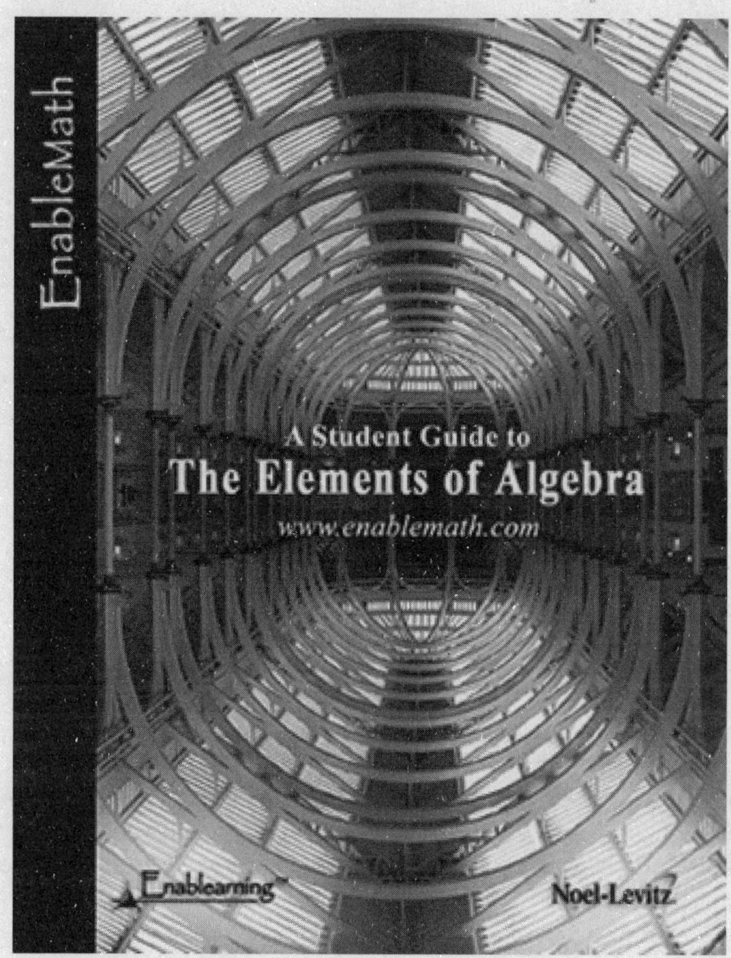

Enablearning, Inc.
Cambridge, Massachusetts

Publisher's Acknowledgements

The Publishers would like to thank a number of extraordinarily talented people for their valuable contributions to the development of the EnableMath Student Guide. Principal contributors of online content from which the images in the guide were derived include Dr. Daniel Himes, Danielle Goodwin, Peter Mili, Arran Bardige, Brenan Bardige, and Diana Szczesuil, who was additionally responsible for online content management. Dr. Daniel Klassen and Dr. George Blakeslee also provided invaluable aid. Finally, we would like to thank Carol Atnip, the principal text author for the Guide. Carol's teaching experience in developmental mathematics and her feel for the subject have resulted in a very clear and concise description of the mathematical concepts.

Art Bardige, President and CEO,
Dr. Laurence Reeves, Chief Operating Officer,
Enablearning, Inc.,
Cambridge, Massachusetts

ISBN 0-9774966-1-9

Cover design by Beryl Simon. Cover photo: Royal Museum in Edinburgh, Scotland, by Art Bardige

EnableMath

The Elements of Algebra

Table of Contents

Modules

User Registration & Login

What you will need to register

- ☐ **EnableMath License Code —** This code is printed on the inside of the front cover of this book.
- ☐ **User name —** Use a valid email address. Your instructor may want you to use your college email address.
- ☐ **Class Code** — Obtain from your instructor.
- ☐ **Computer**
  - ☐ **Platforms —** Windows 98 second edition and above, Mac OS X 10.2 (Jaguar) and above
  - ☐ **Internet Connection**
  - ☐ **Web Browser —** Internet Explorer (version 5 and above), Mozilla Firefox, Netscape (version 6 and above)
  - ☐ **Version 1.4 of Sun's Java Plug-in —** EnableMath technology will automatically detect and redirect the user who does not have this plug-in installed to our Web page for the download.

To complete the registration process

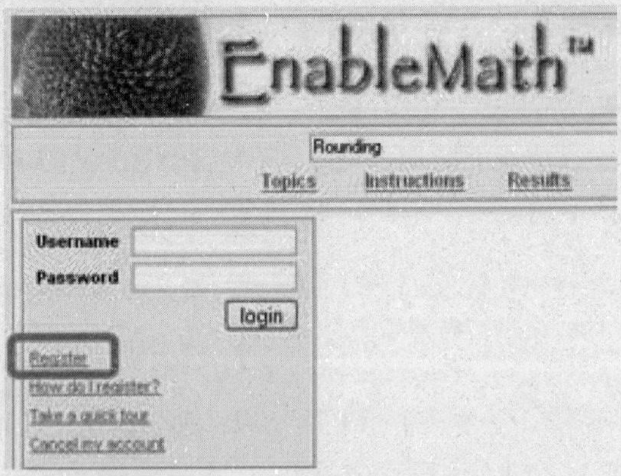

- ☐ Visit us on the Web at **http://*www.enablemath.com***
- ☐ Click on the **Register** link
- ☐ A new Web page will open in your browser window with instructions that will guide you through the registration process.

EnableMath™
Rounding
Topics Instructions Results
Username
Password
login
Register
How do I register?
Take a quick tour
Cancel my account

To login

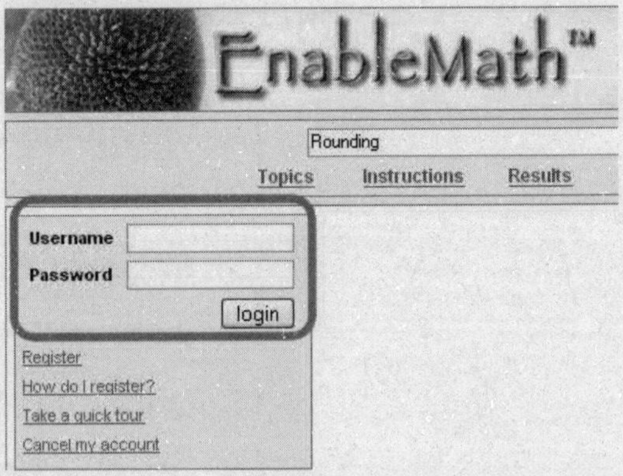

- ☐ Visit us on the Web at **http://*www.enablemath.com***
- ☐ Click on the **Register** link
- ☐ A new Web page will open in your browser window with instructions that will guide you through the registration process.

EnableMath™
Rounding
Topics Instructions Results
Username
Password
login
Register
How do I register?
Take a quick tour
Cancel my account

For support

- ☐ Visit us on the Web at **http://*www.enablemath.com/support***
- ☐ Fill out the form.

Doing Your Homework

The Key to Success

Problems Select an assignment from your syllabus. To do a problem, input your answer and press **Submit**. As you do problems watch your progress on the left side. On the bottom of the screen you can see the **difficulty level** of the current problem (**red bar**) and your **progress** (**green bar)** on the assignment. When you press the **Submit** button, your progress will be updated, green for correct and red for incorrect. Press the yellow flag if you want your answer reviewed.

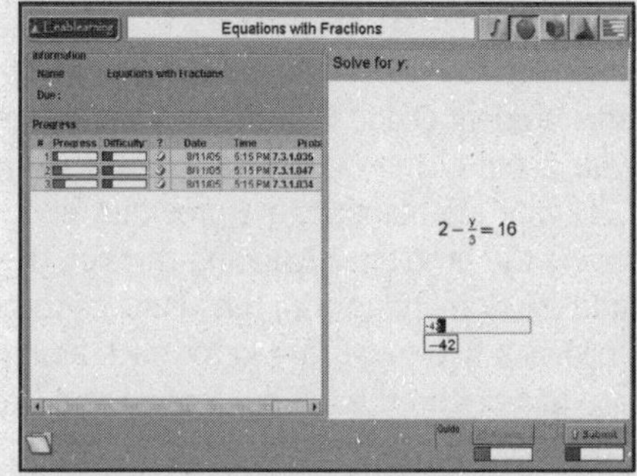

Do your work on paper and enter your answer in the answer box using the *****to multiply, **/** to divide, and **^** to "take the power of". The box below the answer space will show you what you input in mathematical notation.

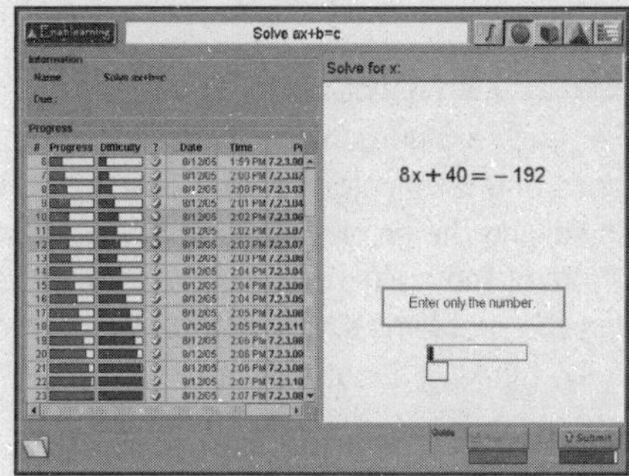

When you reach **mastery** (the green progress bar will be filled in)**,** you have finished the assignment. You will be asked if you want to do more problems or go on to the next assignment. You can see all of the assignments you have done and your **Progress** and **Efficiency** in each by clicking on the **Progress** button.

Syllabus Problems Example Concept Progress

Help To get help with a problem click on the **Example** or **Concept** button on the top of the screen. If you are in an Example or Concept and want to return to the problem click the **Problems** button

Example When you are having difficulty with a problem, click the **Example** button to take you step-by-step through the solution. Choose **Step** in the **Joystick** and push the Joystick up or down. Many Examples are **dynamic**, you can change values and try the example again. Choose a value and change it with the Joystick**.**

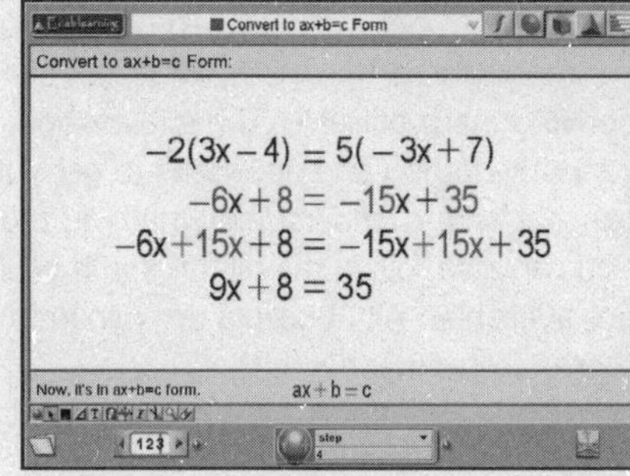

Concept The best way to learn a concept is to play with it. Pick a value to change in the dropdown box next to the Joystick, use the Joystick to change it and watch what happens.

Some **Concepts** and **Examples** have multiple **Points**. Use the **Points** Selector to go from Point 1 to Point 2, etc.

Use the **Student Guide** to help you work through a concept or example.

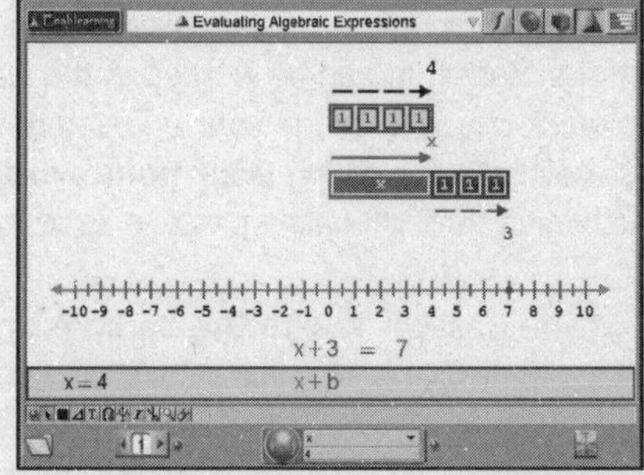

Points Joystick Guide

How to use the Guide

Supporting your Learning

The Student Guide

Provided to support you as you work with the online content, this Student Guide provides guidance specifically for when you're out of the classroom or not working at the college. Relevant mathematics are provided along with assistance for doing the problems, stepping through the dynamic examples, and experimenting with the visual concepts. The guide format follows a two-page spread for each assignment. **Examples** are laid out on the left hand page and **Concepts** are on the corresponding right hand page.

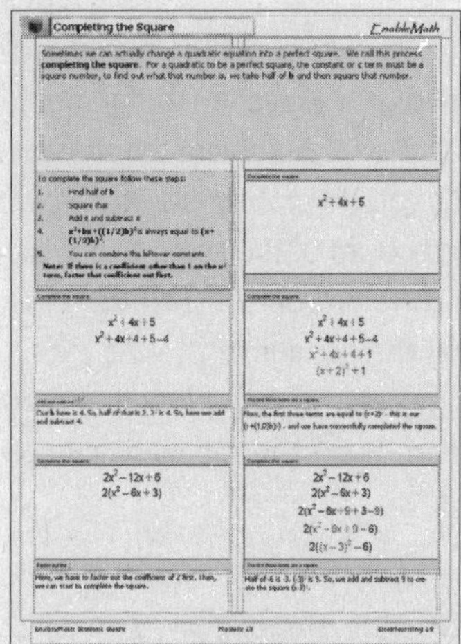

Example

The Examples

For each assignment, an Example page provides formal definitions and terms along with a description of the steps involved in solving the problem types under consideration. Screen shots of the online content are provided as an aid for reviewing the problems step-by-step. Work through examples carefully, thinking about each step in turn. Most of the examples are dynamic; so that you can create new problems by changing values. Develop your understanding of the relevant problem solving process by stepping through solutions one step at a time.

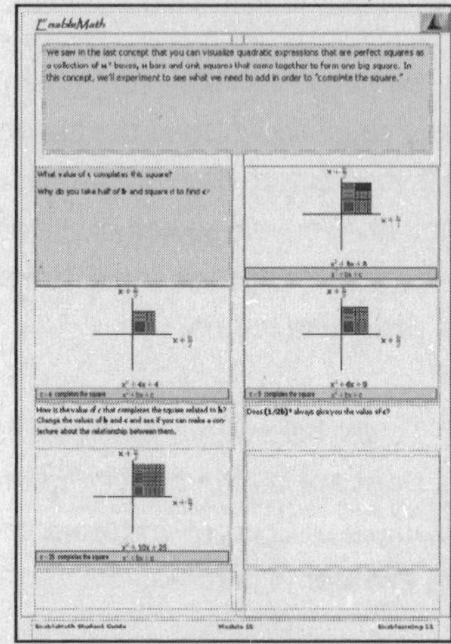

Concept

The Concepts

The Concept page is designed to take you through the visual concept, screen-by-screen, with text explanations of the underlying math pattern. The explanations provide prompts for experimentation and questions to get you to think about the concept and to understand what you are seeing on the screen. You can also follow the pictures in the Guide if a computer is not available. All Concepts are dynamic. Try them. Play with them. Experiment with them!

Sample Problems

Sample Problems*

The Student Guide also contains sample problems for each assignment that can be worked in the classroom or at home as a quick check to gauge your understanding. **They are not a substitute for doing your homework.** Mastery will be achieved through online practice assignments.

***The answer key to the sample problems is found at http://www.enablemath.com/answers**

1. The Whole Numbers

The whole numbers are numbers we use everyday. They form amazing patterns that continue to intrigue everyone, including mathematicians. As you study this module remember that to understand math you have to understand and be fluent in whole number arithmetic. Take the time to play with the Concepts on the computer, they will help you to understand the underlying ideas. Be sure to concentrate when you do your homework problems. The practice will help you gain the fluency that will make all of the rest of math much easier to learn.

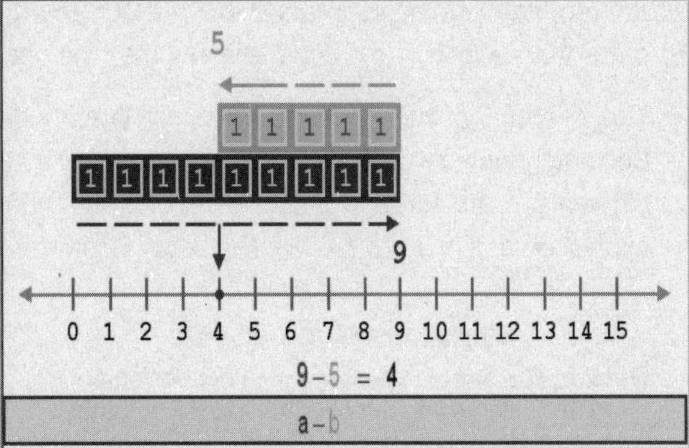

Set notation can be used to describe all sets of numbers including whole numbers, fractions, and decimals. In set notation curly brackets, { }, are used to enclose the members of the set. If there are too many elements in a set to write out and these elements can be determined by a predictable pattern an ellipsis, …, is used to show that the set continues in that pattern forever.

The elements of the whole numbers are linearly ordered, meaning that they form a successive chain. Beginning with zero, whole numbers successively increase in value. There are an infinite numbers of elements in the set, and thus the set of whole numbers has no upper bound. In set notation this is expressed as {0, 1, 2, 3, …}. The set is visualized as evenly spaced tick marks on the Real line.

Important Number Sets

Natural Numbers: Counting numbers beginning with 1 and adding 1 for each successive number with no last number.

Whole Numbers: Elements includes all of the counting numbers and zero.

Even Numbers: Every other Whole number starting with zero, count by 2's {0,2,4,6,...}

Odd Numbers: Every other Natural number beginning with 1, count by 2's {1,3,5,7,...}

The Whole Numbers and The Natural Numbers

Natural Numbers or Counting Numbers: {1, 2, 3, 4, 5,...}

Whole Numbers: {0, 1, 2, 3, 4,...}

The set of Whole Numbers includes zero.

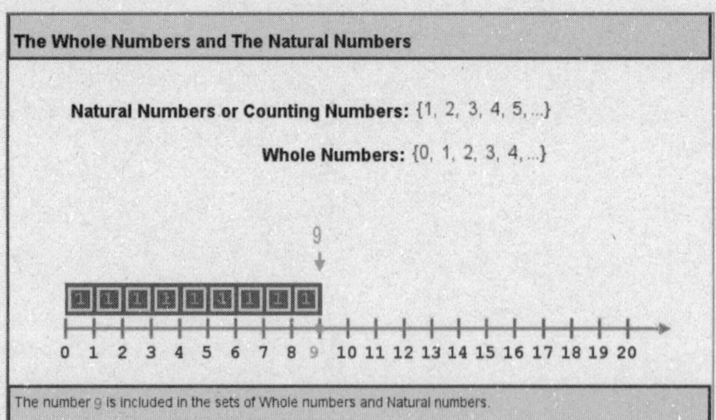

Here the number line contains Whole numbers from 0 to 20. The arrow head on the right end of the line is used to indicate that the Whole numbers continue indefinitely, stepping in order so that each successive number is exactly one unit more than the previous number

Number Line Examples

0 1 2 3 4 5 6 7 8 — 3

44 45 46 47 48 49 50 51 — 51

2 3 4 5 6 7 8 9 10 — 9

25 26 27 28 29 30 31 32 — 25

4 5 6 7 8 9 10 11 12 — 5

104 105 106 107 108 109 — 107

Here are six different number line segments. The red dot indicates the chosen number on the segment or the *graph* of the number.

Visualize numbers and look for patterns on the Real **number line.**

You can learn to visualize and understand mathematical concepts by interacting with the concept visualizations. Using the **joystick**, change the value of **count by** and **number**. Select either **count by** or **number** by pulling down the dropdown menu next to the joystick. **Answer the following questions by experimenting with this visualization.**

This Guide provides questions to focus you as you explore the concept visualizations.

How do you know if a number is even or odd?

If you change the value for **number** to 10 will even or odd pop up on the yellow bar?

If you set the **count by** value to 5, how many clicks for **a** does it take to get to 20?

If you start with 0, how many clicks will it take to get to 18 if you **count by** 6? By 9? By 2? By 3?

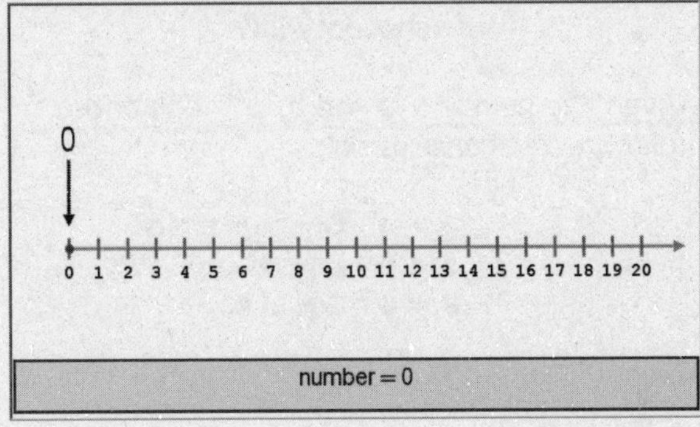

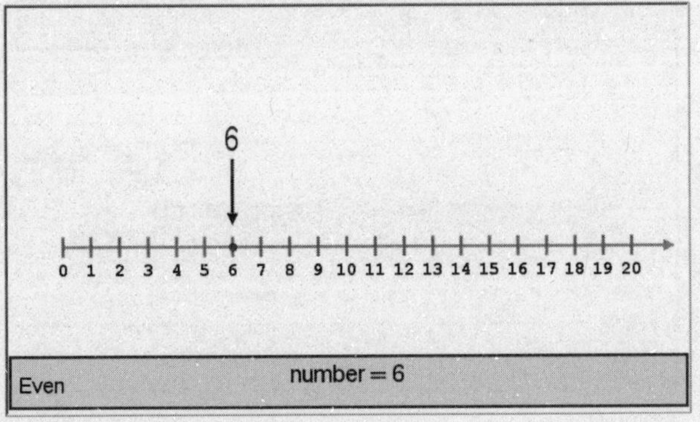

What do you notice about all the even numbers? What **count by** group describes this group of numbers?

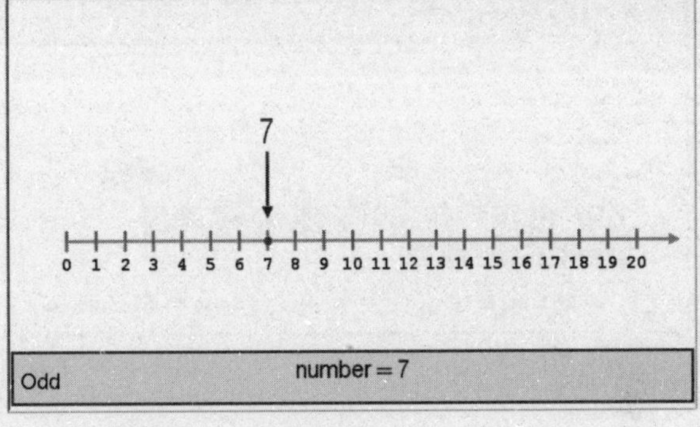

What number do you start with and what number do you **count by** to get the odd numbers?

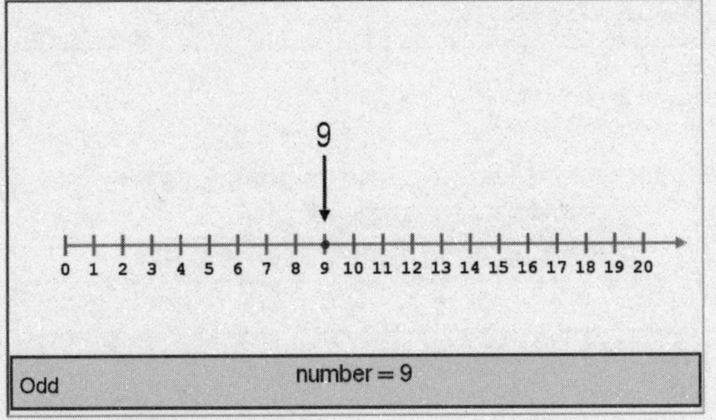

Is 9 in the **count by** 3 family?

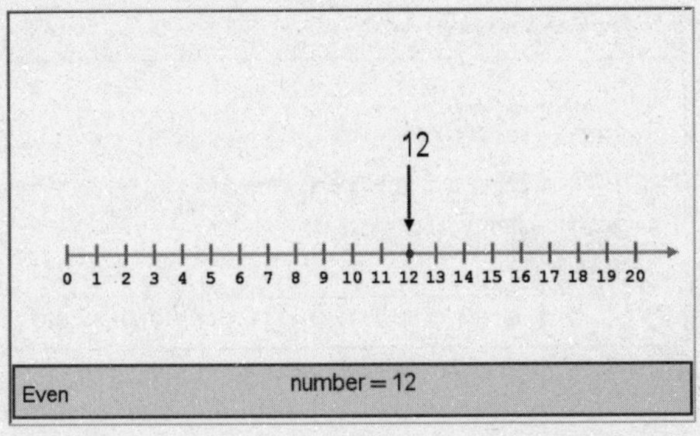

What are all the **count by** groups that have 12 in them?

The whole numbers are a linearly order set, meaning that the relative position and value of the elements can be compared. If you asked to compare any two whole numbers, there are only three possible relationships that can exist between them. One number will either be greater than, less than, or equal to the second number. The statement is known as the **Trichotomy Law**. Numbers represented on a number line always increase in value as you move along the line from left to right.

Trichotomy Law

Given two numbers, **a** and **b**, only one of the following relationships holds:

a > b Greater than
a < b Less than
a = b Equal to

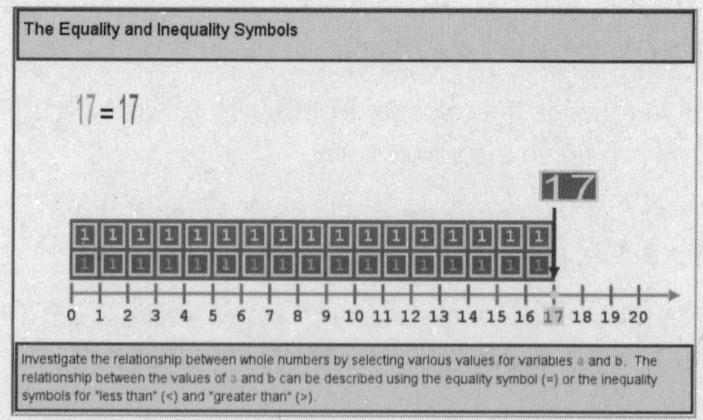

The Equality and Inequality Symbols
17=17
Investigate the relationship between whole numbers by selecting various values for variables a and b. The relationship between the values of a and b can be described using the equality symbol (=) or the inequality symbols for "less than" (<) and "greater than" (>).

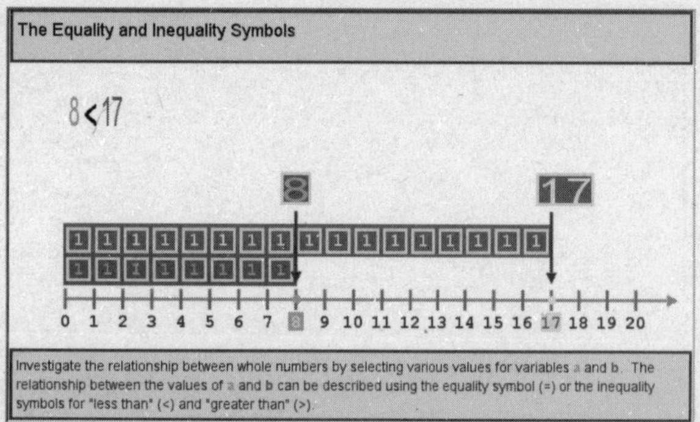

The Equality and Inequality Symbols
8<17
Investigate the relationship between whole numbers by selecting various values for variables a and b. The relationship between the values of a and b can be described using the equality symbol (=) or the inequality symbols for "less than" (<) and "greater than" (>).

Using the joystick, change the values of **a** and **b**. Notice that numbers on the number line increase in value from left to right.

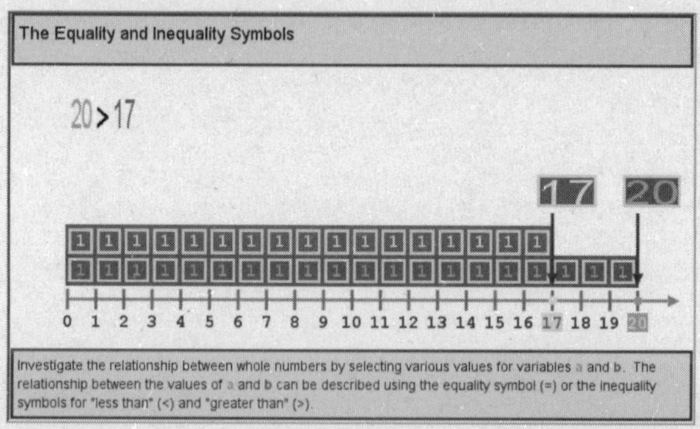

The Equality and Inequality Symbols
20>17
Investigate the relationship between whole numbers by selecting various values for variables a and b. The relationship between the values of a and b can be described using the equality symbol (=) or the inequality symbols for "less than" (<) and "greater than" (>).

A mathematical statement can be evaluated as either **true** or **false**. The above statement is true, because 20 is greater in value than 17.

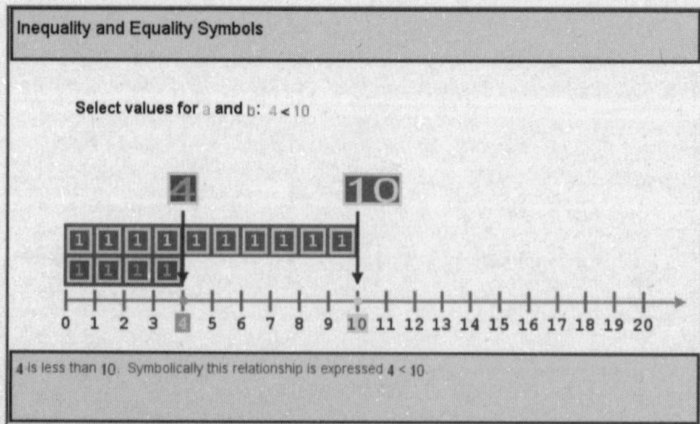

Notice the inequality symbol. The wide open part is positioned toward the larger number and point faces the smaller number. Read left to right, we say that 4 is less than 10. It is also true that 10 is greater than 4.

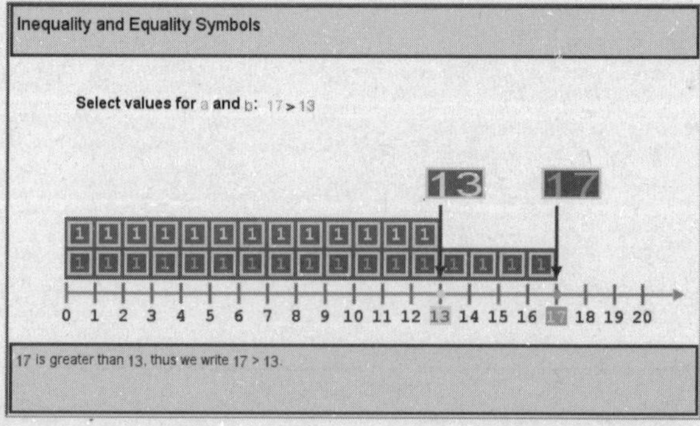

Notice the relative positions of the numbers on the number line. Compare their positions. When a number is less than another, how can you describe its position with respect to the larger valued number?

Number sentences are created using inequality relationship symbols.

>	**greater than**
<	**less than**
=	**equal to**

Ask: If I use write **a** > **b** to indicate a relationship between two numbers, will **a** be positioned to the right or left of **b** on the number line?

Select different values for **a** and **b** until you can understand and predict each relation.

What do you have to do to change 7 < 15 into a statement using greater than?

Can you make two true inequality statements with the same two numbers?

On a number line, if a number is positioned to the left of another number is it greater than or less than?

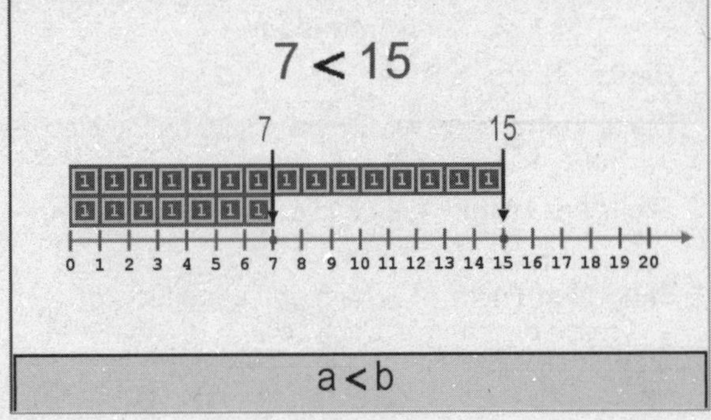

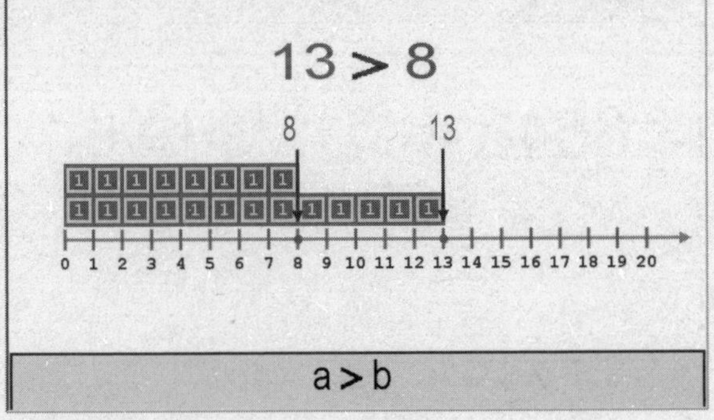

How can the above relationship be expressed using a less than symbol?

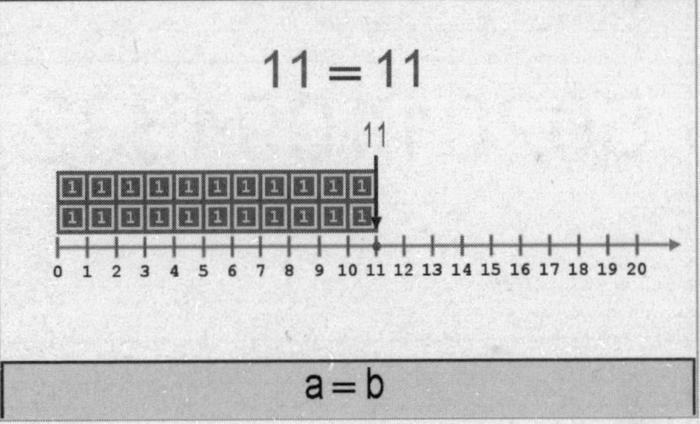

Equal, coincide, same, overlap, equivalent, ...

Place Value & Expanded Form

Numbers are uniquely described by the position or place of their digits. This dependence means that the number 23 is different from 32. Numbers in the base ten number system are made up of digits ranging from 0 to 9. Each place of a number represents ten times more than the place to its immediate right. The value that each digit contributes depends on what place of the number it occupies. The place value of each digit is determined by multiplying the value of the digit times the value of its place.

Numbers can be expressed in **standard** or **expanded form**. For example, 23 = 20 + 3. Here the number 23 is expanded into a summation of its tens place value plus its ones place value.

Terminology

Digits: Numbers 0 - 9

Place Value: The value represented by the place of a digit.

Standard Form: The regular way to write a number.

Expanded Form: The sum of the products of each digit and its place value.

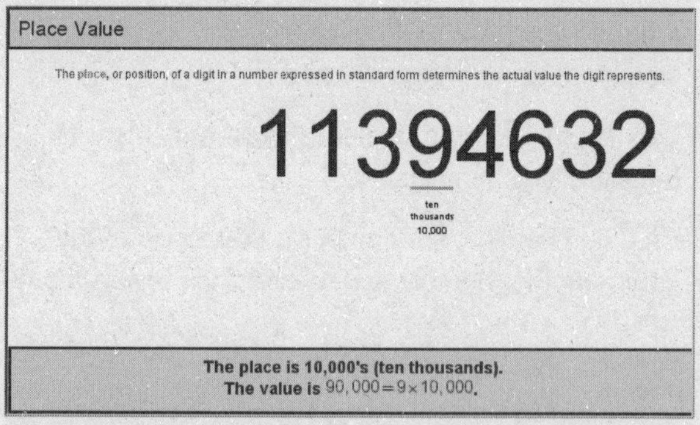

Place Value

The place, or position, of a digit in a number expressed in standard form determines the actual value the digit represents.

11394632

ten thousands 10,000

The place is 10,000's (ten thousands).
The value is $90,000 = 9 \times 10,000$.

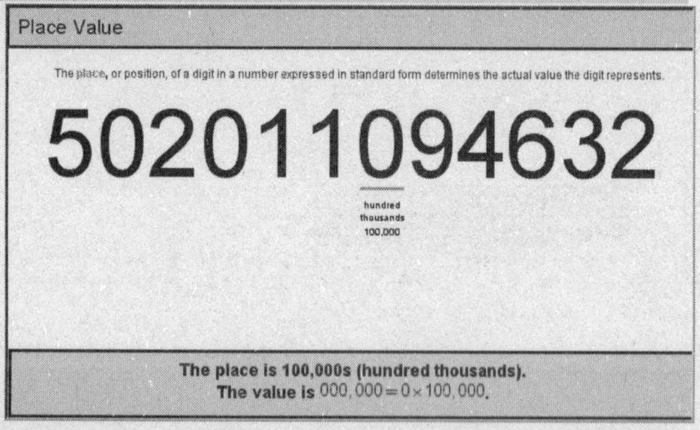

Place Value

The place, or position, of a digit in a number expressed in standard form determines the actual value the digit represents.

502011094632

hundred thousands 100,000

The place is 100,000s (hundred thousands).
The value is $000,000 = 0 \times 100,000$.

0 is in the hundred thousands place. Change the value of each digit and place to investigate other examples. We call this a *dynamic example*.

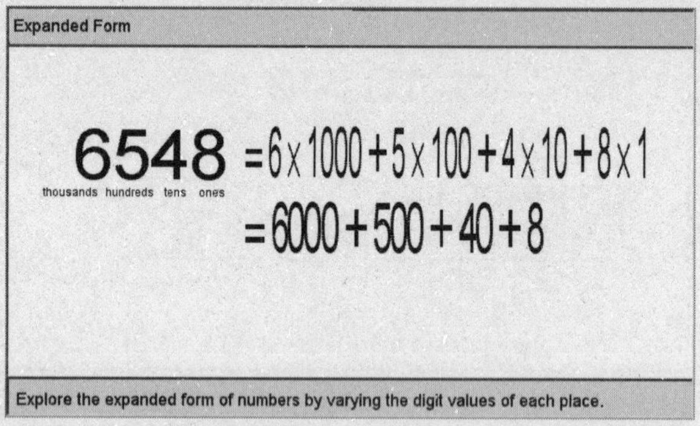

Expanded Form

6548 (thousands hundreds tens ones)

$$6548 = 6 \times 1000 + 5 \times 100 + 4 \times 10 + 8 \times 1$$
$$= 6000 + 500 + 40 + 8$$

Explore the expanded form of numbers by varying the digit values of each place.

The number above is in **expanded form**. Notice that each **digit** has been multiplied by its **place value**.

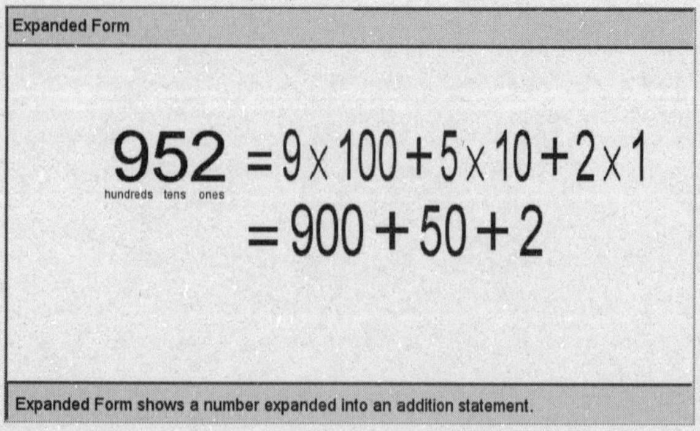

Expanded Form

952 (hundreds tens ones)

$$952 = 9 \times 100 + 5 \times 10 + 2 \times 1$$
$$= 900 + 50 + 2$$

Expanded Form shows a number expanded into an addition statement.

Expanded form explicitly shows the place value of each digit. The standard form implies place value, meaning that the place that 5 occupies relates that its value is 50.

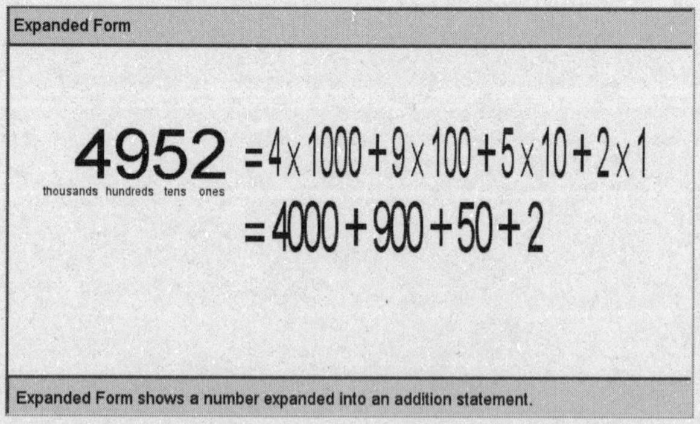

Expanded Form

4952 (thousands hundreds tens ones)

$$4952 = 4 \times 1000 + 9 \times 100 + 5 \times 10 + 2 \times 1$$
$$= 4000 + 900 + 50 + 2$$

Expanded Form shows a number expanded into an addition statement.

Notice that if you add up the sum of place values in expanded form, you do get the standard number.

Place value can be visualized by thinking of columns that increment in value from 0 to 9. Use the joystick to change the value in each column. Incrementing a full column results in the value carrying over to the next higher order stack. If the ones column is filled, then adding one more forces 10 to be carries into the tens column. Since each increment in the tens column represents ten ones, the carried over value fills one increment. The pattern continues. It takes 10 tens to fill up one 100 and ten 100s to fill one 1000.

Be sure to play with place value on screen. It is very valuable for you to really see how this works and to get a natural feel for it.

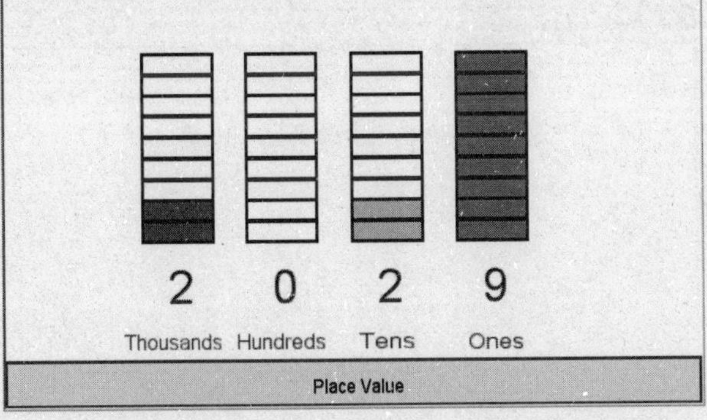

What happens when you add one to the ones column? How many columns change? How many clicks would it take to "fill up" the tens column if you fill it by incrementing the ones column?

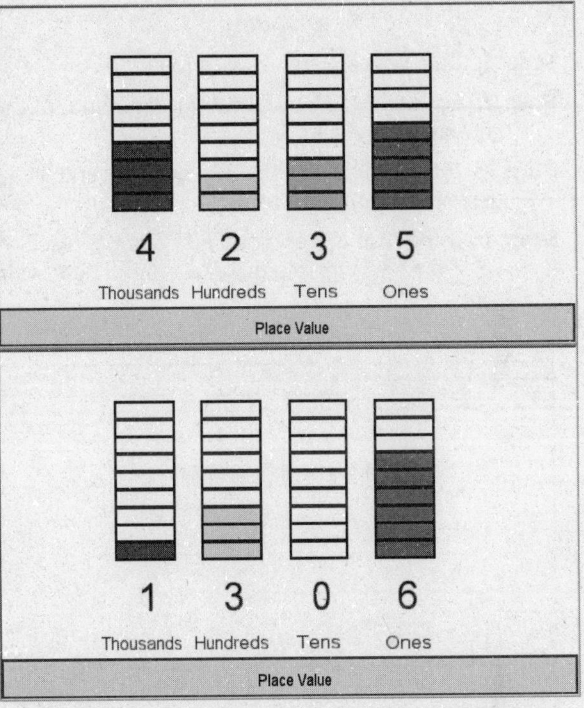

Select the hundreds column. As you increase the digit in the hundreds place, how is the value of the number changing. How much does each click of the joystick increase or decrease the value of the number?

Expanded Form

To see the place value pattern, select a place from the drop down menu. Using the joystick increase the place value until it carries over to the higher order place.

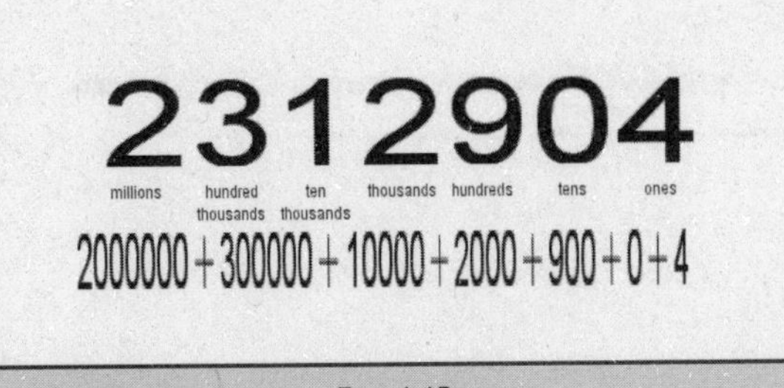

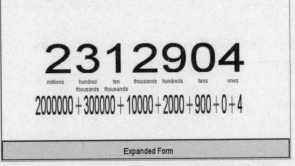

How many clicks does it take to fill the ones place? What happens when you add one more? How many clicks fills up the tens place? What place comes after millions?

Rounding is a process for approximating a number that is often used as a means for simplifying calculations or estimating a solution. For example, the speed of light is 299,792,458 meters per second, but we can **round off** this number to an approximation of 300,000,000 meters per second. This rounded off value is easier to remember, write, and use in computations. Rounded off numbers are "close to" their true value. "Rounding up" means the number is larger than the original and "rounding down" means the number is smaller. If we wanted to we could round the speed of light to 299,792,000 meters per second, which is closer to the true value than 300,000,000 meters per second. The degree to which you round a number affects the accuracy of your calculated solutions.

Rounding

Step 1: Choose the place value to round to.

Step 2: Look at the digit to the immediate right of the chosen place value.

Step 3: If this digit is less than 5, replace it and all digits to its right with zeros.

Step 4: If the digit is 5 or more, add 1 to the place value digit and replace the digits to the right with zeros.

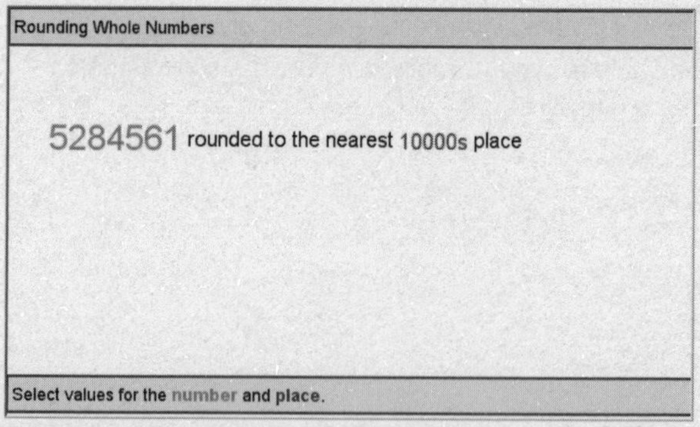

Rounding Whole Numbers

5284561 rounded to the nearest 10000s place

Select values for the number and place.

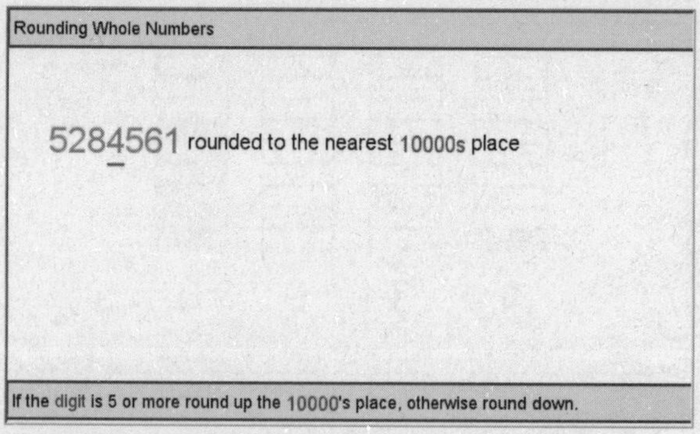

Rounding Whole Numbers

5284561 rounded to the nearest 10000s place

If the digit is 5 or more round up the 10000's place, otherwise round down.

8 occupies the ten thousands place. Since the digit to the right is 4, the rounding rules tell us to round down by replacing all digits to the right of 8 with zeros. The rounded number is 5,280,000.

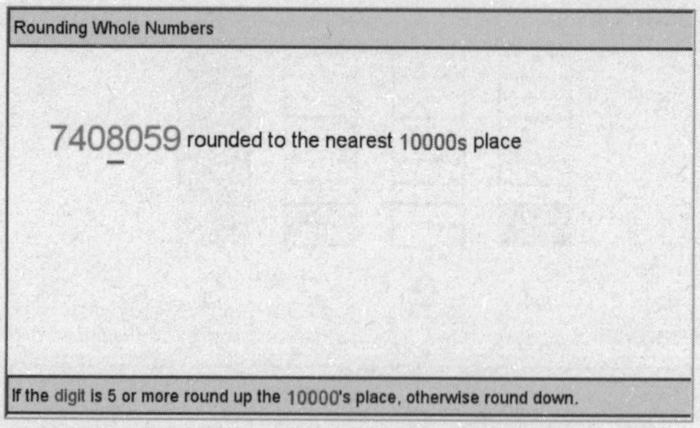

Rounding Whole Numbers

7408059 rounded to the nearest 10000s place

If the digit is 5 or more round up the 10000's place, otherwise round down.

0 occupies the ten thousands place. Since the digit to the right is 8, the rounding rules tell us to round up by adding 1 to 0, and replacing all digits to the right of with zeros. The rounded number is 7,410,000.

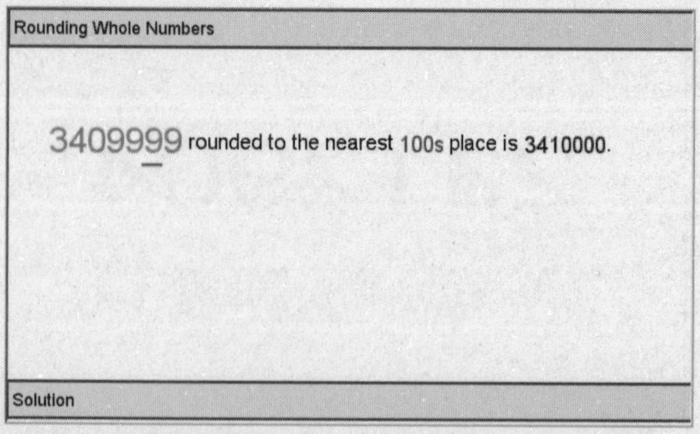

Rounding Whole Numbers

3409999 rounded to the nearest 100s place is 3410000.

Solution

Rounding up the hundreds place adds one to the 9. This added one successively carries into the thousands place and ten thousands place. Final answer?

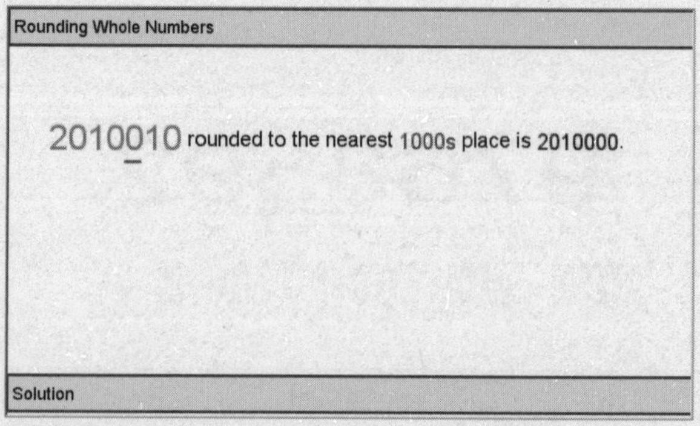

Rounding Whole Numbers

2010010 rounded to the nearest 1000s place is 2010000.

Solution

Rounding down the thousands place by replacing all the digits to the left of the digit in the thousands place with zeros.

Rounding is an approximation method that allows us to express large number in simpler forms that are easier to remember, write, and use. The numbers presented in the visualizations here are fairly small, but the process for rounding a number of any size is exactly the same. Point 1 considers rounding numbers between 100 and 999 to the nearest 10s place. Point 2 examines rounding numbers from 1000 to 9999 to the nearest 100s place. The rounding process is visualized as identifying which endpoint of a number line segment has a value closest to the number to be rounded.

What does it mean to round "up" or "down"?

Which digit do you look to in deciding to rounding a number up or down?

Do you ever subtract 1 from a digit when rounding down?

What do all rounded off numbers end in?

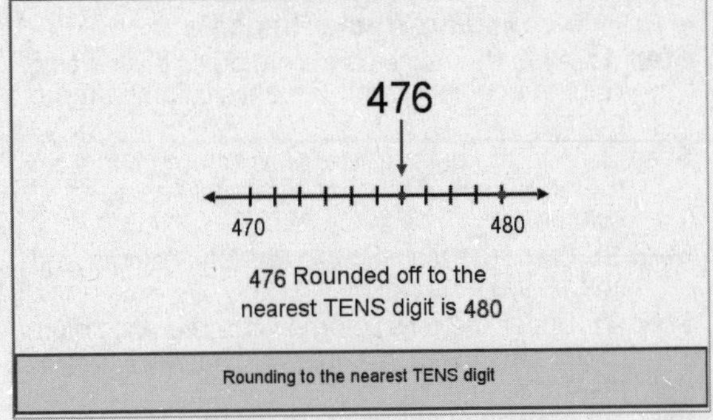

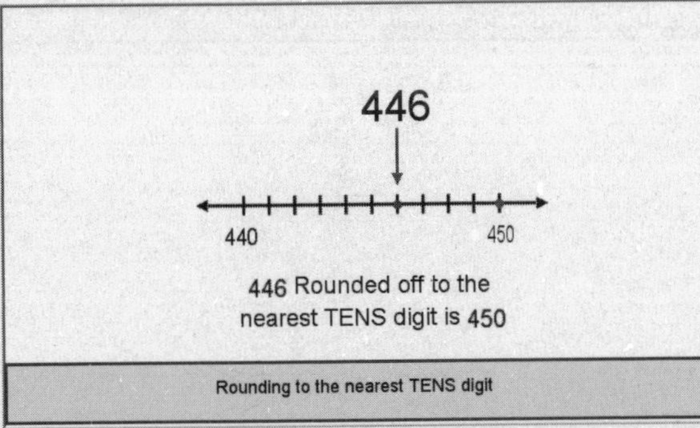

Is the 446 closer to 440 or 450? In the above right, is 476 closer to 470 or 480?

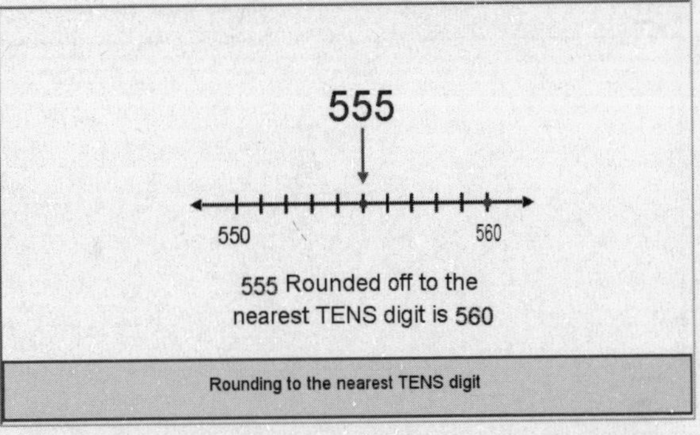

If the digit to the right of the place we want to round is equal to 5, do we round up or down? Math and science usually round up; social science uses an even/odd rule—follow the advice of your instructor.

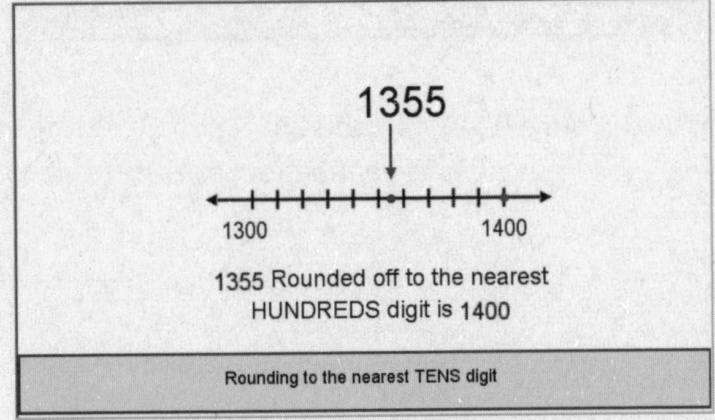

Point 2: What digit do you look at when rounding to the nearest hundred? Is 1355 closer to 1300 or 1400?

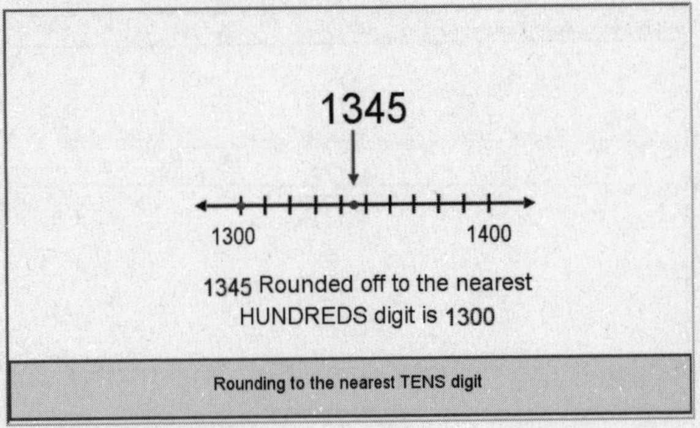

Does the 5 digit in this number affect the rounding process?

Addition is the first of the four *basic operations* that can be used to combine whole numbers. Adding whole numbers is the process of combining or adding up two or more quantities. In word problems the addition process is used to answer questions that ask how many of something you have. This example steps through the addition algorithm for adding two, two-digit numbers, so that you can build your fluency with the process.

The answer to an addition problem is called the **total** or **sum**. The symbol used to perform addition is the plus sign: +. **Carrying** is a process of regrouping.

Adding Whole Numbers

Step 1: Align the numbers according to place value column beginning with the ones column on the right.

Step 2: Add the digits in the ones column and write the ones digit of the answer under the ones column.

Step 3: Carry the tens digit to the tens column and add all the tens digits.

Step 4: Under the tens column write the ones digit of the tens sum and carry the tens digit to the hundreds column.

Step 5: Continue until all columns are added.

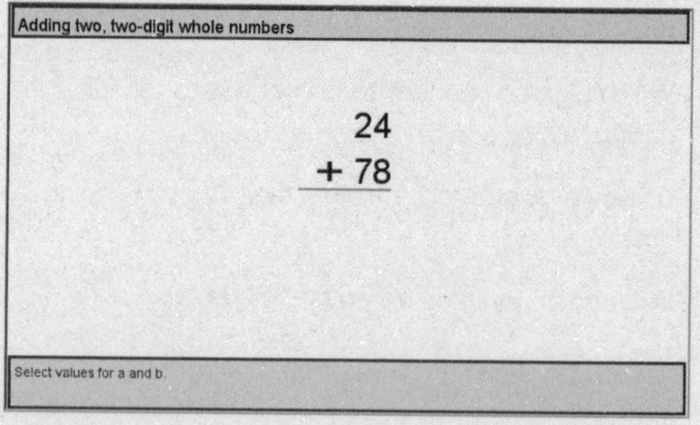

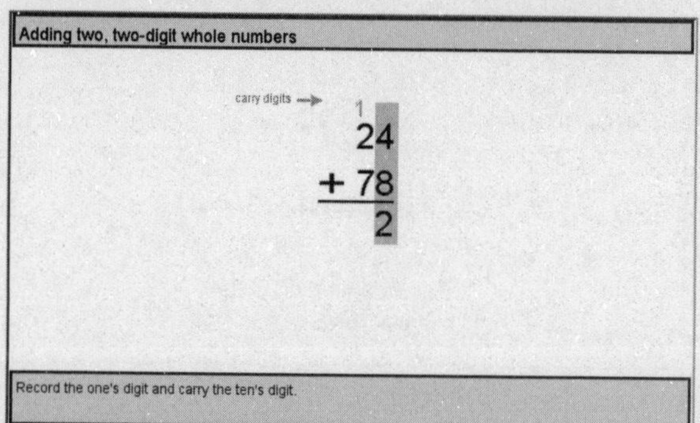

Since 8+4=12, record the 2 in the ones column and carry the 1 to the tens column.

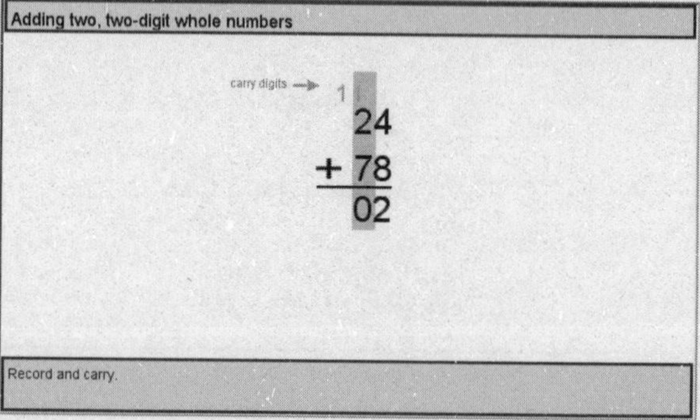

Add the values in the tens column along with the carry digit, Since 2+7+1=10, record the 0 in the tens column and carry the 1 to the hundreds column.

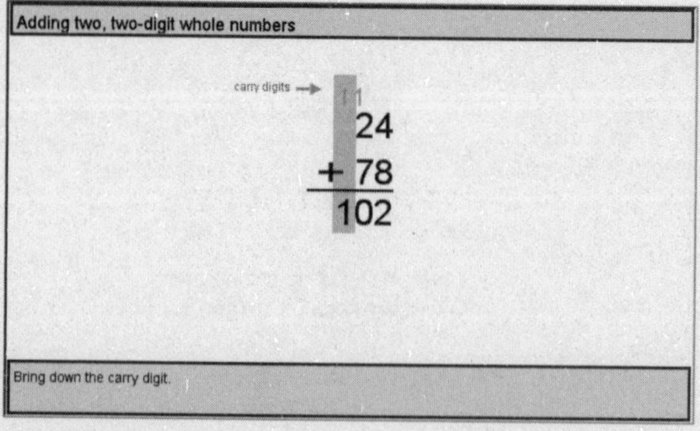

Bringing down the carry digit ends this addition process. The sum 24+78=102

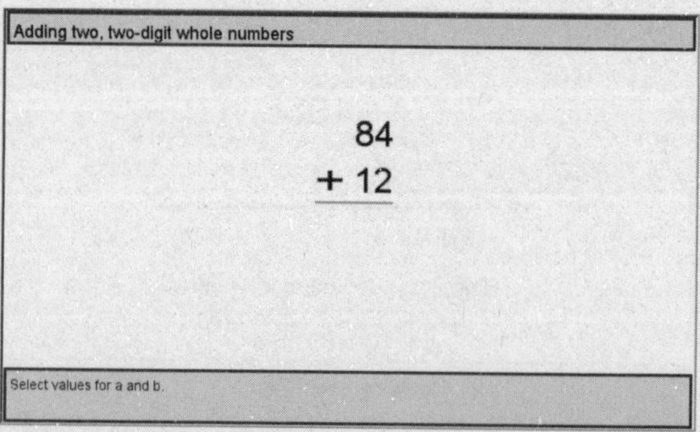

Using the joystick set step to 1 and select new values for **a** and **b**. Step through the addition process. Investigate

We have three different objects on the screen to help us picture addition. The dot on the number line shows the result. The **number bar** shows what addition looks like—count up the number of blue unit squares with the number of yellow unit squares. The **number arrows** or **vectors** give us a shorthand picture of addition. We will use this type of visualization for all addition processes. You can extend this simple visual concept to all whole numbers.

Can two different additions statements yield the same answer?

Does the order matter when adding two numbers?

Do you always get a whole number answer when adding two whole numbers?

When you add two numbers, but the sum is one of the numbers, what did you add?

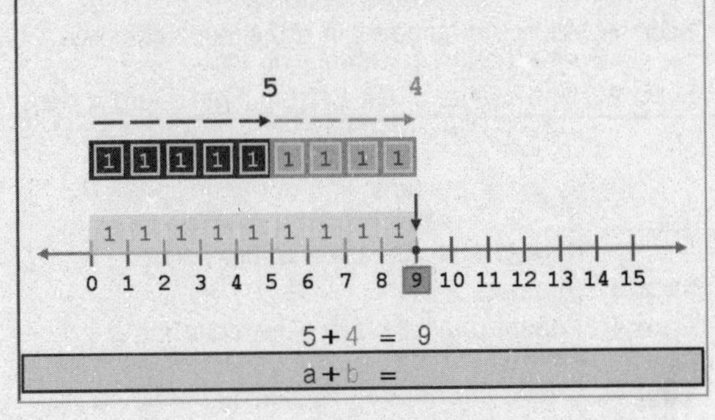

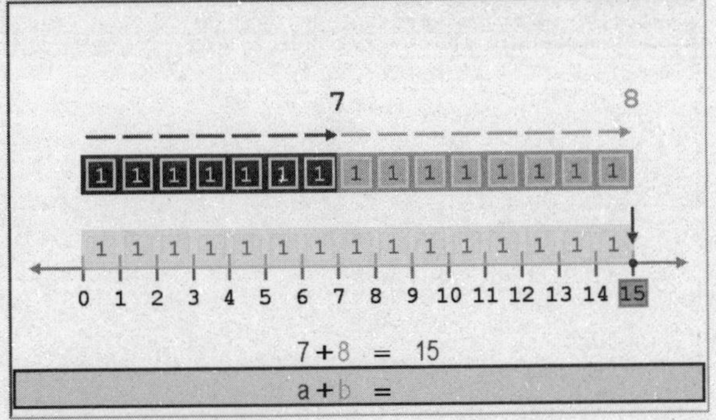

What added to 7 is 15?

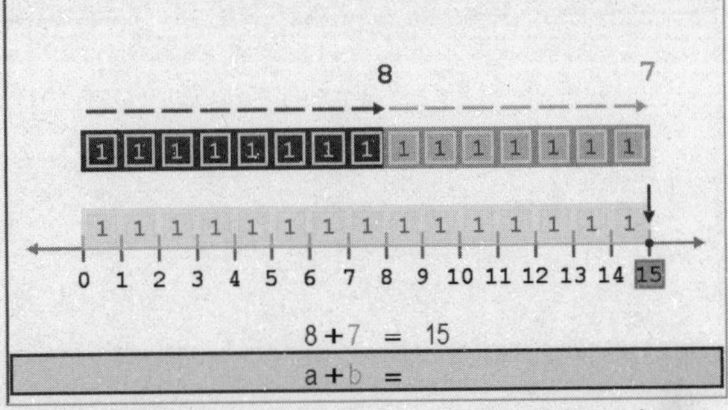

What added to 8 is 15? Does the order in which numbers are added affect their sum?

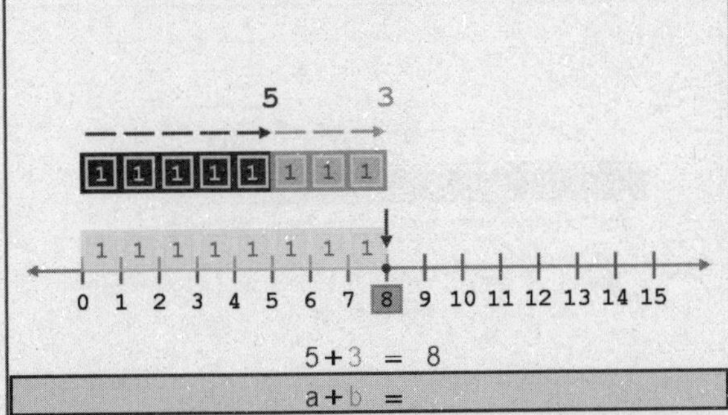

Is adding 5+3 the same as 3+5? Whole numbers are **commutative** under addition, meaning that a+b=b+a. The order in which whole numbers are added does not matter.

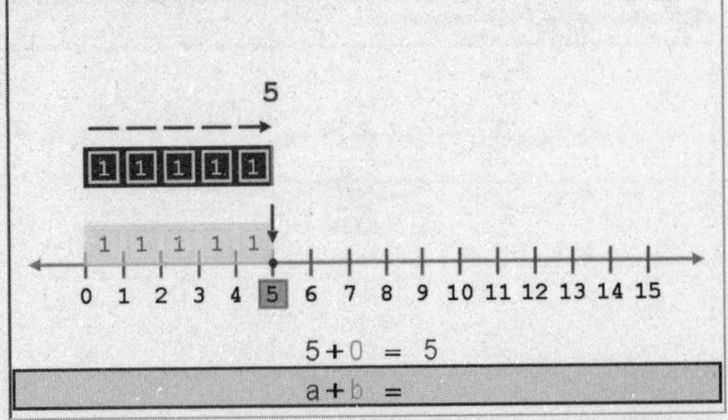

Investigate what happens when you add 0 to any whole number. 0 is the **additive identity** element, which means that adding 0 to any number does not change that number.

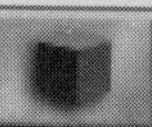

Subtracting Whole Numbers

EnableMath

Subtracting is the opposite of addition. Instead of "counting up" from one number to the other, subtraction is the process of "counting down" or "taking away" one quantity from another. The algorithm for subtraction often uses **borrowing**, a process of regrouping that "takes back" 1 unit from the place value column to the immediate left. Borrowing 1 from the tens place means adding 10 to the ones place. Since addition and subtraction are inverse operations, these processes can be used to undo the another. Addition can be used to check to see if the solution to a subtraction problem, or **difference**, is correct simply by adding the difference to the bottom number. If these values sum to the top number, the calculated difference is correct. Subtraction uses the minus sign, –.

Subtraction

Step 1: Align the numbers in place value columns with the larger number on top.

Step 2: If the value of the bottom digit is larger than the top digit, then borrow 1 from the tens column.

- **A.** Mark the tens digit out and replace it with one less.
- **B.** Add 10 to the ones column digit.

Step 3: Subtract.

Step 4: Repeat until all place value columns are used.

Step 5: Check your answer by adding back.

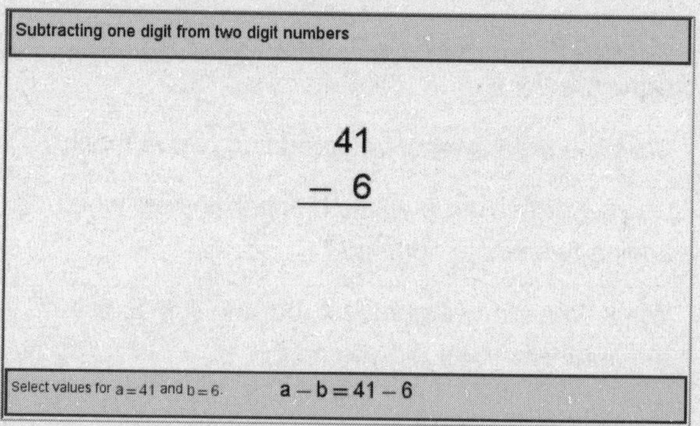

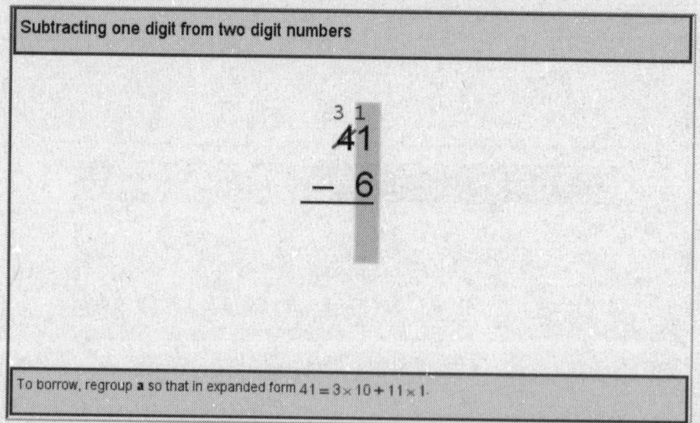

Subtracting one digit from two digit numbers
3 1
41
– 6
To borrow, regroup a so that in expanded form 41 = 3 × 10 + 11 × 1.

Since 6>4, borrow from the tens column. Borrowing is a regrouping process. In this case 41 is regrouped so that 30 is in the tens column and 11 is in the ones column.

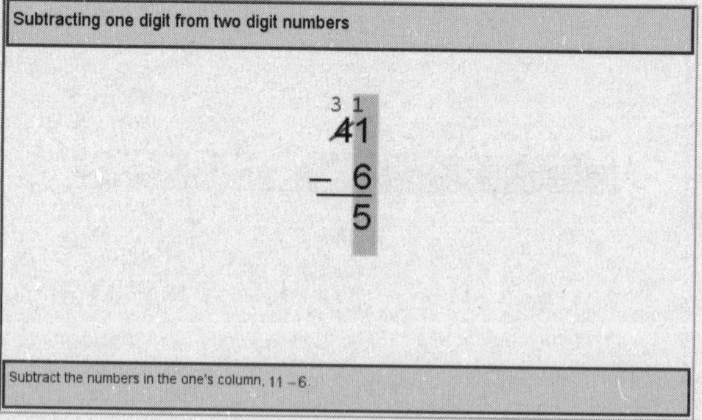

Subtracting one digit from two digit numbers
3 1
41
– 6
5
Subtract the numbers in the one's column, 11 – 6.

Now that the value in the top number's ones place is larger than the bottom numbers, perform the ones column subtraction. **11 - 6 = 5**

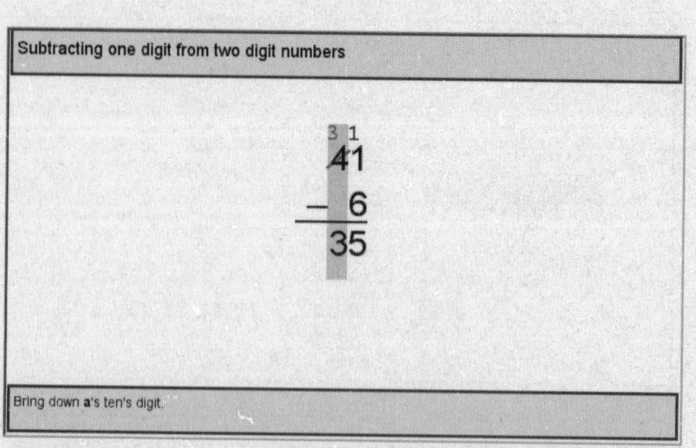

Bringing down the remaining digits in the tens column completes this subtraction process. The difference **41-6=35**. To check your solution, add 35+6 or subtract 41-35.

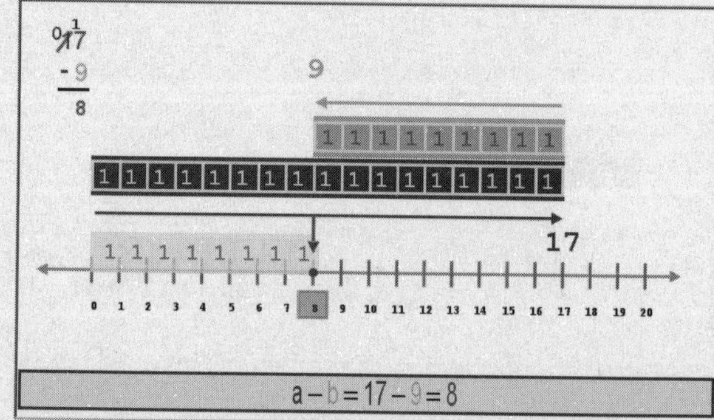

Point 2: Change the values of **a** and **b**. When do you have to borrow? When is borrowing unnecessary? How can you check if a calculated difference is correct?

Picture subtraction as flipping the direction of the number bars and flipping the arrow (vector). When you subtract you reverse direction, and the arrow representing the number changes direction. Instead of "counting up," we "count back" or "take away." Subtraction is the inverse operation to addition.

Is the difference always smaller than either number in the problem?

What happens when you subtract zero from a number?

Does order matter in a subtraction problem?

If you start with 15, what happens to the difference as the number you are subtracting increases?

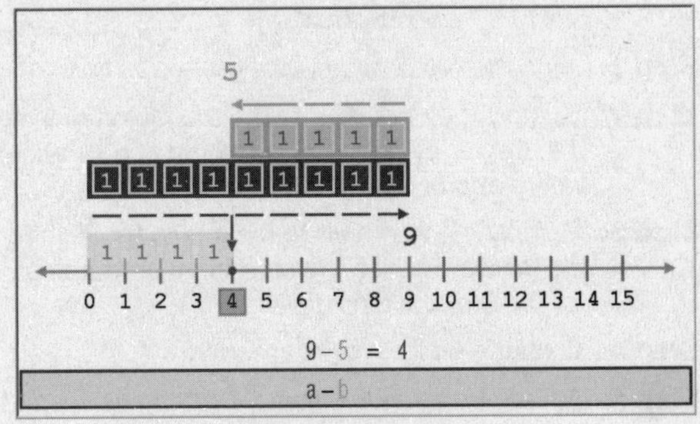

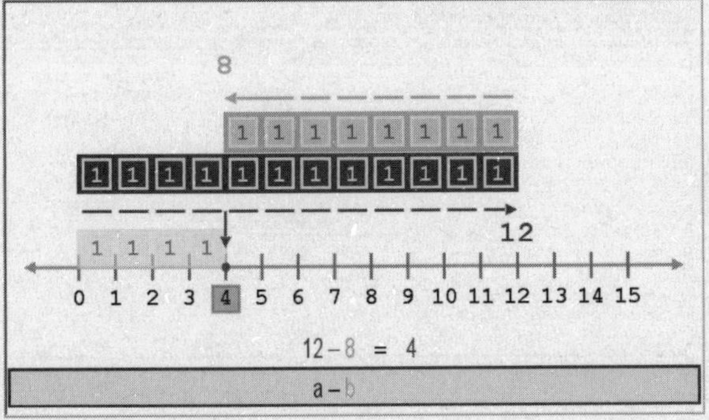

Where would the 8 bar be if you were adding 8 and 12?

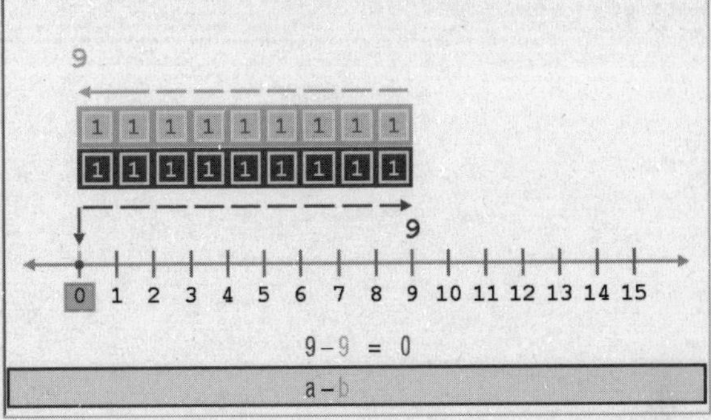

When you subtract a number from itself you get the identity element, or 0. Is this always true? 0 is called the **additive identity**.

Multiplication is a shortened way to perform many additions. For example 3*4 means 3 sets of 4 objects, or three 4s added together. Symbolically, 3*4=4+4+4. While it's easy to write out the addition for small numbers, can you imagine how hard it would be to write the addition problem for 46 sets of 63 objects? For this reason we have an **algorithm** for multiplying that breaks the problem down into **partial products**. The answer is found by adding the partial products.

The answer to a multiplication problem is called the **product** and the numbers multiplied are called **factors**. There are many symbols for the multiplication process including x, ( )( ), and *. We will use all of these symbols.

Multiplication

Step 1: Align the problem by place value columns.

Step 2: Multiply the ones digit to the top factor aligning the answer by place value column and carrying where appropriate.

Step 3: Multiply the tens digit to the top factor aligning the answer by place value column accounting for the 0 of the tens digit.

Step 4: Continue until all digits are used.

Step 5: Add by place value column, carrying as needed.

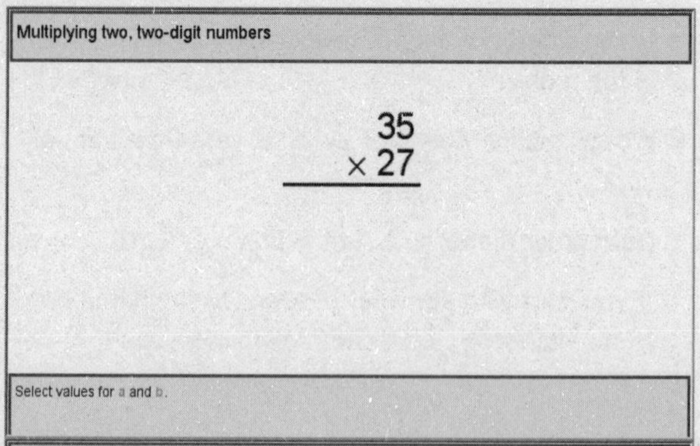

Multiplying two, two-digit numbers

$$\begin{array}{r} 35 \\ \times\ 27 \\ \hline \end{array}$$

Select values for a and b.

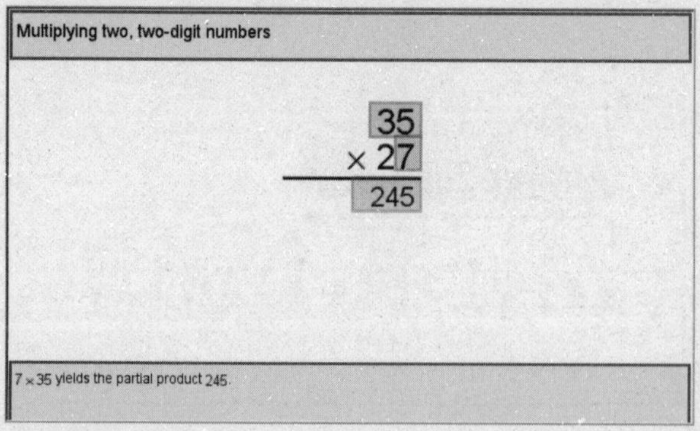

Multiplying two, two-digit numbers

$$\begin{array}{r} 35 \\ \times\ 27 \\ \hline 245 \end{array}$$

7 × 35 yields the partial product 245.

Multiply the top number by the ones digit of the bottom number. Be sure to carry if necessary.

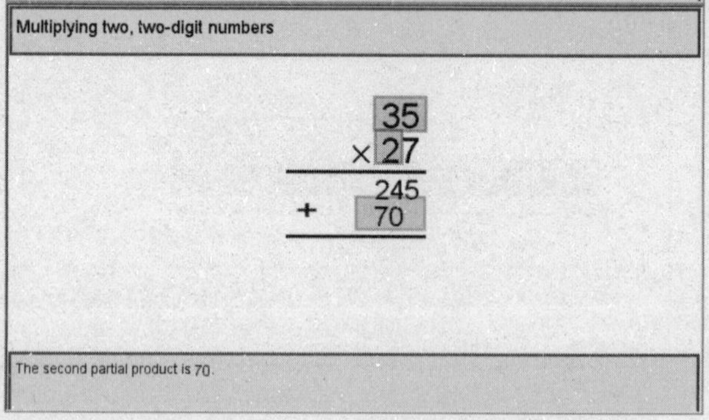

Multiplying two, two-digit numbers

$$\begin{array}{r} 35 \\ \times\ 27 \\ \hline 245 \\ +\ \ 70 \\ \hline \end{array}$$

The second partial product is 70.

Then multiply by the top number by the bottom numbers tens digit. Notice the zero indicating the tens place value.

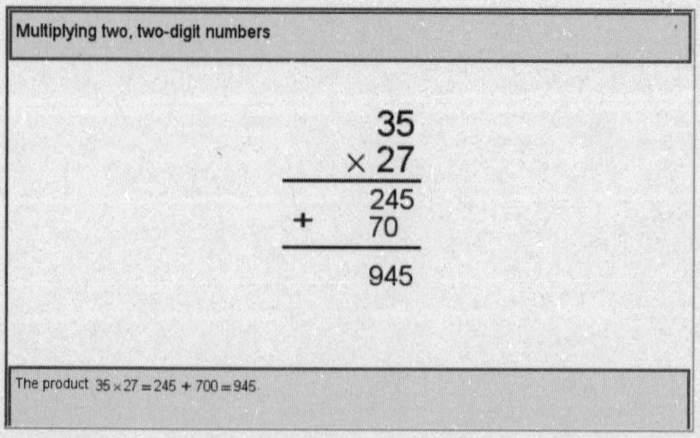

Multiplying two, two-digit numbers

$$\begin{array}{r} 35 \\ \times\ 27 \\ \hline 245 \\ +\ \ 70 \\ \hline 945 \end{array}$$

The product $35 \times 27 = 245 + 700 = 945$.

Once both partial products have been calculated, add them to get the final product.

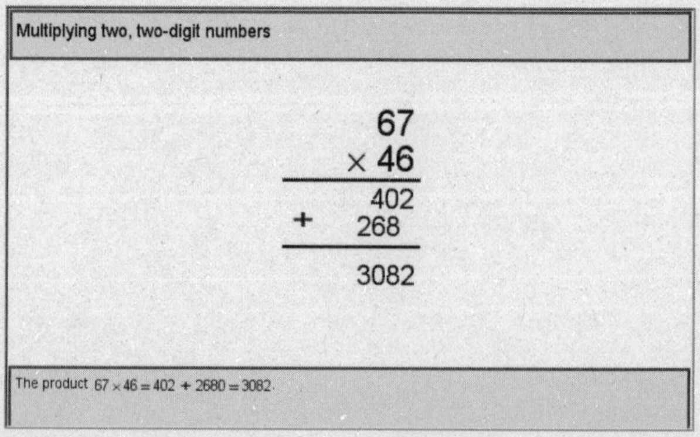

Multiplying two, two-digit numbers

$$\begin{array}{r} 67 \\ \times\ 46 \\ \hline 402 \\ +\ 268 \\ \hline 3082 \end{array}$$

The product $67 \times 46 = 402 + 2680 = 3082$.

You can use the joystick to change the factors. Set step to 1 and use the joystick as you work through the solution one step at a time.

Picture multiplication as a rectangle. The result of a multiplication is called a product (dark blue rectangle) and the numbers we multiply are called the factors (red bars). Notice the pattern for small numbers and generalize to larger numbers.

This visualization is a very good place for you to practice your multiplication facts. Just choose and **a** and **b** and change one of them one number at a time! We strongly suggest that you play with this visualization to strengthen your understanding and fluency with multiplication.

As the factors increase in size does the product also increase in size?

Does order matter for multiplication?

If the product remains the same, but one factor decreases what happens to the other factor?

If you know the product and one of the factors, how can you find out what the other factor is?

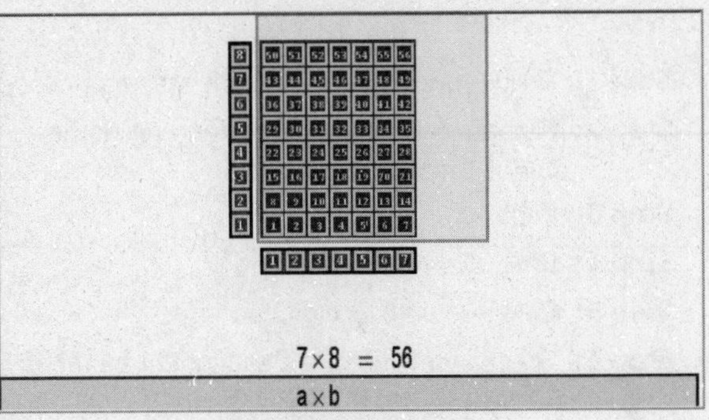

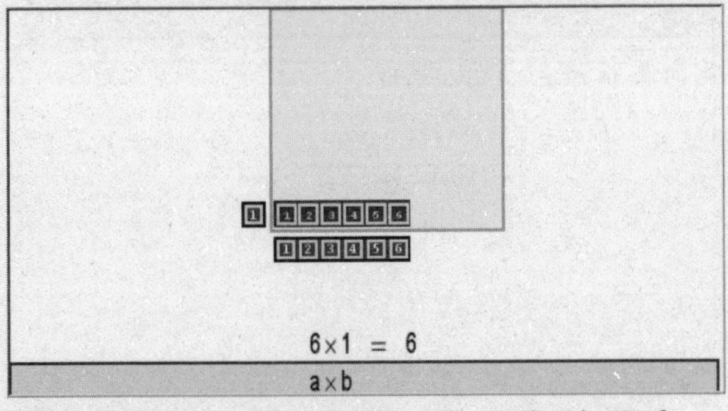

What are the values of any number *1? 1 is the identity for multiplication, we call it the multiplicative identity.

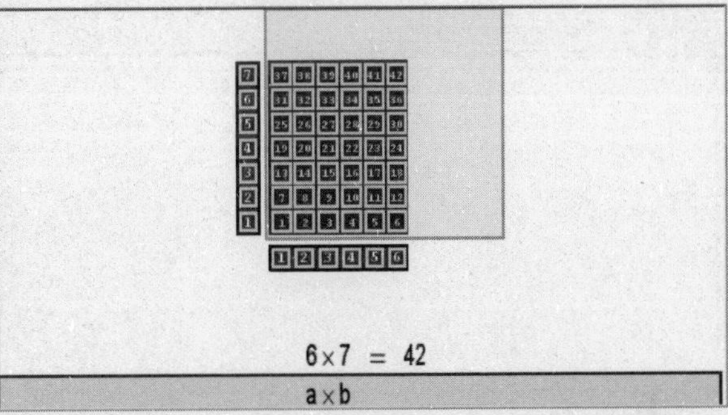

Is 5*8 the same as 8*5? Is multiplication commutative? (Hint: Are the rectangles for any pair of numbers the same size no matter how we turn them?)

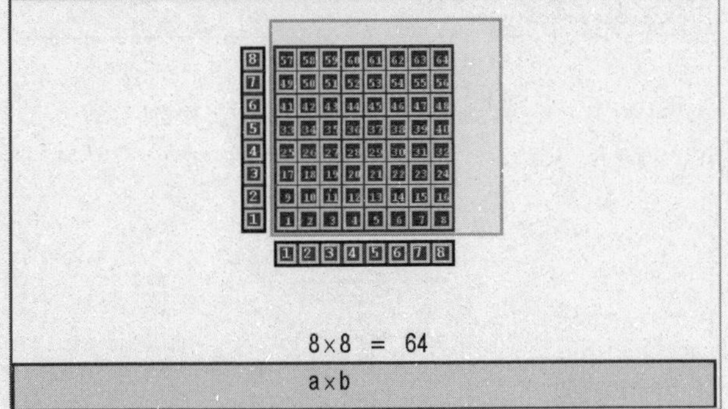

When both factors are the same the product is called a **square number**. Is the shape of every one of these products a square?

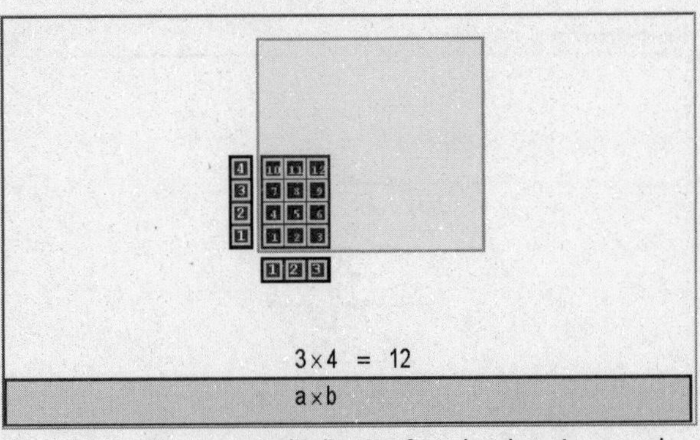

You can practice your multiplication facts by changing **a** and **b.** Say the product aloud as you watch it change,

"3 times 4 is 12."

Dividing Whole Numbers

EnableMath

Division is the opposite operation to multiplication. Division undoes multiplication. When we divide whole numbers, we determine how many times the **divisor** will "go into" the **dividend**. If the divisor does not divide the dividend evenly, what is left over we call the **remainder**.

The answer to a division problem is called the **quotient**, and it includes the whole number answer and the remainder. There are several different symbols used for division: ÷, $\overline{)\quad}$, and /. We use all of them, but prefer the / because it is easy to type on the computer keyboard.

Long Division

Step 1: Divide, put quotient over the last digit used.

Step 2: Multiply quotient to divisor and place the product under the dividend.

Step 3: Subtract.

Step 4: Bring down the next digit.

Step 5: Continue until all digits are used.

Step 6: Check by multiplying the quotient by the divisor and adding the remainder.

Dividing by single digit whole numbers

$$\frac{86}{9} = 9R5$$

Divide and show any remainder.

Dividing by single digit whole numbers

$$\frac{46}{2} = 23$$

Divide and show any remainder.

Point 1: Here we show division by a single digit number. Usually division by one digit is done mentally, but you can follow the same step-by-step process on scratch paper.

Dividing Large Whole Numbers

```
      3
26) 8796
    78
```

Divide and multiply.

Point 2: 26 will divide the first two digits, so the answer is above the last digit used. The product of 3 and 26 is positioned under the two digits used. The next step is to subtract, and then bring down the 9. Repeat process.

Dividing Large Whole Numbers

```
      338 R8
26) 8796
    78
     99
     78
     216
     208
       8
```

The problem is finished!

To divide larger numbers, it may be easier to round the numbers off in your head and think, "How many times will 30 divide 90?" So, 26 goes into 87 about 3 times.

Dividing Large Whole Numbers

```
      135 R16
56) 7576
    56
    197
    168
     296
     280
      16
```

The problem is finished!

Point 2: Change **a** and **b** to create a new problem. Step through each partial quotient working on scratch paper

To divide is to partition or to separate a whole into different groupings. We are asking how many groups of a number can we form. We have three visualizations to show the concept of division. The first visualization shows the relationship of the dividend and divisor on a grid. The quotient is the slope, or steepness, of the line drawn from zero to the top of the dividend; it represents the ratio of dividend to divisor. The second uses the idea of partitioning into groups. The third one uses the idea that division and multiplication are inverse operations. Multiplying is presented as a rectangular array. Can you arrange the rectangle so that one side is the divisor? What do you get for the other side? How does division undo multiplication?

Does order matter for division?

Is there an identity for division?

Can the same problem be modeled by all three methods? What are the connections between the three visualizations?

What is any number divided by itself?

Can you make two division statements from one multiplication statement?

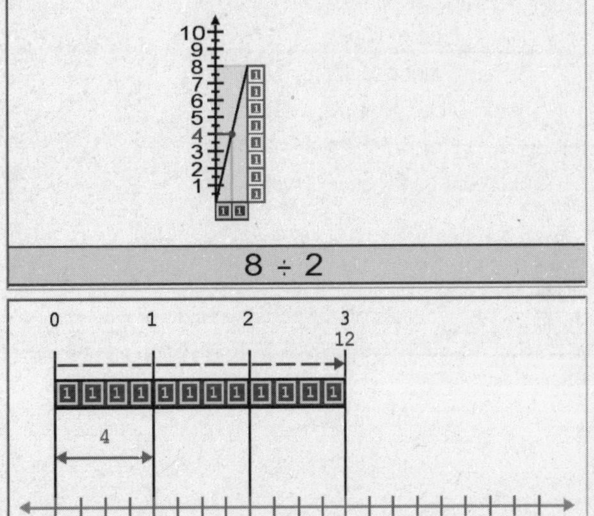

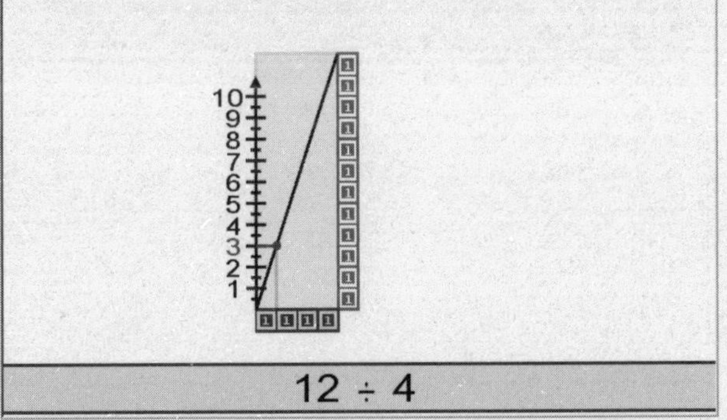

Find the quotient by counting the distance from 1 to the slanted line. Notice the gray line guiding you to the three. What happens if the division doesn't "come out even"? The 15 divided by 4.

How many groups of 4 are in 12? Does this agree with the visualization to the left?

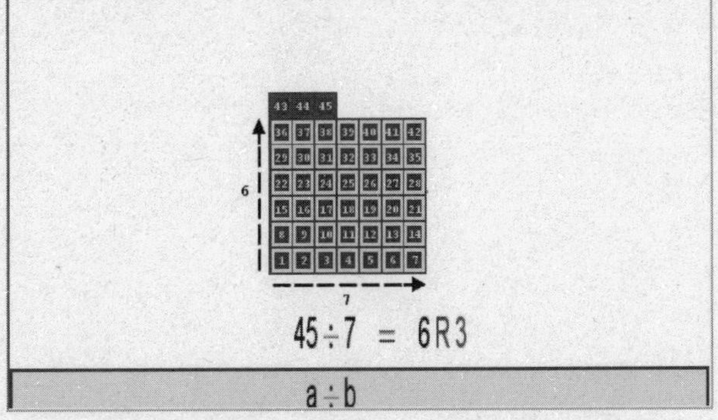

Division is the inverse or opposite of multiplication. We can picture division as taking the rectangle and dividing it into the numbers that formed it.

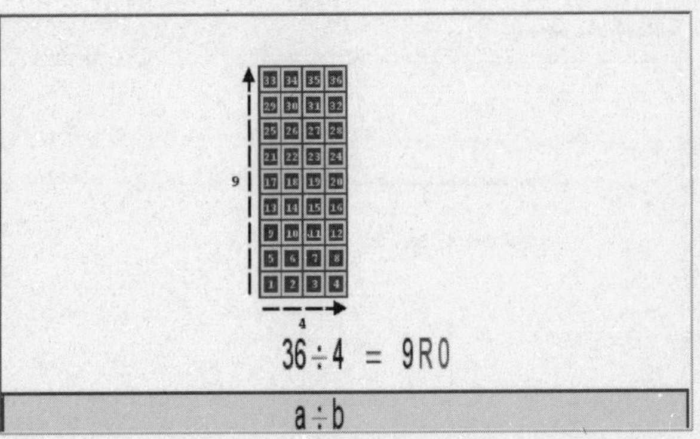

Each rectangle suggests two division problems. What is the other division problem that can be made from the array of unit squares as pictured above?

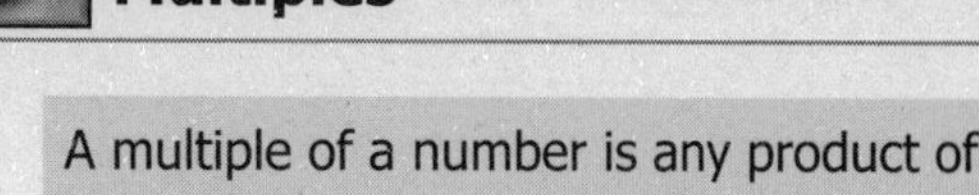

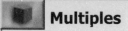

Multiples

A multiple of a number is any product of that number and another number. Multiples make up the "times table" of a number. That is, you can successively "count by" a number to produce a list of multiples. We can list all the multiples of a number using set notation, as in the example below. If you want a particular multiple of a number, say the 5th multiple of 7, then multiply 5*7.

Use multiples when finding the least common denominator, when working with fractions, or to find the least common multiple.

Given any number *n*, find the multiples of that number by the following:

First Multiple: 1*n

Second Multiple: 2*n

Third Multiple: 3*n

Fourth Multiple: 4*n

And so on, as far as you want to go.

Multiples of a number

15 multiples of $96 = 1440$

Multiply the numbers, $15 \times 96 = 1440$.

Multiples of a number

8 multiples of $7 = 56$

Multiply the numbers, $8 \times 7 = 56$.

56 is the 8th element in the 7s times table.

Multiples of a number

The multiples of $8 = \{8 \times 1, 8 \times 2, 8 \times 3, 8 \times 4, \ldots\}$

Select values for the number $a = 8$.

Continue as far as needed.

Multiples of a number

The multiples of $8 = \{8 \times 1, 8 \times 2, 8 \times 3, 8 \times 4, \ldots\}$

The multiples of 8 are $\{8, 16, 24, 32, \ldots\}$

Multiply the numbers, $8 \times 1 = 8$, $8 \times 2 = 16$, $8 \times 3 = 24$, $8 \times 4 = 32$, ...

Multiples of 8 are the multiplication times tables for 8. If a number is a multiple of 8 it is in the times table for 8.

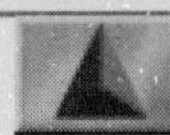

When we list 3, 6, 9, 12, we are counting by 3. These numbers are the **multiples** of 3. Each of the multiples of 3 can be represented by a rectangle with one side equal to 3. If any number can be put into a rectangle (with nothing left over) with one side equal to 3, then that number is a multiple of 3. Each of the rectangles below represent multiples of each of the sides.

Is there another way to arrange 12 unit squares into a rectangle?

Does every number have a set of multiples?

Can a multiple have more than one set of factors?

Is 1 a factor of every number or a multiple of every number?

Is the 8th multiple of 7 and the 7th multiple of 8 the same number?

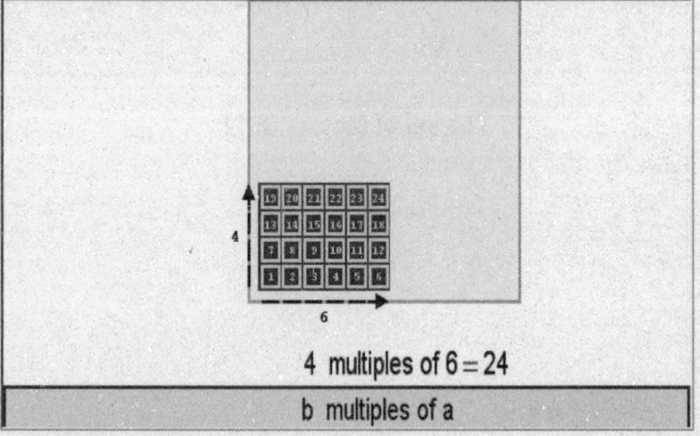

4 multiples of $6 = 24$

b multiples of a

Is there another way to arrange the 24 unit squares to form a rectangle? Is there another statement that can be made with the above array?

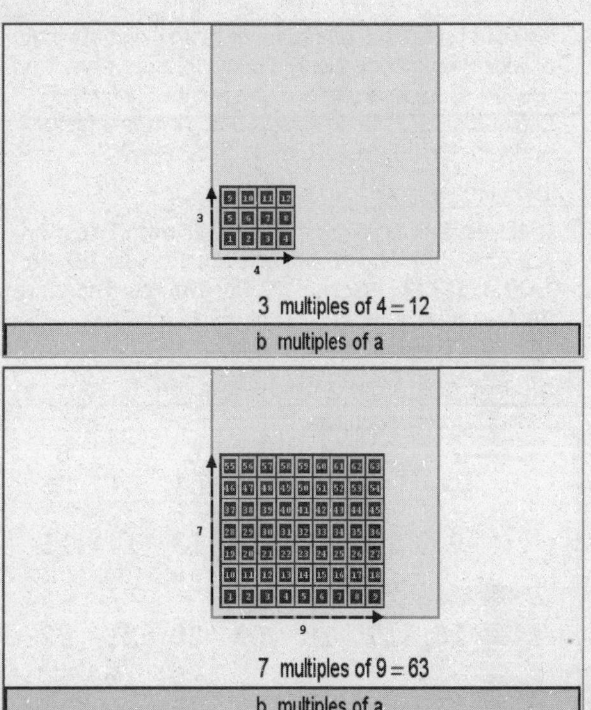

3 multiples of $4 = 12$

b multiples of a

7 multiples of $9 = 63$

b multiples of a

How many multiples of 3 does it take to use up all 63 unit squares?

The factors of a number are numbers that multiply to equal that number. Thinking in reverse; a factor divides a number evenly (with no remainder). We often must break a large number into its multiplicative components, called factors. Factors and factoring are an important tool in working with fractions and algebra problems.

You can list factors of a number by thinking of what divides the number evenly. Begin in order from 1 (of course) successively to half the number (why half? Can you guess?) to be sure you don't miss a factor. And you don't even have to do half. Why?

The number is **36**:

Is 1: yes; 2? Yes; 3? Yes; 4? Yes; 5? No; 6? Yes; 7 No; 8? NO; 9? Yes; 10 No; 11? No; 12: yes; 13? No; 14? No; 15? No; 16? No; 17? No; 18? Yes. Therefore the factors of 36 are: {1,2,3,4,6,9,12,18, 36}.

Here is a list of numbers. Notice we do not start with the number 1.

Next is the list of factors of each number.

2	3	4	5	6	7	8
1*2	1*3	1*4 2*2	1*5	1*6 2*3	1*7	1*8 2*4
9	**10**	**11**	**12**	**13**	**14**	**15**
1*9 3*3	1*10 2*5	1*11	1*12 2*6 3*4	1*13	1*14 2*7	1*15 3*5
16	**17**	**18**	**19**	**20**	**21**	**22**
1*16 2*8 4*4	1*17	1*18 2*9 3*6	1*19	1*20 2*10 4*5	1*21 3*7	1*22 2*11

As you step through the factors of each number, look at them carefully. What factor does every even numbers have in common? Which of the numbers only have one and themselves as factors?

Here is a list of numbers. Notice we do not start with the number 1.

2	3	4	5	6	7	8
9	10	11	12	13	14	15
16	17	18	19	20	21	22

and the list could go on as far we need it to go.

The set of factors of 12:

{1, 2, 3, 4, 6, 12}

List the factors of 12

After finding all the factors of each number you can list them in set notation. This will be helpful when finding the greatest common factor in the next module.

When we visualize a number as a rectangle, its factors are the lengths of its two sides. Most numbers have more than 1 pair of factors. If you can arrange a number of unit squares into a rectangle you can find the factors of the number.

For the visuals presented below, select a number **n** and change **a** to see if it is a factor of **n**. If **a** is a factor of **n** the unit squares will align to form a complete rectangle.

Is 3 a factor of 14? Is 8 a factor of 14?

What number is a factor of every number?

Are factors larger or smaller than the number?

If you know one factor of a number, how can you find another factor?

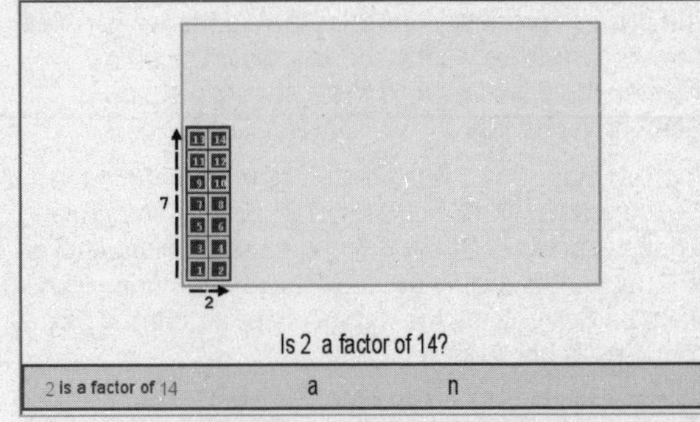

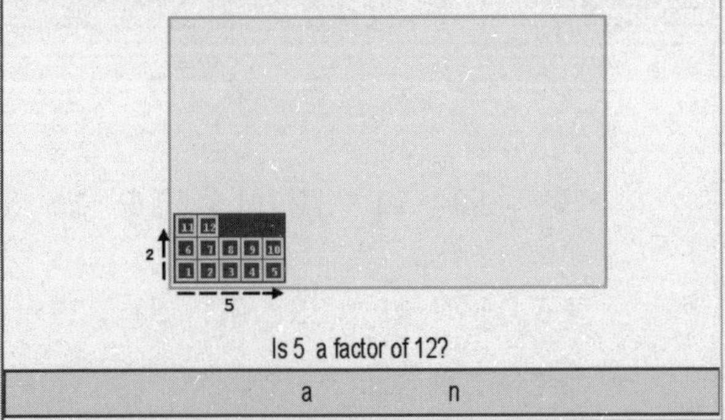

Is there any way to arrange the unit squares so that 5 is a factor of 12? Does 5 divide 12?

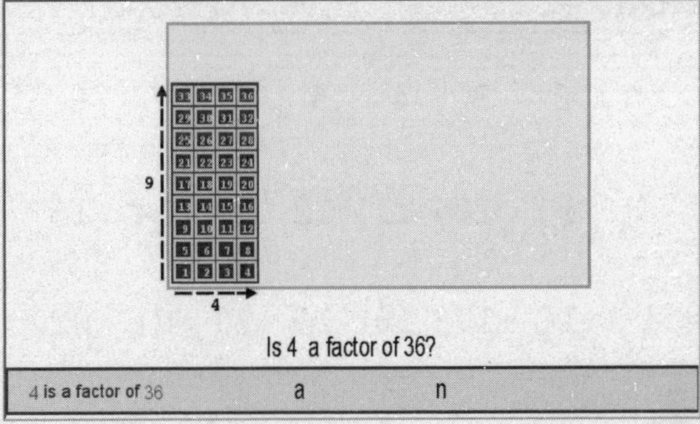

What is another factor pair for 36?

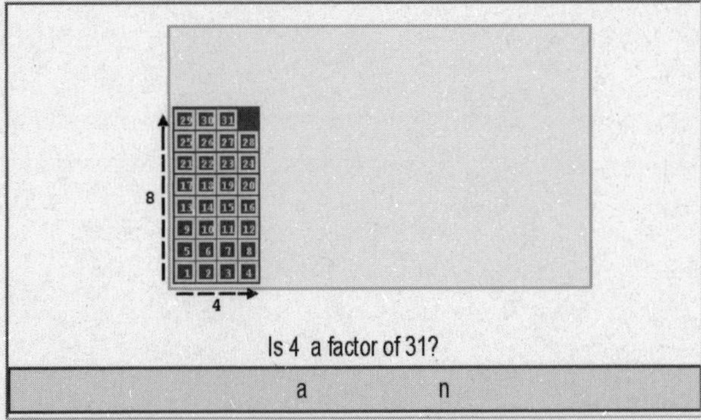

Can you find a number that does not have factors other than 1 and itself?

Prime Numbers

EnableMath

Numbers can be divided into two categories: prime and composite. A **prime number** has only two factors: 1 and the number. A **composite number** has more than two factors. In the module on fractions we will be interested in writing a composite number as the product of prime numbers. You will want to know what the first 10 prime numbers are because those are the one used as prime factors most often.

The process presented in the following frames is called a sieve: What we want to do is sift out the prime numbers by eliminating all the numbers with more than one factor pair.

You can make your own sieve: List the numbers from 2—100; cross off all multiples of 2; circle 3 and cross off all multiples of 3; circle 5 and cross off all multiples of 5...continue circling the next uncrossed number and all its primes until all the numbers are accounted for. Your circled numbers are prime.

The Prime Numbers

A prime number is a number whose factors are only 1 and itself.

Here is a list of numbers. Notice we do not start with the number 1.

2	3	4	5	6	7	8
9	10	11	12	13	14	15
16	17	18	19	20	21	22

and the list could go on as far as we need it to go.

Remember 1 is a factor of every number—we eliminate 1 from consideration.

Next, eliminate on the list any number that has more than one set of factors.

2 1·2	3 1·3	4 1·4 2·2	5 1·5	6 1·6 2·3	7 1·7	8 1·8 2·4
9 1·9 3·3	10 1·10 2·5	11 1·11	12 1·12 2·6 3·4	13 1·13	14 1·14 2·7	15 1·15 3·5
16 1·16 2·8 4·4	17 1·17	18 1·18 2·9 3·6	19 1·19	20 1·20 2·10 4·5	21 1·21 3·7	22 1·22 2·11

List all the factors of every number.

So the prime numbers are 2, 3, 5, 7, 11 ...

Any numbers left standing are called **PRIME numbers**.

The numbers we crossed out are called **COMPOSITE numbers**.

The number 1 is neither prime nor composite.

(2) 1·2	(3) 1·3	~~4~~ 1·4, 2·2	(5) 1·5	~~6~~ 1·6, 2·3	(7) 1·7	~~8~~ 1·8, 2·4
~~9~~ 1·9, 3·3	~~10~~ 1·10, 2·5	(11) 1·11	~~12~~ 1·12, 2·6, 3·4	(13) 1·13	~~14~~ 1·14, 2·7	~~15~~ 1·15, 3·5
~~16~~ 1·16, 2·8, 4·4	(17) 1·17	~~18~~ 1·18, 2·9, 3·6	(19) 1·19	~~20~~ 1·20, 2·10, 4·5	~~21~~ 1·21, 3·7	~~22~~ 1·22, 2·11

This sieve method emphasizes that prime factors are only 1 and the number.

If there is only one way to arrange a number of unit bars in a rectangular array, then we say that number is a prime number. If there is more than one way, then the number is a composite number.

Change **n.** Is that number prime or composite? Change **a** to see if you can form a rectangle with another factor, other than 1. What is the shape of the array if **a** is not a factor of **n**?

How can you tell if a number is prime or composite?

How do you know if you have tested all the possible factor pairs of a number?

How can you be certain a number is prime?

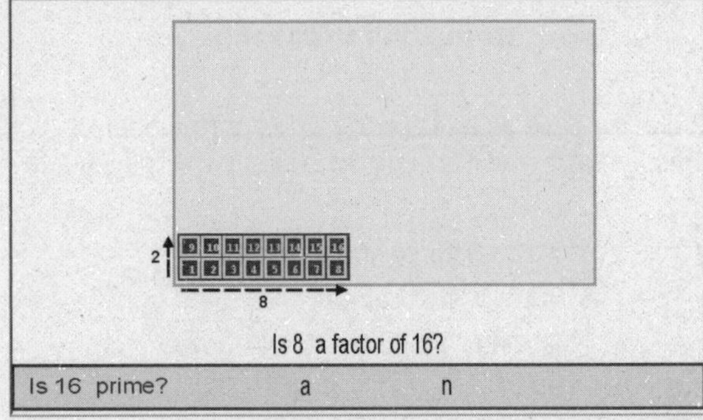

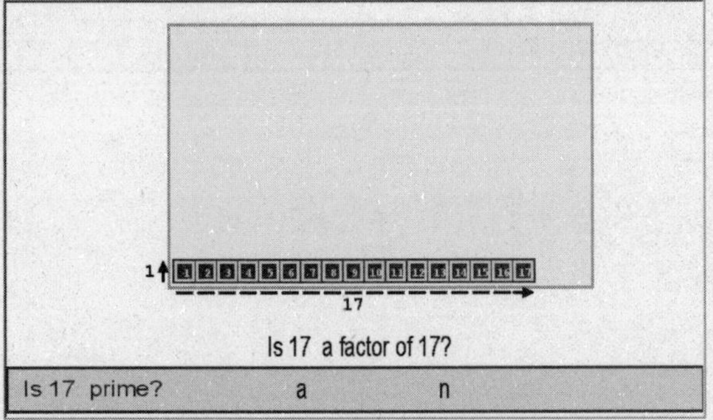

Can you make 17 into another complete rectangle? Is 17 a prime number? (Hint: A prime number cannot form a rectangle other than the 1 by.)

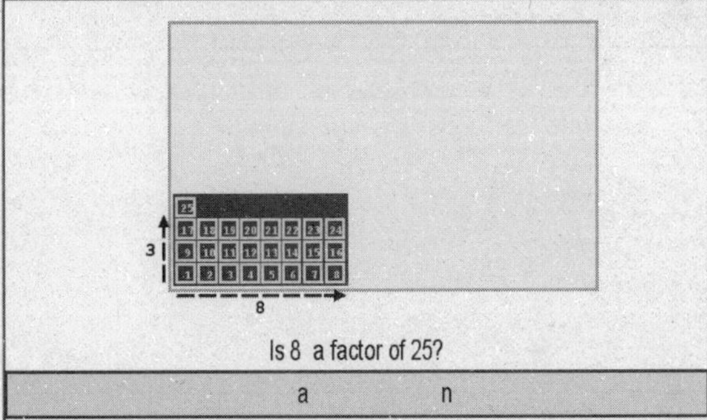

8 is not a factor of 25... so is 25 prime? How many numbers do you have to test to find out for sure?

Remember that multiplication is a short hand way to write repeated additions of the same number. Exponential notation is short hand method to write repeated multiplications of the same number. The **exponent** tells us how many times we use the number as a factor. The **base** is the number or factor that will be multiplied. Exponents are also called **powers.** You can use the words **exponents** and **powers** interchangeably. We say a number is **raised to a power.**

Evaluating exponents

Write the base as a factor the exponent number of times and then perform the multiplications to evaluate.

3^2 is read "three squared"
5^3 is read "five cubed"
2^4 is read "two to the fourth power"

Exponential Notation

$$\text{base}^{\text{exponent}} = 5^3$$

Select values for the **base** and **exponent**.

Exponential Notation

$$5^3 = 5 \times 5 \times 5$$

5^3 is read "5 **cubed.**" It means there are 3 multiples of 5.

Multiply the base times itself the exponent number of times.

Exponential Notation

$$9^5 = 9 \times 9 \times 9 \times 9 \times 9 = 59049$$

To evaluate 9^5 means to multiply 9 by itself 5 times.

Enter any 2—10 value for base and any 1—10 value for exponent. Here, the exponent indicates five factors of the base nine.

Exponents determine the number of times a base is multiplied by itself. The first visualization shows a picture of multiplying the first stack one more base time to get the second stack. In the second visualization, the value for a is indicated by a red dot on the vertical axis and the exponent is indicated along the horizontal axis. No matter what the base is, the visual pattern showing evaluated exponents is the same—a curve upward. Enter a number for **x** and then see what happens when the exponent **n** increases from 1 to 2 to 3 to 4 to 5.

What is the value of any number raised to the 1st power?

Can you predict what any number raised to the 0 power would be?

How much bigger is one stack from the stack to its left?

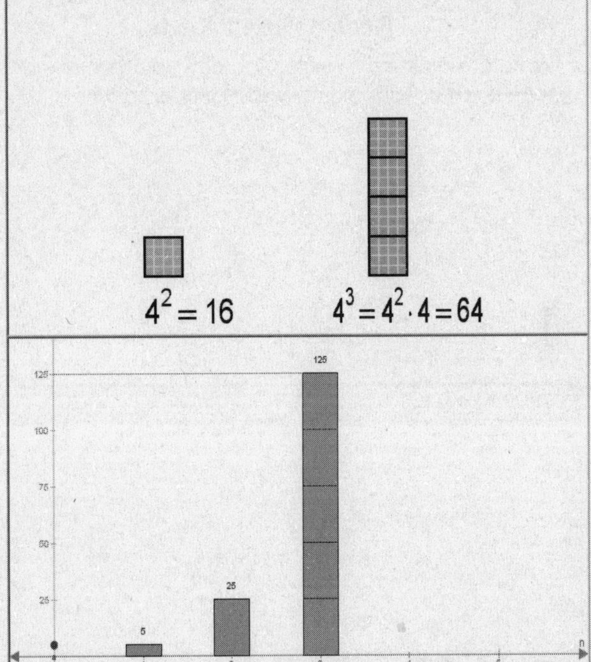

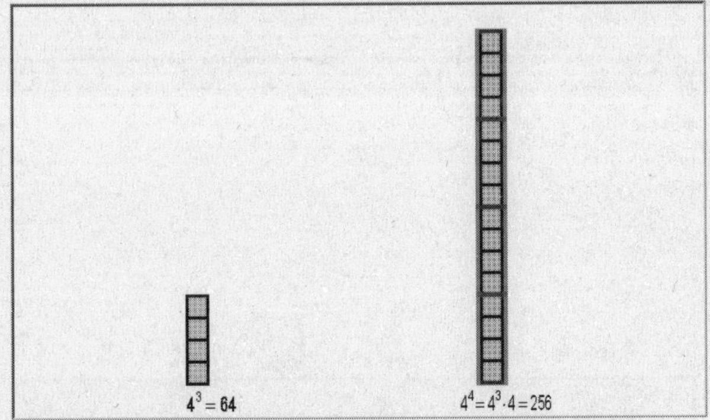

Change the base or exponent. Change the relative sizes by changing canvas. How do you justify that the stack on the right is a multiple of the stack on the left by a factor of your chosen base?

How many fives are in the stack of 25? How many 25's are in the stack of 125? What do you have to do to find 5^4?

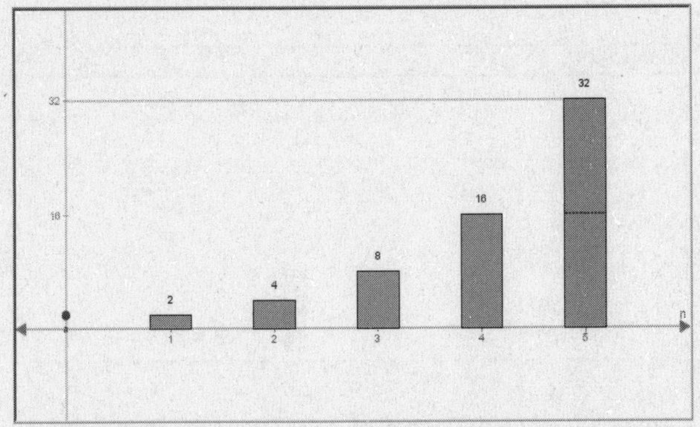

What do you predict is the value of 2^0? What should be the value of 2^6?

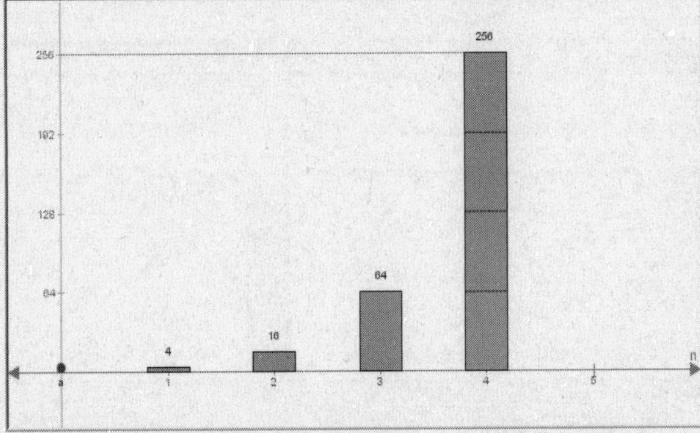

Can you think of a way to connect the powers of 4 with the powers of 2 shown to the left?

Roots

Roots are the opposite of exponents. Square root "undoes" a **perfect square**; cubed root "undoes" a **perfect cube** and so on.

Roots use a **radical** sign: √ - notice the difference between the radical and the long division sign. (There is no divisor space for the radical.)

The inside part is called the **radicand**.

If the root needed is other than square root, use an **index**—written in the crook of the radical in small print.

Finding Perfect Roots

Write the radicand in exponent form and then eliminate the root with the corresponding exponent.

Principle Square Roots

$$\sqrt[2]{\text{radicand}} = \sqrt[2]{81} = \sqrt[2]{9^2} = 9$$

The radical symbol $\sqrt[2]{}$ is used to express **square roots**. Squaring a value and taking the square root of the same value are inverse processes. One operation cancels or undoes the other.

Principle Square Roots

$$\sqrt[2]{\text{radicand}} = \sqrt[2]{196} = \sqrt[2]{14^2} = 14$$

The radical symbol $\sqrt[2]{}$ is used to express **square roots**. Squaring a value and taking the square root of the same value are inverse processes. One operation cancels or undoes the other.

Exponentiation and taking the root of a number are inverse process. One process undoes the other. Successively squaring and then taking the square root of 14, leave the value

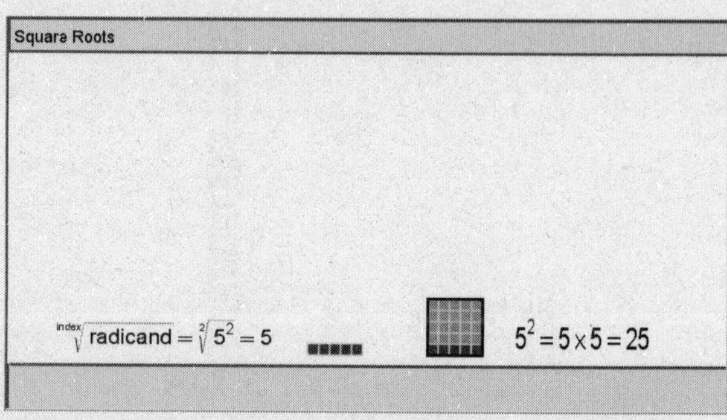

Point 2: Explore other perfect squares by changing the value of **root**. The value of radicand is a perfect square. Its root is the length of one side of the perfect square that is formed by squaring the root.

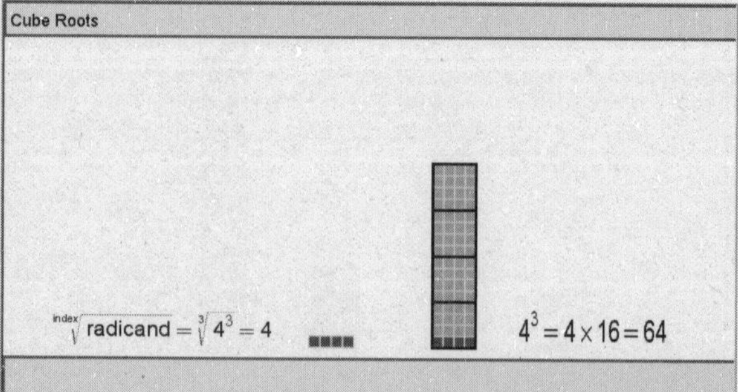

Point 3: Since 64=4x(4x4), the visualization relates the length of the side of a perfect 4x4 square to the root, or

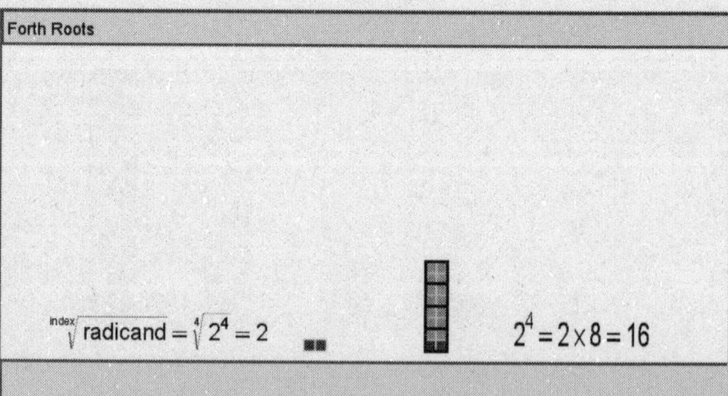

Point 4: The fourth root of 16 is 2. Taking the root of the number is short hand for repeated division. Think: 16/2=8, 8/2=4, 4/2=2. Check: 2x2x2x2=16.

Think of a rectangular array that is in the shape of a perfect square. The square root is the length of one side. Look at the visualizations below. Pick a number for the radicand and a number for the index. When the index is set you can try any number for **x** to see if it is a perfect root. Try setting the **index** to 3 and scan through values for **x** by clicking the joystick. What do you notice about the distance between perfect cubes to get successive cube roots?

Can prime numbers be perfect squares?

Can prime numbers be square roots?

If the radicand is a perfect 4th root will it also have a perfect square root?

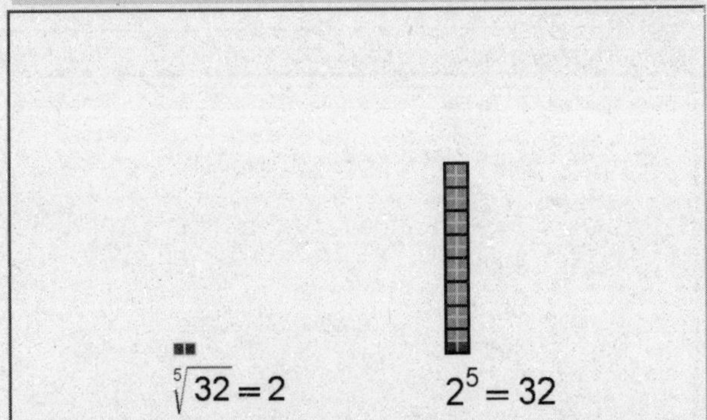

The fifth root of 32 is the same as the base of the number raised to the fifth power to get 32. Change the base and index for other combinations. How are the index and exponent related?

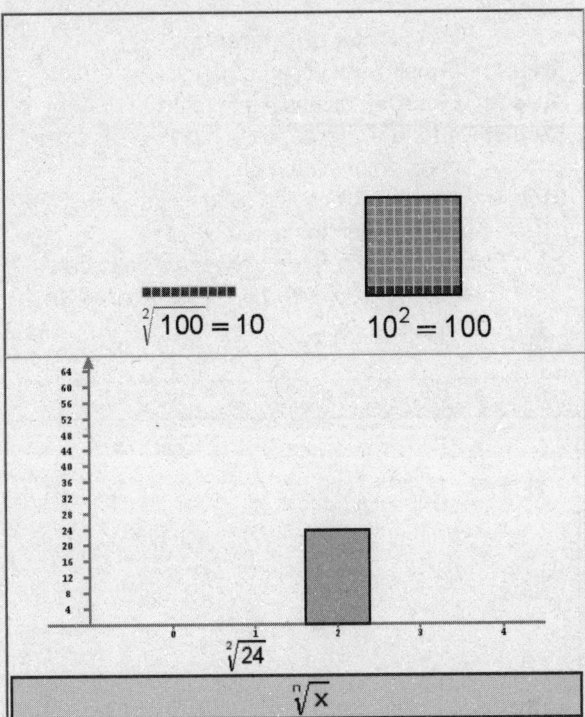

Set the index to 2. Click through x, beginning with x=1, until you have found the first 6 perfect squares.

Order of Operations

EnableMath

When we are performing more than one mathematical operation within an expression, we must know the sequence in which we have to perform each step. An order of operations has to exist or else we would get a different answer each time we carried out a series of mathematical steps for the same mathematical expression. There is a universally agreed upon **order of operations** that is a step-by step process for evaluating any mathematical expression in any field of study.

Order of Operations

Step 1: Simplify within parentheses.

Step 2: Evaluate exponents and roots.

Step 3: Perform multiplication and division as they appear from left to right.

Step 4: Perform addition and subtraction as they appear from left to right.

Hint: Some people like to remember the order by a little saying: PEMDAS—Please Excuse My Dear Aunt Sally.

$$4+8\div 2$$

$$\boxed{4+4=8}$$

Examples using Order of Operations:

2 $3\cdot\underline{(2+1)}-\underline{2^2}+\sqrt{\underline{(16)}}\div 2$

$3\cdot\ (3)\ \ -\underline{2^2}+\ \ 4\ \ \div 2$

The first two steps are underlined in the above problem. Evaluate parentheses first and then exponents. Evaluating roots is done with exponents, but here we show it with the parentheses step because it is important to simplify *within* radicals as if they were in parentheses.

Examples using Order of Operations:

2 $3\cdot\underline{(2+1)}-2^2+\sqrt{\underline{(16)}}\div 2$ Parentheses first

$3\cdot\ (3)\ \ -\underline{2^2}+\ \ 4\ \ \div 2$ Then exponents

$\underline{3\cdot 3}-4+\underline{4\div 2}$ Then multiply and divide

$9-4+2$ Add and subtract from left to right

$5+2$

7

Continuing with the whole problem. Notice that no addition or subtraction is done until the last two steps.

Examples using Order of Operations:

3 $5+5^2-\underline{(4-2)}$ Parentheses first

$5+\underline{5^2}-2$ Then exponents

$\underline{5+25}-2$ Add and subtract from left to right

$\underline{30-2}$

28

Skip steps in the process as necessary. Here there are no multiplications or divisions to perform.

Examples using Order of Operations:

5 $3^2+5\cdot\underline{(8-3)}$

$\underline{3^2}+5\cdot(5)$

$9+\underline{5\cdot 5}$

$\underline{9+25}=34$

Unless parentheses indicate otherwise, always multiply before adding.

How important are parentheses and other grouping symbols in working order of operation problems? Parentheses have the power to change the order of operation for an expression. In the visualization presented here you have the chance to see how parentheses affect the value of a mathematical expression by seeing the same expression in three different stages. Find which set of parentheses gives the biggest answer, or the smallest answer.

How does changing from the position of the parenthesis in case 1 to case 2 change the result? What changes?

Can parentheses be inserted so that they have no affect when the expression is simplified?

$$(1+2)\times 2^3 = 24$$

Case 1: $(a+b)\times c^d$

$$1+(2\times 2)^3 = 65$$

Case 2: $a+(b\times c)^d$

Is there a way to change the parentheses to get an even larger answer?

$$1+2\times(2^3) = 17$$

$$1+2\times 2^3 = 17$$

Case 3: $a+b\times(c^d)$

Are parentheses needed here? What would happen if the parentheses were not used?

$$(5+3)\times 4^2 = 128$$

Case 1: $(a+b)\times c^d$

Compare the problem above to the one to the right. Can the parentheses be moved so that a larger value can be found?

$$5+3\times(4^2) = 53$$

$$5+3\times 4^2 = 53$$

Case 3: $a+b\times(c^d)$

Are the parentheses needed here?

Multiplicative Properties

EnableMath

There are three underlying properties of whole numbers that we use to govern how numbers are combined. These three properties are formally presented here, but we have been using them all along. Along with the identities of addition and multiplication, the **associative**, **commutative** and **distributive properties** justify many of the actions taken in solving problems or even building understanding of new concepts.

Hint: The frames refer to properties of multiplication, but the properties also hold for addition.

Special Properties of Zero and One

1. 0 + a = a (Identity of addition)
2. 1*a = a (Identity of multiplication)
3. 0*a = 0 (Zero product property)
4. a÷0 = undefined

Division by zero is called "undefined" because division by zero is not realizable; it has no physical meaning.

Commutative, Associative and Distributive Properties

Commutative Property: The order in which you multiply two numbers does not affect the result.

2*8=8*2=16

24*3=3*24=72

Commutative, Associative and Distributive Properties

Associative Property: The manner in which you group numbers does not affect the product.

(2*2)*4=2*(2*4)=16

(3*8)*3=3*(8*3)=72

The associative and commutative properties also work for addition. Notice where the parentheses are—it doesn't matter which two you multiply (add) first, you get the same answer.

Commutative, Associative and Distributive Properties

Distributive Property: Multiplication is distributive over addition.

3*(6+4)=3*6+3*4=18+12=30

compare: 3*(6+4)=3*10=30

The distributive property is used time and again to solve problems and justify building new concepts. We use it backwards and forwards. Notice that the number on the outside of the parentheses is multiplied to BOTH inside numbers.

The visualizations below justify the associative, commutative and distributive properties of whole numbers. Use the joystick to change values for **a**, **b**, and **c**.

In which order do you want to multiply two numbers?

If three numbers are being multiplied, which two are combined first?

Which operation comes first multiplication or addition?

When multiplying, which side of the rectangle is the bottom? Which is the vertical side? Does it matter?

Does it matter how the stacks are arranged for multiplication? Which side is the bottom?

Can you visualize the two rectangles formed by the multiplication process in the distributive property visual?

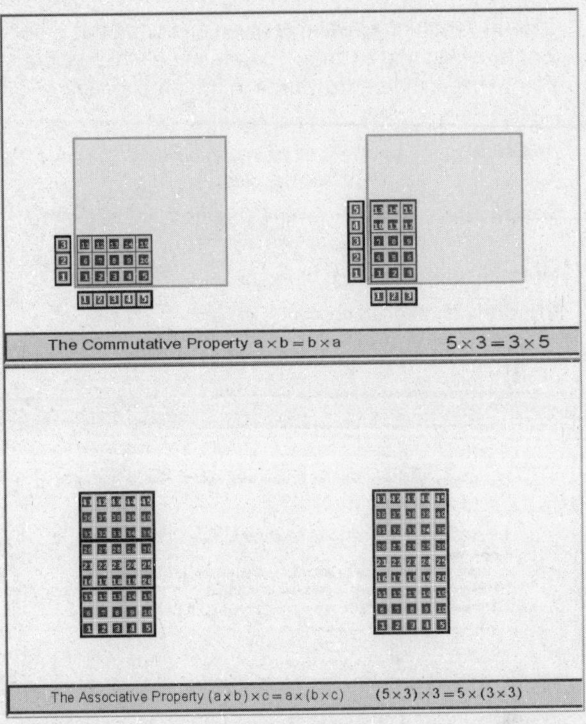

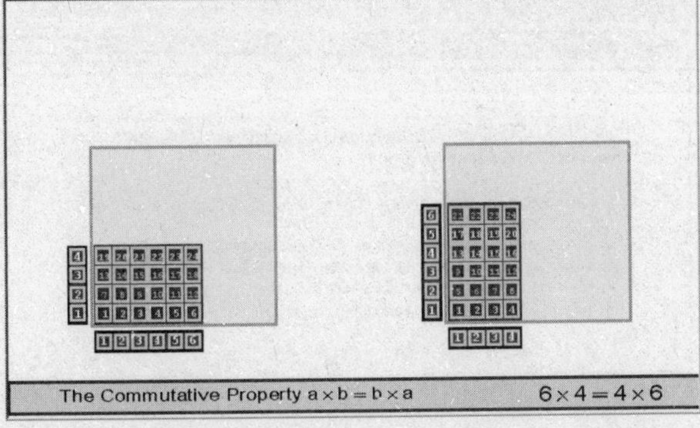

How do you know that order does not matter in multiplication? How do you know the two rectangles are equal?

The first rectangle is three sets of 3x5's. The second rectangle shows (3x3)'s aligned in columns—5 columns of 9.

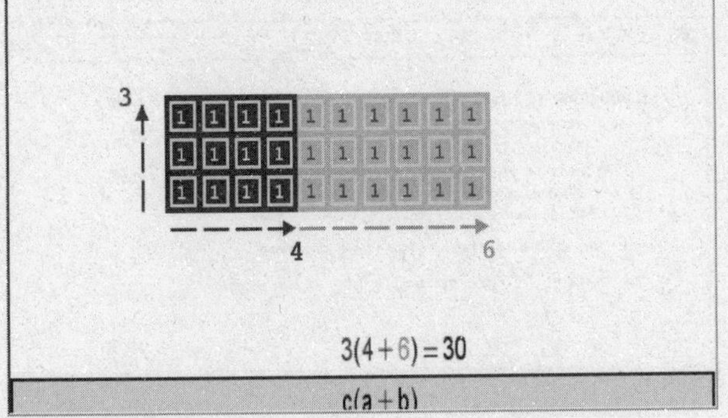

How many blue unit squares and how many yellow unit squares? Is distributive commutative? Does (4+6)3 = 30? Can you model that on screen?

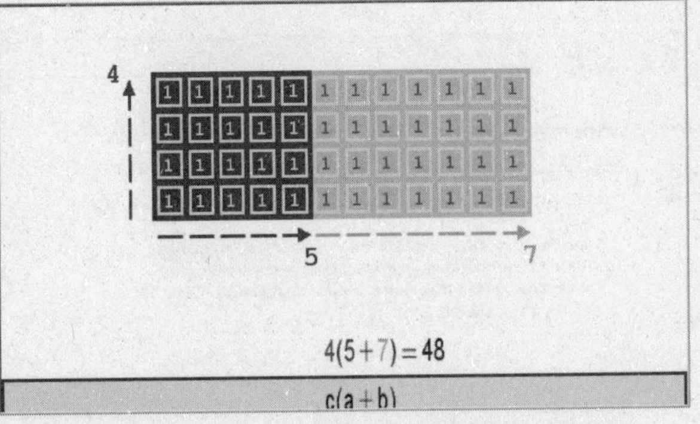

Any numbers work. In later modules we will be using unknown variables to stand in for one of the numbers inside the parentheses. It might look like 4(x + 7). Can you use the distributive property to remove the parentheses?

In solving problems use all the tools that are available. Mathematics gives you tools to solve word problems. The more tools you know how to appropriately use, the better problem solver you will become. You already have some tools: addition, subtraction, multiplication, and division of whole numbers. Now is the time to put those tools to use.

Identify what information is given and what the problem is asking you to find. To determine which operation to use look for key words in the problem statement.

Addition: sum, total, added to, more, how many, how much, increased by, plus

Subtraction: difference, minus, less than, decreased by, how many less, take away

Multiplication: product, times, of

Division: divided by, quotient, per, each

Case I: Addition

If you add 47 chairs to 56 chairs, how many chairs would you have?

Select values for **a** and **b**.

Case I: Addition

If you add 47 chairs to 56 chairs, how many chairs would you have?

1. Record what you know: Two groups of chairs, one with 47 chairs and another with 56 chairs.
2. Idenifty what you are asked to find: The total number of chairs.
3. Determine the necessary math operation: Addition
4. Translate the word problem into a math statement: $47+56=?$
5. Solve: $47+56=103$ total chairs.

Answer

The key word is add.

Case II: Subtraction

If you take 150 chairs from a group of 1149 chairs, how many chairs would be left in the group?

1. Record what you know: Total number of chairs 1149; Number of chairs removed $=150$.
2. Idenifty what you are asked to find: The number of chairs that remain.
3. Determine the necessary math operation: Subtraction
4. Translate the word problem into a math statement: $1149-150=?$
5. Solve: $1149-150=999$ remaining chairs.

Answer

The key word is "take" indicating subtraction. Notice that you must determine which number to subtract—subtraction is not commutative.

Case III: Multiplication

If you have 35 rows of chairs of 28 chairs, how many total chairs are there?

1. Record what you know: Number of rows $=35$; Number of chairs in each row $=28$.
2. Idenifty what you are asked to find: The total number of chairs.
3. Determine the necessary math operation: Multiplication
4. Translate the word problem into a math statement: $35\times 28=?$
5. Solve: $35\times 28=980$ chairs.

Answer

In context you know this is a rectangular array—key word is "of".

Case IV: Division

If you have 13 rows of chairs and a total of 52 chairs, how many chairs are in each row?

1. Record what you know: Number of rows $=13$; Number of chairs $=52$.
2. Idenifty what you are asked to find: The number of chairs in one row.
3. Determine the necessary math operation: Division
4. Translate the word problem into a math statement: $\frac{52}{13}=?$
5. Solve: $\frac{52}{13}=4$ chairs per row.

Answer

Total is NOT the key word here. Use the context of the problem to determine that the total chairs can be visualized

When you are doing word problems draw the same picture representations that you did when you worked on pure arithmetic problems. Only this time, label the objects in the picture. A word problem is an extension of the regular arithmetic problem. We use the same algorithms to solve them. Make up your own word problems to go with each of the visualizations below.

What determines the operation being demonstrated in each of the visuals here?

Other than key words, what clues do you use for working word problems?

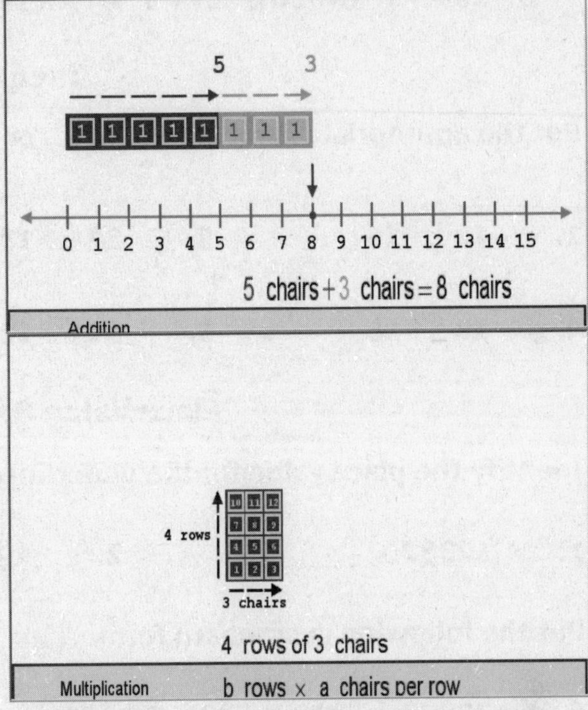

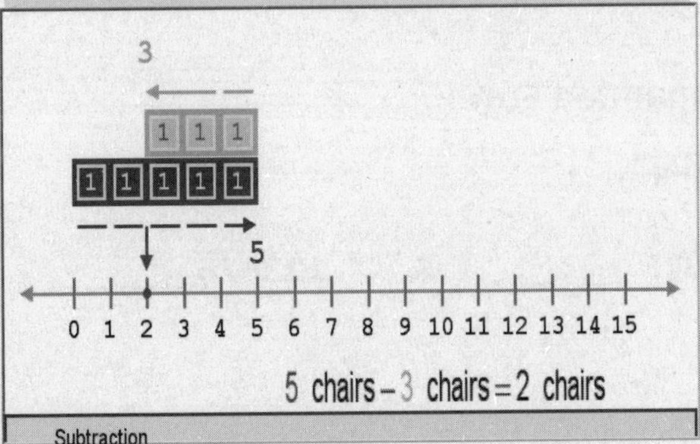

Are we "taking away" three chairs?

If you can draw a picture of the word problem by making a rectangle—what operation is illustrated?

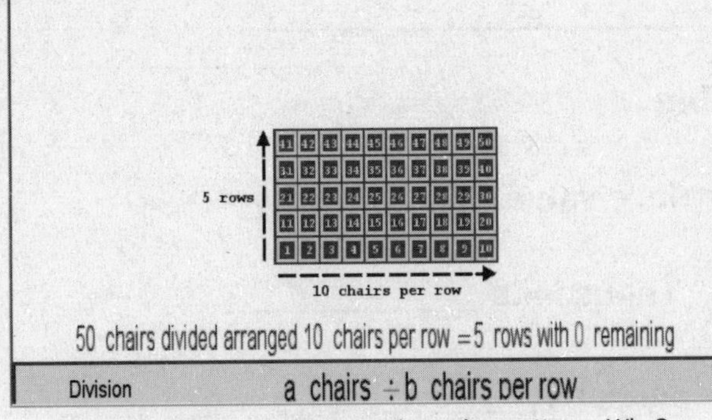

Take care in setting up division—the order matters. Why?

Whole Numbers

1. Is 24 to the LEFT or RIGHT of 43? __________
2. Is 13 to the LEFT or RIGHT of 23? __________
3. Is 24 to the LEFT or RIGHT of 3? __________
4. Is 45 to the LEFT or RIGHT of 43? __________
5. Is 61 to the LEFT or RIGHT of 13? __________
6. Is 33 to the LEFT or RIGHT of 12? __________

Inequalities

Put the appropriate symbol (use >, <, or =) in the box.

1. 12 □ 16 **2.** 32 □ 13 **3.** 56 □ 75

4. 16 □ 16 **5.** 81 □ 66

Place Value & Expanded Form

Identify the place value for the underlined digit.

1. $123\underline{8}76$ ______ **2.** $1\underline{2}3876$ ______ **3.** $12387\underline{6}$ ______

Put the following in standard form.

6. 30000 + 2000 + 500 + 70 + 4 ____________________

7. 6000 + 30 + 1 ____________________

8. 700000 + 9000 + 30 ____________________

Rounding

Round off the 589,627,501 to the indicated place value.

1. Hundreds __________ **2.** Thousands __________

3. Ten thousands __________ **4.** Millions __________

5. Tens __________ **6.** *Billions __________

Adding Whole Numbers

Align in columns and add.

1. 452 + 510 + 331

2. 99 + 120 + 15 + 7

3. 310078 + 45902 + 21991

4. 54 + 3 + 101 + 31

5. 12 + 45 + 21 + 13 + 43

6. 1011 + 3012 + 45 + 120

Subtracting Whole Numbers

Align in columns and subtract.

1. 569 – 347

2. 834 – 198

3. 67103 – 23985

4. 10009 – 8814

5. 260198 — 120755

6. 835611— 200099

Multiplying Whole Numbers

1. Multiply the following:

a. 4 * 7 = ______ **b. 5 * 2 = ______** **c. 4 * 9 = ______**

a. 6 * 3 = ______ **b. 8 * 7 = ______** **c. 6 * 7 = ______**

2. 12985 * 2431

3. 5409 * 387

4. 3281902 * 5482

Dividing Whole Numbers

Divide the following.

1. a. 42 /7 = ______ **b. 24 / 3 = ______** **c. 48 / 6 = ______**

d. 42 /5 = ______ **e. 84 / 9 = ______** **f. 45 / 6 = ______**

2. $38\overline{)2548}$

3. $45\overline{)745902}$

5. $891\overline{)1003567}$

Multiples

1. Find the 12th multiple of 6. ____________

2. Find the 40th multiple of 12. ____________

3. Find 23 multiples of 17. ____________

4. Find 32 multiples of 543. ____________

5. Find the 312th multiple of 567. ____________

Factors

1. Is 8 a factor of 56? ________ 2. Is 7 a factor of 56? ________

3. Is 10 a factor of 55? ________ 4. Is 5 a factor of 45? ________

5. Is 5 a factor of 72? ________ 6. Is 3 a factor of 99? ________

Prime Numbers

1. Is 14 a prime number? ________ 2. Is 26 a prime number? ________

3. Is 23 a prime number? ________ 4. Is 31 a prime number? ________

5. Is 39 a prime number? ________ 6. Is 18 a prime number? ________

Exponents

Write using exponents.

1. 4*4*4*4 = ____________

2. 3*3*3*3*3*3*3= ____________

3. 12*12*12*12*12= ____________

4. 1*1*1*1*1*1*1*1= ____________

Change from exponent form to multiplication.

5. 5^6 = ____________ 6. 7^3 = ____________

Roots

Find the indicates root.

1. $\sqrt{52}$ = ________ 2. $\sqrt[3]{5^3}$ = ________

3. $\sqrt[4]{7^4}$ = ________ 4. $\sqrt{13^2}$ = ________

5. $\sqrt[4]{2^4}$ = ________ 6. $\sqrt{9^2}$ = ________

Order of Operations

1. 18+2(3*3-4)+6=________ 2. $16 - 2^3 \div 4*2$=________

3. 3(9-5) + 5(6-3)=________ 4. $6(7-5)^2 + 9(6-5)^2$ =________

5. Does $4+2^3 = (4+2)^3$? How do you know?

Multiplicative Properties

Rewrite using the appropriate property. Do not simplify.

1. 27*43 2. 99*21 3. 16*(12*15)

4. (12*14)*15 5. 4(5 + 7)

Word Problems

Solve the following problems.

1. **What is the balance of the gift account if Dilbert adds his $12 to the $42 already in the account?**

2. **If Alice spends $25 out of the account total from above for the pointy haired boss's birthday present, how much is left in the account?**

3. **If there are 4 people in the office and they each contribute $23 for their donation to Asock's recovery fund, how much was collected?**

4. **Ratbert decided that the $457 profit from Elbonian munitions sales should be given to the top three performers in the company. How much did each get?**

5. **Two offices combined their resources to send the pointy haired boss to Boston for a lobster fest. Dilbert said he would double their total. If one office gathered $23 and the other office gathered $41, how much money was available to send the boss to Boston?**

2. Fractions

In Module 1 you learned about whole numbers. Here we deal with "part" numbers, numbers that do not represent wholes, but instead represent parts or fractions of wholes. You will find the arithmetic of fractions very different from the arithmetic of whole numbers. For example, multiplying fractions generally makes the result smaller, and dividing makes it larger. Multiplying and dividing fractions are generally easier to do and learn than adding and subtracting, so we study them first. These are some of the things you will come to understand by visualizing fractions as fraction bars.

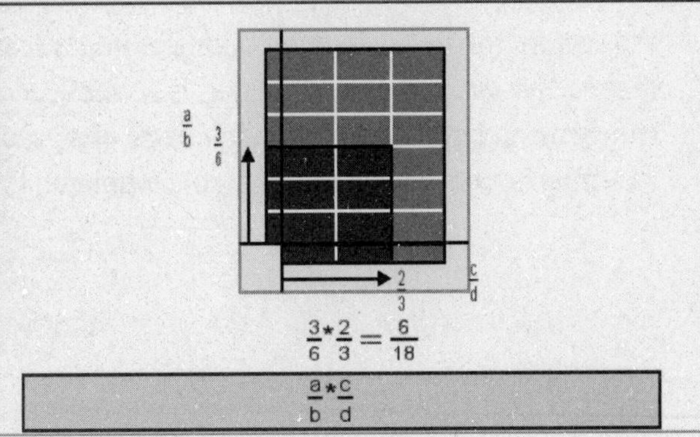

As you know, whole numbers cannot describe every math situation. **Fractions** are introduced to describe and account for parts of a whole unit. Fractions are ratios that tell us how many parts of one thing we have in relation to how many parts the whole has been subdivided or partitioned.

We write a fraction using two numbers and a **fraction bar**, represented as either —, or /. The bar means division, because a fraction is a whole divided into parts. The top number is called the **numerator** and indicates how many parts are used. The bottom number is the **denominator** and indicates how many parts make up a whole unit. $\frac{numerator}{denominator} = \frac{parts}{whole}$

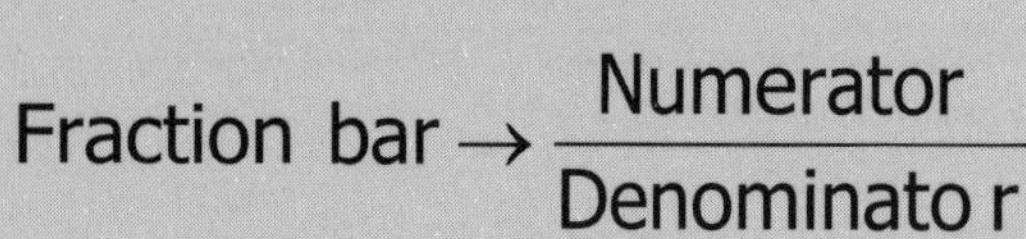

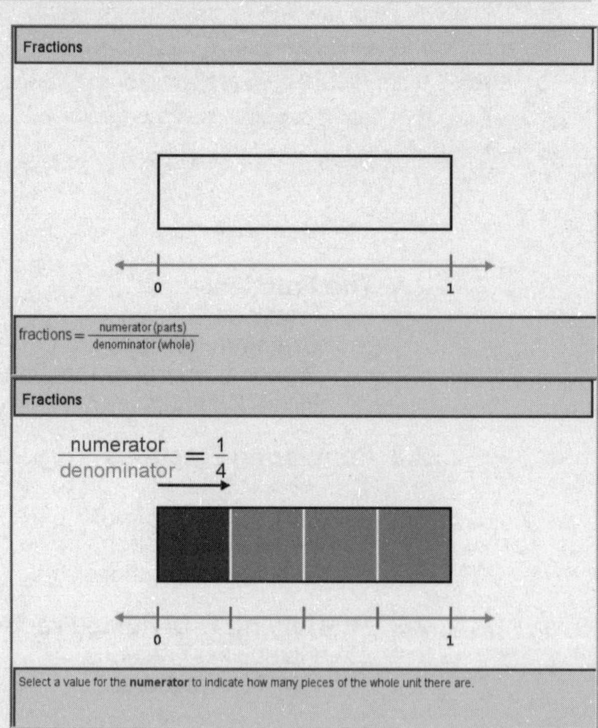

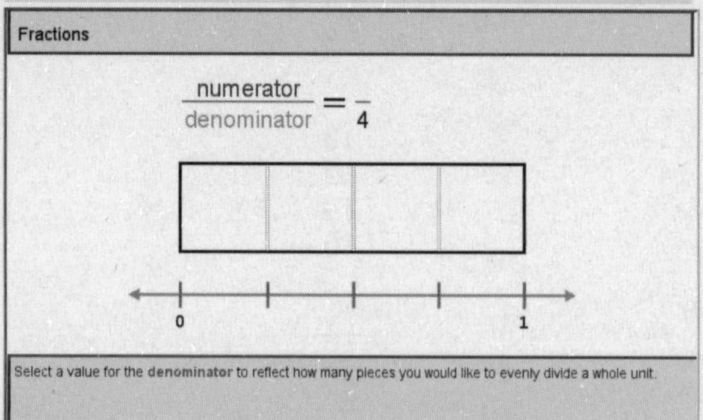

The unit bar is divided into four equal sections. The denominator tells how many equal partitions the whole unit bar is divided into.

The numerator, the top number, tells how many of the parts are used. Above one part is used out of the four parts making the whole unit bar.

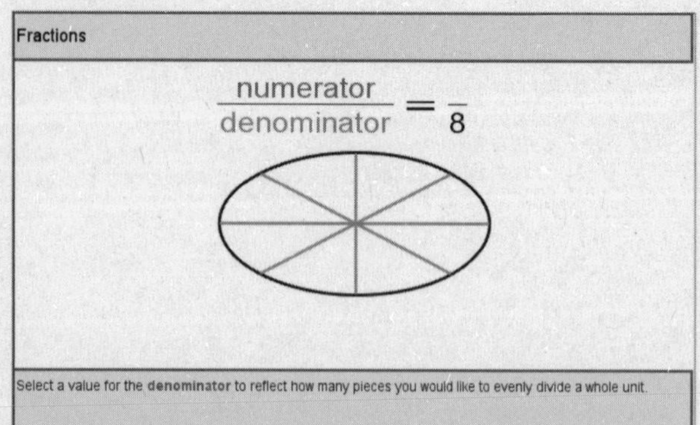

Fractions
numerator / denominator = 8
Select a value for the denominator to reflect how many pieces you would like to evenly divide a whole unit.

Circles can also represent fractions. The denominator tells how many equal size wedges the circle is subdivided into.

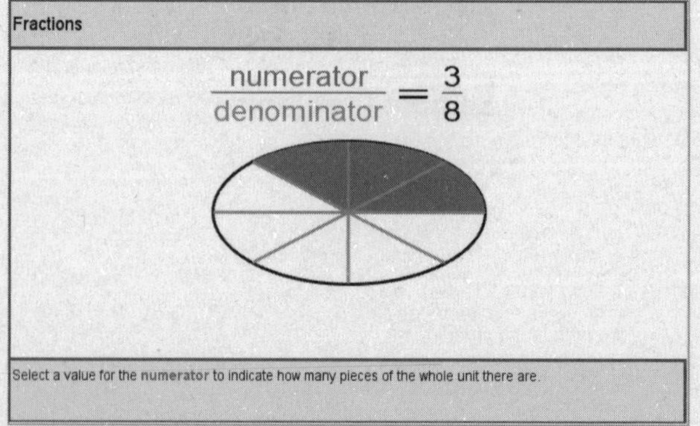

The numerator indicates how many parts of the whole there are. If the circle above represents pizza, there are three pieces left. So, 5/8 of the pizza has been eaten. Yum!

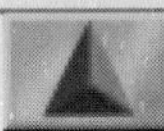

When we put just the whole numbers on a number line we leave huge gaps between them. We will start filling these gaps. The first numbers that we will fill them with are the fractions.

Fractions are visualized using a number bar divided into sections. The number bar is positioned over a number line so that you get a general idea of the size of each fraction compared to the number 1 or one whole. Use the joystick to change the values of the numerator and denominator.

What does the **denominator** (bottom number) count up? What does the **numerator** (top number) count up?

If the numerator increases and the denominator stays the same will the fraction get larger or smaller?

If the numerator stays the same and the denominator increases then will the fraction get smaller or larger?

What is the value of any fraction whose numerator and denominator are the same?

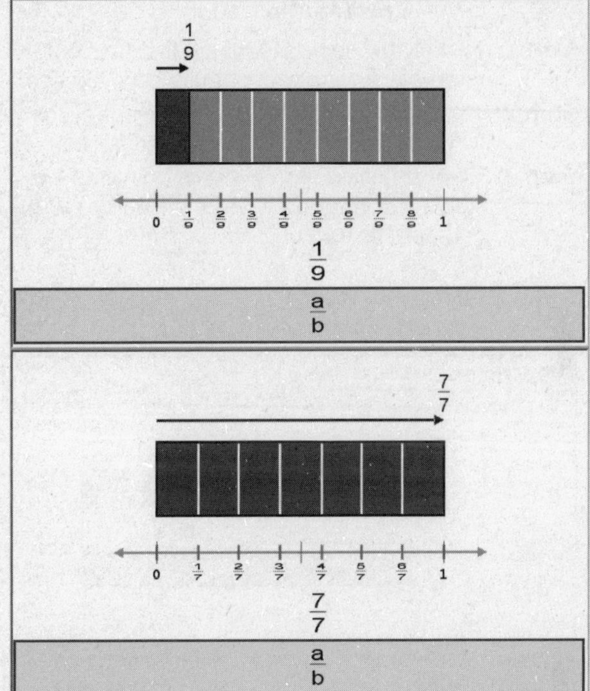

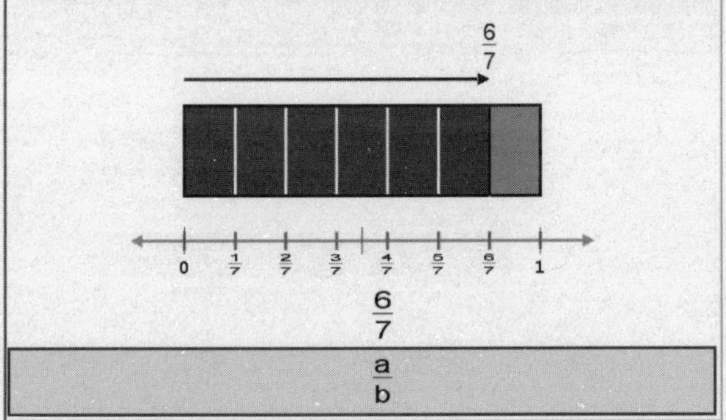

Compare the above fraction with the fraction in the frame below. Which one is bigger?

What is 7÷7?

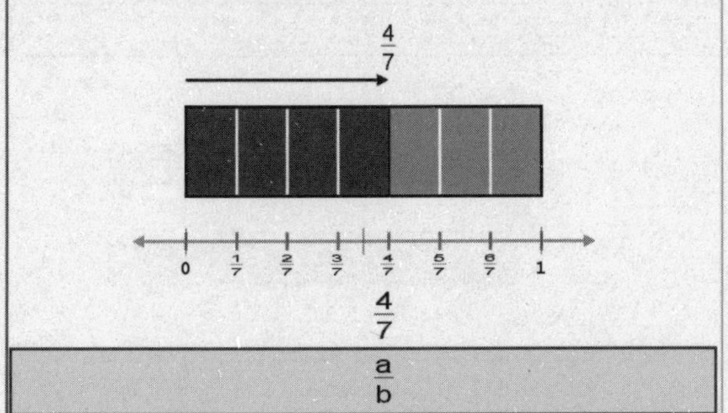

Compare the above fraction with the one to the right. What changed? What stayed the same? Is 4/7>4/9?

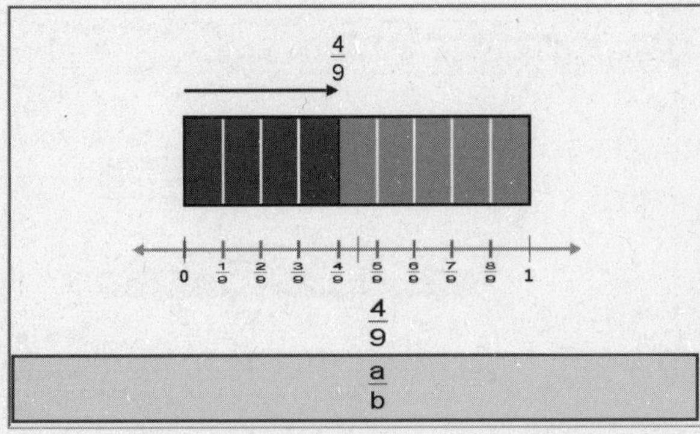

Enter any fraction you want to see a picture of that fraction and its relation to one whole unit.

Just like with whole numbers, when we have two fractions, only one of the following three statements can be true:

The first fraction is greater than the second $\frac{a}{b} > \frac{c}{d}$

The first fraction is less than the second $\frac{a}{b} < \frac{c}{d}$

The first fraction is equal to the second $\frac{a}{b} = \frac{c}{d}$

Cross Multiplication

Step 1: Multiply the numerator of the first fraction times the denominator of the second fraction.

Step 2: Multiply the denominator of the first fraction times the numerator of the second fraction.

Step 3: Compare, in order, the results from step 1 to step 2 and insert the correct inequality symbol between the fractions.

Hint: A quick way to determine the larger fraction is choose the one whose value is closer to 1.

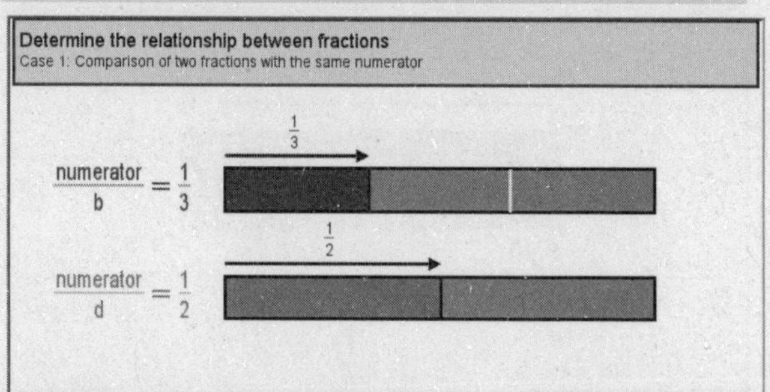
Determine the relationship between fractions
Case 1: Comparison of two fractions with the same numerator
numerator / b = 1/3
numerator / d = 1/2
When two or more fractions have the same numerator, the value of the fraction with the larger denominator is less than the fraction with the smaller denominator, 1/3 < 1/2.

Consider fractions with the same numerator. Change the values of the denominators **b** and **d**. Which whole unit is broken into more partitions? Which whole unit bar's partitions are smaller in size? What is true about the relative size of fractions with the same numerator?

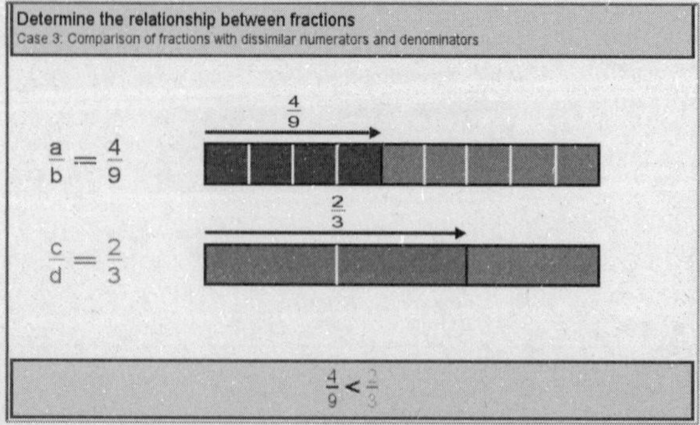
Determine the relationship between fractions
Case 3: Comparison of fractions with dissimilar numerators and denominators
a/b = 4/9
c/d = 2/3
4/9 < 2/3

Comparing fractions with dissimilar denominators and numerators takes more thought. First, think about the how many partitions each is divided into. Then, consider the size of how many of each there are of each in relation to the other.

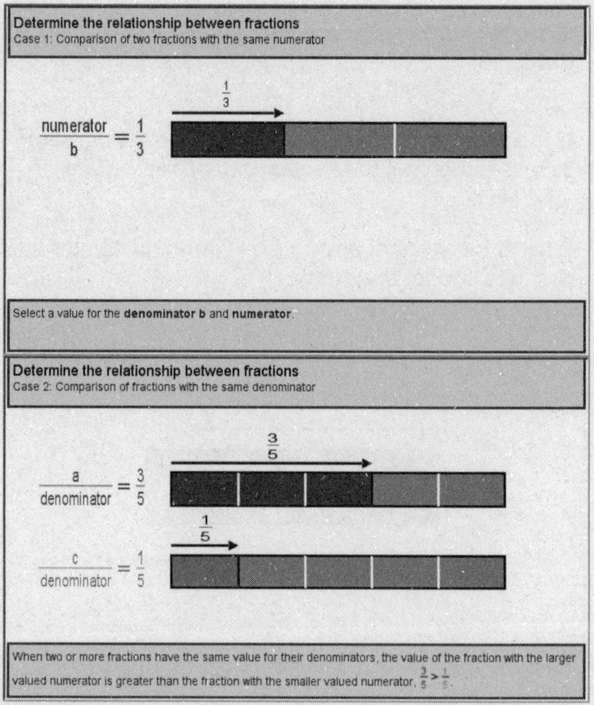
Determine the relationship between fractions
Case 1: Comparison of two fractions with the same numerator
numerator / b = 1/3
Select a value for the denominator b and numerator.
Determine the relationship between fractions
Case 2: Comparison of fractions with the same denominator
a / denominator = 3/5
c / denominator = 1/5
When two or more fractions have the same value for their denominators, the value of the fraction with the larger valued numerator is greater than the fraction with the smaller valued numerator, 3/5 > 1/5.

Consider fraction with the same denominator. How many partitions is each whole unit bar divided into? When **a>c**, which fraction is larger? When **a<c**, which fraction is smaller? What is true about the relative size of fractions with the same denominator?

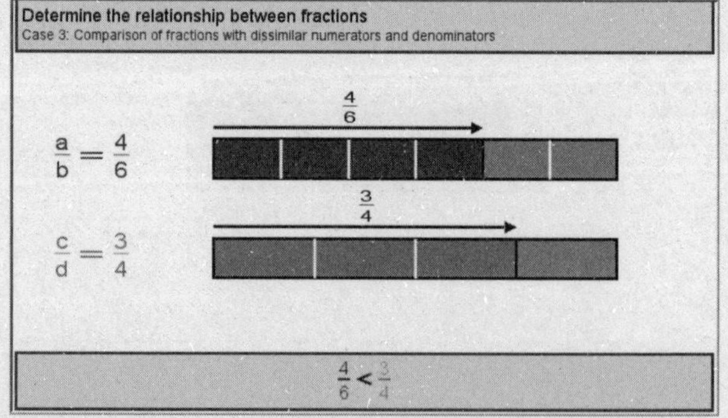
Determine the relationship between fractions
Case 3: Comparison of fractions with dissimilar numerators and denominators
a/b = 4/6
c/d = 3/4
4/6 < 3/4

When fractions are too close in value to estimate which is larger, use cross multiplication to make an accurate determination. Which is larger the product **(a** x **d)** or **(c** x **b)**?

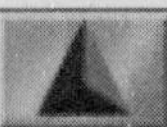

Two fractions can be compared by looking at their fraction bars. Here, two whole unit bars are partitioned and colored based on the values of **a/b** and **c/d**. Then, the fractions are compared and ordered based on their relative size.

Use the joystick to change the values of **a/b** and **c/d** and compare fractions.

What determines how many partitions a whole unit bar is divided into?

What determines the size of parts that make up the fraction? Is each part the same size?

What tells you how many pieces there are?

What would zero fourths look like?

Can a whole unit bar be divided into zero pieces?

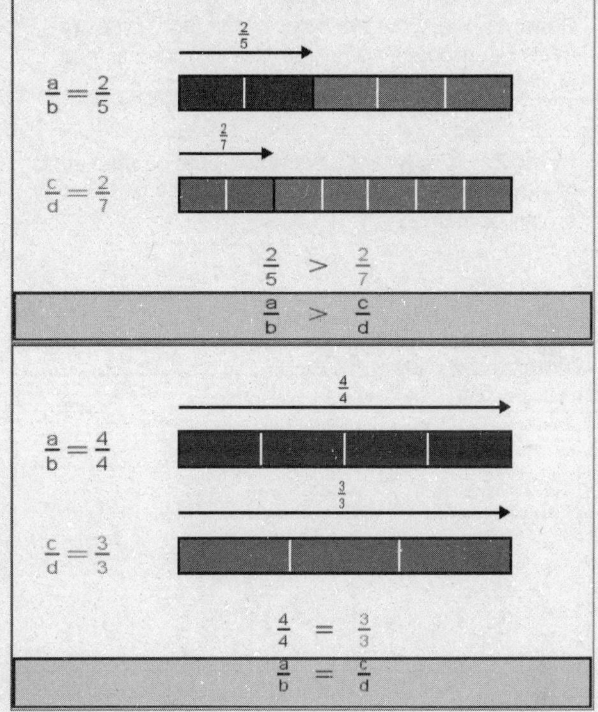

What can you surmise about the fraction with a numerator value equal to the denominator value? Is 4/4 = 3/3?

Is 3/3 = 1 whole unit?

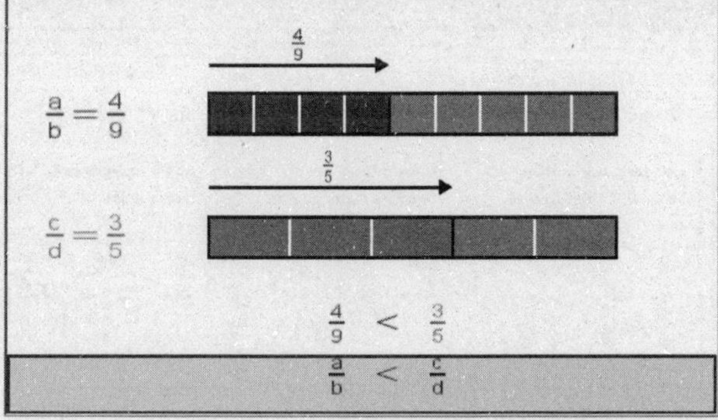

Which fraction has been divided into more pieces? Which fraction has smaller size pieces? How many pieces of each whole unit bar are colored? What determines how many pieces are colored?

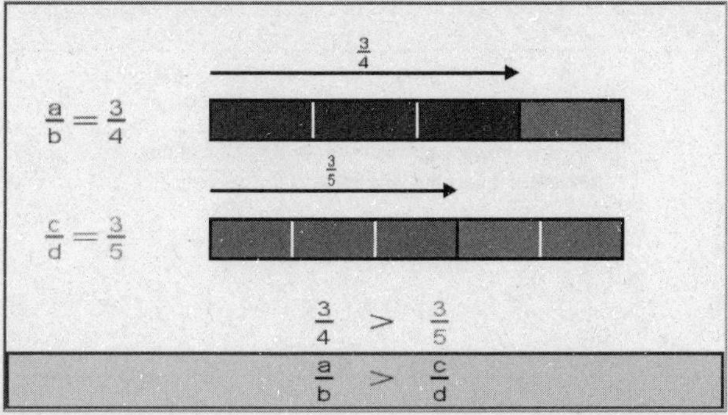

If the numerators are the same which fraction is larger? How can you tell?

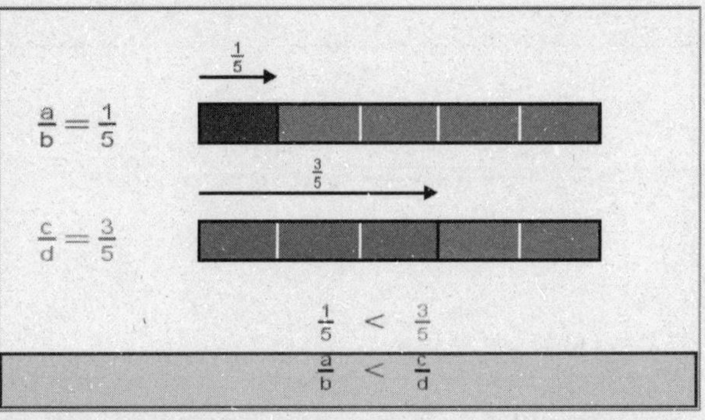

If the denominators are the same what do you look at to order the fractions?

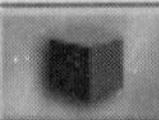

Proper & Improper Fractions

EnableMath

There are two types of fractions, **proper** and **improper**.

For a fraction to be **proper** the value of its numerator must be less than the value of its denominator. **Improper fractions** have numerator values that are greater then or equal to the value of their denominators.

Improper fractions can be equivalently expressed as a **mixed number**, which is a whole number plus a fraction.

Point 1: We show examples of the three types of fractions: proper fractions, improper fractions, and mixed number fractions.

Point 2: Is a dynamic example. Change the values of **numerator/denominator** to verify whether it is proper or improper.

Different kinds of Fractions

Proper Fractions

numerator is smaller than the denominator

$\frac{1}{2}, \frac{3}{5}, \frac{7}{11}$

Different kinds of Fractions

Proper Fractions	*Improper Fractions*	
numerator is smaller than the denominator	numerator is larger than the denominator	
$\frac{1}{2}, \frac{3}{5}, \frac{7}{11}$	$\frac{2}{1}, \frac{7}{5}, \frac{14}{11}$	

Point 1: Notice the difference between the value of the numerators compared to denominators.

Different kinds of Fractions

Proper Fractions	*Improper Fractions*	*Mixed Numbers*
numerator is smaller than the denominator	numerator is larger than the denominator	whole number and a proper fraction
$\frac{1}{2}, \frac{3}{5}, \frac{7}{11}$	$\frac{2}{1}, \frac{7}{5}, \frac{14}{11}$	$1\frac{5}{18}, 5\frac{5}{12}, 1\frac{3}{7}$

For mixed numbers, the whole number part is *added to* the fraction part, but the addition sign is omitted.

$\frac{6}{5}$ is an improper fraction, because the value of the numerator is greater than the value of the denominator.

Point 2: Test values for **a** and **b**. What type of fraction have you created? How do you know?

$\frac{7}{12}$ is a proper fraction, because the value of the numerator is less than the value of the denominator.

Here, the numerator is smaller than the denominator. So, 7/12 is a proper fraction.

If the value of a fraction is less than one, it is called **proper.** If its value is equal to or greater than 1, a fraction is called **improper**.

Locate the fraction on a number line to visualize where the fraction is relative to the closest whole number. If it is to the **left** of 1 then it is a proper fraction; if it's to the **right** of 1 then it's an improper fraction.

Visualize any fraction on the number line by changing the values of the **numerator** and **denominator** with the joystick.

How can a whole number be represented as an improper fraction?

Can a whole number be represented as a mixed number?

If you know a number is a proper fraction, where will it be located on the number line? (Between which two numbers?)

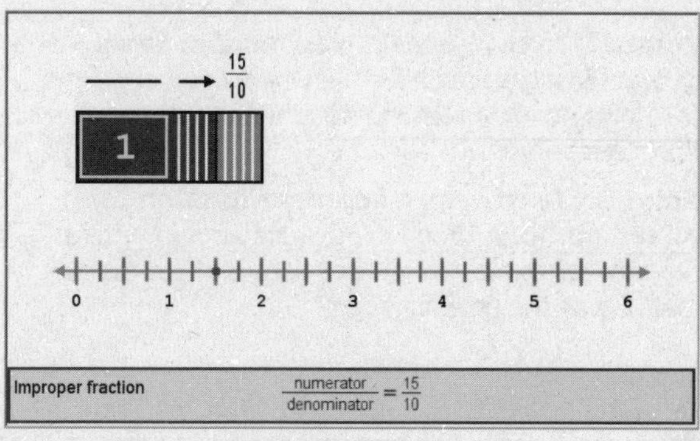

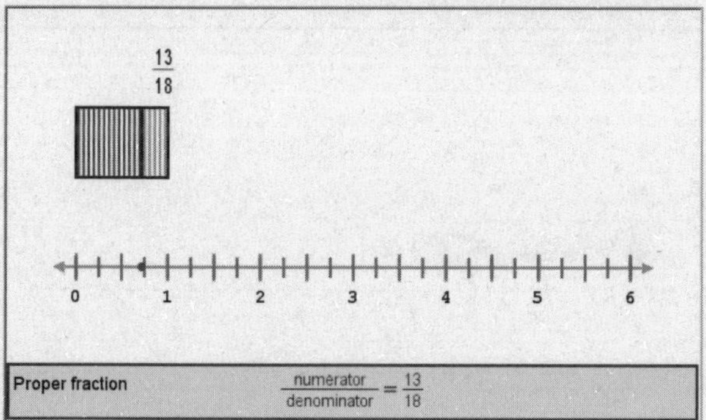

Is the value of a **proper fractions** always less than 1?

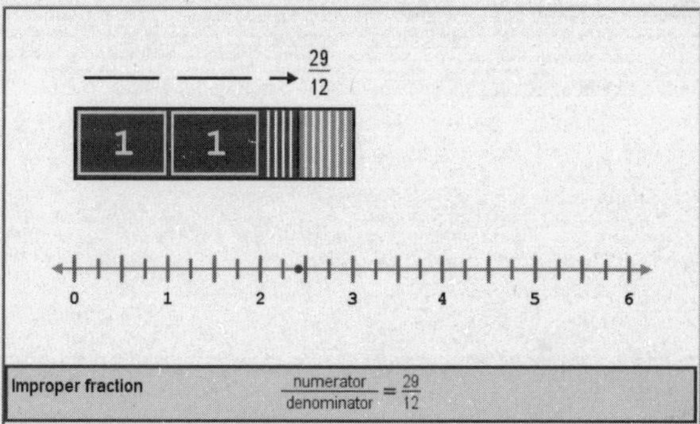

Can you think of the above fraction as 2 plus 5/12? How would you write that as a mixed number?

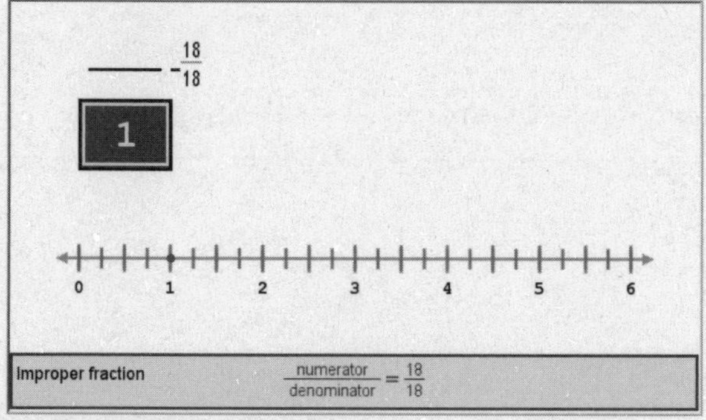

Is the value of an **improper fraction** always greater than 1?

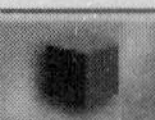

Mixed Numbers

Together a fraction plus a whole number form a **mixed number**. A mixed number has two parts, a whole number plus a fraction. If a fraction is improper, it can be changed to a mixed number. Likewise, a mixed number can be written as an improper fraction.

Point 1: To change the **mixed number to an improper fraction**, multiply the whole number by the fraction's denominator and add the product to the fraction's numerator.

Point 2: To convert an **improper fraction to a mixed number**, divide the denominator into the numerator for the whole number part, and put the remainder as the new numerator.

Convert this mixed number to an improper fraction

$$\text{whole part}\,\frac{\text{numerator}}{\text{denominator}} = 3\frac{1}{5}$$

$$= \frac{3\times5}{5} + \frac{1}{5}$$

$$= \frac{15}{5} + \frac{1}{5}$$

$$= \frac{16}{5}$$

Since the denominators of the two fractions are the same, combine them by adding the numerators together.

Think: **multiply**, then **add**.

Convert this improper fraction to a mixed number

$$\frac{11}{4} = 2\frac{3}{4}$$

$2\ \frac{3}{4}$

1 1

0 1 2 3 4 5 6 7 8 9 10

Place remainder over the denominator.

Use scratch paper if you need to. 11 divided by 4 is 2 with 3 left over (the 4).

Convert this mixed number to an improper fraction

$$\text{whole part}\,\frac{\text{numerator}}{\text{denominator}} = 1\frac{13}{4}$$

$$= \frac{1\times4}{4} + \frac{13}{4}$$

$$= \frac{4}{4} + \frac{13}{4}$$

$$= \frac{17}{4}$$

Since the denominators of the two fractions are the same, combine them by adding the numerators together.

Convert this improper fraction to a mixed number

$$\frac{36}{10} = 3\frac{6}{10}$$

$3\ \frac{6}{10}$

1 1 1

0 1 2 3 4 5 6 7 8 9 10

Place remainder over the denominator.

Remember: The fraction bar means for you to divide. 10 divides 36 evenly 3 times with six tenths remaining.

Fraction bars and the number line are used to visualize improper fractions and mixed numbers. Since improper form and mixed number form represent exactly the same number, these forms are used interchangeably. Whether one is used over the other depends on the context of the situation, but the driving factors are ease of use or ease of communication.

The representation of fractions as bars is similar to the visualization of addition of whole numbers. How is the whole numbers part of a mixed number attached to the fractional part?

Does the denominator always stay the same for both the improper fraction and the mixed number?

Which fraction form is easier to read?

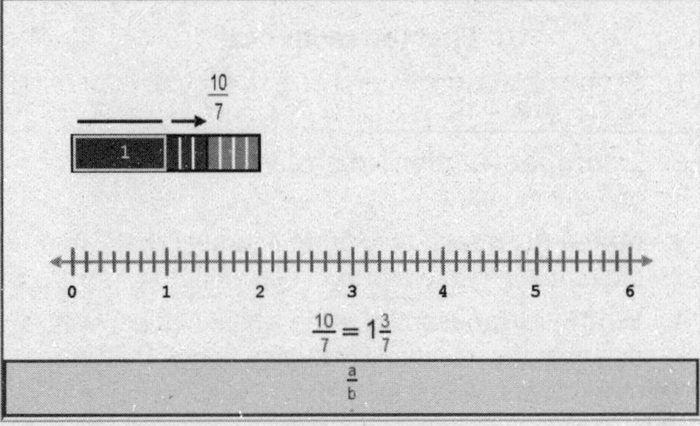

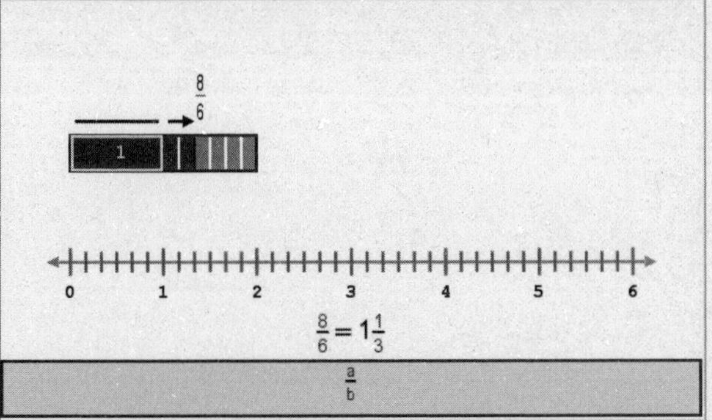

Why does the above mixed number have a denominator of 3? How many 6ths are represented by the fraction part of 1/3?

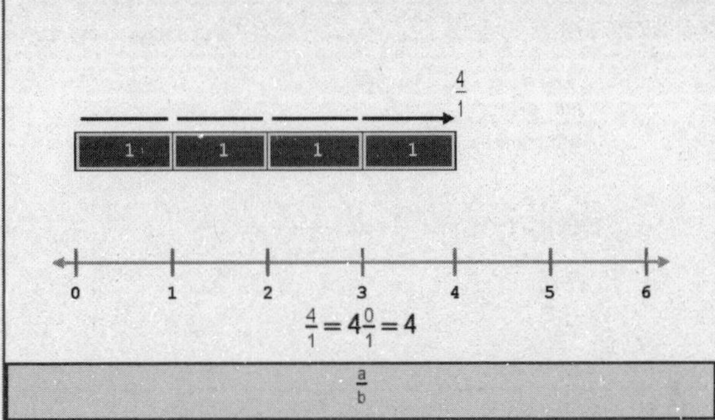

How can a whole number be written as a mixed number? What would the numerator of the fraction part need to be?

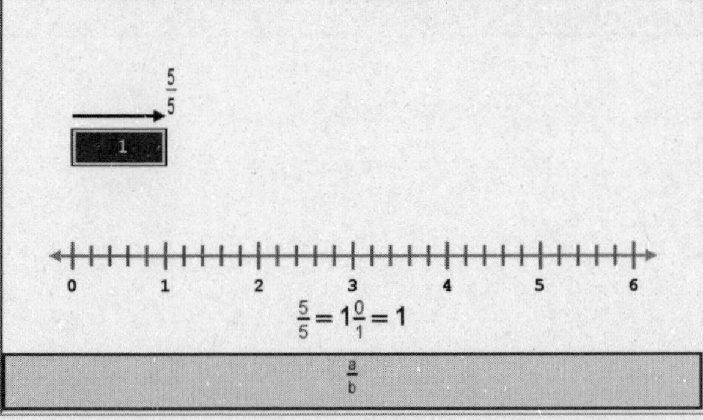

What happens if there is no remainder? What kind of number do you have?

Reciprocals

Another name for the **reciprocal** of a number is **'multiplicative inverse'**. These terms will be used interchangeably. A number times its multiplicative inverse is equal to one. For example,

(4 x 1/4) = 1

(1/2 x 2/1) = 1

(505/8 x 8/505) = 1

For now, practice writing the reciprocal of a number by inverting its numerator and denominator.

Find the reciprocal

1. **Proper fraction**: Interchange the numerator with the denominator.
2. **Improper fraction**: Interchange the numerator and denominator.
3. **Mixed number**: Change to improper first, then interchange numerator and denominator.
4. **Whole numbers**: Write the whole number with a denominator of 1 and then interchange then numerator and denominator.

Finding Reciprocals of fractions

To write the reciprocal of a number interchange its numerator and denominator.

$$\text{number} = \frac{a}{b} \qquad \text{reciprocal} = \frac{b}{a}$$

A number and its reciprocal are inversely related, such that the product of a number and its reciprocal is 1.

$$\frac{a}{b} \times \frac{b}{a} = 1$$

Finding Reciprocals of fractions

$$\frac{\text{numerator}}{\text{denominator}} = \frac{13}{7}$$

$$\text{reciprocal} = \frac{1}{\frac{13}{7}} = \frac{1\times 7}{\frac{13}{7}\times 7} = \frac{7}{13}$$

To find the **reciprocol** of a **number**, interchange its numerator and denominator.

Notice that the reciprocal of an improper is an proper fraction.

Finding Reciprocals of Mixed Numbers

$$\text{whole part}\ \frac{\text{numerator}}{\text{denominator}} = 12\frac{16}{8}$$

$$= \frac{(12\times 8)+16}{8}$$

$$= \frac{112}{8}$$

Calculate terms in numerator, $12\times 8=96$ and $96+16=112$. Write numerator over denominator.

Convert to an improper fraction first.

Finding Reciprocals of Mixed Numbers

$$\text{number} = \frac{112}{8}$$

$$\text{reciprocal} = \frac{8}{112}$$

To find the reciprocal interchange the values of the numerator and denominator. Check: $\frac{112}{8} \times \frac{8}{112} = 1$

The reciprocal of a mixed number is a proper fraction.

Finding Reciprocals of fractions

$$\frac{\text{numerator}}{\text{denominator}} \times \text{reciprocol} = \frac{13}{7} \times \frac{7}{13}$$

$$= \frac{91}{91}$$

$$= 1$$

If their product is 1, then your solution is correct. The product of a **number** and its **reciprocol** is 1.

The product of a number and its reciprocal will always be 1.

The **reciprocal** of a fraction interchanges the values of the fraction's numerator and denominator.

If the original fraction is a proper fraction, will its reciprocal also be a proper fraction?

Does a whole number have a reciprocal?

What is the reciprocal of 4?

What is the reciprocal of 1/4?

Does 1 have a reciprocal?

Does 0 have a reciprocal?

Do all other whole numbers have reciprocals?

How do you find the reciprocal of a mixed number? Will the reciprocal of a mixed number be proper or improper?

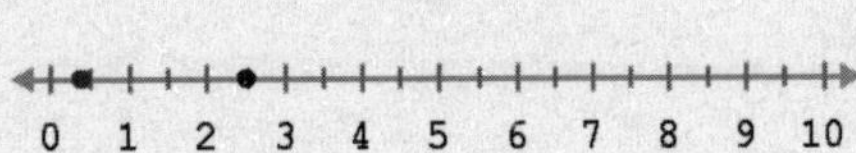

The reciprocal of $\frac{2}{5}$ is $\frac{5}{2}$

The reciprocal of $\frac{a}{b}$

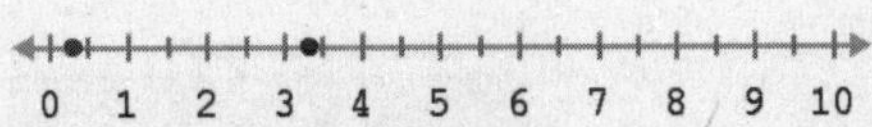

The reciprocal of $\frac{3}{10}$ is $\frac{10}{3}$

The reciprocal of $\frac{a}{b}$

As the original fraction gets smaller, what happens to the reciprocal?

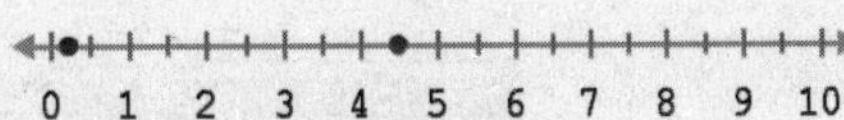

The reciprocal of $\frac{9}{2}$ is $\frac{2}{9}$

The reciprocal of $\frac{a}{b}$

If the original fraction is an improper fraction, will the reciprocal always be a proper fraction?

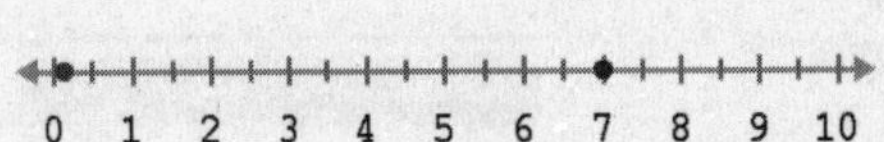

The reciprocal of $\frac{1}{7}$ is $\frac{7}{1}$

The reciprocal of $\frac{a}{b}$

What happens when 1 is the numerator? What kind of number is the reciprocal?

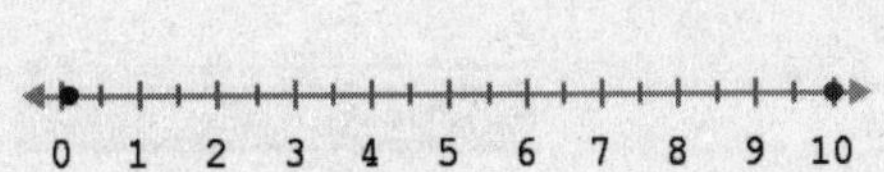

The reciprocal of $\frac{10}{1}$ is $\frac{1}{10}$

The reciprocal of $\frac{a}{b}$

Does the reciprocal of a whole number always make a proper fraction?

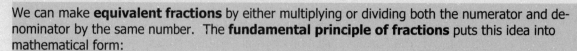

We can make **equivalent fractions** by either multiplying or dividing both the numerator and denominator by the same number. The **fundamental principle of fractions** puts this idea into mathematical form:

$$\frac{ac}{bc} = \frac{a}{b} \textit{ and } \frac{a}{b} = \frac{ac}{bc}$$

A fraction is **reduced** when the common factor **c** is divided out. A fraction is **built up** if a factor **c** is multiplied to both numerator and denominator.

To create an equivalent fraction multiply or divide both the numerator and denominator by the same number.

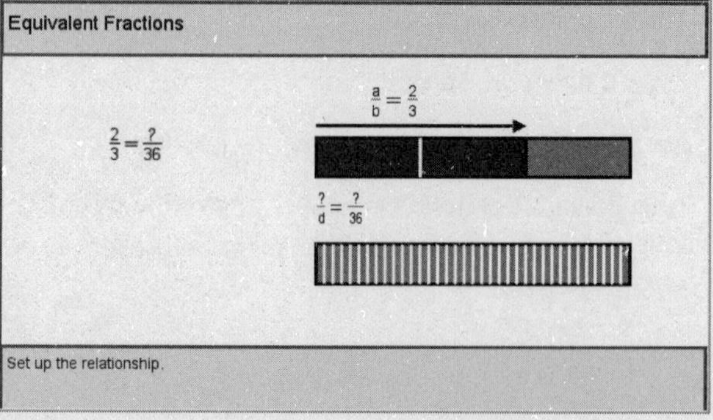

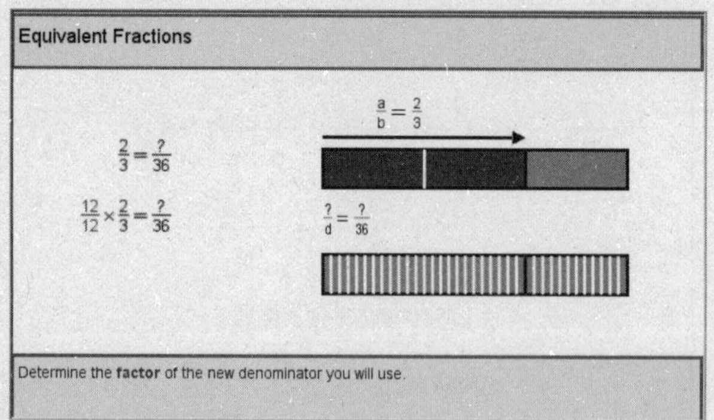

Point 1: Building up 2/3 to 36ths.

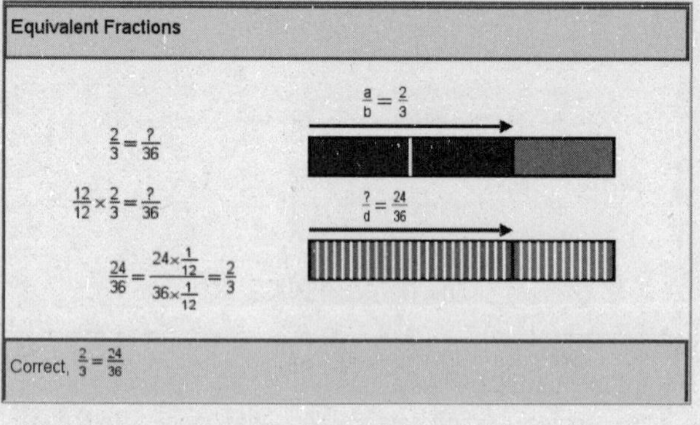

To find the equivalent fraction, how many divisions will need to be made to each 1/3 partition?

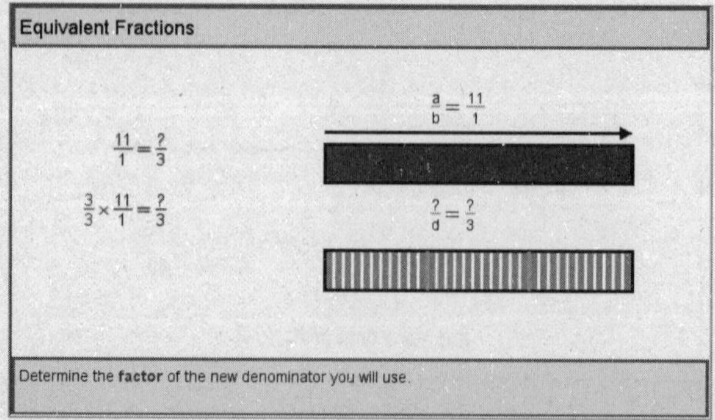

Point 2: Works with whole numbers as well. Find the fractional equivalent to 11. If you want the denominator value to be 3, how many times will each 1/3 section be subdivided?

Use the joystick to change the values and create new problems.

Fractions can be built up like multiples of whole numbers. The fraction 2/3 can be built up to 4/6, or 6/9, or 8/12, or 10/15 and so on. What do you notice is different?

Visualize building equivalent fractions with two fraction bars. The bottom bar shows an equivalent fraction, but with the number of partitions changed.

How many more partitions are there in the bottom fraction bar than the top?

Each partition in the top bar is further in the bottom bar. What determines how many partitions there are?

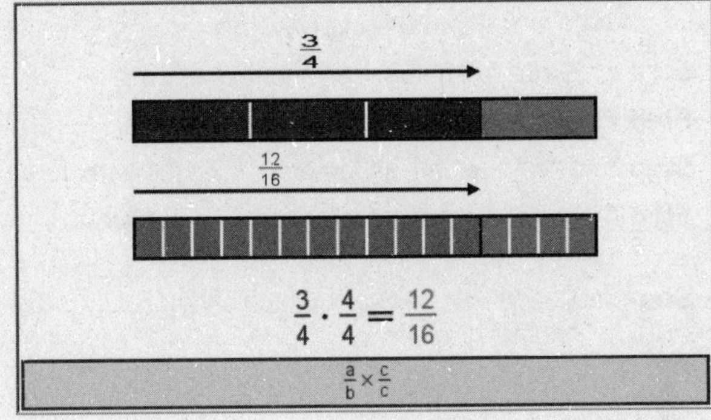

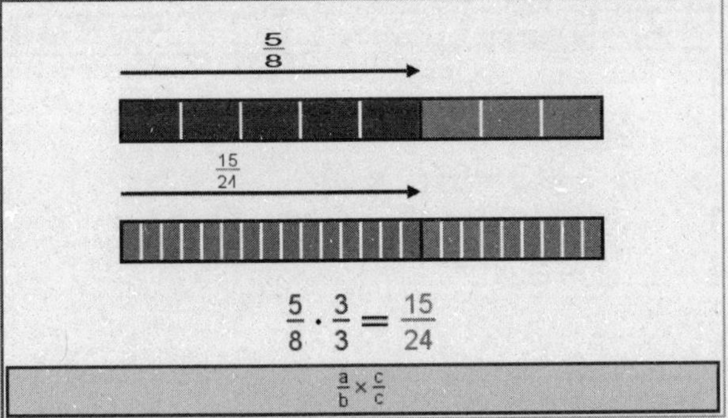

Building by 3. Are there any other fractions that can be built to 15/24?

Prime factorization means to break down a number until all of its factors are prime numbers. The **Fundamental Theorem of Arithmetic** states that every composite number has one and only one prime factorization. That means that every composite number can be factored into a product of prime numbers in only one way.

Recall that repeated multiplications of the same number can be written in exponent form. The base is the number and the exponent is the number of multiplications. If a number has NO multiplications, the exponent is zero. Any number raised to the zero power equals 1: $\mathbf{n^0=1}$, because 1 is the starting point for multiplication, the **multiplicative identity**.

Prime Factorization

Step 1: Write the number as a pair of factors.

Step 2: Write each factor as a pair of factors.

Step 3: Continue until all factors are paired with 1.

Step 4: Write the prime factorization in exponent form by listing all the factors but the 1s.

Step 5: Check your answer by multiplying back to the original number.

Finding Prime Factors of Numbers

$$\begin{aligned} 24 &= 6 \times 4 \\ &= (3 \times 2)(2 \times 2) \end{aligned}$$

Continue dividing factors.

Finding Prime Factors of Numbers

$$\begin{aligned} 24 &= 6 \times 4 \\ &= (3 \times 2)(2 \times 2) \\ &= (3 \times 1)(2 \times 1)(2 \times 1)(2 \times 1) \end{aligned}$$

Stop when the number has been decomposed into its prime factors.

We find the prime factors of 24 by listing all factor pairs until they are expressed as a factor pair with 1 as one of the numbers.

Finding Prime Factors of Numbers

$$\begin{aligned} 24 &= 6 \times 4 \\ &= (3 \times 2)(2 \times 2) \\ &= (3 \times 1)(2 \times 1)(2 \times 1)(2 \times 1) \\ &= 3 \times 2^3 \end{aligned}$$

Write all prime factors with exponents, if possible.

Each of the factors paired with one is a prime factor of 24. Finally, we rewrite the prime factors of 24 with exponents to express how many times a number is a factor of another.

Is $3*2^3 = 24$?

Finding Prime Factors of Numbers

$$\begin{aligned} 130 &= (26 \times 5) \\ &= (2 \times 13)(5 \times 1) \\ &= (2 \times 1)(13 \times 1)(5 \times 1) \\ &= 2 \times 13 \times 5 \end{aligned}$$

Write all prime factors with exponents, if possible.

Any factor pair will work. Try 13*10 as the first pair. Do you still get 2*13*5? Is 2*5*13 the same? Is 2*5*13 = 130?

There is no formula for finding the prime factors of a number which is the heart of modern encryption methods. Thus we will show you how to build numbers from prime factors.

Can you build the first 50 composites as products of primes? Change the base to get another composite number.

Remember: any number to the zero power is 1: $n^0=1$

How do you figure out which prime numbers to use?

Why are the base numbers here only the numbers 2, 3, 5, 7, 11?

What number would you get if all the exponents are set to zero? One?

Can you think of a number from 1-20 that can't be expressed as a product of the listed primes? Which numbers?

30 written as a product of prime factors:

$$30=(2)^1(3)^1(5)^1$$

$(2)^{two}(3)^{three}(5)^{five}$

120 written as a product of prime factors:

$$120=(2)^3(3)^1(5)^1$$

$(2)^{two}(3)^{three}(5)^{five}$

Think of 2^3 as 8. Does 8*15 = 120? Or think of 2^3 as 4*2. Does 12 * 10 = 120? Make other combinations of the given factors. Is there any other number that uses three 2's, a 3 and a 5?

126 written as a product of prime factors:

$$126=(2)^1(3)^2(5)^0(7)^1(11)^0$$

$(2)^{two}(3)^{three}(5)^{five}(7)^{seven}(11)^{eleven}$

Notice that 5^0 and 11^0 are both equal to 1 and can be ignored. Does $2*3^2*7 = 126$?

72 written as a product of prime factors:

$$72=(2)^3(3)^2(5)^0(7)^0(11)^0$$

$(2)^{two}(3)^{three}(5)^{five}(7)^{seven}(11)^{eleven}$

Ignore 5^0,7^0 and 11^0. (Why?) Is there a relationship between the use of 2 as a factor and the number? How do you know if 3 can be used as a factor?

330 written as a product of prime factors:

$$330=(2)^1(3)^1(5)^1(7)^0(11)^1$$

$(2)^{two}(3)^{three}(5)^{five}(7)^{seven}(11)^{eleven}$

If you started this one from the beginning, what factor pair would you use?

In the assignment on equivalent fractions, we were concerned with building fractions to higher terms. Now we want to concentrate on **reducing** or **simplifying fractions**—writing them as equivalent fractions in lowest terms. **Lowest terms** means that the numerator and denominator don't have any common factors.

The best way to do that is to write the numerator and denominator as products of their factors. Then we can divide (or cancel) out any factors they have in common, and the fraction is simplified or reduced.

To reduce to lowest terms: Factor the numerator and denominator and then divide out the common factors.

Reduce fractions to lowest terms

1) Write the fraction as factors of the numerator and denominator.
2) Cancel common factors.

Ex. 1: $\frac{22}{8} = \frac{\cancel{2}\times 11}{\cancel{2}\times 2\times 2} = \frac{11}{4}$

Solution: $\frac{22}{8} = \frac{11}{4}$

Reduce fractions to lowest terms

1) Write the fraction as factors of the numerator and denominator.
2) Cancel common factors.

Ex. 2: $\frac{35}{12} = \frac{5\times 7}{2\times 2\times 3} = \frac{35}{12}$

Solution: There are no common factors

It "looks" like 35/12 should reduce, but they have no common factors. 35/12 is reduced, but it is still an improper fraction and can be changed into a mixed number if needed.

Reduce fractions to lowest terms

1) Write the fraction as factors of the numerator and denominator.
2) Cancel common factors.

Ex. 3: $\frac{26}{40} = \frac{\cancel{2}\times 13}{\cancel{2}\times 2\times 2\times 5} = \frac{13}{20}$

Solution: $\frac{26}{40} = \frac{13}{20}$

Factor and then divide out the common factors. You can check your work by multiplying 26*20 and 40*13. Does this one check?

To find the simplest equivalent fraction, we factor both the numerator and denominator and divide out the factors that are common to both. The result is a fraction in lower terms.

The visualizations below show one fraction bar divided into segments using two colors of dividers. The white dividers show the fraction in higher terms and the red dividers show it in lower terms. Since the fractions are equivalent, the dark colored bar part is the same.

How do you know which fraction bar piece belongs to which fraction?

How do you know what common factor is divided out of a reduced fraction?

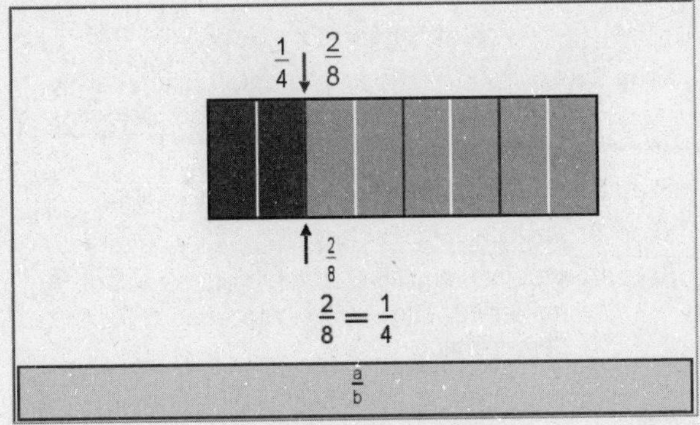

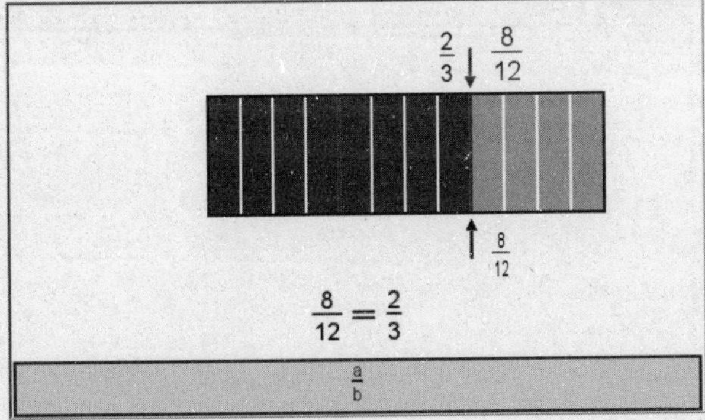

Can 8/12 be reduced to 4/6?

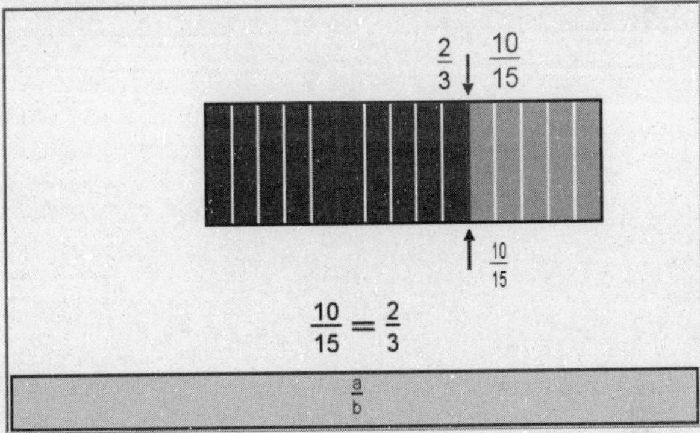

What common factor is divided out?

Multiplying Fractions

EnableMath

Multiply fractions by multiplying numerators and then denominators: $\frac{a}{b} \cdot \frac{c}{d} = \frac{ac}{bd}$

Once the two numerators and two denominators are multiplied, they make one fraction. Reduce the fraction either before or after multiplying. The shortest method is to reduce before multiplying. Write each factor in factored form and divide out common factors—one numerator factor paired with one denominator factor.

Note: Mixed numbers are not considered here, but improper fractions are. You may choose to write improper fraction answers as mixed numbers.

Multiplying Fractions

Step 1: Combine fractions over one fraction bar by multiplying numerators and then denominators.

Step 2: Factor numerators and denominators.

Step 3: Reduce common factors.

Step 4: Multiply remaining numerator factors for the numerator and denominator factors for the denominator.

Multiplying Fractions

$$\frac{a}{b} \times \frac{c}{d} = \frac{5}{8} \times \frac{10}{7}$$

$$= \frac{5 \times 10}{8 \times 7}$$

$$= \frac{50}{56}$$

$$= \frac{25}{28}$$

Reduce fraction. Solution.

Multiplying Fractions

$$\frac{a}{b} \times \frac{c}{d} = \frac{6}{10} \times \frac{15}{18}$$

$$= \frac{6 \times 15}{10 \times 18}$$

$$= \frac{90}{180}$$

$$= \frac{1}{2}$$

Reduce fraction. Solution.

No need to multiply to 90/180 because the next step is to reduce by factoring - so step 2 becomes:

$$\frac{2 \cdot 3 \cdot 3 \cdot 5}{2 \cdot 5 \cdot 2 \cdot 3 \cdot 3}$$

With all top factors dividing out, the numerator is 1.

Multiplying Fractions

$$\frac{a}{b} \times \frac{c}{d} = \frac{7}{12} \times \frac{13}{18}$$

$$= \frac{7 \times 13}{12 \times 18}$$

$$= \frac{91}{216}$$

Since the GCF of 91 and 216 is 1, the solution is in reduced form.

Looking closely at step 1 shows that there are no common factors to divide out.

Multiplying Fractions

$$\frac{a}{b} \times \frac{c}{d} = \frac{8}{12} \times \frac{12}{20}$$

$$= \frac{8 \times 12}{12 \times 20}$$

$$= \frac{96}{240}$$

$$= \frac{2}{5}$$

Reduce fraction. Solution.

Take short cuts by dividing any common factors—one numerator factor with one denominator factor.

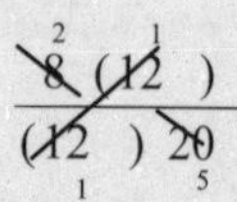

Multiplying Fractions

$$\frac{a}{b} \times \frac{c}{d} = \frac{150}{225} \times \frac{450}{600}$$

$$= \frac{150 \times 450}{225 \times 600}$$

$$= \frac{67500}{135000}$$

$$= \frac{1}{2}$$

Reduce fraction. Solution.

Look for the shortcuts! Reduce before multiplying. No need to do the multiplication if all common factors are reduced. Try it on scratch paper.

Multiplication of fractions is visualized by using a 1 x 1 square. The chosen fractions are represented by fraction bars along the left side and bottom of the square. The product is the interior of the square. Notice that the fractions might not be reduced. When they do, how can you mentally rearrange the dark blue tiles to reduce the product?

Why can the product be represented as a 1 x 1 square?

Is the product of two proper fractions ever larger that 1?

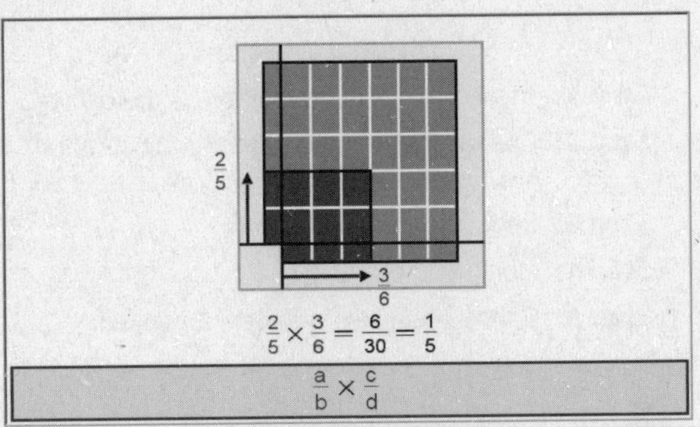

$\frac{2}{5}$
$\frac{3}{6}$
$\frac{2}{5} \times \frac{3}{6} = \frac{6}{30} = \frac{1}{5}$
$\frac{a}{b} \times \frac{c}{d}$

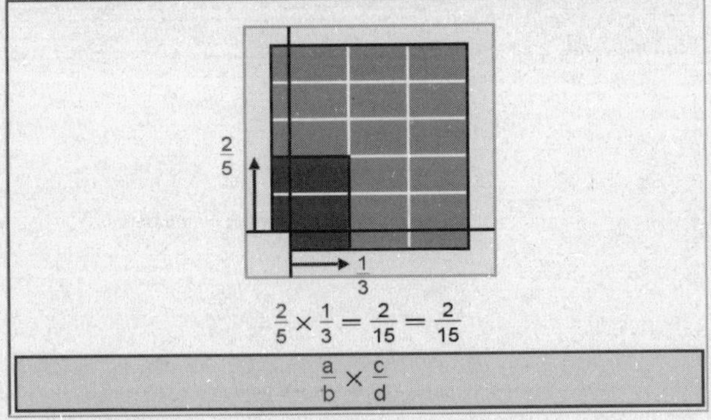

Is 2/15 greater or less than either 2/5 or 1/3?

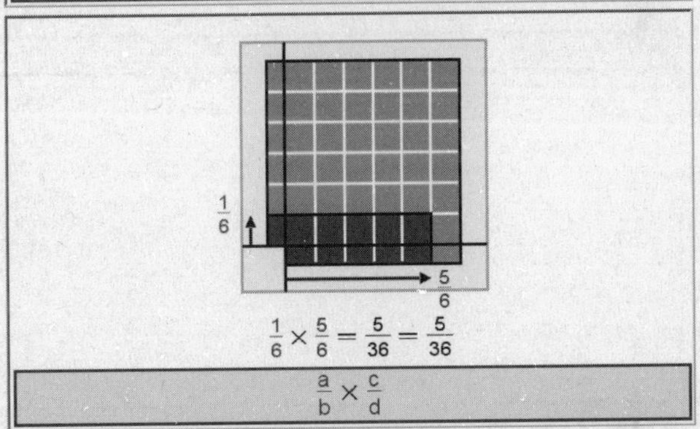

Can the above problem be reduced?

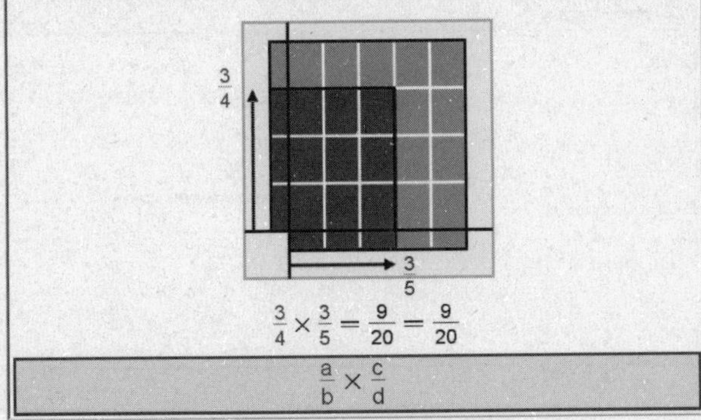

$\frac{3}{4}$
$\frac{3}{5}$
$\frac{3}{4} \times \frac{3}{5} = \frac{9}{20} = \frac{9}{20}$
$\frac{a}{b} \times \frac{c}{d}$

Is multiplication of fractions commutative?

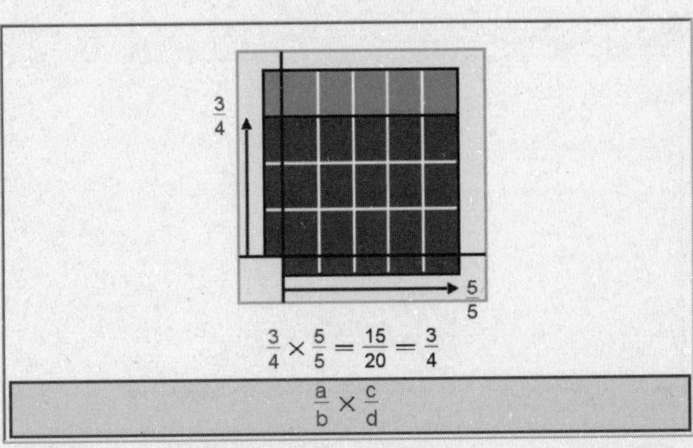

If 5/5 = 1 and 1 is the identity for multiplication, does the identity hold for fractions?

Dividing Fractions

EnableMath

Division is the inverse operation of multiplication. We use that fact to define division of fractions. To divide fractions multiply by the inverse (reciprocal) of the divisor. In symbols:

$$\frac{a}{b} \div \frac{c}{d} = \frac{a}{b} \cdot \frac{d}{c} = \frac{a \cdot d}{b \cdot c}$$

Note: Improper fractions may be converted to mixed numbers. Proper fractions should be put into reduced form.

Dividing Fractions

Step 1: Identify the second fraction as the divisor.

Step 2: Change the problem sign to multiplication AND invert the divisor.

Step 3: Reduce common factors.

Step 4: Multiply.

Step 5: Convert to mixed numbers if needed.

Dividing Fractions

$$\frac{\frac{a}{b}}{\frac{c}{d}} = \frac{\frac{8}{3}}{\frac{7}{9}}$$

$$= \frac{8}{3} \times \frac{9}{7}$$

Take reciprocal of second fraction and change operation to multiplication.

Dividing Fractions

$$\frac{\frac{a}{b}}{\frac{c}{d}} = \frac{\frac{8}{3}}{\frac{7}{9}}$$

$$= \frac{8}{3} \times \frac{9}{7}$$

$$= \frac{72}{21}$$

$$= \frac{24}{7}$$

Reduce the fraction if necessary.

Above is the step-by-step process without showing the reducing step. You can write 24/7 as a mixed number.

Dividing Fractions

$$\frac{\frac{a}{b}}{\frac{c}{d}} = \frac{\frac{8}{3}}{\frac{7}{9}}$$

$$= \frac{8}{\cancel{3}_1} \times \frac{\cancel{9}^2}{7} \quad \text{Reduce common factors.}$$

$$= \frac{16}{7}$$

Calculate the answer.

With reducing by dividing out common factors, the final step is in lowest terms.

Dividing Fractions

$$\frac{\frac{a}{b}}{\frac{c}{d}} = \frac{\frac{5}{9}}{\frac{3}{5}}$$

$$= \frac{5}{9} \times \frac{5}{3}$$

$$= \frac{25}{27}$$

$$= \frac{25}{27}$$

Reduce the fraction if necessary.

Never reduce BEFORE changing the problem to multiplication. Only common factors reduce and the word factor implies multiplication is needed.

Dividing Fractions

$$\frac{\frac{a}{b}}{\frac{c}{d}} = \frac{\frac{6}{9}}{\frac{3}{4}}$$

$$= \frac{{}^2\cancel{6}}{9} \times \frac{4}{\cancel{3}_1} \quad \text{Reduce common factors.}$$

$$= \frac{8}{9}$$

Calculate the answer.

Make sure you divide out one numerator with one denominator.

We visualize division as a right triangle whose slope (slant) represents the value of the quotient. Slope is the steepness of the line defined by the rise divided by the run (length). The numerator fraction bar (the dividend) is vertical and the denominator fraction bar (the divisor) is horizontal.

Division as the inverse of multiplication is shown in the second visualization.

Does the slope line get steeper or less steep as the answer increases?

If the slope is 1, what do you know about the two fractions being divided?

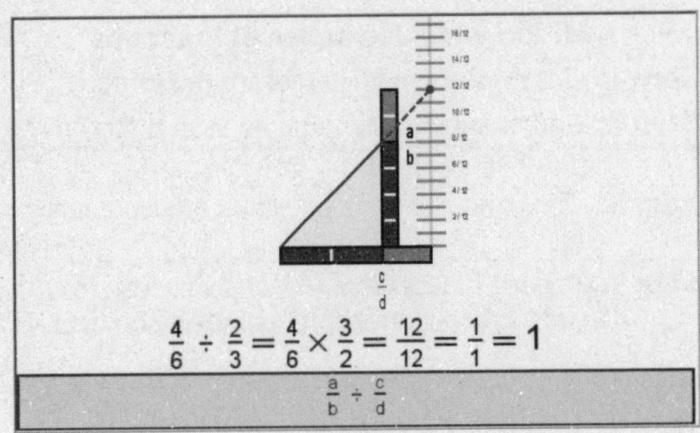

$\frac{4}{6} \div \frac{2}{3} = \frac{4}{6} \times \frac{3}{2} = \frac{12}{12} = \frac{1}{1} = 1$
$\frac{a}{b} \div \frac{c}{d}$

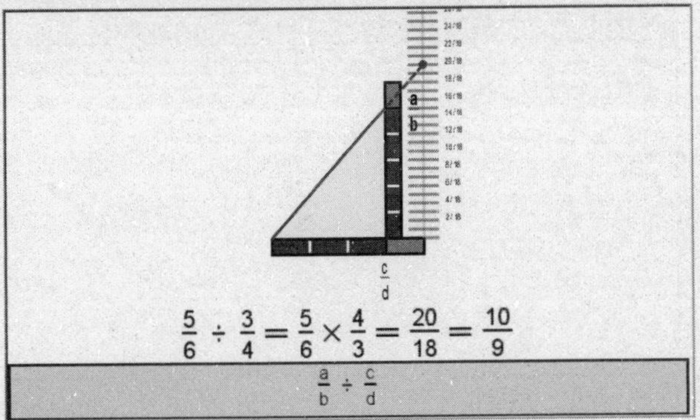

$\frac{5}{6} \div \frac{3}{4} = \frac{5}{6} \times \frac{4}{3} = \frac{20}{18} = \frac{10}{9}$
$\frac{a}{b} \div \frac{c}{d}$

Can you divide out any common factors?

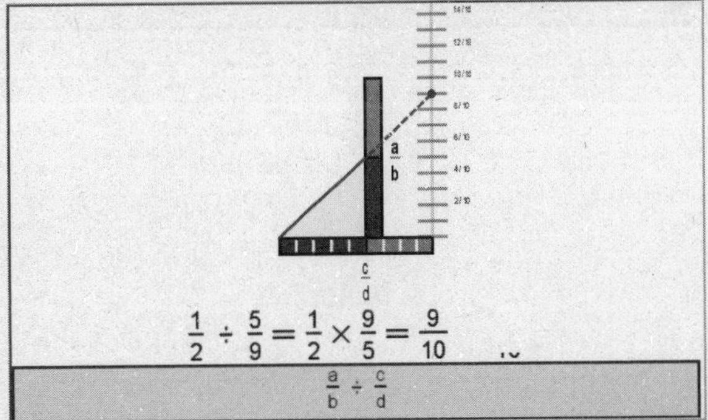

Is the slope of the above line steeper or not as steep as the slope in the frame to the left?

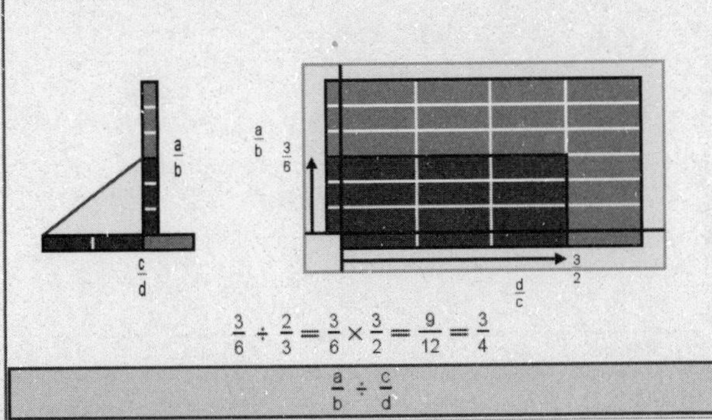

$\frac{3}{6} \div \frac{2}{3} = \frac{3}{6} \times \frac{3}{2} = \frac{9}{12} = \frac{3}{4}$
$\frac{a}{b} \div \frac{c}{d}$

The slope and the product of the dividend and the divisor are pictured above.

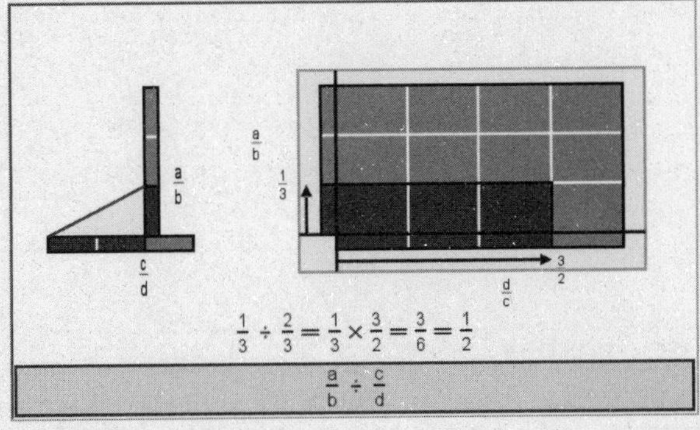

$\frac{1}{3} \div \frac{2}{3} = \frac{1}{3} \times \frac{3}{2} = \frac{3}{6} = \frac{1}{2}$
$\frac{a}{b} \div \frac{c}{d}$

What factors divide out?

Add & Sub Fractions with Like Denominators

EnableMath

Adding fractions is counting up how many same size parts you have. If two fractions have the same denominators, they have the same size parts, so add them by adding numerators. Subtract them by subtracting numerators.

Note: Improper fractions may be converted to mixed numbers. Proper fractions should be put into reduced form.

Addition and Subtraction of Fractions

Step 1: Ensure the denominators are the same.

Step 2: Add or subtract numerators as indicated for the numerator of the answer.

Step 3: The denominator is the common denominator.

Step 4: Reduce if necessary. You may choose to write improper fractions as mixed numbers.

Adding fractions with like denominators

Example 1:

$$\frac{2}{3}+\frac{4}{3}=\frac{?}{3}$$
$$=\frac{2+4}{3}$$
$$=\frac{6}{3}$$
$$\boxed{=2}$$

Put improper fraction into mixed number form. **Solution.**

Adding fractions with like denominators

Example 2:

$$\frac{7}{8}+\frac{3}{8}+\frac{5}{8}=\frac{?}{8}$$
$$=\frac{7+3+5}{8}$$
$$=\frac{15}{8}$$
$$\boxed{=1\frac{7}{8}}$$

Put improper fraction into mixed number form. **Solution.**

You may choose to write 15/8 as a mixed number.

Subtracting fractions with like denominators

Example 1:

$$\frac{17}{26}-\frac{4}{26}=\frac{?}{26}$$
$$=\frac{17-4}{26}$$
$$=\frac{13}{26}$$
$$\boxed{=\frac{1}{2}}$$

Reduce fraction. **Solution.**

Subtraction is counting down same size parts.

Adding Fractions with Like Denominators

$$\frac{4}{8}+\frac{2}{8}=\frac{?}{8}$$
$$=\frac{4+2}{8}$$
$$=\frac{6}{8}$$
$$\boxed{=\frac{3}{4}}$$

Reduce fraction, if possible. **Solution.**

This is a dynamic example. Change **a, b, c,** to see different fractions. Notice the format showing the addition step. This follows the pattern needed for algebra, as does the answer. Your instructor may require you to write an improper fraction as a mixed number or proper fractions in reduced form.

Subtracting Fractions with Like Denominators

$$\frac{10}{9}-\frac{4}{9}=\frac{?}{9}$$
$$=\frac{10-4}{9}$$
$$=\frac{6}{9}$$
$$\boxed{=\frac{2}{3}}$$

Reduce fraction, if possible. **Solution.**

This is a dynamic example. Notice the format showing the subtraction step.

Add & Subtract Fractions with Like Denominators

Visualize addition and subtraction with fraction bars. Adding is joining bars together, subtraction is removing bars. Two questions are answered in fraction addition and subtraction: What size are the pieces and how many are there?

How many pieces are needed to make 1 if the fraction describes ninths?

Can two proper fractions add to an improper fraction?

When subtracting, is the answer always smaller than either fraction?

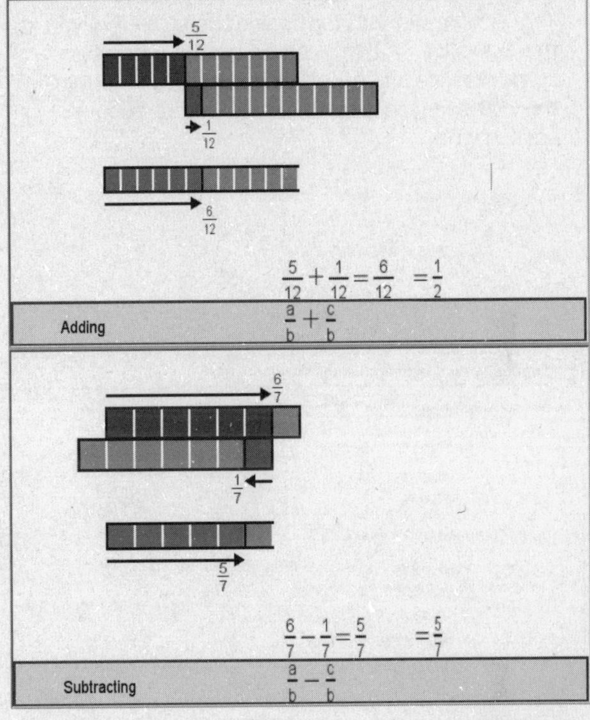

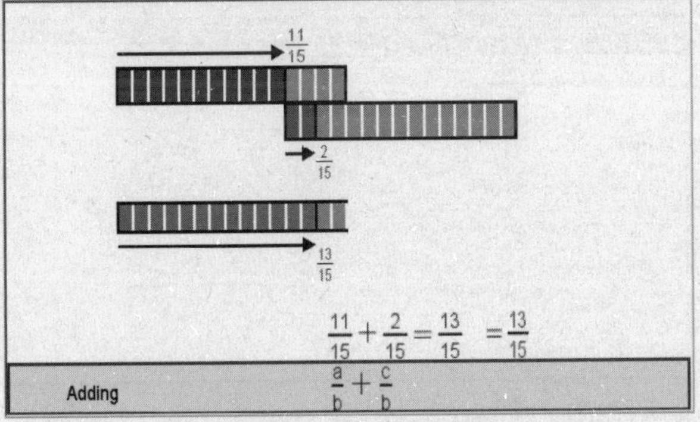

What size are the pieces and how many altogether?

Reverse the arrow for subtraction. What size are the pieces? How many are left? How do you check your subtraction?

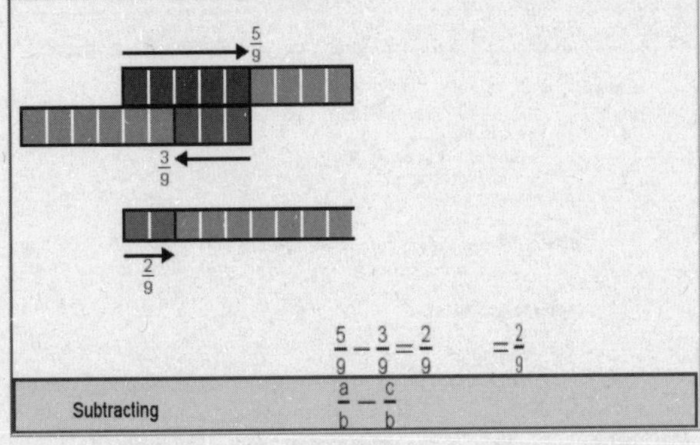

Take away 3/9 from 5/9. What size are the pieces? Does 2/9 + 3/9 = 5/9?

Least Common Denominator

EnableMath

In order to add fractions they must describe the same size pieces—that is, they must have a common denominator. In order to keep work as simple as possible, we use the **least common denominator** (**LCD**). The **LCD** is the smallest multiple common to two or more denominators.

Two similar methods for finding the LCD are given in the examples. A third method can be used after some practice and experience. You can determine the LCD by inspection—mentally, without doing scratch work.

Least Common Denominator

Only fractions with the same denominators can only be added or subtracted.

The least common denominator or LCD of two or more fractions can be used to add or subtract fractions which have different denominators.

The LCD is the smallest number that is divisible by all of the original denominators.

Therefore, the LCD is either larger than all the denominators or equal to the largest denominator.

Finding the Least Common Denominator

1. Write the **denominators.**
2. Factor each denominator into its **prime factors.**
3. Identify each **prime factor**.
4. List each **prime factor** of the denominator 9.
5. List each prime factor of the denominator 12, but do not duplicate a number that is already on the **LCD list.**
7. Multiply the numbers to solve for the **LCD**.

9: (3×3), (3×1)(3×1)

12: (3×4), (3×1)(2×2), (2×1)(2×1)

$LCD = 3 \times 3 \times 2 \times 2 = 36$

The LCD of $\frac{5}{9}$ and $\frac{7}{12}$ is 36.

Test: Divide 9 and 12 into 36. Yes, 36 is a multiple of both 9 and 12.

Finding the Least Common Denominator

1. Write the **denominators.**
2. Factor each denominator into its **prime factors.**
3. Identify each **prime factor**.
4. List each **prime factor** of the denominator 9.
5. List each prime factor of the denominator 12, but do not duplicate a number that is already on the **LCD list.**
7. Multiply the numbers to solve for the **LCD**.

9: (3×3), (3×1)(3×1)

12: (3×4), (3×1)(2×2), (2×1)(2×1)

$LCD = 3 \times 3 \times 2 \times 2 = 36$

The LCD of $\frac{5}{9}$ and $\frac{7}{12}$ is 36.

Any time the two numbers have no common factors, the LCD will be their product.

Finding the Least Common Denominator

1. Write the denominators.
2. Factor each denominator into prime factors.
3. To find the LCD identify each prime factor.
4. List each prime factor of the first number.
5. List each prime factor of the remaining numbers, but do not duplicate a number that is already on the LCD list.
6. Multiply all prime factors in list to get LCD.

4 8 24

2*2 4*2 3*8

2*1*2*12*2*2*13*1*4*2

2*1 2*1 2*2 *2*1

2*1*2*1

2*2 *2*3

LCD is 24

Find the LCD of $\frac{1}{4}$, $\frac{3}{8}$, and $\frac{13}{24}$

Works the same way with more than two numbers.

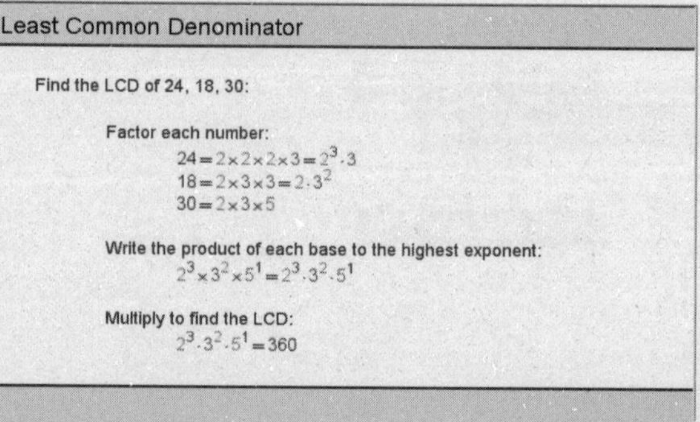

Least Common Denominator
Find the LCD of 24, 18, 30:
Factor each number:
24 = 2×2×2×3 = 2³·3
18 = 2×3×3 = 2·3²
30 = 2×3×5
Write the product of each base to the highest exponent:
2³×3²×5¹ = 2³·3²·5¹
Multiply to find the LCD:
2³·3²·5¹ = 360

Method two is very similar, but makes use of bases and exponents.

Least Common Denominator

For addition and subtraction, the pieces have to be the same size. In order to get the pieces the same size we find the **Least Common Denominator (LCD)**. Visualize this process by looking at three fraction bars.

1. The **top bar** represents the divisions of the first fraction.
2. The **middle bar** represents the divisions of the second fraction.
3. The **bottom bar** shows the **common denominator**. How is the third bar divided? What

What do you look for when finding the LCD?

Is the LCD a **factor** of each denominator or a **multiple** of each denominator?

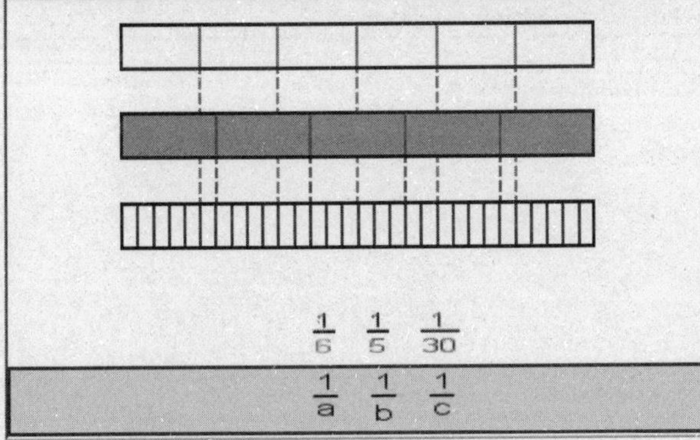

Do 5 and 6 have any common factors?

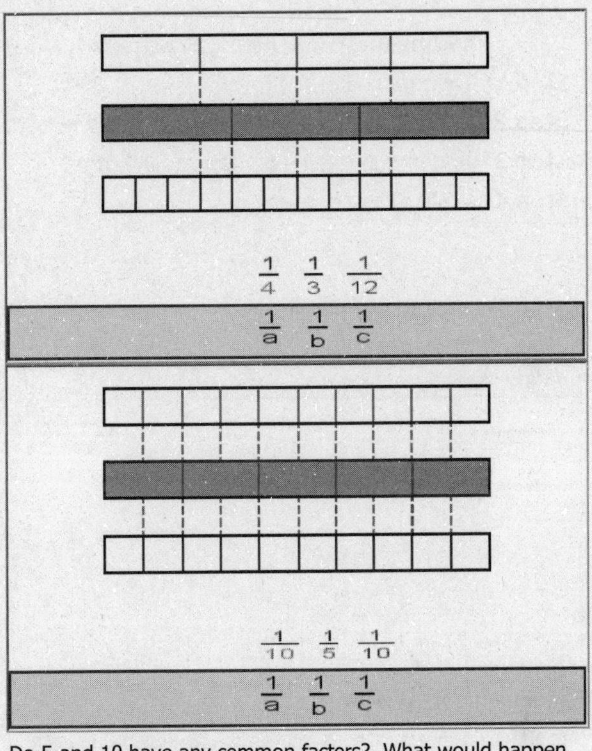

Do 5 and 10 have any common factors? What would happen if they didn't have any common factors?

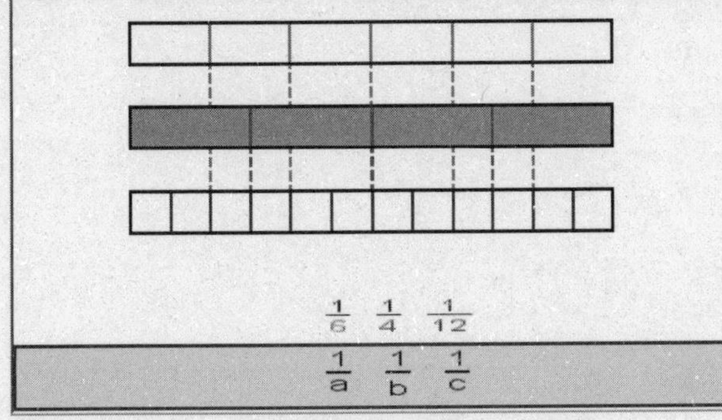

Is there another common denominator for 6 and 4?

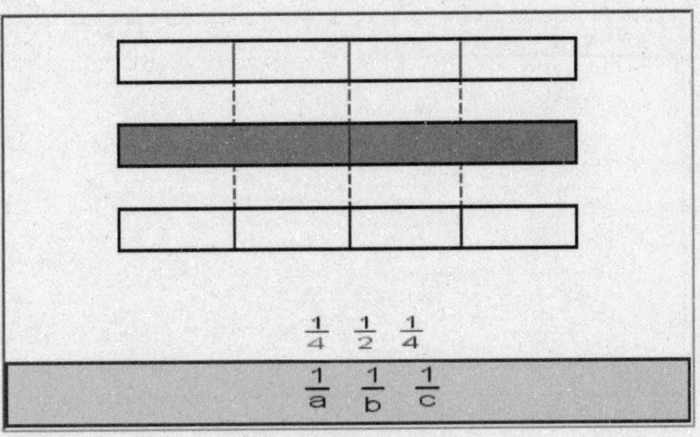

Would 8 work as a common denominator?

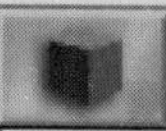

Add & Sub Fractions with Unlike Denominators

EnableMath

Adding and subtracting fractions with unlike denominators is not possible because the parts we need to count up are not the same size. We must use the **fundamental principle of fractions** to write equivalent fractions with the common denominator. For review of this procedure, see Module 2.2 Comparing Fractions. Once the common denominator is found and equivalent fractions are built up, we can combine the numerators to find the sum or difference.

Adding and Subtracting Fractions

Step 1: Determine the LCD.

Step 2: Change to equivalent fractions using the LCD.

Step 3: Add or subtract numerators as indicated.

Step 4: Write in lowest terms.

Adding fractions with unlike denominators

Example 1:

$$\frac{2}{3}+\frac{4}{8}=\frac{?}{24}$$

$$\frac{2}{3}\cdot\frac{8}{8}+\frac{4}{8}\cdot\frac{3}{3}=\frac{?}{24}$$

$$\frac{16+12}{24}=\frac{?}{24}$$

$$\frac{16+12}{24}=\frac{28}{24}$$

$$\boxed{=\frac{7}{6}}$$

Reduce fraction. Solution.

Adding fractions with unlike denominators

Example 2:

$$\frac{7}{8}+\frac{1}{4}+\frac{3}{5}=\frac{?}{40}$$

$$\frac{7}{8}\cdot\frac{5}{5}+\frac{1}{4}\cdot\frac{10}{10}+\frac{3}{5}\cdot\frac{8}{8}=\frac{?}{40}$$

$$\frac{35+10+24}{40}=\frac{?}{40}$$

$$\frac{35+10+24}{40}=\frac{69}{40}$$

$$\boxed{=1\frac{29}{40}}$$

Fraction is in reduced form. Solution.

Multiply by 1 means to build the fraction by multiplying both top and bottom by the same number—whatever factor works to change the denominator to the LCD.

Adding Fractions with Unlike Denominators

$$\frac{6}{3}+\frac{8}{5}=\frac{?}{15}$$

$$=\frac{6\cdot5}{3\cdot5}+\frac{8\cdot3}{5\cdot3}$$

$$=\frac{30+24}{15}$$

$$=\frac{54}{15}$$

$$\boxed{=\frac{18}{5}}$$

Reduce fraction, if possible. Solution.

What whole number is 6/3? Improper fractions work just like proper fractions. You may choose to write the answer in mixed number form.

Subtracting fractions with unlike denominators

Example 2:

$$\frac{11}{12}-\frac{7}{16}=\frac{?}{48}$$

$$\frac{11}{12}\cdot\frac{4}{4}-\frac{7}{16}\cdot\frac{3}{3}=\frac{?}{48}$$

$$\frac{44-21}{48}=\frac{?}{48}$$

$$\frac{44-21}{48}=\frac{23}{48}$$

$$\boxed{=\frac{23}{48}}$$

Fraction is in reduced form. Solution.

Use paper and pencil to work through problem step by step on your own.

Subtracting Fractions with Unlike Denominators

$$\frac{5}{13}-\frac{2}{8}=\frac{?}{104}$$

$$=\frac{5\cdot8}{13\cdot8}-\frac{2\cdot13}{8\cdot13}$$

$$=\frac{40-26}{104}$$

$$=\frac{14}{104}$$

$$\boxed{=\frac{7}{52}}$$

If possible, reduce fraction.

Notice the denominators both show factors of the LCD, 88.

Add & Sub Fractions with Unlike Denominators

If the fractions we are adding or subtracting do not have a common denominator, and then we must find one before we add. Two questions can be asked: what size pieces and how many are there? We need to visualize a new fraction whose denominator is common to both of the ones we are adding or subtracting.

How would you describe the difference between the way we visualize addition and subtraction?

What happens if the common denominator is bigger than the LCD?

How do you check your answer to a subtraction of fractions problem?

Is there a quick way to check addition of fractions?

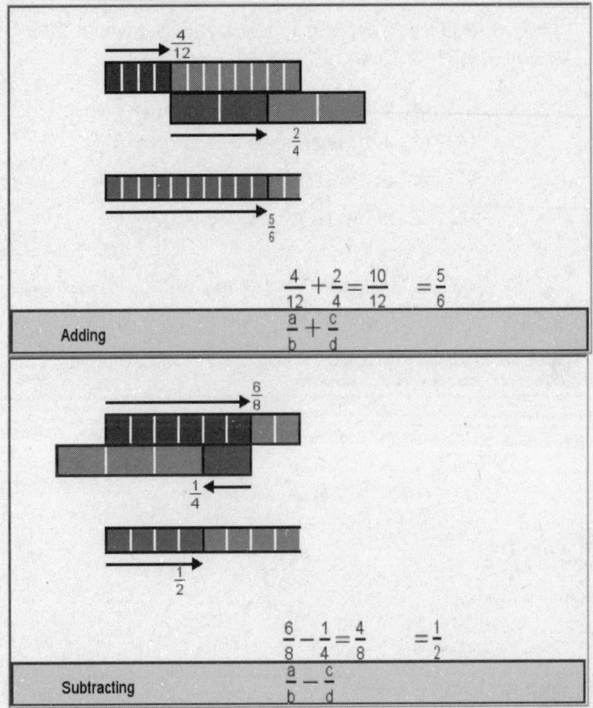

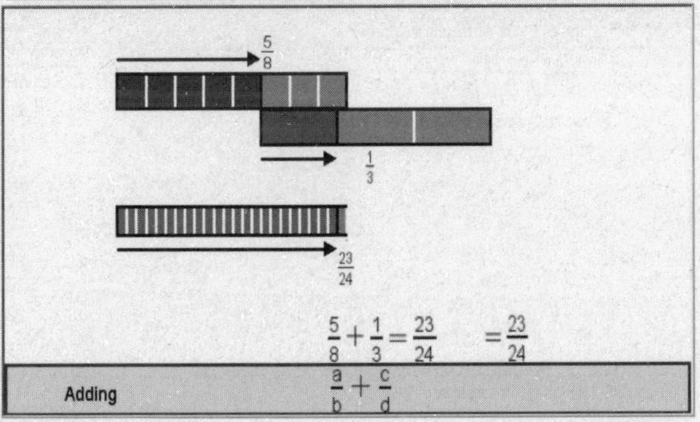

Sometimes the pieces are very small. What do the fractions look like with the LCD?

What is 6/8 in reduced form? Does that help make the problem easier?

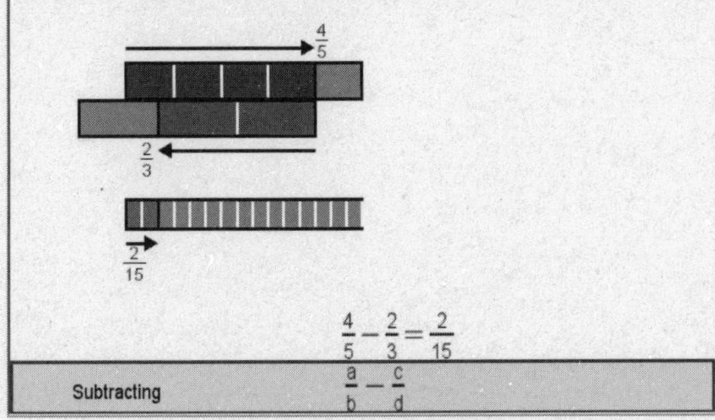

Taking away...What do you have to add to 2 1/5 to get 4/5?

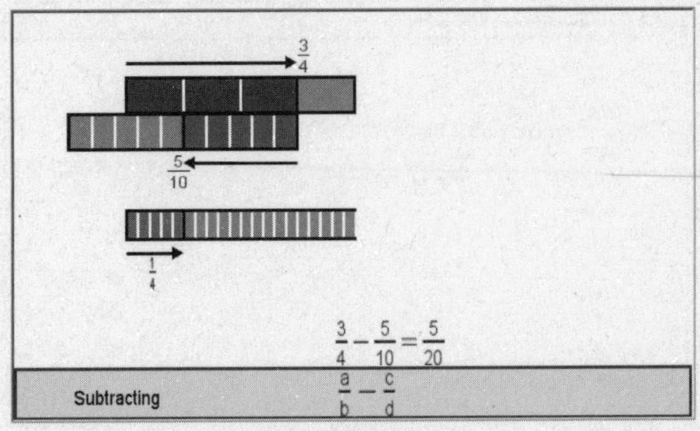

Would 40 work as the CD? Is there an equivalent fraction to 5/10 that would make the problem easier to work? Is 5/20 in lowest terms?

One common application of fractions is finding a part "of" something. What is 1/3 of 12? Or find 1/5 of 25. In the context of fractions, the word "of" means to multiply.

Hint: Remember that any whole number can be written as a fraction whose denominator is 1.

Fraction multiplication and whole number division are closely linked. You can think:

1/2 "of" is the same as dividing by 2.
1/3 "of" is the same as dividing by 3.
1/4 "of" is the same as dividing by 4.
1/8 "of" is the same as dividing by 8.

If an ad says "1/3 off sale" you can find how much you save by dividing the price by 3.

Finding Fractional Parts of Whole Numbers

What is $\frac{3}{6}$ of 10?

$$\frac{3}{6} \times 10 = \frac{3 \times 10}{6} = \frac{30}{6} = 5$$

Reduce the fraction, if necessary.

Finding Fractional Parts of Whole Numbers

What is $\frac{5}{8}$ of 8?

$$\frac{5}{8} \times 8 = \frac{5 \times 8}{8} = \frac{40}{8} = 5$$

Reduce the fraction, if necessary.

Don't forget to divide out common factors.

Finding Fractional Parts of Whole Numbers

What is $\frac{2}{3}$ of 9?

$$\frac{2}{3} \times 9 = \frac{2 \times 9}{3} = \frac{18}{3} = 6$$

Reduce the fraction, if necessary.

Divide out common factors. If you pay 2/3 of a $9 check, how much is your share?

Finding Fractional Parts of Whole Numbers

What is $\frac{3}{5}$ of 7?

$$\frac{3}{5} \times 7 = \frac{3 \times 7}{5} = \frac{21}{5}$$

Reduce the fraction, if necessary.

Think: 3/5 * 7/1. Any common factors to reduce? How could this solution be written as a mixed number?

For this visualization use a fraction bar marked off the fraction amount, the whole number times.

Multiplication is implied by the word "of," therefore, multiply the given values.

Can you have 0 sets of a fraction?

Can you have a fraction of a number and end up with a whole number?

What happens when everything divides out when multiplying a fraction and a whole number?

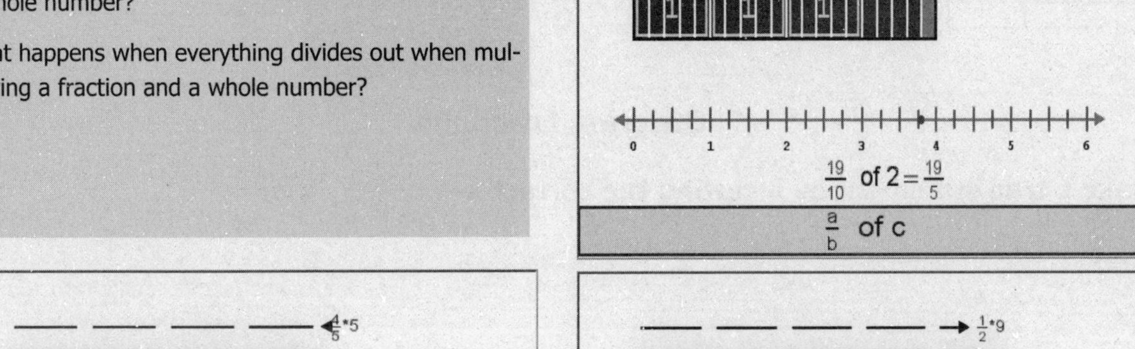

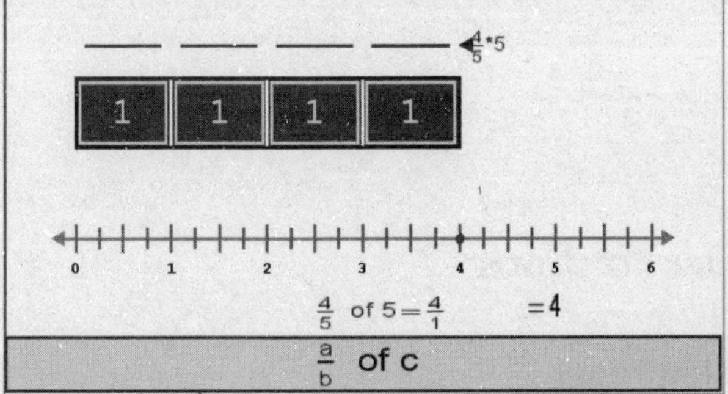

5 sets of 4/5.

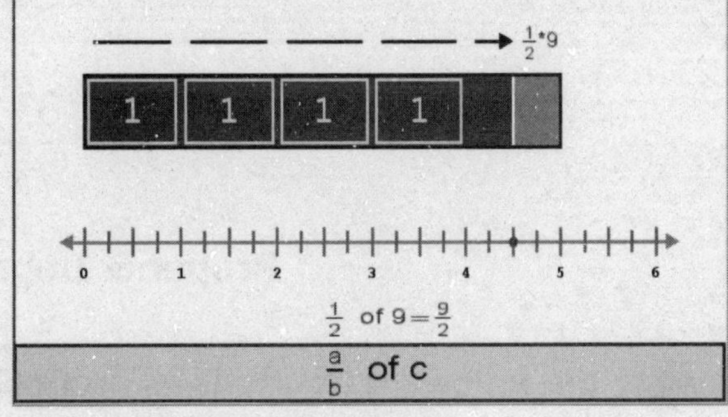

9 sets of 1/2. What is one-half of 9?

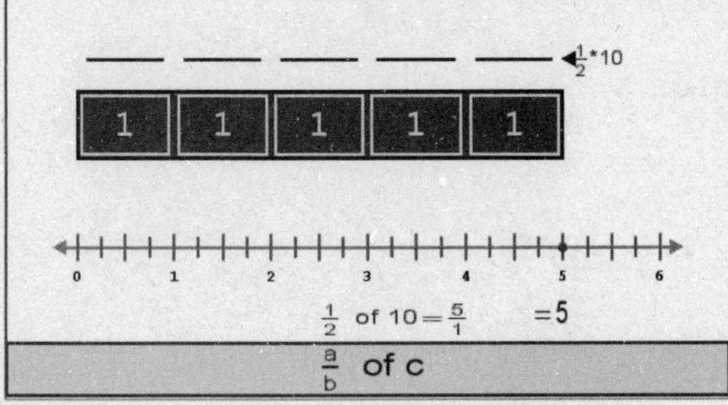

10 sets of 1/2. What is one-half of ten? What is 10/2?

Fractions

Determine what fraction is represented by the following figures.

1. ____________

2. ____________

3. **4.**

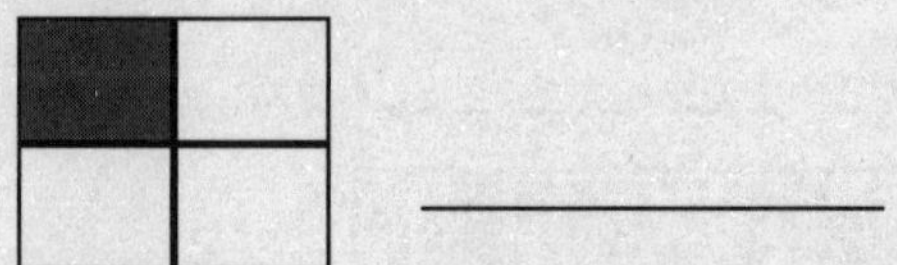

____

____

Ordering Fractions

Make a true statement by inserting the correct symbol: >, < or =.

1. $\frac{3}{5}$ $\frac{1}{2}$ **2.** $\frac{2}{5}$ $\frac{3}{4}$ **3.** $\frac{3}{7}$ $\frac{1}{2}$

4. $\frac{1}{3}$ $\frac{2}{5}$ **5.** $\frac{33}{75}$ $\frac{33}{75}$ **6.** $\frac{31}{50}$ $\frac{31}{70}$

Proper & Improper Fractions

Classify the following fractions as proper or improper.

1. **7/8** ____________ **2.** **9/8** ____________ **3.** **5/3** ____________

4. **8/8** ____________ **5.** **16/25** ____________ **6.** **21/9** ____________

Mixed Numbers

Change the following to proper fractions.

1. **7/5** **2.** **9/4**

3. **28/3** **4.** **22/7**

Convert the following mixed numbers to improper fractions:

5. $1\frac{3}{4}$ **6.** $2\frac{7}{9}$

Reciprocals

Find the reciprocal of each of the following numbers.

1. **7/8** ________ **2.** **9/8** ________

3. **5/3** ________ **4.** **8/8** ________

5. **16/25** ________ **6.** **21/9** ________

Equivalent Fractions

Build the following fractions to the higher terms indicated.

1. $\frac{3}{5} = \frac{\quad}{40}$ **2.** $\frac{7}{12} = \frac{\quad}{48}$

3. $\frac{4}{15} = \frac{\quad}{45}$ **4.** $\frac{2}{9} = \frac{\quad}{45}$

5. $\frac{1}{6} = \frac{\quad}{60}$ **6.** $\frac{3}{25} = \frac{\quad}{100}$

Prime Factorization

Find the prime factorization of the following composite numbers. Use exponent form where appropriate.

1. **48** **2.** **120**

3. **40** **4.** **150**

5. **105** **6.** **144**

Simplifying Fractions

Reduce the following fractions to lowest terms.

1. $\frac{24}{48}$ **2.** $\frac{24}{60}$ **3.** $\frac{12}{30}$

4. $\frac{120}{160}$ **5.** $\frac{50}{75}$ **6.** $\frac{64}{128}$

Multiplying Fractions

Multiply the following fractions. Make sure answers are in lowest terms.

1. $\frac{3}{7} * \frac{1}{2}$

2. $\frac{1}{3} * \frac{2}{5}$

3. $\frac{13}{5} * \frac{1}{26}$

4. $\frac{12}{15} * \frac{35}{14}$

5. $\frac{13}{15} * \frac{11}{12}$

6. $\frac{12}{30} * \frac{15}{18}$

Add & Subtract Fractions with Like Denominators

$\frac{3}{5} + \frac{1}{5}$

3.

$\frac{13}{7} - \frac{6}{7}$

5.

$\frac{13}{15} + \frac{11}{15}$

2.

$\frac{13}{15} - \frac{4}{15}$

4.

$\frac{11}{3} + \frac{2}{3}$

6.

$\frac{12}{15} + \frac{5}{15} + \frac{3}{15}$

Least Common Denominator

Use any method to find the LCD for the following denominators.

1. **12 and 30**

2. **12 and 20**

3. **33 and 45**

4. **8 and 36**

5. **15 and 20**

6. **18 and 24**

7. **15, 27, and 45**

8. **20, 30, and 36**

Add & Subtract Fractions with Unlike Denominators

1. $\frac{3}{5} + \frac{1}{4}$

2. $\frac{13}{15} - \frac{4}{5}$

3. $\frac{13}{7} - \frac{6}{14}$

4. $\frac{11}{12} + \frac{3}{10}$

5. $\frac{11}{15} + \frac{1}{9}$

6. $\frac{8}{15} + \frac{5}{12} + \frac{1}{18}$

Dividing Fractions

Divide the following fractions. Make sure answers are in lowest terms.

1. $\frac{3}{7} \div \frac{1}{2}$

2. $\frac{1}{3} \div \frac{2}{5}$

3. $\frac{5}{13} \div \frac{1}{26}$

4. $\frac{15}{12} \div \frac{35}{14}$

5. $\frac{13}{15} \div \frac{11}{12}$

6. $\frac{12}{30} \div \frac{15}{18}$

Fraction of...

Find the indicated fraction of each of the following whole numbers.

1. **1/5 of 15**

2. **1/2 of 48**

3. **3/4 of 32**

4. **5/12 of 60**

5. **3/8 of 95**

6. **3/25 of 504**

7. **12/17 of 1000**

8. **7/25 of 1250**

3. Decimals

Decimals or, more formally, decimal fractions are fractions whose denominators are powers of 10. They are valuable because they can be written and manipulated in our base 10 place value system just like ordinary whole numbers. Instead of dealing with fractions we can now deal with whole numbers and decimals points. Decimals are used instead of ordinary fractions in everything from money to the price of stocks, from the number of gallons of gas we put in our tanks to measurement in the metric system.

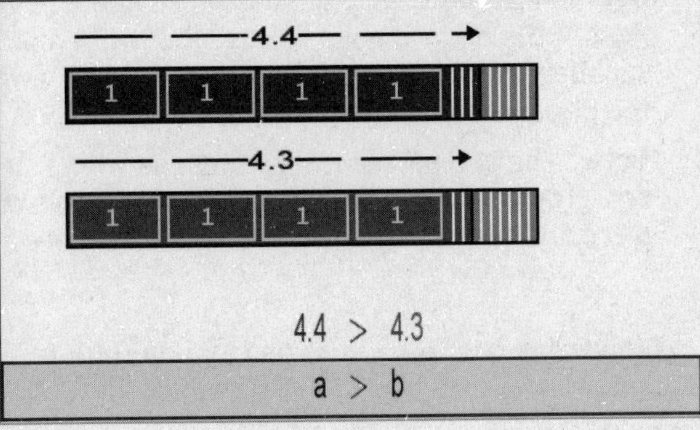

Decimals are another way to express fractions. All **decimal fractions**, as they are formally called, have denominators that are part of our place value system based on powers of 10. We use the **decimal point** to separate the whole numbers from the decimal fractions. The place values to the right of the decimal point represent a fraction of 1 over a power of ten: tenths, hundredths, thousandths, ten-thousandths, and so on. As with whole numbers each place value to the left is 10 times the place value to the right.

Note: The decimal point separates the whole number part from the decimal fraction part of a number. The ones place digit is a number's middle place value. The tens place is to the left of the ones place and tenths place is to the right of the decimal point.

Converting between words and standard form

Change to words: Write the whole number part in the usual way; write 'and' for the decimal point; then, write the fraction part and attach the place value name of the last digit.

Change to standard form: Write the whole number part and add the decimal part by making it the numerator of a fraction that has the place value of the last digit as the denominator. Reduce the fraction part to lowest terms.

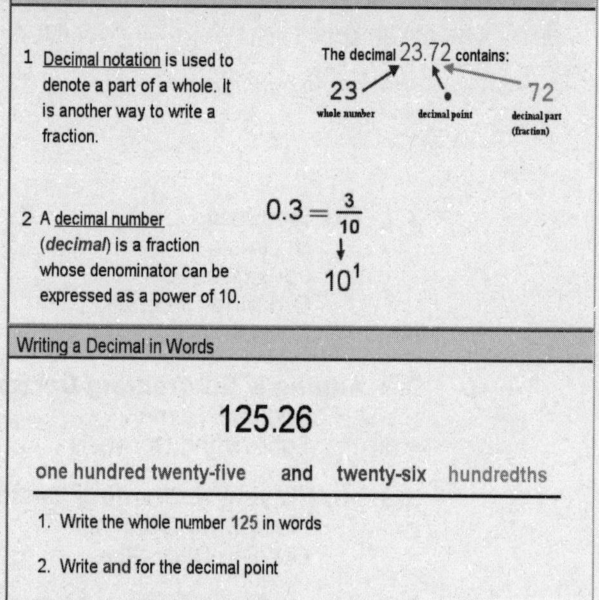

Definitions
1 Decimal notation is used to denote a part of a whole. It is another way to write a fraction.
The decimal 23.72 contains:
23
whole number
decimal point
72
decimal part (fraction)
2 A decimal number (decimal) is a fraction whose denominator can be expressed as a power of 10.
0.3 = 3/10
10^1
Writing a Decimal in Words
125.26
one hundred twenty-five and twenty-six hundredths
1. Write the whole number 125 in words
2. Write and for the decimal point
3. Write the decimal part in words followed by the place value name

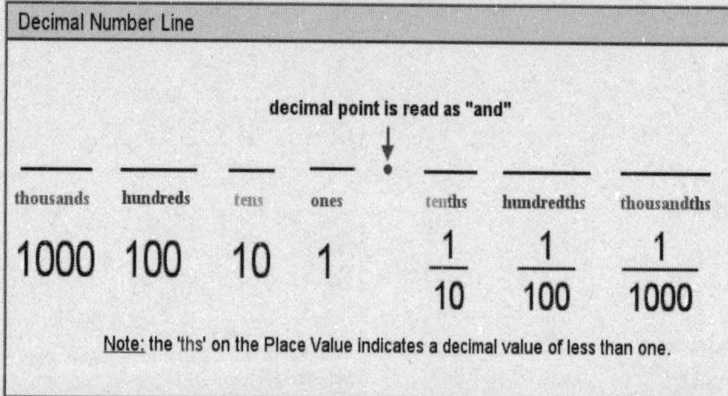

Use the above chart to help identify the place value name for each decimal place. Note the pattern continues in both directions.

The place value name is critical in writing a decimal in word form.

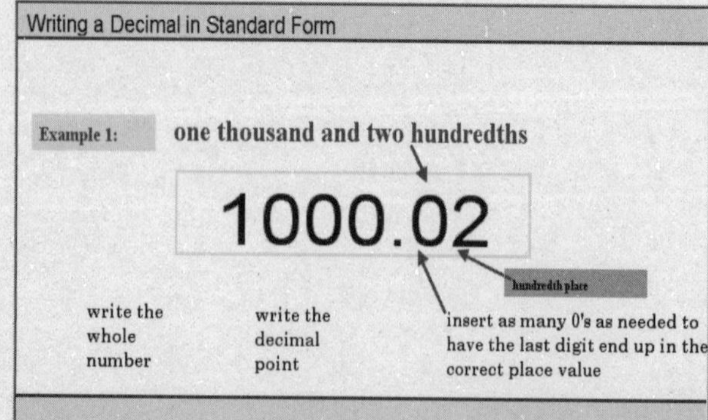

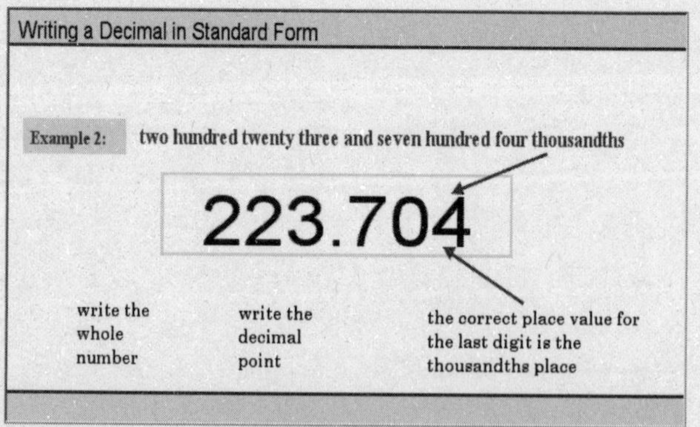

Zeros are used as place holders for decimals just like for whole numbers. The place value name is key to getting correct decimal placement.

The decimal part, seven hundred four thousandths is equivlatent fraction 704/1000.

Understanding place value is critical to being able to use our number system effectively. Determining the difference between 0.03 and 0.3 can be a matter of life and death if you are administering a shot to an infant. It can be the difference between an affordable loan rate and an extremely high credit card rate. There are three visuals to help develop both skill in reading and writing decimal numbers and an intuitive understanding of the relative sizes of these numbers.

Are all decimal numbers mixed numbers with a whole number part and a decimal part?

Can any number be expressed as a decimal number?

How do you know what place value name to attach to the word name of a number?

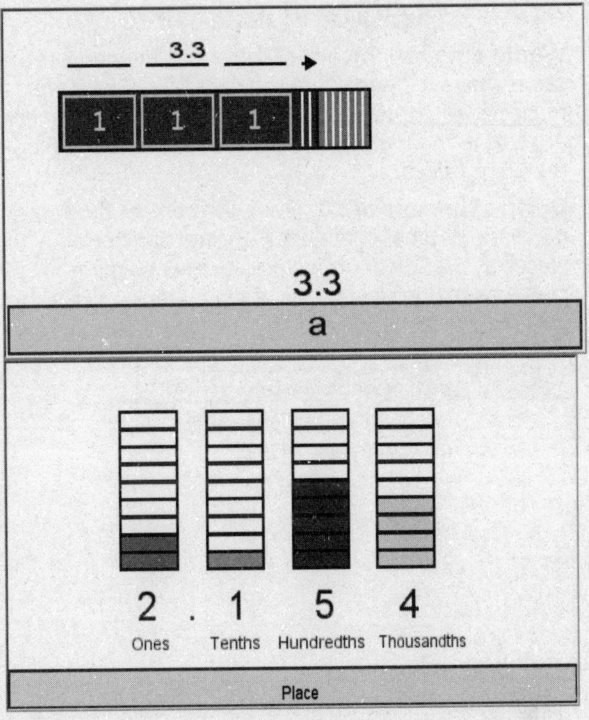

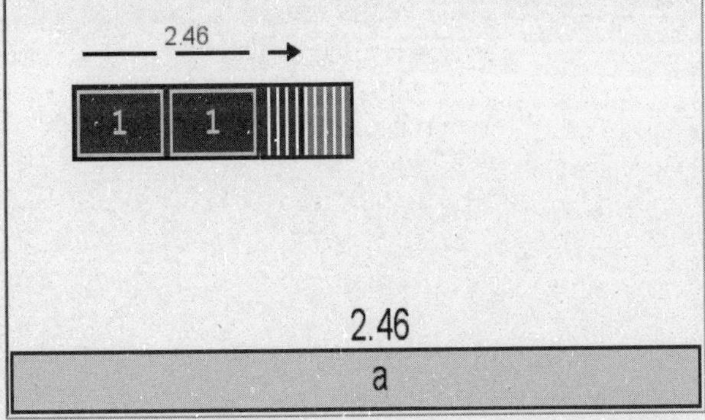

The fraction part gets a little hard to visualize when the pieces get really small. 46/100 is close to 5/10—can you determine if 2.46 is located correctly?

Point 3: Here is a view of place value in decimals as the filling of a stack. What happens when you add 1 to a filled stack?

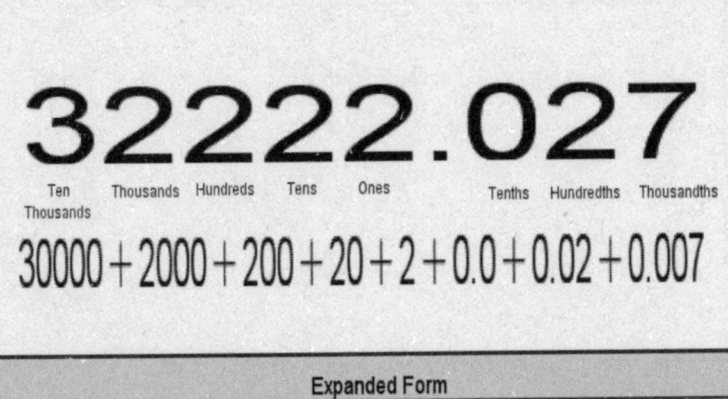

Point 4: Expanded Form -- Here we write a decimal in expanded form. What happens to the hundredths place when you add 3 to the thousandths place?

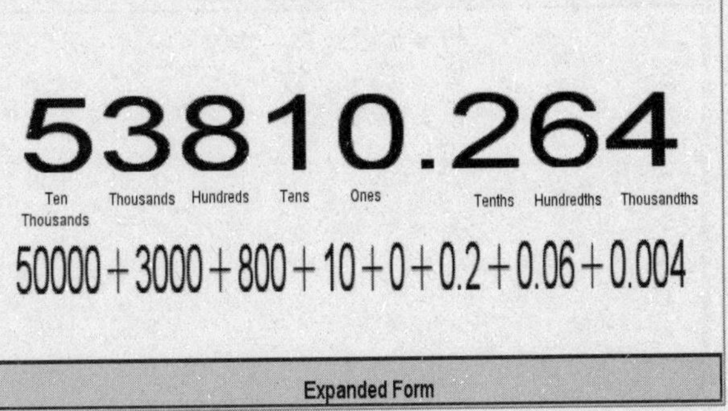

What digit occupies the hundredths place? What digit occupies the hundreds place?

From working with our whole number system, we recognize place values as powers of ten. Since each decimal place to the left is ten times the place to the right, we know 30 is ten times 3 and likewise .3 is ten times .03. Multiplying by ten moves the decimal point one place to the right. Multiplying by one tenth (the same as dividing by ten) moves the decimal point one place to the left.

Below is a chart listing some **Powers of Ten** to show the pattern that makes up our place value number system. The pattern continues in both directions indefinitely. The negative number exponents are shown here just to emphasize the pattern, but will not be covered extensively until a later module.

Multiplying by Powers of 10

Whole number powers of 10: Keep the number the same, move the decimal to the right the same number of places as the power of ten indicates—or the number of zeros of the multiplier. Add zeros if needed to fill the place values.

Decimal powers of 10: Keep the number the same, move the decimal to the left the same number of places as the power of ten indicates—or as many places as the decimal power of ten multiplier. Use place holder zeros as needed.

Powers of ten are 10 raised to an exponent

$$10^3 = 10 \times 10 \times 10 = 1000$$
$$10^2 = 10 \times 10 = 100$$
$$10^1 = 10 \times 1 = 10$$
$$10^0 = 1$$
$$\frac{1}{10^1} = \frac{1}{10} = .1$$
$$\frac{1}{10^2} = \frac{1}{100} = .01$$
$$\frac{1}{10^3} = \frac{1}{1000} = .001$$

Powers of ten are 10 raised to an exponent

$$10^3 = 10 \times 10 \times 10 = 1000$$
$$10^2 = 10 \times 10 = 100$$
$$10^1 = 10 \times 1 = 10$$

Note the pattern as the power decreases. What will the next value going down this table?

Powers of ten are 10 raised to an exponent

$$10^3 = 10 \times 10 \times 10 = 1000$$
$$10^2 = 10 \times 10 = 100$$
$$10^1 = 10 \times 1 = 10$$
$$10^0 = 1$$

And what will be the next value of the power of 10?

Powers of ten are 10 raised to an exponent

$$10^3 = 10 \times 10 \times 10 = 1000$$
$$10^2 = 10 \times 10 = 100$$
$$10^1 = 10 \times 1 = 10$$
$$10^0 = 1$$
$$\frac{1}{10^1} = \frac{1}{10} = .1$$

And the next?

Powers of ten are 10 raised to an exponent

$$10^3 = 10 \times 10 \times 10 = 1000$$
$$10^2 = 10 \times 10 = 100$$
$$10^1 = 10 \times 1 = 10$$
$$10^0 = 1$$
$$\frac{1}{10^1} = \frac{1}{10} = .1$$
$$\frac{1}{10^2} = \frac{1}{100} = .01$$
$$\frac{1}{10^3} = \frac{1}{1000} = .001$$

And 10^{-4}

Multiplying by powers of ten is a mental process of moving the decimal point in a number.

If you multiply a number by 10, or 100, or 1000, how many places do you move the decimal point and in which direction? If you multiply a number by 1/10, 1/100, or 1/000, how many places do you move the decimal point and in what direction? If you multiply by 0.1, 0.01, or 0.001, how many places do you move the decimal point and in what direction?

Do all numbers have a decimal point?

Where is the decimal point in a whole number?

Multiplying by 1/100 is the same as dividing by what number?

Can you work these problems using the multiplication algorithm?

$$5.0860 \times \frac{1}{100} = 0.050860$$

$a = 5.0860$

decimal point moves 2 places to the left — a, decmial point

$$5.0860 \times \frac{1}{10} = 0.50860$$

$a = 5.0860$

decimal point moves 1 places to the left — a, decmial point

Multiplying by 1/10 is the same as multiplying by 0.1 and the same as dividing by what number? If you show the multiplication algorithm, how many decimal places are in the product?

$$5.0860 \times \frac{1}{1} = 5.0860$$

$a = 5.0860$

a, decmial point

Why does the decimal point move to the right? Use the multiplication algorithm to find out!

$$5.0860 \times 10 = 50.860$$

$a = 5.0860$

decimal point moves 1 places to the right — a, decmial point

Which way is that decimal point moving?

$$5.0860 \times 100 = 508.60$$

$a = 5.0860$

decimal point moves 2 places to the right — a, decmial point

Four zeros—four places—which direction? Think: *multiplying*

Ordering Decimals

As with whole numbers and fractions, two decimal numbers are either equal, the first is greater than the second, or the first is less than the second. Place value position critical in determining size of decimal numbers. Match the numbers' place value digits until one is larger and insert the appropriate symbol to make a true statement.

To order decimals we compare digits starting on the left and working toward the right since digits lose value as we move from left to right. Compare each place in turn and when the digits are unequal, then pick the largest value to be first.

You can order a list of numbers in the same way. This is what a spreadsheet does to sort numbers from highest to lowest.

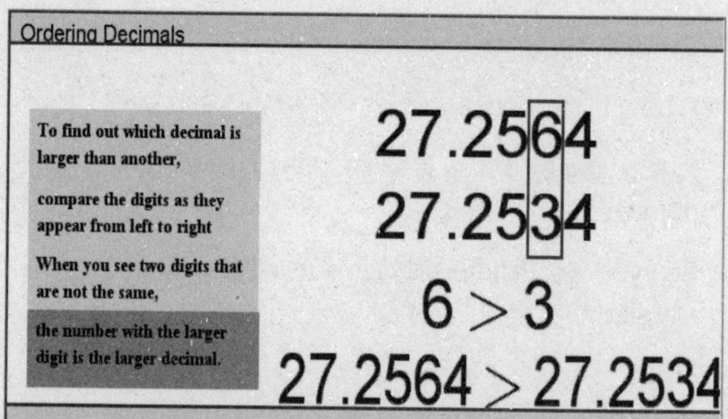

Ordering Decimals
To find out which decimal is larger than another,
compare the digits as they appear from left to right
When you see two digits that are not the same,
the number with the larger digit is the larger decimal.
27.2564
27.2534
6 > 3
27.2564 > 27.2534

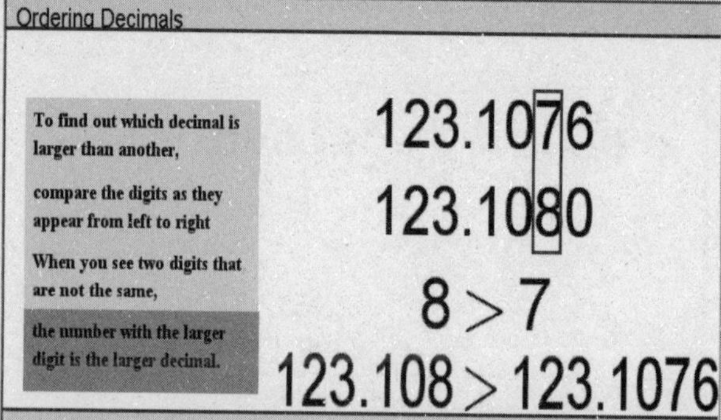

Ordering Decimals
To find out which decimal is larger than another,
compare the digits as they appear from left to right
When you see two digits that are not the same,
the number with the larger digit is the larger decimal.
123.1076
123.1080
8 > 7
123.108 > 123.1076

Look at the part of the number that is not the same. Add place holder zeros to the right of decimal numbers if needed to make the number of decimal places the same.

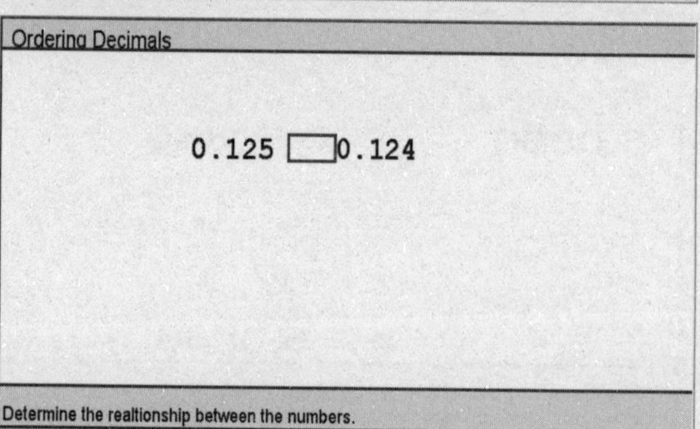

Insert the appropriate symbol to make a true statement (<,>,=).

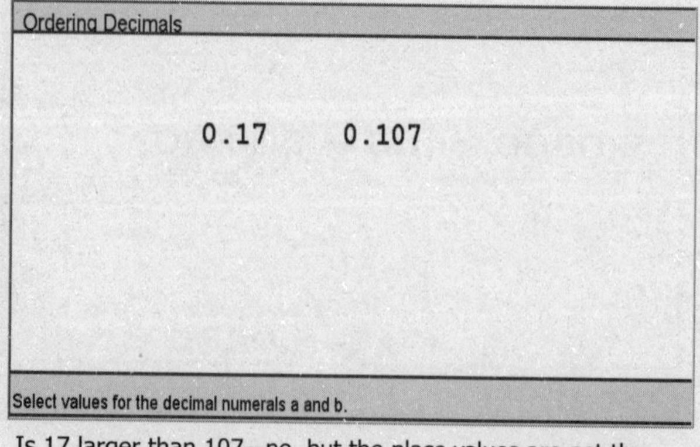

Is 17 larger than 107—no, but the place values are not the same. 0.17 needs one more decimal place before the numbers can be compared.

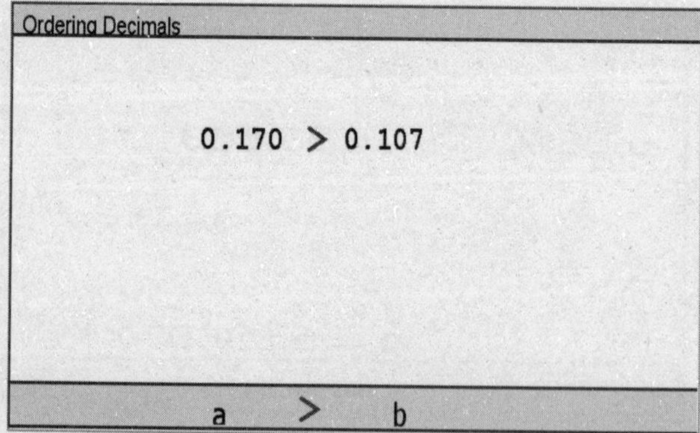

The computer will automatically insert the correct number of zeros. It is now clear that 170 is >107; therefore, 0.17>1.107.

Decimal numbers can be visualized with number bars like fractions. When the divisions get smaller than tenths or hundredths it can be hard to see, so the visualizations here only use one or two decimal places. Use the patterns here to assume that the same approach works for all decimal numbers.

When numbers are very close to being equal, how do you determine which one is larger?

Does the number of digits determine the size of a number?

Does the size digit, disregarding place value, determine the relative size of two numbers?

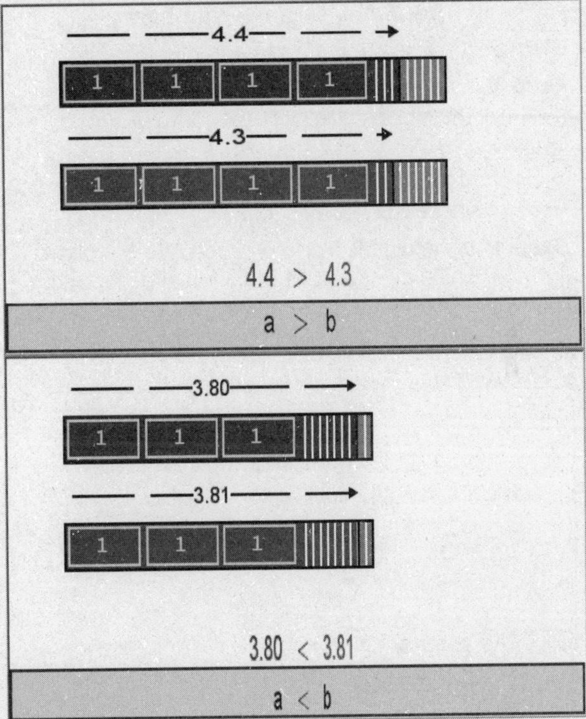

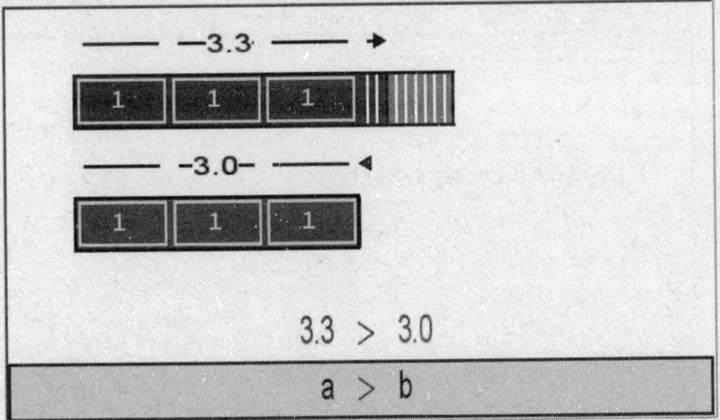

Do the two numbers have the same number of decimal places?

Is 3.81>3.8?

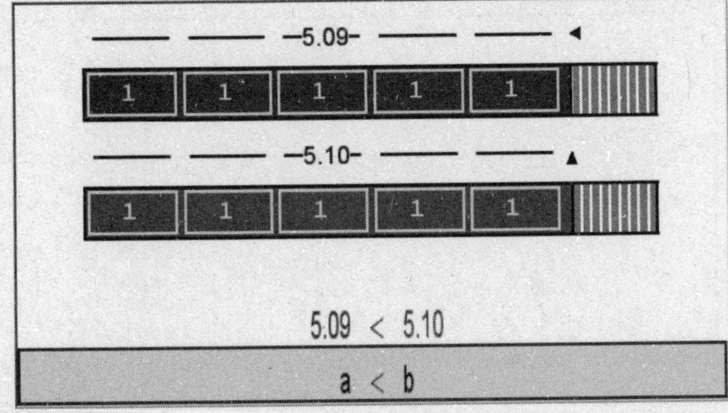

Is 5.09<5.1?

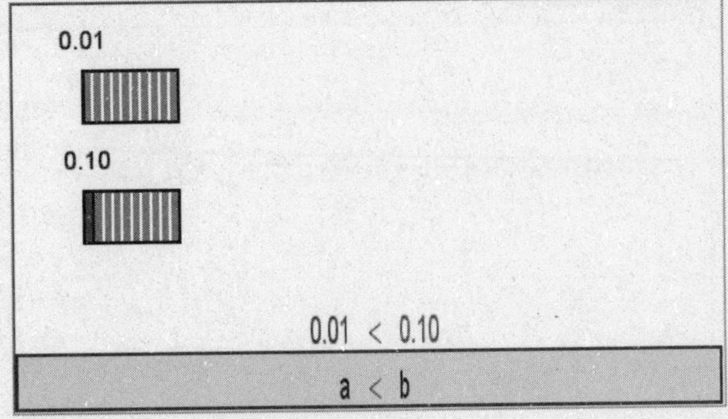

Is 0.1 ten times bigger than 0.01?

The process for rounding decimals is the same as for rounding whole numbers except for one final detail: the decimal place value you are rounding to must be the last digit reported, even if it's a zero. Rounding means to write a number that is "close to" the original number but with fewer non-zero digits.

Rounding Decimal Numbers

Step 1: Choose the place value to round to.

Step 2: Look at the digit to the immediate right of the chosen place value.

Step 3: If the digit is less than 5, discard it and the digits to the right. (Keep all of the digits to the left of the first zero.)

Step 4: If the digit is 5 or more, add 1 to the place value digit, discard the decimal digits to the right (non-decimal digits are replaced by zeros), keep the digits to the left.

Rounding Decimals

1 Round 526.13674 to the nearest thousandth.

Locate the thousandths place value.

Rounding Decimals

1 Round 526.13674 to the nearest thousandth.

Compare the two numbers. ROUND UP by adding 1. The rounded number is:

$7 > 6$ $6 + 1 = 7$ 526.137

RULE: If the digit to the right is 5 or more, ROUND UP by adding 1 to the requested place value. If the digit to the right is less than 5, do not change anything and omit all digits after the requested place value.

Add 1 to the place value digit.

Rounding Decimals

7642.567 rounded to the nearest $\frac{1}{100}$th is 7642.57

If the digit is 5 or more round up, otherwise round down.

Add 1 to the place value digit.

Rounding Decimals

324.979 rounded to the nearest $\frac{1}{100}$th is 324.98

If the digit is 5 or more round up, otherwise round down.

Add 1 to the hundredth place.

Rounding Decimals

324.979 rounded to the nearest $\frac{1}{10}$th is 325.0

If the digit is 5 or more round up, otherwise round down.

This is the same number rounded to tenths. Notice that the tenths place zero must be included to show the place value of the rounded number.

Rounding is visualized by a number line. The two possible round off numbers form the endpoint of the number line with the critical values marked. Choose the value that the number is closest to for the rounded off number. Ask yourself: What two numbers is the given number between? Which number is it closest to?

Why it is 5 and above? Write the numbers 0 to 9 in a row. What side of the middle of that row is 5 on? We are not actually counting from 1 to 10 but for a single digit, we count 0 to 9.

After you know what place value is needed, how do you determine the end points of the number line segment?

What does the red arrow show?

Do you ever subtract 1 from a digit to round off?

Why do we say "round down"?

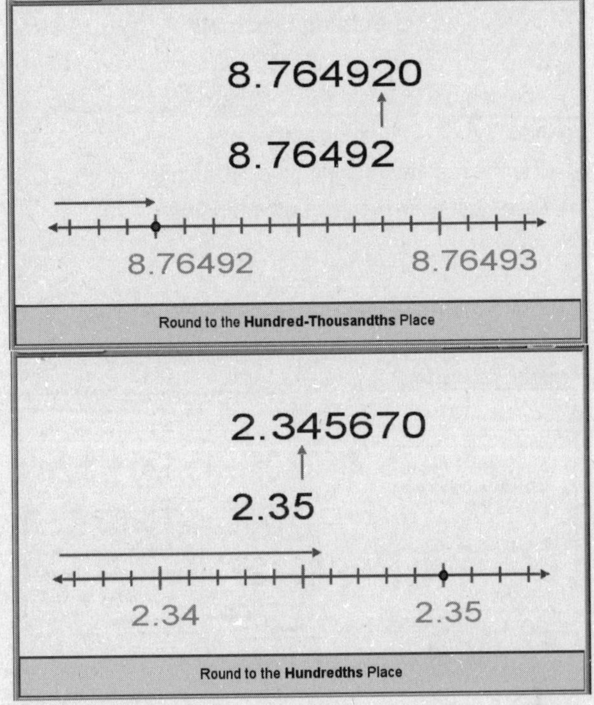

What if the request was to round this number to the nearest hundredth? What would be the end points? What would be the result?

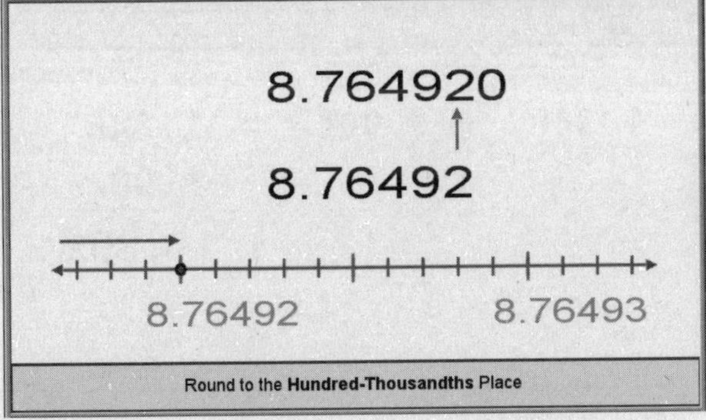

What if you were to round to the 10 thousandths place? Would the result be different?

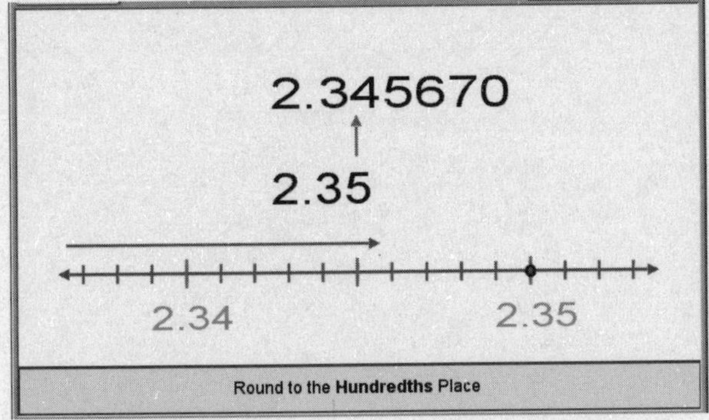

Is the above number closer to 2.34 or 2.35? How did we determine the end points to be 2.34 and 2.35?

The key to adding decimals is to align the decimal points vertically making place value columns. Then we add just like we do whole numbers. The sum has its decimal point aligned, as in the problem, between the ones place and the tenths place.

Adding Decimals

- Addition of decimals is commutative.
- Addition of decimals is associative.
- 0 is the identity of addition of decimals.
- Carry just as in whole number addition.

Adding decimal numbers

Write the decimal numbers so that the decimal points all line up vertically.

1 $32.05 + 15.125 + 3.2$

32.05
15.125
3.2

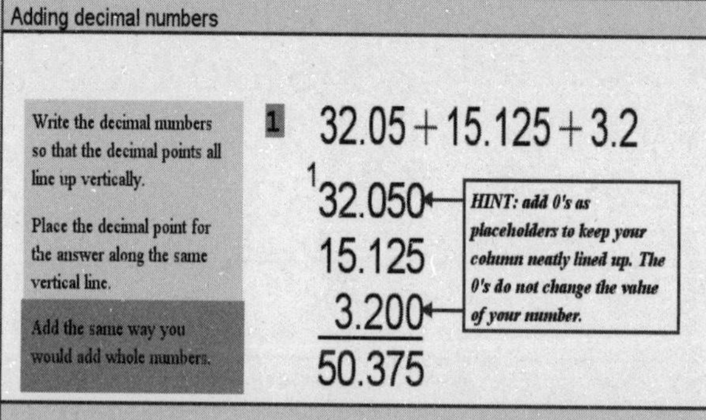

Adding decimal numbers
Write the decimal numbers so that the decimal points all line up vertically.
Place the decimal point for the answer along the same vertical line.
Add the same way you would add whole numbers.
1
32.05 + 15.125 + 3.2
1
32.050
15.125
3.200
50.375
HINT: add 0's as placeholders to keep your column neatly lined up. The 0's do not change the value of your number.

Appending zeros to the right of a decimal number does not change the value of the number. Even up the columns by adding zeros as needed.

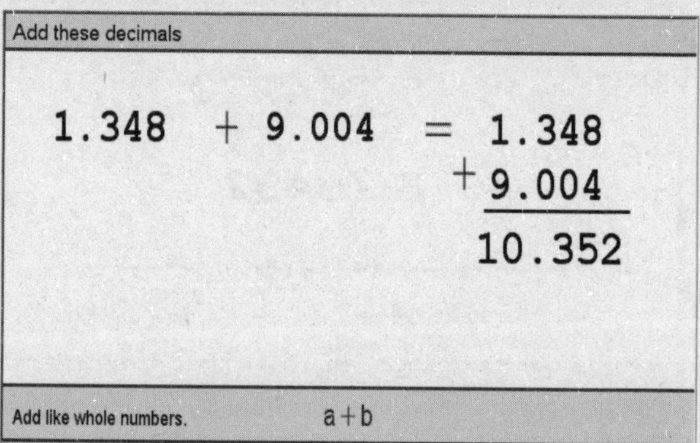

Make sure the decimal is aligned correctly between the ones and tenths columns.

Add these decimals

$$2.9 + 3.004 = \begin{array}{r} 2.900 \\ +\ 3.004 \\ \hline 5.904 \end{array}$$

Add like whole numbers. $a + b$

You can put zeros after the 9 if it helps align the place value columns.

Addition of decimals is exactly like addition of whole numbers and fractions. Decimal bars are put together to represent addition. It is sometimes hard to visualize very small pieces, so try to keep values in tenths or hundredths and assume that the processes and patterns hold for all decimal numbers.

How is a decimal number like a fraction? Is there always a whole number part to a decimal number?

Can you add a whole number and a decimal?

Does a whole number have a decimal point?

If two decimal numbers have both a whole number part and a decimal part, how do you make sure you add the right place value columns?

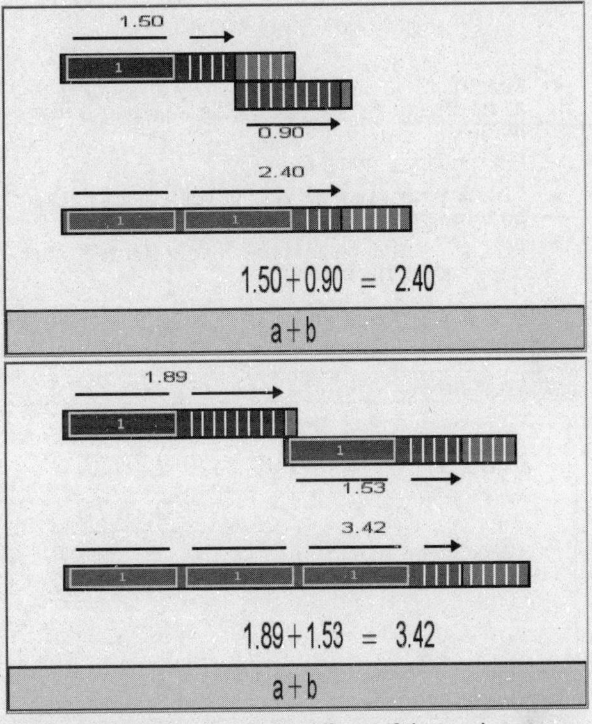

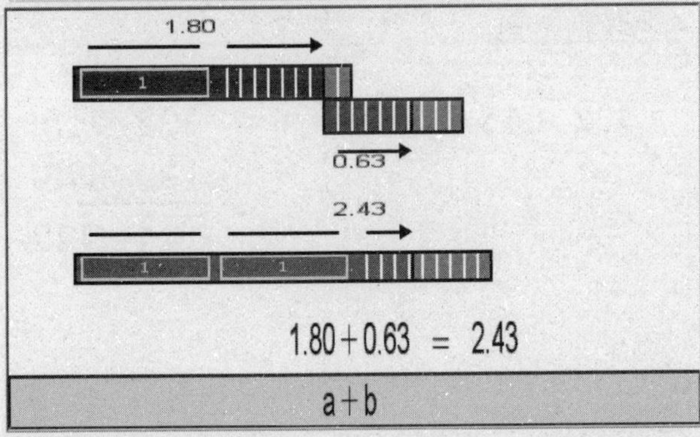

Draw in guide lines as needed to make sure you visualize the sum. Can you carry just like with whole numbers?

How would this visualization be different if the numbers were 0.189 + 0.153?

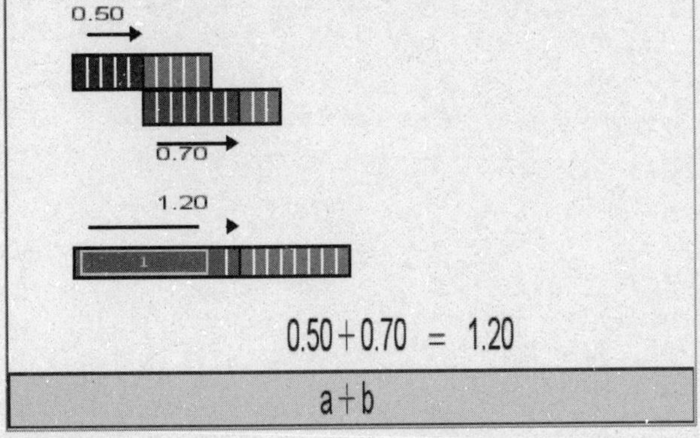

How do you know when you need to carry?

To subtract decimal numbers, it is important to have the same number of digits to the right of the decimal point in each number (add 0's if necessary) so that the correct place values are aligned. Once the problem is set up, subtract decimals just like whole numbers, borrowing when needed.

Subtracting Decimals

- Keep place value columns even by appending zeros as needed to the right of the decimal part of the number.
- Put the larger number on top.
- **Check your answer**: Add the difference to the bottom number to get the top number.
- Put the decimal point in the answer between the ones and tenths place value.

Subtraction of Decimal Numbers

Write the decimal numbers so that the decimal points all line up vertically.

Place the decimal point for the answer along the same vertical line.

Subtract the same way you would subtract whole numbers.

$39.073 - 25.140$

$$\begin{array}{r} 39.073 \\ -25.140 \\ \hline 13.933 \end{array}$$

Subtract these Decimals

$$2.015 - 0.678 = \begin{array}{r} 2.015 \\ -\ 0.678 \\ \hline 1.337 \end{array}$$

Subtract like whole numbers. $a - b$

Step 10-15: When we subtract decimals, we borrow from the places to the left when we need to.

Subtract these Decimals

$$302.015 - 190.678 = \begin{array}{r} 302.015 \\ -\ 190.678 \\ \hline 111.337 \end{array}$$

Subtract like whole numbers. $a - b$

Point 2: **Dynamic Example:** Change **a** and **b** and watch the result. The computer will automatically add zeros to keep the columns even.

Subtraction is the opposite operation from addition so the decimal bars go in opposite direction from addition. Instead of appending the bars we "take away" the subtracted part, reversing the arrow.

Can you take a whole number from a decimal number?

Can you take a decimal number from a whole number?

What happens when you subtract a four digit decimal number from a two digit decimal number?

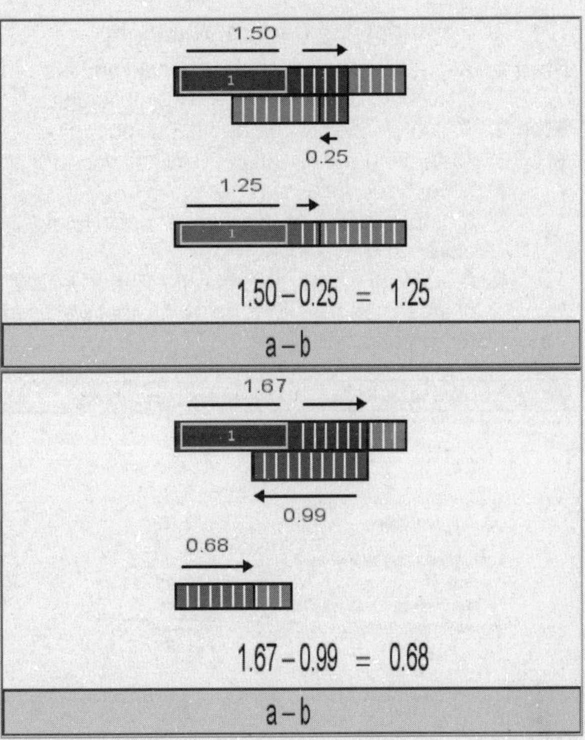

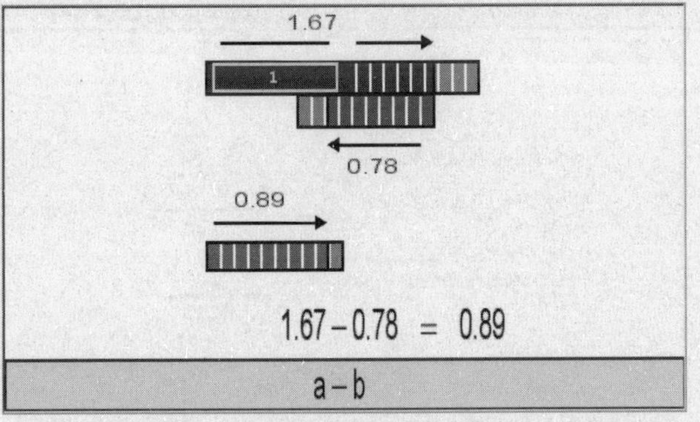

As you increase the subtracted part, what happens to the difference?

What happens when you add one hundredth to the subtracted part?

Multiplying Decimals

Multiplying decimal numbers is a lot like multiplying whole numbers except for figuring out where to put the decimal point in the answer. Use the partial products algorithm for long multiplications that you can't do mentally. Placement of the decimal point depends on the place values of the factors.

Multiplying Decimal Numbers

Step 1: Align the factors just like in whole number multiplication, by aligning the right most digits.

Step 2: Multiply, ignoring the decimal point.

Step 3: Determine the number of decimal places needed for the answer by:

A. Find the total of the number of decimal places in the factors.

B. Counting from the right, insert the decimal point so you have that many decimal places in the product.

Multiply these one-place decimal numbers

1. Count total number of decimal places in multiplicands.
2. Multiply as if they were whole numbers.
3. Place the decimal point to the left the total number counted in step 1.

```
    3.4   1
  * 6.3  +1
  -----
    102
   204
  -----
  21.42  =2
```

a*b

Multiply a one-decimal place number by a two-decimal place number

1. Count total number of decimal places in multiplicands.
2. Multiply as if they were whole numbers.
3. Place the decimal point to the left the total number counted in step 1.

```
    2.47   2
  *  4.7  +1
  ------
    1729
    988
  ------
  11.609  =3
```

a*b

Add the number of decimal places in both factors to find the decimal placement in the answer. Think 1/100 *1/10—the answer should have three decimal places ending in thousandths.

Multipling a two-decimal place number by a two-decimal place number

1. Count total number of decimal places in multiplicands.
2. Multiply as if they were whole numbers.
3. Place the decimal point to the left the total number counted in step 1.

```
     5.28
  *  2.35
  -------
     2640
    1584
   1056
  -------
  12.4080
```

a*b

Think of two decimal places as 1/100ths, so hundredths times hundredths is ten thousandths...the decimal number should end in the ten thousandths place.

Multipling a two-decimal place number by a two-decimal place number

1. Count total number of decimal places in multiplicands.
2. Multiply as if they were whole numbers.
3. Place the decimal point to the left the total number counted in step 1.

```
    0.03
  * 0.02
  ------
       6
      0
     0
  ------
  0.0006
```

a*b

Even if you do not have enough digits in the product, the answer must end in the ten thousandths place...put zeros in as place holders to make the product have the correct place value.

Multipling a two-decimal place number by a two-decimal place number

1. Count total number of decimal places in multiplicands.
2. Multiply as if they were whole numbers.
3. Place the decimal point to the left the total number counted in step 1.

```
    0.95
  * 0.96
  ------
     570
    855
    0
  ------
  0.9120
```

a*b

If you select two 2-decimal place numbers to multiply, will your answer always have 4 decimal places? Ask your instructor if you can eliminate the zero at the end of the product above.

Multiplying decimals, like multiplying whole numbers and fractions, is visualized with a rectangle. The fraction bars across the bottom and up the side are the decimal numbers. We made the grid in 10ths so that it is easy to see, but you can assume the same patterns hold for all place values.

Is multiplication of decimal numbers commutative?

Can a whole number be multiplied by a decimal number?

How do you determine how many decimal places in the product of a whole number and a decimal?

Do all decimals have a whole number part? Do they all have a decimal part?

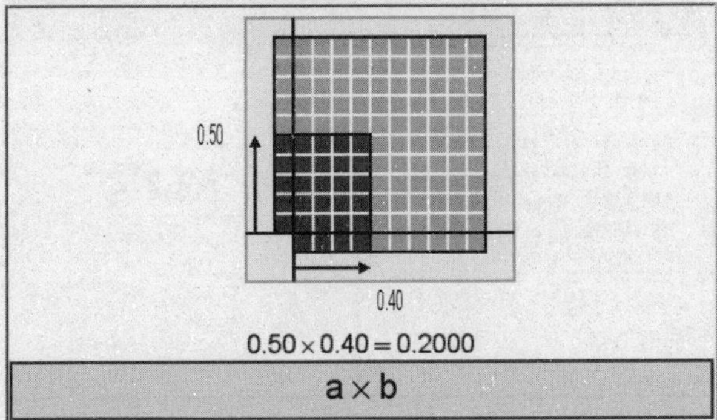

If two decimals are less than 1, is their product less than either of the decimals? Look at this one without all the zeros: 0.5*0.4=0.2—how can that be? Don't we need two decimal places in the answer?

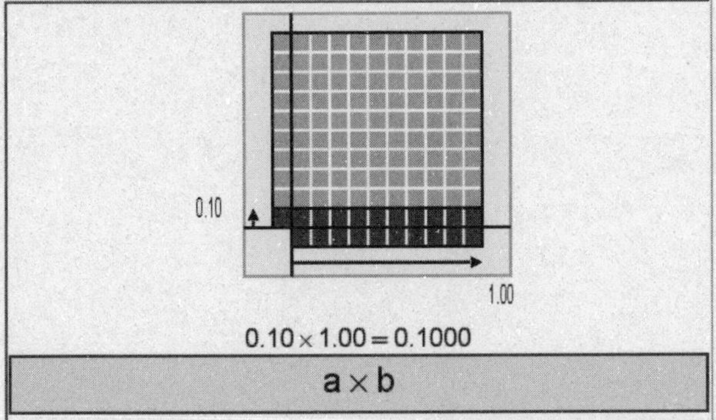

Is the product of a decimal <1 and a one digit whole number, greater than the whole number?

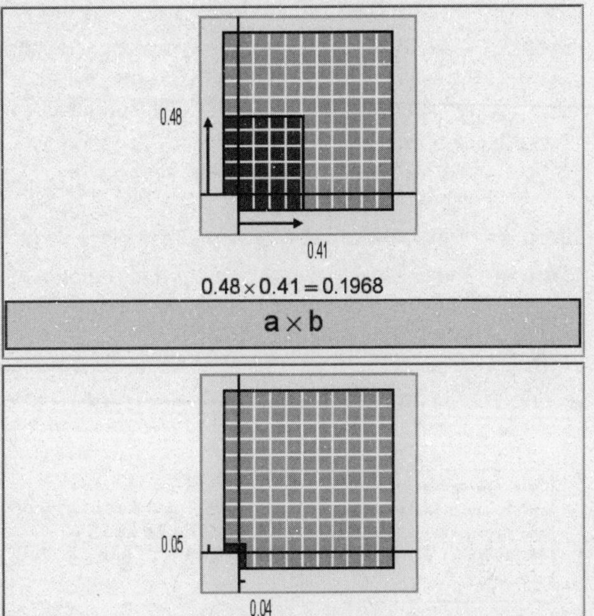

Is the above answer one tenth or one hundredth of the answer to the left?

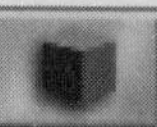

Dividing Decimals

EnableMath

Dividing by fractions requires changing the problem sign to multiplication and inverting the divisor. Dividing by decimal fractions uses that same theory and employs the long division algorithm. When you divide decimal numbers by other decimal numbers, you must change the divisor to a whole number by moving the decimal point to the right—that process is the same as inverting the divisor. You must also move the decimal point in the dividend—like multiplying by the denominator of the decimal fraction.

Decimal Division

Step 1: Make the divisor a whole number by moving the decimal to the right in BOTH the divisor and dividend. Bring the decimal straight up.

Step 2: Use the long division algorithm to divide to one place beyond the needed number of places.

Step 3: Round the answer to the needed place value.

Step 4: Check your answer by multiplying the quotient and divisor and add the remainder (before rounding).

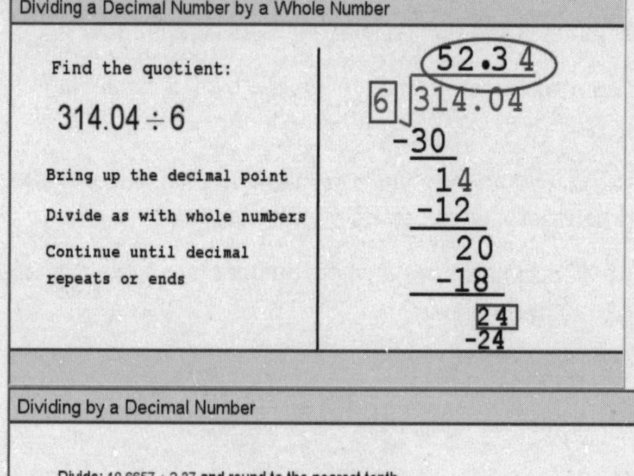

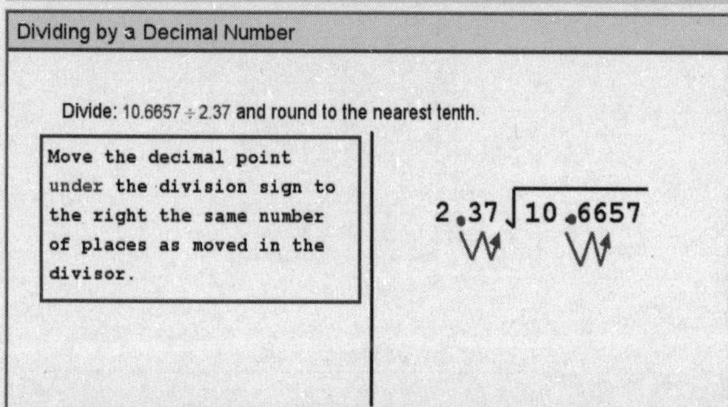

Move the decimal point in both divisor and dividend.

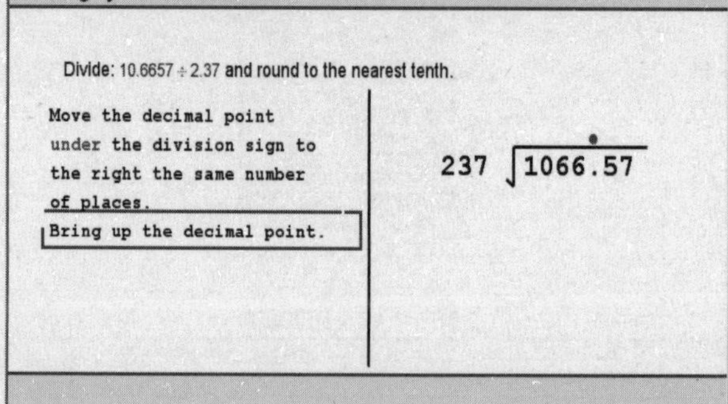

The decimal in the quotient is placed above the decimal in the dividend. Divide like normal using the long division algorithm.

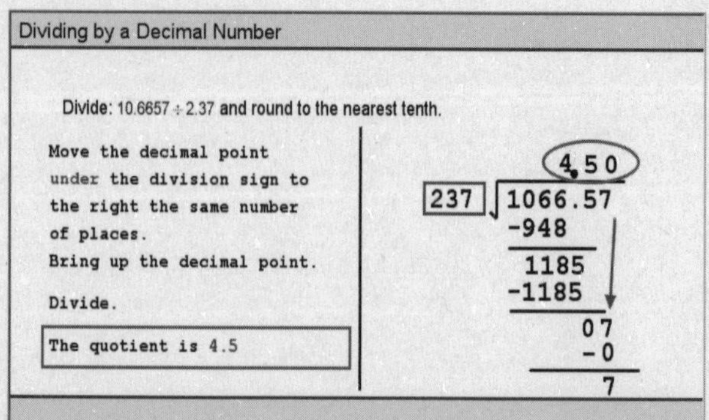

Divide one place beyond, then round.

We picture division as the slope of the line that connects two decimal fraction bars. Think of slope as the steepness of the line measured from the fraction made up of the rise (vertical bar) over the run (horizontal bar). We keep the division to tenths so that you can clearly see the amounts.

If the slope is steep does it mean the divisor is larger than the dividend or smaller? If the slope is flat, what does that tell you about the divisor and dividend?

Can you divide a whole number by a decimal number? Where do you put the decimal in the whole number?

Is division of decimals commutative?

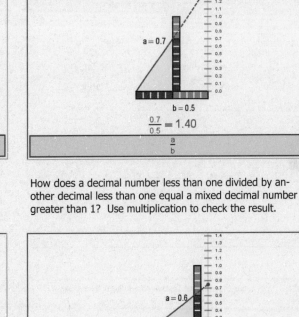

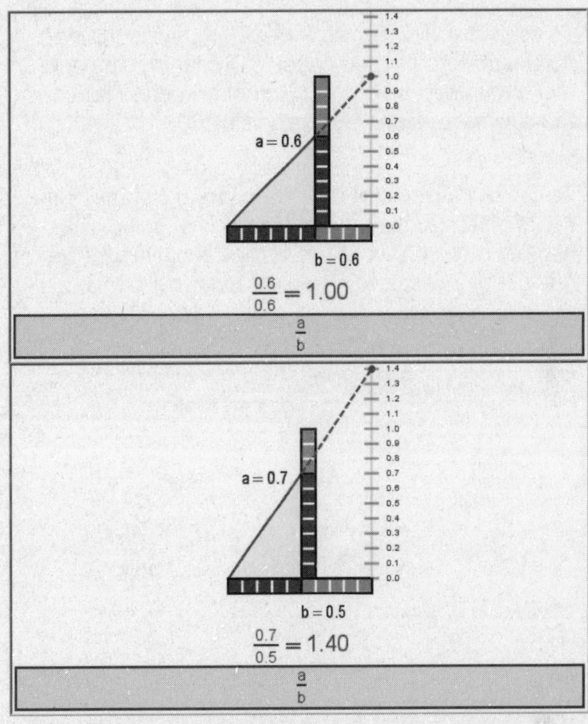

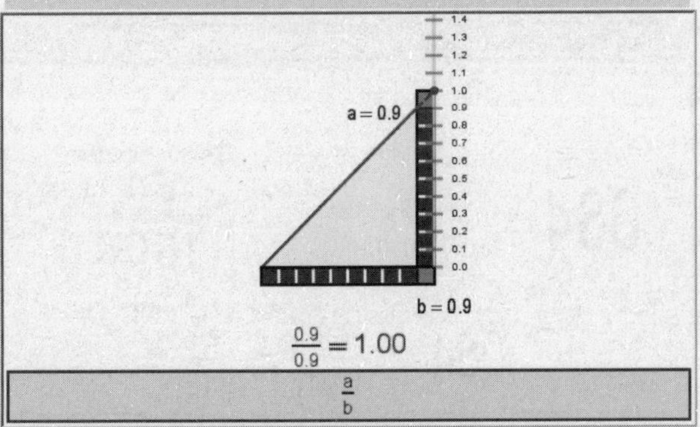

What is any number divided by itself?

How does a decimal number less than one divided by another decimal less than one equal a mixed decimal number greater than 1? Use multiplication to check the result.

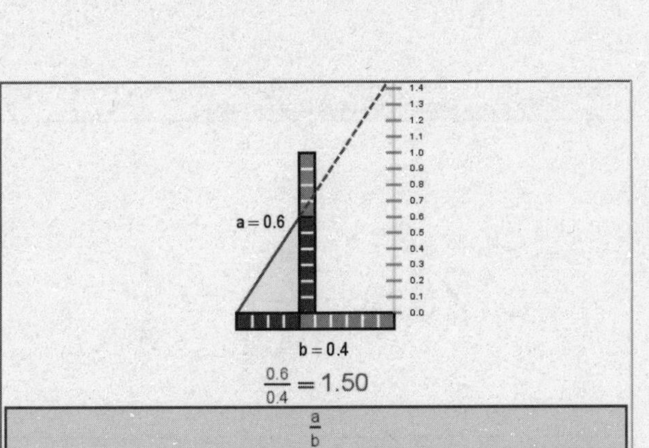

As the denominator gets smaller, does the result get smaller or larger?

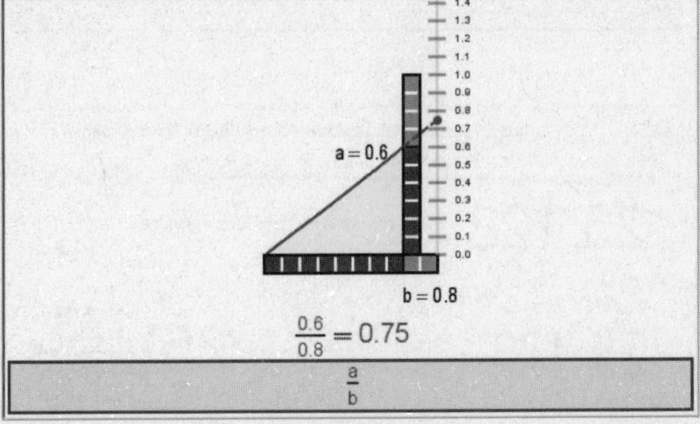

As the denominator gets larger, does the result get smaller or larger?

Converting Fractions and Decimals

EnableMath

Fractions and decimals can be used interchangeably depending on the need of the particular problem or situation. Converting between decimals and fractions can be done by several methods. Decimals are fractions whose denominators are powers of ten—if you can convert a fraction denominator to a power of ten, you can directly translate to decimal form. Decimal numbers translate to fractions by using the last place value as the denominator and then reducing. Below are some other ways to convert between decimals and fractions.

Repeating decimals: Decimals whose last digit (or group of digits) repeats when converting from fraction to decimal. Round to the desired number of places. e.g. 1/3 = .333333... or $0.\overline{3}$

Terminating decimal: Decimals that "come out even" when converting from fraction to decimal—no remainder. Carry out divisions to as many places as needed.

To convert a **fraction to a decimal**, divide the denominator into the numerator. Divide until the decimal terminates or repeats. You may need to round the decimal to a desired place value.

To convert a **decimal to a fraction**, count the number of places to the right of the decimal point. That number is the power of ten in the denominator (the number of zeros used). Reduce to lowest terms.

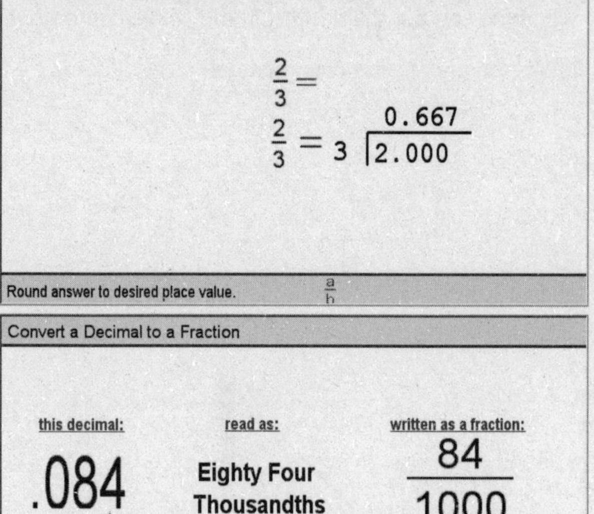

Converting Fractions to Decimals
$\frac{2}{3} =$
$\frac{2}{3} = 3\overline{)2.000}$ 0.667
Round answer to desired place value.

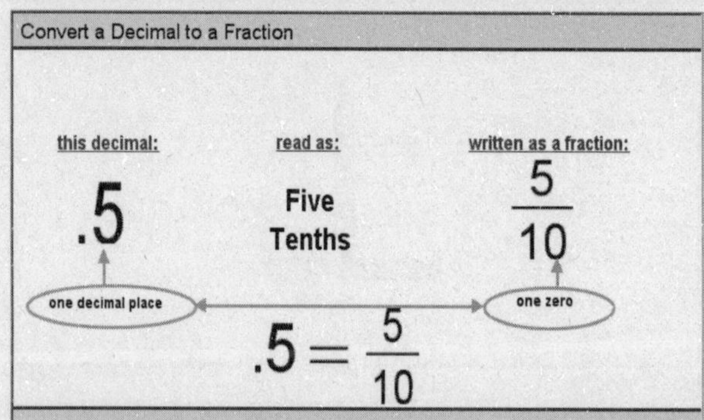

Of course, this must be reduced to 1/2.

Convert a Decimal to a Fraction

this decimal: .084

read as: Eighty Four Thousandths

written as a fraction: $\frac{84}{1000}$

3 decimal places — 3 zeroes

$$.084 = \frac{84}{1000} = \frac{21}{250}$$

Read the place value as the denominator of the fraction.

Convert a Decimal to a Fraction

Note:	The number of places in a decimal is the same as the number of zeroes in the denominator of its equivalent fraction.

25.123 is a mixed number. Write it as a fraction:

whole number — decimal fraction

$$25.123 \longrightarrow 25\frac{123}{1000}$$

Mixed decimals work the same way as mixed number fractions.

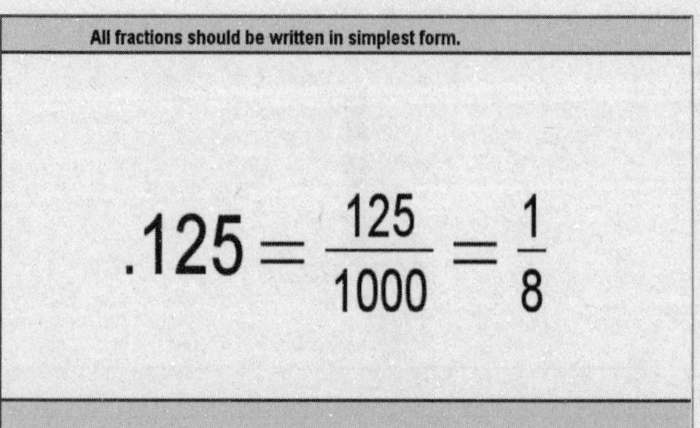

All fractions should be written in simplest form.
$.125 = \frac{125}{1000} = \frac{1}{8}$

Point 3: Some examples of decimal and fraction equivalents. Some of the most common decimal/fraction equivalents should be committed to memory.

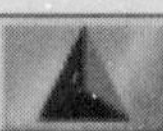

Equivalent fractions measure the same length on a fraction bar. Converting between fractions and decimals can be visualized by taking a look at equivalent bars marked off in either decimal fractions or common fractions.

Can a fraction be changed so that it is easily converted to a decimal without dividing numerator by denominator?

How does a mixed number fraction convert to a decimal number?

What's the common denominator between fifths and tenths? Between fourths and hundredths?

What fractional part of a dollar is 25¢?

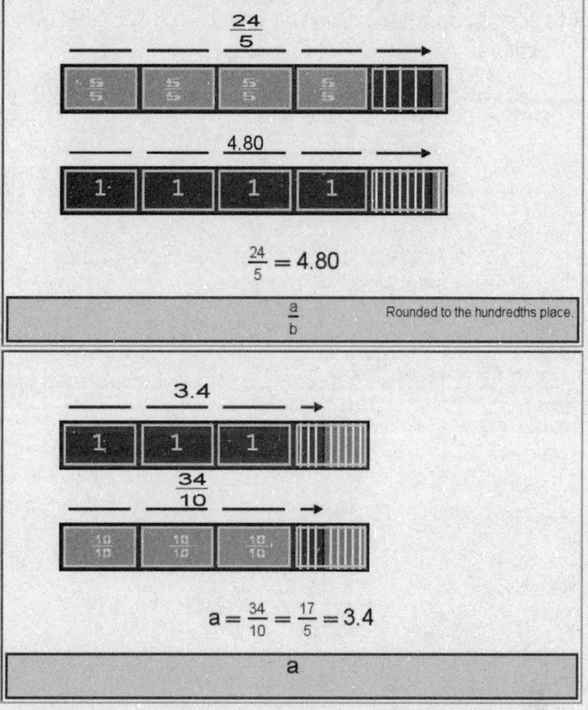

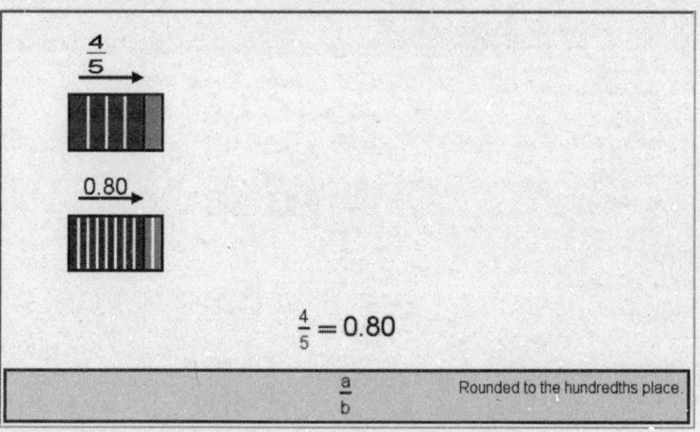

Can 4/5 be represented by a decimal with 1 decimal place? Can it have 3 or 4, or 5 or more decimal places?

What is 17/15 in mixed number form? What does that tell you about changing mixed numbers to mixed fractions?

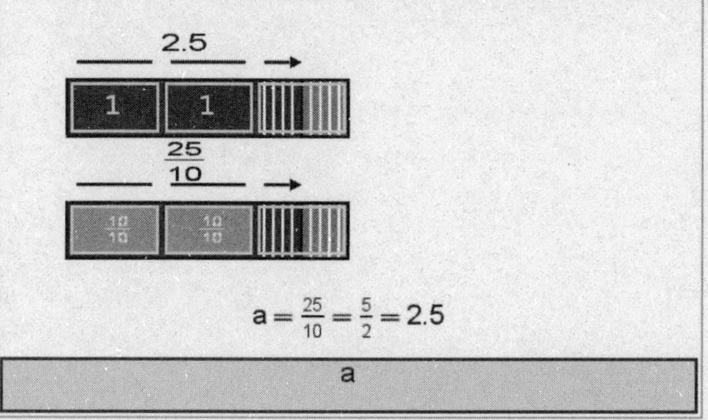

1/2 = 0.5; above we have 2.5. What does 3.5 convert to? 4.5? 5.5? 6.5?

Order of Operations—Decimals

EnableMath

Order of Operations with decimals is just like order of operations with whole numbers. **PEMDAS** is the short cut way to remind you that **P**arenthesis and **E**xponents are evaluated first, then **M**ultiplication and **D**ivision (from left to right) and finally **A**ddition and **S**ubtraction (also from left to right). The fraction bar acts like a set of parentheses—evaluate numerators and denominators separately before dividing to change to decimals.

Order of operations does not change for decimals and fractions. As always:

- Evaluate within parentheses and other symbols of enclosure first.
- Evaluate exponents and roots.
- Evaluate multiplication and division as they appear from left to right.
- Evaluate addition and subtraction as they appear from left to right.

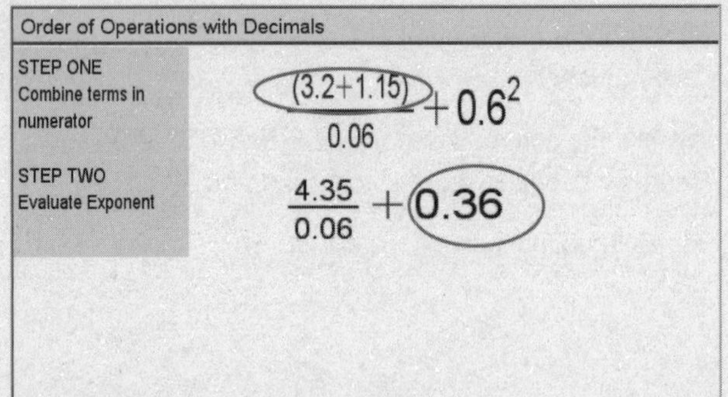

Order of Operations with Decimals

Step	
STEP ONE Combine terms in numerator	$\dfrac{(3.2+1.15)}{0.06}+0.6^2$
STEP TWO Evaluate Exponent	$\dfrac{4.35}{0.06}+0.36$
STEP THREE Divide	$\dfrac{4.35}{0.06}+0.36$
STEP FOUR Add	$72.5+0.36$

Numerators are evaluated in the parentheses step; then exponents—use scratch paper to make sure the decimals are accounted for. Next step is to divide.

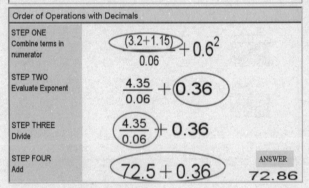

Order of Operations with Decimals

Step	
STEP ONE Combine terms in numerator	$\dfrac{(3.2+1.15)}{0.06}+0.6^2$
STEP TWO Evaluate Exponent	$\dfrac{4.35}{0.06}+0.36$
STEP THREE Divide	$\dfrac{4.35}{0.06}+0.36$
STEP FOUR Add	$72.5+0.36$
ANSWER	72.86

Ready for the last step—add.

Order of Operations with Decimals

Step	
STEP ONE Simplify inside parentheses	$42.27+3*(16.3-12.02)^2$
STEP TWO Exponent	$42.27+3*(4.28)^2$
STEP THREE Multiply	$42.27+3*18.3184$
STEP FOUR Add	$42.27+54.9552$
ANSWER	97.2252

Scratch paper is needed for these problems.

Every time a mathematical expression is evaluated, if the order of operations is followed, we are guaranteed to get the same answer.

Is there a way to manipulate expressions to get a different answer without violating the order of operations?

How important are parentheses in order of operations? How can you get a different answer without changing the position of the numbers or operations?

If a number has one decimal place, then the number is cubed, how many decimal places will the answer have?

Shifting parentheses changes the order of operations.

$(1.7+1.2)\times 2.0^4= \quad 2.9\times(2.0^4)= \quad 2.9\times 16.0=46.400$

$1.7+(1.2\times 2.0)^4=$

$1.7+1.2\times(2.0^4)=$

Shifting parentheses changes the order of operations.

$(1.7+1.2)\times 2.0^4=$

$1.7+(1.2\times 2.0)^4= \quad 1.7+(2.4^4)= \quad 1.7+33.2=34.878$

$1.7+1.2\times(2.0^4)=$

What happens when the parenthesis are in different locations?

Shifting parentheses changes the order of operations.

$(1.7+1.2)\times 2.0^4=$

$1.7+(1.2\times 2.0)^4=$

$1.7+1.2\times(2.0^4)=1.7+(1.2\times 16.0)=1.7+19.2=20.900$

Why can the parentheses be omitted in the above problem without changing the value?

Problem Solving with Decimals

Adding decimal numbers to our problem solving tool kit allows for more true to life problems than just using whole numbers and fractions. Many of the transactions in daily life use **decimal notation**. The word problems presented here are used for finding mileage, gallons of gas, and miles per gallon.

One way to keep track of processes used in problems is by doing **unit analysis**. You know one unit is miles per gallon; one unit is gallons, and one unit is miles. Depending on what the problem wants, you can keep track of what you have and what you need to help set up the problem.

- The word per means divide or the fraction bar.
- MPG is miles per gallon.
- Gallons—how much gas is used.
- Miles—how far traveled.

Calculating Miles Per Gallon

To calculate **miles per gallon (MPG)** for your car, you need to know the number of miles driven and the number of gallons of gas used.

To find **MPG**, simply divide the number of **miles** by the number of **gallons**.

MPG is often expressed as a decimal rounded to one or two decimal places.

Calculating Miles Per Gallon

$$\text{MPG} = \frac{\text{miles}}{\text{gallons}} = \frac{50}{2} = 25.15$$

Calculate the MPG.

Find miles per gallon by treating the per as a fraction bar.

Calculating Miles Driven

$$\text{miles} = \text{MPG} \times \text{gallons} = 16.50 \times 18.5 = 305.25$$

Calculate the miles driven.

Find how many MILES driven if you know your car's miles per gallon and how much gas was used.

Calculating Gallons Consumed

$$\text{gallons} = \frac{\text{miles}}{\text{MPG}} = \frac{34.5}{17.0} = 2.03$$

Calculate the gallons consumed.

If you know how far you need to go and the average miles per gallon your car gets, you can find out how many gallons you will need.

Calculating Gallons Consumed

$$\text{gallons} = \frac{\text{miles}}{\text{MPG}} = \frac{893.2}{17.5} = 51.04$$

Calculate the gallons consumed.

Extend the process: If your car holds 15.2 gallons, how many times will you need to fill your tank?

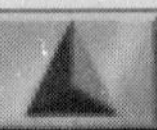

To solve word problems with decimals we use the same images that we have been working with and add units to the numbers.

Addition: two decimal bars attached in the same direction.

Subtraction: two decimal bars in attached opposite directions.

Multiplication: a rectangle.

Division: slope of vertical bar to horizontal bar.

How can using units help in setting up a problem?

Can using units help check the answer?

Can units "cancel" each other out?

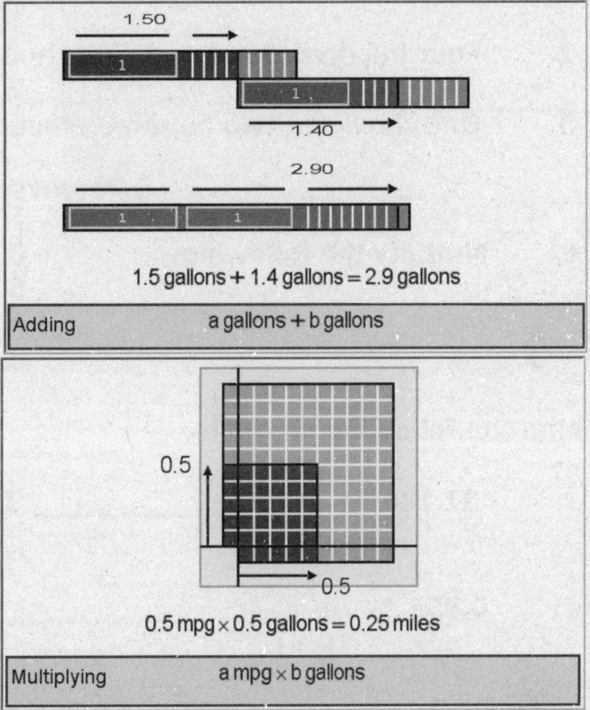

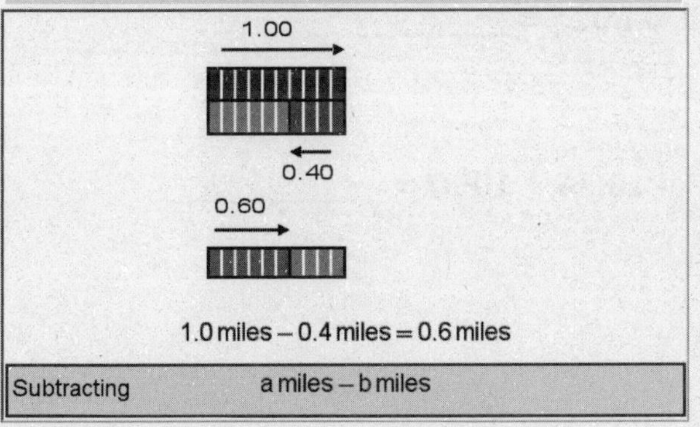

Adding and subtracting—make sure the units match.

O.K...we're just kidding with these units—unless we're talking about a very large boat! A more realistic problem would be hard to visualize using rectangles. How do miles per gallon times gallons equal miles?

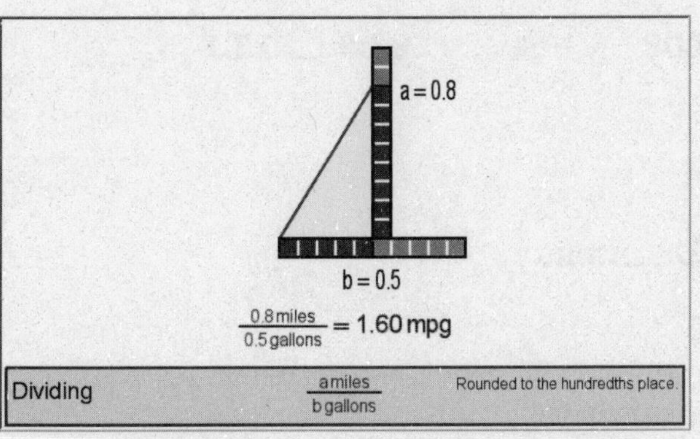

Per means divide. Miles per gallon (MPG) is miles/gallons.

Decimals

Given the number: 35.470928

1. What digit is in the tenths place? ____________
2. What digit is in the hundredths place? ____________
3. What digit is in the tenth-thousandths place? ____________

Write the standard form number for each of the following numbers.

1. Five thousand forty one and five hundred twelve ten thousandths.
2. Four hundred three and nine thousandths.
3. One thousand two hundred eleven hundred thousandths.

Powers of 10

1. Multiply the following:

0.3 * 10 = ____________
0.3 * 1000 = ____________
0.3 * 0.1 = ____________
0.3 * 0.001 = ____________

Find the following products.

2. 32.146 * $\frac{1}{100} =$ ____________
3. 10.78 * 1000 = ____________
4. 0.351 * $\frac{1}{1000} =$ ____________

Ordering Decimals

Insert the appropriate sign: >, <, or =, to make a true statement.

1. 1.2 □ .16
2. 30.2 □ 1.003
3. 56.09 □ 75.1
4. 1.06 □ 1.006
5. 0.81 □ 6.6

Rounding Decimals

Round 392.69548 to the given place value.

1. Tenths ________________
2. Thousandths ________________
3. Tens ________________
4. Hundredths ________________

Adding Decimals

1. 4.73 + 5.682 + 10.003
2. 0.0405 + 1.1009 + 9.9001
3. 590.099 + 32.0189 + 601.3
4. 0.005 + 0.0109 + 0.01991
5. 2.1 + 3.001 + 6.01 + 1.0001
6. 32.035 + 41 + 56.19

Subtracting Decimals

1. 10.003 – 45.682
2. 9.9 –1.1009
3. 590.099 - 32.0189
4. 0.01991– 0.001199
5. 6.01 – 1.0001
6. 32.35 – 5.619

Multiplying Decimals

1. Multiply the following: 0.2 * 0.3 = __________
   0.02 * 0.03 = __________
   0.002 * 0.003 = __________
2. 2.303 * 4.8
3. 5.001 * 3.21
4. 12 * 3.047
5. 2.001 * 9.88
6. 43.209 * 0.0345
7. 29.1 * 0.321

Dividing Decimals

1. Divide the following: 0.2 ÷ 0.3 = __________
   0.02 ÷ 0.03 = __________
   0.002 ÷ 0.003 = __________
2. 2.303 ÷ 4.8
3. 5.001 ÷ 3.21
4. 12 ÷ 3.07
5. 2.001 ÷ 9.88
6. 43.209 ÷ 0.0345
7. 29.1 ÷ 0.321

Converting Fractions and Decimals

Convert the following fractions to decimals.

1. 3/4 **2.** 5/8 **3.** 2 3/5 **4.** 27/50

Convert the following decimals to fractions in lowest terms.

5. 0.250 **6.** 3.05 **7.** 0.325 **8.** 2.003

Order of Operations—Decimals

Evaluate the following. Express all answers in two decimal places.

1. $2.09 + 1.2(5.09 - 3.5)$

2. $\frac{2.1 - 0.03}{(1.1)^2} + 7.2$

3. $2.001 * 5.4 - 3.11 * 1.01$

4. $(1.2)^2 + 0.03(5.4 - 3.75) \div 3$

5. $0.02(0.3)^2 - (0.1)^4 + 0.001$

Problem Solving with Decimals

1. **Your part time job pays $8.03 per hour. If you worked 20 hours last week, how much did you earn?**

2. **Your car gets 15.9 miles per gallon. If you used 6.0 gallons on a recent trip, how many miles did you travel?**

3. **Calculate the miles per gallon for your car, if it used 31.0 gallons of fuel on a trip of 558.00 miles?**

4. **Your car averages 27.5 miles per gallon. If you drove 451 miles, how many gallons of fuel would your car use?**

4. Ratios & Proportions

Ratios and proportions may well be the most important ideas in all of arithmetic; they are the ones we use most often in the real world. If ratio and proportion have confused you try out our visualizations. If you experiment with them, they can help you to understand these powerful ideas and use them in your real world activities.

Picture ratio as a triangle and picture proportion as two similar triangles.

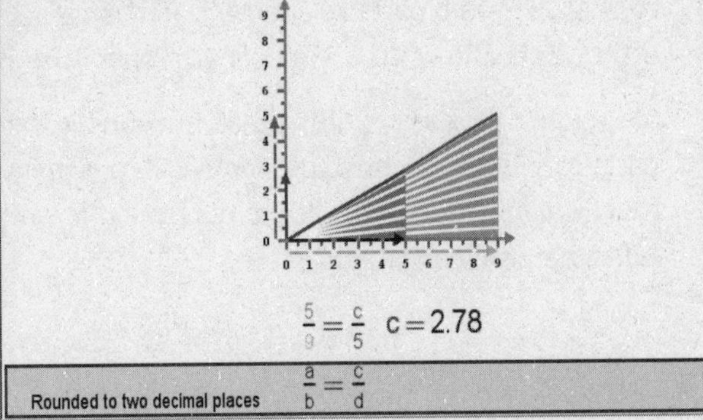

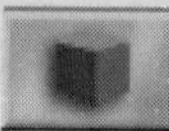

Ratios

EnableMath

A **ratio** is a comparison of two quantities. Ratios are expressed by inserting a colon between the two quantities that are being compared. For example, the ratio of **a:b** means that there are a parts of one thing to b parts of another. Ratios can also be written as fractions. Expressed either way, **a:b** or **a/b**, the written symbols are read, "**the ratio of a to b**."

Although, ratios are expressed as fractions it is important to note that not all ratios represent a parts-to-whole relationship. Some will, but many will not. Writing ratios as fractions is convenient for calculation purposes, but to determine if a ratio represents a true fraction you will have to consider the problem context.

Ratios

- Ratios express a numerical relationship by division between two quantities of a common unit.
- Ratios are expressed using a colon, **a:b**, or like a fraction, **a/b.**
- Ratios should be reduced to lowest terms.
- Ratios can express numerical relationships in either order: **a to b** or **b to a** depending upon their context.

A ratio is a relationship between two quantities.

males: females

Read this ratio as males "to" females.

Two quantities separated by a colon (:). Males "to" females.

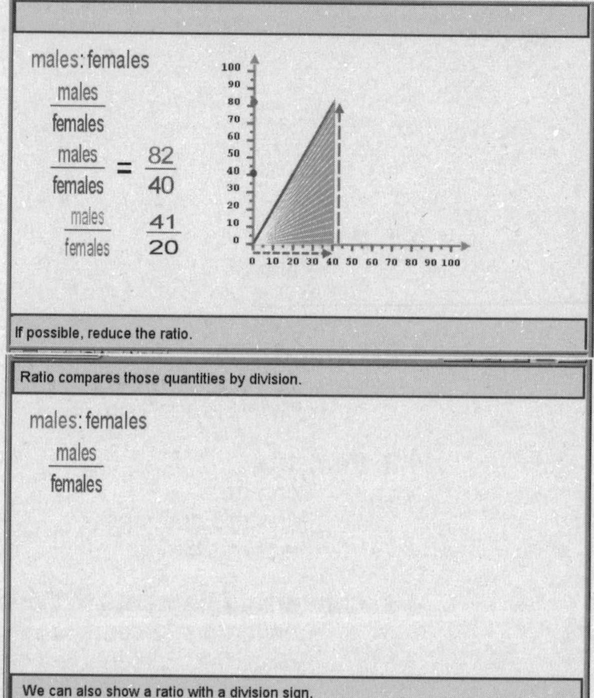

males: females
males / females
males / females = 82 / 40
males / females 41 / 20
If possible, reduce the ratio.
Ratio compares those quantities by division.
males: females
males / females
We can also show a ratio with a division sign.

A ratio can also be written a division.

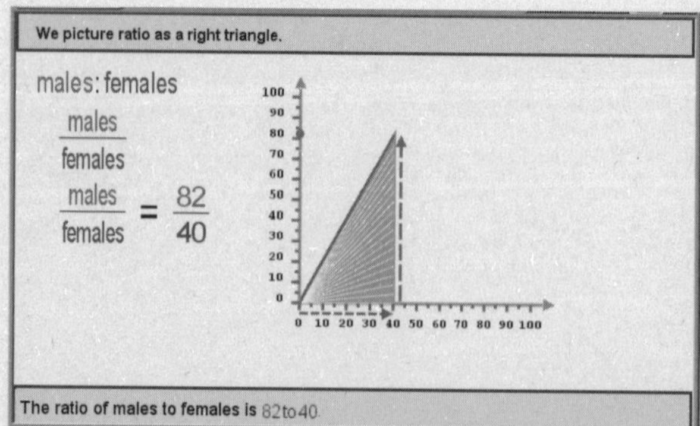

A ratio is a linear relationship between two quantities. The first number (numerator) is the vertical side of the triangle,

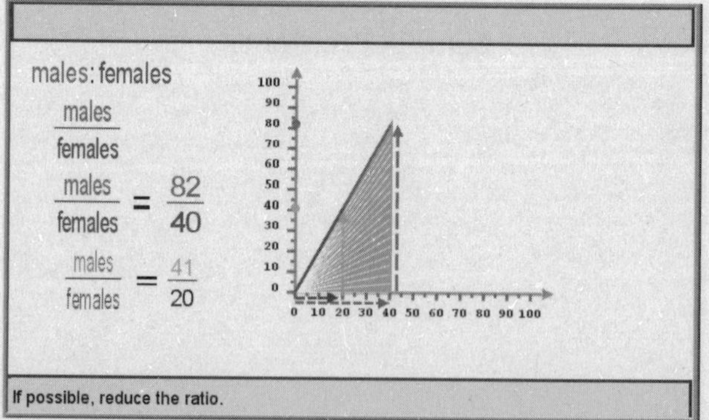

As with fractions, always reduce a ratio to lowest terms. A ratio can be 1:1.

Ratio is one of the most important ideas in mathematics. Ratios compares two quantities. We visualize ratios as right triangles, where the first number represents the length of the vertical side of the triangle and the second number represents the length of the horizontal side.

The value of the ratio is represented by the slope of the triangle's hypotenuse. The higher the value of the ratio, the steeper the slope of the hypotenuse.

In a ratio, what has to happen to the denominator if the numerator increases in value?

How do you know if two ratios are equal?

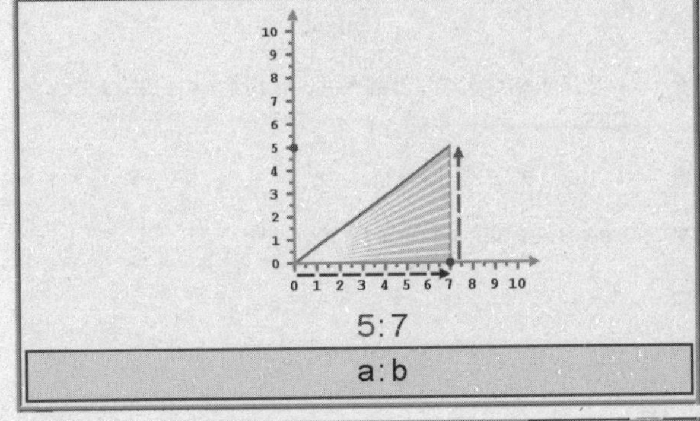

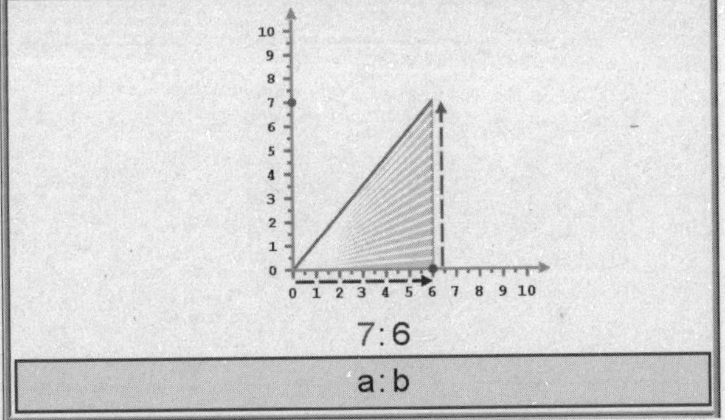

How do you know which ratio to use, 7:6 or 6:7?

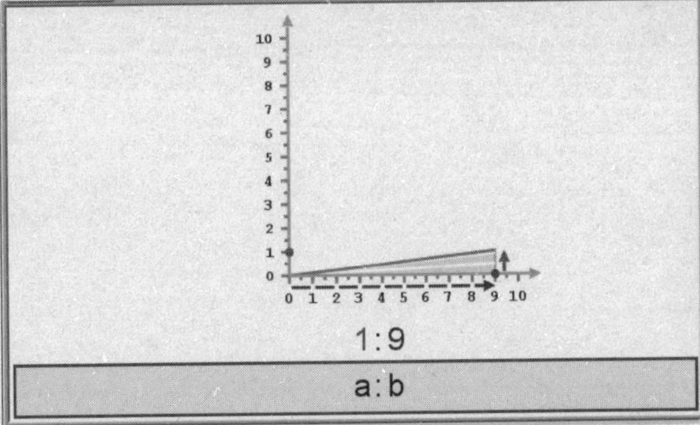

Would we say 9 to 1 or 1 to 9? Does it matter which order we use?

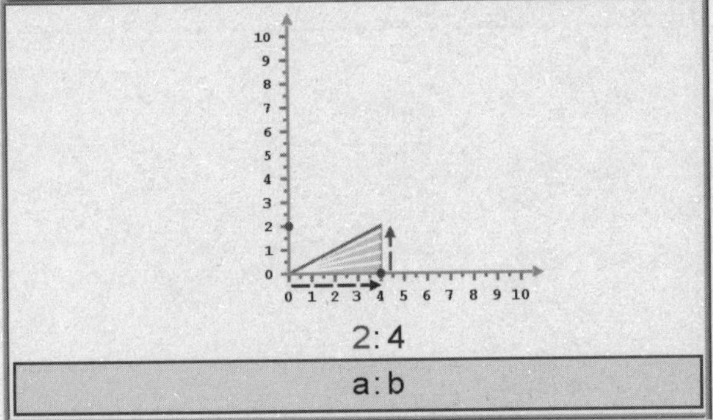

Does the ratio 2:4 have the same value as the ratio 5:10?

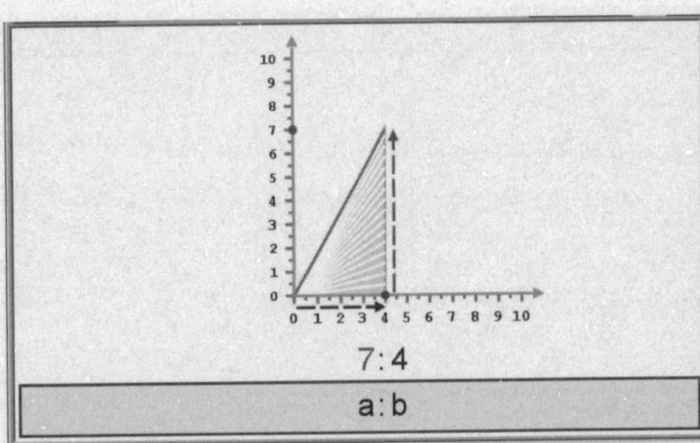

Is 7:4 the same ratio as 2:1?

Rates

EnableMath

A **rate** is a ratio that expresses the relationship between a two measurements that have different units. You can recognize a rate because it is usually expressed with the words **per** or **for**. Some examples include, "miles per gallon," "cost per square foot," "4 for $1," and "10 for $3." The units of a rates are often expressed as a single unit, for instance, mph is used for miles per hour.

Some other applications of the rate concept in the real world include heart rate, currency conversion rates, and interest rates.

Rates

- Comparison of two measurements with different units.
- Reduce rates to lowest terms.
- Keep the units as part of the rate.

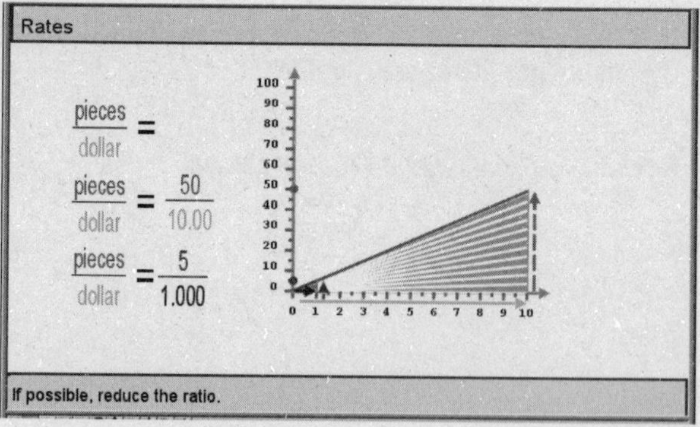

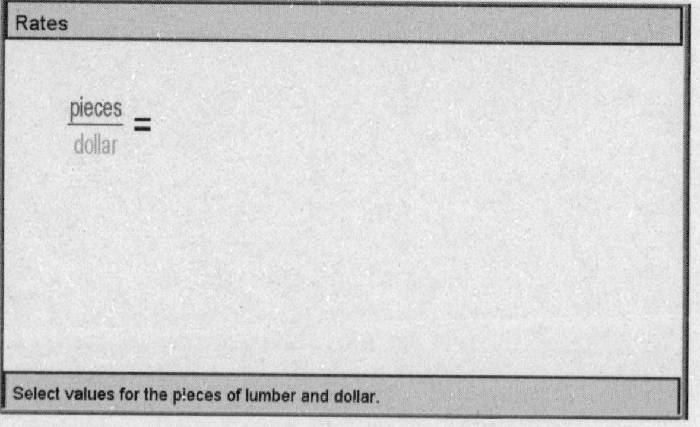

You can use either 'for' or 'per' to express the rate above. "5 pieces per dollar" or "5 pieces for a dollar."

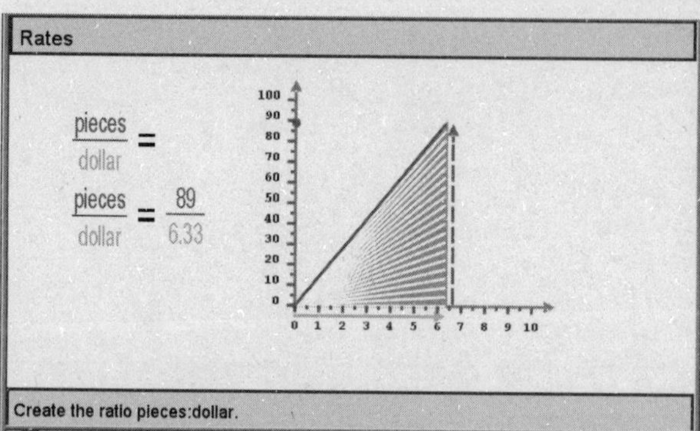

Like ratios, rates can be pictured as right triangles. The length of the vertical side represents the numerator value and the length of the horizontal side represents the denominator value.

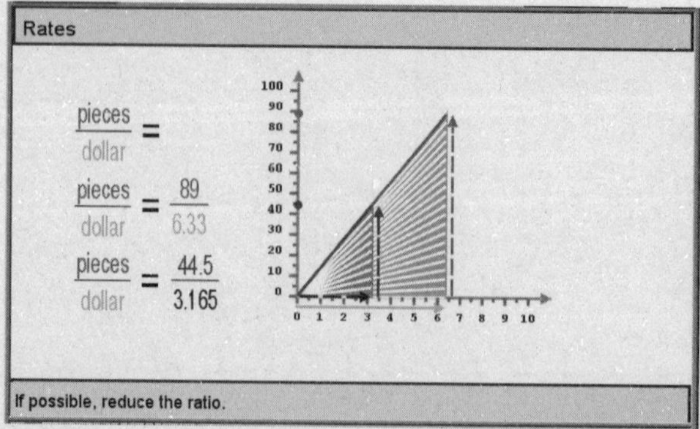

Reduce whenever possible. When appropriate, you can reduce until the denominator is one.

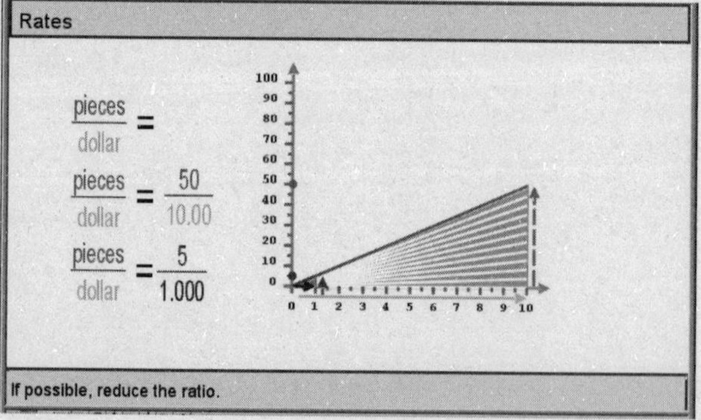

Reducing the values makes it easier to mentally calculate the rate.

Since a rate is a ratio, visualize a rate as the slope of a triangle's hypotenuse.

If the axes of the grid are interchanged, will the rate be expressed in the same order? What will change?

If one term in a rate changes, does the other term change by the same amount?

What determines which is the numerator and which is the denominator?

What determines if the rate should be presented with a denominator of 1 or not?

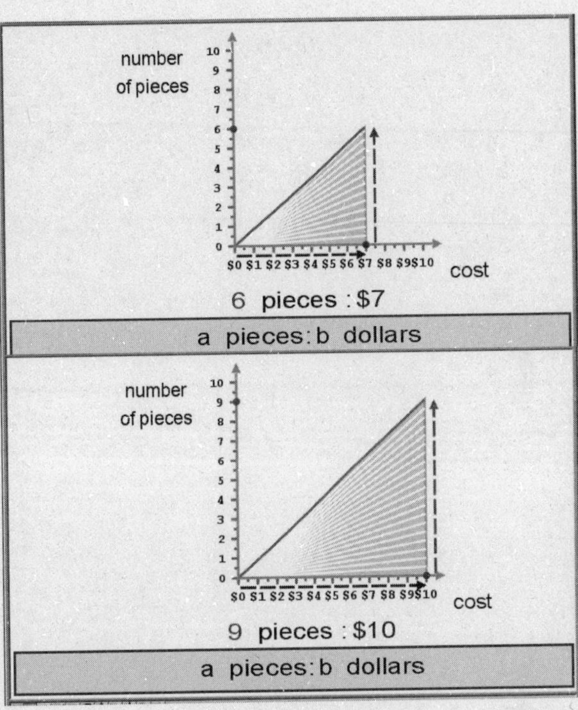

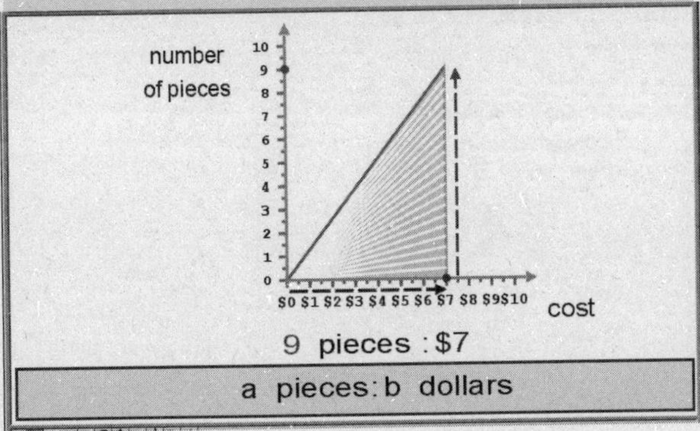

If the number of pieces goes up and the cost stays the same, will the rate (or number of pieces per dollar) increase?

If the cost of the pieces goes down while the number of pieces stays the same, will the rate (in this case the cost per piece) decrease?

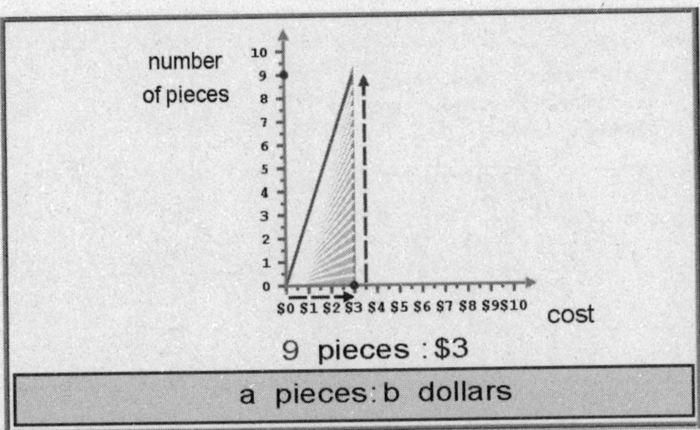

Is this rate expressed in lowest terms? What is the cost for 3 pieces?

Setting up Proportions

A **proportion** is an equivalency statement that says two ratios are equal. Proportions are written as two ratios separated by an equal sign. To be a proportion both ratios must be equal to one another, meaning that the ratios can be reduced to the same value. For example, 5/10 = 1/2 is a proportion.

Use cross products to determine if a proportion is true. Do this by cross multiplying. First multiply the numerator on the left hand side (LHS) of the equation by the denominator on the right hand side (RHS). Then, multiply the denominator on the LHS by the numerator on the RHS. **If the cross products are equal, the ratios are proportional.** If the cross products are not equal, the ratios do not form a proportion.

Proportions

- An equation of two equivalent ratios.
- Quantities that vary in such a way that they have a constant ratio: 5/10=.5 and 1/2=.5
- Use cross products to determine if two ratios are proportional: (5*2)=(10*1)
- For rates, denominator units must match and numerator units must match.

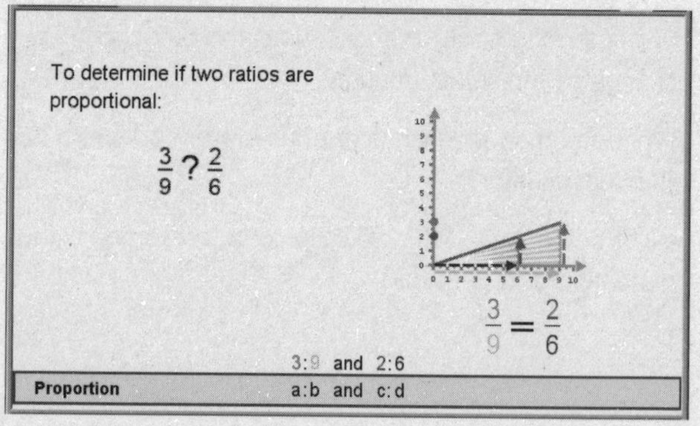

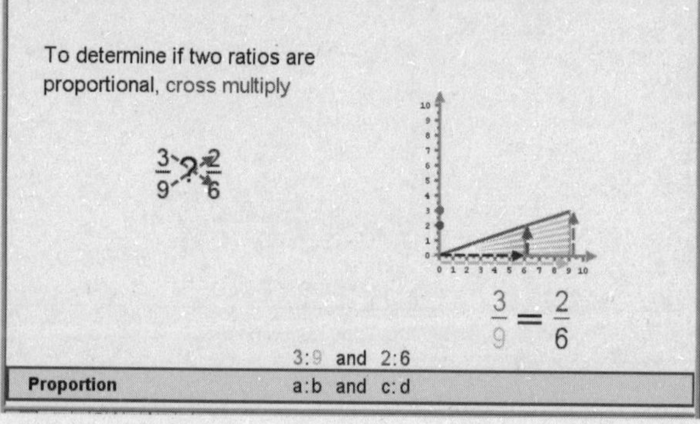

Find the cross product.

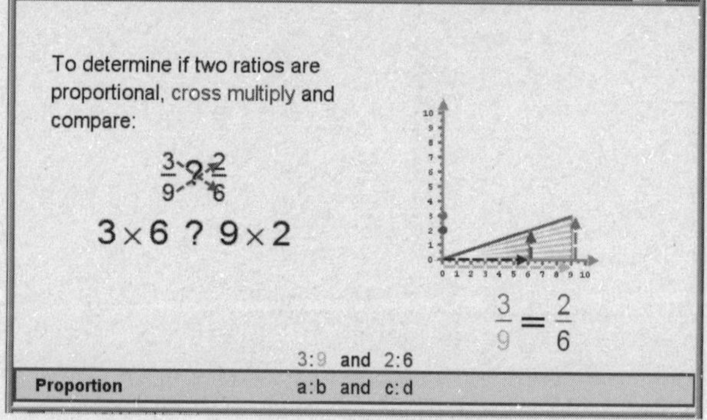

If the cross products are the same the two ratios form a proportion.

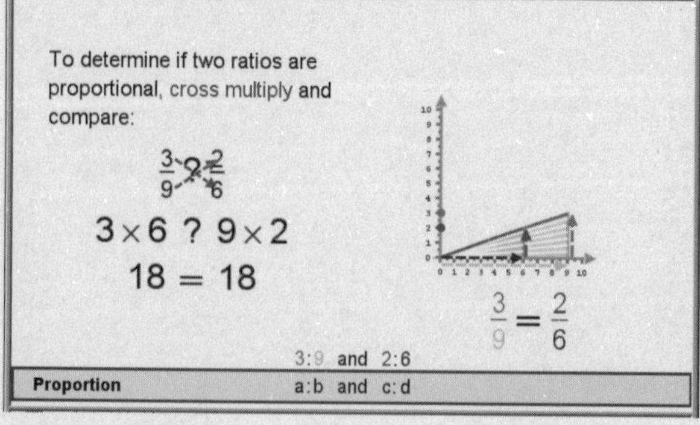

Replace the ? with an =. The two ratios are equal and they form a proportion.

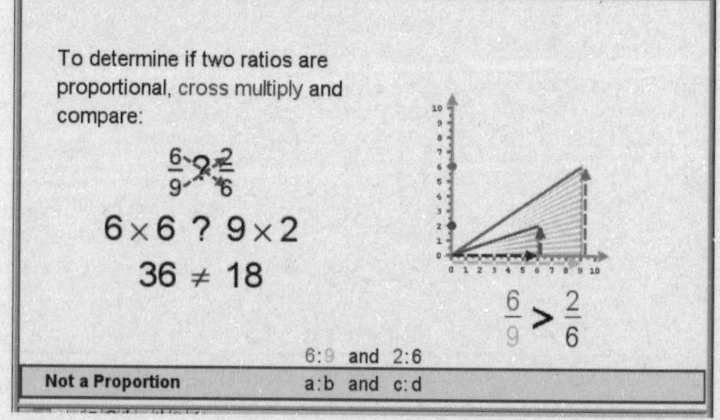

What happens if the two ratios are not equal? They do not form a proportion and you cannot replace the "?" with an equal sign.

Setting up Proportions

Proportions are visualized as **similar right triangles**. Similar triangles have the same shape, because the measure of their angles are the same, their **corresponding sides are in proportion**, and the **slope of their hypotenuses are the same**. A proportion relates the **common ratio** of their corresponding sides.

To maintain a proportional relationship between similar triangles, any change made to the length of one side must be matched with a corresponding scale change in the other.

If you add 1 to both numerators in a proportion, will the ratios still be proportional?

If you add 1 to both numerator and denominator of one ratio, will the ratios still be in proportion?

How does changing one ratio of a proportion affect the proportional relationship?

Does it matter which numerator and denominator you multiply first to find the cross product?

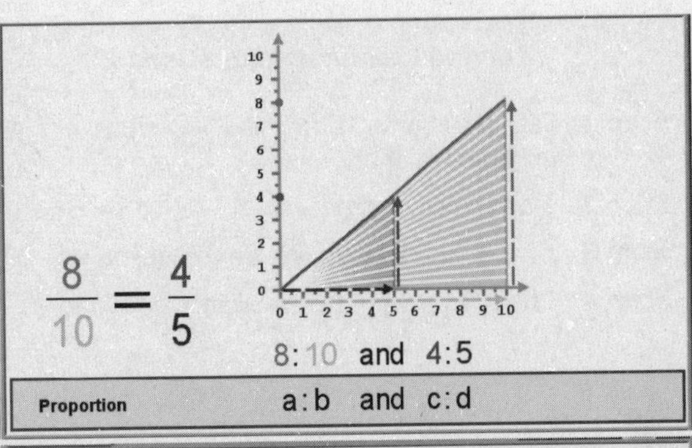

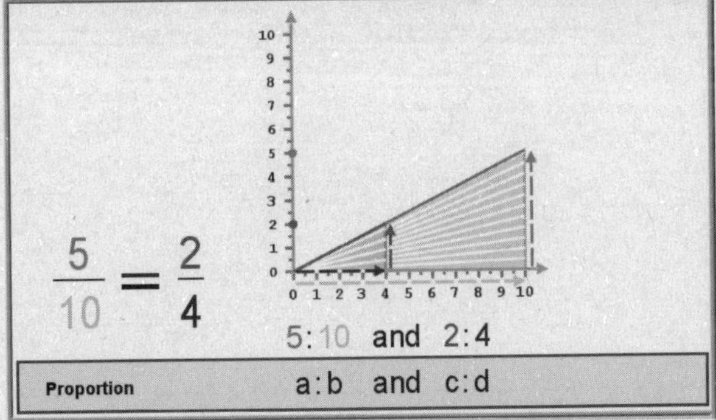

Are the two ratios above in proportion? Can you change one ratio of a proportion without changing the other ratio? What other ratios are proportional to 2/4?

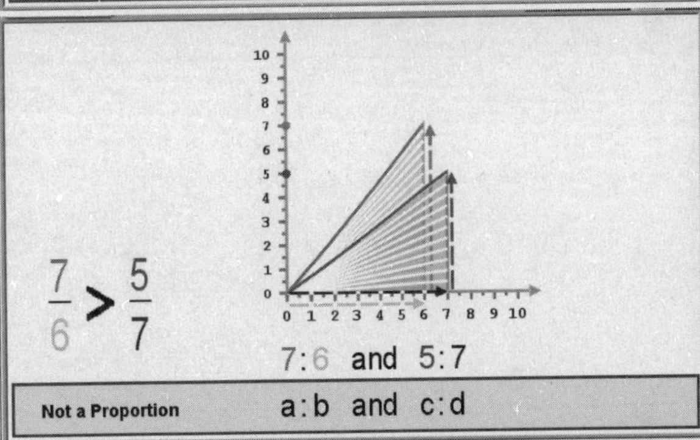

What could you change to make the ratios above a proportion?

Solving Proportions

EnableMath

Solving an proportion is the process of finding the value of an unknown quantity that makes the proportional relationship statement true. To solve a proportion three of the four proportional factors must be known. When three of the proportional values are known, we can use cross multiplication to solve for the missing value. To solve, we compute the cross products, then divide both sides of the equation by the coefficient of the unknown factor. If **a:b=?:d**, then **b?=ad** and **?=(ad)/b**.

Solving Proportion Equations

Step 1: Set up the proportion using two ratios with an unknown quantity.

Step 2: Find the cross products.

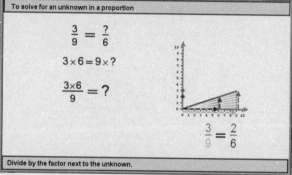

Step 3: Divide by the factor beside the unknown.

Step 4: Check your work by rebuilding the proportions.

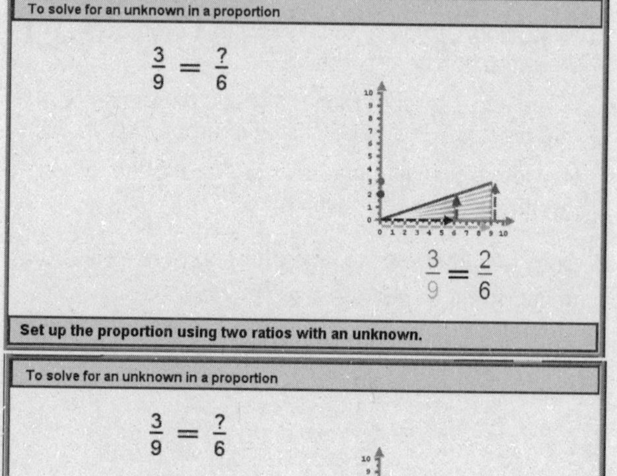

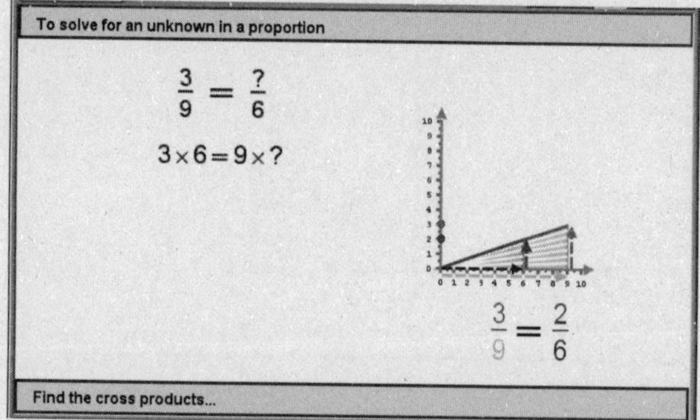

Find the cross product.

Divide by the factor besides the unknown.

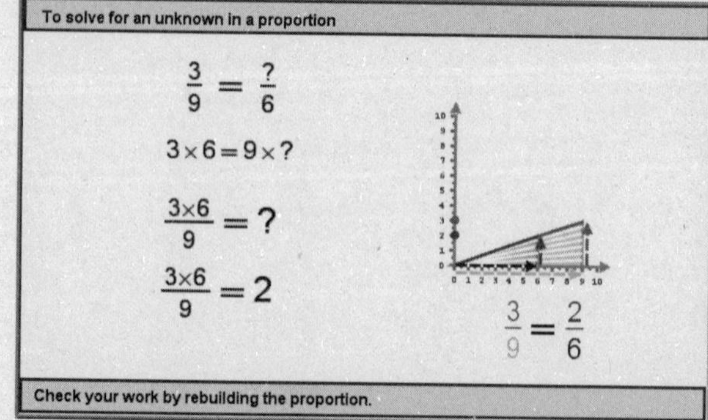

Check your work by rebuilding the proportions. Is 3:9 proportional to 2:6?

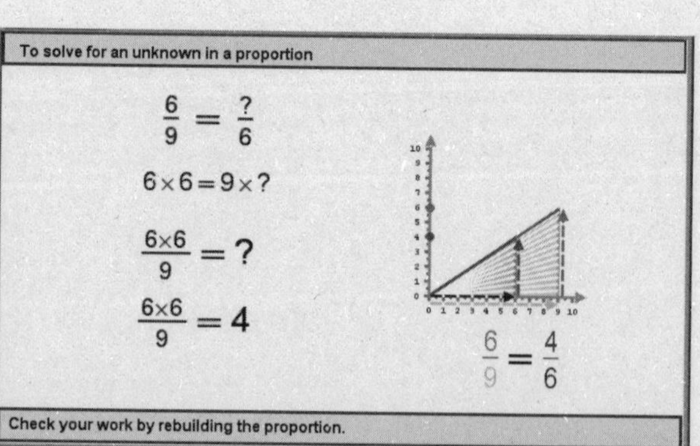

Change the values and try solving other proportions. Look at the concept to see how to solve proportions with unknowns in other positions.

In the real world we regularly need to solve a proportion to find an unknown value. To solve a proportion three of the four proportional factors must be known. Visually this means that the lengths of one of the sides of two similar triangles is unknown.

Use the visualization to investigate the proportionality of the sides. What happens to the value of the unknown side as you increase or decrease the other lengths?

When increasing one value in a linear proportion increases another value in the proportion, we say that these values are **directly proportional**. When increasing one value in the proportion decreases another (or vice versa), we say that these values are **inversely proportional**.

If **a:b=c:d**, then it is also true that length **c** is to **d** as **a** is to **b**, **c:d=a:b**.

Is it also true that length **c** is to **a** as **d** is to **b**, **c:a=d:b?**

How else can the proportionality of the sides of similar triangles be expressed?

Are **a** and **c** directly proportional? How about **b** and **c**?

How do you know the triangles are similar?

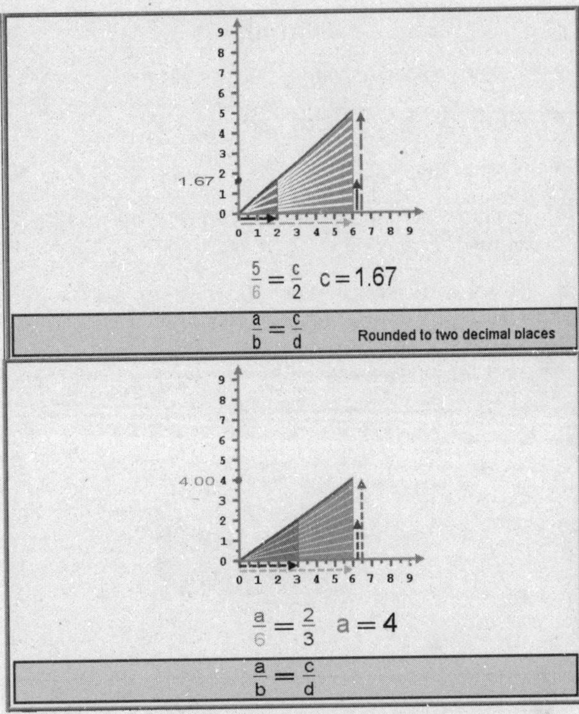

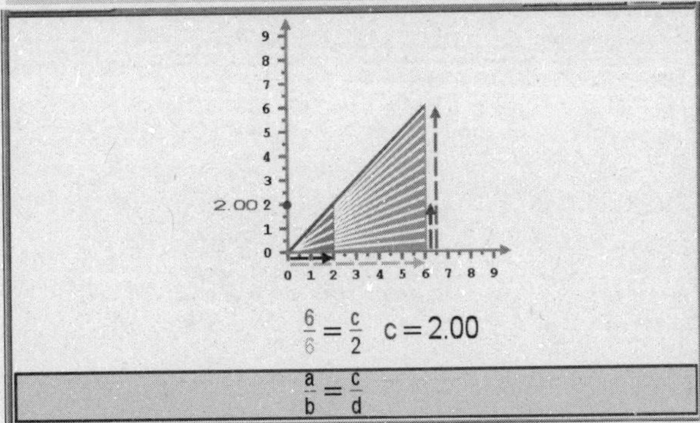

Point 1: Select values for **a**, **b**, and **b**. Solve for **c**. When you increase the value of **b** what happens to the value of **c**? When you increase the value of **a** what happens to the value of **c**? When you increase the value of **d** what happens to the value of **c**? Why?

Point 2: Select values for **b**, **c**, and **d**. Solve for **a**. When you increase the value of **c** what happens to the value of **a**? When you increase the value of **b** what happens to the value of **a**? When you increase the value of **d** what happens to the value of **a**? Why?

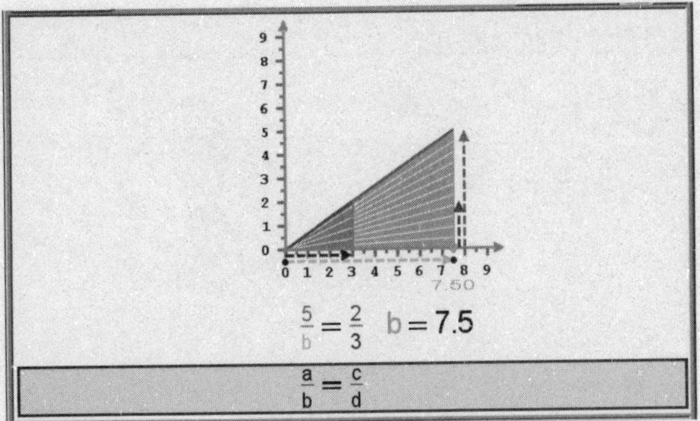

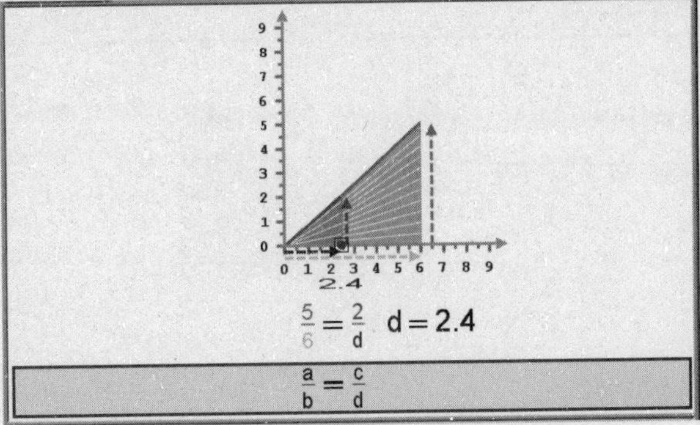

Point 3: Solve for **b**. If you decrease the value of **c** will the value of **b** increase or decrease? Why?

Point 4: Solve for **d**. If you decrease the value of **a** will the

Percents

A **percent** is a ratio of a number to 100. For example, **12:100** means **12 percent**. The percentage symbol, **%**, is used to indicate that a value is a percentage, so **12:100 = 12 percent = 12%**.

Percent means "**per 100**" or "**out of each 100.**" Percents may be expressed as fractions or decimals. Because percent means per 100, percents mean a number of hundredths.

12% = 12/100 = twelve hundredths = .12

Percents

- A ratio expressed with a denominator of 100.
- A fraction expressed as parts per 100.
- Means "per 100."
- Replace the denominator of 100 with the % sign to convert to percent.
- To convert to fraction or ratio form replace the % sign with a denominator of 100.

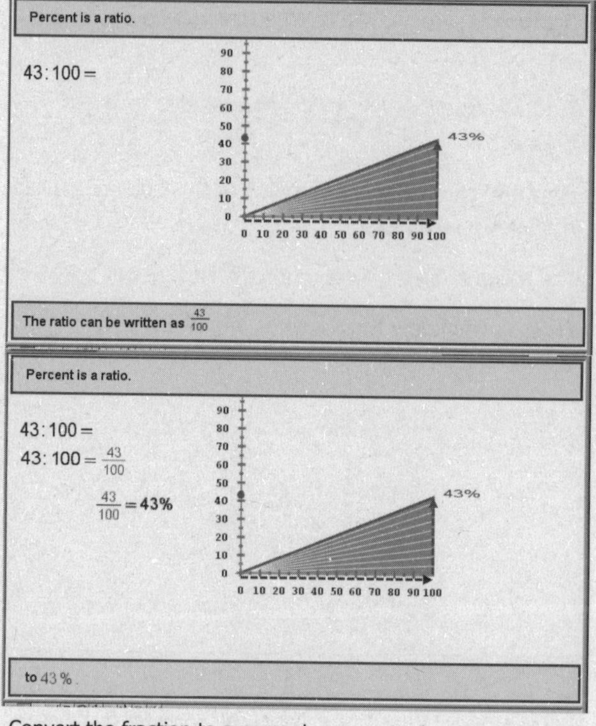

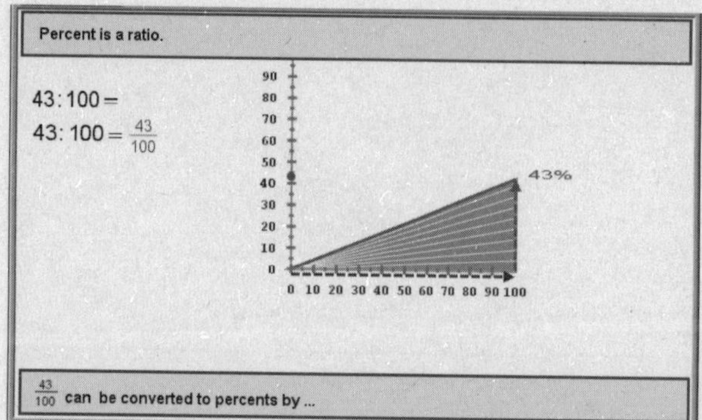

The ratio of 88/100 is 88 per cent (cent means hundred).

Convert the fraction to a percent.

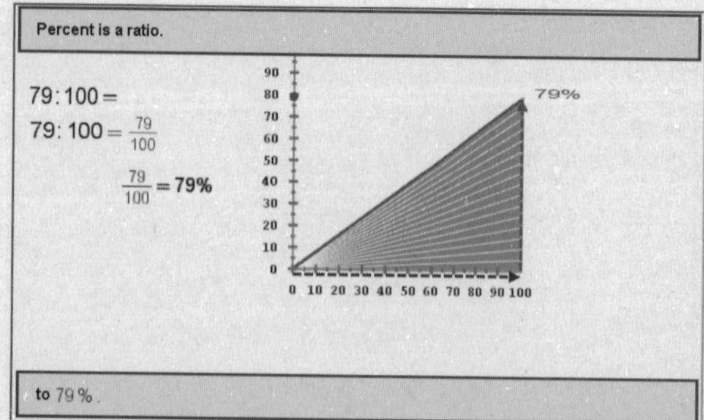

Change the number to change the percentage. Note how the triangle changes, how its slope gets steeper as the percentage grows and get shallower as it decreases.

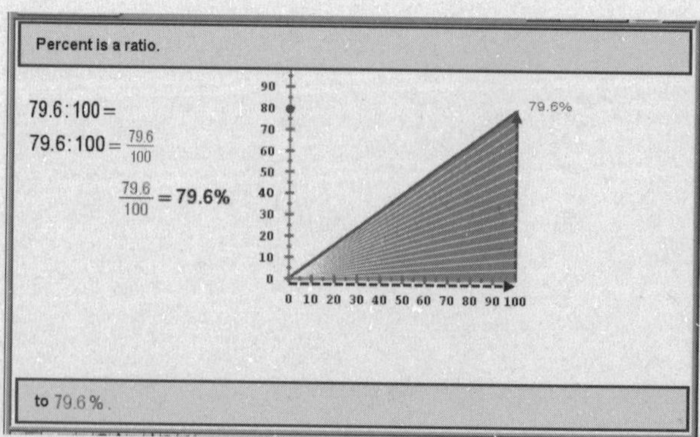

Percents can contain decimals and fractions..

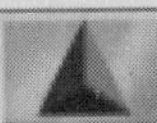

Percent is a ratio that has 100 for its second number, **number:100**. Percents are a standard ratio that we use across every aspect of our society. A percent ratio is represent by a right triangle with a fixed base of length 100 units and a height specified by the value of the **number** variable.

Select different values for **number**. As the value of **number** increases what happens to the slope of the hypotenuse? How does decreasing the value of **number** affect the shape of the triangle?

What percent is represented by 40:100?

What percent is represented by 50:100?

What percent is represented by 98:100?

What percent is represented by 100:100?

What percent is represented by 200:100?

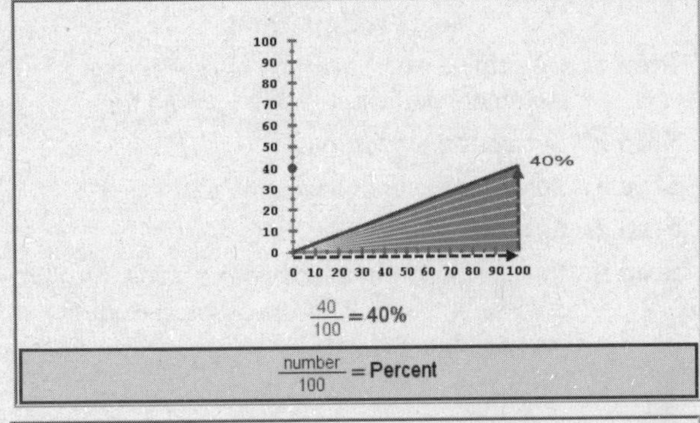

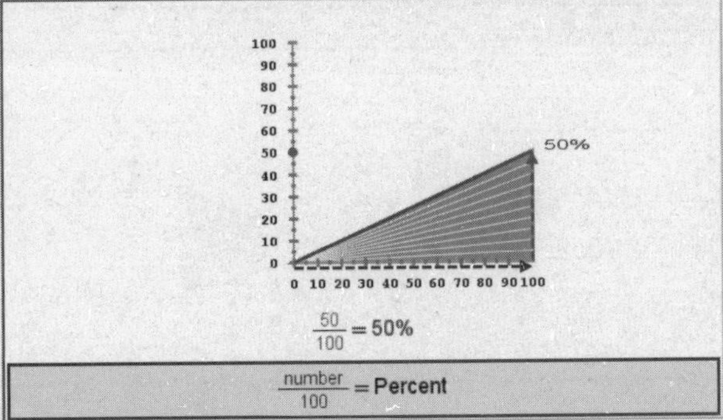

Can a percent be expressed as a reduced fraction? What fraction is represent here?

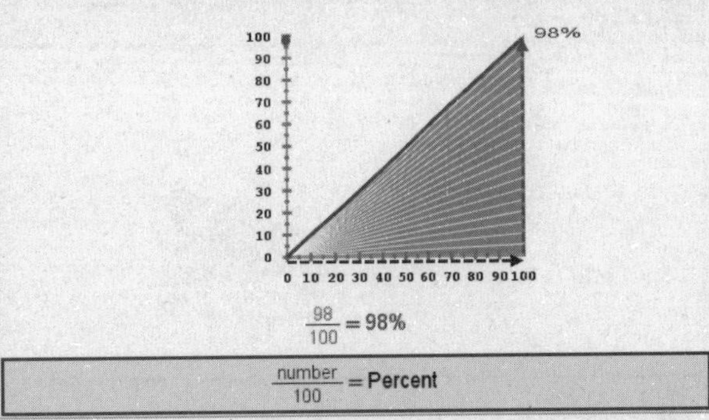

If something is 98% water, what percentage of it is not water?

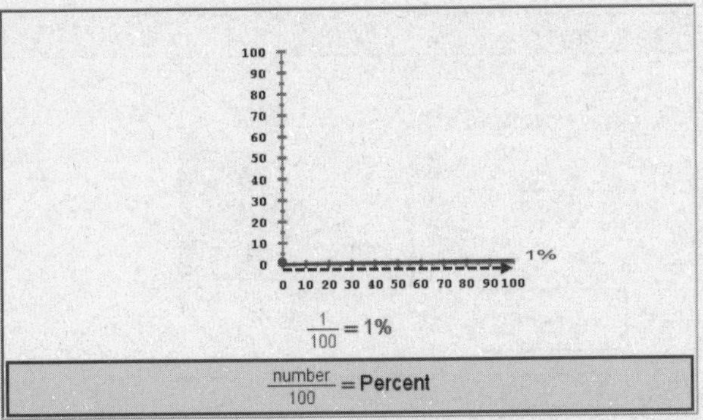

If something is 1% water, what percent is not water?

A **percent equation** is a **proportion** of two part-to-whole ratios, where one of the ratios is a percent.

All percentage problems are of the form: $\frac{part}{whole} = \frac{percent}{100}$

To solve percent equations two of the unknowns must be given in the problem statements. This means that there are only three cases to consider when solving percentage problems.

Case I	Case II	Case III
$part = \frac{percent}{100} \times whole$	$whole = \frac{100}{percent} \times part$	$percent = \frac{part}{whole} \times 100$

Percent Equations

Step 1: Determine what is given in the problem statement and what is to be solved for.

Step 2: Set up the proportion.

Step 3: Solve for the unknown variable.

Step 4: Calculate the solution.

Step 5: Check solution by plugging the value into the original proportion. If the ratios are equal, your solution is correct.

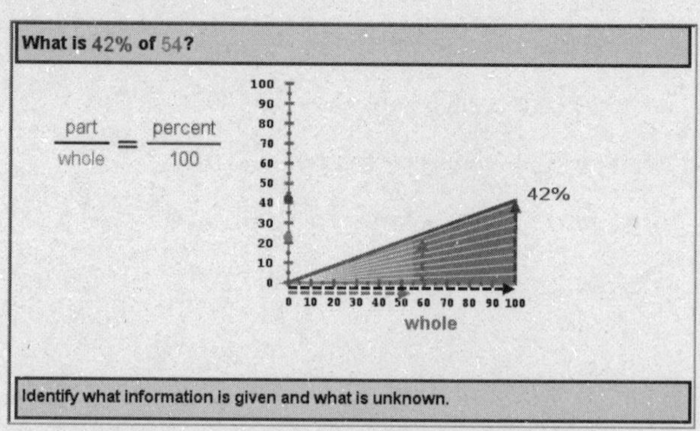

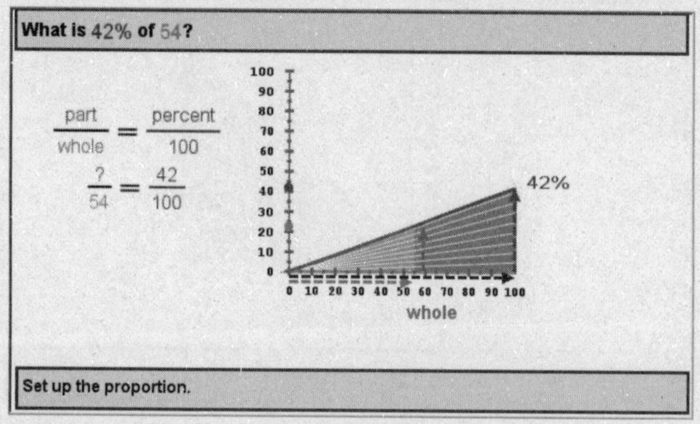

All percent equations are proportional relationships between two part-whole ratios. Read the problem statement and determine what factors are given and what is unknown. Set up the proportional relationship.

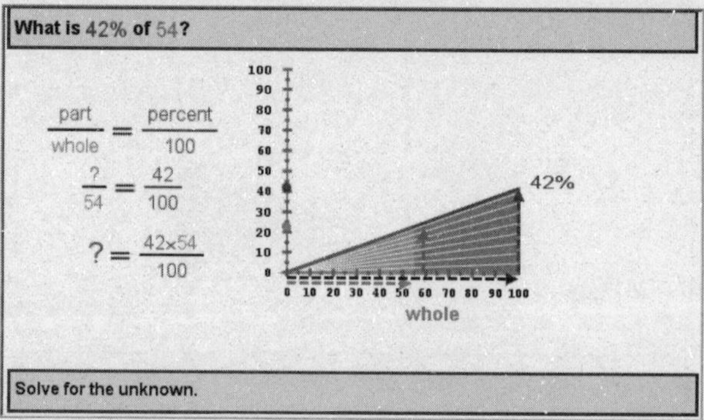

When used in a math problem **'of'** generally means to **multiply**. A "percent of" problem statement translates into an equation by changing the word **'is'** to = and changing the

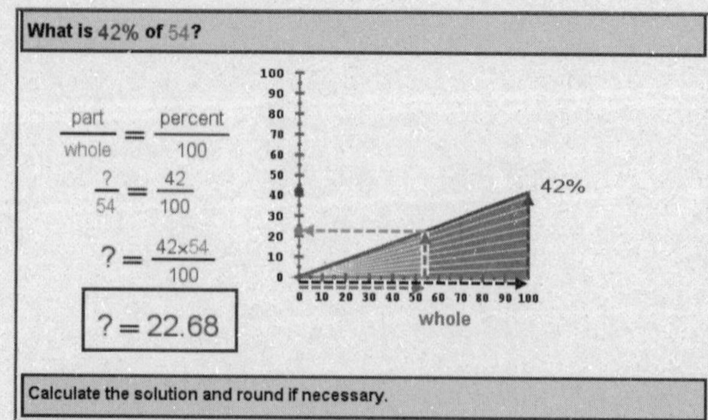

To find 42% of 54, multiply the **whole (or base) amount** by the **percent**. Solve for the unknown and round when necessary. **?=54(42/100)=22.68**

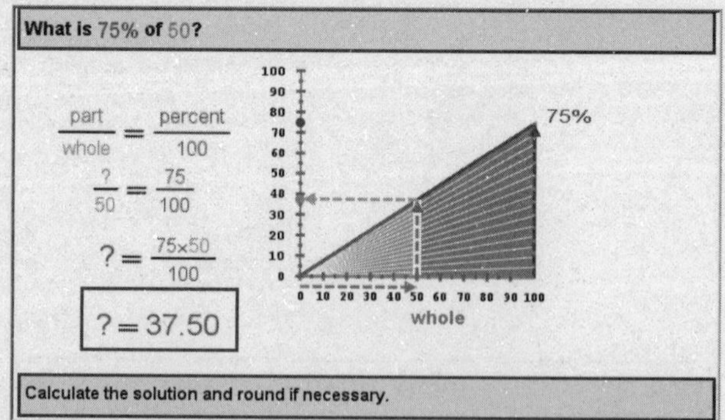

This is a dynamic example, change "**percent**" and "**whole**" to generate new problems.

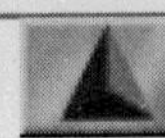

Percent of... equations are visualized as two similar right triangles. The percent ratio is represent by a right triangle with a fixed base of length 100 units and a height specified by the **percent** variable. The base of the second amount represents the original or initial amount of the quantity. It is referred to as the base amount. The height of the triangle represents how much or what part of the base amount there is. The proportional relationship is between two part-to-whole ratios, sometimes taking the form,

$$\frac{part}{base} = \frac{percent}{100}$$

If any two of the proportional factors are known, the third missing factor can be solved for.

Can all percent equations be changed to an equation with a fraction?

If know the value of 25% of something, how much does the rest represent?

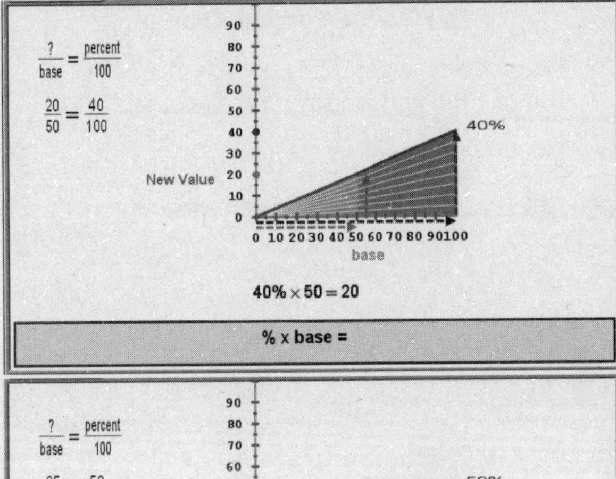

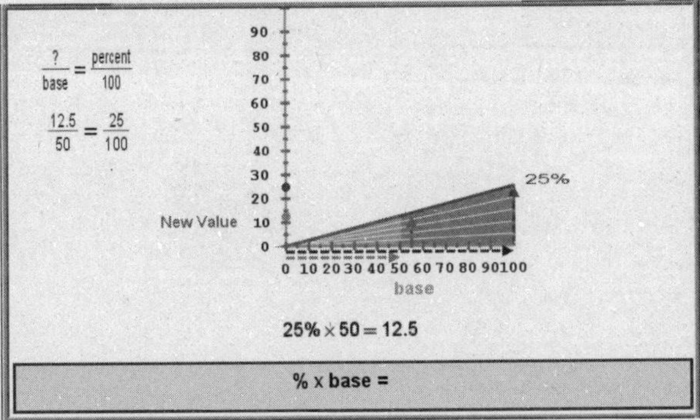

What fractional part is 25%?

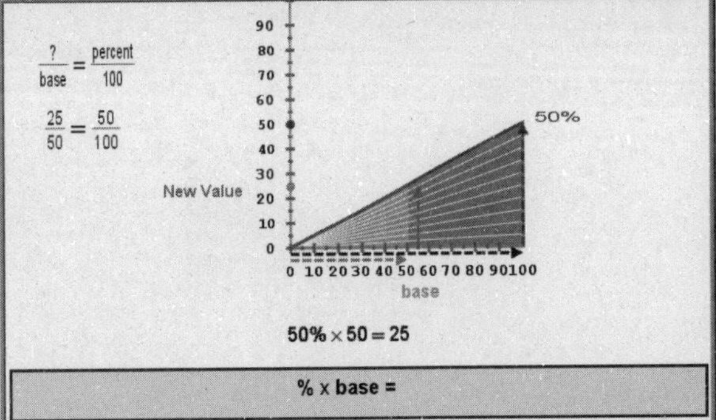

What does the phrase "50-50" mean in terms of percentage?

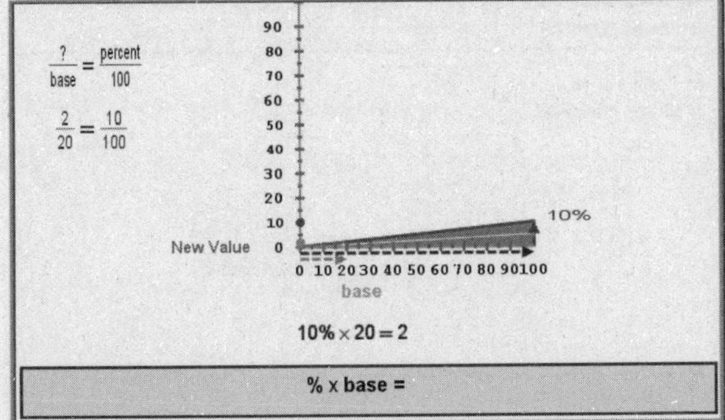

Visually, the above equation is hard to see. What can you do to enlarge the visualization—what do you have to change to make the problem represent the same percentage but easier to see?

Percent Change

EnableMath

Percent change, that is **percent increase** or **percent decrease**, assumes an original, initial, or **base amount**. The amount of change divided by the base and multiplied by 100 gives the **percent change**.

If you treat percent increase problems as proportions you will be able to solve any type of percent change problem. For example you will be able to solve a problem in which you know the base and the percent increase but not know the amount of increase. You will also be able to add the increase to the base price to find a new price. Think about these problems as proportions.

To Find the Percent Change

- Find the amount of increase. You may have to subtract the final amount from the base.
- Divide the increase by the base.
- Multiply by 100 to give you percents.

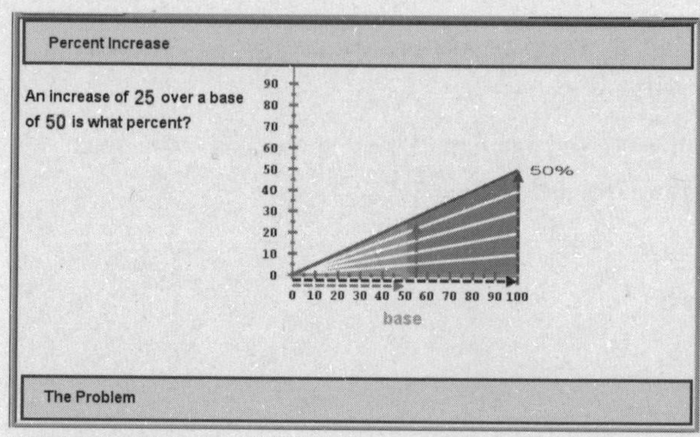

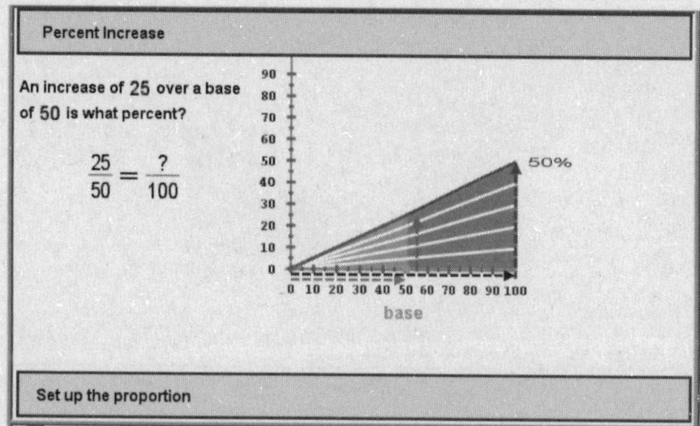

Percent Increase — Begin by setting up the proportion.

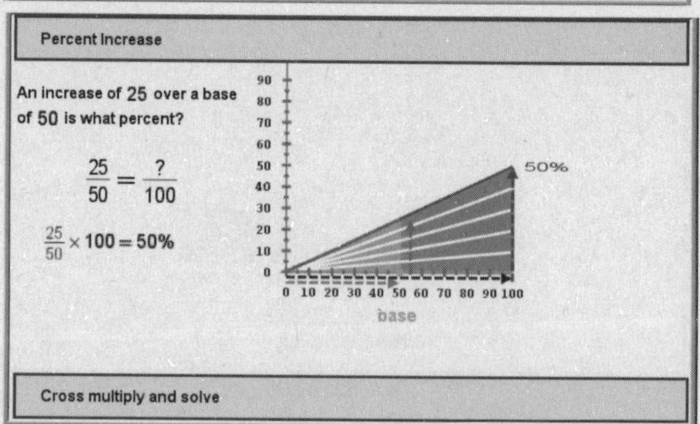

Multiply each side by 100 to find the unknown percentage.

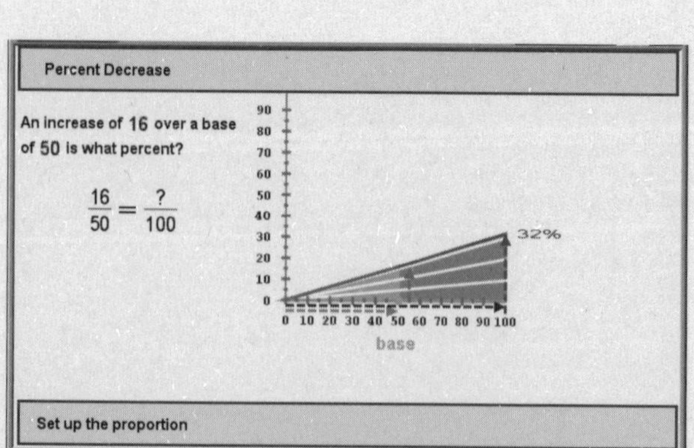

Percent Decrease— Set up the proportion and cross multiply. The only difference between increase and decrease problems is what you do with that answer.

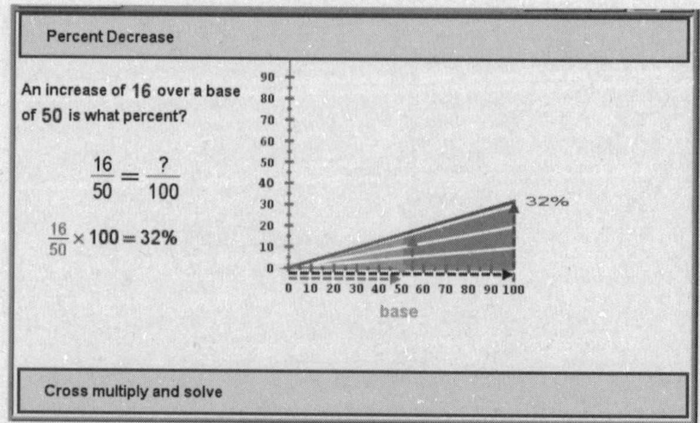

Try the example with different numbers. If you know the base and the percent change, you can find the amount of change by multiplying these terms together.

Percent change is the amount of change divided by a base amount in a ratio to 100—it makes a proportion. We visualize percent change using the same concept as we did with proportion. The aqua triangle represents the ratio of the change to the base. The purple (larger) triangle represents the percentage.

The proportional relationship is given by $\dfrac{change}{base} = \dfrac{percent}{100}$

If the base is 50 and you increase it by 25, what is the percent increase?

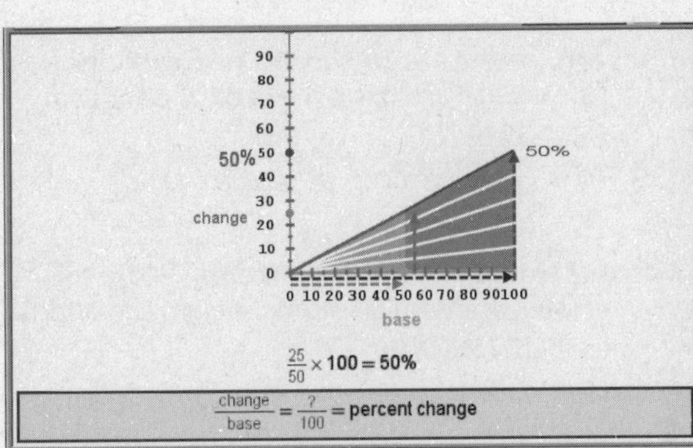

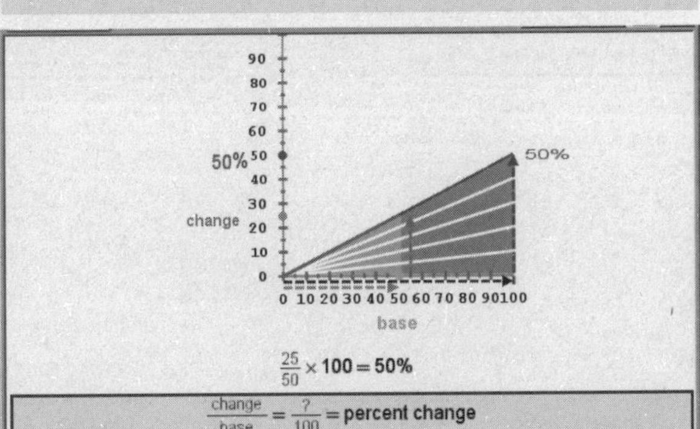

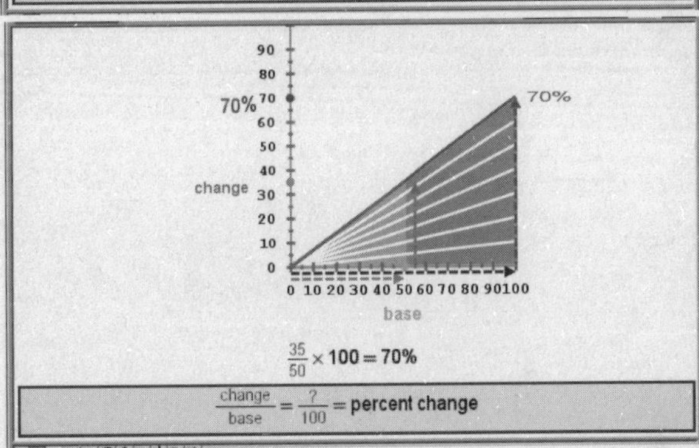

If the base is 50 and your increase is 12, what is the percent increase?

If you change the base to 36 and your increase is 12, what is your percent increase?

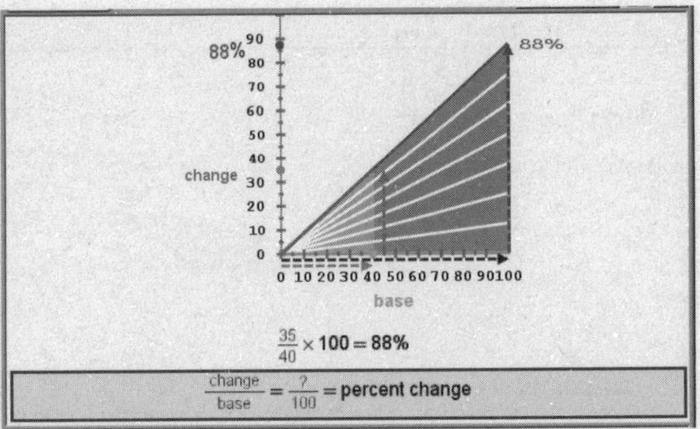

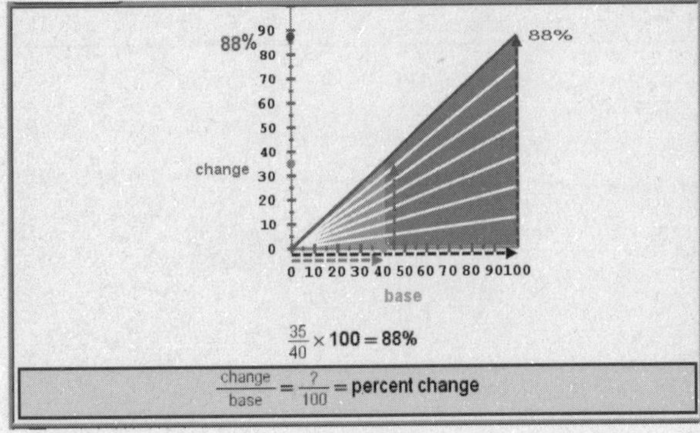

If the percent increase is 20% and the base is 50, how big was the increase?

If the ratio of the increase to the base is 2:3, what is the percent increase?

Converting Percents to Decimals

EnableMath

Computations with percents require that the percentages be converted to decimal or fraction form.

Converting percents to decimals is easiest because it only requires removing the percent sign and dividing by 100. As you recall from Module 3. Decimals, dividing by 100 moves the decimal two places to the left. Of course the process can be thought of as the reverse process of writing a number in percent form.

Convert Percents to Decimals: Take away the percent sign and move the decimal point two places to the left.

Hint: Percent to decimal—divide by 100.

Convert from Decimals to Percents: Move the decimal point two places to the right and attach a percent sign(%).

Hint: Decimal to percent—multiply by 100.

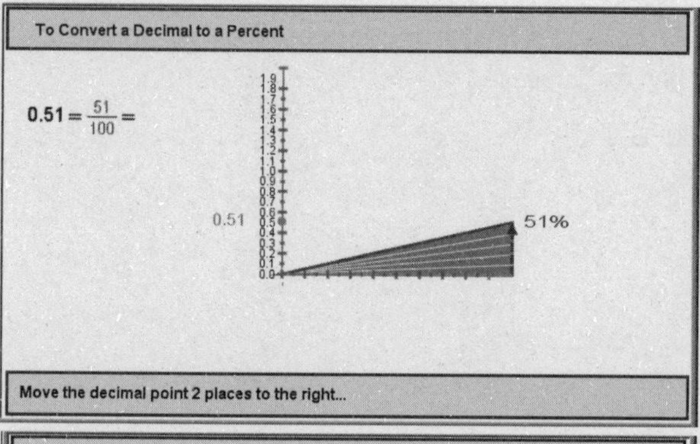

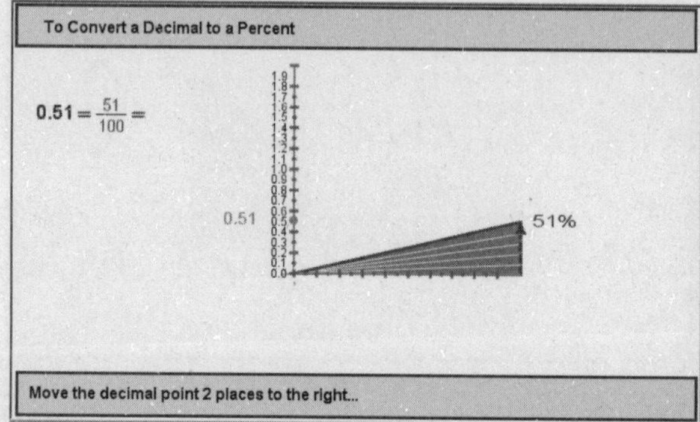

Turn the decimal into a ratio...

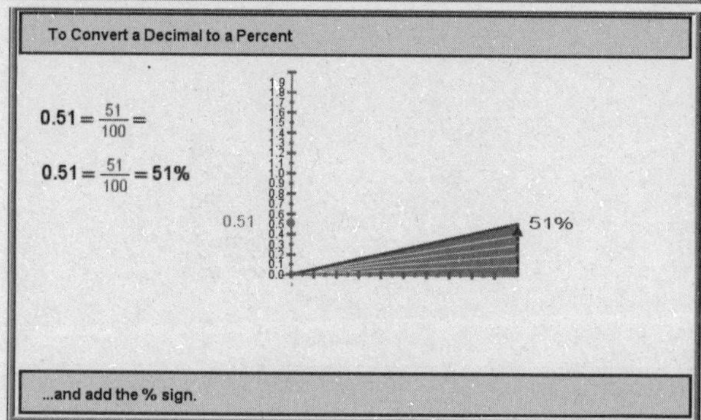

...and the ratio into a percent.

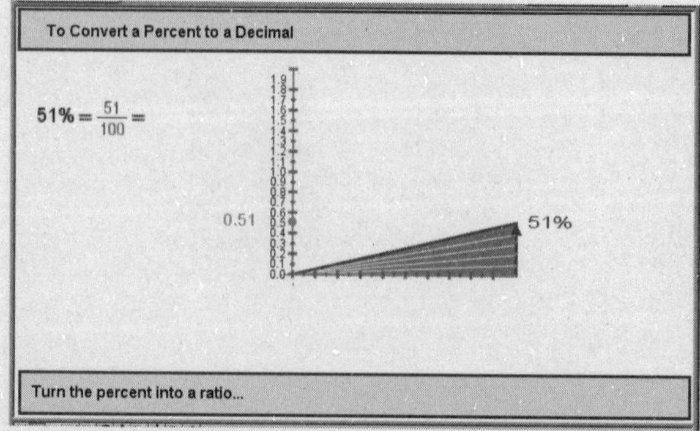

Turn the percent into a ratio...

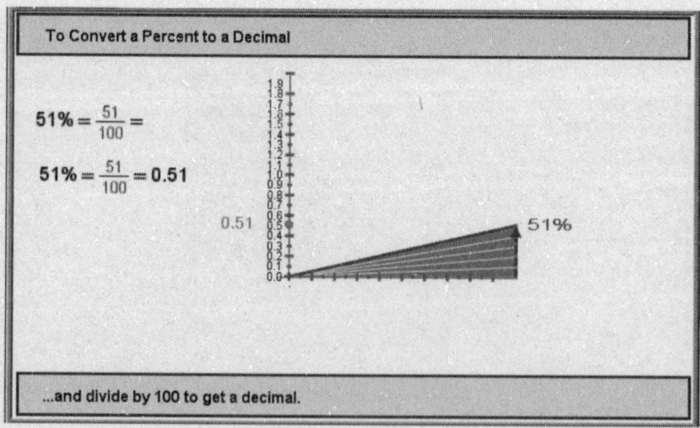

...and divide by 100 to make a decimal.

Converting Percents to Decimals

Percent means per 100—so converting 1 whole to 100 parts is a way of visualizing percentage. We use a number bar divided into 100 segments with a vector (arrow) indicating the percentage. Beneath the number bar is a number line marked from 0 to 1 in tenths and hundredths. The percentage on the number bar matches up with the decimal representation on the number line.

What happens if there is more than 100% of something? What happens if the divisions are too small to be represented on the number line? What is the pattern of numbers between tenths?

Can any amount be divided into 100 parts? Will each of those parts represent 1% of the amount?

If you have $1000 and spend 12% of it—how much did you spend? What decimal amount does each percent represent?

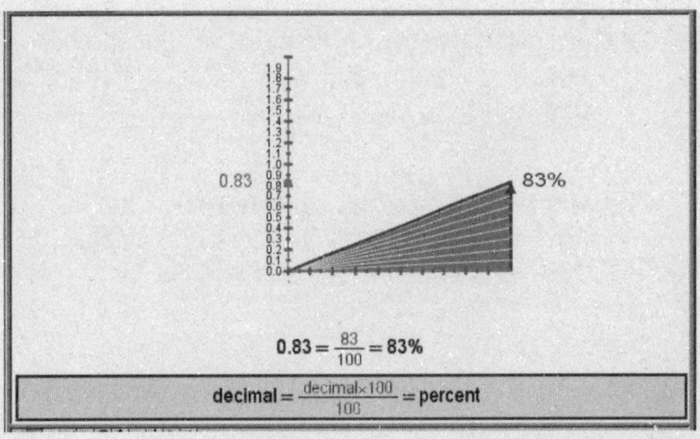

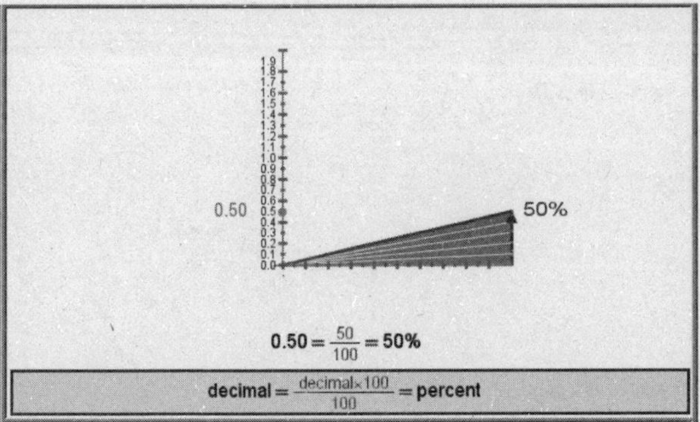

Is 50% more than or less than .55?

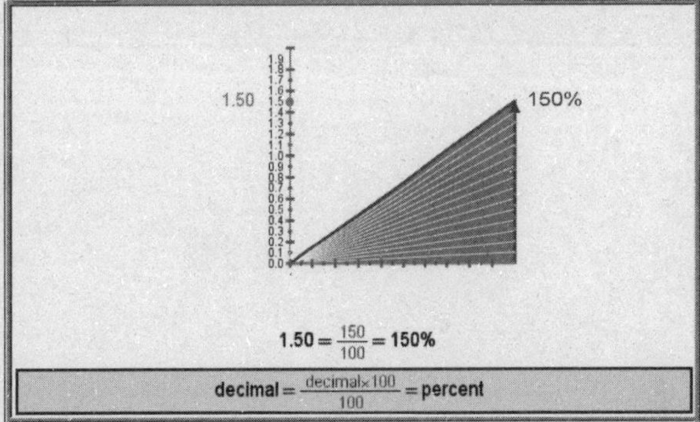

What happens to the decimals when the percentage goes above 100? Remember you can use the scroll wheel to run the decimal up and down — select the joystick first.

Converting Percents to Fractions

EnableMath

Computations with percents require that the percentages be converted to decimal or fraction form.

The definition of percent as per hundred is a direct conversion to fraction form. All that is required is to reduce the fraction to lowest terms. Place value plays an important role in converting to and from decimals, percent and fraction form.

To Convert Percents to Fractions: Put the percent as the numerator with 100 as denominator and reduce to lowest terms.

Convert from Fractions to Percents: Build equivalent fractions to have a denominator of 100—eliminate the 100 and add the %.

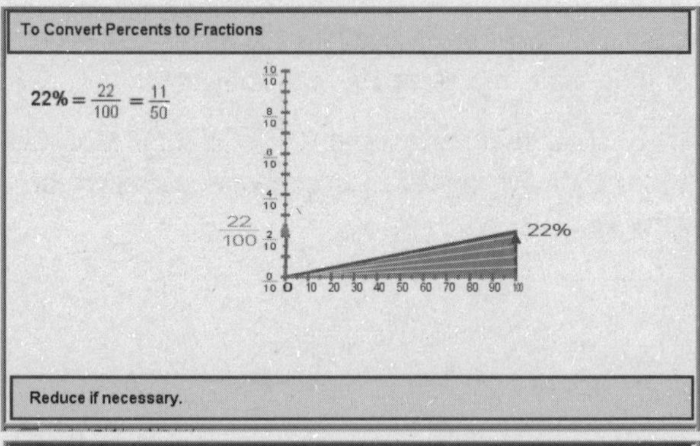

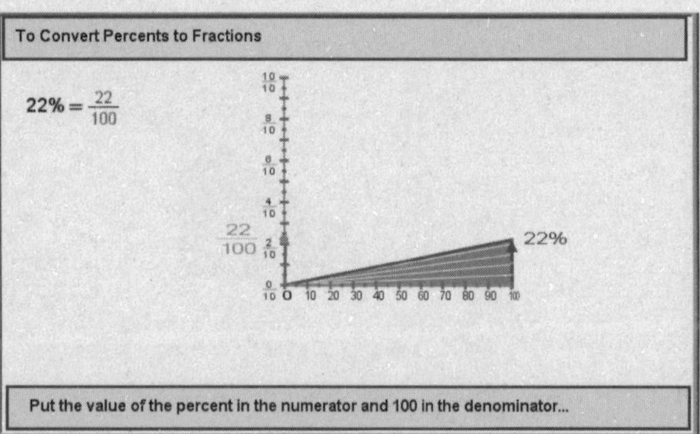

Drop the % sign and put the value over 100.

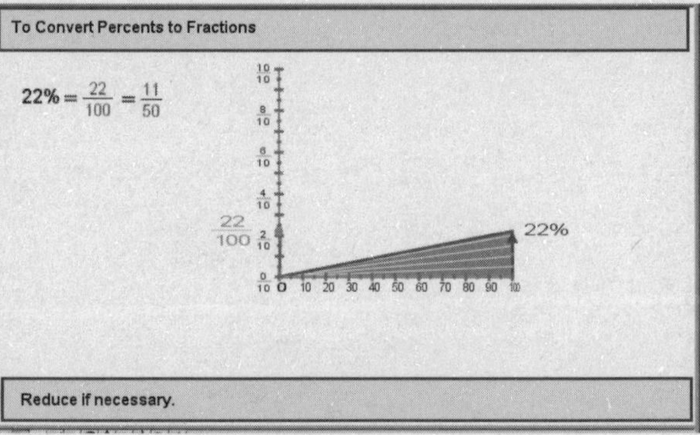

Be sure to reduce your answer to lowest terms.

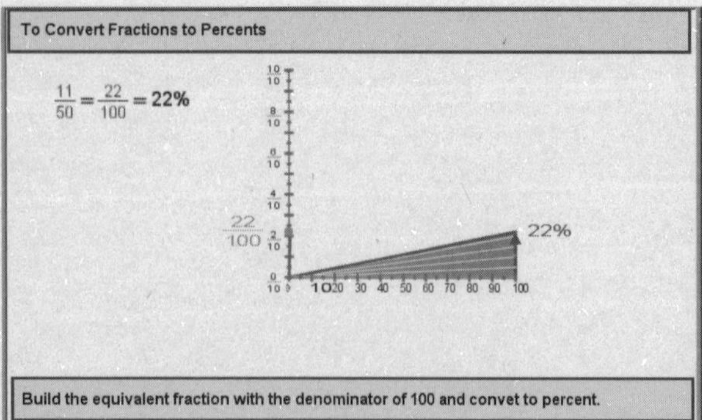

To Convert Fractions to Percents
$\frac{11}{50} = \frac{22}{100} = 22\%$
22%
Build the equivalent fraction with the denominator of 100 and convet to percent.

Build the equivalent fraction over 100 and convert to percent.

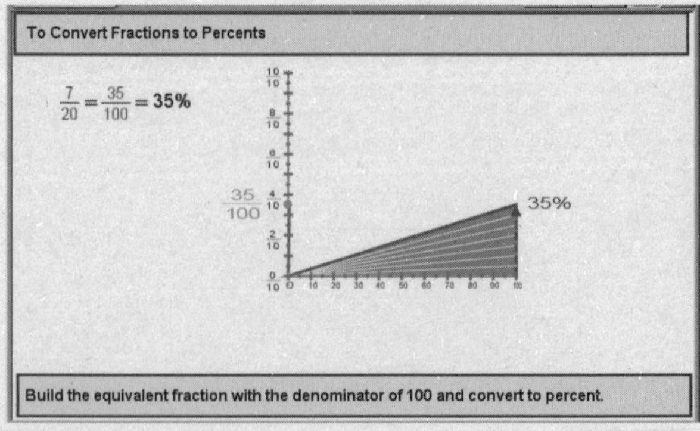

This example is dynamic. Be sure to try other values for the percentage.

Percent means per 100—so converting a percent to a fraction only requires us to put the percent in the numerator and 100 in the denominator.

Be sure to reduce the fraction if you can.

What happens if there is more than 100% of something?

What happens if a percent has a decimal place?

What happens if the percent has a fraction?

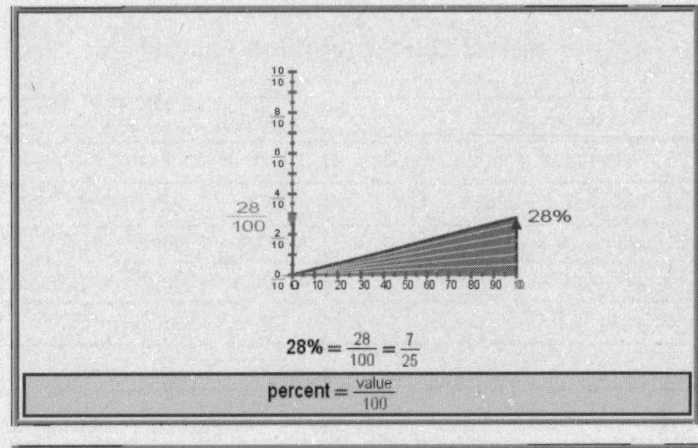

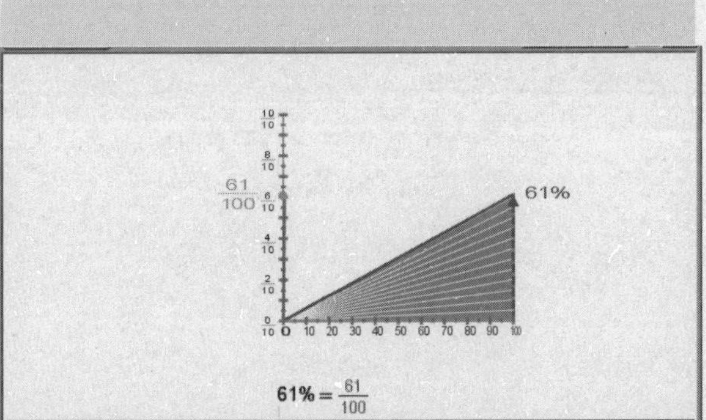

Is 61% greater or less than half?

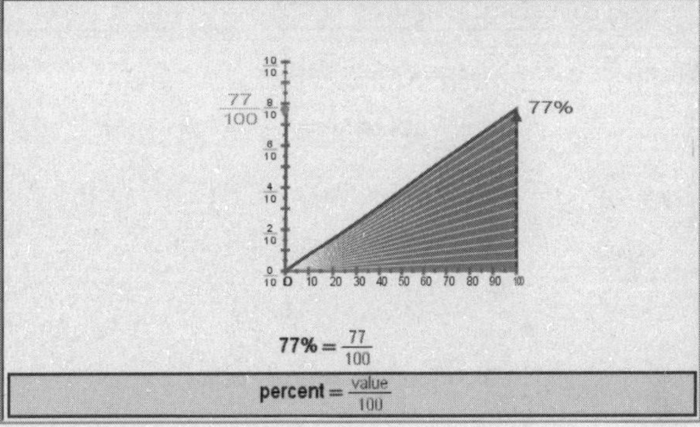

Is 77% greater or less than 3/4?

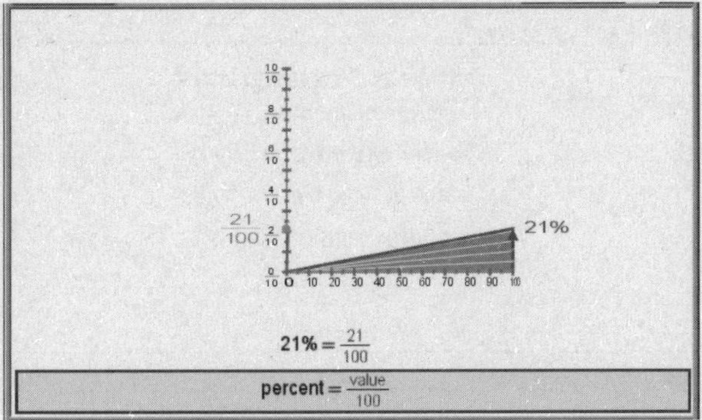

Is 21% less than one-quarter?

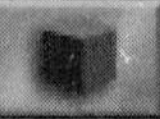

Converting American to Metric Units

EnableMath

To convert between measurement systems we use an agreed upon relationship between the units—their conversion formulas, which are generally rounded to 2 decimal places. Each conversion formula has been solved for a conversion factor that links the two measurement units. To convert from an American unit to metric, multiply the American measurement times the appropriate conversion factor. Alternatively divide the American unit by the metric to American conversion factor.

To convert between American and metric measures you can use a proportion. Set up the first part of the proportion with the given units. The second part of the proportion uses the appropriate conversion from the table. Then solve the proportion making sure that the units divide out except for the new unit.

Select the Conversion Factor

Metric to American	American to Metric
1 centimeter = 0.3937 inches	1 inch = 2.54 centimeters
1 meter = 3.28 feet	1 foot = 0.305 meters
1 kilometer = 0.62 miles	1 mile = 1.6 kilometers
1 kilogram = 2.2 pounds	1 pound = 0.45 kilograms
1 gram = 0.035 ounce	1 ounce = 28.3 grams
1 liter = 1.057 quarts	1 quart = 0.947 liters

Converting Inches to Centimeters

Convert 13.0 inches into centimeters

Select the conversion factor.

Converting Inches to Centimeters

Convert 13.0 inches into centimeters

$$\text{conversion factor} \approx \frac{2.54\text{ cm}}{1\text{ in}}$$

$$13.0\text{ in} \approx 13.0\text{ in} \times \frac{2.54\text{ cm}}{1\text{ in}}$$

$$13.0\text{ in} \approx 13.0 \times 2.54\text{ cm}$$

$$13.0\text{ in} \approx 33.02\text{ cm}$$

Conversion completed.

Converting feet to centimeters: The conversion factor is 1 inch = 2.54 centimeters. Then, one foot is 12 inches and 12 times the conversion factor is the number of centimeters in one foot.

Converting Ounces to Grams

Convert 15.5 ounces into grams

$$\text{conversion factor} \approx \frac{28\text{ g}}{1\text{ oz}}$$

$$15.5\text{ oz} \approx 15.5\text{ oz} \times \frac{28\text{ g}}{1\text{ oz}}$$

$$15.5\text{ oz} \approx 15.5 \times 28\text{ g}$$

$$15.5\text{ oz} \approx 434.0\text{ g}$$

Conversion completed.

Converting one pound to grams—multiply the number of ounces times the conversion factor for ounces to grams.

Is the proportion true? $\frac{16\ ounces}{1\ ounce} = \frac{453.6\ grams}{28.35\ grams}$

Converting Quarts to Liters

Convert 11.5 Quarts into Liters

$$\text{conversion factor} \approx \frac{1.1\text{ qt}}{1\text{ L}}$$

$$\text{new conversion factor} \approx \frac{1\text{ L}}{1.1\text{ qt}}$$

$$11.5\text{ qt} \approx 11.5\text{ qt} \times \frac{1\text{ L}}{1.1\text{ qt}}$$

$$11.5\text{ qt} \approx 11.5 \times \frac{1}{1.1}\text{ L}$$

$$11.5\text{ qt} \approx \frac{11.5}{1.1}\text{ L}$$

$$11.5\text{ qt} \approx 10.45\text{ L}$$

Conversion completed.

Dividing the number of quarts by the liter-to-quarts conversion is the same as multiplying by the quarts-to-liters conversion because the conversion factors are in proportion to each other. The above example converts gallons to liters.

Converting Pints to Liters

Convert 20.0 Pints into Liters

$$\text{conversion factor} \approx \frac{2.11\text{ pt}}{1\text{ L}}$$

$$\text{new conversion factor} \approx \frac{1\text{ L}}{2.11\text{ pt}}$$

$$20.0\text{ pt} \approx 20.0\text{ pt} \times \frac{1\text{ L}}{2.11\text{ pt}}$$

$$20.0\text{ pt} \approx 20.0 \times \frac{1}{2.11}\text{ L}$$

$$20.0\text{ pt} \approx \frac{20.0}{2.11}\text{ L}$$

$$20.0\text{ pt} \approx 9.48\text{ L}$$

Conversion completed.

Converting gallons to liters through pints. There are 2.11 pints per liter so divide the number of pints by 2.11 to convert to liters. Alternatively, multiply 8 pints times 0.47 to convert to liters.

Converting American to Metric Units 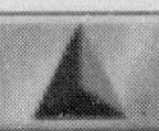

American and metric units were developed completely separately on different standards. The American system (previously referred to as the English system) was originally developed in England and many of the units are based on archaic measures such as the length of a king's step or the distance between the tip of a nose and the end of an index finger. All industrialized countries except the United States have adopted the metric system which is based on powers of 10.

To convert units of measure we build and solve proportions. We visualize proportions as triangles and when the slopes are the same the triangles are in proportion.

Can every American unit be converted to a metric unit and vice versa?

What happens when the unknown measurement is an American unit?

Can the same conversion factors be used?

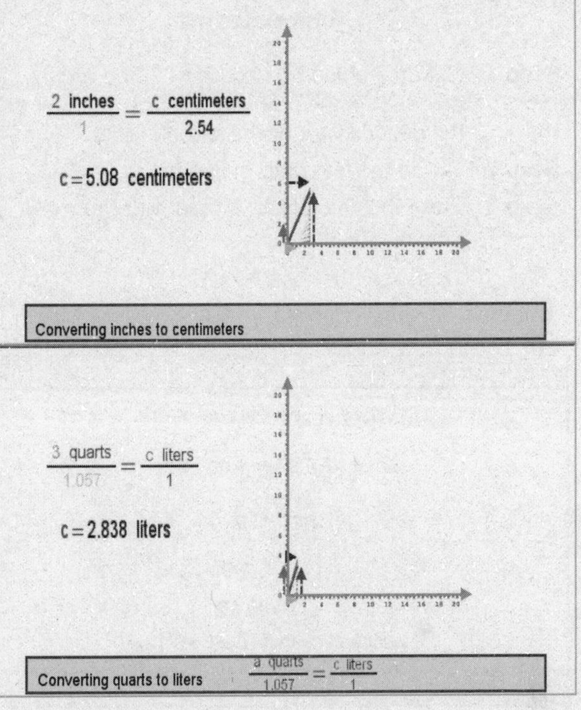

Which represents a larger value liters or quarts?

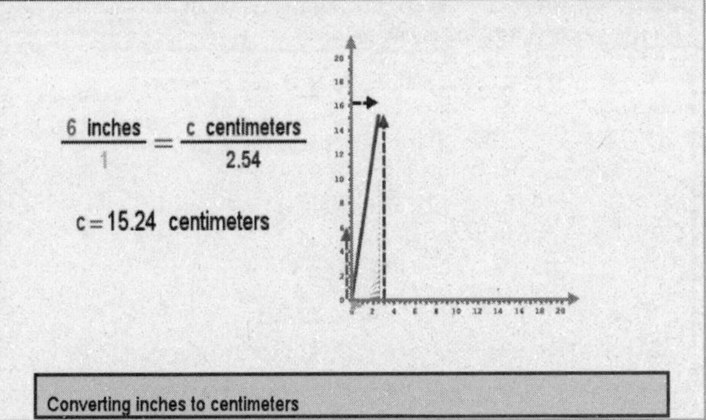

When converting from inches to centimeters, by how much does the number increase?

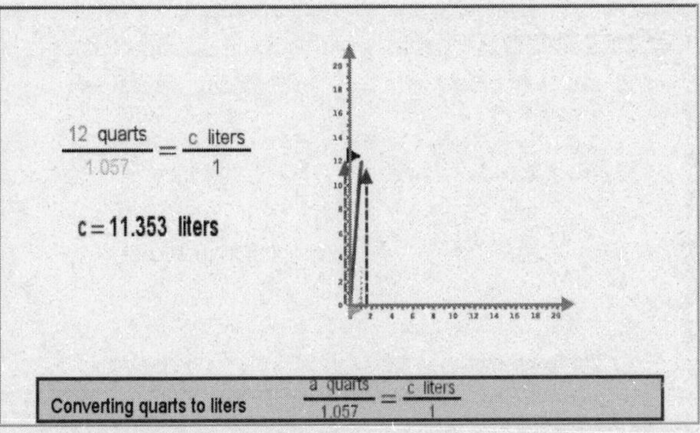

Is a liter of a soft drink larger than a quart of that same soft drink?

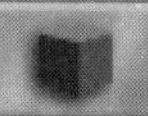

Unit Rates

A **unit rate** is a ratio of some number of items compared to 1 unit. When we solve a unit rate problem, we always create a proportion in which the denominator of the unit rate side is 1. Unit rates are often described as something **per unit,** like miles per hour or cans per dollar. The unit is one hour or one dollar.

Unit Rates

Step 1: Set up a proportion equation in the order called for in the problem with the one unit as the denominator of the second ratio.

Step 2: Divide the first ratio to find the unit rate.

Step 3: State the unit rate as a ratio with the word **per** and the unit.

Find the cost of one ounce.

17 ounces of peanuts cost \$2.04

$17 \text{ oz} : \$2.04 = 1 \text{ oz} : \$n$

$$\frac{17}{2.04} = \frac{1}{n}$$

$17 \times n = 2.04 \times 1$

$n = 0.12$

State the solution.

Find the cost of one ounce.

17 ounces of peanuts cost \$2.04

$17 \text{ oz} : \$2.04 = 1 \text{ oz} : \$n$

$$\frac{17}{2.04} = \frac{1}{n}$$

$17 \times n = 2.04 \times 1$

$n = 0.12$

1 ounce of peanuts cost \$0.12

Cost per ounce

Find the distance travelled in one second.

An object moved 99.36 feet in 3.6 seconds

$99.36 \text{ ft} : 3.6 \text{ s} = n \text{ ft} : 1 \text{ s}$

$$\frac{99.36}{3.6} = \frac{n}{1}$$

$n = 99.36 \div 3.6$

$n = 27.60$

The object travelled 27.60 feet in 1 second.

Feet per second

Determine the better value using unit cost.

35 ounces of detergent cost \$16.60

65 ounces of detergent cost \$24.62

$\$16.60 : 35 \text{ oz} = \$n_1 : 1 \text{ oz}$

$\$24.62 : 65 \text{ oz} = \$n_2 : 1 \text{ oz}$

Write in fraction form.

Comparing two prices on a supermarket shelf. First set up the proportion.

Determine the better value using unit cost.

35 ounces of detergent cost \$16.60

65 ounces of detergent cost \$24.62

$\$16.60 : 35 \text{ oz} = \$n_1 : 1 \text{ oz}$

$\$24.62 : 65 \text{ oz} = \$n_2 : 1 \text{ oz}$

$$\frac{16.60}{35} = \frac{n_1}{1} \qquad \frac{24.62}{65.0} = \frac{n_2}{1}$$

$n_1 = 0.47$

$n_2 = 0.38$

The lower unit cost, \$0.47 or \$0.38 is the better value.

Then solve.

Unit rates are devised to make calculations more efficient. Finding unit rates requires using a proportion and are visualized with similar right triangles. This time, when the first triangle is drawn, the second triangle is constructed from one base unit to the hypotenuse (the slanted line from the origin) and the value is read on the y-axis. Two types of unit rates are examined here: dollars per ounce and feet per second.

Can every ratio be expressed as a unit rate? When should you use a unit rate rather than a lowest terms rate?

How do you know which way to set up a unit rate?

Why is it important to keep the units attached as part of the answer?

What can a unit rate tell you that a lowest term rate can't?

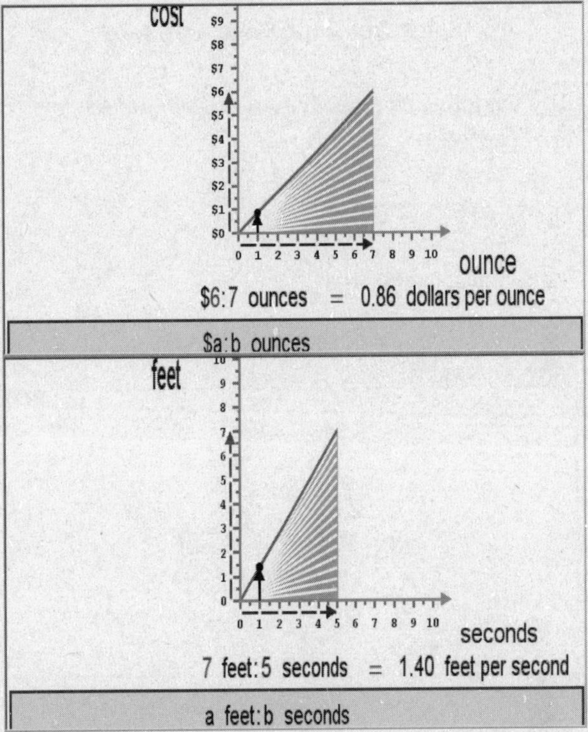

Once you know the unit rate can you use it to find how far something traveled in 12 seconds? 9 seconds? 2 seconds?

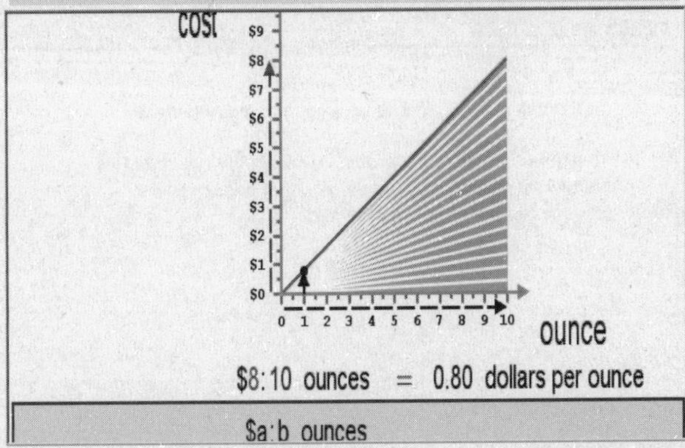

Consumer shopping: Which is the better buy, the rate above or the rate above right?

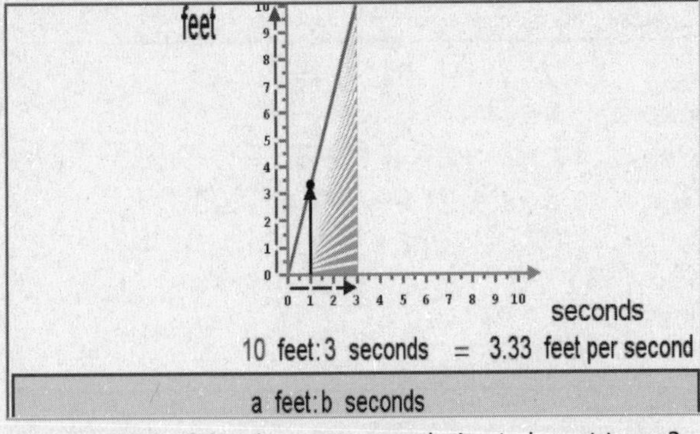

Can you think of the above rate as reducing to lowest terms?

Sales Tax

Sales tax is a rate. A 5% sales tax means that you are required to pay an additional 5% per dollar you spend on an item to the government. You can calculate the sales tax you will owe on items that you purchase using a proportion. The sales tax proportion given below relates the tax amount, the cost of an item, and the rate of sales tax. You can find the unknown part of the proportion if you know any two parts. Cross multiply and divide to get the unknown value.

Sales Tax, Total Cost, and Rate

Use the following proportion to calculate for the unknown value:

$$\frac{tax}{cost} = \frac{rate}{100}$$

Cross multiply and divide.

Calculating Sales Tax

Sales tax is an amount added onto things that we buy, as a percent of the cost of the item.

To calculate the sales tax of an item, we need to know the cost of the item and the sales tax rate. That will allow us to set up a proportion and solve for the tax.

Calculating Sales Tax

$$\frac{\text{tax}}{\text{cost}} = \frac{\text{rate}}{100}$$

$$\frac{\text{tax}}{20.56} = \frac{4}{100}$$

$$\text{tax} \cdot 100 = 4 \cdot 20.56$$

$$\text{tax} = 0.82$$

Solve for tax.

Set up the proportion: The tax you pay per item cost is equal to the percentage sales tax. Solve the proportion by cross multiplying and dividing by 100. Since sales tax is in dollars and cents we round to 2 decimal places.

Calculating Total Cost

Total cost of an item is what we pay for an item, including the tax.

To calculate the total cost of an item, we need to know the cost of the item and the sales tax rate. That will allow us to calculate the tax, which we then add to the cost of the item.

Use the formula to find the tax and add it to the cost.

Using what you know: an alternative is to multiply the cost times (1 + tax rate) to get the total cost.

Calculating Total Cost

$$\frac{\text{tax}}{\text{cost}} = \frac{\text{rate}}{100}$$

$$\frac{\text{tax}}{20.56} = \frac{4}{100}$$

$$\text{tax} \cdot 100 = 4 \cdot 20.56$$

$$\text{tax} = 0.82$$

$$\text{cost} + \text{tax} = 20.56 + 0.82$$

$$\text{total} = 21.38$$

Solve for total cost.

Alternatively, multiply $20.56 *(1+ 4/100).

Calculating the Tax Rate

$$\frac{\text{tax}}{\text{cost}} = \frac{\text{rate}}{100}$$

$$\frac{1.42}{21.99} = \frac{\text{rate}}{100}$$

$$\text{rate} \cdot 21.99 = 1.42 \cdot 100$$

$$\text{rate} = 6.46$$

Solve for rate.

If you know the amount of tax you can find the rate. Cross multiply and divide.

Sales Tax

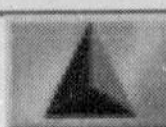

Sales tax is figured as a percentage of the cost of an item. Thus a 5% sales tax is 5% of the cost of the item you are buying. We visualize sales tax in the same way we look at any proportion by setting up triangles. This time, the larger triangle has a base of 100.

Are other taxes figured like sales tax? Can restaurant tips be figured like sales tax?

If the tax rate doubles, does the tax double?

If the cost of an item doubles, and the tax rate stays the same, will the amount of tax double?

Can you determine what the cost of an item is if you know the sales tax and the rate?

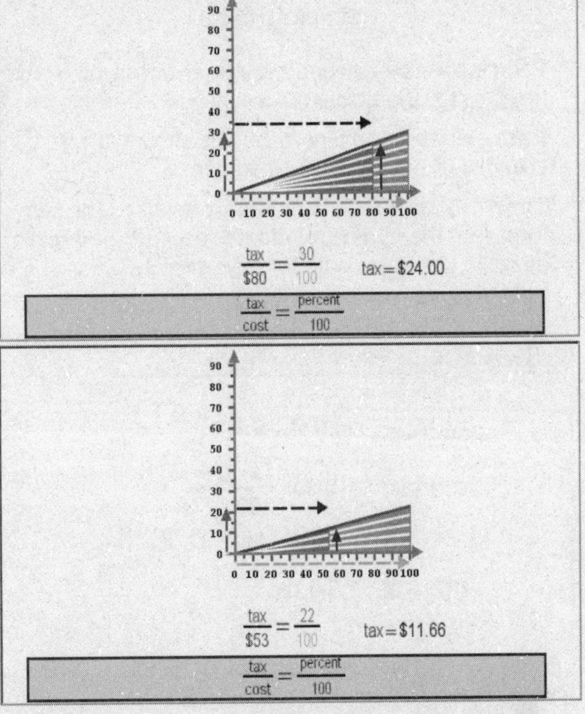

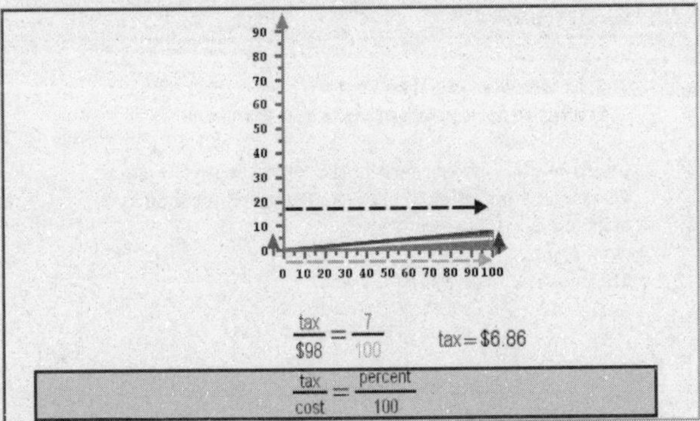

What is the tax on $100? Is the tax on $98 appropriately "close to" $7.00? What would be the tax on an item worth $9800?

What would be the tax on $50? Is the tax of $11.66 "close to" that amount?

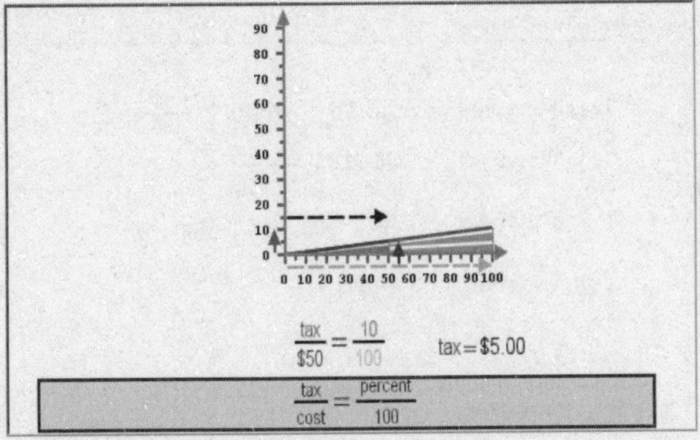

If 10% of an item is $20, how much is the item?

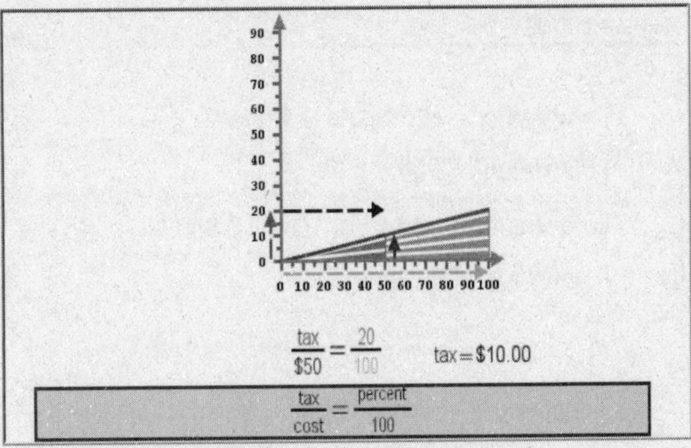

Can you use this to find the tip on a $50 dinner?

Interest is either the amount you are paid on an account or investment, or the amount you must pay to borrow money or defer payment (like using a credit card). The amount of interest on an account is based on the **interest rate**, the **principal** or amount money you have in the account, and the **time** you leave the money in the account.

Simple Interest

Principal—The amount invested or borrowed; sometimes called the amount.

Rate—Given in percent form, rate should always be changed to fraction or decimal form.

Time—Usually given in months, convert to fraction form with the number of months over 12; or if given as daily, use the number of days over 365.

Calculating Simple Interest

Interest that is calculated for an investment just once for a certain period of time is called Simple Interest. The amount invested is called the principal.

Usually the time is given in months and calculated as part of a year. For example, 3 months = 3/12 of a year. The rate of the interest is expressed as a fraction over 100.

The formula for Simple Interest is:

Interest = Principal*Rate*Time

Calculating Simple Interest

$$\text{Interest} = \text{Principal} \cdot \frac{\text{Rate}}{100} \cdot \frac{\text{Time}}{12}$$

$$\text{Interest} = 500 \cdot \frac{5}{100} \cdot \frac{7}{12}$$

$$\text{Interest} = 500 \cdot 0.05 \cdot 0.5833$$

$$\text{Interest} = 14.58$$

Solve for interest rounded to nearest cent.

Finding how much interest is earned in a $500 account at 5% for 7 months.

Calculating Total Value

The total value of an investment is the sum of the principal and the interest earned on the investment over a given time period.

Usually the time is given in months and calculated as part of a year. For example, 3 months = 3/12 of a year. The rate of the interest is expressed as a fraction over 100.

The formula for Total Value is:

Total Value = Principal + Principal*Rate*Time can be shortened to TV = Principal(1+RT).

You must add the principal to the amount of interest earned.

Calculating Total Value

$$\text{TotalValue} = \text{Principal} + \text{Principal} \cdot \frac{\text{Rate}}{100} \cdot \frac{\text{Time}}{12}$$

$$\text{TotalValue} = 500 + 500 \cdot \frac{5}{100} \cdot \frac{7}{12}$$

$$\text{TotalValue} = 500 + 500 \cdot 0.05 \cdot 0.5833$$

$$\text{TotalValue} = 514.58$$

Solve for total value rounded to nearest cent.

Taken one step further, add the interest to the account principal to get the new account total value.

Calculating Total Payment

$$\text{TotalPayment} = \text{Amount} + \text{Amount} \cdot \frac{\text{Rate}}{100} \cdot \frac{\text{Time}}{12}$$

$$\text{TotalPayment} = 1200 + 1200 \cdot \frac{7}{100} \cdot \frac{6}{12}$$

$$\text{TotalPayment} = 1200 + 1200 \cdot 0.07 \cdot 0.5000$$

$$\text{TotalPayment} = 1242.00$$

Solve for total payment rounded to nearest cent.

If you borrow $1200 - you must pay back both the amount you borrowed *and* the amount of interest.

While we rarely pay **simple interest** on money we borrow, it is the place to start looking at interest. Simple interest is based on the amount of money you borrow (principal), the interest rate (%) and the time you borrow it for. The product (**principal** x **rate** x **time**) gives you the interest you pay.

Can you use the visualizations below to predict what larger investments will pay? Instead of $20, what would $20,000 at 10% for 12 months pay?

This visualization combines rate and time since we do not have another dimension to show them both.

What happens if you double the time?

What happens if you halve the rate?

What happens if your principal triples?

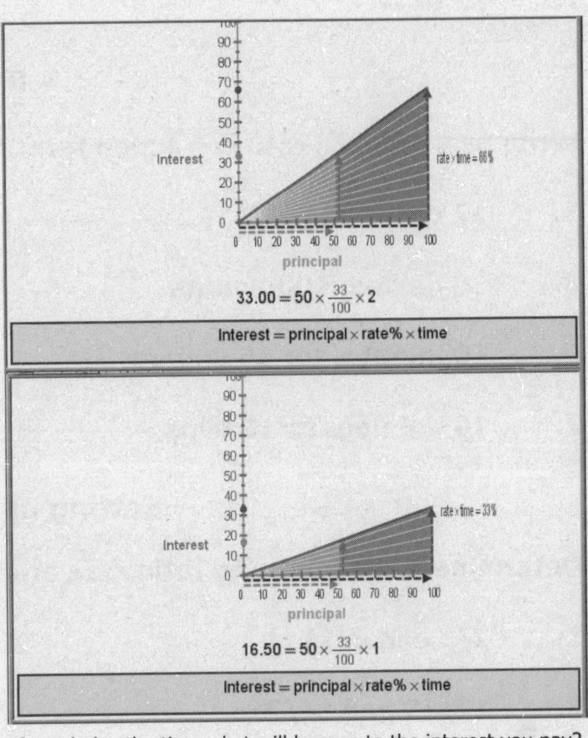

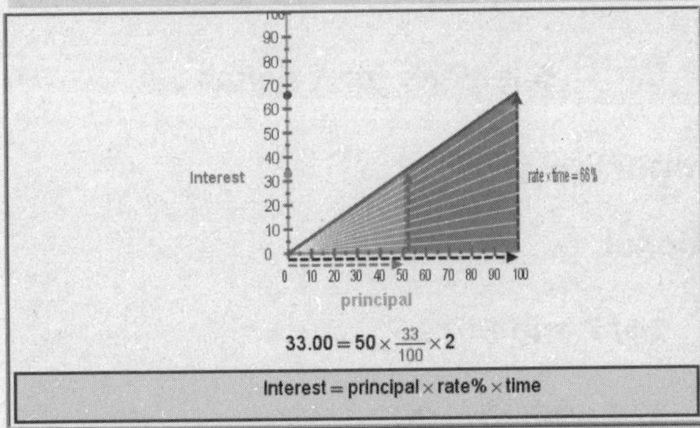

If your interest rate increases by 5% how much more interest will you pay on this loan?

If you halve the time what will happen to the interest you pay?

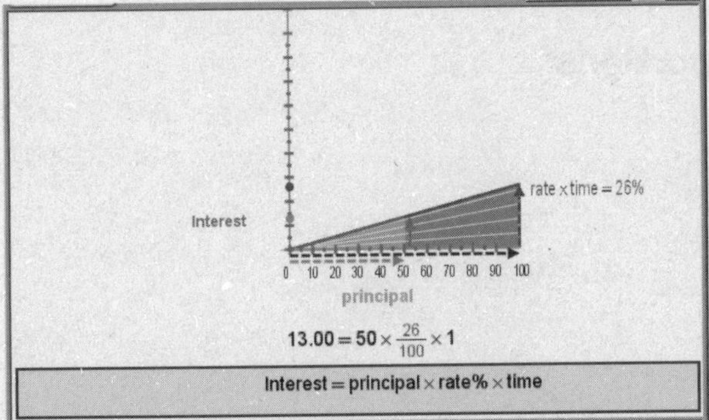

If you lower your rate, how will that affect the interest you will pay?

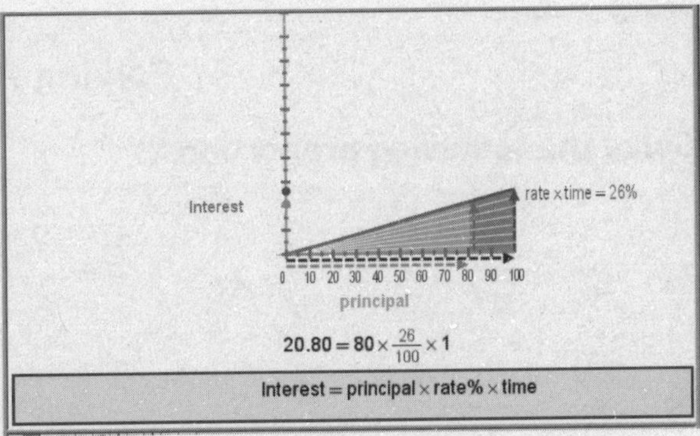

If you raise the principal amount of your loan how will that affect the interest you will pay on it?

Ratios

Write as a reduced ratio in fraction form.

1. 12:18
2. 15:25
3. 30:100
4. 22:11
5. 10 to 15
6. 36 to 40
7. 12 to 17
8. 5 to 1

Rates

Write as a reduced rate in fraction form.

1. 12 cokes : 18 kids
2. 15 toys : 25 tots
3. 30 dollars :100 donuts
4. 22 books :11 babies
5. 10 minutes for 15 dollars
6. 36 people per 12 jobs
7. 10 hot dogs to 12 buns
8. 5 lemons for 1 dollar

Setting up Proportions

Determine if the following ratios are proportional.

1. 2/5 and 6/15
2. 14/7 and 50/25
3. 12/15 and 14/21
4. 1/4 and 25/100
5. 9/6 and 150/100
6. 9/1 and 1/9
7. 35/42 and 10/12
8. 169/39 and 169/26

Solving Proportions

Solve the following proportions.

1. $\frac{5}{8} = \frac{?}{4}$
2. $\frac{4}{7} = \frac{?}{5}$
3. $\frac{3}{8} = \frac{?}{18}$
4. $\frac{9}{81} = \frac{?}{4}$
5. $\frac{25}{81} = \frac{?}{45}$
6. $\frac{5}{3} = \frac{?}{4}$

Percents

1. Change the following ratios to percent form:

12:100 __________ **27:100** __________ **1.98:100** __________

235:100 __________ **12.5:100** __________

2. Change the following fractions to percent form:

$\frac{17}{100}$ ________ $\frac{2.9}{100}$ ________ $\frac{12\frac{1}{2}}{100}$ ________

$\frac{117}{100}$ ________ $\frac{0.17}{100}$ ________

Percent Equations

Solve for the unknown amount.

1. 12% of 56 is what number?

2. What is 45% of 60?

3. 112% of $24,500 is what amount?

4. What is 18% of $45.54?

5. What is 42.3% of 905?

6. What is 0.15% of 6,000?

Percent Change

Solve the following; round to two decimal places if necessary.

1. What is 178 increased by 12%?

2. If your bill for dinner was $54.78 and you leave an 18% tip, what is the new amount?

3. 450 increased by what percent is 512?

4. If gas prices rose from $1.23 last year to $2.39 this year, what was the percent increase?

5. Tuition increased from $12,300 to $15,600; what percent increase was that?

6. My three year old weighed 45 lbs at his check-up last year and 53 lbs this year; what was his percent weight gain?

Percent Change

Solve the following; round to two decimal places if necessary.

1. **What is 178 decreased by 12%?**

2. **If your credit card listed the charge for dinner as $54.78 and you know you left an 18% tip, what was the cost of the meal.**

3. **450 decreased by what percent is 312?**

4. **If gas prices dropped from $2.43 last week to $2.39 this week, what was the percent decrease?**

5. **Interest on an account dropped from $12,300 to $10,600; what percent decrease was that?**

6. **My old dog weighed 56 lbs at his check-up last year and 43 lbs this year; what was his percent weight loss?**

Converting Percents to Decimals

1. **Change the following percents to decimal form:**

12% __________ **27%** __________ **1.98%** __________

235% __________ **12.5%** __________

2. **Change the following decimals to percent form:**

0.11 __________ **1.23** __________ **0.012** __________

0.921 __________ **0.003** __________

Converting Percents to Fractions

1. **Change the following percent to reduced fraction form:**

13% __________ **25%** __________ **1.98%** __________

235% __________ **12.5%** __________

2. **Change the following fractions to percent form:**

13/100 __________ **3/25** __________

1/20 __________ **4/5** __________

Converting American to Metric Units

Use the table to convert the following measurements from American/English to metric (round to the nearest tenth).

	English to Metric
Length	1 inch = 2.54 centimeters
	1 foot = 0.305 meters
	1 mile = 1.6 kilometers
Weight	1 pound = 0.45 kilograms
	1 ounce = 28.3 grams
Volume	1 quart = 0.947 liters

1. 4.5 feet to meters.

2. 120 miles to kilometers

3. 15 quarts to liters

4. 28 feet to meters

5. 185 pounds to kilograms

6. 6 pounds to kilograms

7. If a baby weighs 6 pounds and her car seat weighs 3.2 kg, how much in kilograms do they weigh together?

Unit Rates

Find the unit rate.

1. Five lemons for $1.45, how much each?

2. 12 apples for $3.60, how much for one apple?

3. On a map of Saskatchewan, 5 inches represents 200 miles, what is the number of miles per inch?

4. 120 miles used 4.5 gallons gas, how many miles per gallon?

Which is the better buy?

5. 8 hotdog buns for $1.29 or 12 for $1.95?

6. 18 20 oz snack packs mini Oreos for $3.79 or 3 for $1.00?

7. A six pack microwave popcorn for $3.49 or a three pack for $1.98?

Sales Tax

Find the amount of sales tax.

1. **$18.97 at a sales tax rate of 6%.**

2. **$237 at a sales tax rate of 5%.**

3. **Sales tax in the city is 11%. If I buy $230 worth of merchandise, how much sales tax do I owe.**

4. **If the tax on my $396 hotel room was $31.68, what was the tax rate?**

5. **If my meal cost $26 and the tax was $1.56, what was the sales tax rate?**

6. **Find the sales tax rate if the amount of tax was $20.25 on a bill of $225.**

Simple Interest

1. **Calculate the simple interest earned on an investment of $700 that is invested for 18 months at a yearly rate of 8%.**

2. **Calculate the simple interest earned on an investment of $250 that is invested for 6 months at a yearly rate of 12%.**

3. **Find the interest you owe if you borrow $1200 for 18 months at a yearly rate of 6.5%.**

4. **Calculate the total value of an investment of $600 that is invested for 9 months at a yearly rate of 6%.**

5. Tables & Graphs

Everyday we are bombarded with charts and graphs depicting information gathered from this survey or that telephone marketing poll. To make sense out of all the information swirling around us we use a branch of mathematics called statistics. Scientific research relies on statistical measures to determine whether or not an experiment is successful or whether one procedure is better than another one. This module will introduce you to data into tables, graphing data, and descriptive statistics (mean, median, mode).

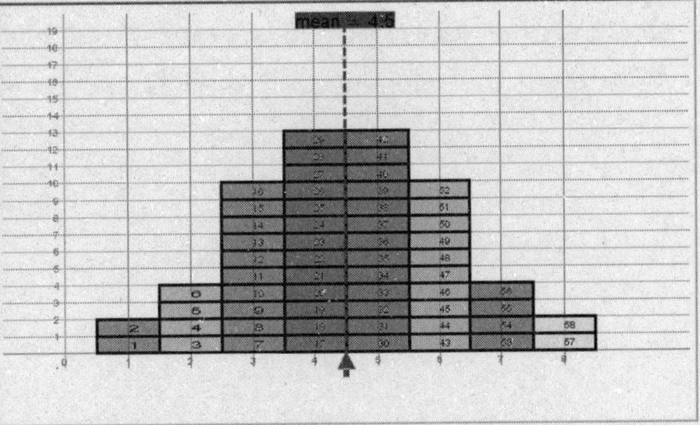

Tables and graphs help us organize information into sets of data to make it more useful and easier to read. Spreadsheets are **data tables**. They organize data by rows and columns. Rows generally contain the **record** and columns the **field**. A record is the data connected to one individual, a person, a course, a city. A field is a type of data such as body weight, height, F's, boys, address, etc.

An **entry** is the value in a cell, the intersection of a column and a row.

Data Tables

Context: Usually the top or title of the table, it provides the reason and general description for the table.

Column: (field), holds one category of information, like name or address.

Row: (record) represents an individual, a person or a thing.

Cell: The intersection of each row and column. A cell holds one piece of data.

Organizing Data into DataTables

Context: An ice cream franchise wants to open a new store in a family neighborhood if there are enough families with children to support it. Information is available through census data.

Organizing Data into DataTables

Context: An ice cream franchise wants to open a new store in a family neighborhood if there are enough families with children to support it. Information is available through census data.

Organization: Arrange relevant data into categories. Name the categories as column headings.

Address	Boys	Girls	Moms	Dads	Total

Organize Data by Categorie

Use the context to define the column (field) headings.

Organizing Data into DataTables

Context: An ice cream franchise wants to open a new store in a family neighborhood if there are enough families with children to support it. Information is available through census data.

Organization: Arrange relevant data into categories. Name the categories as column headings.

Address	Boys	Girls	Moms	Dads	Total

Address	Boys	Girls	Moms	Dads	Total
212Elm	1	1	1	0	3
214Elm	0	3	0	1	4
216Elm	2	2	2		6
218Elm	2	0	1	1	4
220Elm	3	3	1	1	8
Total	10	10	6	4	30

Fill in the Table

We usually enter the data by record, in this case the data associated with and Elm St. address.

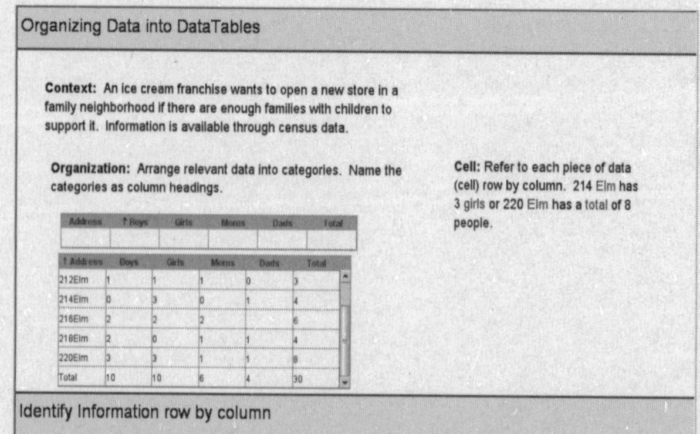

Organizing Data into DataTables

Context: An ice cream franchise wants to open a new store in a family neighborhood if there are enough families with children to support it. Information is available through census data.

Organization: Arrange relevant data into categories. Name the categories as column headings.

Cell: Refer to each piece of data (cell) row by column. 214 Elm has 3 girls or 220 Elm has a total of 8 people.

Address	Boys	Girls	Moms	Dads	Total

Address	Boys	Girls	Moms	Dads	Total
212Elm	1	1	1	0	3
214Elm	0	3	0	1	4
216Elm	2	2	2		6
218Elm	2	0	1	1	4
220Elm	3	3	1	1	8
Total	10	10	6	4	30

Identify Information row by column

How many girls are living at 214 Elm St.?

Our data tables let you sort the data by column. For example, you can sort these math courses by from most to least by the number of students who pass them.

Click on a column head to sort the table by that column. Change the size of the column by dragging the column boundaries in the header left or right.

The table below shows how students faired in math courses at a college. They could withdraw (W), Fail (F), or pass (P).

What is the hardest course to pass?

What is the "easiest" course to pass?

Which course is the most popular?

Which course do students have the most difficulty in?

Course	W	F	P	Total
Basic – Math	40	45	120	205
Introductory – Algebra	70	60	130	260
Intermediate – Algebra	100	60	180	340
College – Algebra	65	85	305	455
Pre – Calculus	20	10	90	120

Course	W	↑ F	P	Total
Pre – Calculus	20	10	90	120
Basic – Math	40	45	120	205
Introductory – Algebra	70	60	130	260
Intermediate – Algebra	100	60	180	340
College – Algebra	65	85	305	455

The above table is sorted by fewest "F's".

What happens if you click on "F" again?

↓ Course	W	F	P	Total
Pre – Calculus	20	10	90	120
Introductory – Algebra	70	60	130	260
Intermediate – Algebra	100	60	180	340
College – Algebra	65	85	305	455
Basic – Math	40	45	120	205

If you sort based on course name, what happens to the cells in the table?

Do the cell entries move with the course?

Course	W	F	P	↓ Total
College – Algebra	65	85	305	455
Intermediate – Algebra	100	60	180	340
Introductory – Algebra	70	60	130	260
Basic – Math	40	45	120	205
Pre – Calculus	20	10	90	120

Which course had the most students?

Which course had the least students?

Graphs are pictures of data. Data tables are usually graphed two columns at a time. One column goes with each axis of the grant.

There are different types of graphs: **pie graph** (chart) or circle graph; **bar graph**; **pictogram** and a **line graph** (or broken line graph). Each conveys a different picture of the data.

Imagine that the data here represents grades on a quiz (**e** means you missed the quiz). You can create a table showing how many students got each grade. You can also create graphs to show your grade distribution.

Data Tables: Values show the **frequency** (how often) it occurs (how many students got each grade).

Pie Graph: Each piece is a percentage of the total.

Bar Graph: Each bar represents the value or frequency of the particular item by height or length.

Pictogram: Pictures represent the data being described with each picture representing an amount or frequency.

Line graph: Each data point is connected by a line.

a	b	c	d	e	f
5	3	3	4	5	6
19%	12%	12%	15%	19%	23%

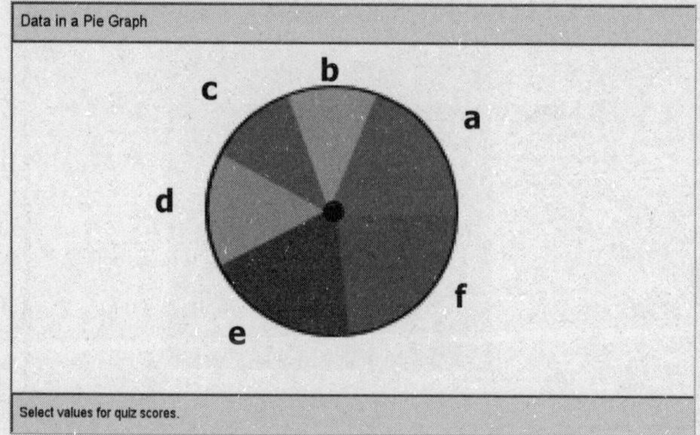

Which grade has the highest percentage?

Which has the lowest percentage?

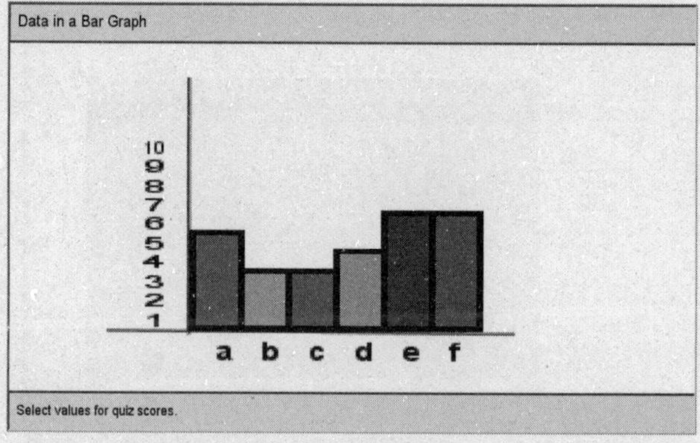

Which grade was received by the lowest number of students? Are there more students with lower grades than higher grades?

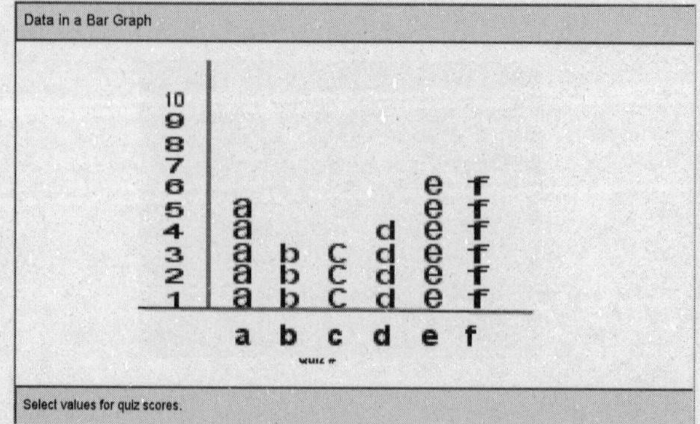

If you were the instructor, would you show this graph to your class?

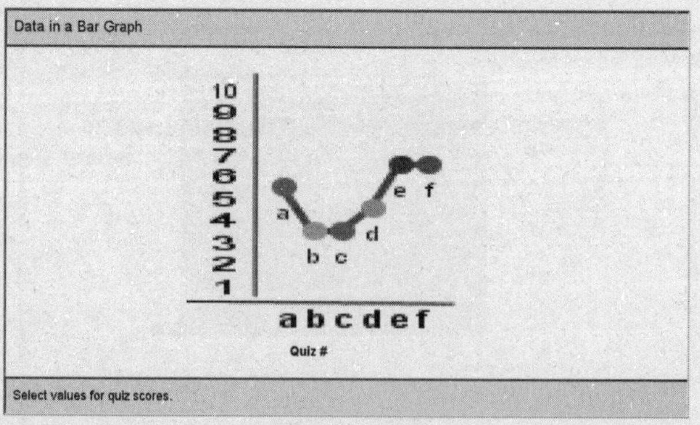

Line graphs show trends. Follow from one point to the next. What question would this graph suggest?

There are different forms of graphing data because there are different arguments that people want to make with that data. Graphs tell stories.

Change the entries in the table and watch each graph make a corresponding change. What stories about the grades on this quiz do these different graphs tell.

What is the difference between data presented in the pie graph and data in the other three graphs?

What picture would you choose for the pictogram of grades?

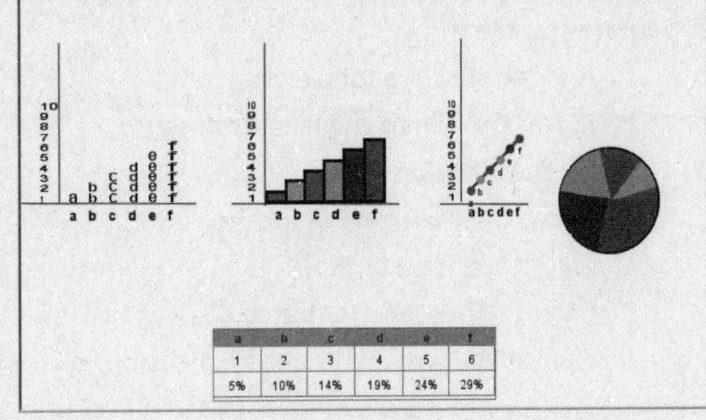

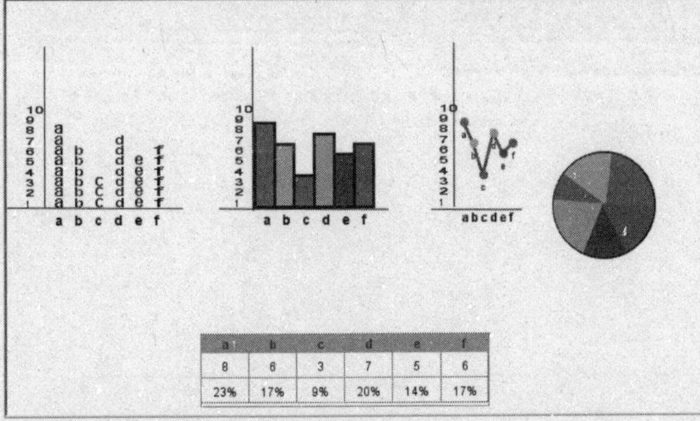

As the data change, the height of the corresponding picto-graph and bar graph change.

What changes in the pie graph?

How does the line graph change?

The **arithmetic mean** is another name for average. To find the mean add up the scores and divide by the number of scores. (The *number of scores* is indicated by the **n**.) Each score is an entry representing whatever is being added. It is always useful to think concretely about statistics and to think about the scores or values connected with activities you like.

The mean describes where the "center" of a set of data is located: the **central tendency** of a set data. The three measures of central tendency are **mean**, **median**, and **mode**. The mean is the most popular. Every average is a mean and it is calculated in the same way.

Calculate the Mean

1. Find the sum of a list of scores.
2. Divide the sum by the number of terms.

Frequency Distribution

1. Set up table columns as needed.
2. Enter each score.
3. Enter the frequency of the score.
4. Multiply the score times the frequency.

The Mean of a list of numbers.

35, 52, 73, 67, 3

$$35+52+73+67+3=230$$

$$\frac{(35+52+73+67+3)}{5}=\frac{(230)}{5}$$

$$\frac{(230)}{5}=\mathbf{46}$$

The Mean of the numbers is **46**

Add the numbers and divide by five. This example is dynamic. Change the numbers with the joystick.

The Mean of a list of numbers.

27, 12, 14, 22, 17

$$27+12+14+22+17=92$$

$$\frac{(27+12+14+22+17)}{5}=\frac{92}{5}$$

$$\frac{92}{5}=\mathbf{18}$$

18.4 is the Mean of the numbers.

Frequency Distribution

Answers on a questionaire are ranked 1 - 5. What is the mean score on the following question ? 12 chose 1; 15 chose 2; 8 chose 3; 7 chose 4; and 8 chose 5.

There are too many scores to add up individually. Remembering that multiplication is a shortened way to add repeated numbers leads to a **frequency** distribution table.

Frequency Distribution

Answers on a questionaire are ranked 1 - 5. What is the mean score on the following question ? 12 chose 1; 15 chose 2; 8 chose 3; 7 chose 4; and 8 chose 5.

a	b	c
Score	Frequency	Value
1	12	12
2	15	30
3	8	24
4	7	28
5	8	40
Total	50	134

Here each score is listed with the number of times it occurred—the frequency. Multiplying the score times the frequency gives the value of that particular score.

Frequency Distribution

Answers on a questionaire are ranked 1 - 5. What is the mean score on the following question ? 12 chose 1; 15 chose 2; 8 chose 3; 7 chose 4; and 8 chose 5.

a	b	c
Score	Frequency	Value
1	12	12
2	15	30
3	8	24
4	7	28
5	8	40
Total	50	134

Mean is usually symbolized by $\bar{x}$.

$\bar{x}$ = (Total Value)/(Total Frequency)

$\bar{x}$ = 134/50 = 2.68

To find the mean, divide the total value by the total frequency.

These visualizations show frequency distribution and mean. Scores can be distributed **normally** as they are in the top right picture called a bell shaped curve. The data spreads the same way on both sides of the mean. Data can also be **skewed** (stretched right or left).

Use the joystick to change the frequency of the scores in each bar. How does each change affect the mean? If more scores are added on the left of the mean, which direction does the mean move? Can a score be added left and right without changing the mean?

Where is the mean in a normal distribution?

Which score moves the mean the least?

Which score moves the mean most?

Does the value of the score affect the mean?

Is batting average a mean?

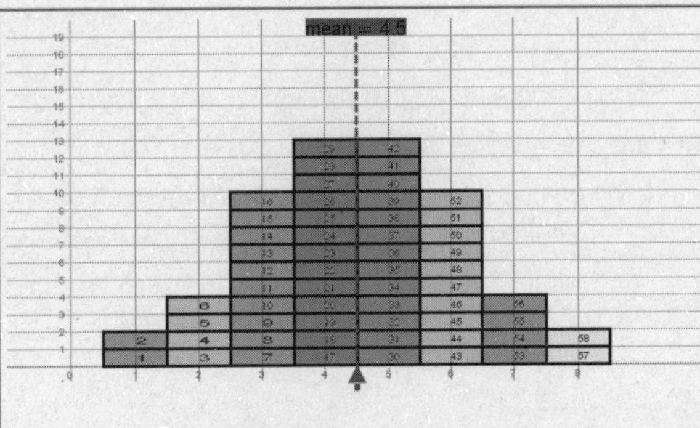

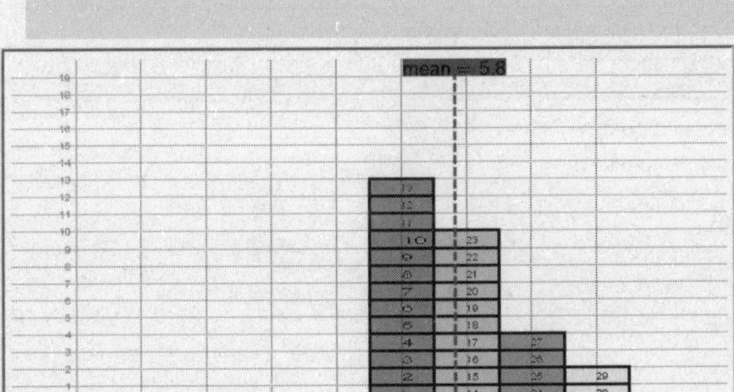

Here the data are skewed to the right. What could the above distribution represent?

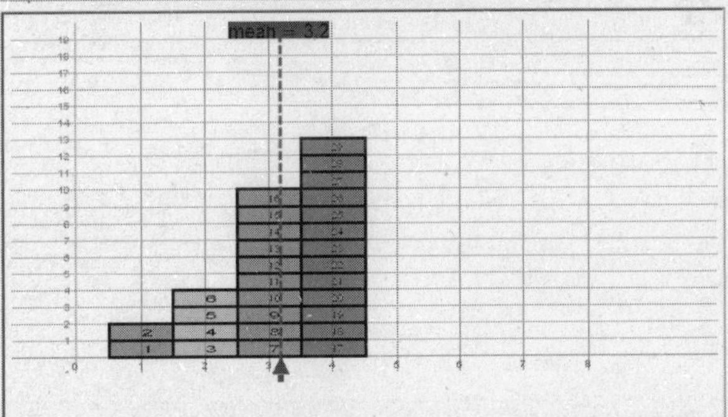

Data are skewed left. What would happen to the mean if you add data with a score of 8?

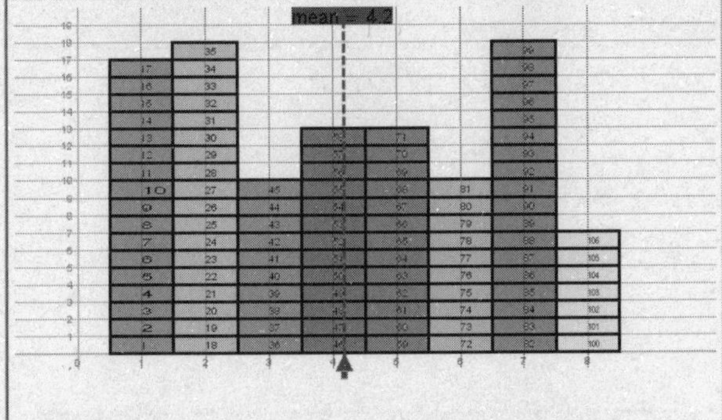

Neither normal nor skewed. How many scores are presented? Change the blue (4) stack. What happens to the mean as blue changes?

The **median** of a set of numbers (scores or values) is the middle number in the sequence, half of the scores will be above and half will be below.

You find the median by choosing the score that is in the middle, by ranking the scores from lowest to highest, completely independent of what the value is.

If there are an odd number of scores, the median is the middle score.

If there are an even number of scores, the median is the average of the two middle scores.

Find the Median

1. Sort numbers, lowest to highest.
2. Find the value at the (n + 1)/2 position.
3. If there is no middle value (there are an even number of values) take the average of the two middle values.

Note: ***n*** *is the number of scores in the data set.*

Median

27, 14, 12, 17, 22

Find the Median of the odd list of numbers.

Median

27, 14, 12, 17, 22
12, 14, 17, 22, 27

The middle number, 17 is the Median.

If there are an odd number of scores, sort the scores from lowest to highest...

Median

27, 14, 12, 17, 22
12, 14, 17, 22, 27
12, 14, (17), 22, 27

The middle number, 17 is the Median.

And the one in the middle is the median.

Median of an even number of numbers

27, 14, 12, 17, 22, 8
8, 12, 14, 17, 22, 27

The Median is 15.5

If there are an even number of scores, sort the scores from lowest to highest...

Median of an even number of numbers

27, 14, 12, 17, 22, 8
8, 12, 14, 17, 22, 27
8, 12, (14, 17), 22, 27

$$\text{Median} = \frac{(14+17)}{2}$$

$$\text{Median} = 15.5$$

The Median is 15.5

And take the average of the two middle scores to find the median.

To picture the median of a bar chart, imagine placing the bars horizontally end to end the way we have done below. The median is the value of the bar at the halfway point.

If there are an odd number of scores then the median is the middle score. If there are an even number of scores then the median is the average of the two middle scores.

How does the median change when we go from a normal distribution to a skewed distribution?

Why does having an even number of scores and having an odd number of scores make a difference in finding median?

Can you determine when to use mean and when to use median by the shape of the graph? Why do we use these two ways to show central tendency?

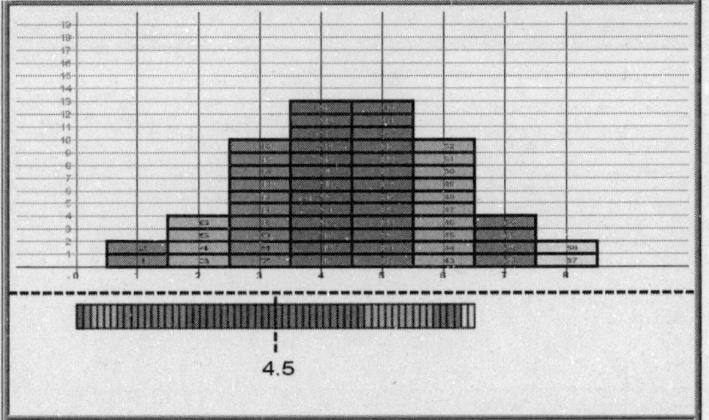

Since there is an even number of data values, this median is half way between the middle values, 4 and 5.

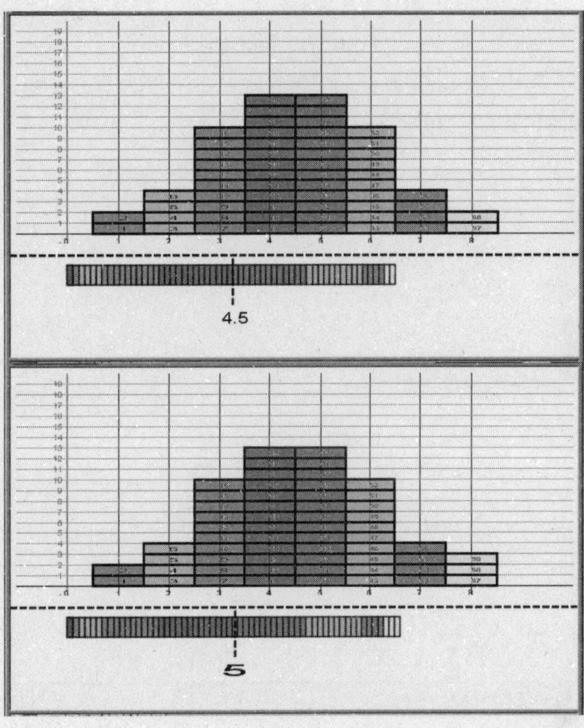

If you add another score at 8, what happens to the median?

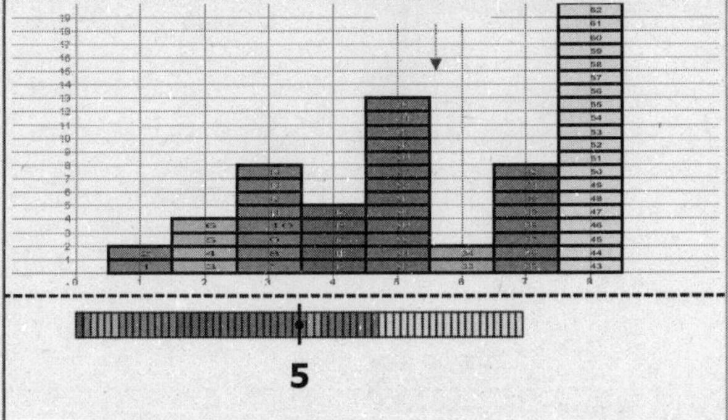

How much did the median move when you skewed the graph? Did it move as fast as the mean moved before?

Mode

Mode is simply the data value(s) that occurs most frequently in the set. Mode is not used as often as mean or median, but it can tell you something about what your data looks like. Some data and graphs do not have modes, while others have two (bimodal) or more modes.

Find the Mode

1. Arrange data in order from lowest to highest score.
2. Identify the score or scores that occur most frequently.

The single Mode of a list of numbers

27, 14, 12, 17, 22, 12, 8

Find the Mode of this list of numbers.

The single Mode of a list of numbers

27, 14, 12, 17, 22, 12, 8
8, 12, 12, 14, 17, 22, 27

The number listed most, 12, is the Mode.

Sort the data from lowest to highest.

The single Mode of a list of numbers

27, 14, 12, 17, 22, 12, 8
8, 12, 12, 14, 17, 22, 27
8, (12, 12), 14, 17, 22, 27

The number listed most, 12, is the Mode.

The mode is always one of the scores in the data set.

Multiple Modes of a list of numbers

27, 14, 12, 17, 22, 12, 8, 17
8, 12, 12, 14, 17, 17, 22, 27
8, (12, 12), 14, (17, 17), 22, 27

The numbers listed most, 12 and 17, are the Modes.

This data is bimodal because both 12 and 17 occur twice. Bimodal data often means that we can divide our data into two separate parts.

No Modes for a list of numbers

27, 14, 12, 17, 29, 32, 8, 5
5, 8, 12, 14, 17, 27, 29, 32
5, 8, 12, 14, 17, 27, 29, 32

No number is listed more than any other, there is no Mode.

No score appears more than once, this data has no mode.

On a bar graph the mode is the value(s) that has the most bars. We can find the mode of a graphed data set by inspection.

If a graph is bimodal, then it has two central tendencies and we often think of it as being made up of two groups of data.

Can you make a bar graph that is bimodal?

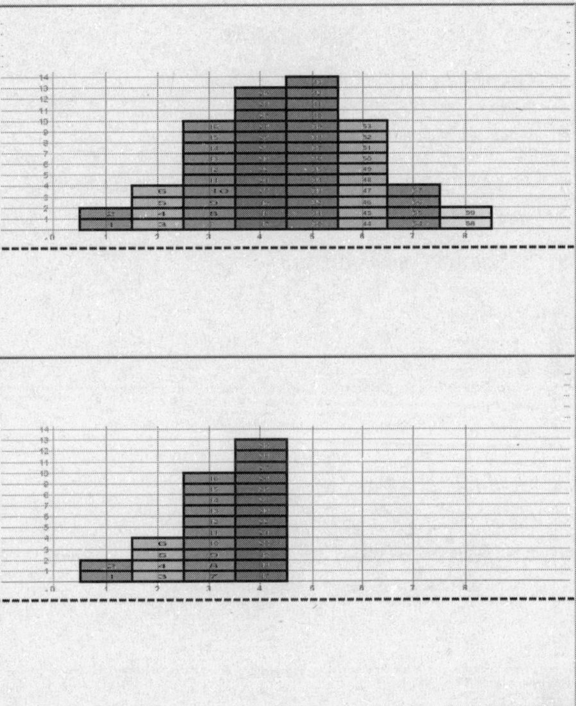

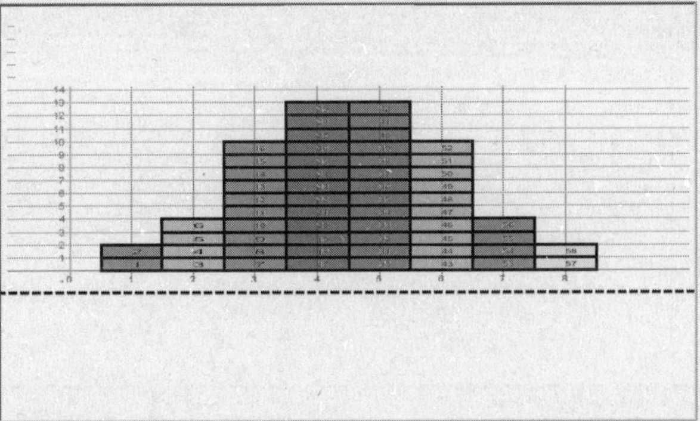

There are two modes, 4 and 5.

There is one mode, 4.

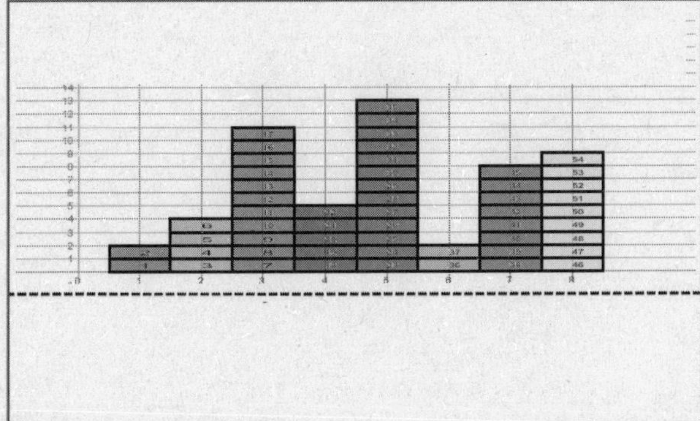

There is one mode, what is it?

What if you added 2 more scores to pink, how many modes would the graph have?

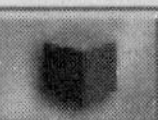

Histograms

EnableMath

In a bar graph, the height of each bar represents the value, score, or number of one item (like make of car). The bars on a bar graph need not touch each other.

In a **histogram**, each bar represents a range of data. The width of the bar has meaning. The height of the bar represents the frequency and the width of the bar represents the **range** or **interval**.

Like a bar graph, a histogram can be vertical or horizontal. The difference is the bars that represent data in a histogram always touch.

Histograms

- Determine the range of each bar.
- Each range must be the same.
- The height of the bar is frequency of occurrence within the range.
- Bars touch each other.

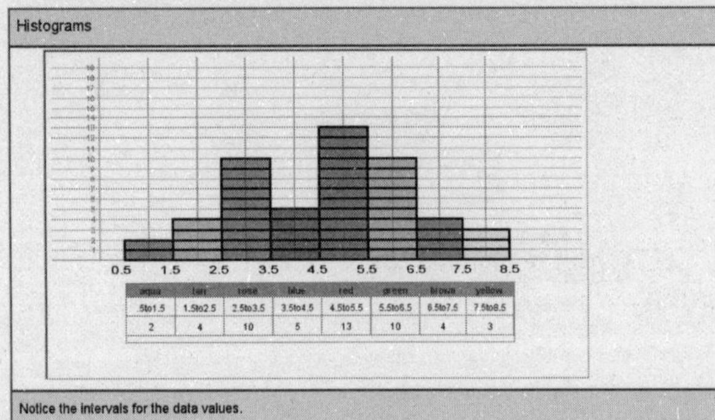

aqua	tan	rose	blue	red	green	brown	yellow
.5to1.5	1.5to2.5	2.5to3.5	3.5to4.5	4.5to5.5	5.5to6.5	6.5to7.5	7.5to8.5
2	4	10	5	13	10	4	3

What range has the greatest number of occurrences?

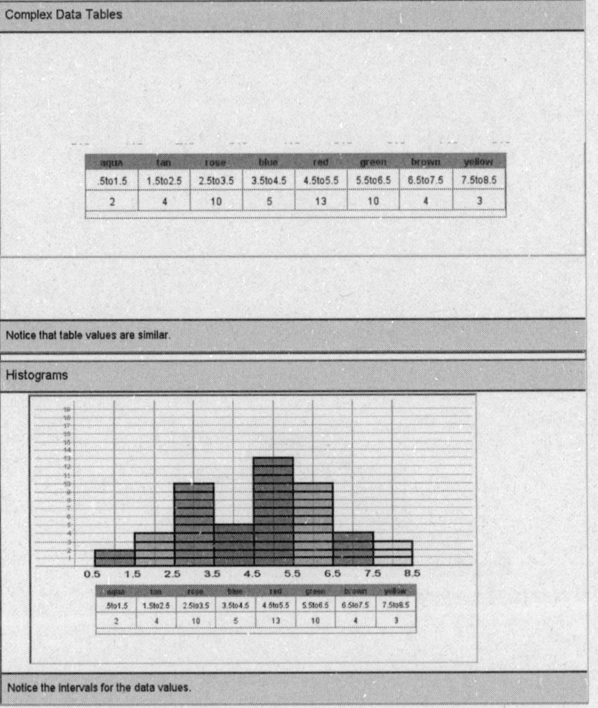

aqua	tan	rose	blue	red	green	brown	yellow
.5to1.5	1.5to2.5	2.5to3.5	3.5to4.5	4.5to5.5	5.5to6.5	6.5to7.5	7.5to8.5
2	4	10	5	13	10	4	3

What range has the least number of occurrences?

A bar graph shows the frequency of individual scores or data. A histogram shows the frequency of a range of scores or data. As you play with these histograms think of real data. For example, a bar graph could be used to show the number of games a team won. A histogram would be used to show the number of players that with batting averages between 300 and 310 or 310 and 320, etc.

What other kinds of data in the real world do we typically see as histograms?

What are the possible scores in each interval?

How does a histogram differ from a bar graph if the data aren't grouped into a range?

How does adding a score affect the intervals?

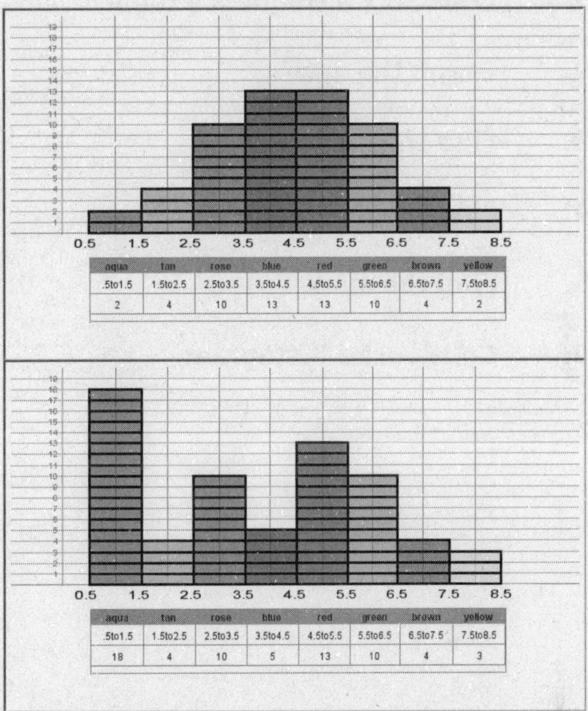

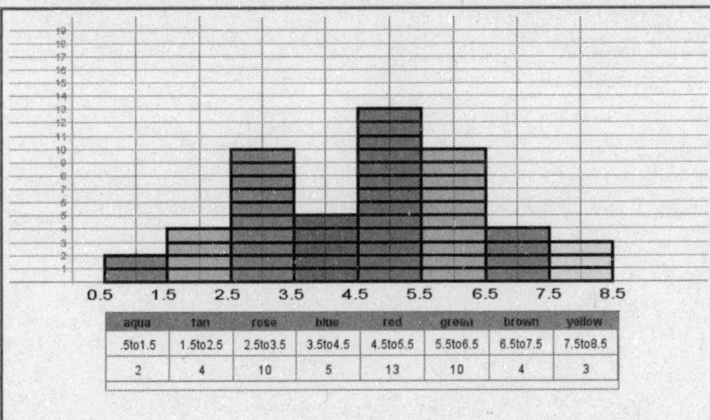

If you add a score of 3.7 to the data, which bar changes?

Could mode be a useful in describing the data above?

Answer the questions below from the information given. Use the following data.

12	14	13	12	15	11
12	13	15	14	11	12
14	11	13	11	12	15

1. **Construct a frequency table.**
2. **Graph the data .**
3. **Find the mean.**
4. **Find the median.**
5. **Find the mode.**
6. **Construct a histogram.**

6. The Real Numbers

In this module we do the arithmetic of the Real Numbers. The real numbers are built up from: the counting numbers, the whole numbers, the integers, the rationals, and the irrationals. As you go through these lessons think about how the operations on each of these sets of numbers are the same and are different from each other.

Most of the visualizations that will be key to your understanding of algebra are introduced in this module. Play with them until you understand their patterns.

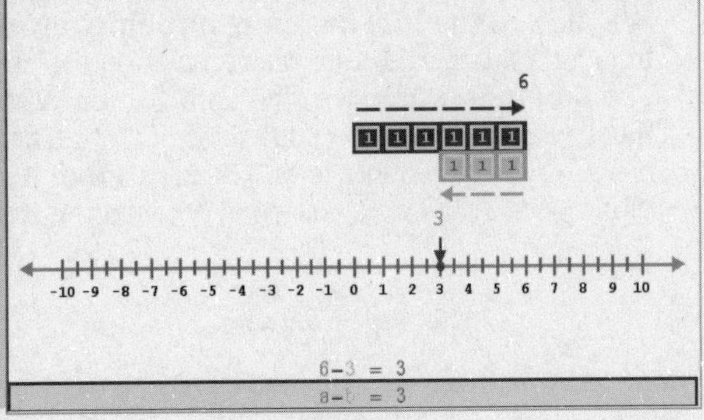

The Real Numbers

EnableMath

We have grouped the numbers we use into collections or sets so that we can see their patterns and define their properties. There are 5 sets of numbers that make up what we call the **Real Numbers.**

We picture the real numbers as points on a line. This is a critical visualization. Each time you think of a number, picture it as a point on the number line. The number line has 0 in the middle. The **Counting Numbers** start with 1. The **Whole Numbers** start with 0. The **Integers** are these whole numbers on both sides of 0 stretching both right and left. The **Rational Numbers** are all ratios of two integers. The **Irrational Numbers** are those that can't be made from a ratio of integers. The entire collection is called the **Real Numbers**.

The Real Numbers

Counting numbers	{1,2,3,4,5,6,...}
Whole numbers	{0,1,2,3,4,...}
Integers	{...-3,-2,-1,0,1,2,3 ...}
Rational numbers	numbers formed by the division of 2 integers.
Irrational numbers	numbers that are not rational like π, $\sqrt{2}$

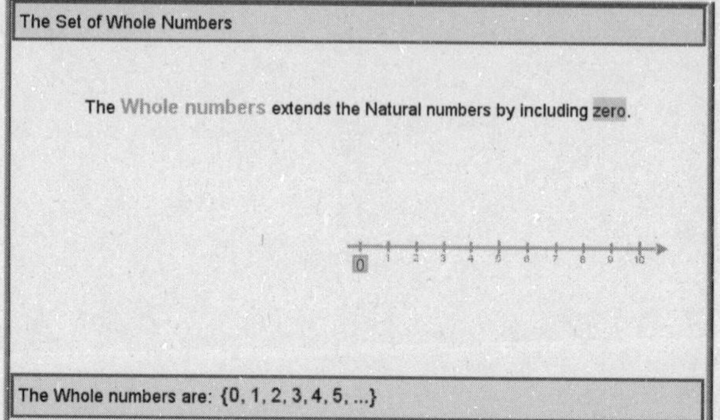

The Set of Whole Numbers
The Whole numbers extends the Natural numbers by including zero.
0 1 2 3 4 5 6 7 8 9 10
The Whole numbers are: {0, 1, 2, 3, 4, 5, ...}

The Whole Numbers include 0 and the counting numbers.

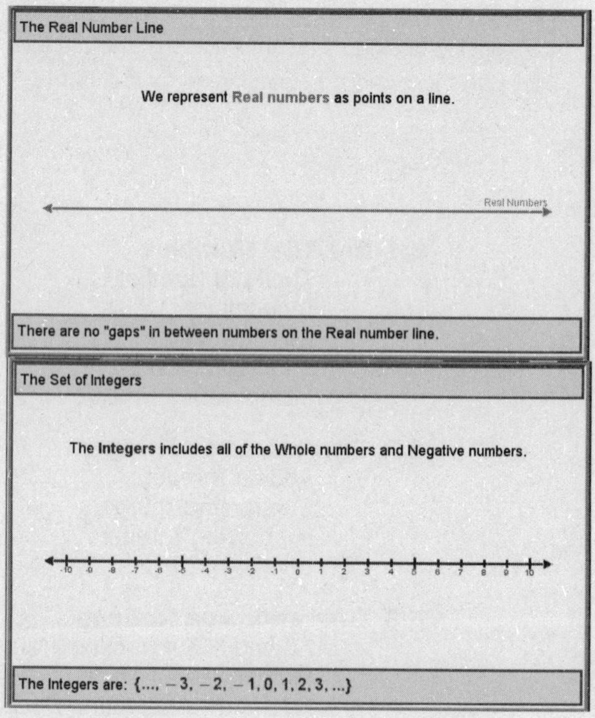

The Real Number Line
We represent Real numbers as points on a line.
Real Numbers
There are no "gaps" in between numbers on the Real number line.
The Set of Integers
The Integers includes all of the Whole numbers and Negative numbers.
-10 -9 -8 -7 -6 -5 -4 -3 -2 -1 0 1 2 3 4 5 6 7 8 9 10
The Integers are: {..., −3, −2, −1, 0, 1, 2, 3, ...}

The Integers include both the positive and the negative "whole" numbers.

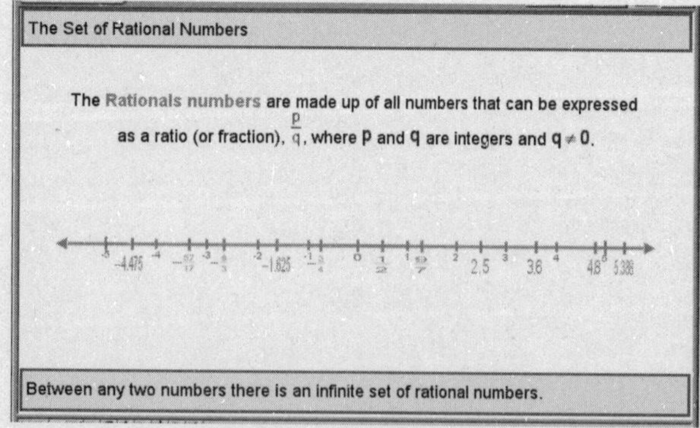

The Set of Rational Numbers
The Rationals numbers are made up of all numbers that can be expressed as a ratio (or fraction), p/q, where p and q are integers and q ≠ 0.
Between any two numbers there is an infinite set of rational numbers.

The Rational Numbers include every number that can be made dividing 2 integers so long as the denominator does not equal 0.

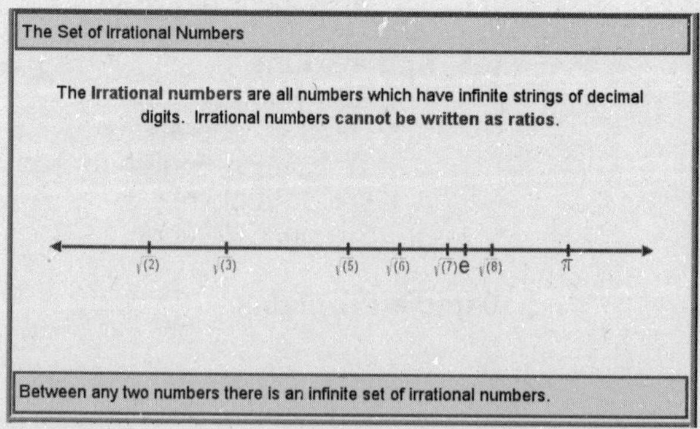

The Set of Irrational Numbers
The Irrational numbers are all numbers which have infinite strings of decimal digits. Irrational numbers cannot be written as ratios.
√(2) √(3) √(5) √(6) √(7) e √(8) π
Between any two numbers there is an infinite set of irrational numbers.

The Irrational Numbers are all the numbers that cannot be made by dividing 2 integers. These are numbers like π, $\sqrt{2}$.

Since you can multiply these irrational numbers by every rational number there are more of them that the rationals.

Picture two numbers like 1 and 2 on a number line. Now picture putting a number halfway between them. Now picture putting another number half way between that 1/2 and 2. You can keep going like this forever. For every two points on a number line you can find a point half way between them. So not only is it important for you to picture the numbers you use on a number line, it is important for you to recognize that you can always find more numbers between any two numbers on the line. As you are introduced to the different sets of numbers in this module, keep in mind where they fit on the number line and the numbers on the line that lie between them.

On this number line we can change the "scale" so that we can see more and more of the numbers between these numbers. No matter how powerful your magnifying glass may be, you will always see more numbers.

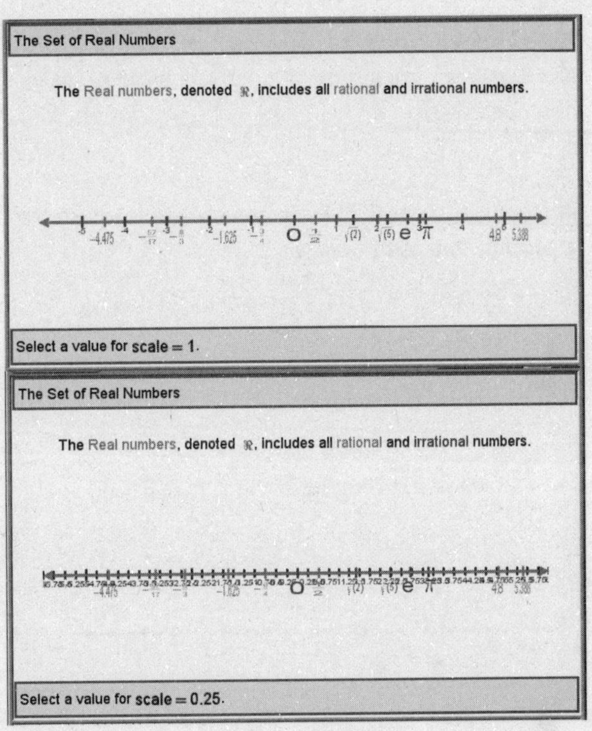

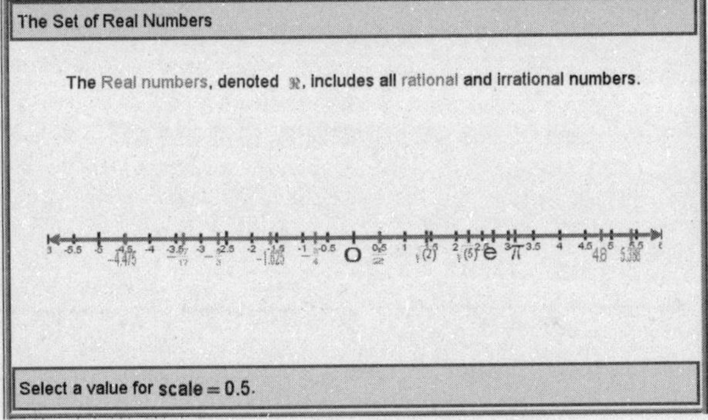

What is happening as you make the scale finer?

What is happening as you make the scale even finer?

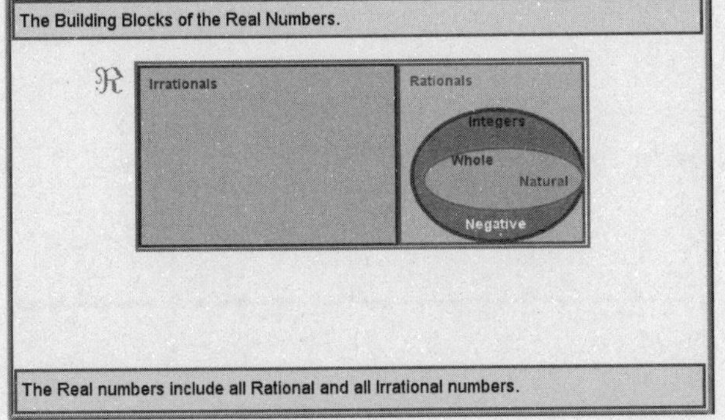

Another way to visualize the real numbers is to think of them as shapes laid over each other. The integers include the whole numbers, the rationals include the integers, and the Reals include the rationals and irrationals.

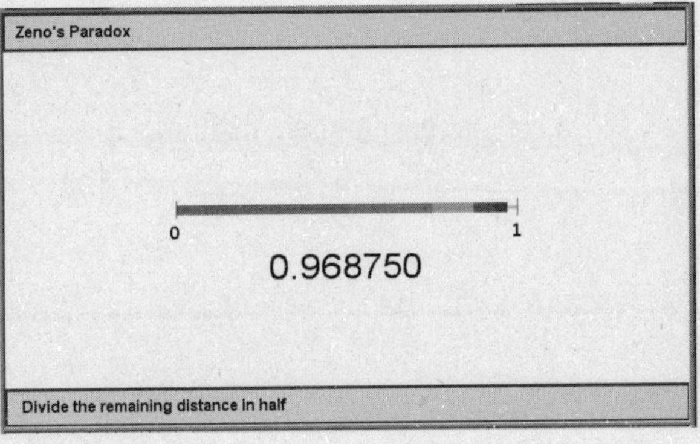

Zeno's Paradox: If you start at 0 and go half way to one with each step. Will you ever get there? Are there an infinity of numbers between 0 and 1?

Given two numbers, **a** and **b**, there are only three possible relationships between the numbers:

Either: **a** is equal to **b** — **a = b**
a is greater than **b** — **a > b**
a is less than **b** — **a < b**

When variables are introduced, a few more relationship symbols are needed:

a does not equal **b** — **a ≠ b**
a is greater than or equal to **b** — **a ≥ b**
a is less than or equal to **b** — **a ≤ b**

The examples presented show what *number line graphs* look like when using some of the relationship symbols described above.

Another way to think of the graph at right is to use the inequality statement **a < 4**.

All numbers to the *left* of **4** are included.

Graph on a number line:

all of the real numbers that are < 4

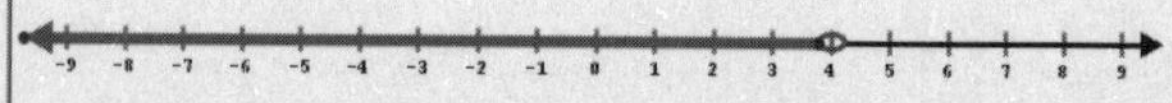

-9 -8 -7 -6 -5 -4 -3 -2 -1 0 1 2 3 4 5 6 7 8 9

Graph on a number line:

all of the real numbers that are ≤ 4

-9 -8 -7 -6 -5 -4 -3 -2 -1 0 1 2 3 4 5 6 7 8 9

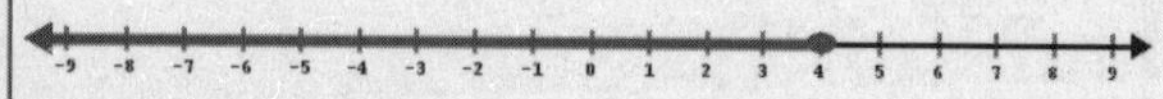

Notice that the graph above uses ≤ and that the circle over 4 is shaded indicating that 4 is included. A inequality statement for the above graph is **a≤ 4.**

Graph on a number line:

all of the real numbers that are > 3

-9 -8 -7 -6 -5 -4 -3 -2 -1 0 1 2 3 4 5 6 7 8 9

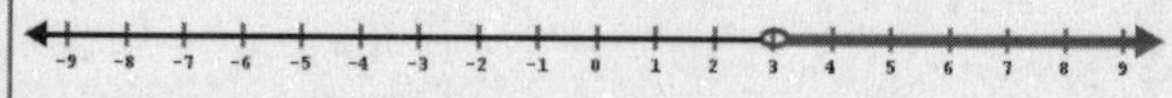

3 is not included. All numbers to the *right* of three are included.

Graph on a number line:

all of the real numbers that are ≥ 3

-9 -8 -7 -6 -5 -4 -3 -2 -1 0 1 2 3 4 5 6 7 8 9

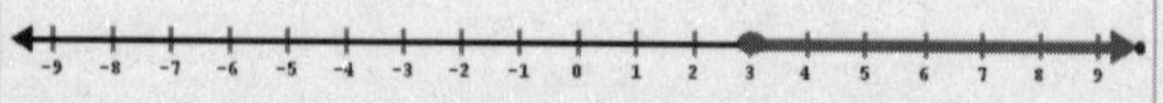

3 is included. Notice that the graph is shaded in the *direction of the inequality symbol.* Will this always be the case?

Graph on a number line:

all of the real numbers that are ≥ 3

-9 -8 -7 -6 -5 -4 -3 -2 -1 0 1 2 3 4 5 6 7 8 9

Two expressions describe the above graph: **a≥3** and **3≤a.**

Relationships between numbers are easy to visualize on a number line. Numbers to the left get smaller; numbers to the right get bigger. Given any two numbers, **a** and **b,** located on a number line, the larger number is located to the right of the smaller number. Conversely, the number to the left is smaller. Some like to think **left** stands for **less than**. Do two statements **a> b** and **b < a** mean the same thing? If **a** is to the right of **b** on the number line, is a>b or is b<a?

Use the joystick to input any **b** and **a** values, from –10 to 10.

What happens as point **b** changes its relationship to point **a**? What would you expect the relationship symbol to do as **a** meets **b** and then moves to the right?

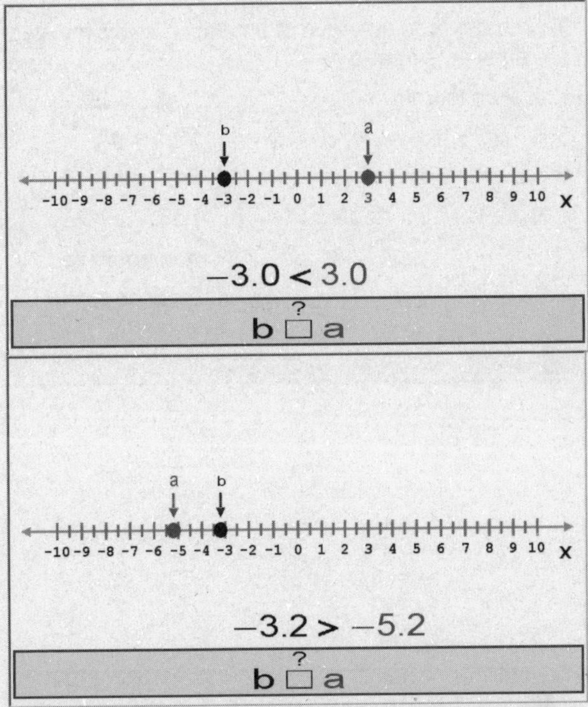

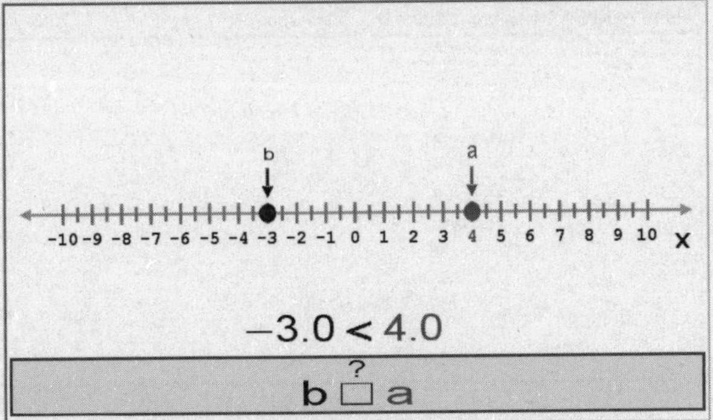

Does this also represent a picture of **4.0>-3.0**? Can any inequality statement be written in two ways?

Given **b= -3.2** and **a= -5.2**, what two inequality statements can be made? Notice that the format of answers will always be presented as **b? a**. We will revisit this when studying, solving, and graphing inequalities.

Absolute Value

EnableMath

Finding the Absolute Value, $|a|$, of a number always returns a positive number or zero. **Absolute value represents the distance on the number line from 0 to the number.** The absolute value symbol is two parallel lines with a number, variable, or expression inside: $|x + a|$.

In the order of operations, simplify the expression within the absolute value symbols on the same level as for parentheses.

To find the absolute value of a number, count how far the number is from zero.

-2 is 2 units from zero so **$|-2| = 2$**

3 is 3 units from zero so **$|3| = 3$**

0 is 0 units from zero so **$|0| = 0$**

a is **a** units from zero so **$|a| = a$ if a is positive or $-a$ if a is negative.**

What happens when you change the value of a?

$|-5| = 5$

|a|

Point 2: Is dynamic. Enter any value for **a** and see the absolute value displayed.

Absolute value is the distance a number is from 0.

Absolute value is always ≥ 0 because it's a distance.

$|3| = 3$

$|-2| = 2$

$|0| = 0$

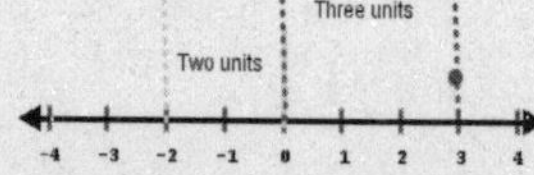

What happens when you change the value of a?

$|-5| = 5$

|a|

Notice that the absolute value of –5 is **$-(-5) = 5$.**

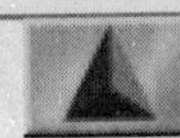

Think of absolute value of a number, **I a I**, as the distance the number is from zero on a number line. These distances from zero are the absolute value of the number, regardless of sign.

Picture a number line with integers as units. Are that 2 and –2 are the same distance from zero? Are 17 and –17? 25 and – 25? Use the joystick to change the value of **a** to find the absolute value by determining the distance a number is from zero on the number line.

Does every real number have an absolute value?

If the absolute value of a negative number is positive, is the absolute value of a positive number negative?

Use the joystick to enter positive and negative numbers to test your answer.

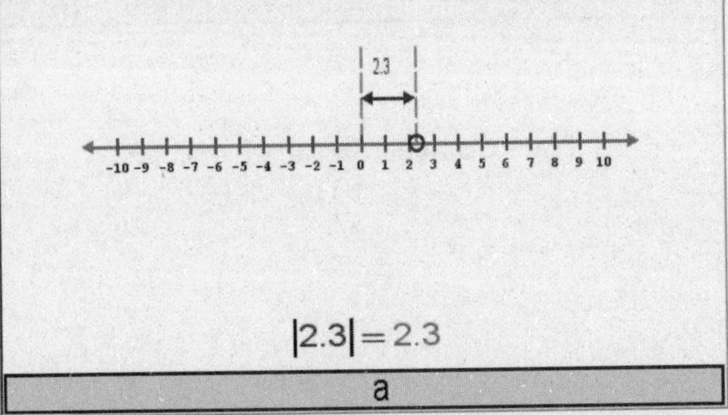

Use the joystick to enter different values for **a**.

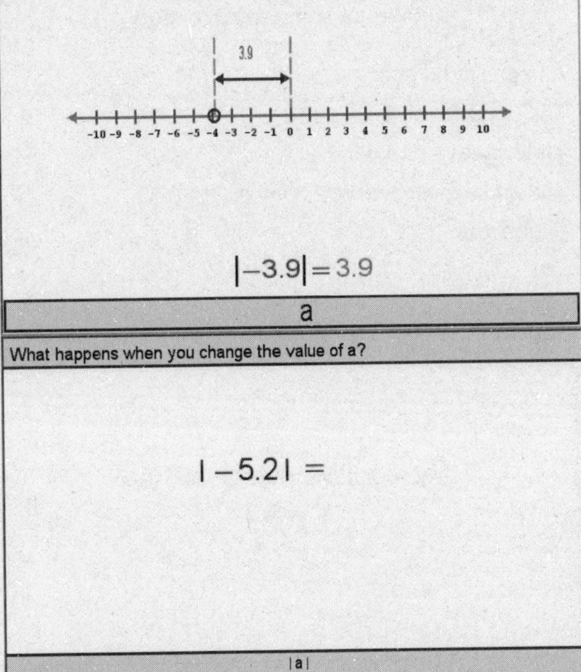

Find the absolute value of **–5.2**. Can it be written in the form of **–(–5.2)**?

Additive Inverse

Zero is called the **additive identity** because adding zero to a number does not change the number. If two numbers add to zero, then the two numbers are called **additive inverses** of each other.

Symbolically: **$a + (-a) = 0$**.

The **additive inverse** of a number is also called the **opposite** of the number because it is the same distance from zero, but in the *opposite direction*. Opposite numbers can also be described as negatives of each other. Therefore, a number and its negative are additive inverses. Informally, opposite and negative can be used interchangeably.

Uses of the negative sign

A negative number	**-3**
The opposite of a number	**- (-3)**
The negative of a number	**- (-3)**
The additive inverse of a number	**- (-3)**
Subtraction	**5 - (-3)**

The additive inverse or opposite of a number is the negative of that number.
The additive inverse of 2 is -2.
The additive inverse of -3 is $-(-3) = 3$.

A negative negative is a positive.

The additive inverse of 6 is:
-6

The additive inverse of -10 is:
$-(-10) = 10$

Point 2: This point is dynamic, enter values from 1 to 10. All the numbers are positive therefore all the answers are negative.

Point 3: Shown in symbols, additive inverse is written as "the negative of", or "opposite of," or as subtraction. Test values from –1 to –10.

Visualize a number line folded at zero so that each number on the positive side of the number line matches up with its counterpart on the negative side. The matches are **opposites** of each other. We say a number and its opposite are **additive inverses** because they add to zero.

Additive inverses can be visualized with number bars as well as on the number line. Make a number bar of any given length. The additive inverse is shown by counting how many number bars of opposite value are required to "get back" to zero.

If **a >0**, will the additive inverse always be a *negative* number?

If **a<0** will the additive inverse always be a *positive* number?

If **a>0** then **-(a)=-a** and if **a<0** then **-(a) = ?**

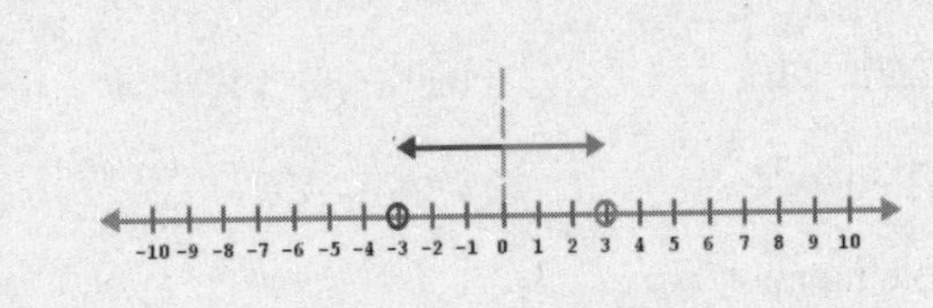

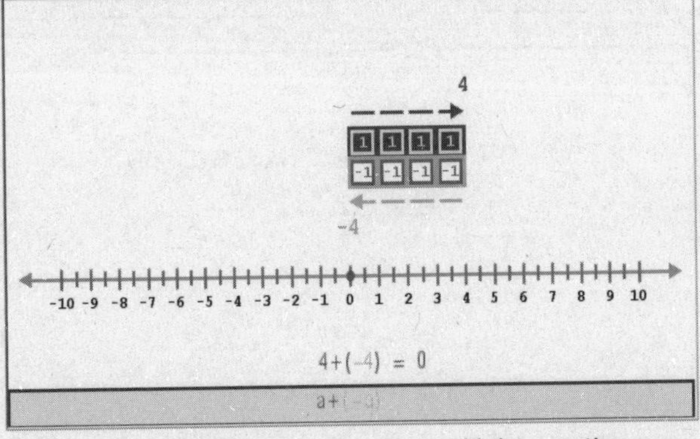

Given a 4 unit number bar, how long would the negative number bar be to get back to 0? Use the joystick to check positive and negative values.

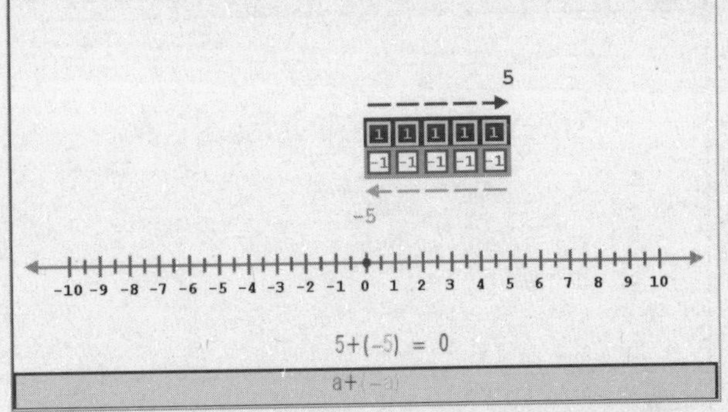

Here the integer 5 (top bar) is 5 units from zero. To get "back" to zero, we need a 5 unit number bar in the negative direction.

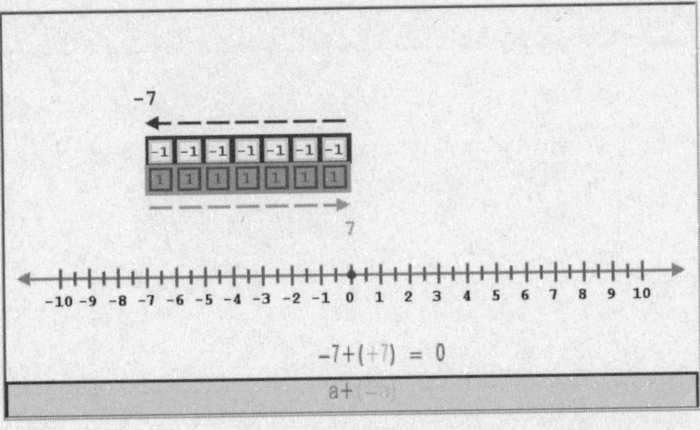

This top bar is negative, so look for positive units to get back to zero.

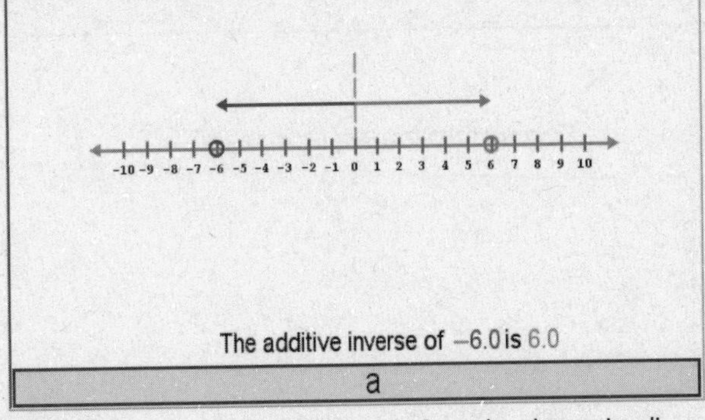

What two statements could be made from the above visualization?

Multiplicative Inverse

EnableMath

A number and its **multiplicative inverse** multiply to equal **1**. The number **1** is the identity for multiplication.

In symbols: $a \cdot \frac{1}{a} = \frac{a}{a} = 1$

The **multiplicative inverse** of a number is also called its **reciprocal**. For any fraction **a/b** the multiplicative inverse or reciprocal is **b/a**. Simply invert (flip) the denominator and numerator. For whole numbers, rewrite with a denominator of 1 and then flip it.

Number Form	Multiplicative Inverse
Fraction a/b	b/a
Whole number a	1/a
Negative fraction -a/b	-b/a
Irrational number π	$1/\pi$

The multiplicative inverse of a number is the reciprocal of that number.

The multiplicative inverse of $\frac{2}{3}$ is $\frac{3}{2}$.

The multiplicative inverse of $\frac{-5}{2}$ is $\frac{2}{-5}$.

The multiplicative inverse of 3 or $\frac{3}{1}$ is $\frac{1}{3}$.

The multiplicative inverse of $\frac{6}{7}$ is:

$\frac{7}{6}$

Point 2: To find the multiplicative inverse of fractions switch the numerator with the denominator.

Points 2—5 are dynamic—change the values for **a** or **b**.

The multiplicative inverse of $\frac{7}{4}$ is:

$\frac{4}{7}$

Notice that the fraction above is an improper fraction. Change mixed numbers to improper fractions before finding the multiplicative inverse.

The multiplicative inverse of -8 is:

$\frac{1}{-8}$

Point 5: Whole numbers can always be written as fractions by making the denominator 1. Invert to find the reciprocal.

When you multiply a number by its multiplicative inverse, you always get 1.

$\frac{-2}{3} * \frac{3}{-2} = 1$

Just as adding a number and it's additive inverse resulted in the additive identity, multiplying a number and it's multiplicative inverse results in the multiplicative identity, 1.

Multiplication can be visualized as a rectangle. The sides of the rectangle are the **factors**. In the case of finding the product of multiplicative inverses, the area of the rectangle is always **1**.

The models depicted here are limited to **a** and **1/a** for ease of visualization for –5 through 5. Use your imagination to extend the images to include other common fractions.

As **a** gets larger, what happens to **1/a**? What happens to the shape of the area?

Can you reverse the process? If you start with 1/a, what is the multiplicative inverse?

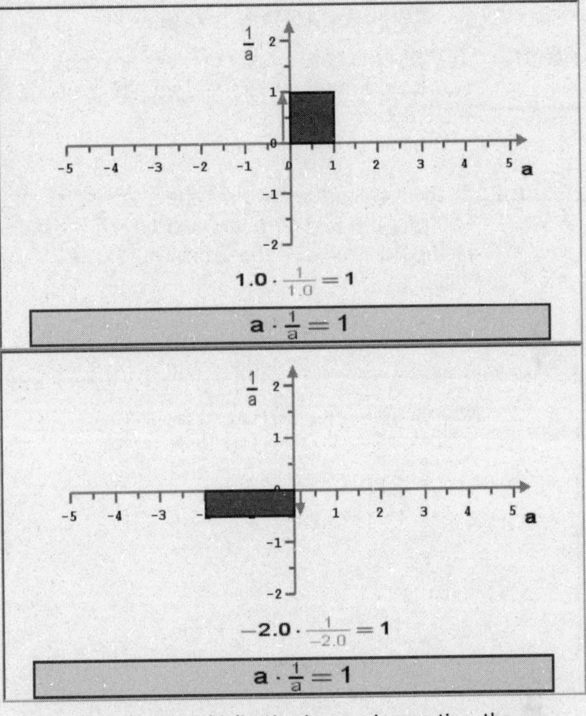

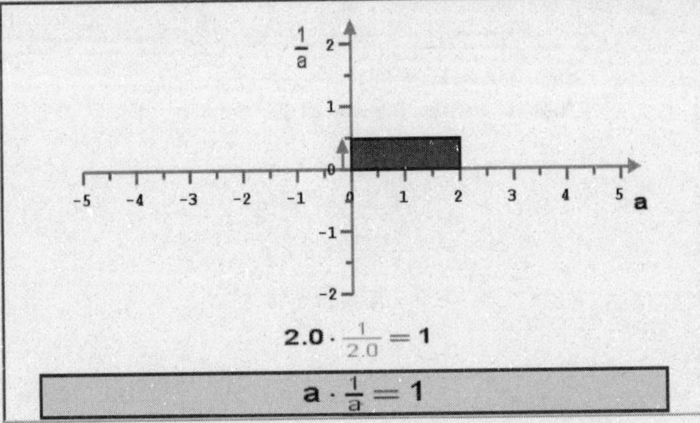

2 and 1/2 are reciprocals therefore their product is 1.

Notice that if one multiplicative inverse is negative, the other one is also negative.

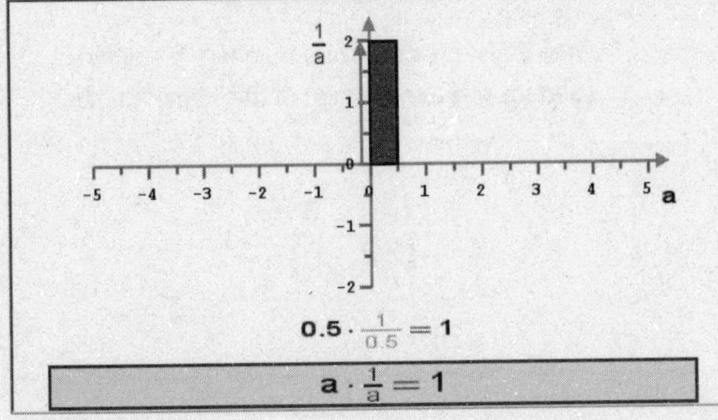

Rewrite 0.5 as 1/2. What is 1/0.5?

Adding Integers

EnableMath

The **integers** are made up of the whole numbers, their opposites, and zero. Integers are sometimes called **signed numbers** because of the use of + or – to denote whether they are positive or negative. Numbers added together are called **addends** or **terms**, and the answer is called the **sum** or **total**.

Negative numbers will always be preceded by a **–** sign. Positive numbers will usually not use **+** unless there is some chance of ambiguity. A number without a sign will *always* be assumed to be positive.

*If you see two signs together, an operator and a + or – to indicate positive or negative numbers, the symbol **closest** to the number indicates its sign.*

Rules for Adding Integers

Rule 1: If the signs of the two numbers are the same, add the numbers and attach the common sign to the sum.

Rule 2: If the signs of the two numbers are different, subtract the two numbers and attach the sign of the number with the largest absolute value.

Add:

When the signs of the two numbers are the same, add and keep the sign of the numbers.

$$-14+(-25)$$
$$-(14+25)$$
$$-39$$

The answer is negative. a + b

Add:

When the signs of the two numbers are different, subtract and use the sign of the 'larger' number.

$$33+(-8)$$

The signs are different. a + b

The "larger" number really means the number with the larger absolute value.

Add:

When the signs of the two numbers are different, subtract and use the sign of the 'larger' number.

$$17+(-32)$$
$$-(32-17)$$
$$-15$$

The answer is negative. a + b

Subtract and use the sign of the larger absolute value. The larger number is 17 BUT the larger absolute value is 32.

Add:

When the signs of the two numbers are different, subtract and use the sign of the 'larger' number.

$$-20+37$$
$$(37-20)$$
$$17$$

The answer is positive. a + b

Which has the larger absolute value: -20 or 37? Use the joystick to try other combinations by changing **a** and **b**.

Add:

When the signs of the two numbers are different, subtract and use the sign of the 'larger' number.

$$-30+6$$
$$-(30-6)$$
$$-24$$

The answer is negative. a + b

The answer is negative because $|-30|>|6|$.

Adding two integers can be visualized by attaching number bars together and measuring their sum on the number line. Positive integers form to the right, one block per unit; negative numbers form to the left, one block per unit. Begin each sum at zero.

Does order matter when adding integers?

How do the rules fit with the bars? Look at the models below. Can you describe the models using the rules for adding integers?

How do you check to see if you have found the correct answer to an addition problem?

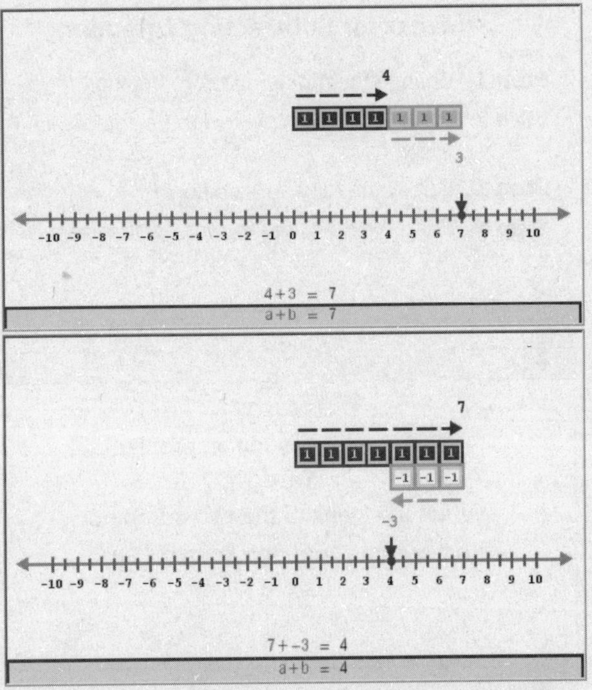

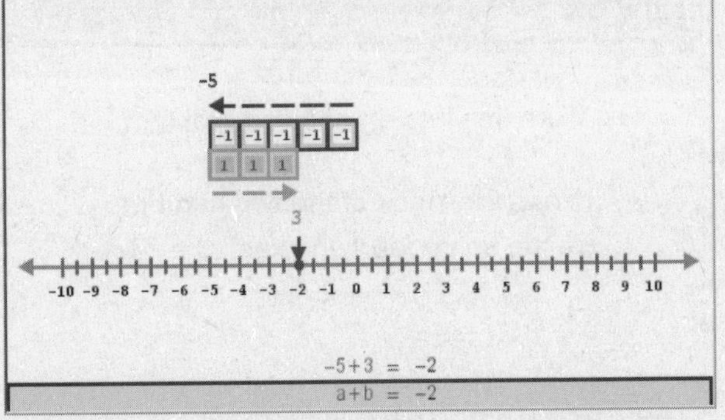

Notice above, the –5 arrow points to the left. At the head of the arrow +3 points back to the right. By the rule: 5 – 3 = 2 and are there more negative blocks than positive blocks?

Here is the case where the signs are different but the largest absolute value is positive. Do you see why we can say "... attach the sign of the 'larger' number "?

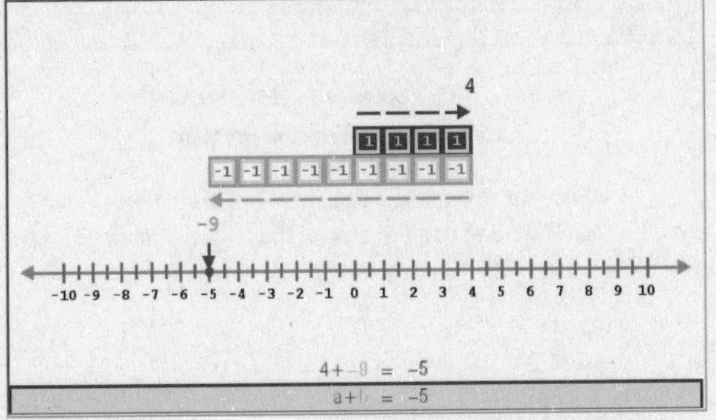

Begin with a positive number and add a negative number. Is the negative number larger or smaller? Is the **absolute value** of the negative number larger or smaller?

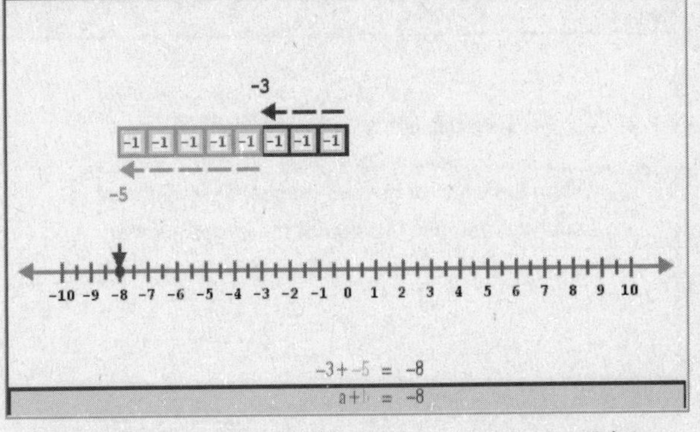

Two negative numbers added together. Use the joystick to add any combination of integers from –10 to 10.

Subtracting Integers

EnableMath

Addition and subtraction are **inverse processes**. Look back at the concept visualizations for addition. Adding a positive integer with a negative integer looked exactly like subtraction. From that idea we can define subtraction as *adding the additive inverse of the second term to the first term.*

Remember that the sign of the integer is immediately to the left of the number. If it isn't clear from the problem, try rewriting it using parentheses around each integer with its sign.

The answer to subtraction is called the **difference**. Some terms indicating subtraction are: *Adding the opposite, minus, take away, less than.*

Process for Subtracting Integers

Step 1: Change the problem sign to addition.

Step 2: Change the second term to its additive inverse.

Step 3: Follow the rules for addition.

Step 4: Check your answer for arithmetic errors.

Subtract:

$a - b$

Turn this into an addition problem.

$= a + (-b)$

Follow the rules for adding integers.

a–b

Subtract:

$-14 - 27$

Turn this into an addition problem.

$= -14 + -27$

When the signs of the two numbers are the same, add and keep the sign.

$= -41$

a–b

Point 1: The additive inverse of 27 is –27. Check in the original problem: –14 – 27 = – 41. Does –41 + 27 = –14?

Subtract:

$21 - (-12)$

Turn this into an addition problem.

$= 21 + 12$

When the signs of the two numbers are the same, add and keep the sign.

$= 33$

a–b

Point 2: Notice the additive inverse of –12 is 12.

Subtract:

$24 - 31$

Turn this into an addition problem.

$= 24 + -31$

When the signs of the two numbers are different, subtract and use the sign of the larger number.

$= -7$

a–b

Point 3: A positive number *take away* a larger positive number yields a negative number.

Subtract:

$-13 - (-11)$

Turn this into an addition problem.

$= -13 + 11$

When the signs of the two numbers are different, subtract and use the sign of the larger number.

$= -2$

a–b

Point 4: Subtracting a negative number from a negative number. Use the joystick to create other examples.

Subtraction is visualized in the same way as for addition. Picture two number bars, arrow to the right for positive, arrow left for negative. Instead of attaching unit bars to the right for addition of a positive number, attach them in the *opposite direction,* ***left,*** to indicate subtraction. Similarly, if subtracting a negative integer, attach it to the ***right*** *as if adding a positive integer*.

Use the joystick to explore other examples and watch what happens as the bars move through positive an negative values for **a** and **b**.

Is the idea of "taking away" 3 of the 6 bars presented at right?

Can you "take away" a negative number from a negative number?

Can you subtract a negative number from zero?

How are the visualizations different from the visuals for addition?

Does order matter when subtracting integers?

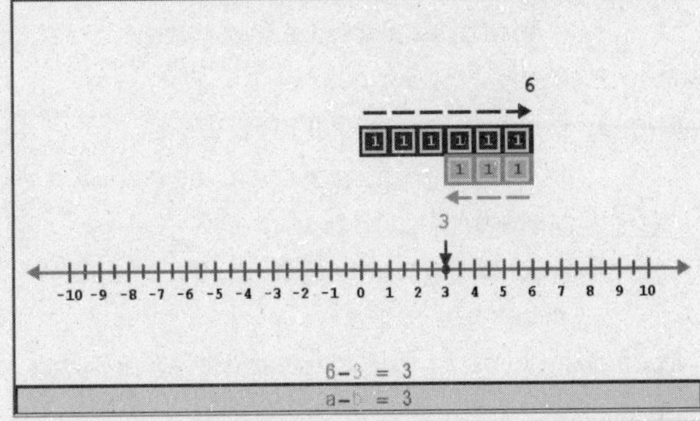

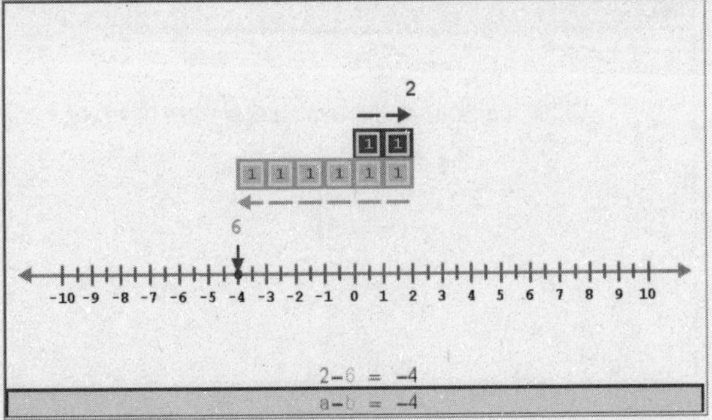

How would you rewrite this problem as an addition problem? How would you check this answer?

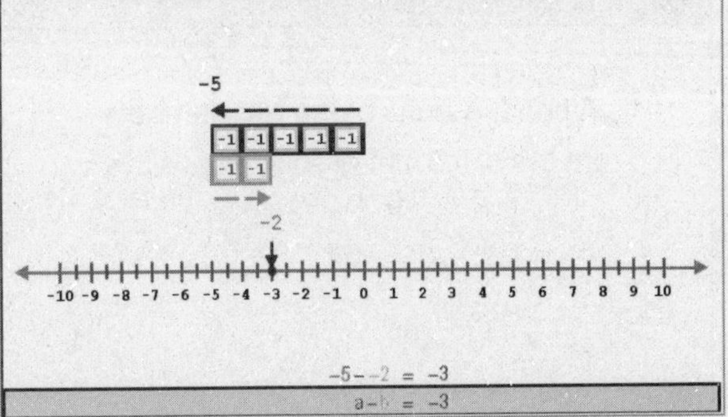

Notice that subtracting a negative results in adding a positive. Show this problem in symbols.

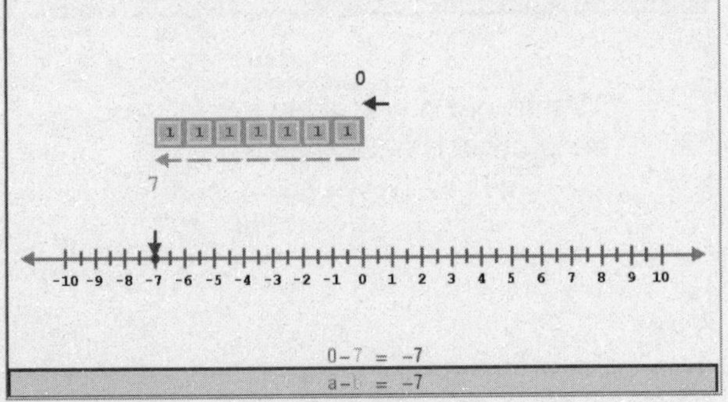

Can you subtract a positive number from zero?

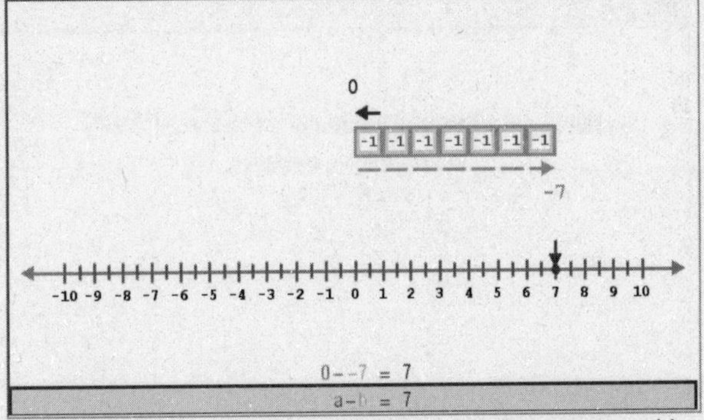

If you subtract a negative from zero, is that the same as adding a number to zero? Think of a real world example of how this might work.

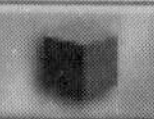

Multiplying Integers

Multiplication of integers is a two-step process. First, multiply the numbers normally. Then determine the sign by the rules given below.

The answer to multiplication is called the **product**. The numbers being multiplied are called **factors** or multipliers.

The product of **a** times **b** will be shown with either a raised dot, **a•b**, or an asterisk, **a*b**. Sometimes there may be confusion about seeing two signs together. Rewrite using parentheses. Remember that the sign of the number is the sign to its immediate left.

Multiplication of Integers

Step 1: Multiply the two numbers.

Step 2: Determine the sign of the product.

a. If the signs are the same, the product is positive.

B. If the signs are opposites, the product is negative.

Quick answer check : *Divide product by either factor.*

Multiply:

When the signs of the two numbers are the same, the product is positive.

$9 \cdot 8$

$= 72$

a·b

Multiply:

When the signs of the two numbers are the same, the product is positive.

$-6 \cdot (-9)$

$= 54$

a·b

Point 2: Negative factors yield positive products. Quick check: 54/(-9) = -6 or 54/(-6) = -9.

Multiply:

When the signs of the two numbers are different, the product is negative.

$3 \cdot (-5)$

$= -15$

a·b

Point 3: Signs are not the same, therefore, the product is negative.

Multiply:

When the signs of the two numbers are different, the product is negative.

$-6 \cdot 7$

$= -42$

a·b

Point 4: Different signs for the factors result in a negative answer. What happens if there are *more than two* factors?

Multiply:

When zero is one of the two factors the product is always zero.

$8 \cdot 0$

$= 0$

a·b

Don't forget: Multiplication by zero is always zero.

Multiplication can be visualized by using a rectangle imposed on a grid. The grid is divided into four sections called **quadrants**. Factors are unit bars located to the side and below the grid. The product is found by counting up the number bars that form the rectangle in one of the quadrants. Each quadrant has a sign of either positive or negative, depending on which number line segments are used to make up the boundaries. *Up* and *right* are positive directions, *down* and *left* are negative directions.

Quadrant I is positive: positive (right) and positive (up).
Quadrant II is negative: negative (left) and positive (up).
Quadrant III is positive: negative (left) and negative (down).
Quadrant IV is negative: positive (right) and negative (down).

You can use the joystick to try out any positive or negative integer in the given range.

In which quadrant is 3x4 located?

Which two quadrants are positive?

Which two quadrants are negative?

How does the picture justify that a negative number times a negative number is a positive number?

Does order matter when multiplying integers?

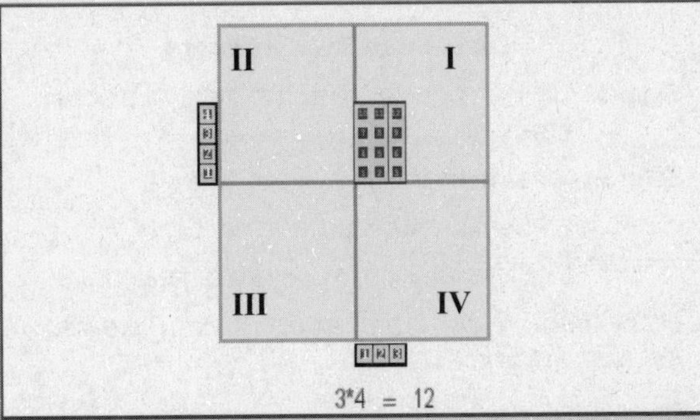

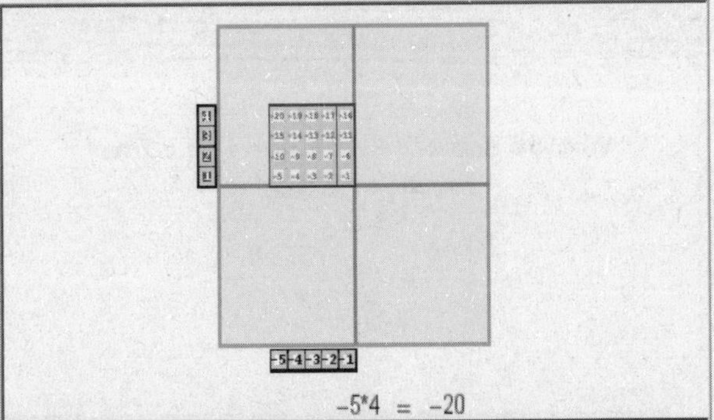

Notice above that the 5 number bar is located to the left of the center line, thus negative. The 4 number bar is up from the horizontal center line, thus positive. Is the product positive or negative?

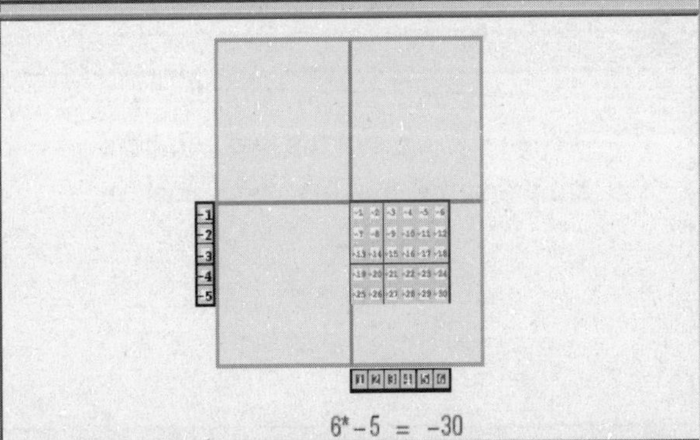

Positive 6 times negative 5 puts the rectangle in Quadrant IV, which is negative. Will all positive numbers times all negative numbers result in a product in quadrant IV?

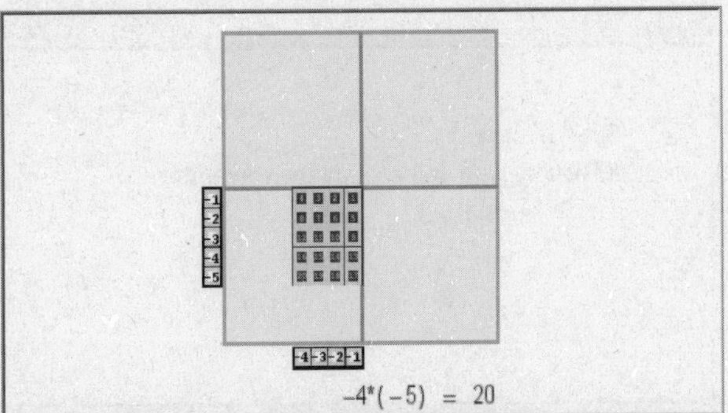

Notice both bars are negative. Is the answer positive or negative? Which quadrant holds the product?

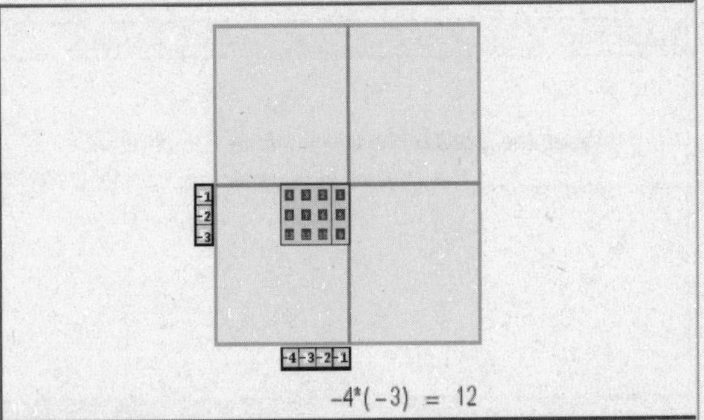

Something to think about: If you dieted for 4 months and lost 3 pounds per month, How much *MORE* did you weigh 4 months ago?

Dividing Integers

EnableMath

Dividing is the opposite of multiplying. Division of integers has a two step process for finding the answer: First divide normally, then determine the sign of the answer. Determining the sign of the answer is exactly the same process as for multiplication. If the signs are the same the answer is positive. If the signs are opposite, the answer is negative.

The answer to division is called the **quotient**. The terms are called **divisor** and **dividend**. The quotient of **a divided by b** is usually indicated by either a slash, **a/b**, or a fraction with the divisor as the denominator.

Division of Two Integers

Step 1: Divide normally. Use two decimal places if necessary.

Step 2: Determine the sign of the answer:

a. Same signs = positive quotients.

b. Different signs = negative quotient.

Quick check: Multiply the quotient times the divisor to get the dividend.

Divide:

When the signs of the two numbers are the same, the quotient is positive.

$$\frac{15}{3}$$
$$= 5$$

Divide:

When the signs of the two numbers are the same, the quotient is positive.

$$\frac{-12}{-4}$$
$$= 3$$

Points 1 & 2: Signs are the same, therefore, the answer is positive.

Divide:

When the signs of the two numbers are different, the quotient is negative.

$$\frac{70}{-7}$$
$$= -10$$

Point 3: The signs are not the same, therefore, there is a negative answer. Quick check: Is −10 *(−7) = 70?

Divide:

When the signs of the two numbers are different, the quotient is negative.

$$\frac{-12}{6}$$
$$= -2$$

Point 4: Different signs result in a negative answer.

Divide:

Special quotients:

division by zero and zero as the numerator:

$\frac{-12}{0} = \text{undefined}$ and $\frac{0}{5} = 0$

Know these two special cases. Use the quick-check method to remember which is which.

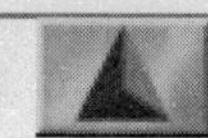

Division can be pictured as a right triangle with the legs of the triangle the dividend (the up or down leg) and divisor (the left or right leg). The quotient is represented by the ratio of the two sides: the slope (steepness) of the hypotenuse. As with multiplication, the quadrant determined by the divisor and dividend provides the **sign** of the quotient.

You can also visualize division as "un-multiplying." If you start with the product rectangle and have set one side of that rectangle as the divisor, then what is the length of the other side (the other factor)?

Is 4/2 as in Quadrant I? Is the quotient positive? Notice the red line. The steepness of that line is 2; the quotient of the problem.

Where is the red dot in relation to the divisor?

Does order matter in division?

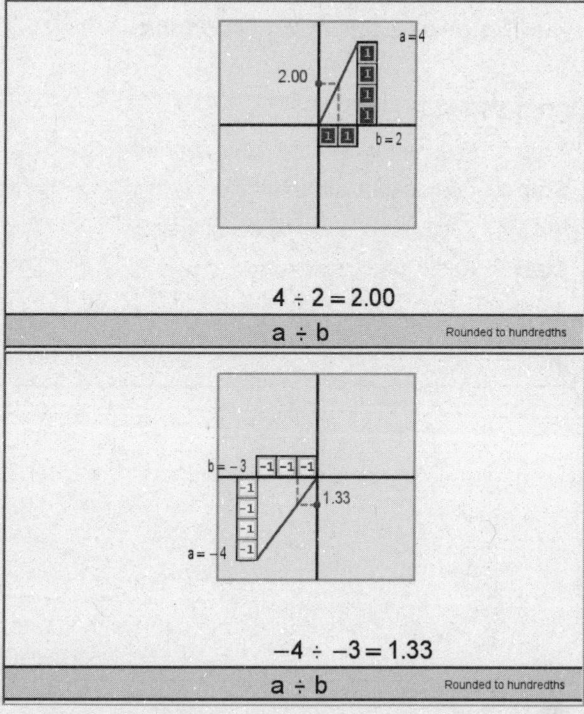

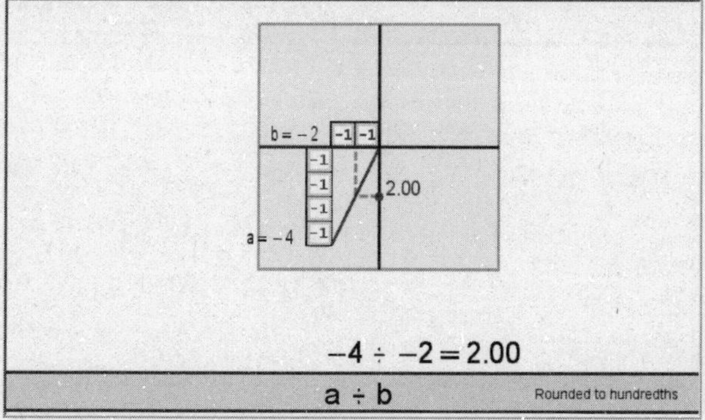

Divide a negative number by a negative number—positive quotient. What is the relationship between the red dot and the unit one?

Notice how steep the line is in the negative direction. Are –4/-3 and 1.33/1 proportional?

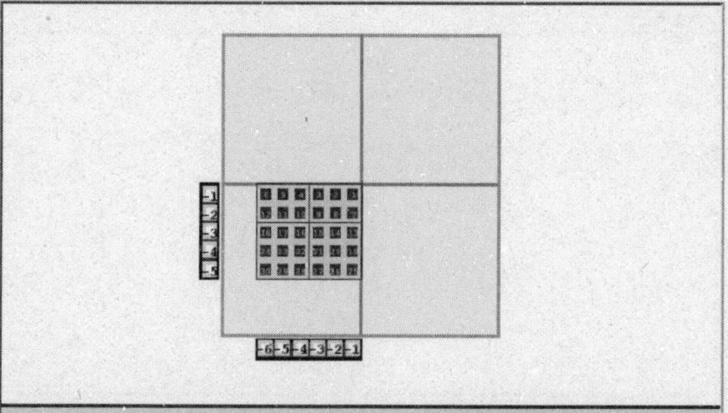

Recall the model for multiplication. If there are +30 units in the rectangle and I know one side is –5, what is the other side?

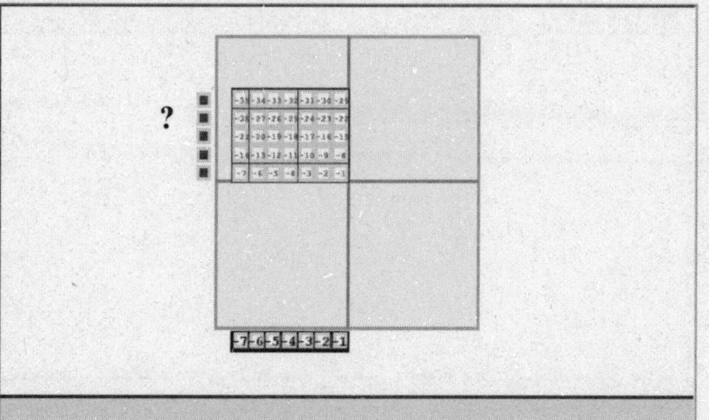

Above, there are 35 units pictured, with –7 units across the bottom, representing 35/(-7). How many units are in the red number bar on the side? Are they positive or negative? How do you know?

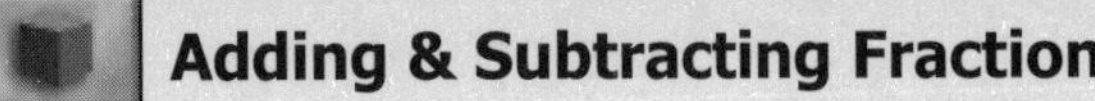

Adding & Subtracting Fractions

EnableMath

Signed fractions can be added or subtracted following the same procedure as for positive fractions. Establish a common denominator, preferably the lowest common denominator (LCD). Change to equivalent fractions with the LCD, and then add or subtract. To review finding the LCD, go to *2.4 Least Common Denominator.*

Signed fractions may need to be rewritten to place the negative sign in a better location. See the first frame below for equivalently signed fractions. Use the most convenient equivalent form for any particular problem.

Adding and Subtracting Fractions:

Step 1: Find the LCD.

Step 2: Write equivalent fractions over one LCD.

Step 3: Add or subtract numerators.

Step 4: Keep the LCD as the denominator.

Step 5: Reduce to lowest terms.

Signed Fractions

Positive fractions $\frac{a}{b}=\frac{(-a)}{(-b)}$

Negative fractions $-\frac{a}{b}=\frac{(-a)}{b}=\frac{a}{(-b)}$

Add:

$$\frac{7}{8}+\frac{-3}{5}$$
$$=\frac{7(5)}{8(5)}+\frac{-3(8)}{5(8)}$$

Make a common denominator.

The LCD of 8 and 5 is 40. The equivalent fractions are built by multiplying both numerators and denominator by the same factor.

Add:

$$\frac{7}{8}+\frac{-3}{5}$$
$$=\frac{7(5)}{8(5)}+\frac{-3(8)}{5(8)}$$
$$=\frac{35+(-24)}{40}$$
$$=\frac{11}{40}$$

Once the numerators are written over the common denominator, perform the indicated operation, and add or subtract integers as indicated.

Subtract:

$$\frac{1}{8}-\frac{5}{6}$$
$$=\frac{1(3)}{8(3)}-\frac{5(4)}{6(4)}$$

Make a common denominator.

Point 2: The LCD is 24. Change 1/8 by a factor of 3 (top and bottom) and change 5/6 by a factor of 4 (top and bottom).

Subtract:

$$\frac{1}{8}-\frac{5}{6}$$
$$=\frac{1(3)}{8(3)}-\frac{5(4)}{6(4)}$$
$$=\frac{3-20}{24}$$
$$=\frac{-17}{24}$$

Subtract to find the new numerator. In this case, the resulting fraction is negative. Can this be written in a different way?

Addition and subtraction of fractions is visualized with two fraction bars. Arrows indicate positive or negative quantities as well as addition (right) or subtraction (left). The results are displayed on a bar divided to show the common denominator (not necessarily the LCD).

Use the joystick to investigate different combinations of signed fractions. Notice what happens as fraction denominators get larger — are the models easier to see? What happens as the denominators get smaller? Why can't the denominators use negative numbers (hint: see the first frame on the example page)?

How do the visualizations incorporates each step in the addition process.

Why are the denominators are always positive? How can you write a fraction with a negative denominator?

Will the LCD be the same whether the denominators are positive, negative or both?

Does order make a difference in either addition or subtraction of fractions?

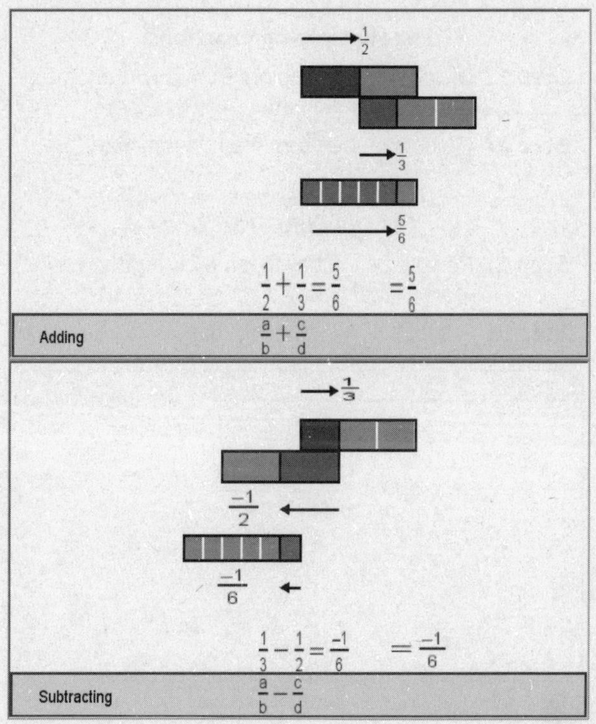

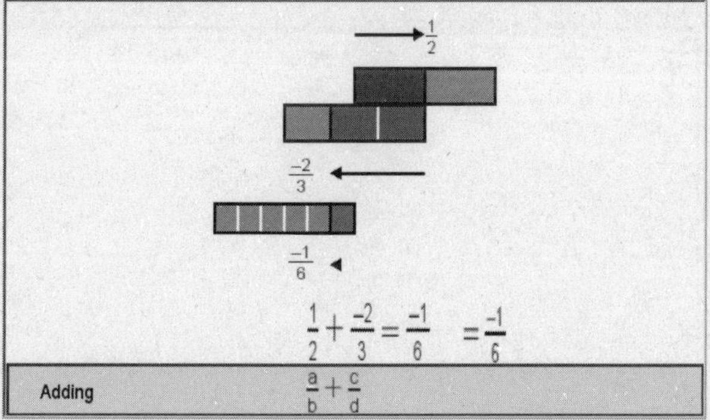

Why is the arrow pointing to the left for adding −2/3? Look closely at this and at **Point 2**. How are they different?

Point 2: Subtracting is visualized in the same way except the arrow is reversed to show subtraction as the opposite of addition.

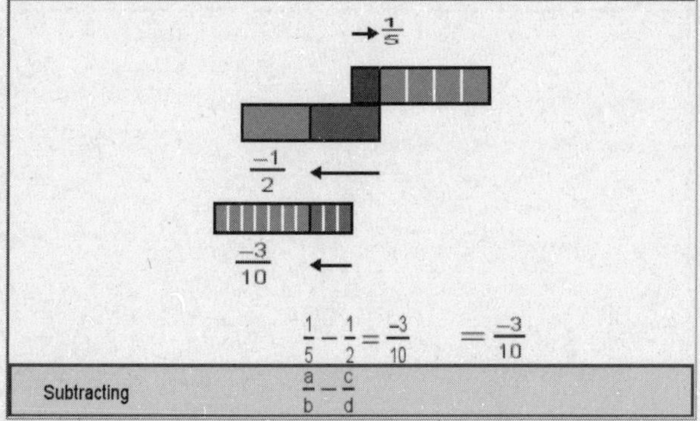

Notice the sign of the answer. Write out the steps in the problem and compare to the model above. Why is the answer negative?

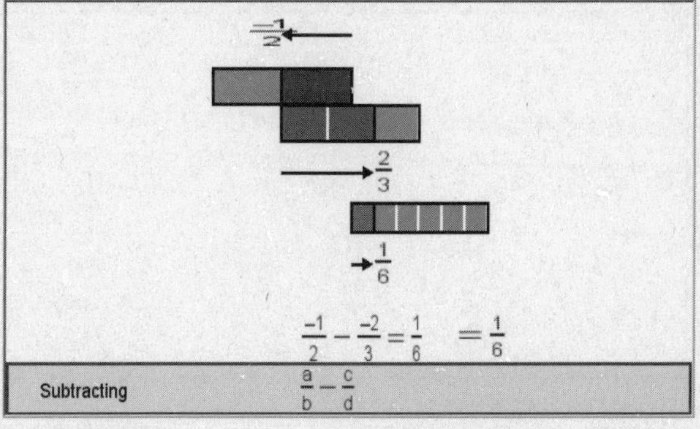

Subtract TWO negative fractions. Notice the direction of the arrow for the −2/3 bar. Can this be rewritten as an addition problem?

Multiplying & Dividing Fractions

Multiply two fractions by multiplying their numerators and then their denominators. It is almost always easier to **reduce fractions before multiplying** by dividing out common factors from any numerator with any denominator. Always double check to make sure your answer is in lowest terms by factoring the numerator and denominator and dividing out any common factors.

Multiplication and division are inverse operations. We use this idea to change division problems into multiplication problems. The quotient is found by multiplying by the reciprocal of the divisor — the multiplicative inverse of the second fraction.

For Multiplying Fractions

Step 1: Divide common factors from any numerator with any denominator.

Step 2: Multiply numerators then denominators.

For Dividing Fractions

Step 1: Rewrite as multiplication by using the reciprocal of the divisor.

Step 2: Proceed as for multiplication.

Multiplication of Fractions

$$\frac{a}{b}\cdot\frac{c}{d}=\frac{ac}{bd}$$

Division of Fractions

$$\frac{a}{b}\div\frac{c}{d}=\frac{a}{b}\cdot\frac{d}{c}=\frac{ad}{bc}$$

Multiply:

$$\frac{5}{14}*\frac{-7}{9}$$

$$=\frac{5}{2(\not{7})}*\frac{-1(\not{7})}{9}$$

Pull out common factors from the numerator and denominator.

Point 1: Step 2 identifies the common factor of 7 and divides it out.

Multiply:

$$\frac{5}{14}*\frac{-7}{9}$$

$$=\frac{5}{2(\not{7})}*\frac{-1(\not{7})}{9}$$

$$=\frac{5}{2}*\frac{-1}{9}$$

$$=\frac{-5}{18}$$

Steps 3 and 4 show the multiplication after dividing out the factor 7. Note the sign rule. How else could the answer be presented?

Divide:

$$\frac{-7}{8}\,/\,\frac{5}{12}$$

$$=\frac{-7}{8}*\frac{12}{5}$$

Multiply by the reciprocal of the second fraction.

Point 2: Step 1 shows the conversion to multiplication.

Divide:

$$\frac{-7}{8}\,/\,\frac{5}{12}$$

$$=\frac{-7}{8}*\frac{12}{5}$$

$$=\frac{-7}{2(\not{4})}*\frac{3(\not{4})}{5}$$

$$=\frac{-7}{2}*\frac{3}{5}$$

$$=\frac{-21}{10}$$

Steps 3 — 5 show the multiplication process: Divide common factors; Multiply numerators; Then, multiply denominators. How do you know if this answer is in the lowest terms?

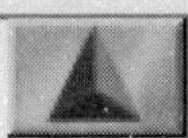

Multiplication and division of fractions are visualized like integers. Multiplication uses a rectangle showing the portion used (before reducing to lowest terms). The quadrants represent the signs of the answers.

We represent division with a right triangle. The quotient is the slope of the hypotenuse. The visualizations are useful to get an intuitive understanding of division and not meant to be used as a method for solving problems. Use the joystick to change values for **a, b, c, d** and notice what happens to the steepness of the hypotenuse line.

What if one of the fractions is negative? Where would the rectangle be located?

Are the sign rules for multiplication and division of fractions are the same as for integers?

How do you know when a fraction is in lowest terms?

Does order make a difference in multiplication or division of fractions?

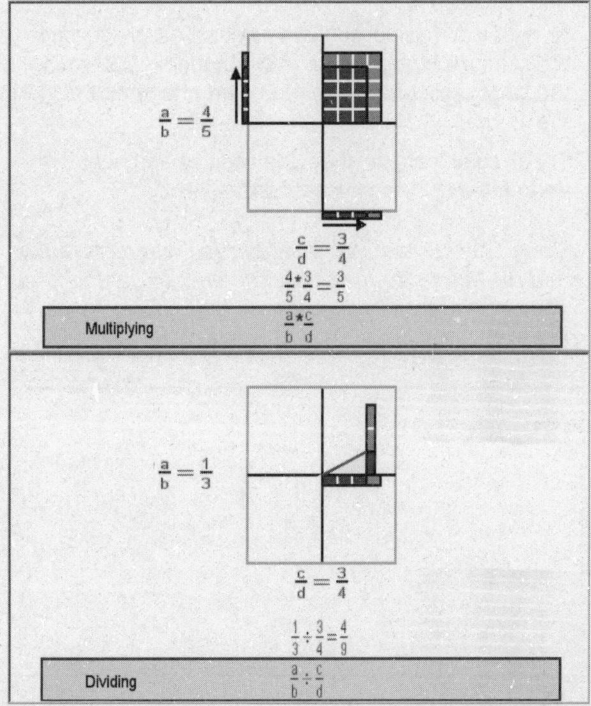

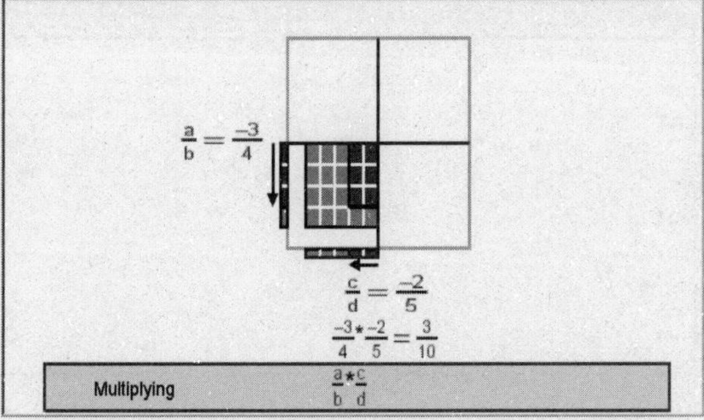

Two negative fractions yields a positive answer just like with integers. Is 3/10 in lowest terms?

Above shows the ratio 1/3 to 3/4. The slope of the line is positive 4/9. What happens to the slope if one of the fractions is negative?

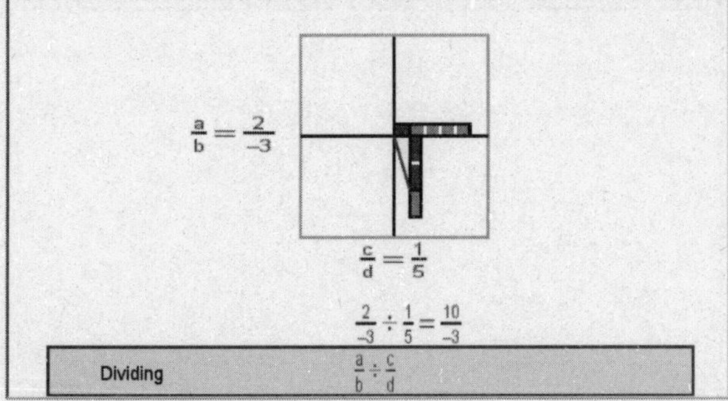

When the first fraction is negative and the second fraction is positive, the results will be in Quadrant IV. Notice that the denominator is negative in the answer; is there another way to write the fraction?

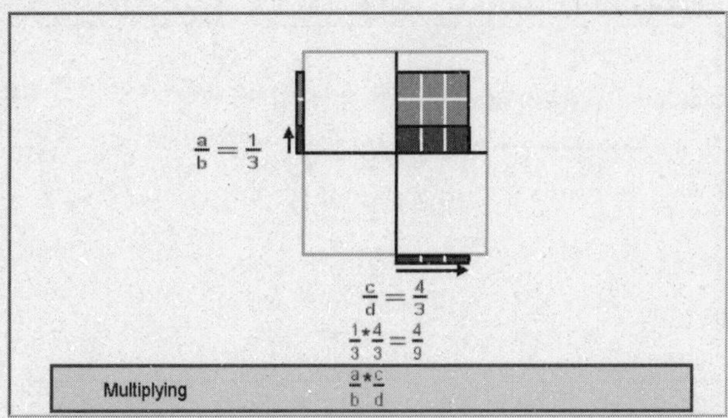

Can division be visualized with a multiplication rectangle? Think about what would have to change for the above frame to represent a division problem.

Adding & Subtracting Decimals

EnableMath

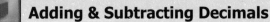

Determining the sign of the answer to signed addition and subtraction problems is exactly the same as for integers.

To add two decimal numbers: if the signs are the same add, use the common sign for the answer; if not subtract, use the sign of the larger absolute value decimal.

To subtract two decimal numbers: change to addition AND change the sign of the second decimal; follow the process for adding.

Practice with adding and subtracting signed decimals to one decimal place to reinforce adding inte-

At right is a decimal addition. Note the signs are not the same; subtract the decimal numbers. Determine the larger absolute value, 45.3, and attach that sign to the answer.

Try all combinations of adding positive and negative decimals with these dynamic examples.

Quick Check: Add back if subtraction was performed: add the answer to the smaller number to get the larger number. Follow all sign rules.

Add:

$$45.3+(-27.6)$$
$$=17.7$$

a+b

Add:

$$-14.9+16.7$$
$$=1.8$$

a+b

Signs are not the same: subtract and attach the sign of the larger absolute value, +.

Add:

$$-14.9+-16.7$$
$$=-31.6$$

a+b

If a problem has no parenthesis between the operator sign and the negative sign, then the sign closest to the number is the sign of the second term. Addition problem; signs are the same so add; attach the sign of the addends, in this case a (-).

Subtract:

$$-28.2-6.4$$
$$=-34.6$$

a−b

Subtraction: change to addition of the opposite of the second term. (-28.2 + -6.4)

Subtract:

$$-16.3-(-12.3)$$
$$=-16.3+12.3$$
$$=-4.0$$

a−b

Point 4: Change subtraction to addition; change the sign of the second addend. Follow rules for addition.

We visualize the addition and subtraction of signed decimals, as we did for integers or fractions by using bars and arrows (vectors), to indicate positive or negative direction.

Use the joystick to construct show addition and subtraction to one decimal place. Imagine what a visualization would look like to 2, 3, or more places.

Is zero still the additive identity? Does order matter in addition or subtraction of decimals?

Notice that the visualizations sometimes combine signs to simplify presentation; why does that work?

How are negative decimals presented? What color is the second term? What does the gray shaded region represent in a decimal bar? What direction will the arrow be pointing if you subtract a negative value?

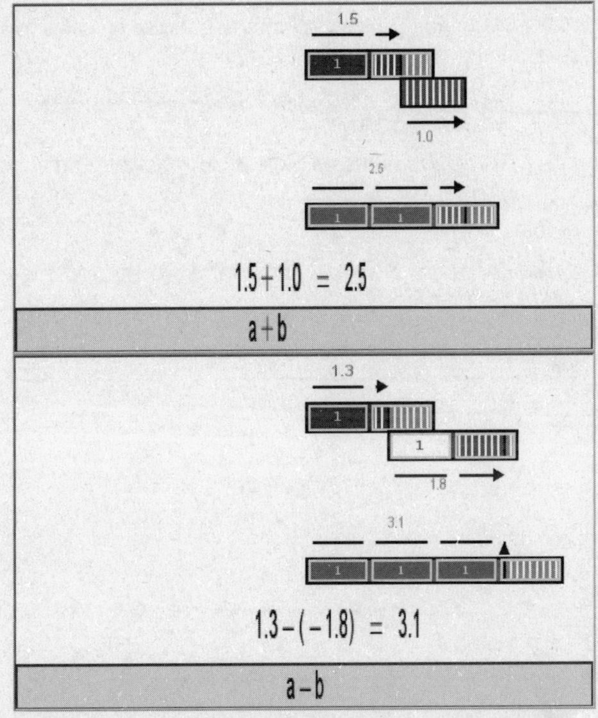

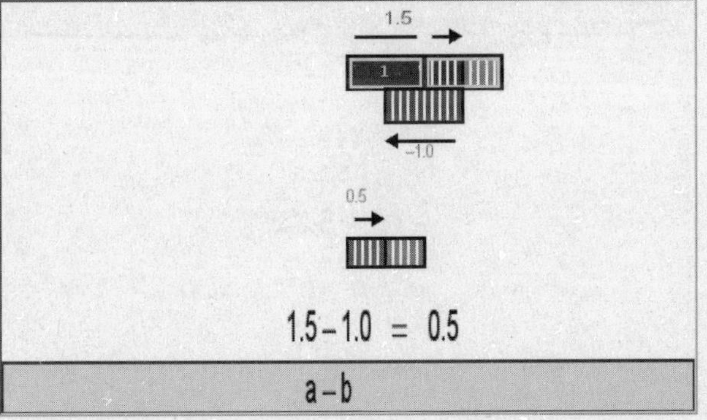

What would the screen be like if this problem were changed to 1.5 + (-1.0)?

Notice the direction and color of the attached bar representing – (–1.8). What will this problem look like when it is re-written as an addition problem?

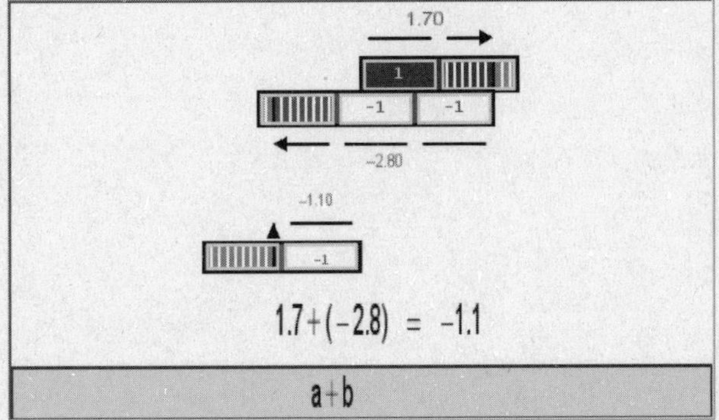

Notice this looks just like subtraction. Can we write it as a subtraction problem?

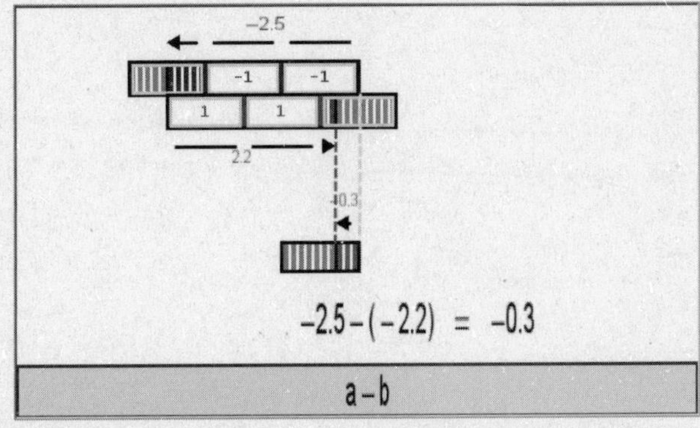

Sometimes a visualization can get complicated. Here the answer bar is very small. You can draw guide lines by clicking on the tool bar triangle and selecting the line drawing tool to help you "see" this by drawing on the screen.

Multiplying & Dividing Decimals

Multiplying and dividing signed decimals use the same sign rules as multiplying and dividing integers and fractions. To review multiplication and division of decimals and decimal placement in the product and quotient see *3.3 Multiplying Decimals*. Multiplication can be written in any of the following ways: a*b, a(b), (a)(b), or a·b. Use parentheses when multiplying decimals so that the decimal point and operator aren't confused.

Round off decimal division to two decimal places unless directed otherwise. Use ≈ to indicate approximately equal.

Multiplying and dividing decimals use the same rules for determining the sign of the answer:

1. If the two numbers have the same sign, the answer is positive.
2. If the two numbers have different signs, the answer is negative.

Quick Check: for division: multiply the answer and divisor to get the dividend.

Multiply:

$$-6.3 \cdot 5.4$$
$$= -34.02$$

Note: This problem can also be written as (-6.3)(5.4).

Point 1: Use scrap paper or a calculator to determine the product, then follow the sign rules.

Multiply:

$$(-0.3)(-0.002)$$
$$= 0.0006$$

For decimal placement: count up the number of decimal places in each factor- that total is the number of decimal places in the product.

To the determine the sign of the answer: positive for same signs; negative for different signs.

Divide and round to the nearest hundredths:

$$\frac{44.8}{-5.3}$$
$$\approx -8.45$$

Point 2: Use scrap paper or a calculator to determine the quotient to two decimal places.

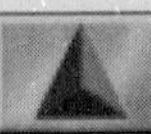

Multiplication is visualized with a rectangular grid. The sides of the rectangle represent the factors. For decimal numbers, the product rectangle is divided into 100 cells. In order to see this clearly, keep the range of **a** and **b** to tenths (between –1 and 1). Use the joystick to check out all combinations of positive and negative decimals.

Division uses a right triangle to show the ratio of **a** to **b**. The slope of the hypotenuse line shows this relationship. Use the joystick to investigate the location of the triangle and the steepness of the line.

The Quadrants show where the products and quotients are positive and negative depending on the signs of **a** and **b**. What factors have products in quadrants II and IV? What is the sign of the **a** factor if the product is in Quadrant III? What is the sign of the **b** factor if the product is in Quadrant III?

Does order make a difference in multiplication or division of decimals?

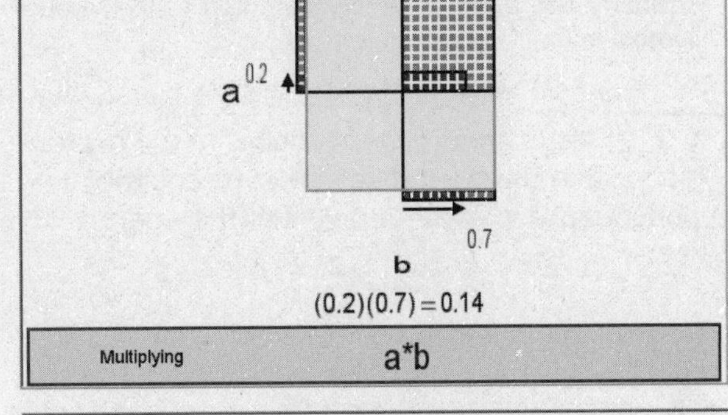

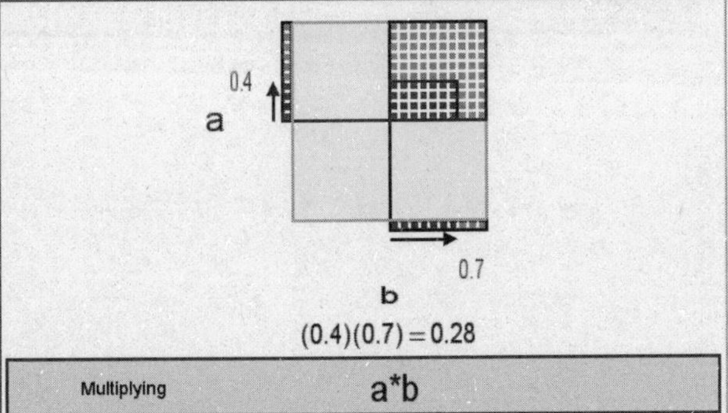

If **a** was positive and **b** was negative, where would the grid be located?

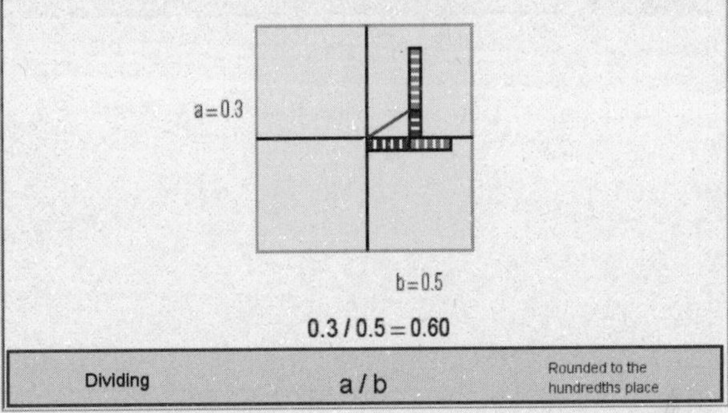

Point 2: Division of positive decimals.

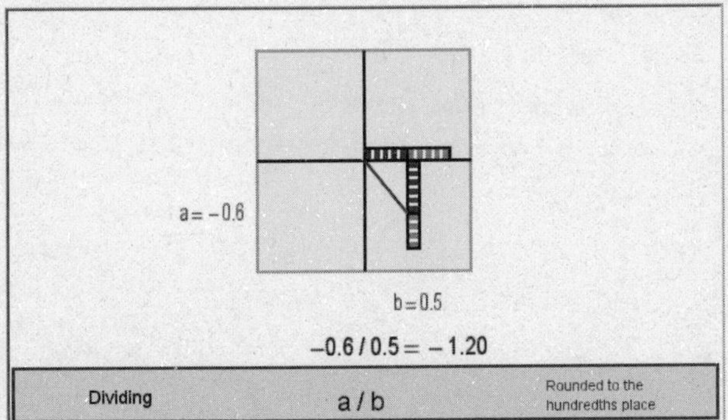

Remember Quadrant IV indicates negative **a** and positive **b**.
Is the line slanted more or less than the line in Point 2 above?

Use **exponents** for a shorthand way to write repeated multiplications. The **exponent** indicates how many times the **base** is multiplied by itself. To *evaluate an exponent expression* means to calculate the value of the repeated multiplications. Use the following pattern for evaluating the base, **b**, raised to the exponent, **n:**

$$b^n = \underbrace{b \cdot b \cdot b \ldots \cdot b}_{n}$$

Special cases:

$b^0 = 1$ for all numbers

b^{even} = positive number for any **b.**

b^{odd} = positive if **b** is *positive*; negative if **b** is *negative*

Identify the base: The exponent applies to the one symbol immediately to its left:

$(-2)^2$ and -2^2 are not the same.

$(-2)^2$ means the exponent applies to the expression within the parentheses; -2^2 means the exponent applies to the **2** only, not the - part.

$(-2)^2 = 4$ and $-2^2 = -4$

Exponent pattern for any number:

$a^0 = 1$

$a^1 = a$

$a^2 = a \cdot a$

$a^3 = a \cdot a \cdot a$

Evaluate:

$$(-2)^3$$
$$= (-2)(-2)(-2)$$
$$= -8$$

Point 1: The base is −2. How many times is −2 multiplied by itself? The exponent is 3, therefore, the answer is: three times.

Evaluate:

$$(-2)^4$$
$$= (-2)(-2)(-2)(-2)$$
$$= 16$$

Notice an even exponent gives a positive answer *even though* the base is negative.

Evaluate:

$$(2-4)^2$$
$$= (-2)^2$$
$$= (-2)(-2)$$
$$= 4$$

Simplify within the parentheses first to find out what the base is going to be. The exponent **2** applies to the ***expression*** within the parentheses.

Positive and negative numbers have different patterns for exponents. Positive integers show rapid growth as the exponent increases for any base. Negative integers show a saw tooth pattern depending on whether the exponent is even or odd. In the visualizations below, the value *a* is shown on the vertical axis and the exponent is shown on the horizontal axis. Use the joystick to change the base and exponent.

Why should the pattern be different for positive and negative numbers? Can you predict what the sign will be if a negative number is raised to an even exponent? Can you predict what the sign will be if the exponent is odd?

What is any number raised to the 0 power? What is any number raised to the 1st power?

If 4^3 is 4 times 4^2, what is $(-4)^2$ times (-4)?

What is the connection between the number of factors and the exponent of a number raised to a power?

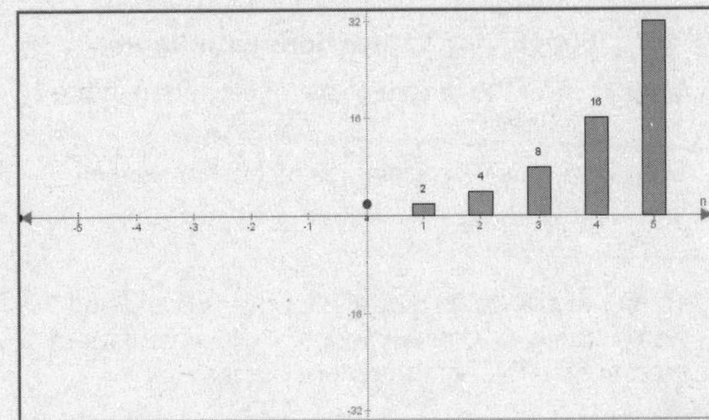

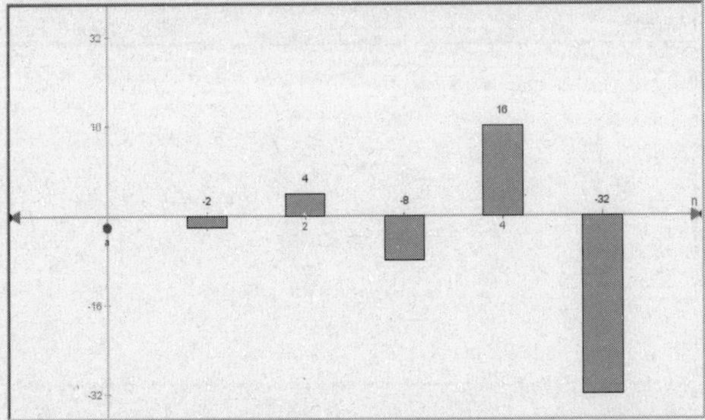

If a= −2, how many factors of −2 are there if the exponent is 2? If the exponent is 3? 4? 5?

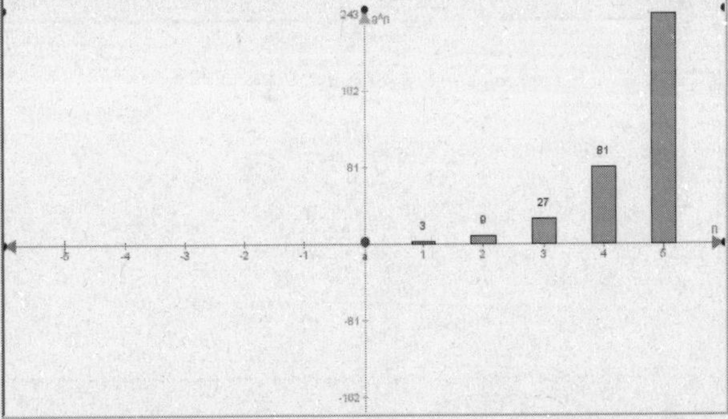

The pattern for 3 is similar to the pattern for 2 above.

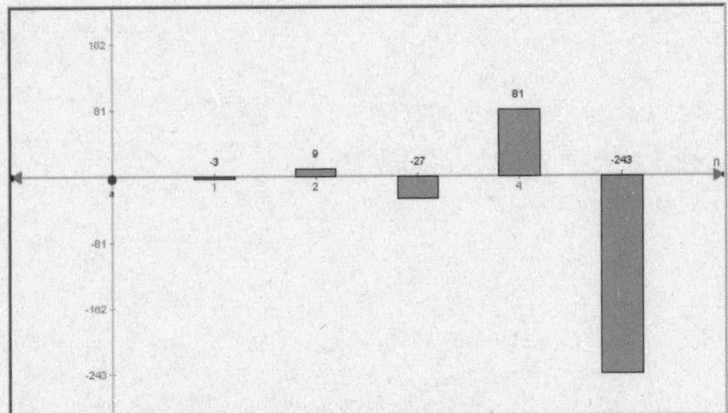

Powers of (-3) are shown above. Will the next exponent yield a positive or negative result? What can you predict about the sign of (-3) raised to any even exponent? What will the sign be for any odd exponent?

Root or radical expressions are the **opposite process** of exponentiation. A symbolic explanation shows that the radical index undoes the exponent. The symbol √ is called the **radical** and indicates that the **root** is to be found. The **n** is called the **index** or **nth root** of the radical, **b.** We are using **b** to connect the idea of **base**.

$$\sqrt[n]{b^n} = b$$

When no index is used, the square root (index of 2) is understood.

Simplifying Expressions with Roots

Step 1: Find the indicated root of each term in the expression.

Step 2: Simplify by adding or subtracting as indicated.

To find the indicated root: Factor the radicand and rewrite using exponent notation. Follow the pattern presented to the right to reduce the radical.

Let b represent any number.

$$\sqrt{b^2} = \sqrt{b \cdot b} = b$$

$$\sqrt[3]{b^3} = \sqrt[3]{b \cdot b \cdot b} = b$$

$$\sqrt[4]{b^4} = \sqrt[4]{b \cdot b \cdot b \cdot b} = b$$

Add

$$-\sqrt{100} + \sqrt{64}$$
$$-\sqrt{10^2} + \sqrt{8^2}$$
$$= -10 + 8$$
$$= -2$$

Point 1: Think backwards: What squared is 100? What squared is 64? Notice the sign indicating the negative square root of 100.

Multiply

$$-\sqrt[3]{8} \cdot \sqrt[3]{27}$$
$$-\sqrt[3]{2^3} \cdot \sqrt[3]{3^3}$$
$$= -2 \cdot 3$$
$$= -6$$

Point 2: What cubed is 8? What cubed is 27? Make a list of the first ten squares, cubes, and fourth powers, to help you quickly and mentally work out these problems — No calculator needed!

Add:

$$-\sqrt[4]{16} + \sqrt[3]{125}$$
$$= -2 + 5$$
$$= 3$$

What to the fourth power is 16? What to the third power is 125? (Always notice where the negative signs are and what they mean.)

Square roots "undo" square exponents — they are opposite processes. To visualize the process, place two column bars on a scale to measure the height of the bar. The larger bar represents the exponential value and the smaller bar represents the root.

Use the joystick to investigate some perfect squares, cubes, fourth powers, and roots. Watch the relative heights to get an intuitive feel for the processes.

At right is a picture of 16 or 4^2, and square root of 16.

Below is a picture of 16 or 2^4, and the fourth root of 16. Compare relative sizes for the roots.

How "fast" do perfect 4ths get out of range of the scale?

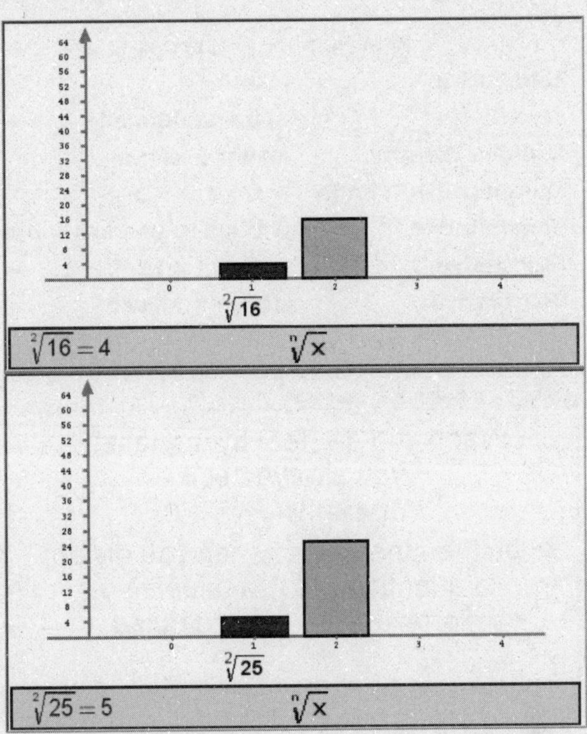

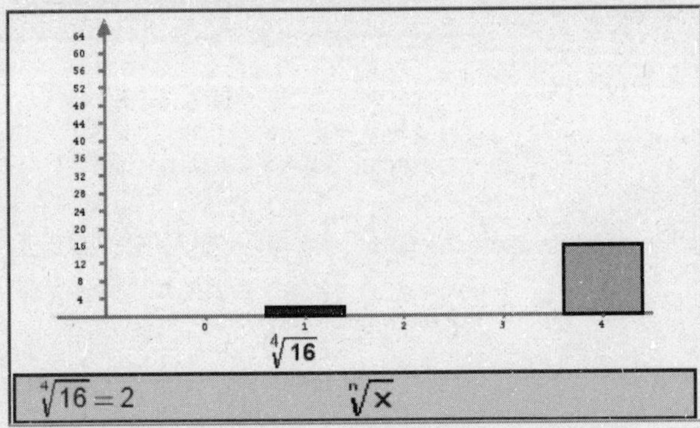

The fourth root of 16 is 2. Compare this to the square root of 16 above. What are the relative sizes of the roots?

The square root of 25 or 5^2. Notice that the tall bar is 5 times bigger than the smaller bar.

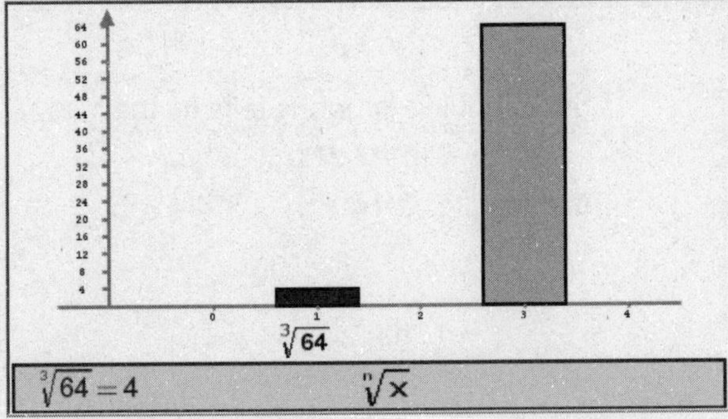

Above, the larger bar is 16 times bigger than the smaller bar. Why?

The **Real Numbers** form a system developed from a basic set of principles, properties and rules that are applied as needed to solve problems and build new concepts. Along with the identity elements, special properties of zero, and the inverses of addition and multiplication, the **Associative, Commutative, Distributive Properties** make up the foundation of our number system. Below is a list (sometimes called the **Field Properties** or **Axioms**) of these basic principles and their symbolic representation.

Real Number Properties

Zero Factor	**ax0=0**
Zero Divisor	**a/0 = undefined**
Additive Identity	**a+0 = 0+a = a**
Multiplicative Identity	**ax1 = 1xa = a**
Commutative	**a+b = b+a and axb = bxa**
Associative	**a+(b+c) = (a+b)+c**
Distributive	**a(b+c) = ab+ac**

When you multiply a quantity by 0, you always get 0. For example, 2*0 = 0.

Divisions involving zero are tricky!

When you divide 0 by a quantity, you always get 0. For example, $\frac{0}{3} = 0$. On the other hand, when you divide a quantity by 0, it's undefined. For example, $\frac{6}{0}$ is undefined.

Division by zero is undefined; there is no rule about division into zero.

The Commutative Property

For addition, the commutative property tells us that

a + b = b + a

For example, 3 + 4 = 4 + 3

For multiplication, the commutative property tells us that

a * b = b * a

For example, 3*4 = 4*3

Order does not matter when combining two real numbers by adding or multiplying them. Notice that subtraction and division are not included. However, if you can convert subtraction to addition and division to multiplication, you can then

The Associative Property

For addition, the associative property tells us that

a + (b + c) = (a + b) + c

For example, 3 + (4 + 5) = (3 + 4) + 5

For multiplication, the associative property tells us that

a * (b * c) = (a * b) * c

For example, 3*(4*5) = (3*4)*5

If you have three numbers (or more) to add, it does not matter which two you add first. Same with multiplication. Subtraction and division are excluded unless they can be rewritten.

The Distributive Property

The distributive property tells us that

a * (b + c) = a * b + a * c

For example, 3*(4 + 5) = 3*4 + 3*5

Multiplication is distributive over addition: you can choose to add first or multiply first. This property is extremely useful in algebra where it is used to simplify and factor expressions.

The real number properties are very basic ideas that are easily visualized by the processes we have already seen: multiplication with rectangles and addition with bars and arrows.

Use the joystick to explore what happens as the numbers increase.

Can you identify which property is illustrated before looking at the description?

Will a number and it's additive inverse always have the same size arrow?

Will a number and it's multiplicative inverse always have the same size area?

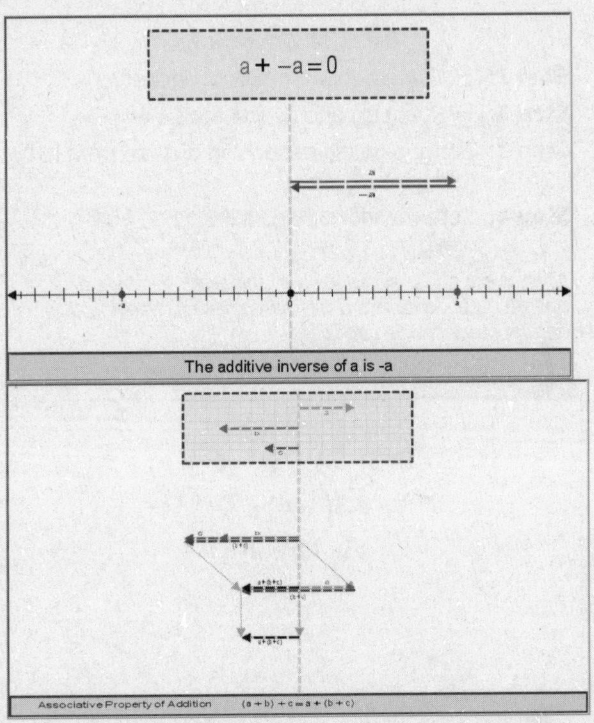

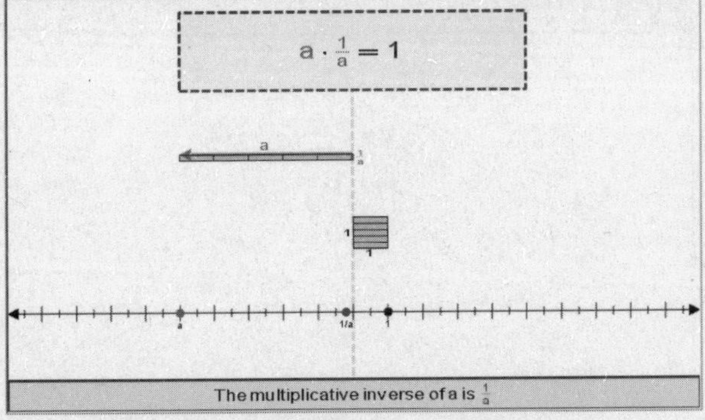

Are the areas the same? Are there the same number of rectangles that make up the larger block and the long bar?

Associative Property of Addition $(a+b)+c=a+(b+c)$

Use the step variable to explore how the above visual changes. Which is a simpler visualization for you?

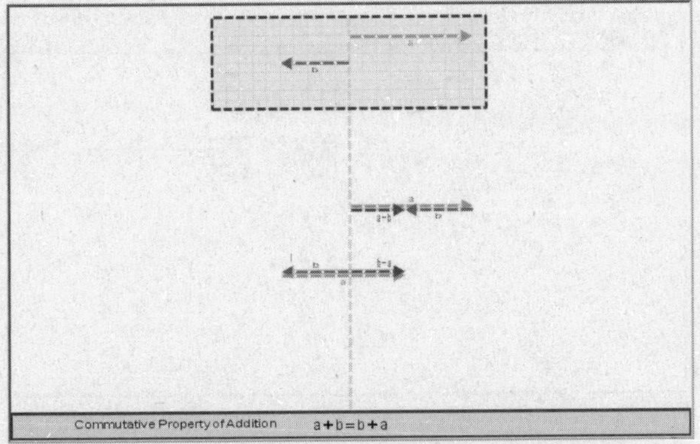

Step through this one. Are the resultant bars the same length?

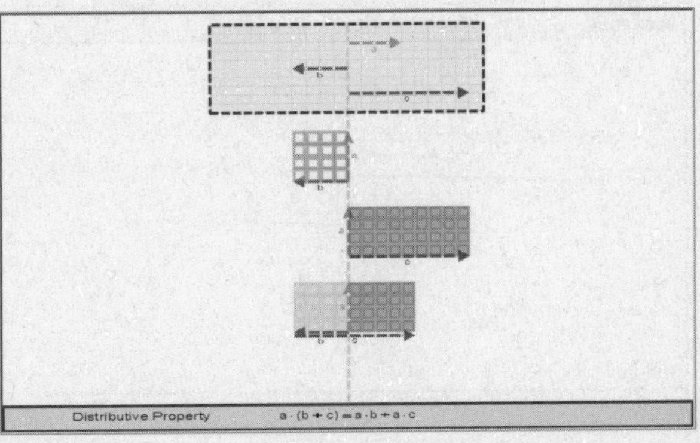

Which is simpler adding first or multiplying first?

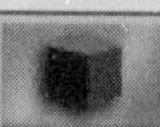

Order of Operations

Numerical expressions are combinations of numbers, operations, and symbols of enclosure. *Evaluating* numeric expressions means to find the numerical value for the expression. There is a universally accepted *hierarchical* process for evaluating numerical expressions called the **order of operations.** Addition and subtraction are at the bottom of the hierarchy. Multiplication and division supersede addition and subtraction. Exponents and roots supersede multiplication. Symbols of enclosure change the hierarchy, therefore, they must be evaluated first.

Hint: In reading class, you might parse a sentence to analyze the grammar and usage of words. For evaluating expressions, first parse the expression into terms. Note where the addition and subtraction symbols are. Just as for sentences, this helps break down the problem into smaller segments. It also helps to make sure addition and subtraction are the last operations performed.

Order of Operations

Step 1: Evaluate within symbols of enclosure.

Step 2: Evaluate exponents and roots.

Step 3: Perform multiplication and division from left to right.

Step 4: Perform addition and subtraction from left to right.

At right are two expressions with the same numbers and operators, but example II has parentheses, changing the natural order of operations.

Example I
No Parentheses
four terms

$$\begin{aligned}&2 - 3 * 4 + 5 - 6^2\\&= 2 - 3 * 4 + 5 - 36\\&= 2 - 12 + 5 - 36\\&= -10 + 5 - 36\\&= -5 - 36\\&= -41\end{aligned}$$

Example II
With parentheses
two terms

$$\begin{aligned}&(2 - 3) * 4 + (5 - 6)^2\\&= (-1)4 + (-1)^2\\&= (-1)4 + 1\\&= -4 + 1\\&= -3\end{aligned}$$

Evaluate:

$$\begin{aligned}&-3(2-6)+2(-2+7)\\&=-3(-4)+2(5)\\&=12+10\\&=22\end{aligned}$$

Point 1: In the above model, the addition sign separates the problem into two smaller problems. You evaluate –3(2-6) and 2(-2+7) and then add them together.

Evaluate:

Two terms $\underline{4(-10+7)} - \underline{(-2)^2}$

Step 1 $=4(-3)-(-2)^2$

Step 2 $=4(-3)-4$

Multiply left to right.

Point 2: Steps 1 and 2 are shown above. Simplify within parentheses and then evaluate exponents. Notice that the terms are underlined. Why do we count only two terms for this expression?

Evaluate:

$$\begin{aligned}&4(-10+7)-(-2)^2\\&=4(-3)-(-2)^2\\&=4(-3)-4\\\text{Step 3}\quad&=-12-4\\\text{Step 4}\quad&=-16\end{aligned}$$

Point 2: Steps 3 and 4 finish the problem.

Evaluate:

$$\begin{aligned}&-6(2-3)^4+\sqrt{4}\\&=-6(-1)^4+\sqrt{4}\\&=-6(1)+2\\&=-6+2\\&=-4\end{aligned}$$

Point 3: Parentheses first; then exponents and roots; then multiplication; finally addition. How many terms? Do you have to wait until step 2 to evaluate square root of 4?

There is a standard process for evaluating numerical expressions called the **order of operations**:
Parentheses; **E**xponents; **M**ultiplication & **D**ivision; **A**ddition & **S**ubtraction

PEMDAS is a mnemonic to help you remember the order. Order of operations is a hierarchy that starts by eliminating parentheses. Then, evaluate in order of the biggest changes to smallest. Parentheses are evaluated first because they have the power to change the order of operations.

Use the joystick to investigate how the value of the expressions change based on placement of parentheses. Which position yields the largest value? Which yields the smallest value?

What effect do parentheses have on the order of operations?

Do exponents always get evaluated first? Are addition and subtraction always last?

When are parentheses needed and when are they optional?

Order
( )
a^b
× ÷
+ −

$$(1.2 + 1.8) \times 2.0^3 = 24$$

parentheses position = 1 $(a + b) \times c^d$

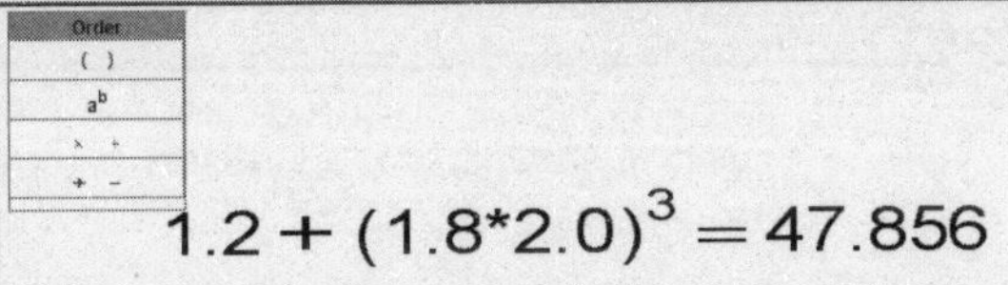

parentheses position = 2 $a + (b*c)^d$

What's different about the above expression and the one above right?

Order
( )
a^b
× ÷
+ −

$$1.2 + 1.8*(2.0^3) = 15.6$$
$$1.2 + 1.8*2.0^3 = 15.6$$

parentheses position = 3 $a + b*(c^d)$

Pay very close attention to where the exponent is and what the base of the exponent is. Here the exponent applies to the 2 only, not including the 18. Why?

Order
( )
a^b
× ÷
+ −

$$5.0 + (3.0*2.0)^1 = 11$$

parentheses position = 2 $a + (b*c)^d$

Are the parentheses needed here? Why or why not?

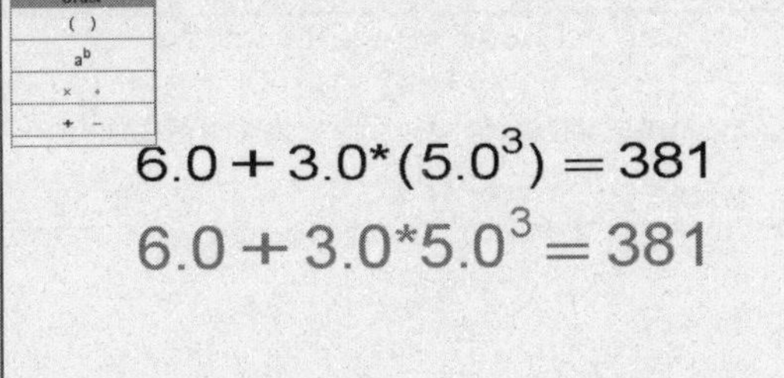

parentheses position = 3 $a + b*(c^d)$

What's the largest number you can find for any of the three positions?

Math "phrases" (expressions) are made up of symbols: numbers, letters, operators (like +, -, *, /), and symbols of enclosures (...). Like sentences in English, math sentences are made up of phrases linked with verbs or verb phrases: *equals* or *is equal to*. Translating between English and math requires a few special word patterns and usages with specific meaning in mathematics. Translate word for word, making sure each symbol has a word or phrase equivalent.

To translate between verbal and symbolic

1. Determine if the problem is a phrase or sentence by locating the "verb" (equal sign).
2. On paper, mark each phrase with parentheses, or by underlining, or by using color.
3. Mark the operator words/symbols either in color or by underlining them.
4. Translate each word or phrase for its corresponding symbol.

Phrases that translate to "x":

a number
an unknown quantity
some number

Phrases that translate to "-":

minus
decreased by
the difference between
less than (Take care! This phrase works backwards!)

Points 3: Subtraction requires extra attention. English phrases for subtraction are sometimes the reverse in mathematical symbols. You can usually tell by the context of the problem.

Phrases that translate to " * ":

times
of (usually used when multiplying by fractions)
the product of
multiplied by
twice (which is 2*), thrice (which is 3*), etc.
one – half of (which is $\frac{1}{2}$*), one – third of (which is $\frac{1}{3}$*), etc.

Point 4: Multiplication has some very different English translations. Use the term or phrase which gives the clearest meaning in the context of the problem.

Translate:

1. The total of five and some number is twelve.

$$x+5=12$$

2. Four less than a number is equal to the square of that number.

$$x-4=x^2$$

3. Twice some number is the opposite of that number divided by four.

$$2x=\frac{-x}{4}$$

Point 9: Make sure each symbol is accounted for by the verbal equivalent.

Translating English sentences into mathematical symbols can be visualized by associating words with pictures. Addition is shown with connecting number bars; Multiplication is shown with rectangles. Imagine more complex expressions and equations by combining two or more of these simple pictures into one visualization.

Drawing a picture and describing that picture in English is also a good technique to help with translating between English and math. The conceptual visualizations we use in this course are the pictures you might want to draw.

Associate "more than" to the picture for addition. What would "less than" look like? (Remember the rules for subtracting integers: Change to addition of the opposite.)

Can more than also be used for multiplication? How do you tell the difference?

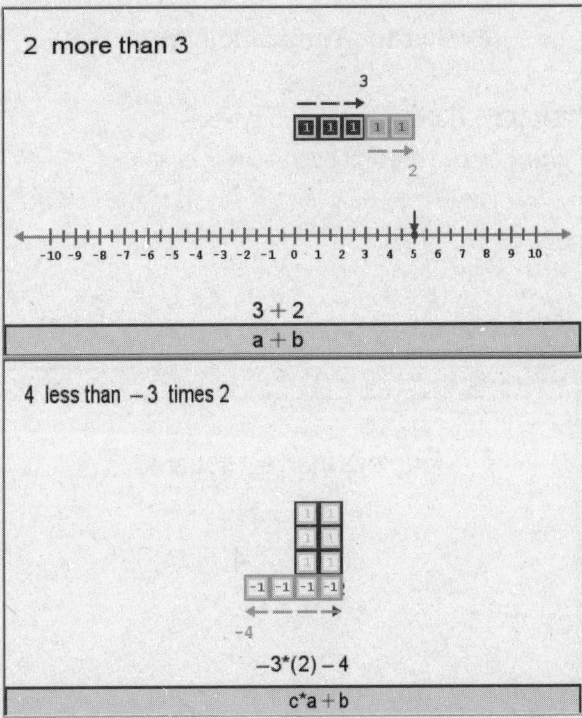

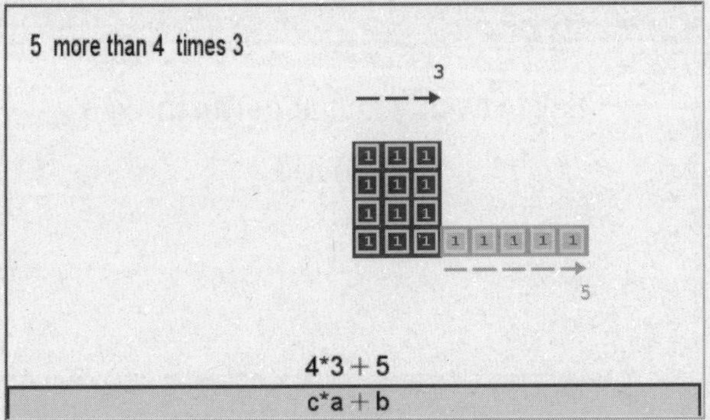

Multiplication and addition are represented above.
How would the picture change for subtraction?

Subtraction from a product. How would it change to show subtraction of −4?

Evaluating translation problems is a two-step process. First, translate from English into symbolic form and then, use **order of operations** to evaluate the resultant mathematical expression.

Hint: Translate each word or phrase into a corresponding math symbol. Remember that words for subtraction must be carefully considered to determine order.

Evaluating Translation Problems

Step 1: Translate into math symbols.

Step 2: Use order of operations to evaluate.

Translate and simplify:

the total of five and seven

$$5+7$$
$$=12$$

Translate and simplify:

four less than six squared

$$6^2-4$$
$$=36-4$$
$$=32$$

Point 2: Subtraction: Note that "four less than" is written as –4.

Translate and simplify:

half of twenty four added to three

$$\tfrac{1}{2}(24)+3$$

Point 3: "Half of" is multiplication by the fraction 1/2. How else could this be interpreted to get the same answer? What answer should we get?

Translate and simplify:

the opposite of 21 divided by seven

$$-21/7$$
$$=-3$$

Point 5: Division with opposite. How else could this be written?

Translate and simplify:

twice three and four tenths divided by one and seven tenths

$$2(3.4)/1.7$$
$$=6.8/1.7$$
$$=4$$

Point 5: Translating and simplifying works with all numbers including decimals. Use scratch paper or a calculator for complicated divisions.

Visualize translation problems using number bars for adding and rectangles for multiplying. For adding and subtracting number bars, look for the answer on the number line below the bars. Count up the number bars for multiplication with addition. Remember reverse colors indicate negative. You can use the joystick to change any of the values.

Many of these visualizations can have several English translations. Once the problem is expressed in symbolic form, is there only one correct way to evaluate it?

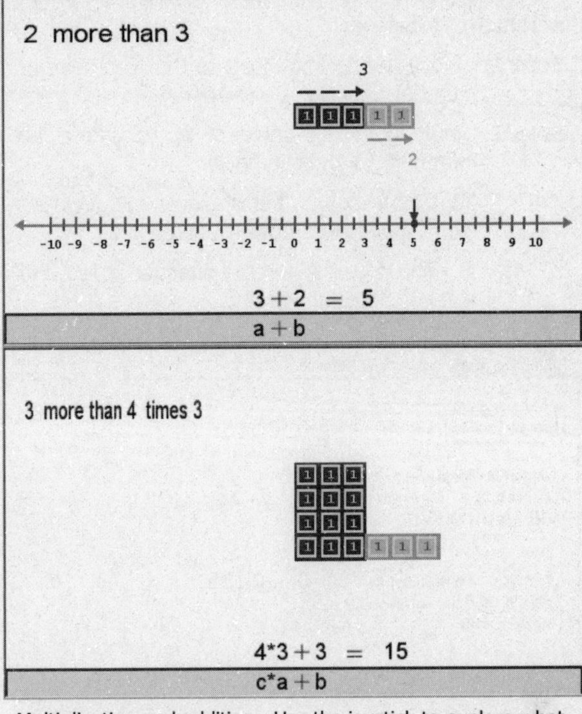

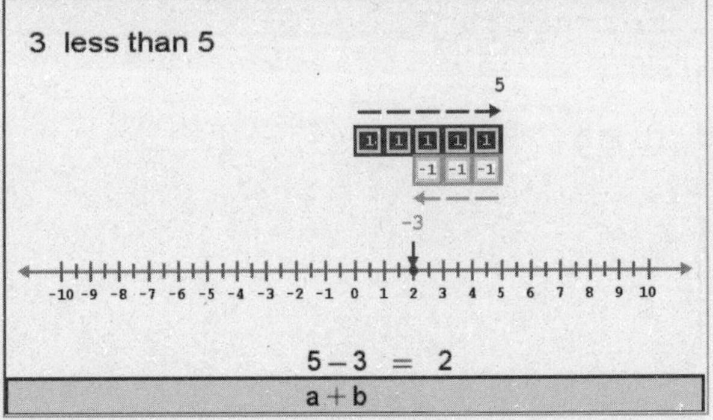

What would this look like for "five more than negative three"?

Multiplication and addition. Use the joystick to explore what happens as **b** decreases.

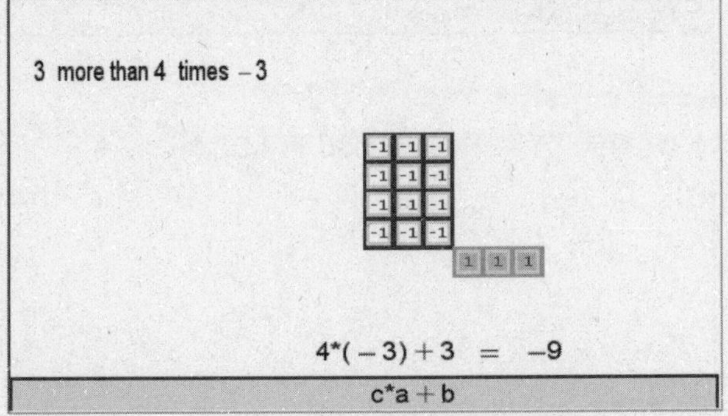

Notice the reversed unit bars to indicate negative bars. How do you accommodate the +3 unit bars with the –12 unit bars to get –9 unit bars?

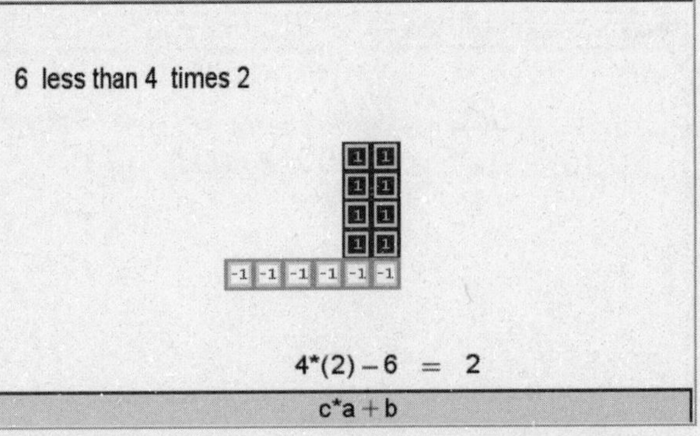

Notice that all but two bars "add out." Think of a simple "story" to describe this picture. (What food would you picture like this, and what happens when you start eating it??)

Scientific Notation

EnableMath

Scientific Notation makes working with very large or very small numbers a little easier. A number written in scientific notation has just one digit to the left of the decimal point, and the decimal is multiplied by a power of ten. The key to scientific notation is to count the number of places you moved the decimal point to make the number have just one digit to the left of the point. The exponent is based on the number of places moved.

For now, we indicate the DIRECTION moved with the sign of the exponent: move left uses a + and move right uses a –.

Scientific Notation:

Step 1: Move the decimal point so that you have a number between 1 and 10.

Step 2: Multiply times a power of ten to restore the number. To find the power:

A. Count the number of places the decimal point moved and note the direction.

B. The power is + if the direction is left and – if the direction is right.

Writing Decimals in Scientific Notatio

Example One

578.48

1. Move the decimal point so there is just one digit to its left, and round the number to the nearsest hundredth.

5.78

2. Multiply the number by the power of ten that would restore the original number.

$578.48 = 5.78* 10^{2}$

Writing Decimals in Scientific Notatio

Example Two

0.00456

1. Move the decimal point so there is just one digit to its left, and round the number to the nearsest hundredth.

4.56

2. Multiply the number by the power of ten that would restore the original number.

$0.00456 = 4.56* 10^{-3}$

4.56 is a number between 1 and 10. Notice that the exponent is (–) because the decimal point moved right three places.

Writing Decimals in Scientific Notation

$0.991 = 9.91 * 10^{-1}$

Now multiply by a power of ten to keep the same value.

Move the decimal one place to the right to get a number between 1 and 10. 10^{-1} really means 1/10. Multiply 1/10 times 9.91 to get 0.091.

Writing Decimals in Scientific Notation

$9000 = 9.00 * 10^{3}$

Now multiply by a power of ten to keep the same value.

Make 9000 look like a number between 1 and 10 by moving the decimal point three places to the left.

Writing Decimals in Scientific Notation

$0.09 = 9.00 *10^{-2}$

Now multiply by a power of ten to keep the same value.

Move the decimal two places to the right. You can then append as many zeros as you need. Multiply times a power of ten.

Scientists work with very small numbers when counting atoms and very large numbers when counting distances to the stars. Sometimes the number of zeros are too big to be understood at a glance, so they make good use of *scientific notation* to standardize their work.

Scientific notation is a standard way of writing numbers that is used, as the name implies, throughout the sciences. A number is always written as a power of 10 with just one digit to the left of the decimal point. Build numbers in scientific notation by entering a value for **a** and changing the power of 10 to see which way the decimal moves and the value of the number.

What does multiplying by a power of 10 do to a number?

If you multiply by 10^7, what does that do to a number?

What does multiplying by 10^{-5} do to a number?

$$2.031 \times 10^2 = 203.1$$

$a \times 10^n \quad 1 \le |a| < 10$

$$2.031 \times 10^6 = 2031000$$

$a \times 10^n \quad 1 \le a < 10$

How many places and in what direction will the decimal point be moved?

The Real Numbers

List all that apply by letter to describe the following numbers:

A. Counting B. Whole C. Integers D. Rational E. Irrational F. Real

1. 23 ______________________________
2. -13 ______________________________
3. 11/12 ______________________________
4. 5.100 ______________________________
5. 3.10100100010000... ____________________
6. 0 ______________________________

Inequalities

Draw a number line for the given inequality.

1. All real numbers > 3 ________________________
2. All numbers less than –2 ________________________
3. All numbers ≥ 5 ________________________

Fill in the correct symbol (>, <, =).

4. 2.11_______ 3 5. -7/17_______-7/17 6. -99_______-98

Absolute Value

Find the absolute value of the given numbers.

1. -9 ________
2. 9 ________
3. -1.23 ________
4. 0 ________
5. 1 ________
6. -a ________

Additive Inverse

Find the additive inverse of the given numbers.

1.	-92	________	2.	23	________
3.	1.9	________	4.	0	________
5.	-3.58	________	6.	a	________

Multiplicative Inverse

Find the multiplicative inverse of the following numbers.

1.	3/5	________	2.	-1/2	________
3.	4	________	4.	-7/8	________
5.	1	________	6.	a	________

Adding Integers

Find the sum

1.	12 + (-3)	________	2.	-7 + 8	________
3.	-8 + (-3)	________	4.	9 + (-5)	________
5.	-2 + (-7)	________	6.	-1 + -1	________

Subtracting Integers

Find the difference

1.	11 – (-4)	________	2.	-6 – 9	________
3.	-7 – (-4)	________	4.	8 – (-4)	________
5.	-3 – (-6)	________	6.	-1 – -1	________

Multiplying Integers

Find the product.

1. **11 * (-3)** ________ **2.** **-6 * 8** ________

3. **-7 * (-3)** ________ **4.** **8 * (-5)** ________

5. **-3 (-7)** ________ **6.** **-3 * -1** ________

7. **0* (-3)** ________

Dividing Integers

Find the quotient

1. **12 /(-3)** ________ **2.** **-72/8** ________

3. **95 /(-5)** ________ **4.** **-10 /-1** ________

5. **0/(-3)**________

Adding & Subtracting Fractions

1. $\frac{-7}{8}+\frac{3}{4}=$ ________ **2.** $\frac{-7}{8}-\frac{3}{4}=$ ________

3. $\frac{-7}{10}+\frac{-1}{3}=$ ________ **4.** $\frac{-1}{8}-\frac{-3}{4}=$ ________

5. $\frac{1}{6}+\frac{-3}{12}=$ ________ **6.** $\frac{-7}{12}-\frac{-3}{4}=$ ________

Multiplying & Dividing Fractions

1. $\frac{3}{-8}\cdot\frac{14}{-9}=$ ________ **2.** $\frac{-1}{4}\cdot\frac{8}{-9}=$ ________

3. $\frac{4}{15}\cdot\frac{9}{-2}=$ ________ **4.** $\frac{-1}{-6}\cdot\frac{-6}{-5}=$ ________

5. $\frac{9}{-14}\div\frac{-3}{-7}=$ ________

Adding & Subtracting Decimals

1. 9.042 + (3.87) = __________ 2. 14.01 – (12.078) = __________

3. -44.12 +(-5.332) = __________ 4. - 3.15 – (-221.56)= __________

5. 12.1 + (-13.005) = __________ 6. 1.002 – (- 5.7) = __________

Multiplying & Dividing Decimals

1. (-4.5)(5.1) = __________ 2. (-1.2)(-3.5) __________

3. (0.012)(-1.3) = __________ 4. (9.3)(-1.1) __________

5. $\frac{-3.232}{1.6} =$ __________ 6. $\frac{-1.48}{0.99} =$ __________

Evaluating Exponents

1. 2^4 = __________ 2. $(-2)^4$ = __________

3. 5^0 = __________ 4. $(-3)^3$ = __________

5. $(2-3)^4$ = __________ 6. $(1-(-3))^2$ = __________

Evaluating Roots

1. $\sqrt{16}-\sqrt{25}$ = __________ 2. $\sqrt{9}+\sqrt{25}$ = __________

3. $\sqrt{169}-\sqrt{100}$ = __________ 4. $\sqrt[3]{27}+\sqrt[3]{8}$ = __________

5. $\sqrt{49}+\sqrt{25}$ = __________ 6. $\sqrt[4]{16}-\sqrt[3]{125}$ = __________

Order of Operations

1. $2(1-5)+3(2-6) =$ ______ 2. $5-3(2-9)+3(1-4) =$ ______

3. $-2(3+5)-3^2 =$ ______ 4. $(1.2 + 2.8) * (0.5)^2 =$ ______

5. $-2(6+1)^2+\sqrt{25} =$ ______ 6. $-2.3(6.1-5.0)^2+\sqrt{36} =$ ______

Translating English to Math

Translate into math symbols:

1. A total of 3 and some number is –7
2. The sum of half a number and three is two times that number cubed.
3. Negative three times a number is the opposite of that number divided by seven.
4. One third of a number is two times the number squared.

Word Problems

Translate and evaluate the following:

1. The difference of seven and five squared
2. Negative one-half added to the opposite of three
3. Twice the quotient of seven and seventy
4. The ratio of two and five tenths and four and one-half
5. The cube of the quantity two and two tenths decreased by one and two tenths

Properties of Real Numbers

Identify the property illustrated by the following statements.

1. $12(5-7) = 60-84$ 2. $12*0 = 0$
3. $15+38+5+2 = 15+5+38+2 = 60$ 4. $2/3\,(3/3) = 6/9$
5. $48+17+13 = 48+30$ 6. $(17+3)-3 = 17$

Scientific Notation

Convert the following to standard notation:

1\. a) $3.72 * 10^4$ b) $3.721 * 10^8$ c) $4.44 * 10^3$

2\. d) $1.24 * 10^{-8}$ e) $3.15 * 10^{-4}$ f) $32.1 * 10^{-6}$

Write the following numbers in Scientific Notation.

3\. a) 0.00029 b) 0.0000315 c) 0.000000123

d) 32700000 e) 502000000 f) 471500000

7. Solving Linear Equations

Linear equations are the simplest equations; yet they are the most useful equations in all of mathematics because you can **always solve** a linear equation. In linear equations the **variable is to the first power**. They are called linear because when we graph them, **they produce a straight line.** We use them everywhere — to calculate a tip, interest on a loan, or speed for a car. If you really understand how to solve linear equations, then you will understand algebra.

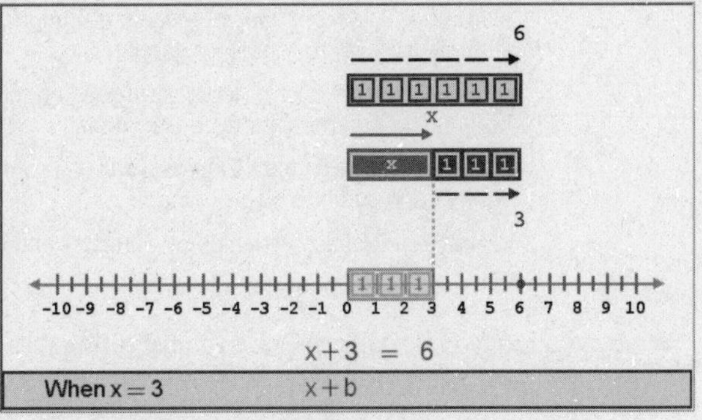

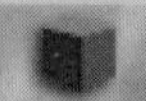

Evaluating Algebraic Expressions

Algebraic expressions are mathematical phrases composed of variables, constants, and grouping symbols linked together by mathematical operations. Unlike a verbal phrase that can be understood with a glance, algebraic expressions must be decoded symbol by symbol.

Variable — A symbol that represents a number, an unknown, or a changing quantity. We usually use letters, (generally **x, y, z**) to represent variables.

Constant — A number or letter that does not change its value. Often letters **a, b,** or **c** represent constants when stating a general pattern or formula.

Algebraic (or Variable) Expression — A combination of numbers and variables linked by **operations** (+,-,*,/,^,√) and symbols of grouping.

Evaluate — Replace variables by numbers and calculate the value of an expression.

We evaluate algebraic expressions by substituting given values for the letters.

Step 1: Substitute the given values for each letter.

Step 2: Evaluate the expression using order of operations.

Substitute:

Let $a = 2$ and $b = -3$.

$$\text{Then, } a^2 + b^2 = (2)^2 + (-3)^2 = 4 + 9 = 13$$

$a^2 + b^2$

Substitute:

Let $a = -4$ and $b = 3$.

$$\text{Then, } a^2 + b^2 = (-4)^2 + (3)^2 = 16 + 9 = 25$$

$a^2 + b^2$

Point 1 & 2: Use order of operations: First square both numbers and then add them. **Point 3: Dynamic Example** — Change the values of **a** and **b** with the joystick to change the problem.

Substitute:

Let $a = 2$ and $b = -3$.

$$\text{Then, } 3a + b = 3(2) + -3 = 6 - 3 = 3$$

$3a + b$

Points 4 & 5: : Use order of operations: First multiply then add or subtract. **Point 6: Dynamic Example —** Change the values of **a** and **b** with the joystick to create new problems.

Substitute:

Let $r = -2$.

$$\text{Then, } -6r^2 + 6r - 9 = -6(-2)^2 + 6(-2) - 9 = -6(4) + 6(-2) - 9 = -24 - 12 - 9 = -45$$

$-6r^2 + 6r - 9$

You can replace the variables with parentheses, and then insert the given value within the parentheses. That way you will be sure to correctly account for sign changes, correctly evaluate exponents, and highlight the next operation.

Substitute:

Let $r = 3$.

$$\text{Then, } -6r^2 + 6r - 9 = -6(3)^2 + 6(3) - 9 = -6(9) + 6(3) - 9 = -54 + 18 - 9 = -45$$

$-6r^2 + 6r - 9$

Points 7-9 are dynamic. You can change the value of the variable to evaluate the expression.

To visualize a **variable** or "**unknown**" we can picture it as a bar — "a variable bar" – that can be different lengths depending upon its value. One or more variable bars can be attached to a number bar to represent an expression.

Think of algebra as the study of variables, in the same way that arithmetic is the study of numbers.

Use the joystick to watch what happens as the variable bar changes values. Notice that as the variable bar gets larger the value of the expression gets larger.
What happens when the value of **x** gets smaller?
What happens when **x** becomes a negative number?
What happens when **x** is zero?

Can **x** be any number? How do you know?

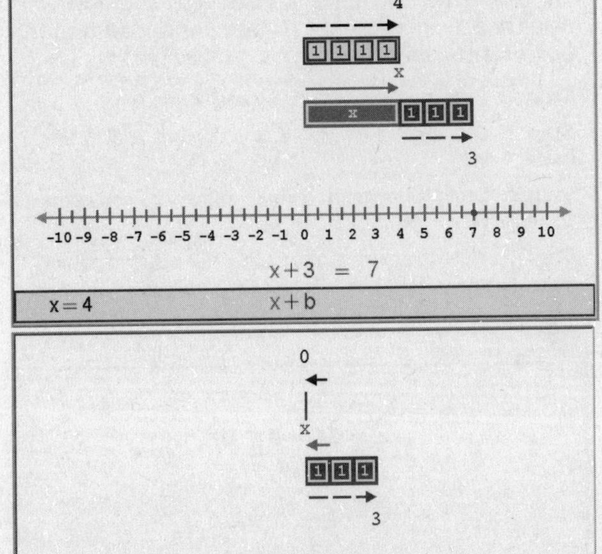

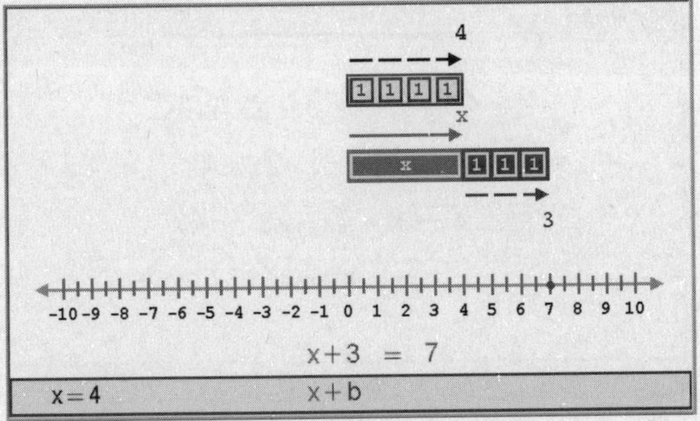

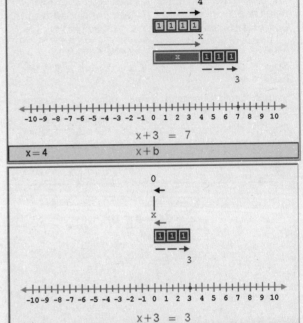

To evaluate an algebraic expression we substitute a value for the variable. Here we are substituting 4 for **x**.

If **x=0,** what is **x+3?**

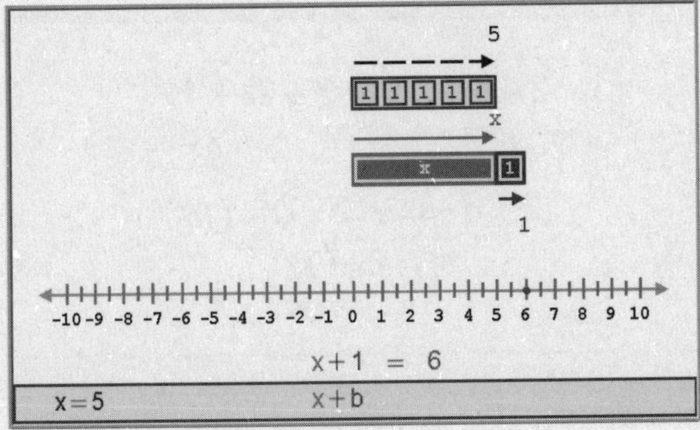

If **x+1=6,** what is the value of **x?**

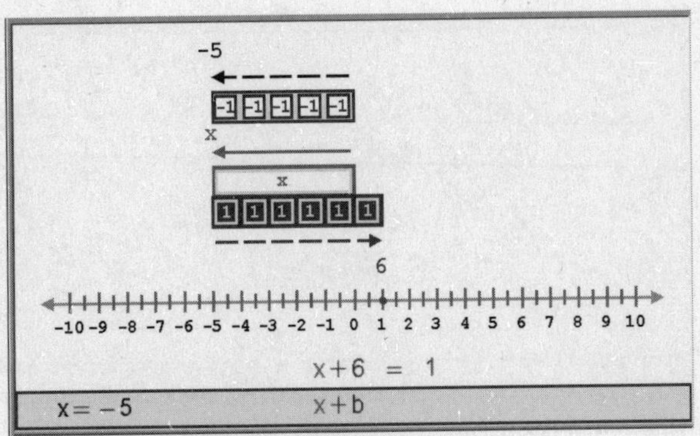

If **x+6=1,** what is the value of **x?**

Combining Like Terms

EnableMath

Terms are algebraic expressions separated by addition or subtraction. Terms can be single numbers, variables, a product of numbers and variables, or variables raised to an exponent. We **simplify** algebraic expressions by combining "like terms." Like terms have the same variables raised to the same exponents.

Term — An expression containing constants and/or variables that are linked only by operations (*,/,^,√).
Like Terms — Terms with the same variables raised to the same exponents.

Coefficient — Usually a number or constant multiplied by the variable in a term. By convention, the coefficient is always written before the variable.

Combining Like Terms — Adding or subtracting like terms to **simplify** the expression.

To tell whether two terms are **like**, look at the variables and their exponents. If they are **the same for both terms**, then those terms can be combined.

Step 1: Combine the constants by adding them.

Step 2: Combine the terms with **x** in them by adding their coefficients.

Step 3: Combine the terms with $\mathbf{x^2}$ in them by adding their coefficients.

Step 4: Write the expression in either the descending or ascending order of the exponents of the variables.

What are like terms?

constants $1, 5, -2$

x terms $x, 2x, -3x$

x^2 terms $x^2, 3x^2, -4x^2$

Combine like terms:

$$2-3x-5+6x$$
$$2-3x-5+6x$$
$$2-5-3x+6x$$
$$-3+3x$$

$a+bx+c+dx$

Point 2: First gather like terms (we colored them alike on the screen), and then combine them.

Combine like terms:

$$2-4x-2x^2+3-2x+4x^2$$
$$2-4x-2x^2+3-2x+4x^2$$
$$2+3-4x-2x-2x^2+4x^2$$
$$5-6x+2x^2$$

$a+bx+cx^2+d+ex+fx^2$

Point 3: Coefficients do not make terms different, but exponents do. The bottom expression is in its **simplest form.**

Combine like terms:

$$2-4x-2x^2+3-2x+4x^2$$
$$2-4x-2x^2+3-2x+4x^2$$
$$2+3-4x-2x-2x^2+4x^2$$
$$5-6x+2x^2$$

$a+bx+cx^2+d+ex+fx^2$

Notice that we are making use of the commutative and associative properties of addition to regroup and combine like terms.

Combine like terms:

$$2-4x-2x^2+3-2x+4x^2$$
$$2-4x-2x^2+3-2x+4x^2$$
$$2+3-4x-2x-2x^2+4x^2$$
$$5-6x+2x^2$$

$a+bx+cx^2+d+ex+fx^2$

This expression could also have been written in *descending order* as:

$$\mathbf{2x^2-6x+5}$$

Combining means to **count up** or **add up** how many of something you have. Picture **like terms** as being **same-sized bars** in an expression. You want to count up how many same-size bars you have and how many unit bars you have, and report the result in an orderly fashion. A simple way to count up is to add coefficients.

Simplify expressions by **combining like terms**.

When we think about it visually, we combine (add up) the number bars, we combine (add up) the variable bars, and we combine variables to powers.

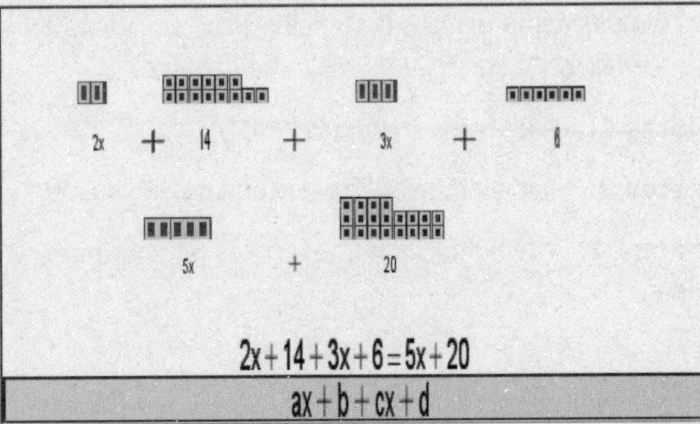

3x + 2 + 4x + 3

7x + 5

$3x+2+4x+3=7x+5$

$ax+b+cx+d$

1x + 3 + 1x + 7

2x + 10

$1x+3+1x+7=2x+10$

$ax+b+cx+d$

Can you combine a term that has only a number bar with a term that has both a number bar and a variable bar?

Can you combine 3x and x*3?

Hint: In any term, when we multiply a number and a variable, we do not need the multiplication sign — it is understood!

Multiplying Monomials

EnableMath

Monomials are algebraic expressions that have only **one** term. Nomial means *term* or *name*, and mono means *one*. The **product** of two monomials is also a monomial. **Binomials** have **two** terms, **trinomials** have **three** terms, and **polynomials** have **many** terms.

Multiplying Monomials — The product of two monomials is the product of their constants times the product of their variables. Their product is another monomial.

Identity Property — The identity for multiplication is 1. Any number or expression, multiplied by 1, does not change. **1*a = a.**

Inverse Property — The inverse of multiplication is division. $\frac{a}{a} = a(1/a) = 1$

To multiply monomials, first multiply the constants (coefficients), and then multiply the variables.

Step 1: Multiply the constants.

Step 2: Multiply the variables by adding exponents.

Point 1: We multiply a number times another number.

Multiply:

$$6(-7)$$
$$= -42$$

a(b)

Multiply:

$$5(2x)$$
$$= 10x$$

a(bx)

Point 2: A number times a variable (number * variable).

Multiply:

$$x(3x)$$
$$= 3x^2$$

x(ax)

Point 3: A variable times a variable — be sure to add the exponents. Remember: **x** means $\mathbf{x^1}$.

Multiply:

$$-4x(-2x)$$
$$= 8x^2$$

ax(bx)

Point 4: Multiply the coefficients and add the exponents of the variables. Watch out for the signs.

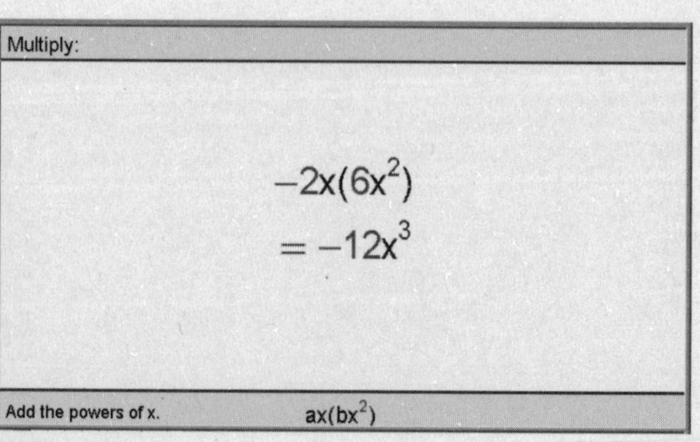

Point 5: Again, add the exponents.

When you think about multiplication picture a rectangle. **A product is always a rectangle, and its size is found by multiplying the lengths of the two sides (the factors).** Picture variable bars and numbers as the sides of the rectangle. Notice that the larger box containing the product is like a graph. Consider that quadrant I is positive, factors are up and right; II is negative, factors are up and left; III is positive, factors are down and left; and IV is negative, factors are down and right. This is a powerful visualization that will ensure the **correct sign** of your answer—one of the pitfalls of every algebra student!

Change **a** and **b** as well as **x** to make this visualization dynamic.

If the product is positive, where are the factors located? If the product is negative, where are the factors located?

Are there any products that cannot be represented by a rectangle?

Are the sides of the products interchangeable—does changing the order change the answer?

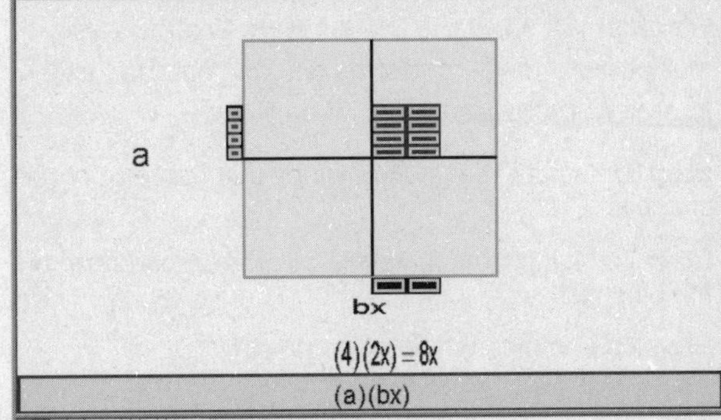

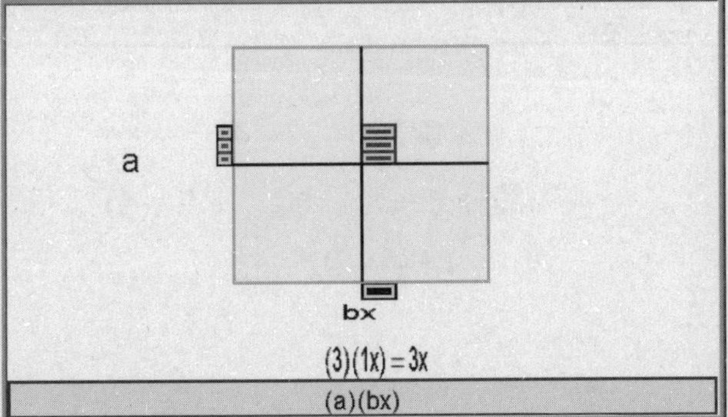

If **x=5**, is **3*x=15**?

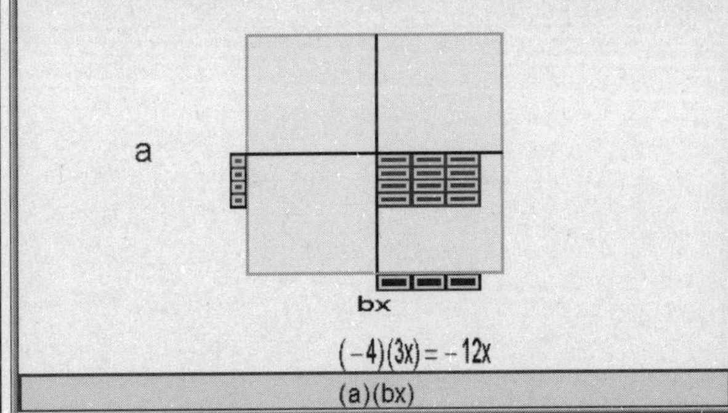

If **a<0** and **b>0**, will their product be positive or negative?

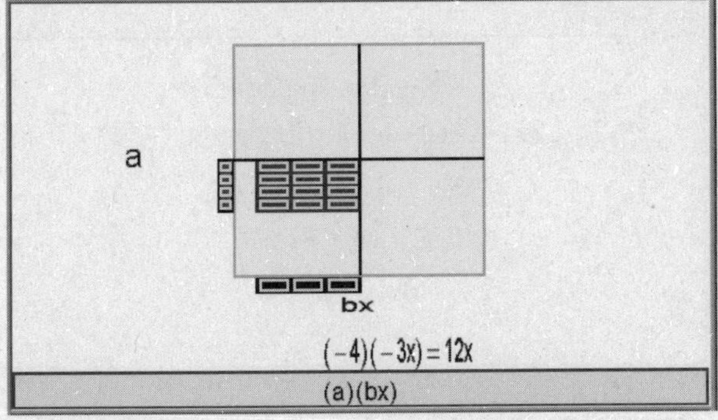

If **a<0** and **b<0**, will their product be positive or negative?

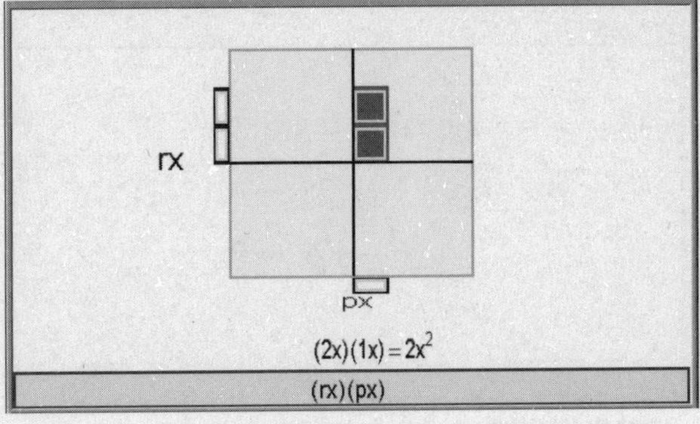

What would **2x*x** look like? What does **2x*2x** look like?

The distributive property allows us to multiply algebraic expressions with two or more terms. It is useful in simplifying algebraic expressions by allowing the removal of parentheses so that like terms can be combined.

The Distributive Property : **a(b+c) = ab+ac** for any real numbers a, b, c.

The Commutative Property : **a+b=b+a or a*b=b*a.** Order does not matter for addition or multiplication.

The Associative Property : **a+(b+c)=(a+b)+c or a*(b*c)=(a*b)*c.** Grouping does not matter for addition or multiplication.

We often talk about the **Distributive Property** as multiplying through, or distributing, the outside factor to each of the inside terms.

Step 1: Multiply the monomial by the first term of the binomial.

Step 2: Multiply the monomial by the second term of the binomial.

Step 3: Combine like terms to simplify.

Distribute:

$$2(3x+6)$$
$$2(3x)+2(6)$$
$$6x+12$$

Distribute:

$$-2x(3x+4)$$
$$-2x(3x)+-2x(4)$$
$$-6x^2-8x$$

Point 2: This is an example of the **Distributive Property** in which both the monomial and the binomial terms have variables.

Distribute:

$$-3(2x^2-3x-4)$$
$$-3(2x^2)+-3(-3x)+-3(-4)$$
$$-6x^2+9x+12$$

Point 3: The **Distributive Property** holds no matter how many terms there are. Be sure to rewrite your answer in descending order of the variables, as it is done here.

Distribute:

$$4x(-3x^2+3x-2)$$
$$4x(-3x^2)+4x(3x)+4x(-2)$$
$$-12x^3+12x^2-8x$$

Point 4: Be careful of the signs of the products.

Distribute:

$$2(-3x+2)-4x(2x-3)$$
$$2(-3x)+2(2)+-4x(2x)+-4x(-3)$$
$$-6x+4-8x^2+12x$$
$$6x+4-8x^2$$
$$-8x^2+6x+4$$

Point 5 & 6: First, distribute. then add the terms to simplify.

The **Distributive Property** may be the most important property in mathematics, for it **combines multiplication and addition**, and allows us to **multiply across any number of terms**.

We start out with the simplest case of a monomial times a binomial. But, we can apply the Distributive Property to the product of any two polynomials. Think of the Distributive Property as multiplication, and visualize the process with rectangles, as before.

If the monomial factor is negative is the product negative? If the monomial factor is positive will the product always be positive?

How do you know which direction to align the factors on the frame?

Will the product always make a rectangle?

How do you know if the product is positive or negative?

Can you determine the sign of the product just by looking at the coefficients?

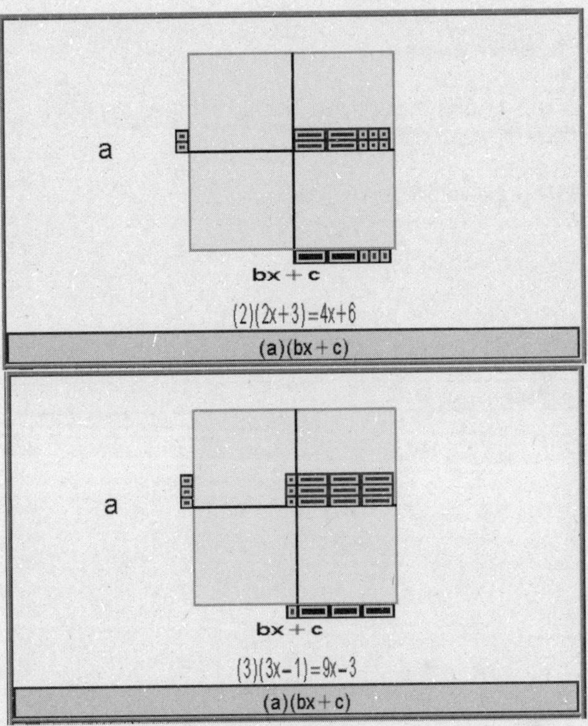

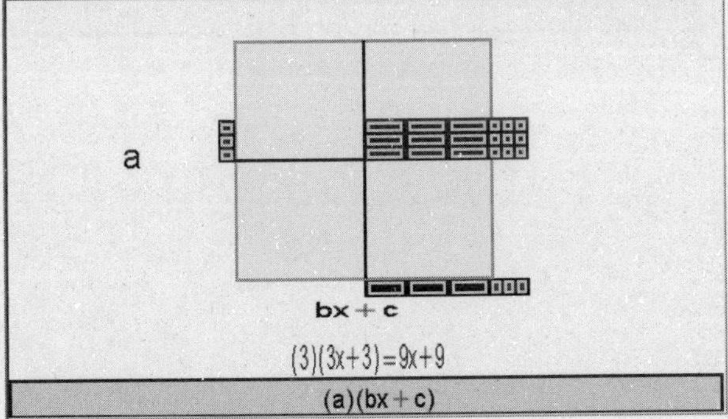

Is **3(3x+2) > 2(3x+3)** ?

Is **3(3x-2) > 9x+6**? What does the rectangle look like if **c<0** ?

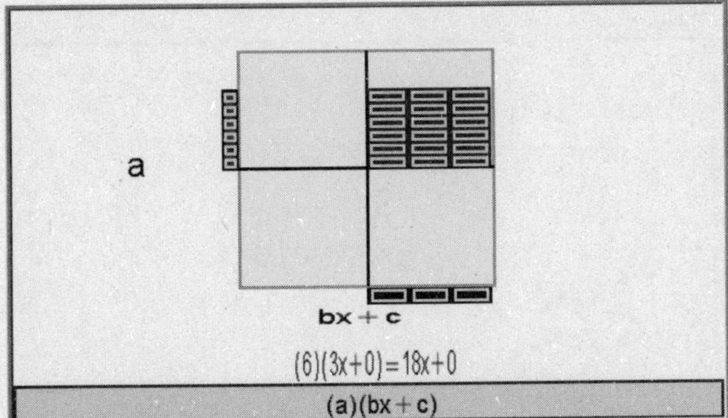

Can you go backwards as well? Does **xb+xc=a(b+c)?** Is this true for every number?

Hint: This is what we call factoring: Start with a product and find its factors.

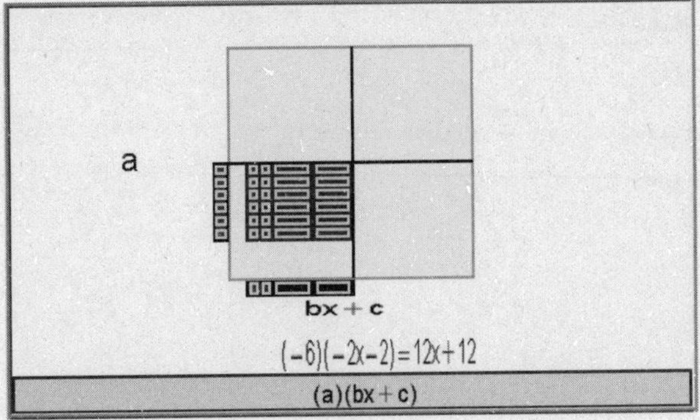

If all of the coefficients are negative, will the resulting coefficients be positive or negative?

Solving x+b=c

An **equation** is made up of two expressions separated by an equal sign (=). We call the expressions "**sides**" of the equation.

Equations can be rewritten without affecting the equality if both sides are changed by the same amount. For example, we can add, subtract, multiply, or divide both sides of an equation by the same number, without changing the equality.

Solving an equation means finding the value of **x** that makes a true statement.

One of the simplest linear equation looks like **x+b=c.** Notice that the variable, **x,** is to the first power. Equations like this are sometimes called **first degree equations** or **linear equations**.

To solve x+b=c

Step 1: Add the additive inverse of b (-b) to each side of the equation.

Step 2: Simplify both sides.

Solve for x:

$$x+2=7$$

x+b=c

Solve for x:

$$x+2=7$$
$$x+2-2=7-2$$

Subtract 2 from both sides. x+b=c

The additive inverse of 2 is −2. Therefore, add −2 to both sides of the equation.

Note: Sometimes we think "add the opposite of b to c."

Solve for x:

$$x+2=7$$
$$x+2-2=7-2$$
$$x=5$$

x+b=c

Always simplify to solve for x. This is the value of x that makes the equation true.

Hint: Always check your work. Does **(5)+2=7**?

Solve for x:

$$x-4=2$$
$$x-4+4=2+4$$
$$x=6$$

x+b=c

If the **b** term is **negative**, we **add** it to both sides...

Solve for x:

$$x+3=-7$$
$$x+3-3=-7-3$$
$$x=-10$$

x+b=c

...and if it is **positive,** we **subtract** it.
In this **dynamic example,** change **b** and **c** to make a new problem.

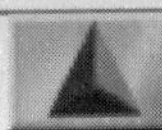

The concept of **solving an equation** is to find out how big the **x** variable has to be in order for the two sides to be the same. We can visualize an equation as two bars, one for each side. We place them, one above the other, to make them easy to compare. Solving the equation means finding a value for **x** that makes both bars the same length.

Use the joystick to change the value of **a** and **b** for different equations.

What happens when **b** is negative?
What happens when **c** is negative?
If **c** is negative will **x** always be negative?

Is adding the additive inverse always like subtracting? How do you know if you should add or subtract a number to both sides?

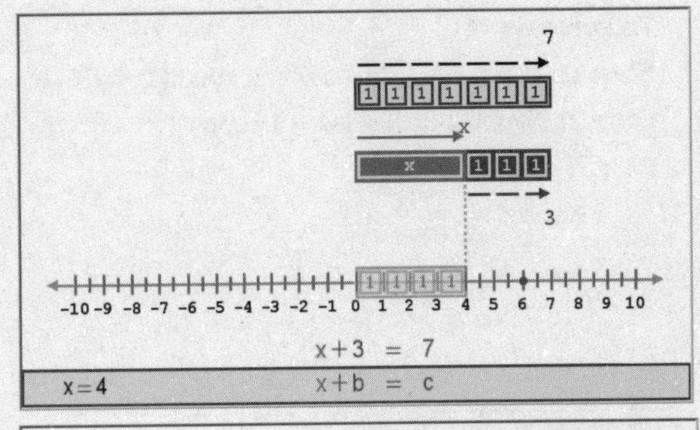

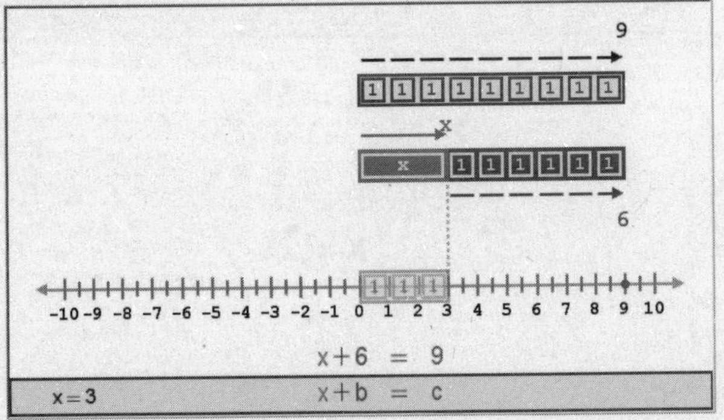

For x+6=9, if you subtract 6 from both sides, is x=3 the solution?

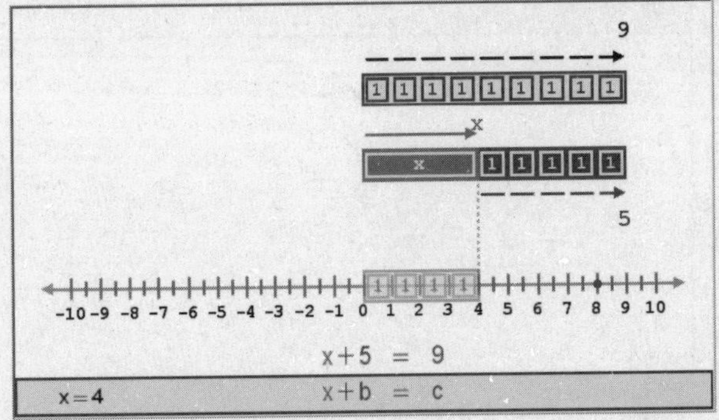

If x+b-b=c-b, does **x** always equal **c-b?**

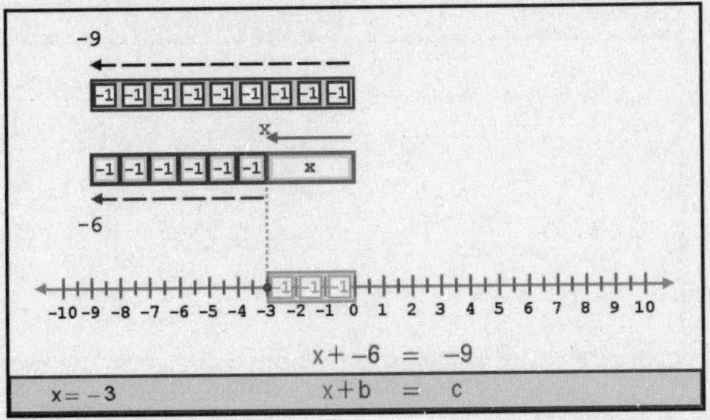

If x-6=-9, is x<0?

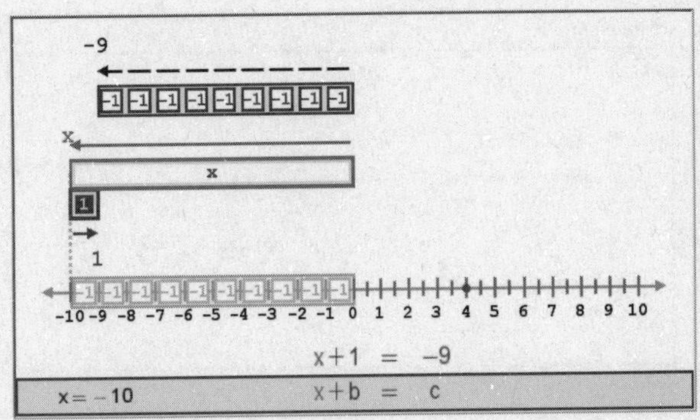

If x+1=-9, is x<0?

Another simple form of a linear equation is **ax=c**. To solve this type, we multiply both sides by the multiplicative inverse of **a** (the coefficient of **x**) and then simplify. Multiplying both sides of an equation by the same non-zero number does NOT affect the equality of the equation.

Things to remember:

- Multiplicative inverse (reciprocal) of a: The number multiplied by a, that gives the product of 1. If a is a whole number, then the inverse of a is 1/a.
- Multiplying by 1/a is the same as dividing by a.

To solve ax=c

Step 1: Multiply both sides of the equation **by 1/a.**

Step 2: Simplify both sides. **x=c/a**

$$\left(\frac{1}{a}\right) ax = \left(\frac{1}{a}\right) c$$

$$\frac{a}{a} x = \frac{c}{a}$$

$$x = \frac{c}{a}$$

Solve for x

$$3x = 9$$

Select values for a = 3 and c = 9.

Solve for x

$$3x = 9$$

$$\frac{3x}{3} = \frac{9}{3}$$

Divide both sides by a. ax = c

The multiplicative inverse of 3 is 1/3, therefore, multiply both sides by 1/3.

Solve for x

$$3x = 9$$

$$\frac{3x}{3} = \frac{9}{3}$$

$$x = 3$$

Solution ax = c

Simplify to **solve for x**. This is the value of **x** that makes the equation true.

Hint: Check your work: Does **3(3) = 9**?

Solve for x

$$-2x = 6$$

$$\frac{-2x}{-2} = \frac{6}{-2}$$

$$x = -3$$

Solution ax = c

Divide both sides by **−2** and simplify. Watch for sign rules.

Solve for x

$$-4x = -8$$

$$\frac{-4x}{-4} = \frac{-8}{-4}$$

$$x = 2$$

Solution ax = c

Divide by **−4**. Watch out for signs.

In the last lesson, we solved equations fitting the pattern of **x+b=c**. Notice that the coefficient of the **x**-variable was always **1**. What happens if the coefficient of **x** is not **1**? How do we solve the linear equation?

Our goal for solving **ax=c** is to make the coefficient of **x** be **1**. [Think about it this way: We want to find out how big *one* **x** is before we find out how big *ax*'s are.] To do this, we multiply the coefficient **a** by its multiplicative inverse, **1/a**, and of course, we have to do the same thing to both sides to keep the equation in balance.

Use the joystick to control **c**, and make **c** smaller and smaller. What happens to **x** as **c** changes to negative? If **a** is negative, what happens to **x** as you decrease **c**?

How do we know to make the **x-bars 4** units long?

How do you check your work?

Can you divide both sides by the same non-zero number?

How do you know if the answer is positive or negative?

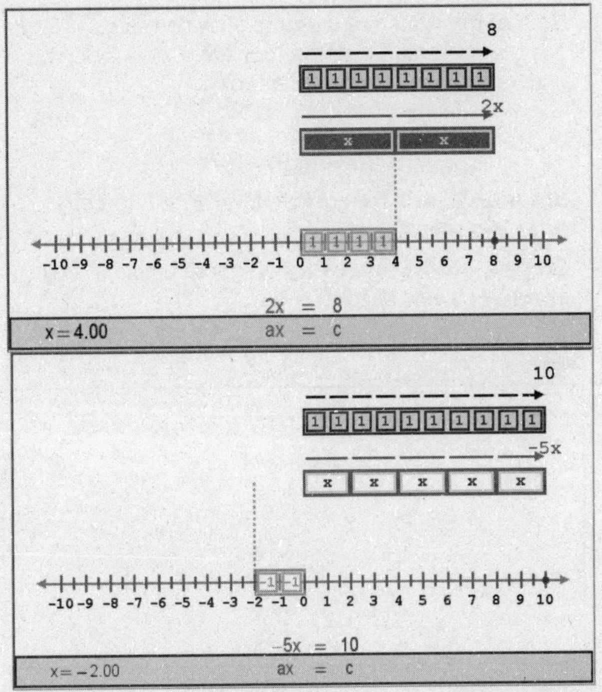

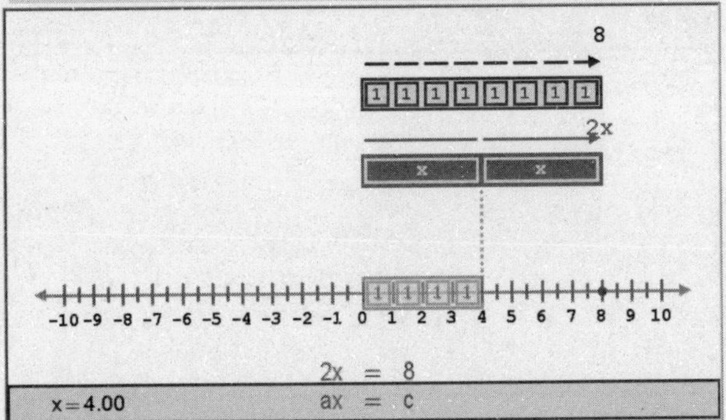

Is (1/2)2x = x? Is (1/2)*8 =8/2? Did we divide by 2 or multiply by 1/2?

What is the multiplicative inverse of **–5**?

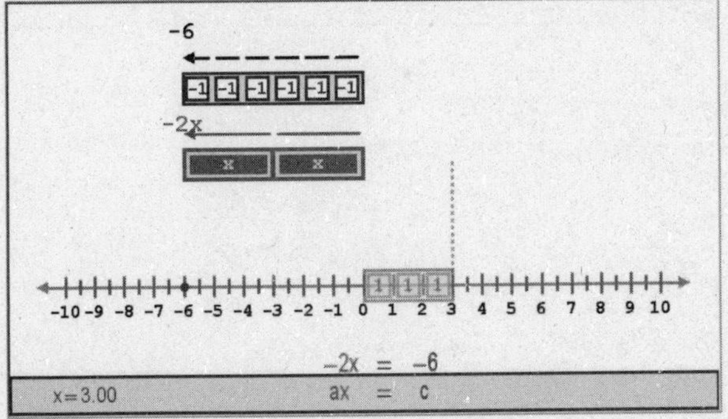

Is **x** a positive or negative number?

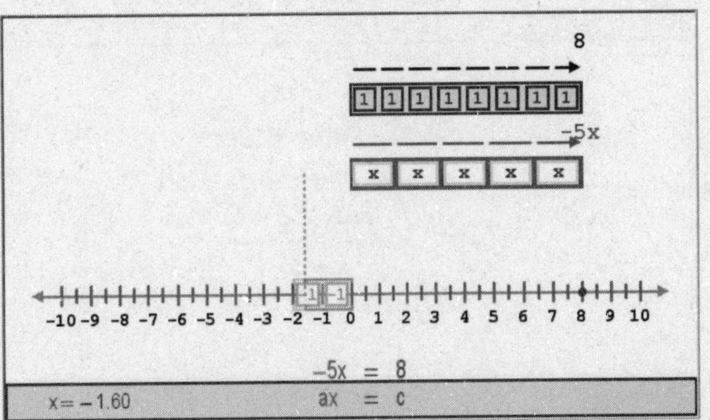

Can this equation be solved with an integer?

Solving ax+b=c

EnableMath

Solving a full linear equation **ax+b=c** combines the steps presented in the last two assignments to find the value of **x** that makes the equation true.

We often say, "**Solve for x**", and we mean: Manipulate the equation to get **x** by itself, on one side of the equal sign.

We do this by first adding (or subtracting) and then multiplying (or dividing) the **same** numbers to **both** sides of the equation.

Each of the examples presented has five steps. (Step 1 is the presentation of the problem.) At right is the general pattern for solving ax+b=c.

Solving ax+b=c

Steps 1-3: Add the additive inverse of **b** to both sides and simplify.

Steps 4—5: Multiply both sides by the multiplicative inverse of **a** and simplify.

Solve for x:

$$ax+b=c$$
$$ax+b-b=c-b$$
$$ax=c-b$$
$$\frac{ax}{a}=\frac{c-b}{a}$$
$$x=\frac{(c-b)}{a}$$

ax + b = c

Solve for x

$$8x+6=-7$$
$$8x+6-6=-7-6$$

Subtract 6 from each side. ax + b = c

Steps 1—3: The additive inverse of 6 is **−6,** so add **−6** to both sides of the equation and simplify.

Solve for x

$$8x+6=-7$$
$$8x+6-6=-7-6$$
$$8x=-13$$
$$\frac{8x}{8}=\frac{-13}{8}$$
$$x=-1\frac{5}{8}$$

Combine like terms, divide both sides by 8, and put result in simplified form. ax + b = c

Step 4—5: Multiply both sides by **1/8** to solve for **x** and simplify.

We can say, "Divide through by **8.**"

Solve for x

$$-3x+5=-4$$
$$-3x+5-5=-4-5$$
$$-3x=-9$$
$$\frac{-3x}{-3}=\frac{-9}{-3}$$
$$x=3$$

Combine like terms, divide both sides by −3, and put result in simplified form. ax + b = c

Add **−5** and then divide by **−3**. Substitute **3** for **x** in the original equation to check the answer.

Solve for x

$$-3x-2=10$$
$$-3x-2+2=10+2$$
$$-3x=12$$
$$\frac{-3x}{-3}=\frac{12}{-3}$$
$$x=-4$$

Combine like terms, divide both sides by −3, and put result in simplified form. ax + b = c

Add **2** and then divide by **−3**. How do we know to divide through by **−3** rather than **+3**?

Check: Does (-3)(-4)-2=10?

Every **linear equation** can be put into the form **ax+b=c**. To solve it, first add the additive inverse to both sides, and then, multiply both sides by the multiplicative inverse.

Use the joystick to change **a**, **b**, and **c** to solve for **x**.

How do the steps in solving an equation make use of the order of operations? Why do we add or subtract before we multiply or divide?

Where are **c**, **b**, **a**, and **x** in the image to the right? What happens when you change each one of these quantities?

When solving an equation, if a number is added to a variable quantity, what operation is called for? If a number is multiplied by a variable quantity, what operation is called for?

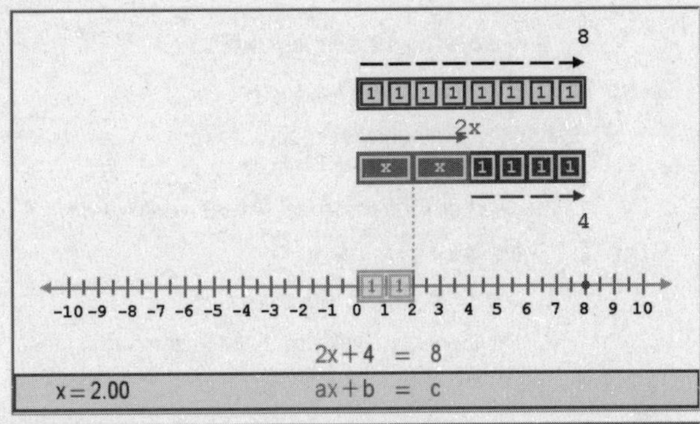

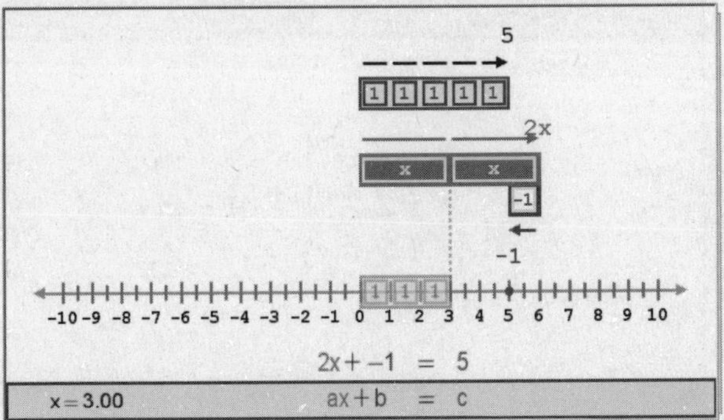

Here, **x=3** solves the equation. What is the direction of the arrow of the −1 unit? Is it "taking away" from the two **x=3** bars? Does that make the lengths of the top bar and bottom bar the same.

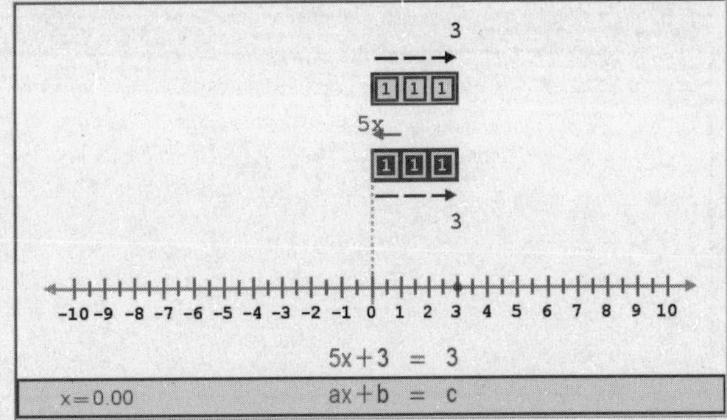

Can **x=0?** How do you know when **x=0?.**

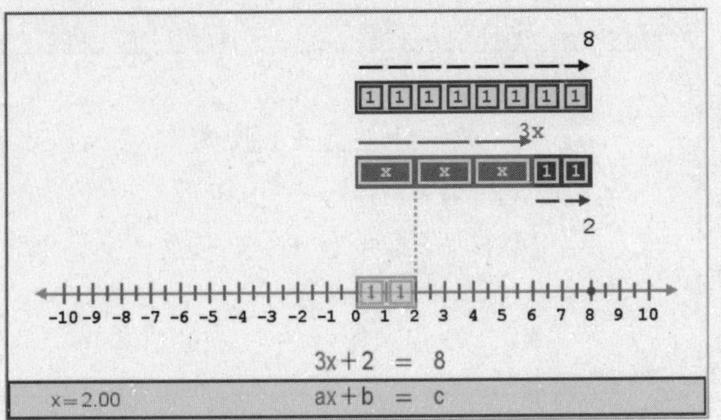

Back track: Visualize taking away **2**, and then divide the result by **3**.

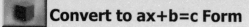

Convert to ax+b=c Form

To solve more **complex or multi-step linear equations**, we first convert those equations to standard form **ax+b=c**. We first gather all of the variable terms on the left side by **adding** their additive inverses (or opposites) to both sides of the equation, and then combining like terms. This is called "**isolating the variable**."

Once the equation is in **ax+b=c** form, we know how to solve it: **Add** the additive **inverse of b** to both sides and simplify. Then, **multiply** each side by the **multiplicative inverse of a** and simplify.

Solving linear equations

Step 1: Convert to **ax+b=c** form:

1. Use Distributive Property to remove parentheses and combine like terms.
2. Add or subtract to get **x**-terms on the left.

Step 2: Solve **ax+b=c** for **x**:

1. Add —b to both sides.
2. Multiply both sides by 1/a. (Divide both sides by a)

Solve for x:

$$ax+b=c$$
$$ax+b-b=c-b$$
$$ax=c-b$$
$$\frac{ax}{a}=\frac{c-b}{a}$$
$$x=\frac{(c-b)}{a}$$

ax + b = c

Convert to ax+b=c Form:

$$2x+2=1+3x$$

ax + b = c

Notice in the problem above, that the variable term is on both sides of the equation. In order to solve for **x**, we need to **have x on one side only**.

Convert to ax+b=c Form:

$$2x+2=1+3x$$
$$2x-3x+2=1+3x-3x$$
$$-1x+2=1$$

Now, it's in ax+b=c form. ax + b = c

Above, we identify the additive inverse of the variable term, **-3x**, to move it to the other side and combine like terms. Notice that –1x and –x are the same. Now solve for **x**.

Convert to ax+b=c Form:

$$3x+2-5x-4=-2x-2+5x+10$$
$$-2x+-2=3x+8$$
$$-2x-3x-2=3x-3x+8$$

Subtract 3x from both sides. ax + b = c

Here, we combine terms as the first step, then add the opposite of 3x (-3x) to both sides. What does the next step do?

Convert to ax+b=c Form:

$$-2-(-4x-4)=5+(2x+7)$$
$$-2+4x+4=5+2x+7$$
$$-2+4x-2x+4=5+2x-2x+7$$
$$2x+2=12$$

Now, it's in ax+b=c form. a – (bx + c) = d + (ex + f)

Remove parentheses first—note the sign changes on the right side. Next add or subtract to move the x-term from the right side to the left side. Combine like terms. Now solve for **x**.

Convert to ax+b=c Form

An equation can have many terms, but as long as no term has a variable to a power higher than **1,** it will still be a linear equation. We can solve any linear equation. First, convert it to the standard **ax+b=c** form: Put all of the terms with a variable in them on the left side and combine them. Then, solve it by moving all of the constant terms to the right side, and combine them as well.

Can an equation be equal to zero? If **ax+b=0**, what must be the relationship between the two terms **ax** and **b**? When we get into solving polynomial equations (equations with terms to higher powers), we will often set them **=0**.

Why are the two bars the same length when x=3?

How do you know when the equation is solved?

How do you know if it is the only solution?

How do you check your answer?

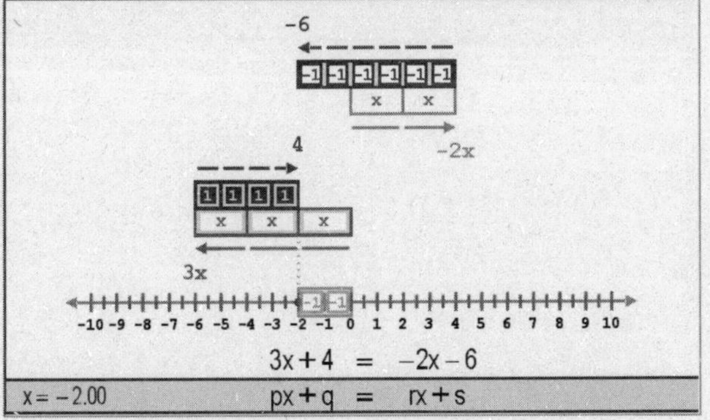

What happens to the bars as **x** gets larger? What happens when **x** gets smaller? (Notice that each bar is being evaluated for the value of **x**, shown on the number line.)

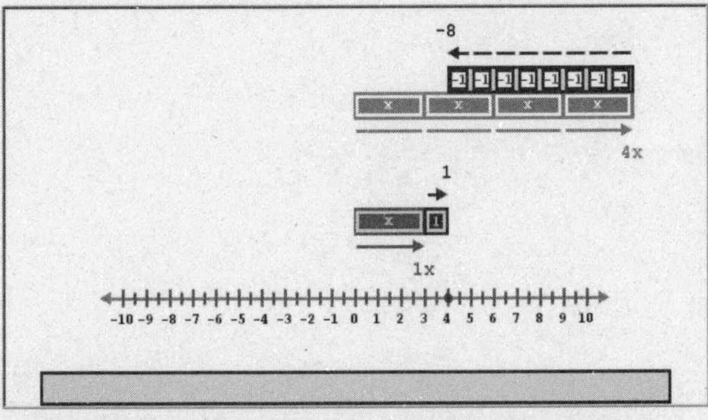

This is the correct representation for finding the solution to **x+1=4(x-2).** What is the intermediate step? What is the solution? How do you know?

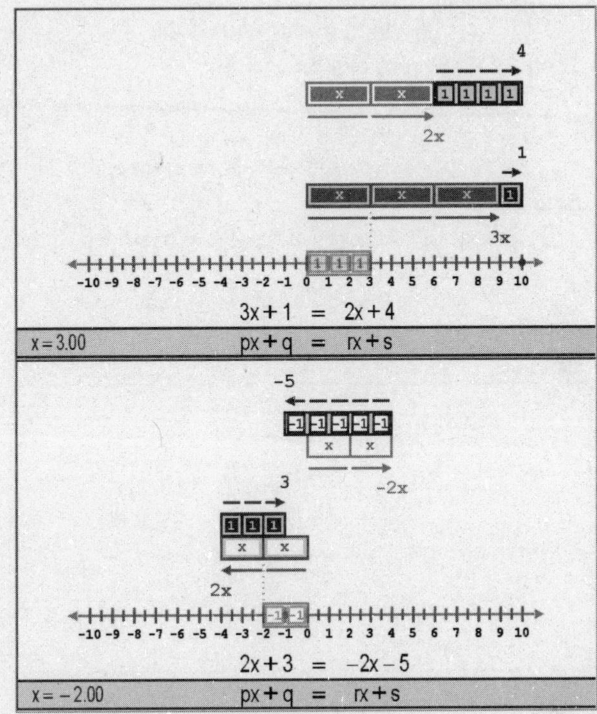

What tells you **x = -2** is the correct answer?

Is it the only answer?

How do you know?

Linear equations with fractions can be solved by putting them into **ax+b=c** form. Fractions, however, often cause difficulty because of the possibility of arithmetic errors. We can eliminate much of the fraction arithmetic by multiplying both sides of the equation by the **Lowest Common Denominator (LCD)** of all the fractions. This is called "**clearing fractions**."

Solving linear equations

Step 1: Convert to **ax+b=c** form:

1. Use Distributive Property to remove parentheses and combine like terms.
2. Add or subtract to get **x**-terms on the left.

Step 2: Solve **ax+b=c** for **x**:

1. Clear fractions by multiplying **a**, **b**, and **c** by the **LCD**.
2. Add **—b** (the additive inverse) to both sides.

Solve for x:

$$\frac{-3}{4}x+\frac{5}{6}=\frac{11}{24}$$

ax + b = c

Solve for x:

$$\frac{-3}{4}x+\frac{5}{6}=\frac{11}{24}$$
$$\frac{-3}{4}x+\frac{5}{6}-\frac{5}{6}=\frac{11}{24}-\frac{5}{6}$$
$$\frac{-3}{4}x=\frac{11}{24}-\frac{20}{24}$$
$$\frac{-3}{4}x=\frac{-9}{24}$$
$$\frac{-3}{4}x=\frac{-3}{8}$$
$$\frac{-4}{3}\left(\frac{-3}{4}x\right)=\frac{-4}{3}\left(\frac{-3}{8}\right)$$
$$x=\frac{1}{2}$$

ax + b = c

Point 1: Worked without clearing fractions.

Solve for x:

$$\frac{1}{2}x-\frac{2}{7}=\frac{4}{35}$$
$$\frac{1}{2}x-\frac{2}{7}+\frac{2}{7}=\frac{4}{35}+\frac{2}{7}$$
$$\frac{1}{2}x=\frac{4}{35}+\frac{10}{35}$$
$$\frac{1}{2}x=\frac{14}{35}$$
$$\frac{1}{2}x=\frac{2}{5}$$
$$2\left(\frac{1}{2}x\right)=2\left(\frac{2}{5}\right)$$
$$x=\frac{4}{5}$$

ax + b = c

Point 2: Worked with clearing fractions.

Solve for x:

$$\frac{2}{3}x+1=\frac{4}{3}x+5$$
$$\frac{2}{3}x-\frac{4}{3}x+1=5$$
$$\frac{-2}{3}x+1=5$$
$$\frac{-2}{3}x=4$$
$$-2x=3\cdot 4$$
$$x=\frac{3*4}{-2}$$
$$x=-6$$

$\frac{a}{b}x+c=\frac{d}{b}x+f$

Point 3: You can clear fractions whenever it is convenient. What is the multiplicative inverse of –2/3? When can that be used?

Solve for x:

$$\frac{2}{3}(1x+2)=\frac{1}{3}(4x+5)$$
$$3*\frac{2}{3}(1x+2)=3*\frac{1}{3}(4x+5)$$
$$2(1x+2)=1(4x+5)$$
$$2x+4=4x+5$$
$$2x-4x+4=5$$
$$(2-4)x+4=5$$
$$(2-4)x=5-4$$
$$(-2)x=1$$
$$x=\frac{-1}{2}$$
$$x=\frac{1}{-2}$$

Reduce. $\frac{a}{b}(cx+d)=\frac{f}{g}(hx+j)$

Point 4: Clearing fractions *before* removing parentheses provides a short-cut. Be careful to multiply every term by the LCD.

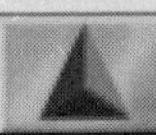

Fractions follow the same rules as integers, therefore, visualize solving **equations with fractions** using the same processes as with integers. Fractions are shown as partially-shaded bars.

The process of solving equations with fractions can be exactly the same as for solving equations with integers, or you can choose to add a step to **clear the fractions** by "multiplying through" by the **Lowest Common Denominator (LCD)**.

What does the red dot indicate?

Can you backtrack? Undo the last operation first—is that the same as subtracting 3?

Then the next to the last thing—is that the same as dividing by 2/3?

Can **x = 0**? Can **f=0**? Can **g = 0**? Can **c = 0**?

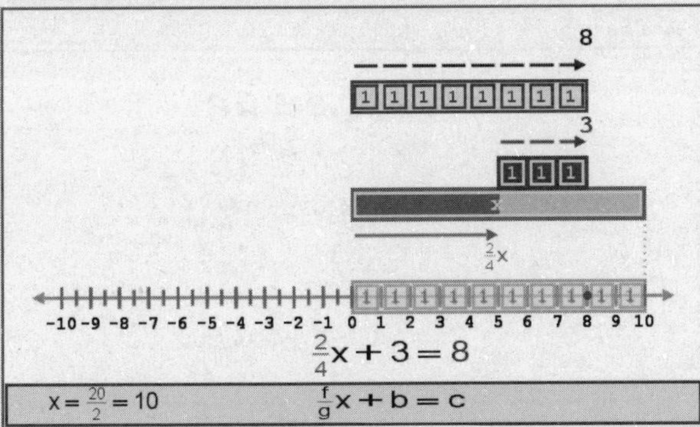

Now change **g** (the denominator) to **4**. What is the value of **x** that solves this equation? **1/2** of **2** is what?

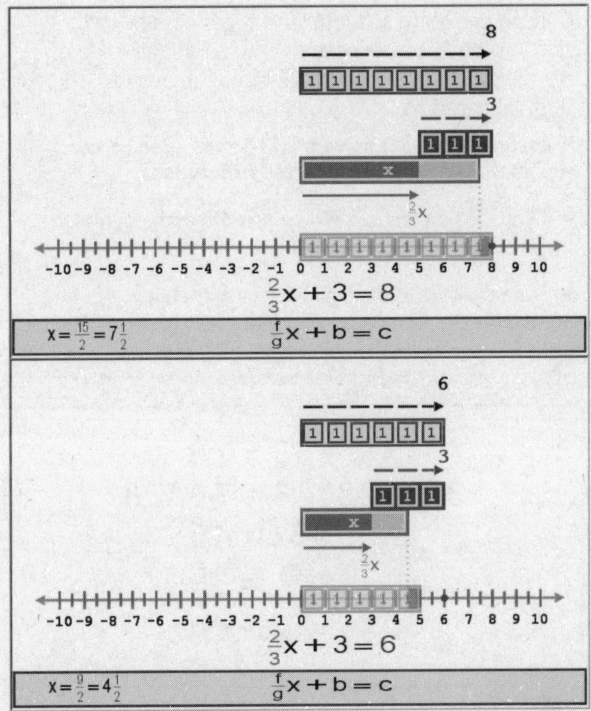

What value of **x** makes this linear equation true? If **2/3** of **x** **equals 2,** then **x=3**.

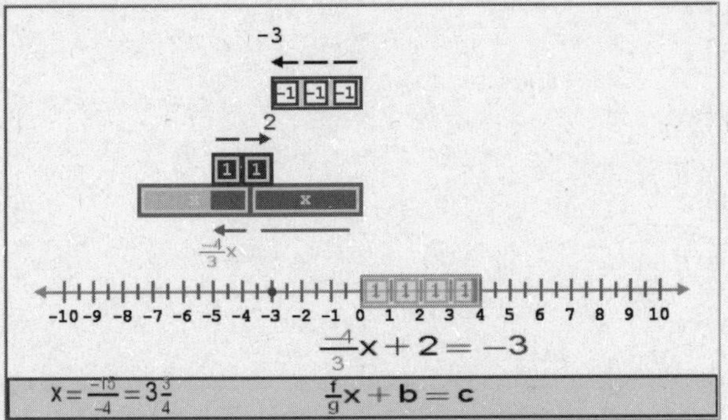

Multiply a number by **–4**, divide that result by **3,** add **2**. What do you get? Make up some more problems like this and then show them with the visualization.

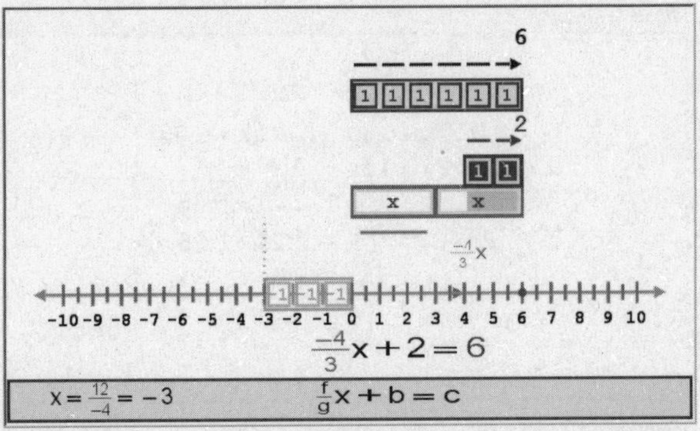

If the fractional coefficient of **x** is less than 0, then will **x** be negative for every value of **b** and **c**? Here, **x** is negative because **c-b>0**.

Equations with Decimals

EnableMath

We can solve **equations with decimals** in the same way that we solve integer linear equations, or we can solve them like fraction equations by "clearing the decimals." Most of the time, clearing the decimals is not necessary, but if you would prefer to work with **whole numbers**, multiply both sides by the power of ten that will clear the decimals.

Solving decimal equations might require division, resulting in answers with long decimal parts. Be sure to round them off to the indicated place value. To review the process for rounding decimals, go to Module 3.1.4 Rounding Decimals.

Solving decimal equations or integer equations that don't come out even requires the additional step of deciding how many decimal places the answer will be approximated to.

*** Assume that all answers will be rounded to two decimal places unless directed otherwise.**

- Rounded-off answers will be noted with the sign ≈ to indicate "approximately equal."
- The example to the right is an integer equation but the answer is a decimal approximation to two decimal places.

Solve for x:

$$3(2x-3) = 2(-1x+9)$$
$$6x-9 = -2x+18$$
$$6x-9+2x = 18$$
$$6x+2x = 18+9$$
$$(6+2)x = 18+9$$
$$8x = 27$$
$$x = \frac{27}{8}$$
$$x \approx 3.38$$

Round to two decimal places. $a(bx+c)=d(fx+g)$

Solve for x:

$$3.8x+2.8 = 7.3$$
$$3.8x+2.8-2.8 = 7.3-2.8$$
$$3.8x = 4.5$$
$$\frac{3.8x}{3.8} = \frac{4.5}{3.8}$$
$$x \approx 1.18$$

Round to 2 decimal places. $ax+b=c$

This example is in **ax+b=c** form. Solve as before, or clear the decimal by multiplying by 10.

Solve for x:

$$-2.8x-2.4 = 9.6$$
$$-2.8x-2.4+2.4 = 9.6+2.4$$
$$-2.8x = 12.0$$
$$\frac{-2.8x}{-2.8} = \frac{12.0}{-2.8}$$
$$x \approx -4.29$$

Round to 2 decimal places. $ax+b=c$

Dynamic Example: Put in your own problem to work, step-by-step, to its solution.

Solve for x:

$$0.125(2x-2) = 0.250(-2x+9)$$
$$0.25x-0.25 = -0.5x+2.25$$
$$0.25x-0.25+0.5x = 2.25$$
$$0.25x+0.5x = 2.25+0.25$$
$$(0.25+0.5)x = 2.25+0.25$$
$$0.75x = 2.5$$
$$x = \frac{2.5}{0.75}$$
$$x \approx 3.33$$

Round to two decimal places. $a(bx+c)=d(fx+g)$

Will multiplying by 1000 help you solve this problem?

Solve for x:

$$-0.6x+0.3+0.2x-0.3 = 0.3x-0.2+0.3x-0.3$$
$$-0.6x+0.3+0.2x-0.3-0.3x-0.3x = -0.2-0.3$$
$$-0.6x+0.2x-0.3x-0.3x = -0.2-0.3-0.3+0.3$$
$$-1.0x = -0.5$$
$$x = \frac{-0.5}{-1.0}$$
$$x = 0.50$$

Round to 2 decimal places. $ax+b+cx+d=fx+g+hx+j$

Some of these steps can be eliminated by combining like terms. Can you find them?

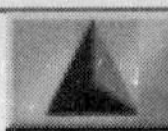

We show the decimal value of each of the bars with shading, because the decimal lines would be too close together to count them or to see them distinctly. You have to imagine that each bar is divided into either 10 or 100 equal parts. As usual, the best way to understand this concept is to experiment with this visualization by changing the values, or parameters, of the equation. Pay particular attention to what happens when each component changes **from positive to negative**.

How do you change a whole number to a decimal?

If there are no directions, then round answers to the nearest one hundredth (2 decimal places) or to the number of decimal places in the factors.

How do you know how many decimal places to carry?

Can you round off before solving for **x**? How do you clear decimals form an equation? Does that effect the answer?

Can decimal equations be written as fraction equations?

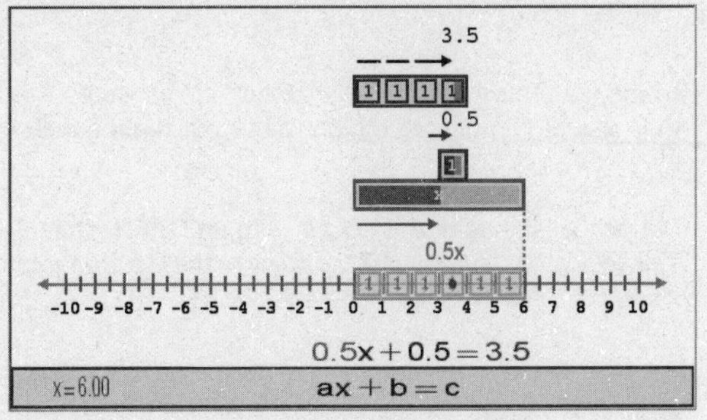

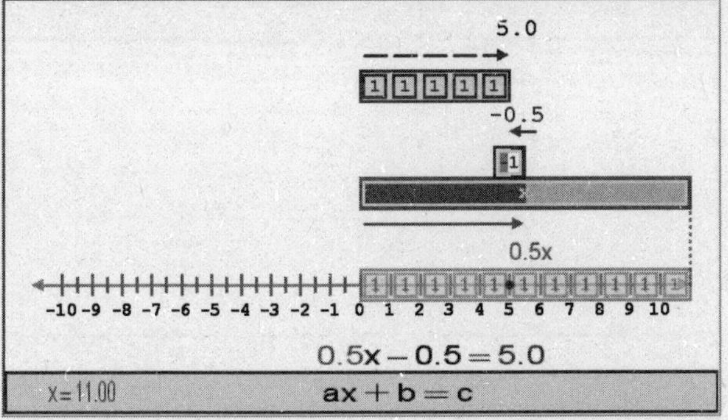

If **a =0.5** and **c=0.5**, that what is **x** if **b=-1**? If **b=-0.1**, will **x** be larger or smaller?

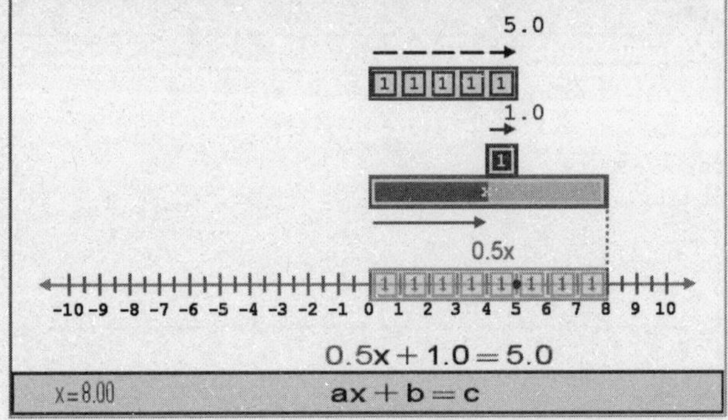

Here, **a**, **b**, and **c** are all positive values. Is **x** positive or negative? Will the x-bars get shorter or longer as **a**, **b**, and **c** change?

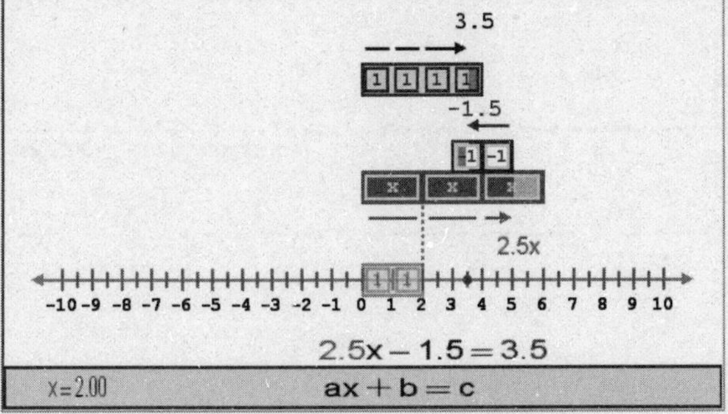

Can a decimal equation have an integer answer?

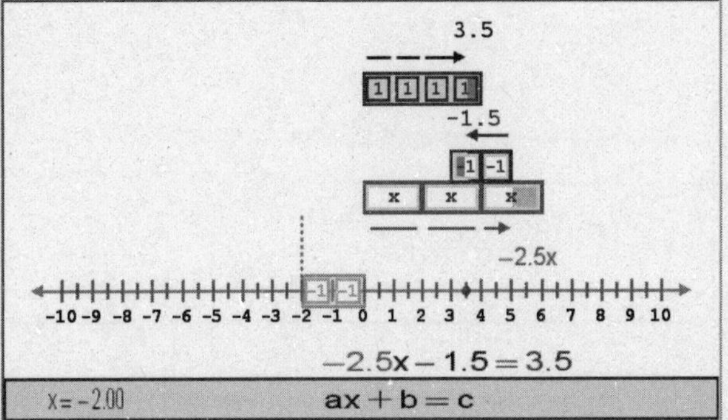

Notice the difference between the figure above and the one to the left. What changed? What stayed the same?

Graphing Inequalities

Inequalities employ one of the following four signs:

< – less than

> – greater than

≤ – less than or equal to

≥ – greater than or equal to

On a number-line graph, inequalities picture a range of values indicated by the **variable**, the **inequality symbol**, and the **value**. The figures below show each type of inequality, with their graph.

In the figure at the right, the number line indicates that anything in the red region will satisfy the inequality.

Notice that the point **4** is shown with an **OPEN** circle. This indicates that **4** is **NOT** a point in the solution for **x<4**.

Graph:

$x < 4$

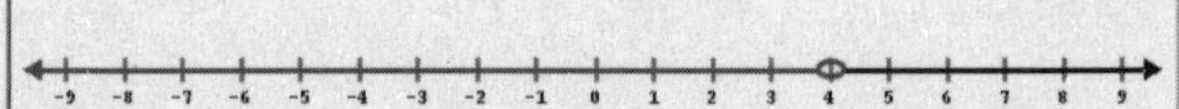

Graph:

$x \leq 4$

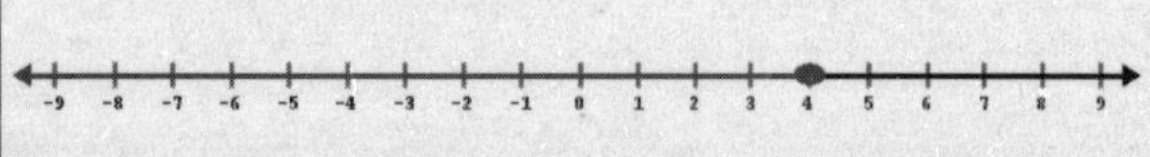

Above, the inequality is **less than or equal to**, therefore, the point **4 is** included in the solution and has a **CLOSED** circle.

Graph:

$x > 3$

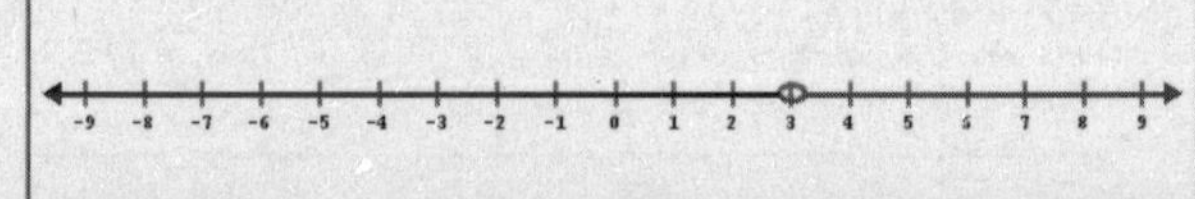

Greater than graphs values to the right of the indicated value. Once again the **3** is an **OPEN** circle indicating that **3** is **NOT** included in the range of solutions.

Graph:

$x \geq 3$

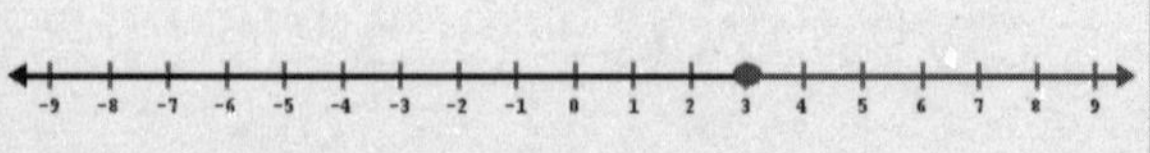

Greater than or equal to requires a **CLOSED** circle.

O x>-1
O x<-1
O x≥-1
O x≤-1

For the online homework problems, you will be asked to pick which inequality is represented by a given graph.

Linear inequalities have a range of solutions, not just one value for the variable. We show that range on a number line by graphing the solution as a thick arrow over the range of answers, beginning with an open circle or a closed circle over the critical value. The open circle does NOT include the value; The closed circle DOES.

x>a and **x<a;** use an **open** circle over **a**.

x≥a and **x≤a;** use a **closed** circle over **a**.

Use the joystick to enter a value to check against the given inequality.

At right, what happens to the inequality symbol as you change the values of x_1 represented on the number line by the black dot?

What does the direction of the inequality graph have to do with the direction of the inequality isymbol n the statement?

What is an alternative way to write **x>3**?

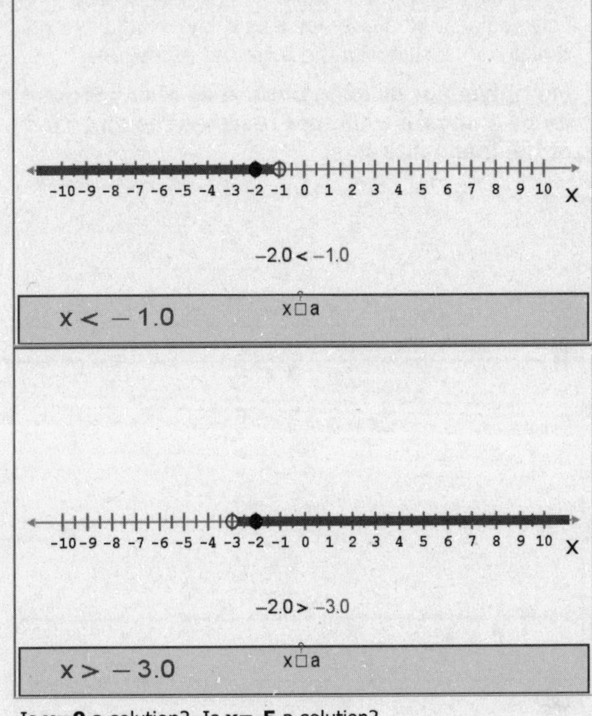

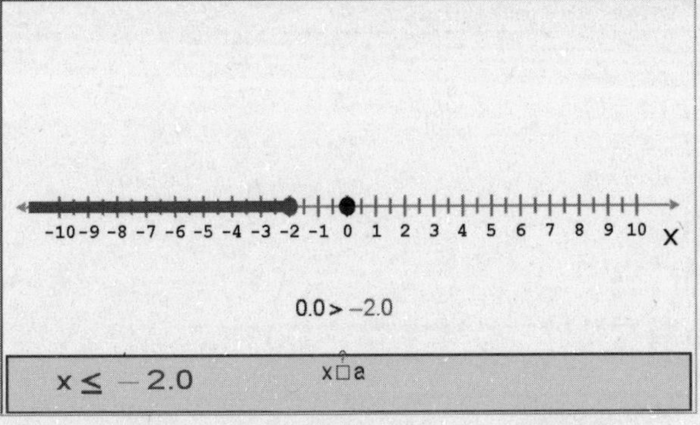

Is **x=-2** included in the solutions? How do you know?

Is **x=0** a solution? Is **x= 5** a solution?

Is **x=0** a solution? Is **x=-5** a solution?

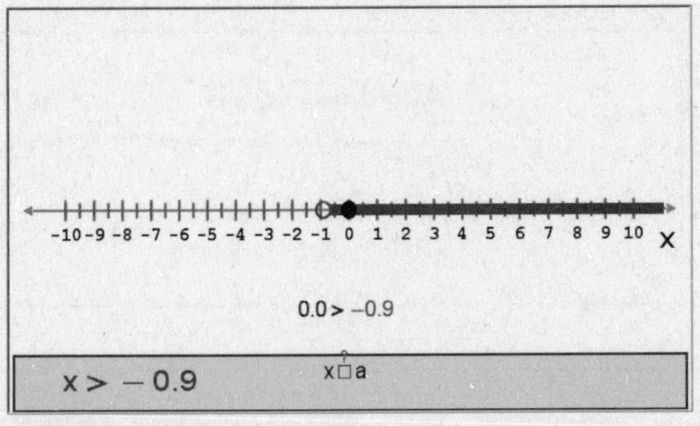

Is **x=0** a solution? Is **x= -0.9** a solution? What happens as **x** gets closer and closer to **–0.9**?

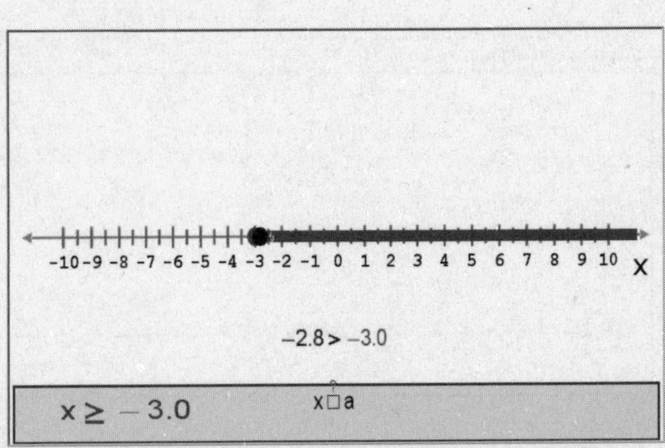

If the inequality is shown in the form ofvariable, inequality sign, constant (such as **x>3**), what pattern have you noticed relative to the inequality sign and the direction of the graphed arrow? How would you graph **x≥2**?

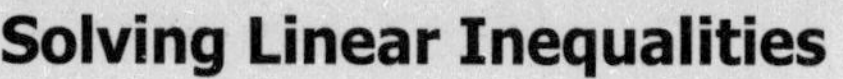

Solving Linear Inequalities

To solve a **linear inequality** means to **find the range of answers that makes the statement true**. The process of solving linear inequalities is the same as for solving linear equations except for one important difference. The direction of the inequality must be reversed, **if and only if** it is multiplied (or divided) by a negative number.

There are two steps in solving linear inequalities:

> **Step 1:** Find all solutions.
> **Step 2:** Graph the range of answers on a number line.

Solve a linear inequality for **x** as if the inequality sign was an equal sign with the following exception:

Multiplying or dividing both sides of an inequality by a negative number reverses the direction of the inequality sign.

Solve for x and graph the solution:

$$2x - 3 < 5$$

$$2x - 3 + 3 < 5 + 3$$

$$2x < 8$$

$$\frac{2x}{2} < \frac{8}{2}$$

$$x < 4$$

-9 -8 -7 -6 -5 -4 -3 -2 -1 0 1 2 3 4 5 6 7 8 9

$ax + b < c,\ a > 0$

In the above frame, **2** is positive. Multiply both sides by **1/2** and do not change the **< (less than)** sign.

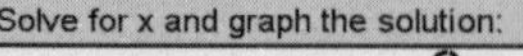

Solve for x and graph the solution:

$$2x - 3 < 5$$

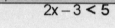

-9 -8 -7 -6 -5 -4 -3 -2 -1 0 1 2 3 4 5 6 7 8 9

$ax + b < c,\ a > 0$

Solve for x and graph the solution:

$$-3x + 4 < -2$$

$$-3x + 4 - 4 < -2 - 4$$

$$-3x < -6$$

$$\frac{-3x}{-3} > \frac{-6}{-3}$$

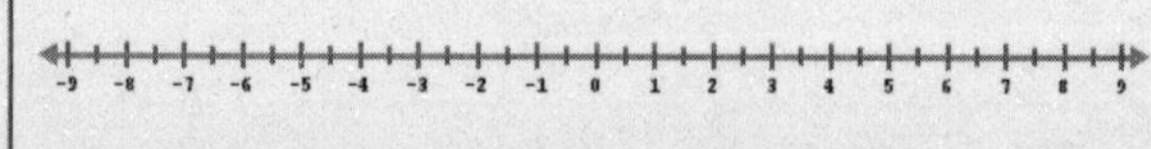

-9 -8 -7 -6 -5 -4 -3 -2 -1 0 1 2 3 4 5 6 7 8 9

Reverse inequality! $ax + b < c,\ a < 0$

Divide both sides by **−3**, and change **less than** to **> (greater than)**.

Solve for x and graph the solution:

$$-4x + 1 \geq 5$$

$$-4x + 1 - 1 \geq 5 - 1$$

$$-4x \geq 4$$

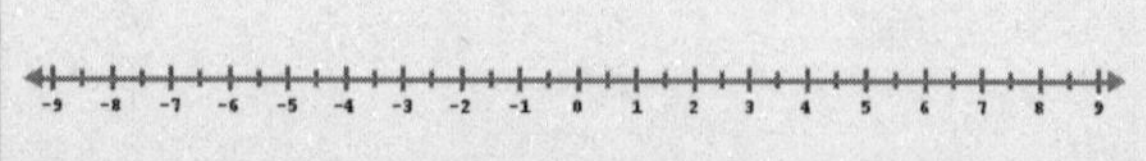

-9 -8 -7 -6 -5 -4 -3 -2 -1 0 1 2 3 4 5 6 7 8 9

$ax + b >= c,\ a < 0$

Did adding **−1** to both sides change the inequality sign? Why not?

Solve for x and graph the solution:

$$-4x - 3 \geq 5$$

$$-4x - 3 + 3 \geq 5 + 3$$

$$-4x \geq 8$$

$$\frac{-4x}{-4} \leq \frac{8}{-4}$$

$$x \leq -2$$

-9 -8 -7 -6 -5 -4 -3 -2 -1 0 1 2 3 4 5 6 7 8 9

$ax + b >= c,\ a < 0$

Don't forget to graph the solution. Check your solution: Pick a number on each side of the critical point (in this case **−2**) to test. Is **0** a solution? Is **−4** a solution?

Inequalities introduce the idea of finding a range of answers to an equation, not just one value. The concept of solving inequalities is exactly the same as for solving an equation, thus the visualization is the same with the exception that the range of answers is graphed along the number line.

Make sure you investigate all four cases (**<, >, ≤, ≥**) and notice what happens when you enter negative values for **a**.

How does the inequality symbol change the process for solving equations?

How do you know if a number is in the solution set of an inequality?

Test the solutions for the inequality at right: Does **x=3** work? How about **x=0**? Does **x=2** work?

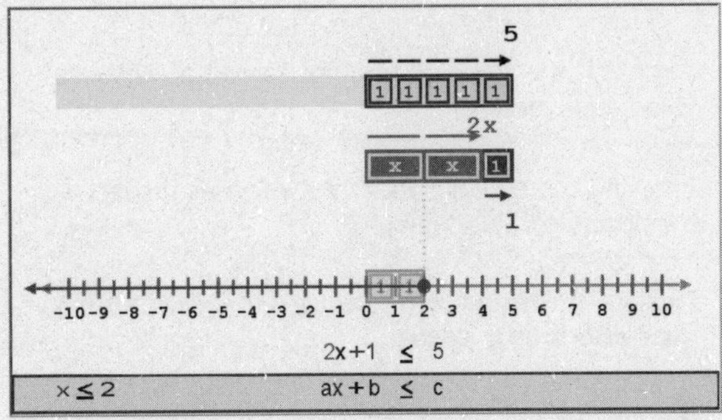

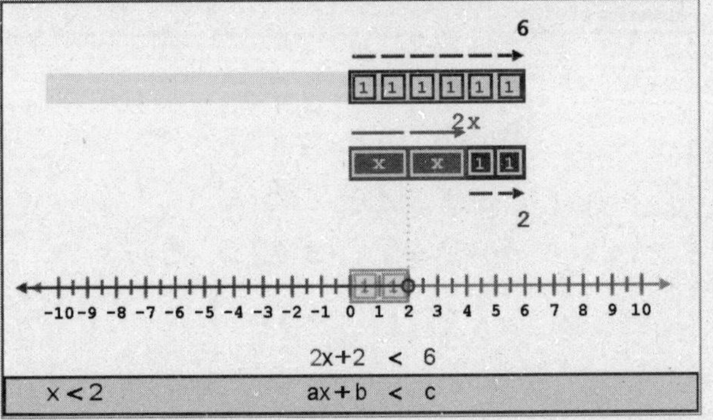

Above **x=2**. Clearly, both sides equal 6 (the red dot fills the circle over the 6). Why is **x=2** NOT the solution?

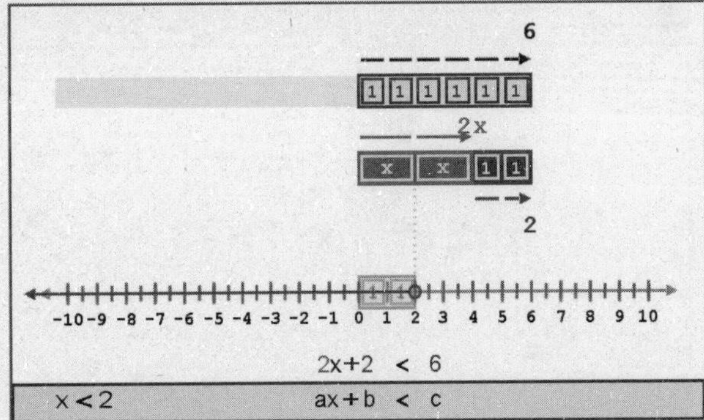

What happens when values for **x** get larger and larger? What happens when values for **x** get smaller and smaller? Is **10** a solution? Is **–10** a solution?

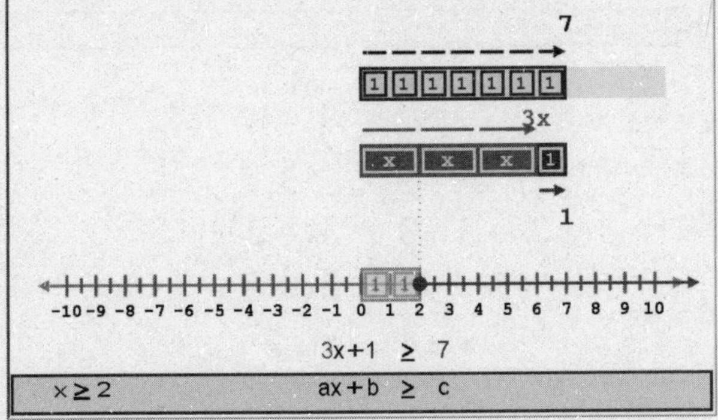

Can you tell where the red dot is located?
How do you know if this is a picture of the correct solution?

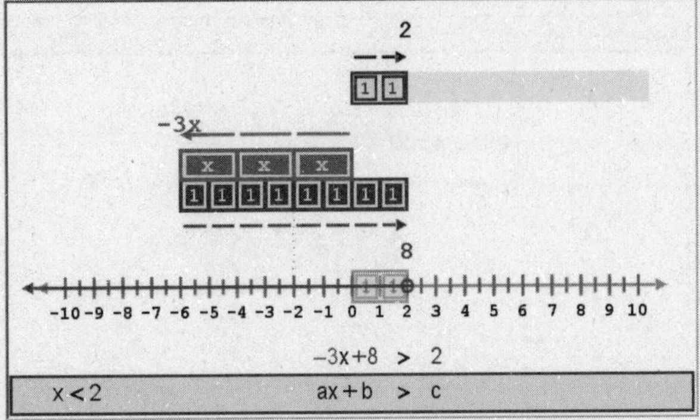

Why is this NOT a picture of the correct solution?
Is **0** a solution? Is **10** a solution? Is **–10** a solution?

Absolute Value Equations

Absolute value of a number can be defined as a number's distance from zero on a number line. A number and its opposite have the same absolute value. For example, **|3| =3**, and **|-3| =3**.

All absolute value equations have two answers: One for the **positive** case and one for the **negative**.

To solve absolute value equations:

- **Isolate the absolute value expression on the left side of the equation.**
- **Make two equations, one for the positive case and one for the negative case.**

In the problem sets we display the solution in *set notation* as **{a, -a}**.

The curly braces { } indicate a set of numbers.

At right is the standard form for solving an absolute value equation.

Breaking the equation into the two cases takes away the absolute value symbols.

Note: The symbol **±** will be used to indicate **both plus and minus cases**.

Solve for x:

$$|x| = a$$
$$x = \pm a$$
$$x = a \;,\; x = -a$$

Solve both equations.

Solve for x:

$$|x+2| = 3$$
$$x+2 = \pm 3$$
$$x+2=3 \;,\; x+2=-3$$

Solve both equations.

An absolute value expression equals a constant (case I as **+3** and case II as **−3)**. Notice that when the two cases are accounted for, the absolute value sign is eliminated. Solve the two equations normally.

Solve for x:

$$|x-2|-5 = 0$$
$$|x-2| = 5$$
$$x-2 = \pm 5$$
$$x-2=5 \;,\; x-2=-5$$
$$x=7 \;,\; x=-3$$

These are the solutions.

First, isolate the absolute value expression by adding **+5** to both sides. Then, solve the two cases and report the answer as **{-3, 7}**, in numeric order.

Solve for x:

$$3|x| = 6$$
$$|x| = 2$$
$$x = \pm 2$$

Solve both equations.

Isolate the absolute value part by dividing by **3**.

Solve for x:

$$-2|3x-9| = -6$$
$$|3x-9| = 3$$
$$3x-9 = \pm 3$$
$$3x-9=3 \;,\; 3x-9=-3$$
$$3x=12 \;,\; 3x=6$$
$$x=4 \;,\; x=2$$

Divide both sides by 3 to solve.

Isolate the absolute value expression first, then break into two cases and solve normally.

Absolute value takes into account **both the positive outcome and negative outcome** of an expression or value.

An intuitive sense of absolute value is that of distance. Distance does not have direction, it cannot be negative. Two units from zero (distance) is the same for both the positive **+2** and the negative **−2** direction.

Picture absolute value equations like other linear equations, with two bars, one above the other. But, this time, the top bar is a picture of both the positive outcome and the negative outcome. The task is to find **TWO** values for the variable, one equaling the negative part of the top bar and one equaling the positive part of the top bar.

What are the two equations needed to solve the absolute value equation at right? The expression bar on bottom shows one solution: when **x = -5**. The figure below shows the same equation with the other solution, **x=1**.

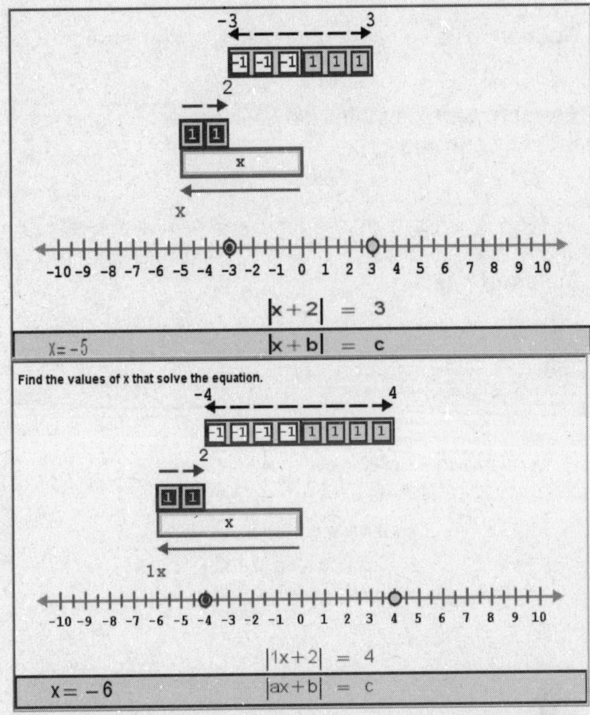

Above shows the negative case for the given equation. What does the equation look like?

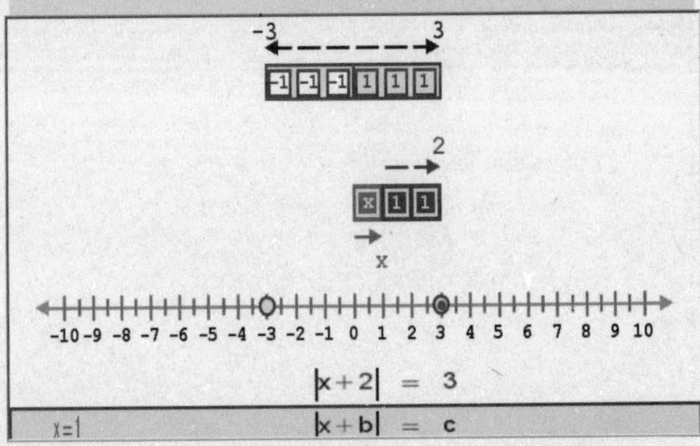

Could **x=0** ever be a solution? Could an absolute value equation ever have just one solution?

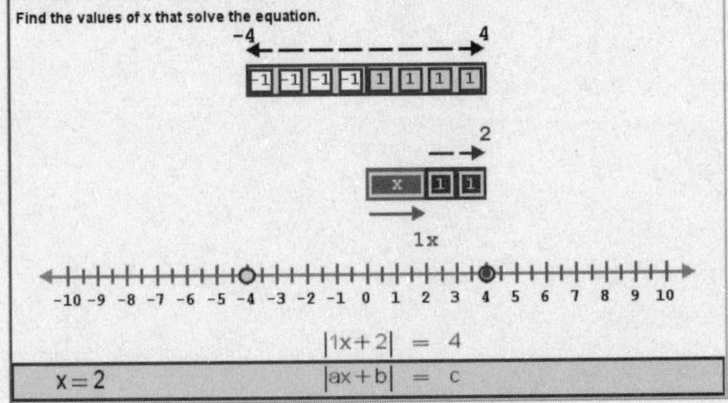

Here is the positive solution for **|x+2| = 4**. Will **x** always have a positive solution **and** a negative solution?

Sets are collections of things. Members of the set are called **elements**. In algebra, the sets and elements we are interested in describing are **numbers**. Sets can be described in three ways:

Roster: List all elements in the set. Use braces, **{ }**, and separate elements by commas.

Set-builder notation: Use a rule, like a formula or equation, and show it between braces.

Graphing: Draw a picture of the set, on a graph or on a number line.

Sets are given a name, generally a capital letter.

Elements are presented between braces **{ }** and separated by **commas**.

In **step 3**, since there are no even integers between **2** and **4,** the set **C** is shown as a pair of empty braces { }, the **empty set**.

Write these sets in roster notation:

1. The set, A, of all odd integers between 2 and 10.
   $A = \{3, 5, 7, 9\}$
2. The set, B, of all prime, numbers less than 14.
   $B = \{2, 3, 5, 7, 11, 13\}$
3. The set, C, of all even integers between 2 and 4.
   $C = \{\}$ (sometimes denoted by $\emptyset$).

Write this set in set builder notation:

The set, A, of all odd integers between 2 and 10.

$A = \{x \mid 2 < x < 10, x \in \text{odd integers}\}$

| is the symbol for such that.

, translates to and.

$\in$ means is a member of the set.

Each of the symbols in the above figure plays an important role in determining the meaning of the rule for **set A**. Translated to English: "**A** is the set of all **x**'s such that **x** is between **2** and **10** and **x** is an **odd integer**."

Write these sets in set builder notation:

1. The set, A, of all real numbers less than or equal to 7.
   $A = \{x \mid x \leq 7, x \in \text{real numbers}\}$
2. The set, B, of all prime numbers between 4 and 14.
   $B = \{x \mid 4 < x < 14, x \in \text{prime numbers}\}$

Point 3: Notice the rule, and then notice the *type* of number **x** can be.

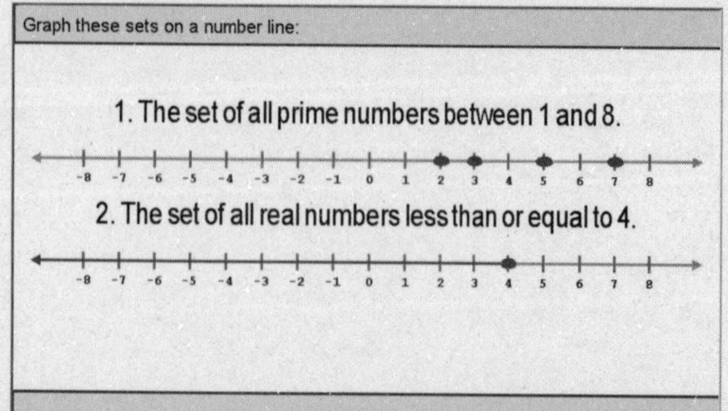

Point 4: Discrete values are shown as dots over the numbers; Continuous values are shown with a solid line. Can you describe these two sets in set-builder notation?

Showing pictures of sets by graphing on a number line is a way to quickly determine whether a given value satisfies the conditions of the set or not.

In the models pictured here, the graph directly corresponds to the set builder notation listed below it. Change the **x** value to see the changes reflected in both the graph and the rule.

What kind of number can **x** be? Can it be any real number in the range?

How would the graphs look if the rules added that **x** must be an integer?

How would the rules change to show that **x** must also be less than **10**?

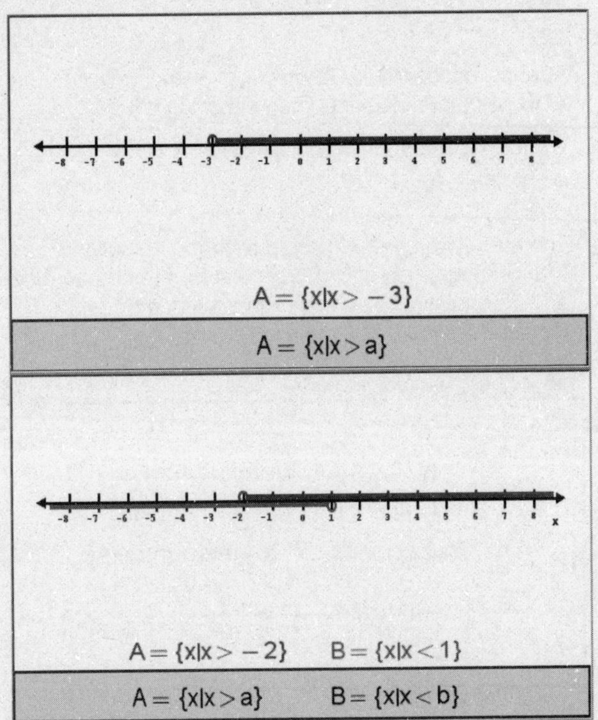

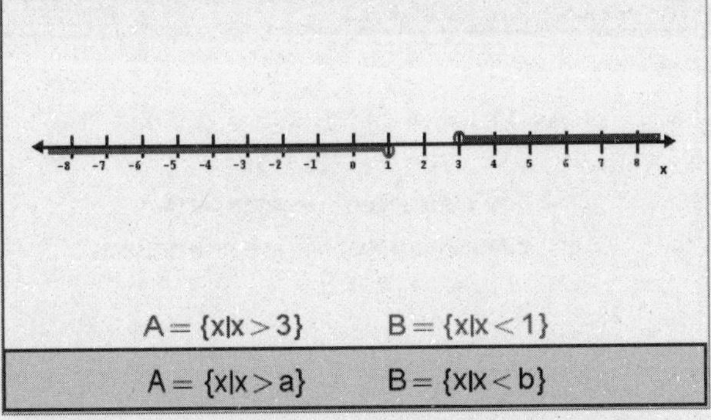

Point 2: Above are two inequalities graphed on the same number line. What part of the graph can NOT satisfy either condition? Is there a way to describe the values between **1** and **3**?

Is there a way to describe the overlapping part?

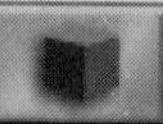

Union & Intersection

Union means to join things together.

Intersection is the point where two things cross each other.

In math, **union** and **intersection** are **operations** we perform on **sets**.

If we want to **combine two or more sets**, we use **union.**

If we only want to **find what is common to the sets,** we use **intersection**.

At right, notice that **AUB** only lists elements once. **AUB** has more elements than either **A** or **B**.

What does the intersection (**A∩B**) of **A** and **B** look like? See below.

There are two types of problems in the homework: Interpreting union and intersection from a number line and determining the union or intersection by listing elements. All are multiple choice.

Find the union of these two sets:

$A = \{1, 2, 3, 4, 5\} \cup B = \{3, 4, 5, 6, 7\}$

$A \cup B = \{1, 2, 3, 4, 5, 6, 7\}$

The union, $\cup$, is the set of all of the elements appearing in at least one of the sets.

Find and graph the union of the sets:

$A = \{x | 1 < x < 4,\ x \in \text{real numbers}\}$

$B = \{x | 3 < x < 7,\ x \in \text{real numbers}\}$

$A \cup B = \{x | 1 < x < 7,\ x \in \text{real numbers}\}$

Points 2 and **3** picture union. Notice that **AUB** has a larger range than either set **A** or set **B**. Graph sets **A** and **B** on the same number line to see what overlaps. What happens to the part that overlaps? Hint: For sets, elements never get listed more than once.

Find the intersection of these two sets:

$A = \{1, 2, 3, 4, 5\} \cap B = \{3, 4, 5, 6, 7\}$

$A \cap B = \{3, 4, 5\}$

The intersection, $\cap$, is the set of all of the elements appearing in both of the sets.

Think of intersection as "sharing." What elements do the sets have in common?

Find and graph the intersection of the sets:

$A = \{x | 0 < x < 6,\ x \in \text{odd integers}\}$

$B = \{x | 4 < x < 8,\ x \in \text{odd integers}\}$

$A \cap B = \{x | 4 < x < 6,\ x \in \text{odd integers}\}$

Points 5 and 6 picture intersection. Notice that the value for **x** is a single point. This is the only point occurring in **BOTH** sets.

Find and graph the intersection of the sets:

$A = \{x | 1 < x < 4,\ x \in \text{real numbers}\}$

$B = \{x | 3 < x < 7,\ x \in \text{real numbers}\}$

$A \cap B = \{x | 3 < x < 4,\ x \in \text{real numbers}\}$

What would the graphs of **A** and **B** look like? Which part would correspond to the intersection?

Visualize **union** of sets as putting two sets together. On a number line we picture each set as a colored bar and their union is the two bars pictured together as one.

Visually **intersection** is the same as overlapping. In the number lines pictured below two inequalities are pictured on the same number line and the graph of the intersection is the overlapping part.

Can the union of two sets ever be smaller than either of the sets? Can the union of two sets ever be the same as one of the sets?
Can the intersection of two sets ever be larger than either set? Can the intersection of two sets ever be the same as one of the sets?
Which represents "more" union or intersection?
Which is usually "less" union or intersection?

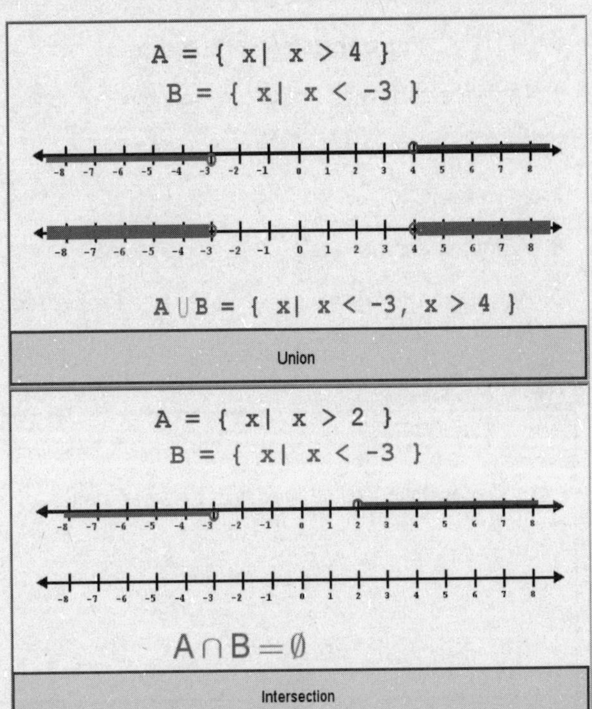

$A = \{ x \mid x > -3 \}$

$B = \{ x \mid x < 2 \}$

$A \cap B = \{ x \mid -3 < x < 2 \}$

Intersection

What would the graph look like if the inequalities were changed to **x≥-3** and **x≤2**?

Why is the bottom graph blank?

The earliest **problems in algebra** were not written symbolically but were described in verbal languages. We still have to translate problems that we describe in our verbal language into mathematics language. In mathematics, each symbol corresponds to a word or phrase. Decoding verbal language into symbolic code is done **word-by-word**.

In translating from verbal to symbolic language, the unknown will be referred to as "what number" or "a number" or "an integer." Once the translation is complete, solve the resulting equation for the unknown, using algebra. Don't forget to verify answers and make sure the solution answers the given question.

Hint: Consecutive numbers: x, x+1, x+2,... Consecutive even or odd: x, x+2, x+4,...

For translation problems

1. Translate each word into a corresponding symbol.
2. Simplify the equation into **ax+b=c** form.
3. Solve for **x.**
4. Verify the answer.
5. Make sure the original question has been answered.

The sum of twice a number and three is seven.

sum is the operation
and indicates the two addends
is means the equal sign
twice a number is the same as 2x

$$2x + 3 = 7$$

Translate and solve for x:

Two less than negative three times a number is ten.

$$-3x-2=10$$

Solve for x.

Point 2: Notice that subtraction is often written out of order, that is, "two less than" means "(some number) – 2".

Find 3 consecutive integers whose sum 45.

$$\begin{aligned} x &= \text{lowest integer} \\ x+1, x+2 &\Rightarrow \text{next consecutive integers} \\ x+(x+1)+(x+2) &= 45 \end{aligned}$$

Translated equation.

Point 3: Three consecutive integers are defined. Once the problem is set up, use algebra to solve. Don't forget to list all three integers for the answer.

Find 3 consecutive odd integers whose sum is 39.

$$\begin{aligned} x &= \text{lowest integer} \\ x+2, x+4 &\Rightarrow \text{next consecutive odd integers} \\ x+(x+2)+(x+4) &= 39 \\ 3x+6 &= 39 \\ 3(x+2) &= 39 \\ x+2 &= 13 \\ x &= 11 \\ x+4 &= 15 \\ 11+13+15 &= 39 \end{aligned}$$

11, 13, 15

Answer.

Points 5 and 6: Consecutive even or odd problems are worked exactly the same way. Why?

Find 3 consecutive even integers whose sum is 24.

$$\begin{aligned} x &= \text{lowest integer} \\ x+2, x+4 &\Rightarrow \text{next consecutive even integers} \\ x+(x+2)+(x+4) &= 24 \\ 3x+6 &= 24 \\ 3(x+2) &= 24 \\ x+2 &= 8 \\ x &= 6 \end{aligned}$$

Solve for x.

This is not a full-credit answer. Why not?

Once verbal problems are translated into symbolic form, they become algebraic equations and can be **visualized**, like all equations, **as two bars**, one above the other. **When the bars are equal in length, the equation is solved.**

Translate sentences into symbols, **word-for-word**. Sentences must have a verb to be complete. Equations must have an equal sign. Usually, the verb "is" translates into the equal sign (=).

Does every equation have one answer? Can an equation have more than one answer? Can an equation have no answer?

Does the answer have to be a Real number? Can the answer be negative? Is the solution of the equation always the answer to the question? How do you know if your answer is reasonable?

Can x = 0? Can b = 0? Can c = 0?

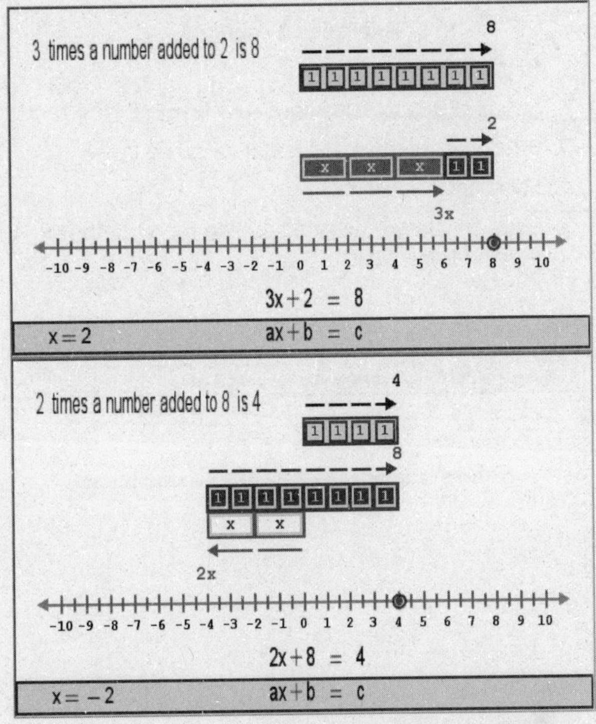

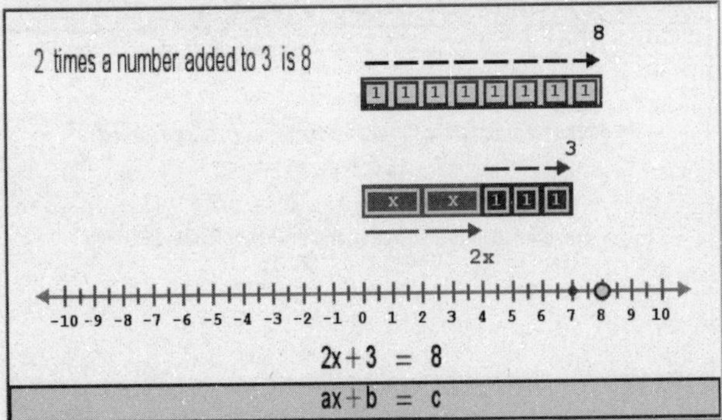

Will **x** be an integer? Find the value for **x**.

Use the joystick to investigate different values for **a, b, c,** and **x.** Here, **a, b,** and **c** are all positive integers, but **x** is negative.

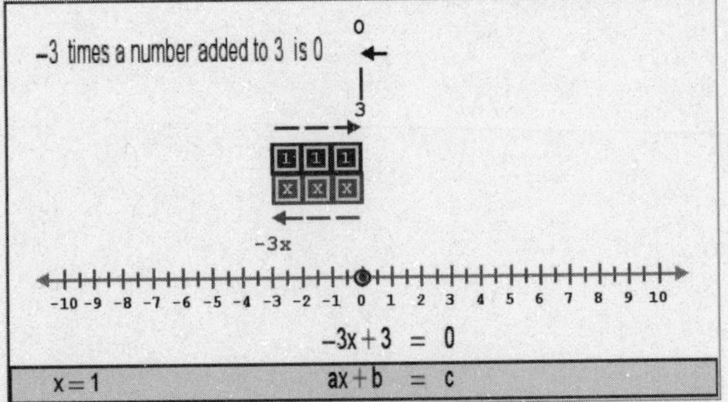

What property does this represent when **x=1**?

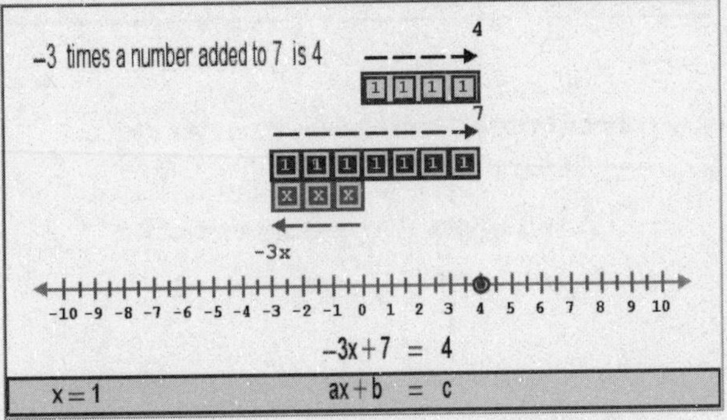

Can this equation have another verbal translation? Make up a story that has this representation.

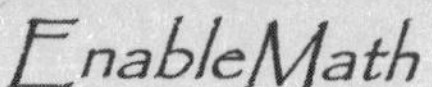

Tolerance problems use the absolute value concept to define the upper and lower limits of a process or a measurement. Recall that absolute value equations have two solutions, one where the expression is positive and one where the expression is negative.

$$|x - p| = t$$

$$x - p = t \text{ and } x - p = -t$$

Tolerance Problems

1. Identify **x**, **p**, and **t**.
2. Set up absolute value equation: **|x-p|=t**.
3. Break into positive and negative cases.
4. Solve each equation.
5. State the answer, making sure to report both upper and lower limits.

Calculating Tolerance:

Some things have tolerance limits they must adhere to. For instance, a coffee machine that dispenses 7 ozs. (p) into an 8 oz. cup, has a tolerance (t) of 0.7 ozs. This prevents the cup from being overfilled and customer dissatisfaction at receiving too little. The equation of tolerance is: $|x - p| = t$. In this case, it is: $|x - 7| = 0.7$, which when solved, yields two equations: $x - 7 = 0.7$ and $x - 7 = -0.7$. So, there are upper and lower limits of 7.7 and 6.3 ozs., respectively.

Calculate the acceptable upper and lower voltage limits:

A motor is designed to run at 220 volts plus or minus 20 volts.

$$|x - 220| = 20$$

Translate into an absolute value equation.

First, translate into an absolute value equation. Notice that the variable will take on two values, one for the positive **t** and one for the negative **t**.

Calculate the acceptable upper and lower voltage limits:

A motor is designed to run at 220 volts plus or minus 20 volts.

$$|x - 220| = 20$$

$$x - 220 = 20 \;,\quad x - 220 = -20$$

So, the upper limit is 240 volts, and the lower limit is 200 volts.

Another way to write the two equations is $x - 220 = \pm 20$. Don't forget to resolve the two cases for the answer.

Calculate the acceptable upper and lower limits:

A doctor prescribed 3 cc of medication with a tolerance of 0.05 cc.

$$|x - 3| = 0.05$$

$$x - 3 = 0.05 \;,\quad x - 3 = -0.05$$

So, the upper limit is 3.05 cc, and the lower limit is 2.95 cc.

Medicines: Knowing about tolerance can be a life-saver.

All measurements are inexact. Tolerance takes into account the **plus/minus factor** used in everyday language to account for the variance between measures.

Tolerance is an application of absolute value equations which have both positive and negative cases.

Visualize tolerance with two bars, but the top bar has two sides, one positive and one negative. Solutions align with either the positive side or the negative side.

How do you verify that **x=8** is a solution of the equation at right? Do the limits found by the equation represent the only voltage that works the motor? Does 8.5 volts make the motor work?

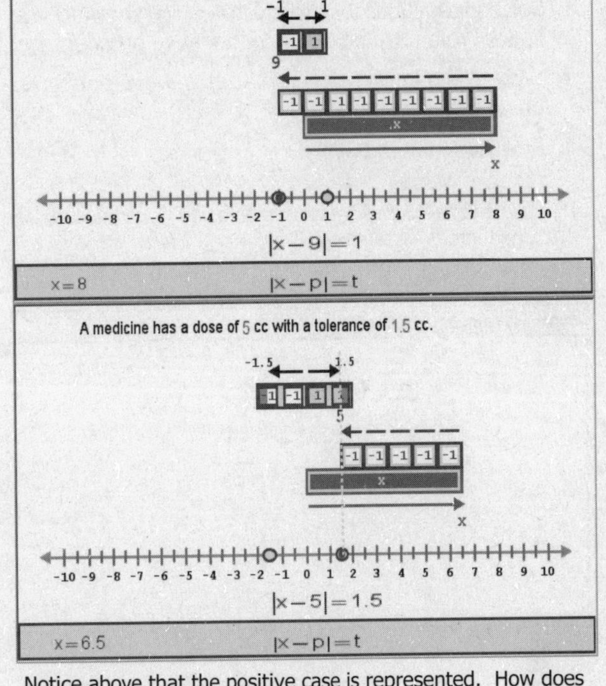

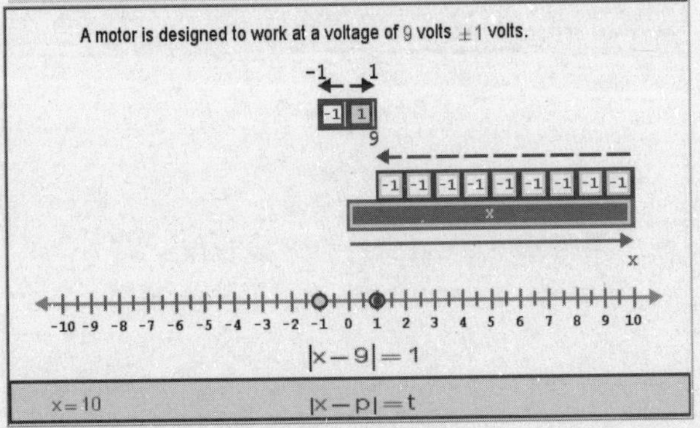

Above is the positive case representation for the motor problem. If 10 volts works, does 10.5 volts work?

Notice above that the positive case is represented. How does **x** change for the negative case?

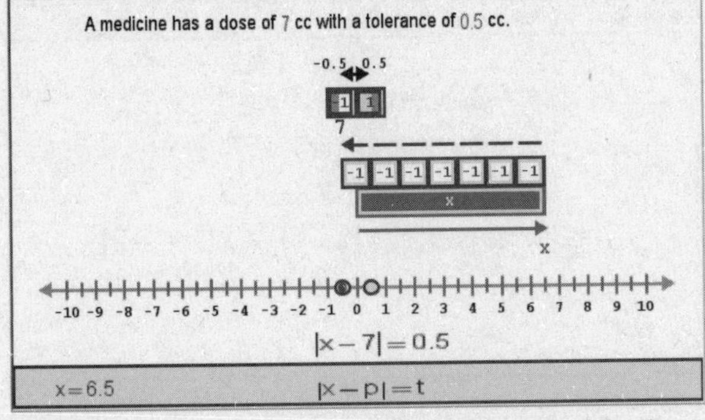

What are the upper and lower limits of measurement for the above dose of medicine? Is the upper or lower limit pictured?

Two inequalities may be joined to make one statement called a **compound inequality**. Compound inequalities make extensive use of set notation. Answers may represented on a number line, in inequality form, or in set notation.

Caution:

1. Sometimes, compound inequalities with "and" have **no** solution.
2. Sometimes, compound inequalities with "or" have all **real numbers** as solutions.

Compound Inequalities

1. Solve inequalities for the unknown. (Remember the special rule for multiplying by negative numbers.)
2. Write using intersection (∩) for the word 'and' and union (**U**) for the word 'or'.
3. Rewrite in set notation.

Hint: U usually requires two statements and ∩ can usually be combined into one statement.

Compound inequalities are formed by joining two or more inequalties together using the words and or or. And translates to intersection ($\cap$), and or translates to union ($\cup$).

Solve this compound inequality:

$$3x<9 \text{ and } 2x+3>-1$$
$$x<3 \text{ and } 2x>-4.$$
$$x<3 \text{ and } x>-2.$$

In the above compound inequality, both inequalities have been solved for **x**. Note the use of the word 'and'.

Solve this compound inequality:

$$3x<9 \text{ and } 2x+3>-1$$
$$x<3 \text{ and } 2x>-4.$$
$$x<3 \text{ and } x>-2.$$
This translates to $\{x|x<3\}\cap\{x|x>-2\}$.

So, the solution is $\{x|-2<x<3\}$.

Continue by changing to set notation, using ∩ for "and." The two statements are combined into one — Think: "x is between −2 and 3."

Solve this compound inequality:

$$3x>9 \text{ or } 2x+3<-1$$
$$x>3 \text{ or } 2x<-4.$$
$$x>3 \text{ or } x<-2.$$

Translate.

Solve the inequalities separately. Notice the word 'or'.

Solve this compound inequality:

$$3x>9 \text{ or } 2x+3<-1$$
So, $x>3$ or $2x<-4$.

Then, $x>3$ or $x<-2$.

This translates to $\{x|x>3\}\cup\{x|x<-2\}$.

Continue by changing 'or' to U and writing as two statements in set notation. Why can't this be written as one statement?

Two inequality statements combined with the words "and" or "or" define a set of numbers. The two sets are either joined, indicating union, or separated, indicating intersection. Visualize the solutions of two inequalities on one number line. Unions are when the ends are the solutions—the middles are not part of the solution set. Intersections are the overlapping middles—the solutions are between two critical values.

Union connects two disjoint sets.

Intersection show solutions between two critical values.

How do you know if a specific value is in the solution set of a compound inequality?

What are other descriptions for intersection?

How do you know if you can write a compound inequality in one statement or two?

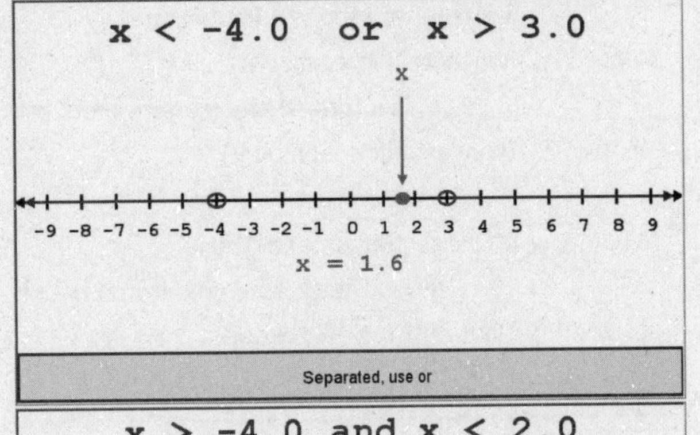

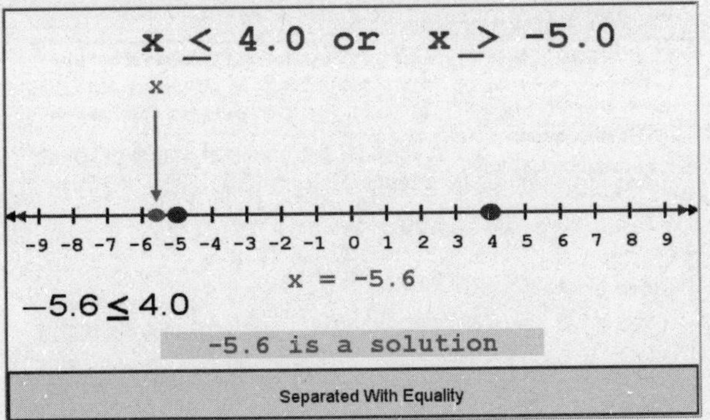

Notice the equal marks under the inequalities. The critical values are included in the solution set. Is **x=0** a solution? Why can't we describe the solution set as numbers between –4 and 5?

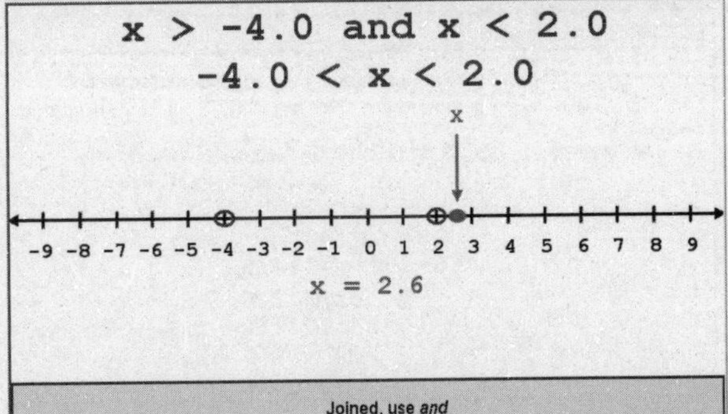

This solution set for **x** is between the two numbers –4 and 2. Check it out: What does the graph of **x<2** look like? What does the graph of **x>-4** look like? The above graph shows the overlapping parts.

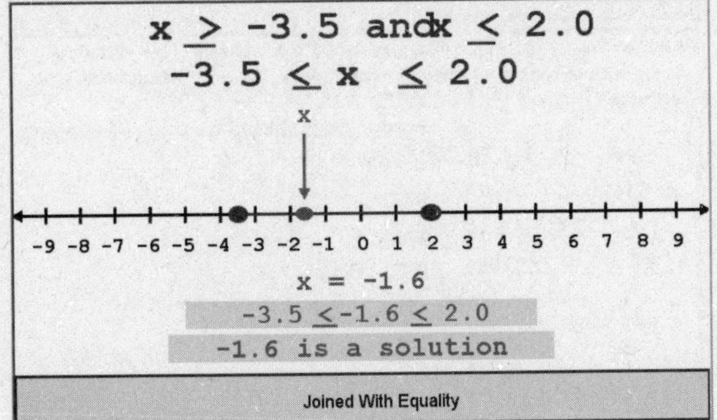

Are the endpoints included in all numbers between –3.5 and 2.0? Clearly, **x=-1.6** is a solution.

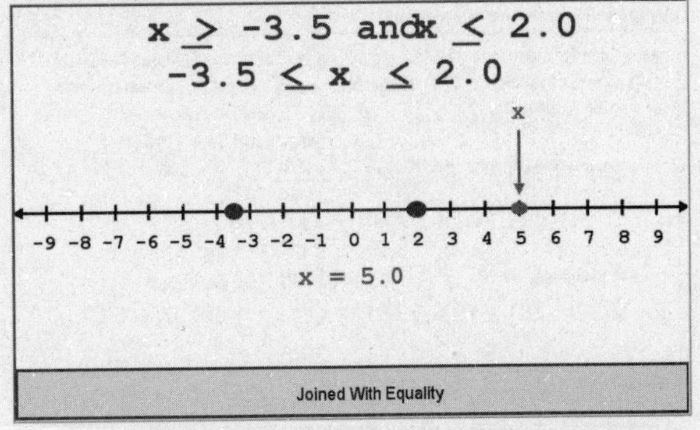

Is **x=5** a solution? Is **x=-7** a solution? Test points in the set and on both sides of the set.

Mixture

Mixture problems usually require combining two different "mixtures" into one "bucket." The "mixtures" can differ in **amount** and **concentration**. The amount can be given in weight, volume, number of items, money, etc. The concentration will be given as a percent, or as a cost per item. Each problem will have the format:

Mixture I + Mixture II = New Mixture

Setting up Mixture Problems

Mixture I: (concentration x amount)

10% x (times) an unknown amount

Mixture II: (concentration x amount)

5% x 3 liters

New Mixture: (concentration x amount)

8% x 3 liters + an unknown amount

Mixture I + Mixture II = New Mixture

How much should we add?

How many liters of a 10% alcohol solution should be mixed with 3.0 liters of a 5% alcohol solution to make a solution that is 8% alcohol? Round to the nearest hundredth.

how much alcohol in unknown qty + how much alcohol in 3.0 = how much alcohol in final solution

Mixture I + Mixture II = New Mixture

This is what your equation will say.

How much should we add?

How many cups of pure oil should be added to 2.00 quarts of a gasoline mixture which is 5% oil to make a gasoline mixture which is 20% oil? Round to the nearest hundredth.

unknown amount of oil + amount of oil in initial mixture = amount of oil in final mixture

$x \Rightarrow$ cups of pure oil

There are four cups in a quart. $x+(4)(2.00)(0.05) = [x+(4)(2.00)]\cdot(0.20)$

$$x+(4)(2.00)(0.05) = x\cdot(0.20)+1.60$$
$$x(1-0.20)+0.40 = 1.60$$
$$(0.80)x = 1.20$$
$$x = 1.50 \quad \text{rounded to hundredths}$$

Check your work. $1.50+(4)(2.00)(0.05) = [1.50+(4)(2.00)]\cdot(0.20) = 3.10$

$$x = 1.50$$

Answer.

The concentration of pure oil is 100% or 1, thus Mixture I is **1x** or **x**. Remember to make sure all measuring units agree.

What is the final cost per ounce?

A "secret" flavoring is made by blending 3 different herbs: 150 ounces of an herb costing $4.00 per ounce, 200 ounces of an herb costing $3.00 per ounce, and 150 ounces of an herb costing $2.00 per ounce. How much does it cost (to the nearest cent) to make one ounce of the secret flavoring?

$x \Rightarrow$ cost per ounce of secret flavoring

$$150(4.00)+200(3.00)+150(2.00) = (150+200+150)x$$
$$600+600+300 = (500)x$$
$$1500 = (500)x$$
$$x = 3.00 \quad \text{to the nearest cent}$$

Check your work.

$$150(4.00)+200(3.00)+150(2.00) = (150+200+150)3 = 1500.00$$
$$x = 3.00$$

Answer.

Three "buckets" into one. Notice on the right that the three amounts in ounces were added for the amount of the final mixture.

What is the final cost per gallon?

A fuel blend is made form a mixture of 2.00 quarts of oil at $1.30 per quart added to 1.50 gallons of gasoline at $2.00 per gallon. What is the cost (to the nearest cent) of a gallon of the mixture?

$x \Rightarrow$ final cost per gallon

$$2.00(1.30)+1.50(2.00) = (\tfrac{2.00}{4}+1.50)x$$
$$2.60+3.00 = 2.00x$$
$$5.60 = 2.00x$$
$$x = 2.80 \quad \text{to the nearest cent}$$

Check your work.

$$2.00(1.30)+1.50(2.00) = (\tfrac{2.00}{4}+1.50)(3) = 5.60$$
$$x = 2.80$$

Answer.

Find the cost of each mixture. Here, the concentration is given as cost in dollars. Notice, in **Mixture I**, the conversion was accounted for in the cost. But, for the New Mixture, quarts were converted to gallons.

How much should be drained?

A radiator holds 16 quarts of a mixture containing 40% antifreeze. How much should be drained and replaced with pure antifreeze to have 16 quarts of a mixture with 50% antifreeze?

$x \Rightarrow$ amount that should be drained in quarts

$$x+(16-x)0.40 = (16)(0.50)$$
$$x+(16)(0.40)-x(0.40) = 8.00$$
$$x(1-0.40)+6.40 = 8.00$$
$$x(0.60) = 8.00-6.40 = 1.60$$
$$x = 2.67 \quad \text{Round to the nearest hundredth.}$$
$$2.67+(16-2.67)0.40 = 8.00 \quad \text{Check your work.}$$
$$x = 2.67$$

Answer.

Two ideas here: The full radiator holds 16 quarts, therefore, the Mixture amounts are **x** and **16 – x**. Pure antifreeze is 100% or 1.

When you buy quantities of items you pay the value per item times the number of items; you can think of this as "how much times how many." In mixture problems you have equations in which the variable takes on one of the above meanings. You will be solving for either a quantity (amount) or a value (concentration) for both parts of the mixture.

The equations are visualized in the same way as before, as bars, one above the other, searching for the value for the unknown that makes them equal in length.

What's the difference between the amount of something and the concentration of something? What's the difference between a quantity and a value?

How do you know if a given value is a quantity or a value?

How do you know if you are solving for a quantity or a value?

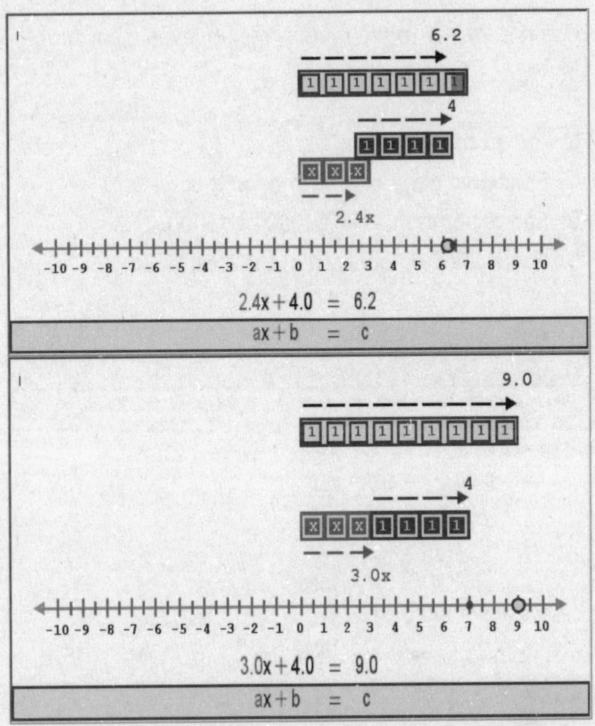

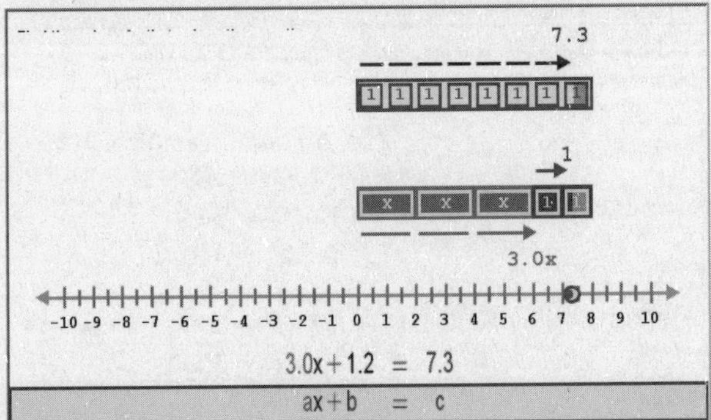

In the above **x** can represent either the amount of a substance or the concentration. How much of **x** is needed to balance the equation?

How much of a $3 mix of nuts should be added to 2 pounds of $2 peanuts to make 3 pounds of $3 nuts?

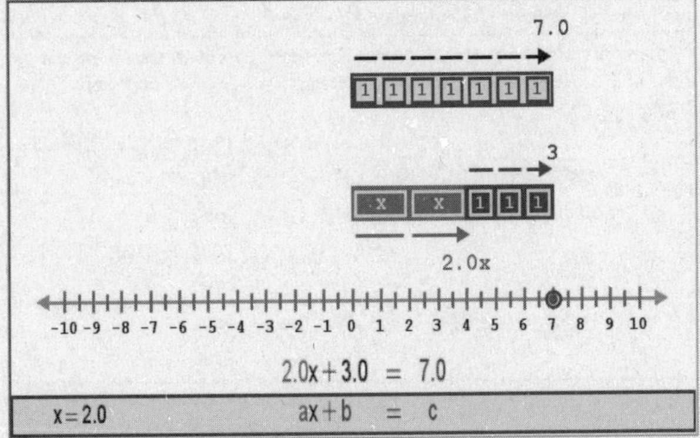

Make up a simple mixture problem for this model.

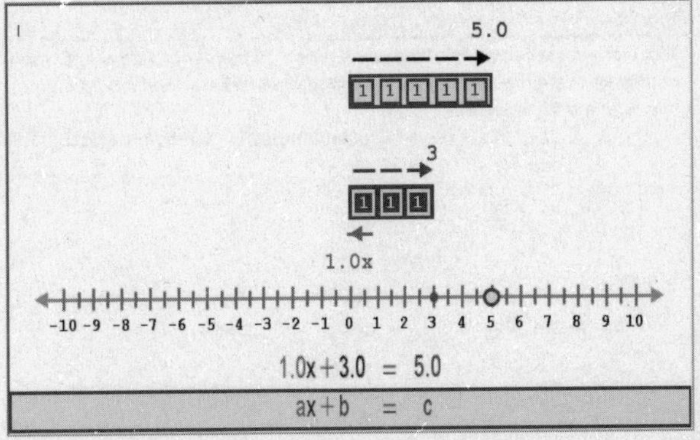

Let **x** represent volume of a "pure" substance. How much of **x** is required for the above mixture?

Investment

EnableMath

Investments of money earn interest (**I**) based on the amount or principle (**p**), the rate (**r**) of return, and the time (**t**) kept in the investment. The formula for simple interest is **I = prt**.

In the problems considered here, time (**t**) is always 1, therefore, we can shorten the formula to **I = rp**. The investments will be divided into two accounts, **principle 1 with rate 1** and **principle 2 with rate 2**. Rates will be given as percents and must be converted to decimal equivalents.

Use the format to the right to set up investment problems.

Divide up the money, **x**, as

1. Fractional parts of **x** such as **x/2** or **x/4**
2. Specific amounts like $1000 or $5000
3. Unspecified amounts from the total

Interest = Rate x Time x Principle
or
I=prt

Investment Problems
Interest on Account I + Interest on Account II = Total Interest
r1*p1 + r2p2=T

Investment: one amount a fraction of the other

Amy invests some money at an interest rate of 10 % and half as much at a rate of 8%. If the interest for one year from both investments is $ 210, how much did she invest at 10%?

$x \Rightarrow$ Amount invested at 10%

$$\frac{x}{2}*0.08 + x*0.10 = 210$$
$$x\left(\frac{0.08}{2} + 0.10\right) = 210$$
$$0.140x = 210$$
$$x = 1500$$
$$\frac{1500}{2}*0.08 + 1500*0.10 = 210$$
Check your work!
$$x = 1500$$

Answer.

Match the fractional part of the principle with the correct rate. The total interest is the sum of the interests in the two accounts. Do the arithmetic on scratch paper.

Investment: investments differ by stated dollar amount

Lou invests some money at an interest rate of 10% and $1000 more than that amount at a rate of 12%. After one year, the interest returned is $560. How much did Lou invest at 10%?

$x \Rightarrow$ Amount invested at 10%

$$x*0.10 + (x + 1000)*0.12 = 560$$
$$x*(0.10 + 0.12) + 120 = 560$$
$$0.22x = 440$$
$$x = 2000$$
$$2000*0.10 + (2000 + 1000)*0.12 = 340$$
Check your work!
$$x = 2000$$

Answer.

The two accounts differ by $1000. Is there another way to set this one up?

Investment: unknown settlement

Tony received a settlement for a large sum of money. He invested half at a rate of 10% and one-fourth at a rate of 12%. After one year, the interest he received was $8000. How much was the settlement?

$x \Rightarrow$ Total amount of money received

$$\frac{x}{2}*0.10 + \frac{x}{4}*0.12 = 8000$$
$$x\left(\frac{0.10}{2} + \frac{0.12}{4}\right) = 8000$$
$$0.08x = 8000$$
$$x = 100000$$
$$\frac{100000}{2}*0.10 + \frac{100000}{4}*0.12 = 8000$$
Check your work!
$$x = 100000$$

Answer.

Two accounts, both are fractions of the total. Do the arithmetic on scratch paper. (Hint: You can use decimal equivalents for the fractions if you want.)

Investment: splitting a total investment

An investor invests a total of $10000, some at an interest rate of 8% and the rest at a rate of 10%. After one year, the investment interest was $990. How much was invested at 8%?

$x \Rightarrow$ Amount invested at 8%

$$x*0.08 + (10000 - x)*0.10 = 990$$
$$x(0.08 - 0.10) + 10000*0.10 = 990$$
$$-0.02x = 990 - 1000 = -10$$
$$x = 500$$
$$500*0.08 + (10000 - 500)*0.10 = 990$$
Check your work!
$$x = 500$$

Answer.

"Total - some" is a trick to finding how much is in two piles of stuff. If x is "some" and $10000 is "total" then the two principle amounts are **x** and **$10000 - x**.

Simple interest and is found by multiplying the principle by the rate: **I=pr**. If we add interest earned from two accounts at different principles and rates we can simplify the equation to the standard form: **ax + b = c** and solve for **x**. Visualize solving the equation as before with two bars, one above the other, searching for the value of **x** that makes the bars the same size. Remember that this time the **x** represents money in an account.

Does the answer to the equation always answer the question? How do you know if you have the correct answer?

How do you combine two accounts into one equation?

If you know the amount of interest from an account, can you determine what the interest rate was? What else do you need to know?

If you know the principle, what else do you need to know to determine the interest earned?

Using algebra, how many different ways can you describe distributing $100 over two accounts?

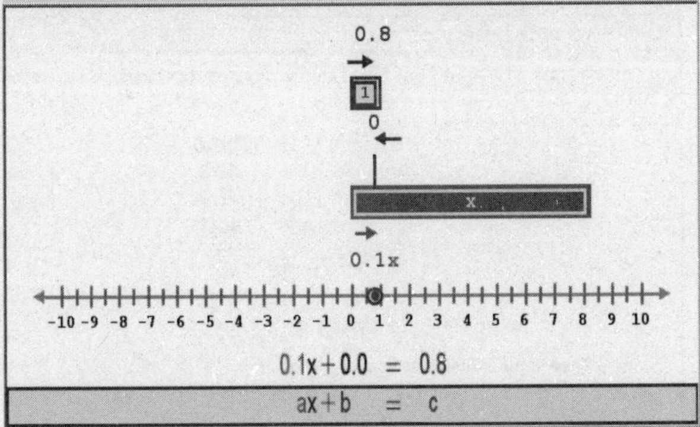

What amount should you invest at **10%** to earn **$800**?

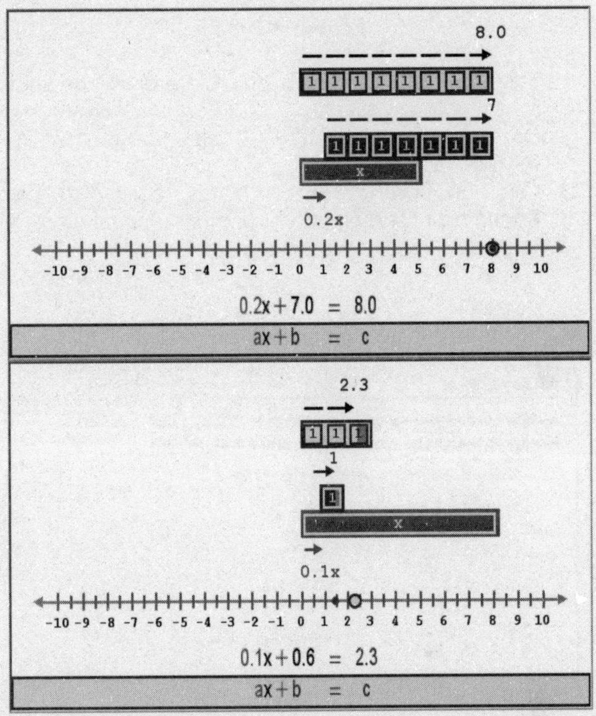

If you have two accounts, how much is needed in account 1 at **10%** if account 2 earned **$600** and the total interest is **$2300**?

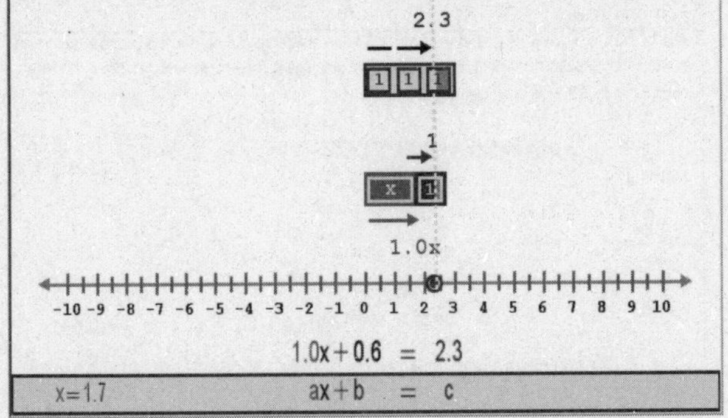

How much interest does account 1 earn if account 2 earns **$600** and the total interest for the two accounts is **$2300**?

Motion problems, or distance-rate-time problems, always use the following formula:

distance=rate*time.

If you know any two of the quantities, you can use algebra to solve for the third quantity.

More complex motion problems fall into two major categories: One where the distances are equal and one where the distances are added. Times and rates will vary, depending on the situation presented. Use your life experience and common sense to guide you in working through motion prob-

Problem types

1. Solve for distance, rate or time. Use **d=rt** and solve for the missing quantity.
2. Opposite directions: Different rates (or times); add for total distance.
3. Catch-up: Different rates (or times); equal distances.
4. Round trip: Different rates (or times); equal distances.

Motion Problems

Distance is equal to rate times time.

$d \Rightarrow$ distance
$r \Rightarrow$ rate
$t \Rightarrow$ time

d=rt; r=d/t; t=d/r

Distance

A jogger goes out for a run on a sunny afternoon. She runs 6 miles per hour on average. If she runs for 2 hours, how many miles does she run?

$d \Rightarrow$ distance
$$d = 6 \cdot 2$$
$$d = 12$$

The jogger ran 12 miles.

Answer the question. $d = r \cdot t$

Points 1—3: Solve for the unknown quantity, (distance, rate, or time).

Motion in Opposite Directions

Two planes take off from the same airport and fly in opposite directions. On average, one travels at 80 miles per hour and the other at 110 miles per hour. How long after they leave will they be 450 miles apart?

$t \Rightarrow$ time
$$80 \cdot t + 110 \cdot t = 450$$
$$(80 + 110)t = 450$$
$$190t = 450$$
$$t = \frac{450}{190}$$
$$t = 2.37$$
$$80 \cdot 2.37 + 110 \cdot 2.37 = 450$$

They will be 450 miles apart after 2.37 hours.

Answer the question. $r1 \cdot t + r2 \cdot t = d$

Notice that the rates are different for each plane, and that the unknown is time. Two distances, expressed as **rt,** are added for total distance.

Motion with different rates and times

The B train leaves the station 2 hours after the A train, with an average speed that is 25 miles per hour faster than the A train. They travel on parallel tracks. If the B train catches up to the A train in 5 hours, what is the average speed of the A train?

$r \Rightarrow$ rate of A train

A train   B train
$$r \cdot (5 + 2) = (r + 25)(5)$$
$$r \cdot 7 = (r + 25)(5)$$
$$7r = 5r + 125$$
$$2r = 125$$
$$r = 62.50$$
$$62.50 \cdot 7 = (62.50 + 25)) \cdot 5$$

The speed of the A train is 62.50 miles per hour.

Answer the question. $r \cdot t = (r + s)(t - h)$

When the trains catch up with each other, they have traveled the same distance. Is train A slower or faster?

A Round Trip

A pilot flies to an airport and then returns. The average speed on the trip to the airport was 90 miles per hour and took 3 hours. Find the average speed on the return trip, if the total round trip flying time was 5 hours.

$r \Rightarrow$ rate on return trip

trip to the airport   return trip
$$90 \cdot 3 = r(5 - 3)$$
$$270 = r(2)$$
$$\frac{270}{2} = r$$
$$135 = r$$
$$90 \cdot 3 = 135 \cdot (5 - 3)$$

The average speed on the return trip was 135.00 miles per hour.

Answer the question. $s \cdot t1 = r(t2 - t1)$

Notice that the time for going to the airport was given, as well as the time for the total trip. Subtract to find the time for the return.

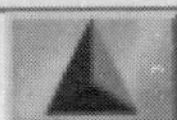

Motion problems or distance-rate-time problems can be visualized, much like the simple equation **ax=c**.

Two bars, one above the other, represent both sides of the equation. When the bars are the same length, the equation is solved. Here, **a**, **x**, and **c** take on specific meaning and can be replace with **rate*time=distance**, or **rt=d**.

In motion problems, any of the three values for **rate**, **time** or **distance**, may be the unknown quantity. How do you determine which is the unknown quantity?

How far do you walk if your speed is 3.5 mph for 2.3 hours? (Visualized at right.)

If you drive 350 miles in 5 hours, how fast did you drive?

How long did it take you to ride your bike 15 miles at a rate of 25 mph?

If you drive to the store and back in 25 minutes at an average rate of 30 mph, how far away is the store?

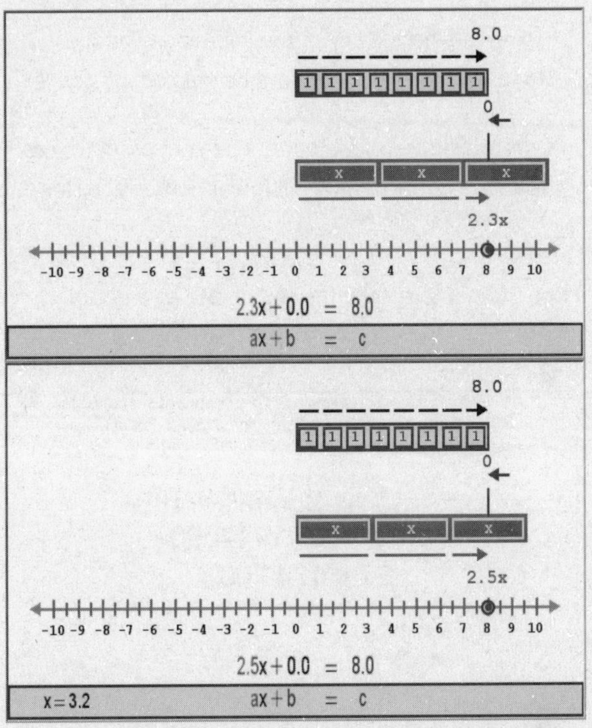

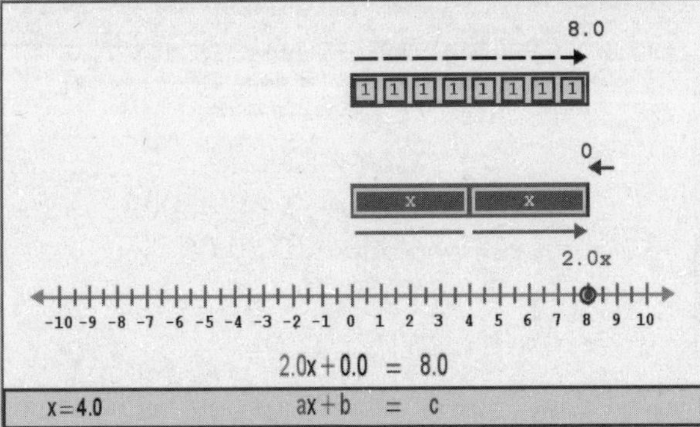

How long does it take to walk 8 miles at 2 mph?

How long does it take if you increase your speed to 2.5 mph?

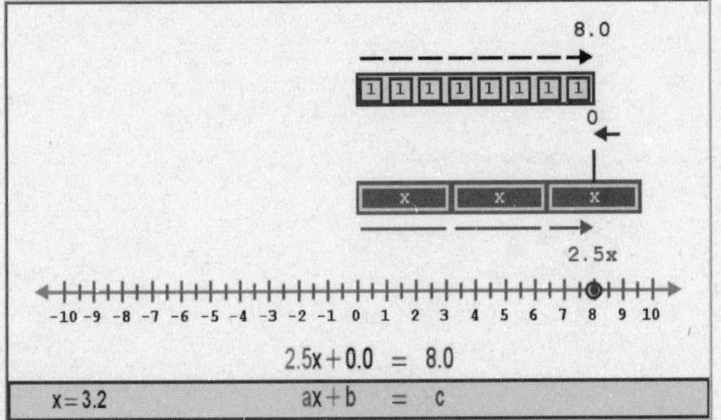

How far will you go in 4 hours? (Hint: Change **c** to find out.)

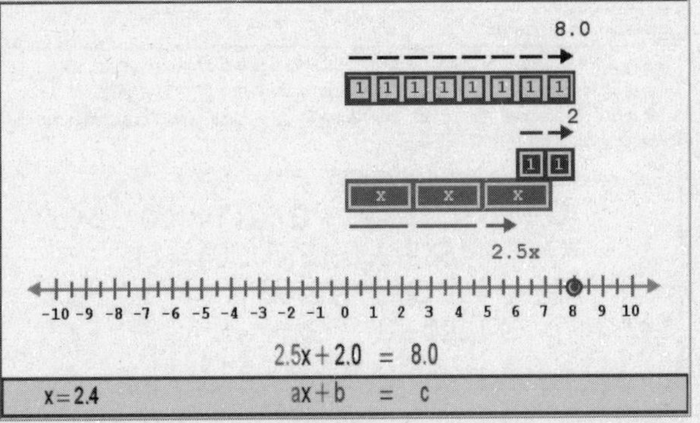

Kira is out for an 8-mile walk. You join her after she has already completed 2 miles. If you walk for 2.5 hours, what is your average speed?

Commission is when someone gets paid based on how much they sell. Commissions are usually figured as a **percentage of total sales**.

Commission = Rate x Sales

Commission problems are worked exactly like motion problems (**d=rt**) except that the quantities represent money rather than distance and the rate is a percent, not speed.

Income can include any of the following quantities:

Base salary—what you earn before commission is added.

Commission—calculated as a percent of total sales.

Variable commission—different percentage rates for sale ranges.

Don't forget to rewrite the stated rate as a decimal.

C = Commission
r = Rate of Commission in percent
s = Total amount of sales

C = r s

Commission

Ani works as a furniture salesman and is compensated at a commission rate of 12%. Last month, Ani sold $14500 worth of furniture. What were his earnings for that month?

$$C \Rightarrow \text{Commission}$$
$$C = 0.12 \cdot 14500$$
$$C = 1740.00$$

Ani earned $1740.00.

Answer the question.

In the simplest case, the commission (C) equals the commission rate times the amount of the products they sold.

Notice that the rate is rewritten as a decimal number.

Base Salary plus Commission

Sally works selling automobiles. She is compensated with a monthly base salary of $2600 along with a commission rate of 14%. Last month, Sally sold automobiles worth a total of $48000. What were her earnings for that month?

$$C \Rightarrow \text{Commission}$$
$$C = 2600 + 0.14 \cdot 48000$$
$$C = 2600 + 6720.00$$
$$C = 9320.00$$

Sally earned $9320.00.

Answer the question.

Commission is used as a reward for good salesmanship. Notice that the commission is added to find the total earnings.

Variable Commission

Harry is a hardware salesman. He is compensated with a commission rate of 7% on sales up to his quota of $6400 along with a commission rate of 12% on all sales over his quota. Last week, Harry's total sales were $14500. What were his earnings for that week?

$$C \Rightarrow \text{Commission}$$
$$C = 0.07 \cdot 6400 + 0.12(14500 - 6400)$$
$$C = 448.00 + 0.12(8100)$$
$$C = 448.00 + 972.00$$
$$C = 1420.00$$

Harry earned $1420.00.

Answer the question.

To find the two different sales amounts, subtract the first amount from the total.

Commissions are awards based on sales. Simple commission is a form of the standard equation **ax=c**. Base salary plus commission is a form of **ax + b = c**.

All commission problems can be visualized as equations with two bars, one above the other. When the equation is solved, the bars are equal.

For commission problems, find the rate, the sales, or the commission using **C = rs**

How do you know which quantity represents a rate in a problem? How do you know which problem represents sales? Is commission always the unknown? Is commission always less than sales? Can someone's salary of base plus commission be greater than the amount of sales? If you know what your commission is, how do you find out what your rate of commission is?

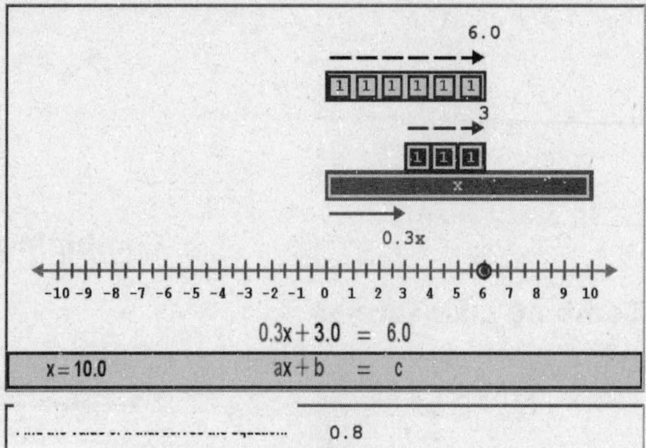

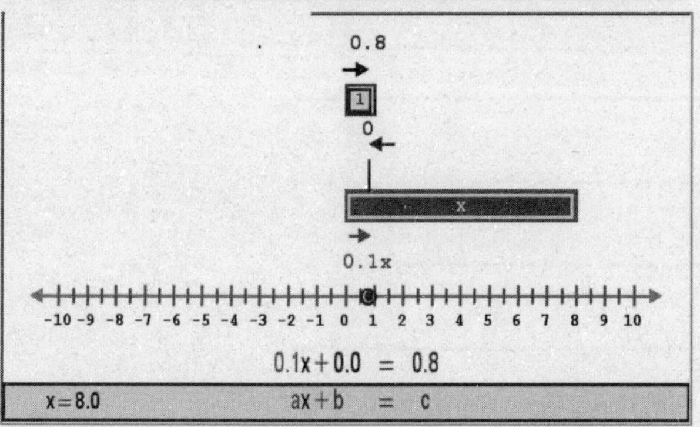

If the commission rate is 10%, and you sell $8 worth of merchandise, you will earn $0.80.

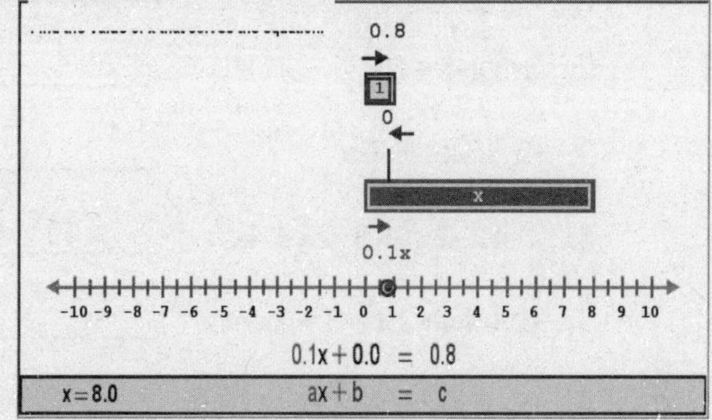

How much will you earn if you sell $8 million of stock?

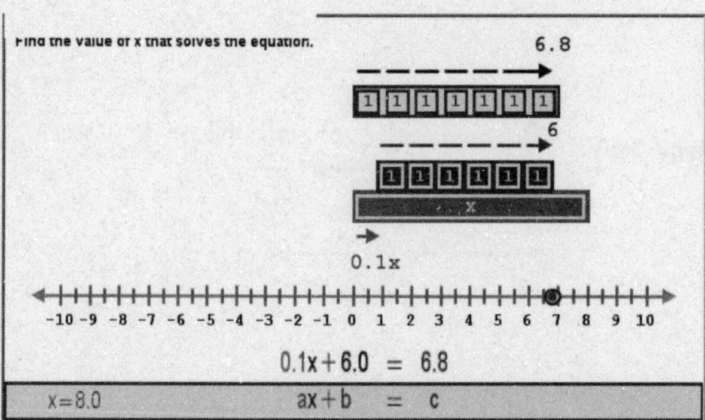

If your base salary is $6000, and you sell $8000 worth of cell phones at 10% commission, how much do you earn?

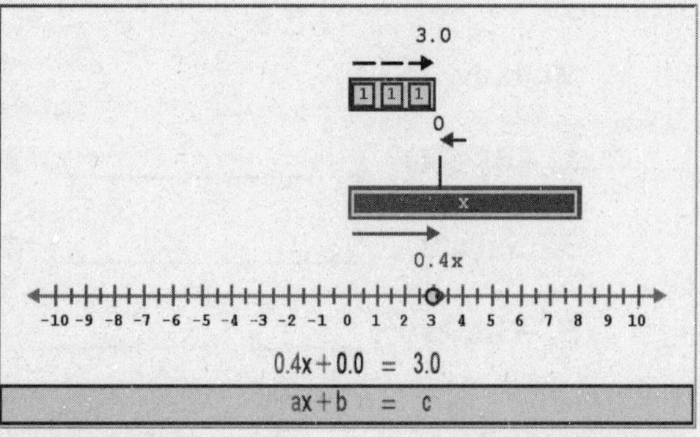

Find the rate if you make $3 on commission for selling $12 worth of candy.

Evaluating Variable Expressions

Evaluate $a^2 + b^2$ when:

1. a=5, b=2 ________
2. a=-5, b=2 ________
3. a=-5, b=-5 ________
4. a=25, b=-9 ________

Evaluate 3a-b when:

5. a=-6, b=-8 ________
6. a=9, b=-8 ________

Combining Like Terms

Combine Like Terms:

1. 2x+9+x-4 ____________________
2. 2-3x-5+6x ____________________
3. -2+3x+5-6x ____________________
4. $2-4x-2x^2+3-2x+4x^2$ ____________________
5. $-2+4x+2x^2-3+2x-4x^2$ ____________________
6. $-2-4x-2x^2-3-2x-4x^2$ ____________________

Multiplying Monomials

Multiply.

1. -6(-3x) ____________ 2. -9x(2x) ____________

3. $5x(x^2)$ ____________ 4 $-7(-x^2)$ ____________

5. $–3x(2xy^2)$ ____________

The Distributive Property

Multiply.

1. $-9(7x+1)$ ______________ 2. $-6(x-2)$ ______________

3. $x(4x-6)$ ______________ 4. $2x(-7x^2+4x+8$ ______________

5. $-3(5x+4)-4(2x+3)$ ______________

6. $3x(x-2)-3(x+7)+2(5x-1)$ ______________

Solving x+b=c

Each of the following equations is in x+b=c form. Solve for x.

1. $x-5 = 10$ __________ 2. $x+5=10$ __________

3. $x-2=6$ __________ 4. $x+7=-3$ __________

5. $x-11=4$ __________ 6. $x-1=0$ __________

Solving ax=c

Each of the following equations is in ax=c form. Solve for x.

1. $-5\ x= 10$ __________ 2. $12x=-120$ __________

3. $-2x=6$ __________ 4. $7x=-35$ __________

5. $-x=4$ __________ 6. $-11x=0$ __________

Solving ax+b=c

Each of the following equations is in ax+b=c form. Solve for x.

1. $3x-5 = 10$ __________ 2. $-2x+5=11$ __________

3. $-8x-2=6$ __________ 4. $5x+7=-3$ __________

5. $7x+14=14$ __________ 6. $3x-12=0$ __________

Convert to ax+b=c and Solve

Use Distributive Property to remove parentheses and combine like terms. Solve for x by converting to ax+b=c form. Put the value for x on the blank.

1. 3x-5 = x-11 __________
2. -2(x+3)=5-3x __________
3. x-2-3x-5=-6x+2-x+6 __________
4. 2(x+7)=-(3x+1) __________
5. 3(1+2x)+4=2+5(x+1) __________
6. -3(-2x-1)=5(x-1) __________

Equations with Fractions

Put answers in reduced fraction form. Show your work.

Solve for x:

1. $-\frac{3}{5}x+\frac{2}{3}=\frac{1}{2}$

2. $\frac{2}{5}x-\frac{1}{4}=\frac{7}{10}$

3. $\frac{5}{7}x-4=\frac{1}{2}x+\frac{2}{3}$

4. $\frac{3}{4}(2x-5)=\frac{1}{3}(3-7x)$

5. $\frac{1}{2}(x-3)=\frac{3}{4}(x-1)$

Equations with Decimals

Solve for x: (Round answers to two decimal places when appropriate.)

1. 2.1x – 5.1 = 4.8 ________
2. 3.1– 4.8x = 2.9 ________
3. 0.2x+ 4.1 = -5.9 ________
4. 2.1x-0.4+0.3x-1.2=3.1x-1.2-2.5x-.07 ________
5. -2.1(3x—5) = -1.1(2x+3) ________

Graphing Inequalities

Graph the following inequalities on the number line provided.

1. $x \geq -2$
2. $x < 5$
3. $x \leq -4$
4. $x > -1$

5. Write an inequality that describes the following graph.

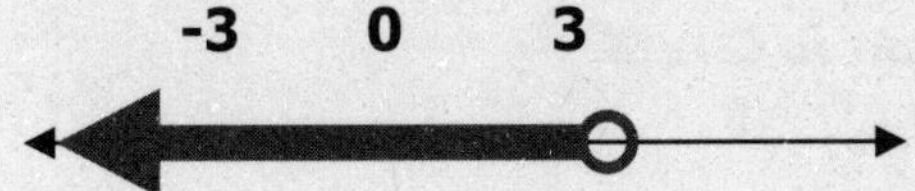

Solving Linear Inequalities

Solve the linear inequalities

1. $b - 9 > -3$ ______________________
2. $3c - 7 \leq 2$ ______________________
3. $2x - 5 < 5x + 13$ ______________________
4. $-2 < -x + 1/2$ ______________________
5. $-3 - 2x + 3 - 5x \geq -8 + 2x$ ______________________

Absolute Value Equations

Solve for x; use roster notation for answers.

1. $|x| = 3$ ______________________
2. $|x + 2| = 7$ ______________________
3. $|x - 1| + 3 = 7$ ______________________
4. $2|x| = 12$ ______________________
5. $3|5x - 1| = 12$ ______________________

Sets

Set A = { 2, 4, 6, 8, 10, 12} and set B = { 1, 3, 6, 9, 12, 15}

1. List the elements in $A \cup B$

2. List the elements in $A \cap B$.

3. Use set builder notation to describe set A.

4. List the elements in the following set: $\{x \mid -2 < x < 3 \text{ and } x \in \text{integers}\}$

5. Use set builder notation to describe the set of all x's such that x is an odd whole number less than 10.

6. If set C = $\{x \mid x>3\}$ and set D = $\{x \mid x<0\}$, what is $C \cap D$?

Union and Intersection

1. Find A U B if A = {3,5,7} and B = {2,3,4,5,6,7,8}

2. Find $A \cap B$ if A = {-1,0,1,2,3,4,5,6} and B = {x I x is an even integer}

3. Find $A \cap B$ if A = {x I x<0} and B = {x I x>3}

4. {x I x> -2} U {x I x<2}

5. {☺,😐,☹} ∩ {☹,😐} U {☺,😐}

Solving Translation Problems

Translate and solve the following problems. Show both the equation and the answer.

1. Negative four times a number added to two is thirty-eight.

2. One less than negative nine times a number is fifty-three.

3. Find three consecutive integers whose sum is 87.

4. Find three consecutive even integers whose sum is 42.

Tolerance Problems

Find the following limits.

1. A small motor is designed to run at 196 volts with a tolerance of 11.5 volts. Calculate the acceptable lower and upper limits of the voltage for this motor.

2. A beverage dispenser is designed to fill a 16 ounce cup with a tolerance of 0.3 ounces. Calculate the acceptable lower and upper limits in ounces for this dispenser.

3. A beverage dispenser is designed to fill a 10.0 ounce cup with a tolerance of 0.4 ounces. Calculate the upper limit.

4. A patient requires a 9 cc dosage of a medicine at regular intervals. The tolerance of each dose is 0.12 cc. What is the least amount the patient can take at each interval and still be within the recommended allowance.

Compound Inequalities

Use set notation to describe the solutions to the following problems.

1. $4x>16$ and $x+11<36$

2. $8x<24$ or $x+12>35$

3. $11x+3>58$ and $2x-5<11$

4. $-7x+14>0$ and $-7x-1<76$

5. $-4x-5<-13$ or $-6x+5>71$

Mixture Problems

1. How many liters of a 70% bleach solution should be mixed with 10 liters of a 5% bleach solution to make a solution that is 44% bleach? Round to the nearest hundredth.

2. How many quarts of a 95% alcohol solution should be mixed with 8 quarts of a 30% alcohol solution to make a solution that is 65% alcohol? Round to the nearest hundredth.

3. A "secret" flavoring is made by blending 3 different spices: 250 ounces of a spice that costs $7.50 per ounce, 300 ounces of a spice that costs $4 per ounce, and 400 ounces of a spice that costs $2 per ounce. How much does it cost (to the nearest cent) to make one ounce of the secret flavoring?

4. A radiator holds 13 liters of a mixture containing 20% antifreeze. How much should be drained and replaced with pure antifreeze to have 13 liters of a mixture with 55% antifreeze? Round to the nearest hundredth.

Investment Problems

1. Alexa invests some money at an interest rate of 14% and one-fourth as much at a rate of 10%. If the total interest for one year from both investments is $1320, how much did she invest at 14%?

2. Shante invests some money at an interest rate of 11% and $2000 more than that at a rate of 7%. If the total interest for one year from both investments is $1040, how much did she invest at 11%?

3. Max received a settlement for a large sum of money. Last year, he invested three-eighths of it an interest rate of 13% and one-eighth of it at a rate of 5%. If the total interest for one year from both investments is $2420, how much was the settlement?

4. Bianca invested a total of $5500, some at an interest rate of 10% and the rest at a rate of 7%. After one year, the investment interest was $460. How much did she invest at 10%?

Motion Problems

1. A jogger goes out for a run on a sunny afternoon. She runs 2.7 miles per hour on average. If she runs for 1.3 hours, how many miles does she run? (Round to the nearest 10th.)

2. Two planes take off from the same airport and fly in opposite directions. On average, one travels at 85 miles per hour and the other at 174 miles per hour. How long after they leave will they be 1208 miles apart?

3. A commuter train leaves the station 1.0 hour after a freight train, with an average speed that is 28 miles per hour faster than the freight train. They travel on parallel tracks. Six hours after the commuter train leaves, it catches up to the freight train. What is the average speed of the commuter train?

Commission Problems

1. Sean is a shoe salesman who gets paid on a straight commission basis. Last week, he had total sales of $9050.00. If Sean's commission rate is 9%, what were his earnings for the week?

2. Liza works in magazine sales. She gets paid a salary of $325.00 a week plus a 4% commission on her total sales. Last week, she sold $1300.00 worth of magazines. What were her earnings for the week?

3. Gregory works Saturday and Sunday selling newspapers and magazines. He gets paid $27.00 a day plus a 11% commission on his total sales. His sales last weekend were $429.00. How much did he earn?

4. Allie is a travel agent for an airline. She earns a commission rate of 5% on ticket sales up to $11495.00 along with a commission rate of 8% on ticket sales over $11495.00. Last week, Allie's total ticket sales were $18383.00. What were her earnings for the week?

8. Graphing Linear Equations

The graph of a linear equation in two variables is a straight line, which is the reason that this form of equation is called linear.

This module covers elementary graphing, the slope of graphs of linear equations, and the graphing of inequalities as well as equalities.

Graphs enable us to visualize these equations. By the time you are finished you should be able to look at a linear equation or inequality and picture its graph in your mind.

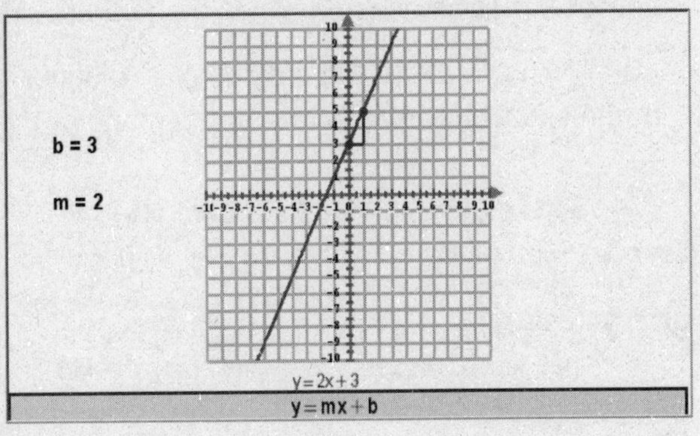

Ordered Pairs as Solutions

In their simplest form, linear equations in two variables look like **Ax + By = C** where **A**, **B**, and **C** are constants and **x** and **y** are variables. We use these capital letters in this particular form of the linear equation by tradition. Solutions to the equation are ordered pairs **(a,b)** where **a**, *the first listed*, is always the **x-value** and **b**, *the second listed*, is always the **y-value**. We generally use lower case a and b or x and y for ordered pairs. Point **(a,b)** is said to satisfy the equation if the equation is balanced (true) when **a** and **b** are substituted for **x** and **y**, respectively.

FOR ANY EQUATION: All ordered pair solutions that satisfy (balance) the equation are on the graph of the equation and all points on the graph of the equation satisfy the equation.

Testing Ordered Pair Solutions (a,b)

Step 1: Substitute **a** for **x** and **b** for **y** in the given equation.

Step 2: Simplify both sides of the equation, independently. (In these examples, only the left side needs to be simplified.)

Step 3: Compare—If left and right sides of the equation are equal, then the ordered pair is a solution.

Is (-4,-2) a solution to the equation?

$$2x - 3y = -2$$

Let $x = -4$ and $y = -2$.

$$2(-4) - 3(-2) = -2$$
$$-8 + 6 = -2$$
$$-2 = -2$$

-2 is equal to -2. $2x - 3y = -2$

Is (-1,0) a solution to the equation?

$$3x + y = -3$$

Let $x = -1$ and $y = 0$.

$$3(-1) - 3(0) = -3$$
$$-3 + 0 = -3$$
$$-3 = -3$$

-3 is equal to -3. $3x + y = -3$

The ordered pair (-1,0) is a solution to 3x + y = -3.

Is (1,2) a solution to the equation?

$$2x - 3y = -2$$

Let $x = 1$ and $y = 2$.

Then, $2x - 3y = 2(1) - 3(2) = 2 - 6 = -4$.

So, $(1, 2)$ is not a solution of $2x - 3y = -2$.

$2x - 3y = -2$

Point 2: After simplifying the left side of the equation, compare –4 and –2; the point does **NOT** satisfy the equation, therefore it is not a solution.

Is (-3,4) a solution to the equation?

$$x^2 + y^2 = 25$$

Let $x = -3$ and $y = 4$.

Then, $x^2 + y^2 = (-3)^2 + (4)^2 = 9 + 16 = 25$.

So, $(-3, 4)$ is a solution of $x^2 + y^2 = 25$.

$x^2 + y^2 = 25$

Points 3 and 4: Test ordered pair solutions to equations that are not linear— the process is the same: substitute, simplify, and compare.

Is (-2,2) a solution to the equation?

$$x^2 + y^2 = 25$$

Let $x = -2$ and $y = 2$.

Then, $x^2 + y^2 = (-2)^2 + (2)^2 = 4 + 4 = 8$.

So, $(-2, 2)$ is not a solution of $x^2 + y^2 = 25$.

$x^2 + y^2 = 25$

Simplify the left side of the equation and compare it to the right side. 8≠25; therefore (-2,2) is not a solution.

Linear equations in two variables (Ax + By = C) have an infinite number of solutions (ordered pairs) which we can display on a graph as a **straight line** – hence the name **linear equation.** To determine if an ordered pair is a solution **substitute** the ordered pair for **x** and **y**, then **simplify**, and finally **compare** both sides of the equation.

Visualize the equation as a balance at the equal sign. When the two sides are the same, the balance is maintained.

Test ordered pair solutions by using the joystick to change values for **x** and **y**. Change the equation by changing **A**, **B**, or **C**. Notice, at right, that the left side of the equal sign is being simplified to **14** on the second line. Then compare that **14** with the right side of the original equation. Make sure you explore enough ordered pairs to get a mental picture of **the process: Substitute, simplify, compare.**

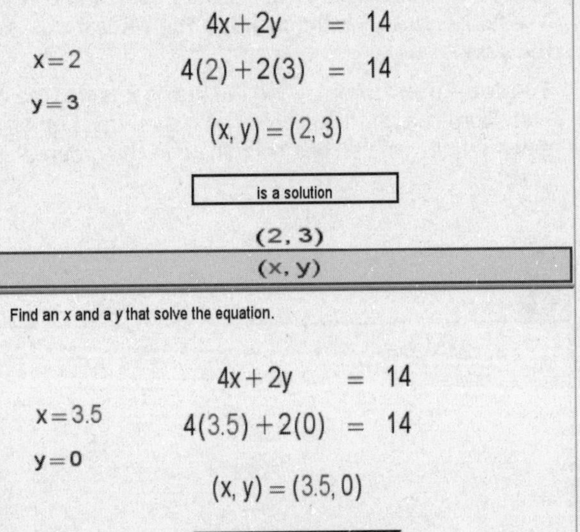

Find an *x* and a *y* that solve the equation.

$$4x + 2y = 14$$

x = 0, y = 7

$$4(0) + 2(7) = 14$$

$$(x, y) = (0, 7)$$

is a solution

(0, 7)

(x, y)

What happens to the first term of the equation when **x=0**?

Find an *x* and a *y* that solve the equation.

$$4x + 2y = 14$$

x = 3.5, y = 0

$$4(3.5) + 2(0) = 14$$

$$(x, y) = (3.5, 0)$$

is a solution

(3.5, 0)

(x, y)

What happens to the second term of the equation when **y=0**?

Find an *x* and a *y* that solve the equation.

$$3x + 4y = 9$$

x = 3, y = 0

$$3(3) + 4(0) = 9$$

$$(x, y) = (3, 0)$$

is a solution

(3, 0)

(x, y)

To easily find an ordered pair that solves the equation, set **x** or **y** equal **0**, then find the other part of the ordered pair.

Find an *x* and a *y* that solve the equation.

$$-3x + 4y = 12$$

x = 2, y = 5

$$-3(2) + 4(5) = 14$$

$$(x, y) = (2, 5)$$

is not a solution

(2, 5)

(x, y)

Notice that **−3(2) + 4(5) = 14** and that **14≠12**, so (2,5) is not a solution.

Plotting Ordered Pairs

EnableMath

Ordered pairs are called **points** when they are displayed on a graph. A **graph** is an organized display of points in a plane. Two number lines crossing at point **(0,0)**, the **origin**, form the **axes** of the grid of the graph. Ordered pairs are made up of the **x–** and **y-coordinates** of the point on the graph. The axes divide the grid into four quadrants, labeled **I, II, III,** and **IV**.

Quadrant I includes all points where **x** and **y** coordinates are *positive*.
Quadrant II has points with *negative* coordinates for **x** and *positive* coordinates for **y**.
Quadrant III are points where **x** and **y** coordinates are *negative*.
Quadrant IV has points of *positive* **x** coordinates and *negative* **y** coordinates.

At right is a grid with the center marked at point **(0,0)** and the Quadrants labeled as I, II, III, and IV. The horizontal axis is the **x-axis**. The vertical axis is the **y-axis.**

To plot a point: trace along the **x**-axis **x**-units (the first coordinate in the ordered pair); then trace up or down **y**-units (the second coordinate of the ordered pair).

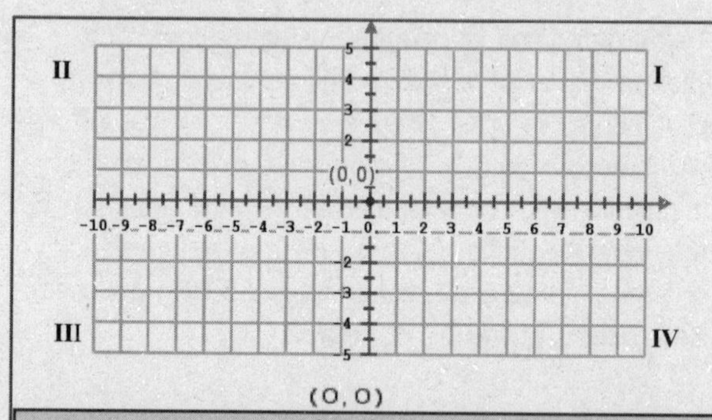

(0, 0)

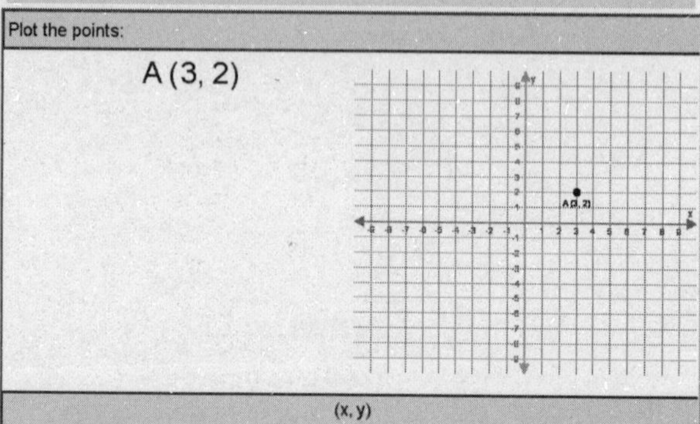

To plot **(3,2)** go **3 units** to the right on the **x-axis**; then go up **2 units** and make a dot. Label the point **A** or **(3,2)**.

Plot the points:

A (3, 2)
B (– 1, – 2)
C (0, 0)

(x, y)

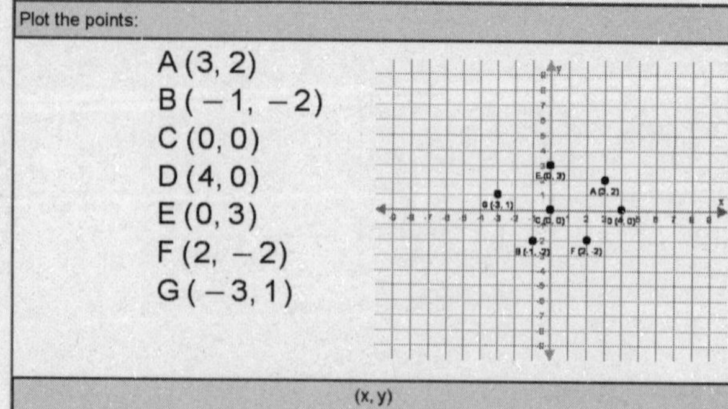

Points **B** and **F** have negative **y** coordinates. Point **F** is in Quadrant IV—therefore the **x**-coordinate must be positive. Point **B** is located in Quadrant III. Is its **x** coordinate positive or negative?

Quad means four. Quadrants are the four parts of what are called Cartesian or rectangular coordinate system graphs. We saw them first in multiplying integers and we will deal with them often in the future. You should play with moving the point around these four quadrants until you can quickly visualize which quadrant any ordered pair will fall into.

Thinking ahead: A collection of graphed ordered pair solutions to an equation will form a picture of the equation. The solutions to a linear equation in two variables will form a line.

Use the joystick to see where different ordered pairs are located on the grid.

What set of ordered pairs are located on the **x**-axis?

What set are located on the **y**-axis?

If an ordered pair is located in Quadrant III, what sign will the **x**-coordinate have?

If all **x**-coordinates must be positive—which Quadrants will be used?

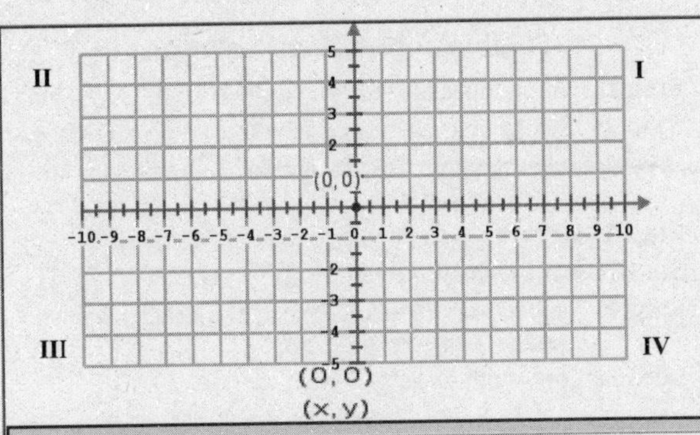

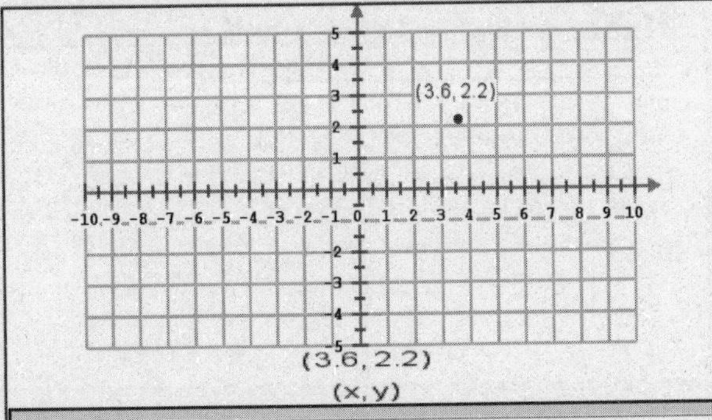

Above is a point in Quadrant I How many units above the **x**-axis is this point? How far to the right of the origin?

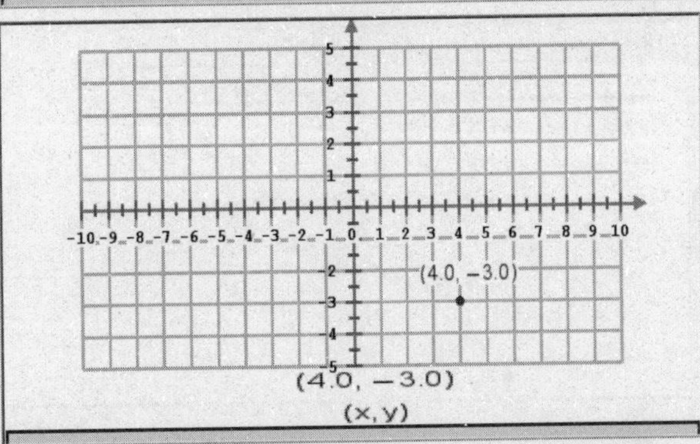

Above is a point in Quadrant IV. What is the sign of the **x** coordinate? What are the coordinates of the point one unit above **(4, -3)**? Two units above **(4,-3)**? What are the coordinates of the point **m**-units above **(4,-3)**?

Table of Values

EnableMath

Write the equation in **y = ax + c** form to make it easier to find the ordered pairs. We do this systematically by creating a **table of values**. The first column lists the **x**-coordinates; the middle column shows the work for finding the **y**-coordinate, and the third column lists the ordered pair.

Finding ordered pair solutions

Step 1: Put the equation into **y = ax + c** form.

Step 2: Choose any value for **x** and list it in the **x**-column.

Step 3: Substitute the chosen value for **x** and simplify to find the value for **y**.

Step 4: Write the ordered pair in the third column.

Step 5: Plot the point.

Step 6: Repeat 3 or 4 times, selecting negative as well as positive numbers and zero.

Step 7: Connect the points.

Plot the graph of f(x)=2x+1 using a table of values:

x	2x+1	(x, 2x+1)

Plot the graph of f(x)=2x+1 using a table of values:

x	2x+1	(x, 2x+1)
−2	2(−2)+1=−3	(−2, −3)
−1	2(−1)+1=−1	(−1, −1)
0	2(0)+1=1	(0, 1)

Use any value for **x**. Choose easy values that "come out even" so that they can be easily plotted. Zero is always a good choice.

Plot the graph of f(x)=2x+1 using a table of values:

x	2x+1	(x, 2x+1)
−2	2(−2)+1=−3	(−2, −3)
−1	2(−1)+1=−1	(−1, −1)
0	2(0)+1=1	(0, 1)
1	2(1)+1=3	(1, 3)
2	2(2)+1=5	(2, 5)

The last step is to connect all the points to see the picture of the line. From the picture you can estimate other values not in the table. Where does the line cross the x-axis? At what point will the line enter Quadrant III?

Plot the graph of f(x)=2x+1 using a table of values:

x	2x+1	(x, 2x+1)
−2	2(−2)+1=−3	(−2, −3)
−1	2(−1)+1=−1	(−1, −1)
0	2(0)+1=1	(0, 1)
1	2(1)+1=3	(1, 3)
2	2(2)+1=5	(2, 5)

Connect the points.

Often we can use mental arithmetic. Pick any value for **x**; solve for **y** and organize the results in a **chart.**

A **table of values** is a chart, in this case, listing ordered pair solutions to equations. Using a table of values will help you organize and keep track of your work. You can organize your work into any type of table, but consider making enough columns to give a clear picture of what has or needs to be done.

Use the joystick to change the equations and see what happens as **x** changes.

Think of a **table of values** as a sequence of ordered pairs, that for every **x** in the table there is a value for **y**. You can make the table of values as long as you want and put in any values that you want, but tables for linear equations need only be 3 or 4 points. It is a good idea to make one of the points at **x=0** to show you where the graph crosses the **y**-axis, and **y=0** to show you where the graph crosses the **x**-axis.

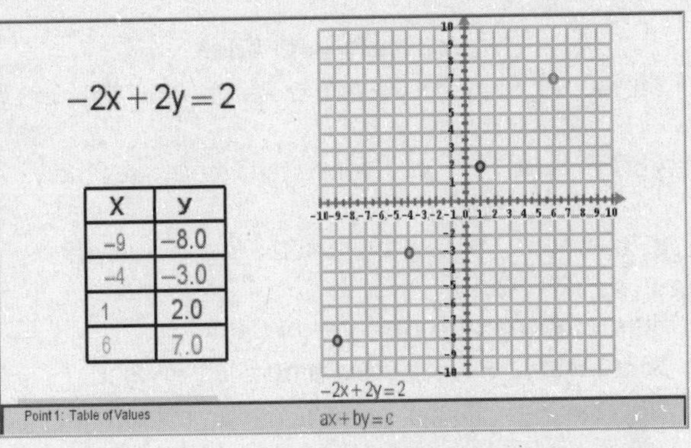

$-2x+2y=2$
X | y
-9 | -8.0
-4 | -3.0
1 | 2.0
6 | 7.0
$-2x+2y=2$
Point 1: Table of Values
$ax+by=c$

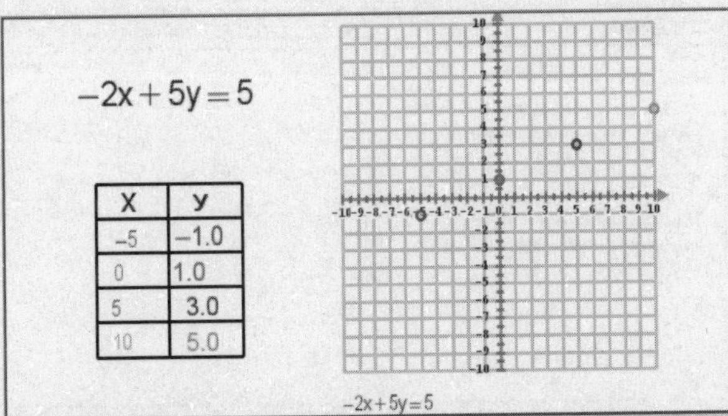

$-2x+5y=5$
X | y
-5 | -1.0
0 | 1.0
5 | 3.0
10 | 5.0
$-2x+5y=5$

Four values for **x** have been chosen and corresponding values for **y** have been calculated. The next step is to connect the dots.

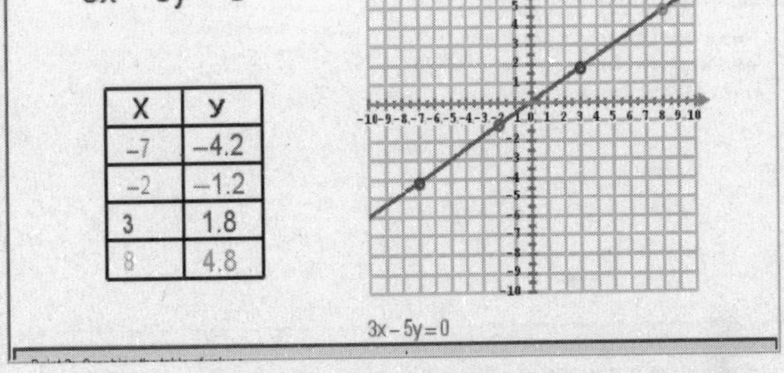

Notice that chosen values for **x** didn't "come out even" for **y**. The coordinates might be hard to plot. A graph is an estimation not an exact representation of the picture of the equation.

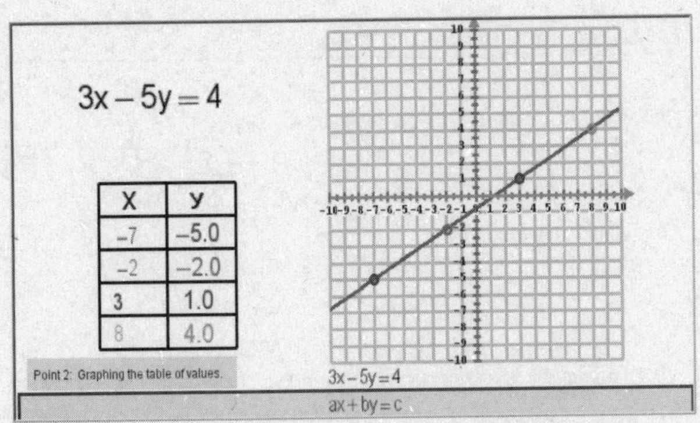

$3x-5y=4$
X | y
-7 | -5.0
-2 | -2.0
3 | 1.0
8 | 4.0
Point 2: Graphing the table of values.
$3x-5y=4$
$ax+by=c$

These points were chosen because all the coordinates are whole numbers and easy to plot. What is the value for **y** when **x=0**? What's the value for **x** when **y=0**?

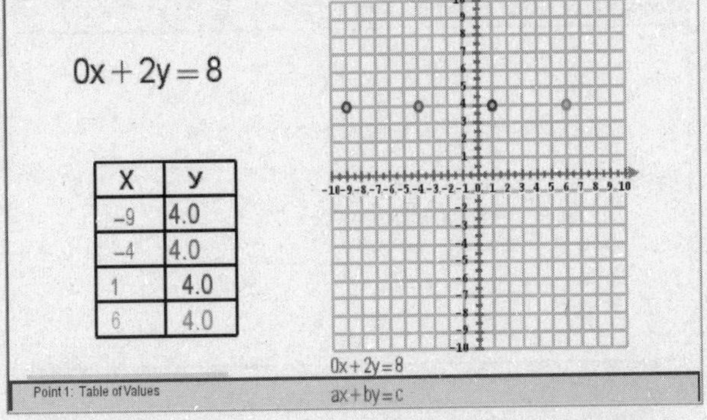

Change the coefficient of **x** to be **0**. What happens to the line? What values can **x** be? What value will **y** have when **x** is 5? What value will **y** have when **x** is **–5**? What value will **y** have for all values of **x**?

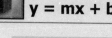

In Module 7. Solving Linear Equations, linear equations in one variable were written in **ax + b = c** form. Linear equations in two variables can be written so that the **y**-variable is alone on the left side of the equal sign (solved for **y**). The equation becomes **y = mx + b** and is called the **slope-intercept form**. The letters **m** and **b** take on special meaning, directly connecting the equation to the graph of the line.

Equations in **y = mx + b** form cross the **y-axis** at the point **(0, b)** and have a **slope** of **m**. If the slope **m>0,** the line is **increasing** (slanted upward to the right); if **m<0** the line is **decreasing** (slanted downward to the right). If **m=0**, the line is horizontal.

Vocabulary for lines

Slope: **m**, the measure of the steepness of the slant of a line.

y-intercept: the point where the line crosses the y-axis. **(0,b)**

x-intercept: the point where the line crosses the x-axis. **(x,0)**.

Slope-intercept form: **y = mx + b.**

Increasing: Slanted upward from left to right.

Decreasing: Slanted downward from left to right.

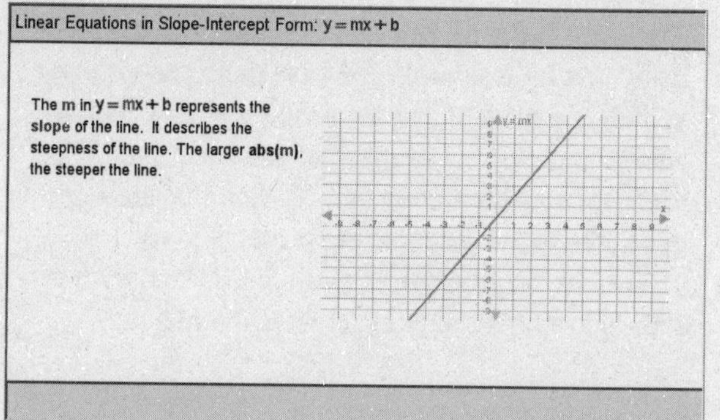

Linear Equations in Slope-Intercept Form: y = mx + b
The m in y = mx + b represents the slope of the line. It describes the steepness of the line. The larger abs(m), the steeper the line.

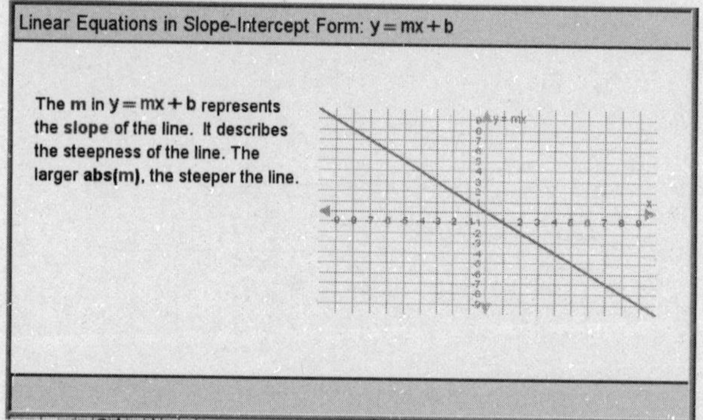

Linear Equations in Slope-Intercept Form: y = mx + b
The m in y = mx + b represents the slope of the line. It describes the steepness of the line. The larger abs(m), the steeper the line.

The top right picture shows a rising slope. The image above shows a falling slope. Use the joystick to step through more examples. Note the change in the slant as the slope changes from negative to positive.

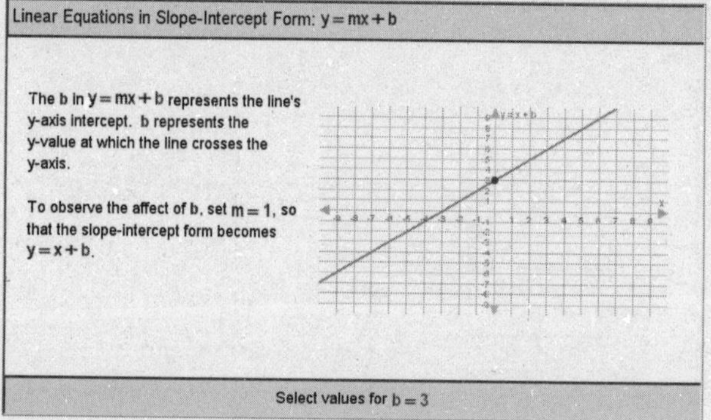

Linear Equations in Slope-Intercept Form: y = mx + b
The b in y = mx + b represents the line's y-axis intercept. b represents the y-value at which the line crosses the y-axis.
To observe the affect of b, set m = 1, so that the slope-intercept form becomes y = x + b.
Select values for b = 3

Here the line crosses the **y**-axis at point **(0,3).** From the equation, **b** is the **y**-intercept. From the graph above, we can see that the equation is close to being revealed: **y = mx + 3**.

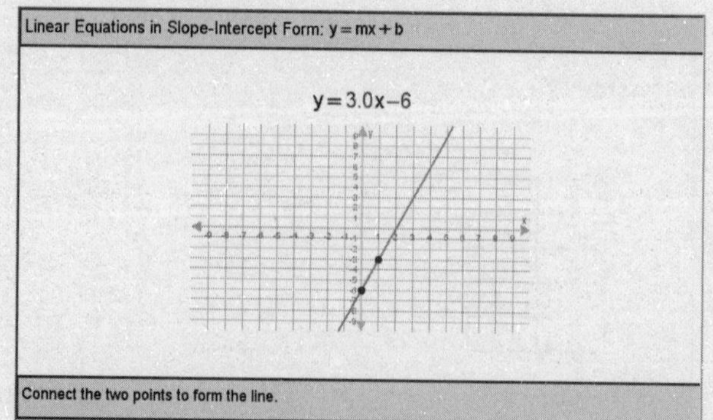

Changing the y-intercept moves the line up or down depending on the value of **b**. The lines above cross the **y-axis** at **(0,3)**; **(0,0)**; and **(0,-2)** respectfully.

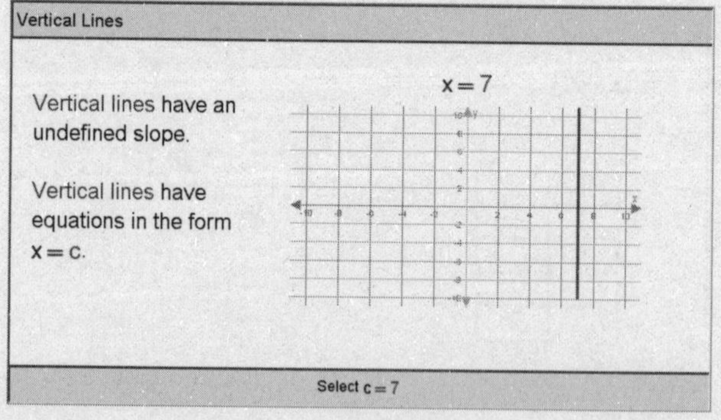

Vertical Lines
Vertical lines have an undefined slope.
Vertical lines have equations in the form x = c.
x = 7
Select c = 7

Vertical lines are parallel to the y-axis; it has no "slant", so we say the slope is undefined. 8.3 gives an algebraic meaning to the slope being undefined. **Horizontal** lines are parallel to the

The slope-intercept form of a linear equation, **y = mx + b**, gives important information about the graph of the line. From just looking at the equation we know where it crosses the **y**-axis; the value of the **slope**, and whether it slants upward (a rising line) or downward (a falling line).

Use the joystick to change the value of **m** to see how the slope affects the line. Make sure to set **m=0**, and sweep through positive and negative values. Change **b** to watch what happens to the line.

How does slope, m, affect the line? What happens when m gets smaller and smaller? What happens as m increases? Describe what the line looks like when m=0. What happens when the line is vertical? What is the slope of a vertical line? What does the value of b do to the line? When b increases what does the line do? When b decreases, what does the line do?

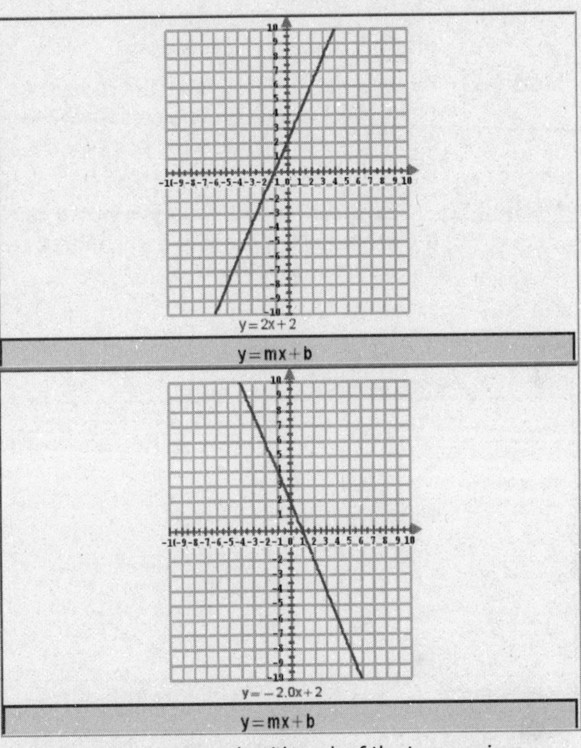

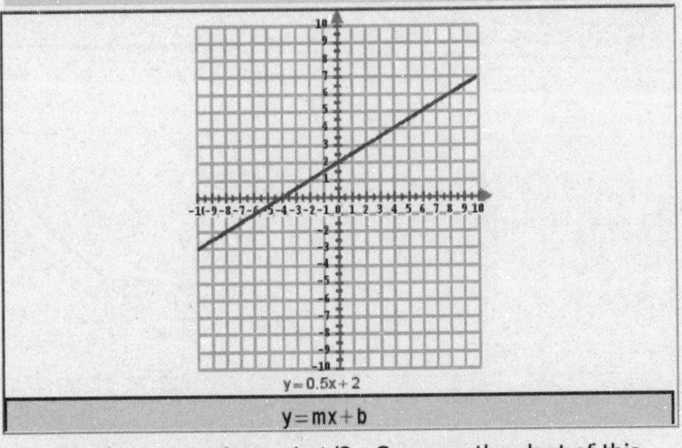

For the above equation **m** is 1/2. Compare the slant of this line with the line above right with **m** = **2**. Which one is steeper?

Compare the above graph with each of the two previous graphs. What's different about this line? What's the slope of this line?

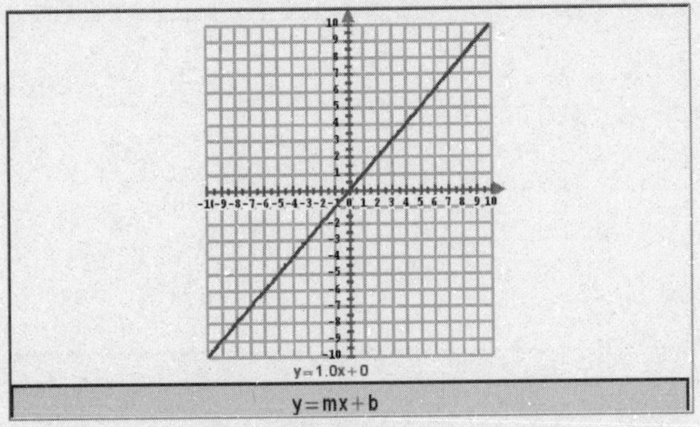

In the above graphs the y-intercept was 2. Here **b=0**. What happened to the line?

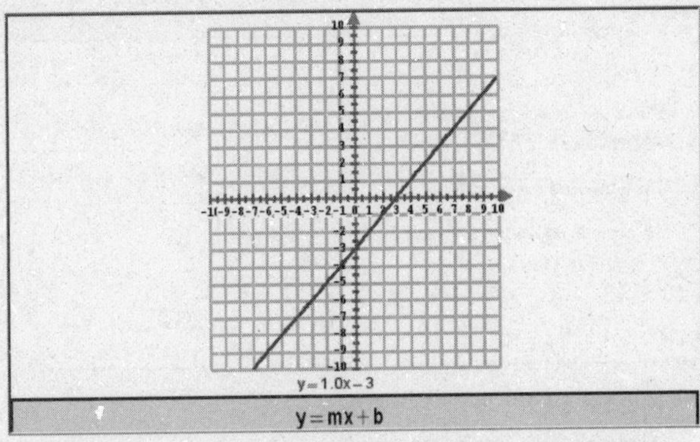

Compare this graph with the one on the left. What's different? Slope is the same but **b** has changed. What did changing **b** do to the line?

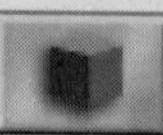

x– and y– Intercepts

EnableMath

It is useful to know where the graph of the line crosses or **intercepts** the **x-** and **y-**axes. You can find the **x**– and **y**-intercepts by looking at the graph or by manipulating the equation. The line crosses the **x**-axis when **y=0** and crosses the **y**-axis when **x=0**, thus substitute **0** for **x** to find the **y**-intercept and **0** for **y** to find the **x**-intercept. When an equation is in **y = mx + b** form, the **y**-intercept is **b**.

To find the **x**-intercept: substitute **0** for **y** and solve for **x**,

$$0 = mx + b$$
$$-mx = b$$
$$x = -b/m$$

Finding x- and y-intercepts

Method I: By Inspection—The **y**-intercept, **b**, is the point **(0,b)** where the line crosses the **y**-axis. The **x**-intercept is the point **(x,0)** where the line crosses the **x**-axis.

Method II: By Equation—In the form **y = mx + b** the **y**-intercept is **b** and the **x**-intercept is the expression **–b/m**.

Find the x- and y- intercepts graphically

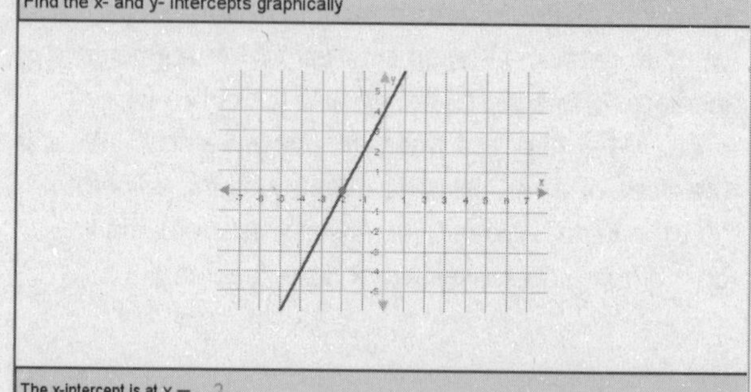

The x-intercept is at $x = -2$.

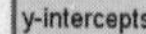

Find the x- and y- intercepts graphically

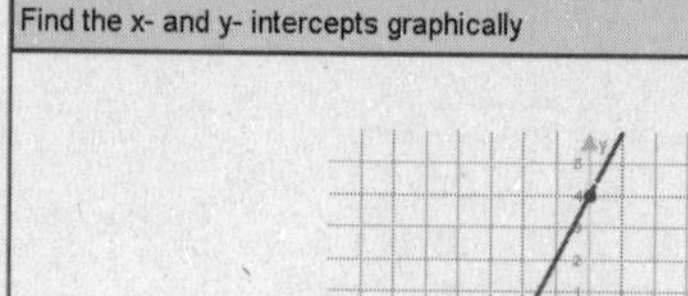

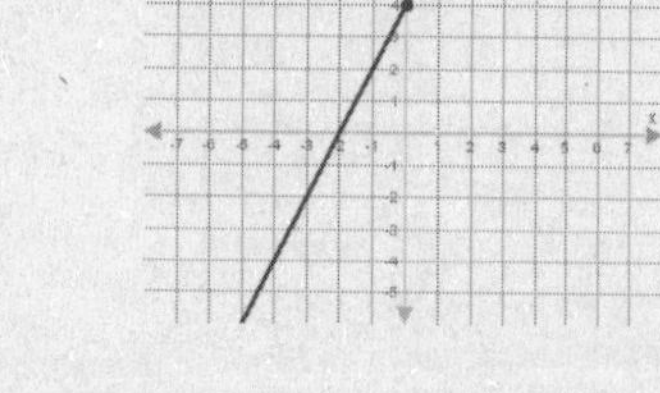

The y-intercept is at $y = 4$.

Points 1 and 2: Find the intercepts by inspecting the graph. Be as precise as possible—all problem answers are given as whole numbers.

y-intercepts

If a linear equation is in $y = mx + b$ form, b is the y-intercept.

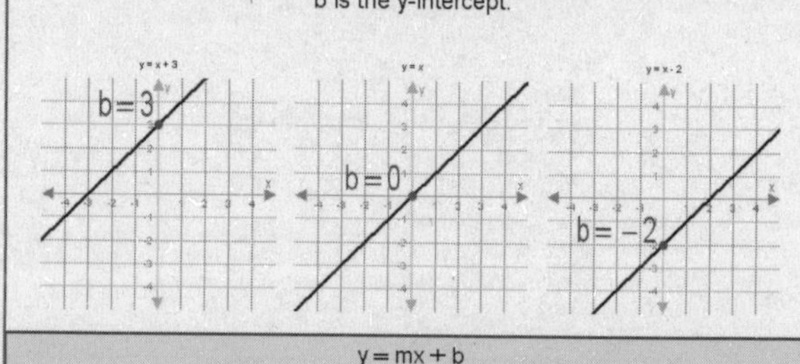

$y = mx + b$

Point 3: For equations in **y=mx+b** form the **y**-intercept is **b**.

x-intercepts

If the linear equation is in $y = mx + b$ form, the x-intercept is $x = -\frac{b}{m}$.

This is the value of x when $y = 0$.

For example, the line $y = 2x + 4$ has an x-intercept at $x = -\frac{b}{m} = -\frac{4}{2} = -2$

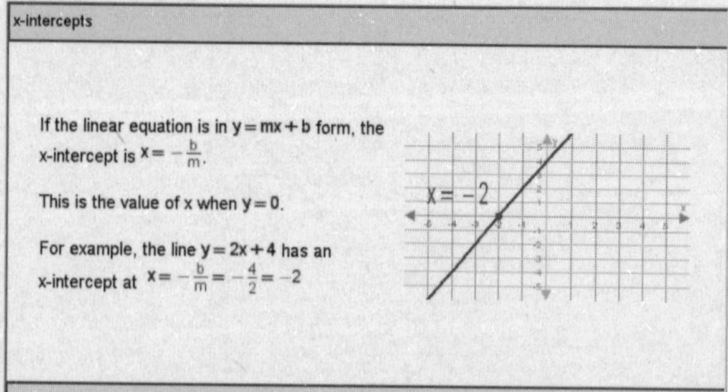

$y = mx + b$

Point 4: Find the **x**-intercept by simplifying **–b/m**.

Find the x- and y- intercepts of:

$y = -3x - 6$

y-intercept: $b = -6$

x-intercept: $\frac{-b}{m} = \frac{-6}{3} = -2$

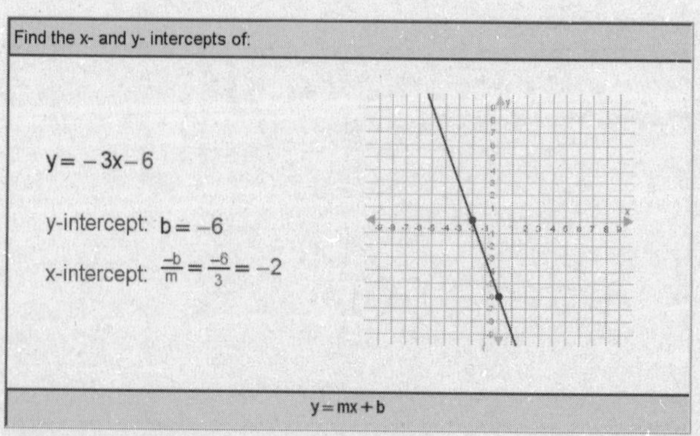

$y = mx + b$

Point 5: Find the **x-** and **y-intercept.**

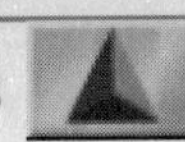

The points where the graph of a line crosses the **x**– and **y**-axes are called the **x**– and **y**-intercepts, respectively. The two points can be found by visual inspection (reading the graph), or by manipulating the equation into **y = mx + b** form and letting **x** or **y** be zero. But what information can the **x**- and **y**-intercepts give about the graph of the line?

Can both intercepts be positive?

Can they both be negative?

Can one or the other be zero?

At right the slope of the line is increasing. Notice that the **x**-intercept is negative. Is the **x**-intercept always negative when the slope is increasing?

How would the **y**-intercept change if the slope remained the same but the **x**-intercept was positive?

Is that possible?

What happens when the **y**-intercept is zero?

What if the **x**-intercept is zero?

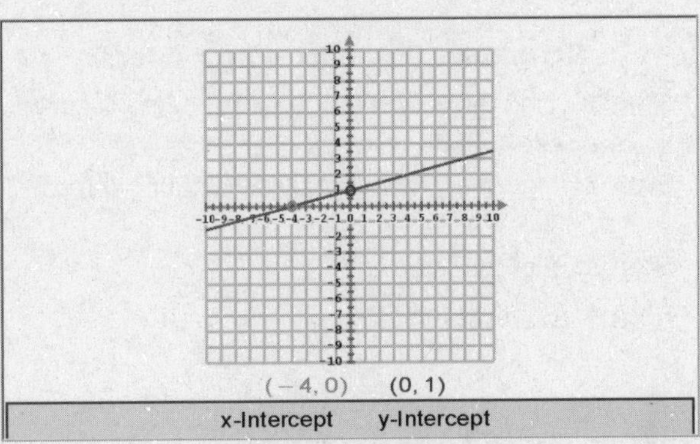

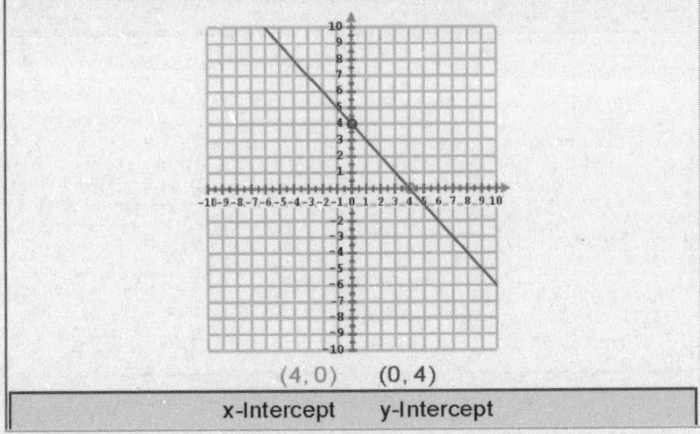

Above both intercepts are positive and the line is falling. Is it possible to have a rising graph with both intercepts positive?

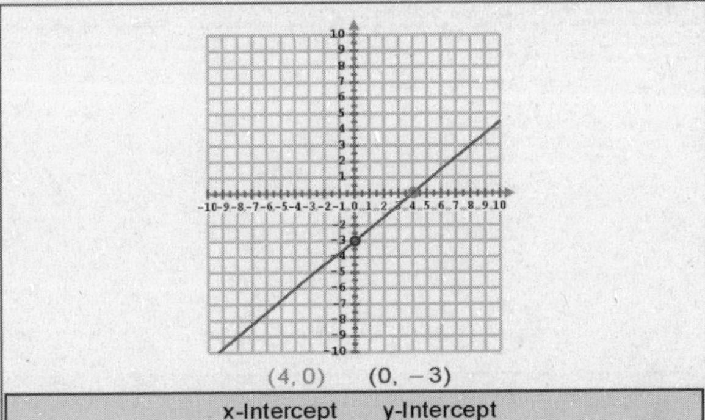

We can say the x-intercept is 4, but the point where the line intersects the x-axis is (4,0). Likewise, -3 is the y-intercept, and the point (0,-3) is where the line crosses the y-axis.

Linear equations in **standard form** look like **Ax +By = C**. You can find the **x**– and **y**-intercepts of lines in this form by substituting **0** for **x**, solve for **y**; and then substituting **0** for **y**, solve for **x**. Plotting the intercept points and connecting them with a line graphs the equation: It takes two points to form a line.

Two key ideas to remember:

1. Wherever a graph crosses the y-axis, the x-coordinate is always 0.
2. Wherever a graph crosses the x-axis, the y coordinate is always 0.

To graph a line in Ax + By = C form

Step 1: Find the **x**-intercept by substituting **0** for **y**; solve for **x**.

Step 2: Find the **y**-intercept by substituting **0** for **x**; solve for **y**.

Step 3: Plot the intercepts.

Step 4: Connect the dots.

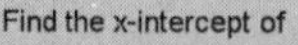

Find the x-intercept of

$$2x - 3y = -6$$

$$2x - 3(0) = -6$$
$$2x = -6$$
$$x = -\frac{6}{2}$$
$$x = -3$$

The x-intercept is at $x = -3$.

Find the y-intercept of

$$2x - 3y = -6$$

$$2(0) - 3y = -6$$
$$-3y = -6$$
$$\frac{-3}{-3}y = -\frac{6}{3}$$
$$y = -3$$

The y-intercept is at $y = -3$.

Here is the process for finding the **y-intercept.**

Use the x- and y- intercepts to graph

$2x - 3y = -6$

x-intercept

$$2x - 3(0) = -6$$
$$2x = -6$$
$$x = -\frac{6}{2}$$
$$x = -3$$

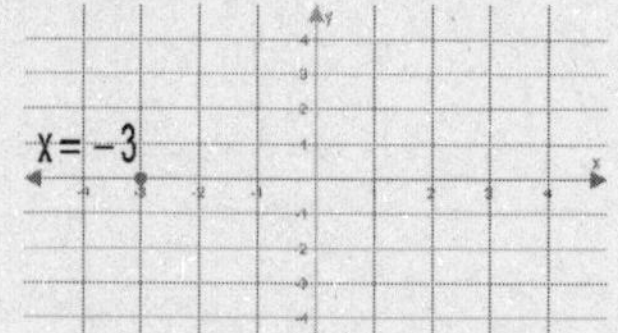

Ax + By = C

Once the x-intercept is found to be –3, plot the point (-3,0).

Use the x- and y- intercepts to graph

$2x - 3y = -6$

y-intercept

$$2(0) - 3y = -6$$
$$-3y = -6$$
$$-\frac{3}{3}y = -\frac{6}{3}$$
$$y = -3$$

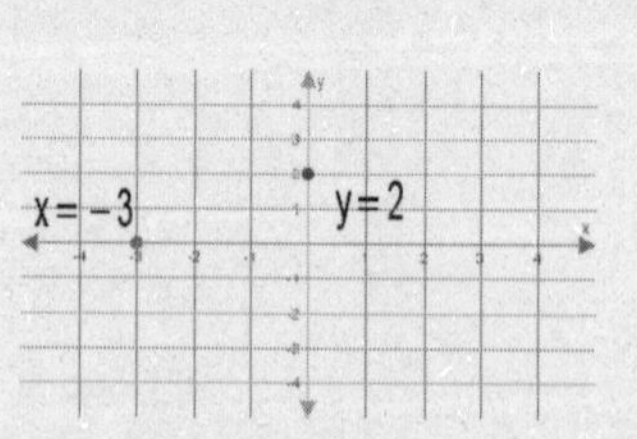

Ax + By = C

Next plot the y-intercept, 2, at the point (0,2).

Use the x- and y- intercepts to graph

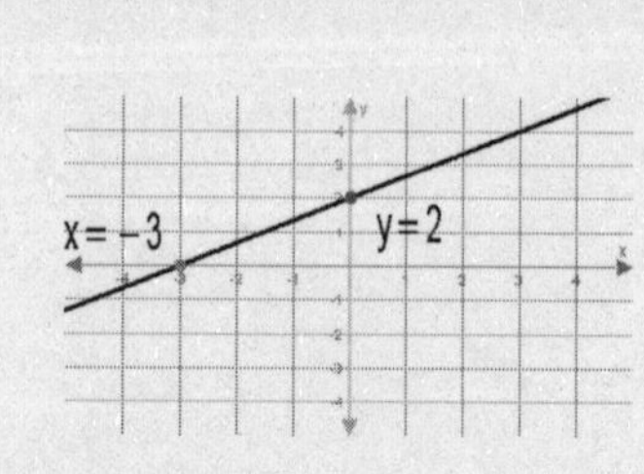

Connect the points. Ax + By = C

Last—connect the dots to show the graph of the line.

 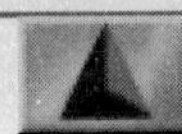

For linear equations in **standard form, Ax +By = C**:

- What do the intercepts tell us about the graph of the line?
- If the intercepts are both positive, what will the line look like?
- If they are both negative, what will the line look like?
- What can you tell about the intercepts if the slope is increasing?

Can the **y**-intercept be positive if **C** is negative?

Can the **y**-intercept be negative if **C** is negative?

What will the line look like if the **x**-intercept is positive and the y-intercept is negative?

Will there always be two different intercepts? (Will there ever be a time when the two intercepts are equal?)

What determines if the intercept is positive or negative?

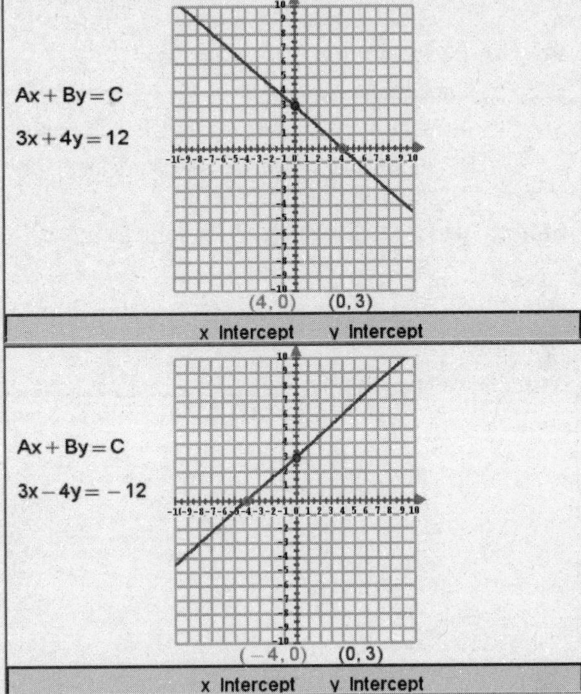

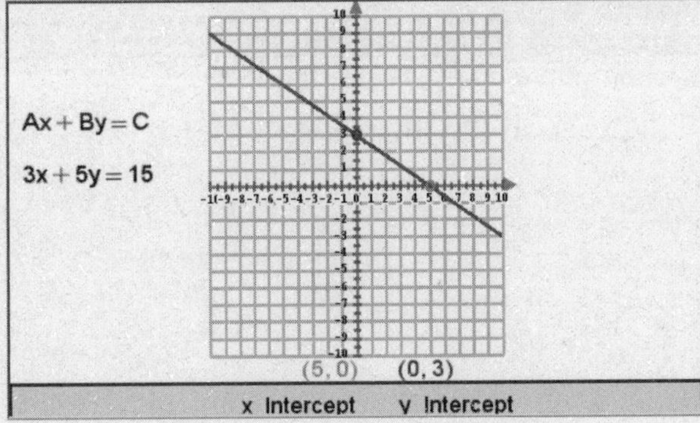

What is the **y**-intercept? What is the **x**-intercept?

This graph has a negative **x**-intercept. Is the slope of this line increasing or decreasing.?

Calculating Slope

EnableMath

Slope is the ratio of the change in distance between the **y**-coordinates (called the **rise**) to the change in distance between **x**-coordinates (called the **run**) for any two points on a line. Calculate the slope by dividing the difference in **y** by the difference in **x**. Since any two points determine a line, it makes no difference which is point 1 or point 2; the slope ratio will be the same.

Given any two points on a line, **P_1 (x_1,y_1)** and **P_2 (x_2,y_2)**: $$m = \frac{y_2 - y_1}{x_2 - x_1}$$

Slope can be written with the symbol **Δ** meaning "the change in." $$m = \frac{\Delta y}{\Delta x}$$

Calculating Slope

Step 1: Decide which is point 1 and point 2.

Step 2: Build the ratio:

A. Subtract **y**-coordinates for the numerator.

B. Subtract corresponding **x**-coordinates for the denominator.

Step 3: Reduce to lowest terms (or write as a decimal).

The slope (m) between two points (x_1, y_1) and (x_2, y_2) is equal to:

$$m = \frac{y_2 - y_1}{x_2 - x_1}$$

The slope is the change in height (rise) divided by the change in length (run).

Calculate the slope between the two points:

(−1, −2) and (1, 4)

$$m = \frac{y_2 - y_1}{x_2 - x_1}$$

(x_1, y_1) and (x_2, y_2) $m = \frac{y_2 - y_1}{x_2 - x_1}$

Point 2: Calculating the slope begins with the given points and the formula. Above, we chose **(-1,-2)** as point 1 and then point 2 is **(1,4)**.

Calculate the slope between the two points:

(−1, −2) and (1, 4)

$$m = \frac{y_2 - y_1}{x_2 - x_1}$$

$$m = \frac{4-(-2)}{1-(-1)}$$

$$m = \frac{6}{2}$$

$$m = 3$$

(x_1, y_1) and (x_2, y_2) $m = \frac{y_2 - y_1}{x_2 - x_1}$

Find the change in **y** by substituting 4 for y_2 and −2 for y_1.
Find the change in **x** by substituting 1 for x_2 and −1 for x_2.
Simplify the numerator and then the denominator.
Reduce to lowest terms, in this case, it is a whole number.

Calculate the slope between the two points:

(3, 5) and (1, −2)

$$m = \frac{y_2 - y_1}{x_2 - x_1}$$

$$m = \frac{-2-5}{1-3}$$

$$m = \frac{-7}{2}$$

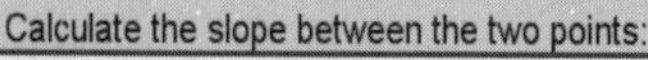

Point 3: Leave fractions in improper form so that the rise/run ratio can be easily used. Above, the rise is down 7 and the run is right 2.

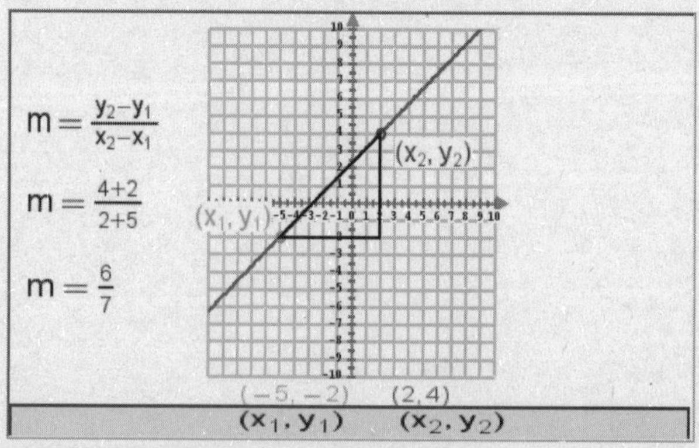

$$m = \frac{y_2 - y_1}{x_2 - x_1}$$

$$m = \frac{4+2}{2+5}$$

$$m = \frac{6}{7}$$

(−5, −2) (2,4)

(x_1, y_1) (x_2, y_2)

On the graph above from point 1 trace over 7 and up 6 to get to point 2. Pick any other point on the line; count over positive 7 and up 6 to get another point on the line.

Slope describes the steepness of something like a hill, or the slant of a roof. In mathematics, slope is also a measure of steepness, but we define it carefully as the ratio of the change in **y**-coordinates to the change in **x**-coordinates between two points on a line.

We show the rise over the run and the slope as a right triangle beginning at point 1 **(0,0)** moving up positive **5** units and right positive **4** units lands back on the line at point 2 **(4,5)**. Use the joystick to change the points to explore the effects of slope and to get an intuitive feel for slope. If **m** is large, will the line be steep or flat? If **m** is between 0 and 1, will the line be steep or flat? What happens when **y** changes but **x** does not change? What if the rise is zero? What does a negative slope do?

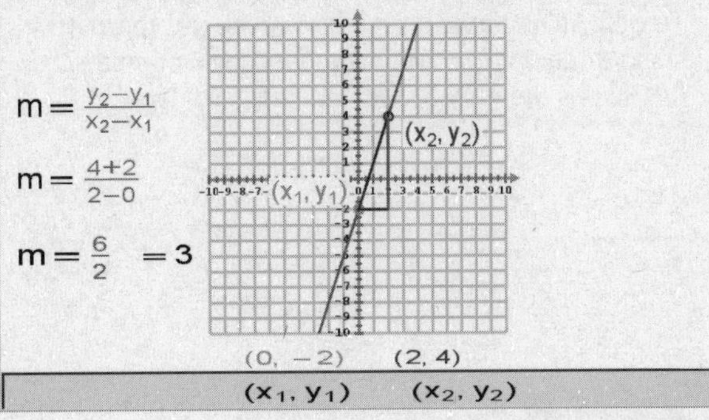

$m = \frac{y_2 - y_1}{x_2 - x_1}$
$m = \frac{4+2}{2-0}$
$m = \frac{6}{2} = 3$
(x_1, y_1)
(x_2, y_2)
(0, −2) (2, 4)
(x_1, y_1) (x_2, y_2)

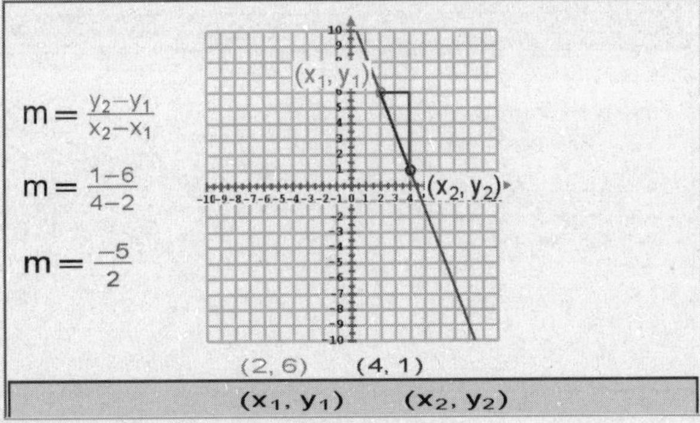

$m = \frac{y_2 - y_1}{x_2 - x_1}$
$m = \frac{1-6}{4-2}$
$m = \frac{-5}{2}$
(x_1, y_1)
(x_2, y_2)
(2, 6) (4, 1)
(x_1, y_1) (x_2, y_2)

When **m** is negative, the line is falling.

What is the slope if point 1 is **(2,6)** and point 2 is **(4,1)**?

Does order make a difference?

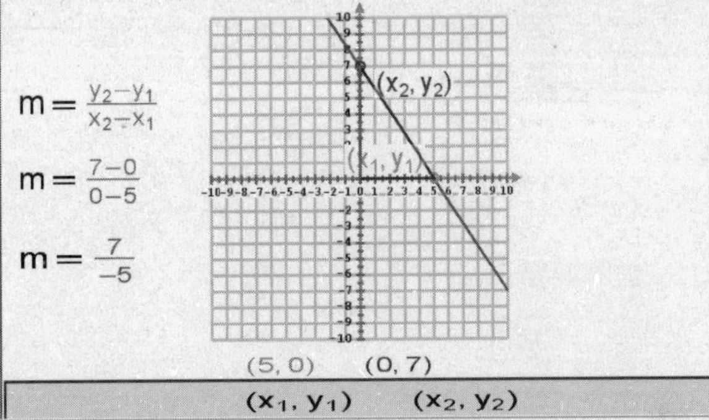

$m = \frac{y_2 - y_1}{x_2 - x_1}$
$m = \frac{7-0}{0-5}$
$m = \frac{7}{-5}$
(x_2, y_2)
(x_1, y_1)
(5, 0) (0, 7)
(x_1, y_1) (x_2, y_2)

This shows the importance of the **x**– and **y**-intercepts and their relationship to slope. If both intercepts are positive, will the slope always be negative? If both intercepts are negative will the line be rising or falling?

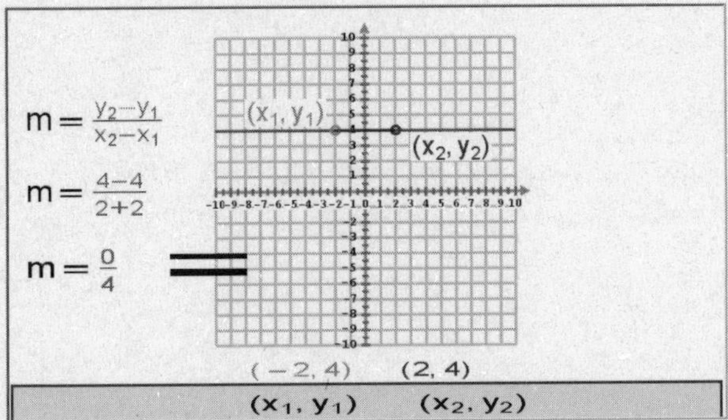

Special case I: What if the rise is zero? What is **m**?

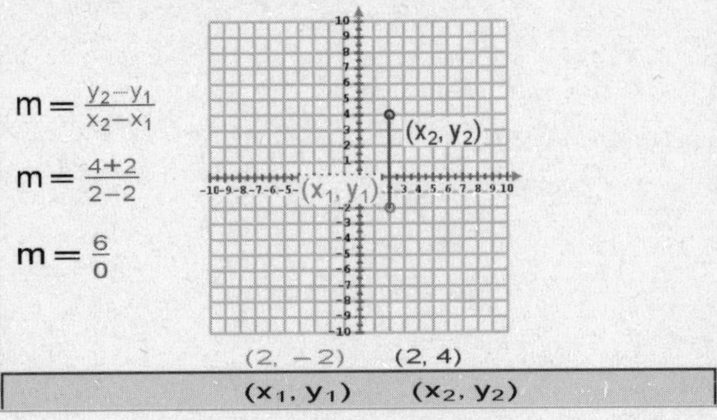

Special case II: What if the run is zero? What is m? We say that **m** is **undefined** when the run is 0.

Parallel Lines

Parallel lines have no now common points; parallel lines do not cross. Two lines that have the same slope are parallel; conversely two lines that are parallel have the same slope.

To determine if two lines are parallel, put them in slope-intercept form and compare their **m** values. If the slopes are equal, then the lines are parallel.

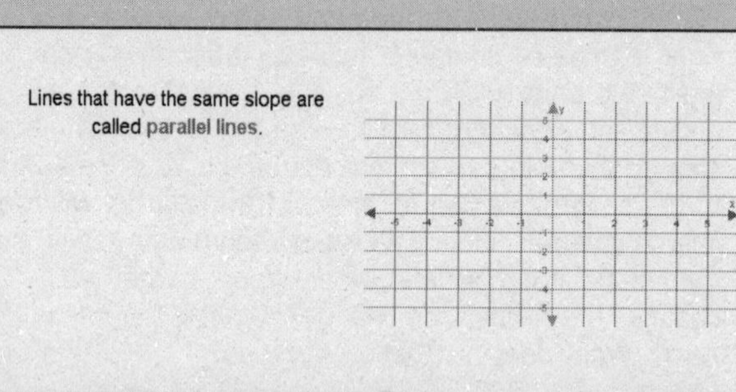

Lines that have the same slope are called parallel lines.

For example,
$L_1: y = 2x - 2$ & $L_2: y = 2x + 3$

$\mathbf{m_1 = m_2}$ so the lines are parallel.

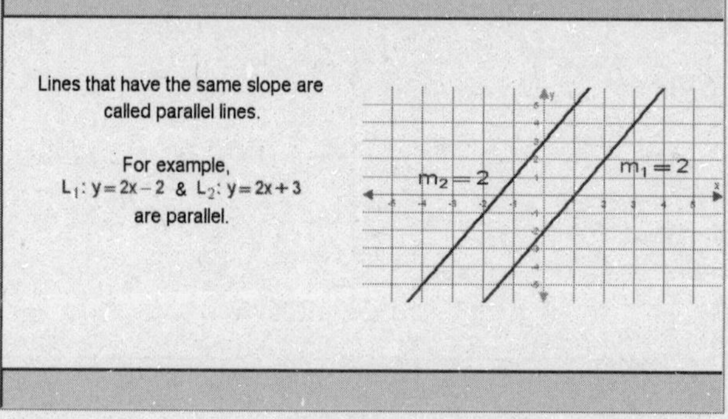

Examine the slopes: $\mathbf{m_1 = m_2}$; therefore, the lines are parallel.

Parallel lines are considered a special case because they never intersect. Lines that have the same slope are parallel. Determining if two lines are parallel requires determining if the slopes are equal.

Use the joystick to change slope and intercepts for parallel lines. How does changing intercepts affect the lines? Does changing $\mathbf{b_1}$ impact $\mathbf{b_2}$?

At the right **m=2** for each of the two parallel lines. The intercepts are different for the two lines. What happens as the intercepts get closer and closer together? Do the lines merge into one? What affect does the slope have on the intercepts? Does changing the slope change the intercepts?

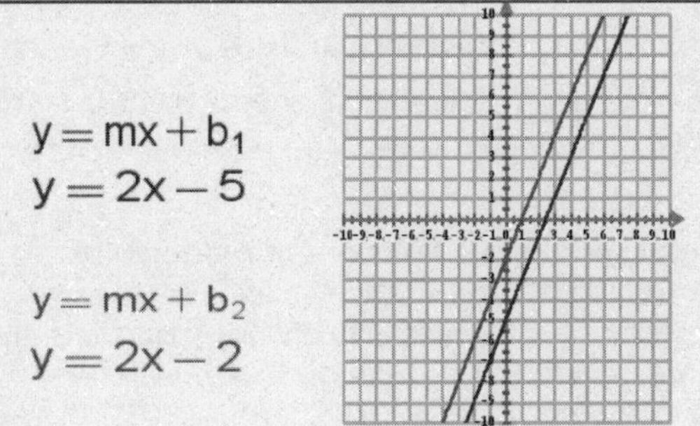

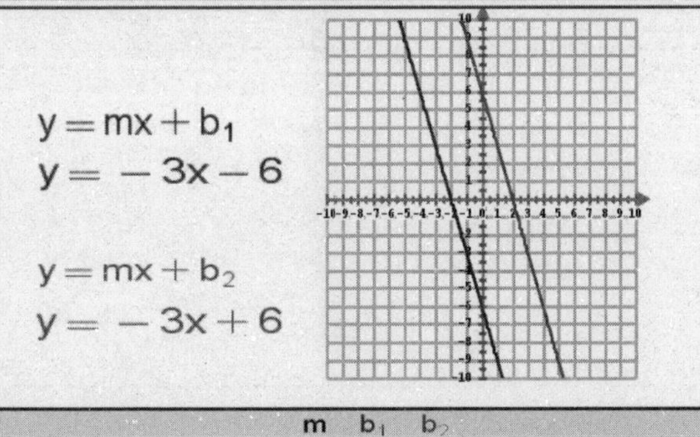

What is **m** for the two lines above? Where do the two lines cross the **y**-axis?

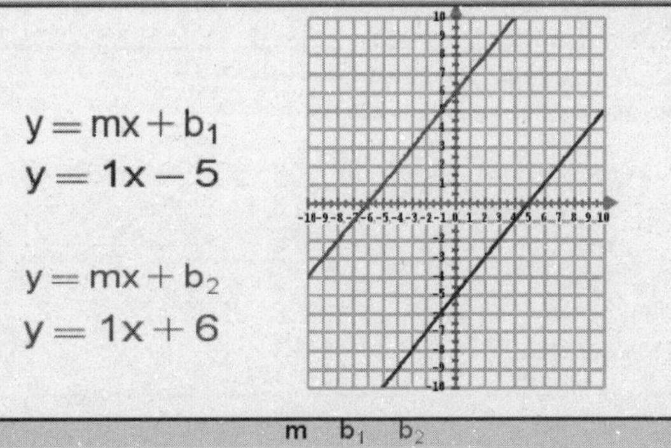

Slope is positive 1. If two lines are parallel, is there any relationship between their y-intercepts?

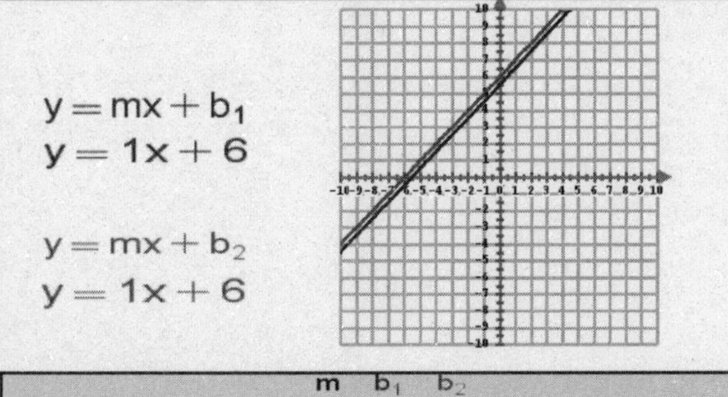

What happens as the distance between intercepts decreases? What happens when the intercept has the same value for both lines?

Perpendicular Lines

EnableMath

Lines that intersect forming a right (or square) angle are called **perpendicular lines**. In order for two lines to cross at right angles, their slopes must have opposite signs because one line will be increasing while the other line will be decreasing. Thus one line will have a positive slope and its perpendicular partner will have a negative slope.

The values of the slopes will be **m** and the reciprocal of m or **1/m,** because the rise of one line will become the run of the other and vise versa (see the **Concept**).

Perpendicular lines

If line 1 has slope of **m**, then all lines perpendicular to line 1 have slope of: $-\dfrac{1}{m}$.

To determine if two lines are perpendicular: Write each equation in slope-intercept form to compare slopes. If the slopes are negative reciprocals, the lines are perpendicular. Quick check: the product of slopes of perpendicular lines is –1.

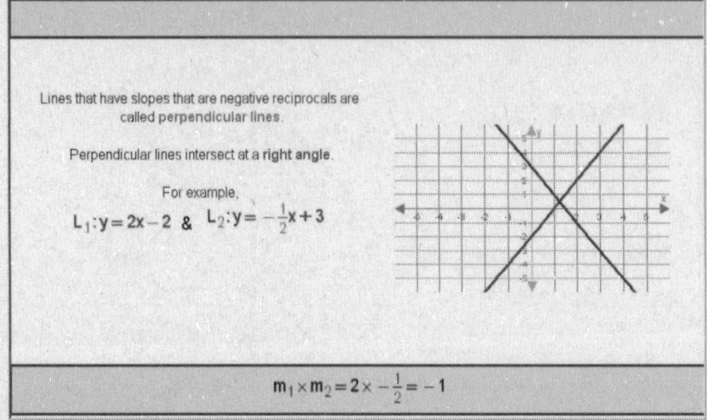

Lines that have slopes that are negative reciprocals are called perpendicular lines.
Perpendicular lines intersect at a right angle.
For example,
$L_1: y = 2x - 2$ & $L_2: y = -\frac{1}{2}x + 3$
$m_1 \times m_2 = 2 \times -\frac{1}{2} = -1$

2 and –1/2 are negative reciprocals—the lines are perpendicular.

Quick test: Is their product is –1?

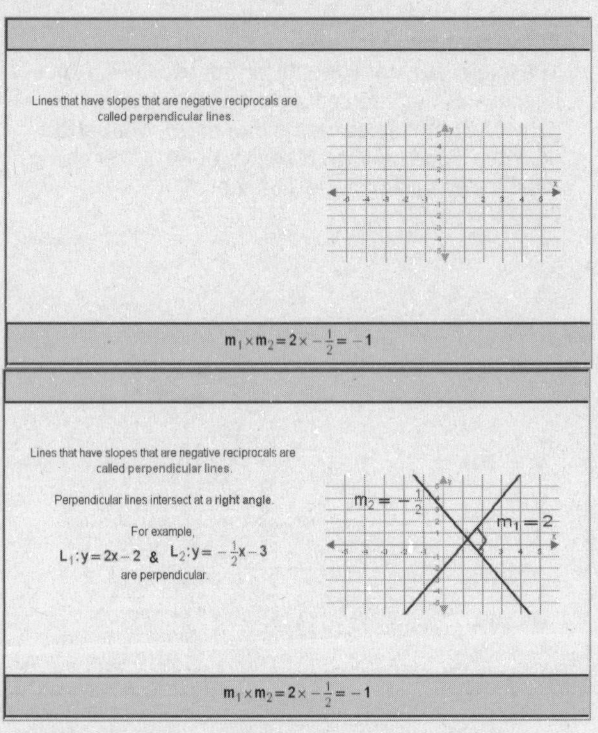

Lines that have slopes that are negative reciprocals are called perpendicular lines.
$m_1 \times m_2 = 2 \times -\frac{1}{2} = -1$
Lines that have slopes that are negative reciprocals are called perpendicular lines.
Perpendicular lines intersect at a right angle.
For example,
$L_1: y = 2x - 2$ & $L_2: y = -\frac{1}{2}x - 3$
are perpendicular.
$m_2 = -\frac{1}{2}$
$m_1 = 2$
$m_1 \times m_2 = 2 \times -\frac{1}{2} = -1$

Examine the slopes: 4 and –1/4 are negative reciprocals therefore, these lines are perpendicular.

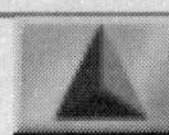

Perpendicular lines intersect at right angles. This is an interesting relationship between their slopes. Visualize two lines drawn on a graph—if the point where they cross forms right or square angles, the lines are perpendicular. Since it is often hard to determine if angles are perfectly square, it is necessary to look at the equations of the lines in slope-intercept form. If the slopes are negative reciprocals (if their product is –1) the lines are perpendicular.

Use the joystick to play with perpendicular lines. Change the slope and the **y**-intercepts to see how each change affects the graph of the lines.

Why is the slope of a perpendicular line always the negative reciprocal?

You will be able to see why if you look at **Point 2**, where we have drawn the right triangles to show the slope of each line. Watch those triangles as you change **m**.

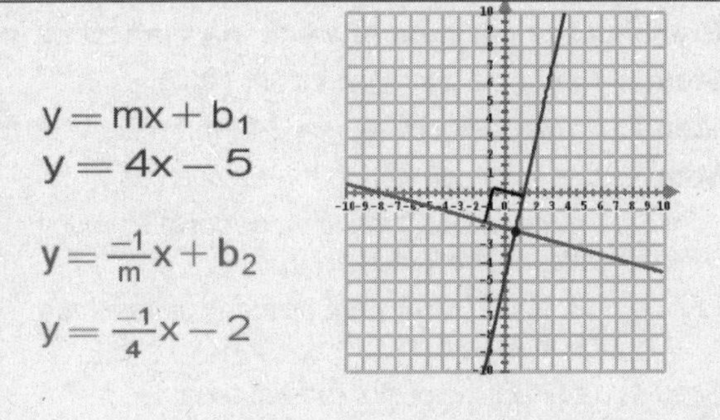

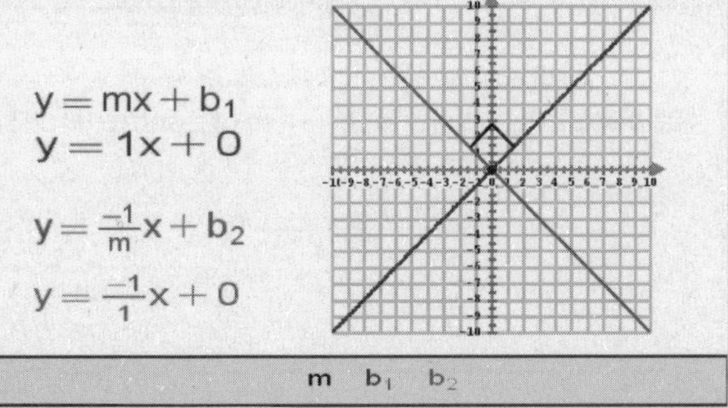

Set both **b1** and **b2** are equal to 0 and the slope **(m)** to 1. The slope of the perpendicular line will be –1. Is the slope of the perpendicular line 1 if the slope of the original line is –1?

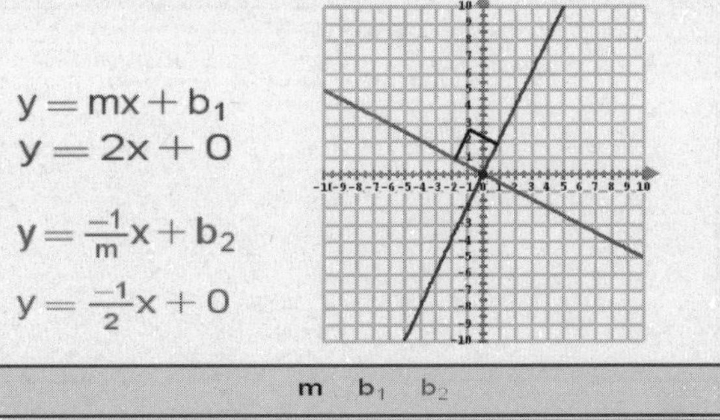

Now change the slope to 2, what happened to the slope of the perpendicular line? Change the slope to 3, what happened to the slope of the perpendicular line?

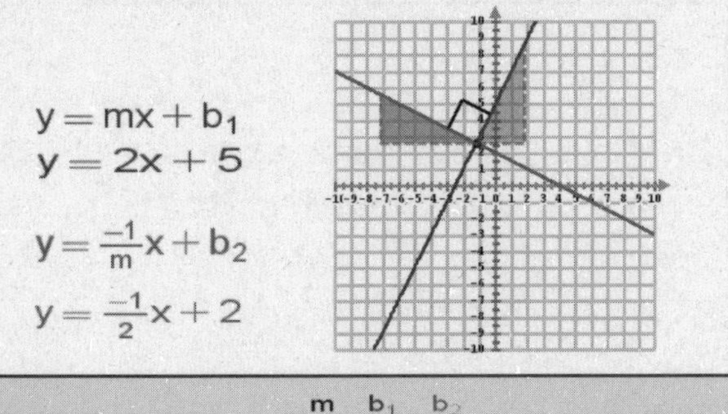

Point 2: Let's look at why. If we draw right triangles that allow us to measure the slope of each line, we can see that for perpendicular lines the rise of one becomes the run of the other and vice versa.

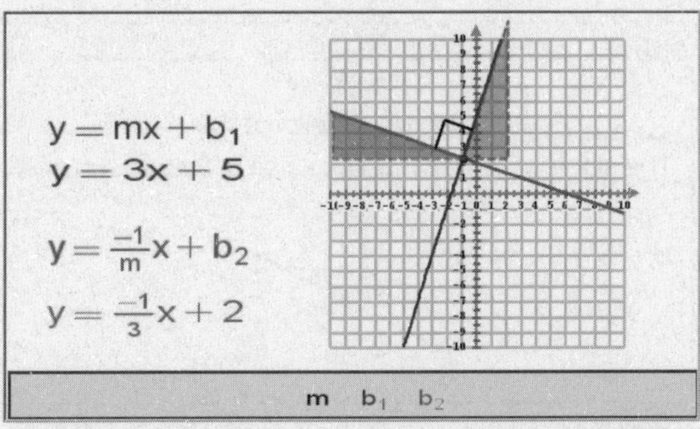

That makes the slope of the perpendicular line the inverse of the slope of its partner and this inverse is negative because we are now subtracting x_1 from x_2.

An equation in **slope-intercept** form, **y = mx + b**, gives enough information to graph the line by using the intercept as the first point and then using the slope's rise over run ratio to find a second point. Once the two points have been graphed, connect the dots to form the line.

For any given equation written in **y = mx + b** form, the slope and **y**-intercept can be read directly from the equation. The slope is equal to **m (**the coefficient of **x)**, and the **y**-intercept is located at **b** on the **y**-axis, point (**0,b**).

Graphing the equation of a line in y=mx+b form

Step 1: Graph the **y**-intercept point **(0,b)**.

Step 2: Write the slope in $\frac{\textbf{rise}}{\textbf{run}}$ form.

Step 3: Use the slope to find the second point.

A. From **(0,b)** move up or down as many units as rise indicates.

B. Move left or right as many units as run indicates.

Step 4: Connect the points to form the line.

The y = mx + b form of an equation is referred to as the slope – intercept form of a line. Given a slope (m) and the y – intercept (b), the equation of the line is simply y = mx + b. For example, if $m = \frac{-1}{3}$ and b = 2, then the equation of the line is $y = \frac{-1}{3}x + 2$.

y = mx + b

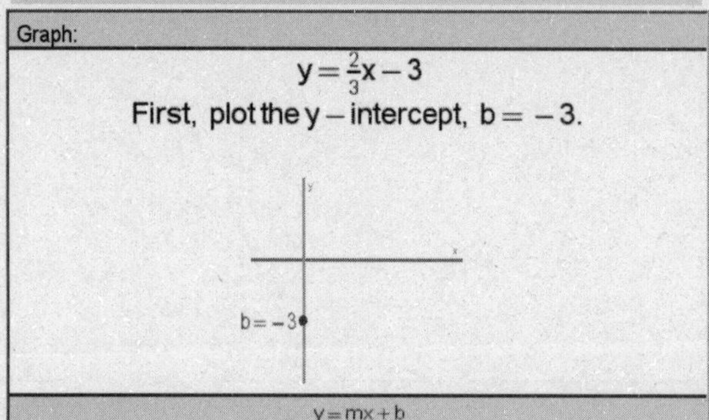

Identify the slope and y-intercept from the equation. Plot the y-intercept.

Graph:

$y = \frac{2}{3}x - 3$

First, plot the y – intercept, b = –3.

The slope is $\frac{2}{3}$, which means a rise of 2 and a run of 3.

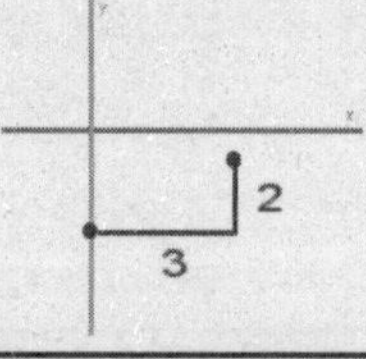

y = mx + b

The slope is in rise/run form. From point **(0,b)** move up 2 units and right 3 units. Make a point.

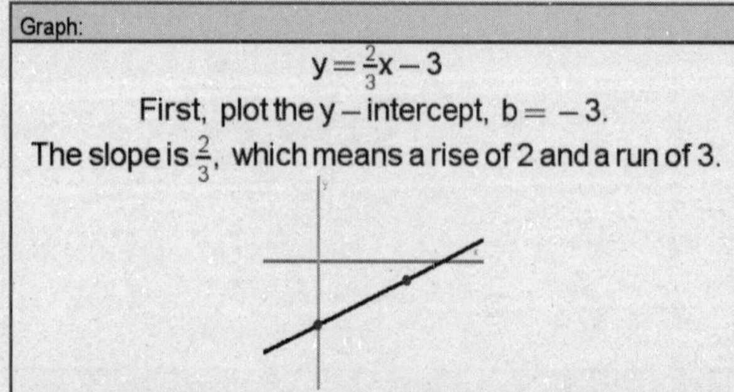

Connect the dots to construct the line.

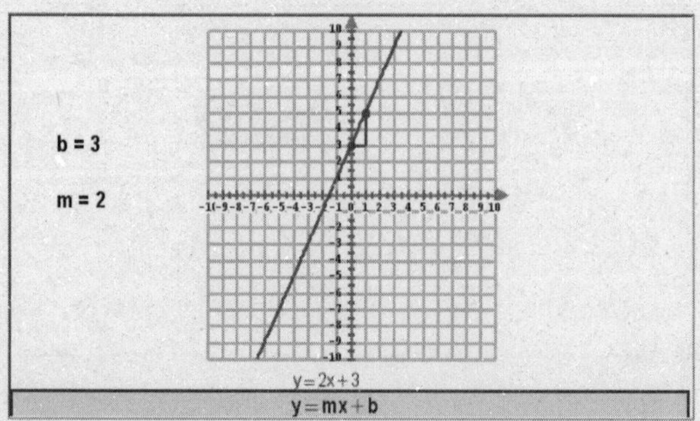

Intercept is +3 and slope is 2. Plot the point (0,3). Write the slope in rise/run form: 2/1. From point (0,3) go up 2 and right 1. Connect the points to draw the line.

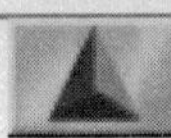

The slope-intercept form of a line, **y = mx + b**, gives enough direct information to graph the line without going through the process of making a chart and plotting several points. By just looking at the equation (mathematicians say, "by inspection") **m** is the **slope** and **b** is the **y-intercept**. Plotting the **y**-intercept and using the slope for rise/run generates as many extra points as needed.

Use the joystick to see whole number slopes. Watch as the red triangle finds new points. Remember that the slope ratio holds true from any point on the line to any other point on the line.

At the right **m=2** and **b=3**. How far back to the line if you traveled down (negative) two? Down 4? Up 6? What is the slope ratio in each case?

Change **b**. What effect does changing **b** have on the line?

Does changing **b** change the slope of the line?

What does making **b** negative do to the line?

What affect does **m** have on the line?

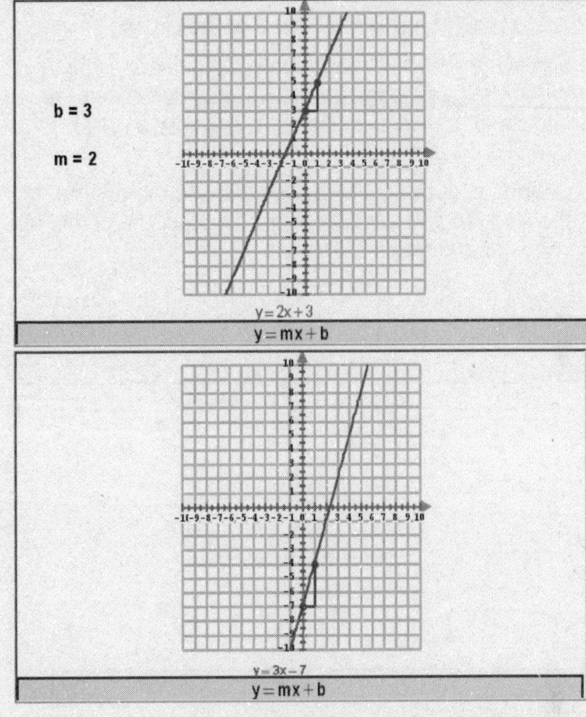

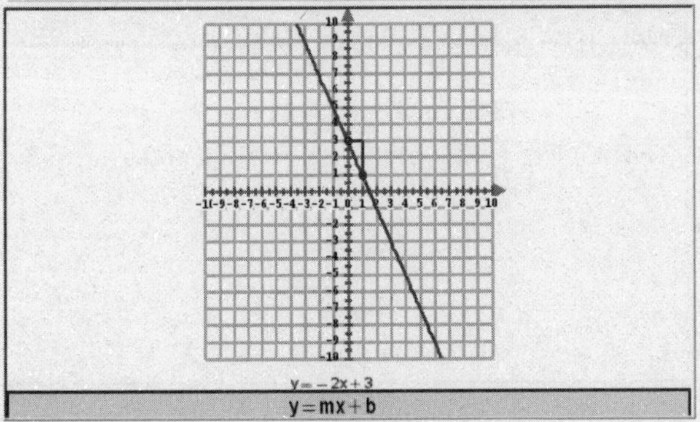

Negative or decreasing slope. What does changing **b** do to the line?

Positive or increasing slope. What does changing **b** do to the line?

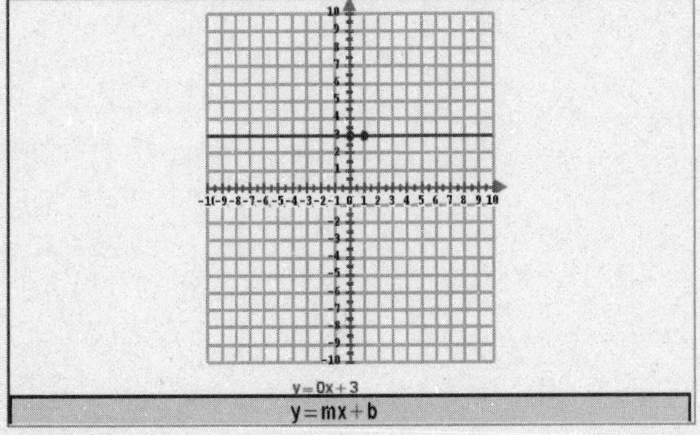

Special case I: Zero slope is no slope. Make a horizontal line through b.

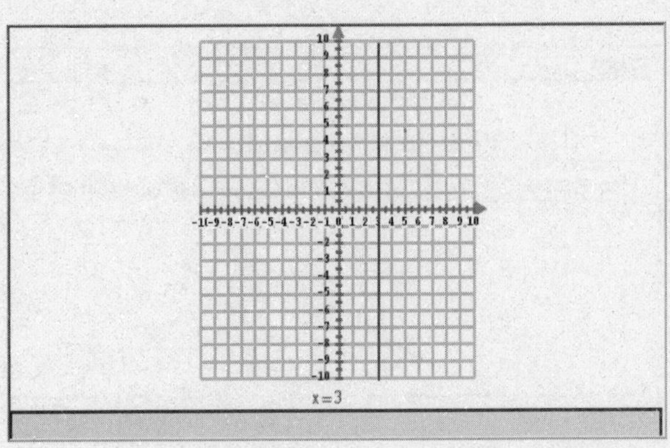

Special case II: No matter what **y** is, **x** will always be 3. Make a vertical line at **x=a**. Is this still in slope-intercept

Point-Slope Equation

EnableMath

Return to the formula for slope: $m = \frac{y_2 - y_1}{x_2 - x_1}$.

Rearranging the equation by clearing the fraction yields an awkward but very useful equation for a line, the **point-slope equation**: $y - y_1 = m(x - x_1)$. Notice that the first **x** and **y** have no subscripts. Any point on a line (x_1, y_1) and its slope are enough information to write the equation and graph the line.

Given a slope and a point (x_1, y_1)

Equation: Write the equation of the line by substituting the given point for y_1, x_1, and given slope, **m**, into the point-slope equation, $y - y_1 = m(x - x_1)$. (Simplify as directed.)

Graph: Plot the point (x_1, y_1) and use the rise/run of the slope to find another point. Connect the points to construct the graph of the line.

The $y - y_1 = m(x - x_1)$ form of an equation is referred to as the point – slope form of a line. Given a point (x_1, y_1), and a slope (m), the equation of the line is simply $y - y_1 = m(x - x_1)$. For example, if the point $(1, 2)$ is on the line and $m = -3$, then the equation of the line is $y - 2 = -3(x - 1)$.

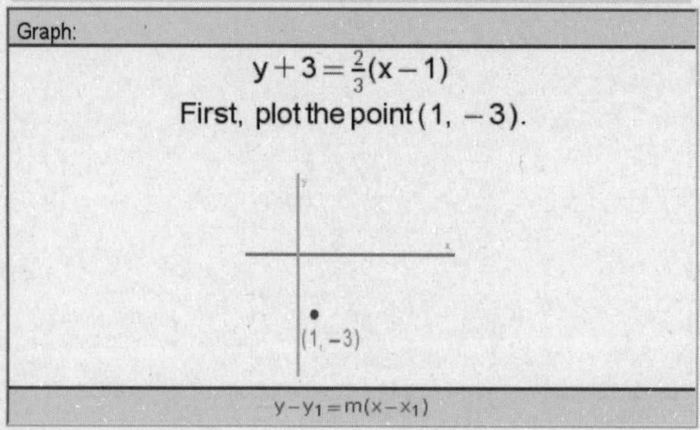

From an equation in point-slope form use the pattern of the formula to identify x_1 and y_1. Plot the point.

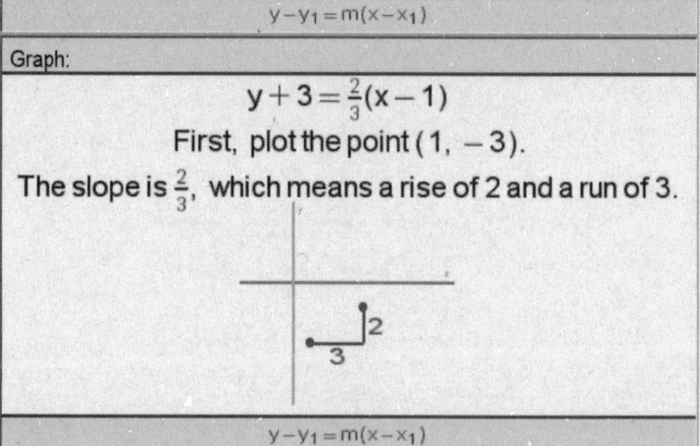

y−y1=m(x−x1)
Graph:
y+3=2/3(x−1)
First, plot the point (1, −3).
The slope is 2/3, which means a rise of 2 and a run of 3.
2
3
y−y1=m(x−x1)

Use the rise/run of **m** to get another point.

Graph:

$y + 3 = \frac{2}{3}(x - 1)$

First, plot the point $(1, -3)$.

The slope is $\frac{2}{3}$, which means a rise of 2 and a run of 3.

Connect the points. $y - y_1 = m(x - x_1)$

Connect the dots. Are there other points that could be used as a quick check?

The **point-slope form** of an equation is developed from the formula for slope. Knowing one point and the slope is enough to construct the graph and form the equation of a line.

Given point $(\mathbf{x_1,y_1})$ and slope **m** the equation of the line is: $\mathbf{y - y_1 = m(x - x_1)}$. Notice that y and x are variables in the equation of the line and thus do not have subscripts.

Use the joystick to see what happens as each component changes. The red triangle will not necessarily move to the given point, but will maintain the slope ratio of rise/run from a point on the line to another point.

From the given equations to the right, identify $\mathbf{x_1}$, $\mathbf{y_1}$, and **m**. How does changing one component change the line? Does changing either $\mathbf{x_1}$ or $\mathbf{y_1}$ change **m**? Does changing **m** alter $\mathbf{x_1}$ or $\mathbf{y_1}$? As $\mathbf{x_1}$ changes from positive to negative what happens to the line? As $\mathbf{y_1}$ changes from positive to negative what happens to the line? As **m** changes from positive to negative what happens to the line?

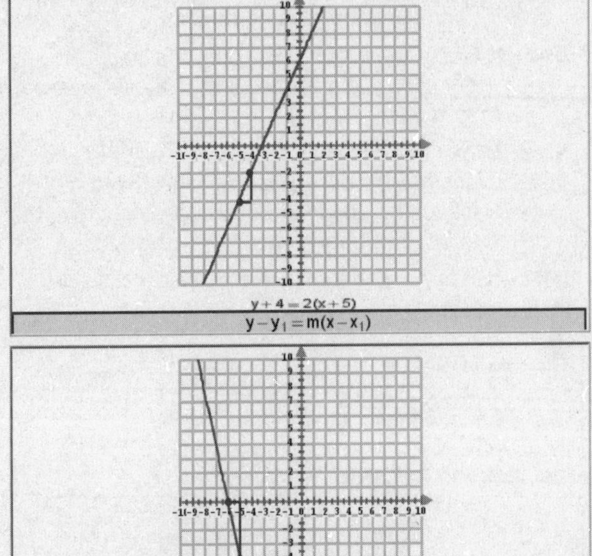

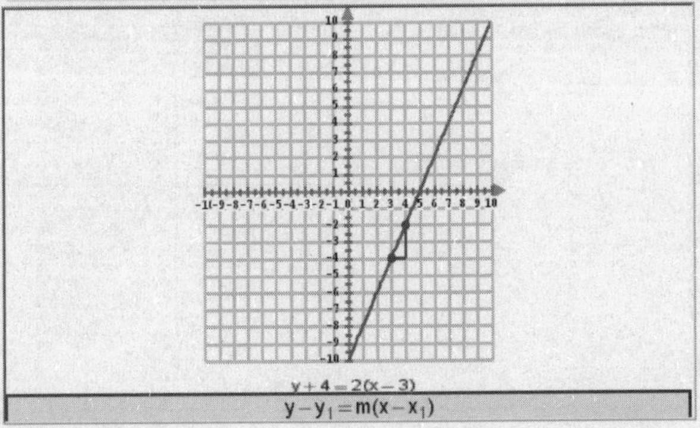

Changing $\mathbf{x_1}$ from –5 to +3 moves the line horizontally along **the x**-axis.

Changing **m** from **2** to **–4** moved the line but not the given point **(-4,-5)**; the slope of the line is decreasing.

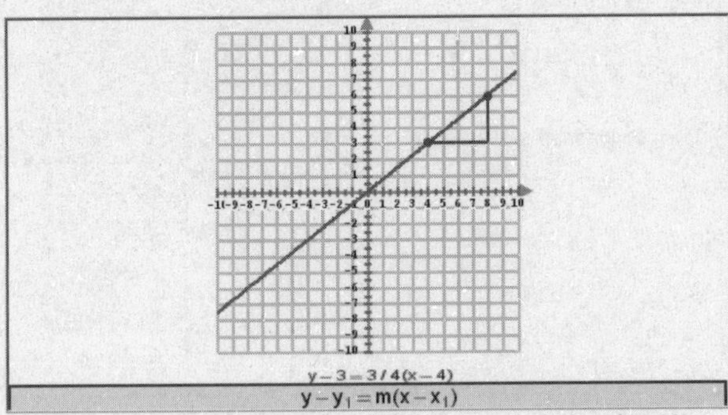

Name two other points on this line. Notice that the slope is a fraction—enter fractions in decimal form under the chosen variable beside the joystick.

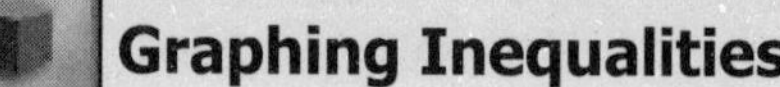

Graphing Inequalities

EnableMath

Linear inequalities in two variables use the same forms as linear equations except that the inequality symbols replace the equal signs. Just as graphing inequalities in one variable produces a set of points on a number line, graphing inequalities in two variables produces a set of points in the plane. An inequality divides the plane of the graph into three parts: the graph of the line; the portion of the plane satisfying the inequality; and the portion NOT satisfying the inequality. The portion satisfying the inequality is shaded to show inclusion.

Graphing Inequalities

Step 1: Graph the line, disregarding the inequality — if > or < use a dashed line, if ≥ or ≤, use a solid line.

Step 2: Test one point for shading, usually test the point (0,0); if the point satisfies the inequality, shade in the portion containing the point; if not, then shade the other side.

If the line is in y=mx+b form, < shades left and > shades right.

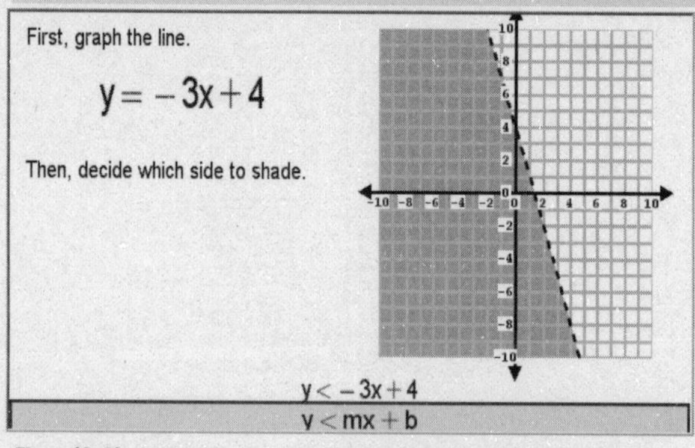

Test (0,0): is 0<4?; yes, so shade the side including zero. Notice the dashed line; points on the line are NOT included in the solution set.

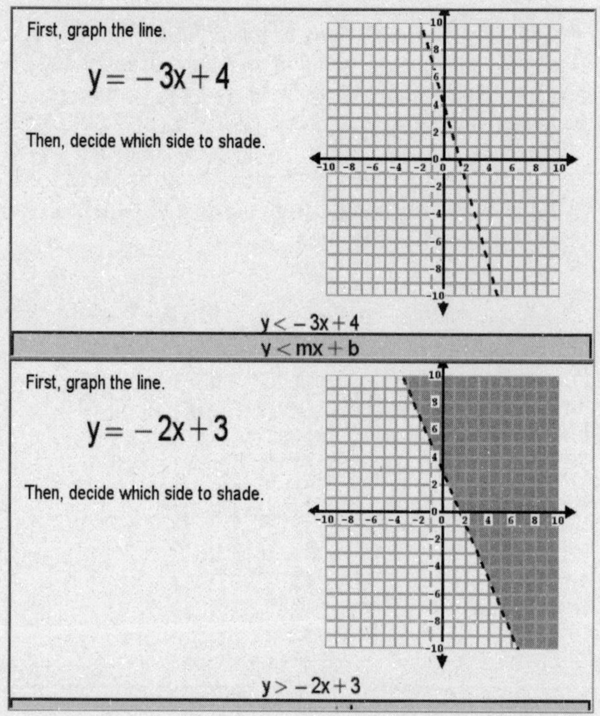

Try point (0,0): 0>3? No, shade the right side.

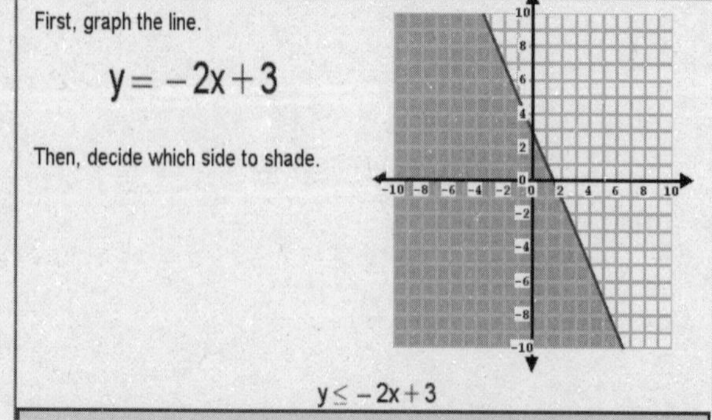

First, graph the line.
y = −2x + 3
Then, decide which side to shade.
y ≤ −2x + 3

Test (0,0): 0≤3? Yes; shade the side containing zero. Note that the line IS included in the solution set.

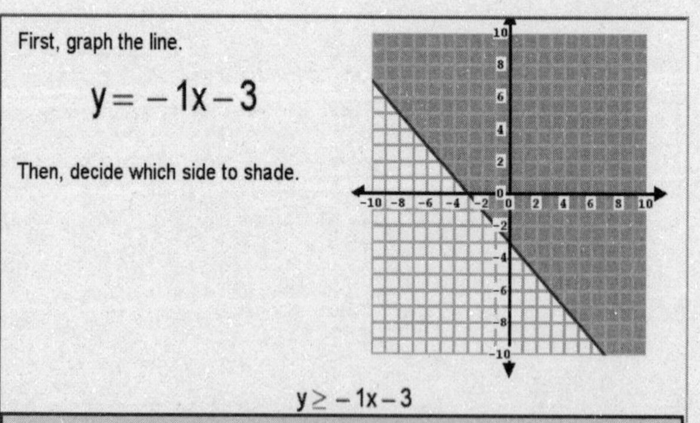

First, graph the line.
y = −1x − 3
Then, decide which side to shade.
y ≥ −1x − 3

Test (0,0): 0≥-3? Yes; shade in the side containing zero.

Solutions to inequalities in two variables are shown as a shaded region on a graph. The inequality divides the graph into three parts: the line, the portion in the solution set, and the portion not in the solution set.

As you use the joystick to change the inequalities, notice how changing the inequality sign effects the region shaded. Change one component at a time to see how each impacts the solution set region.

Each of the visualizations are presented in **y=mx+b** form, with the equal sign replaced with an inequality symbol. How do you determine which side to include? Will the y-intercept help decide which region to include? What role does the slope play in determining the solution set region?

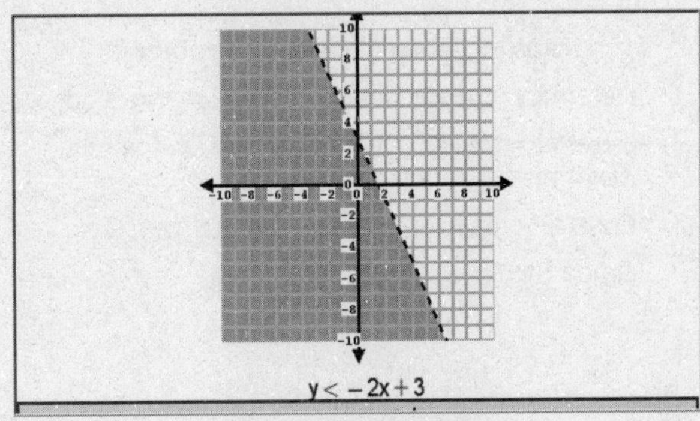

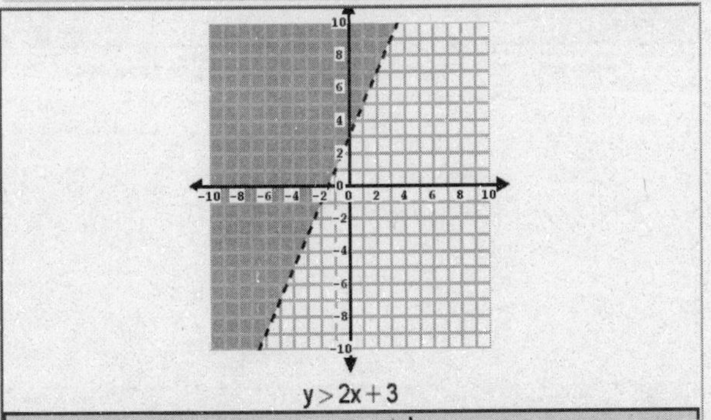

The inequality is "flipped" and the slope is opposite of the visualization above right.

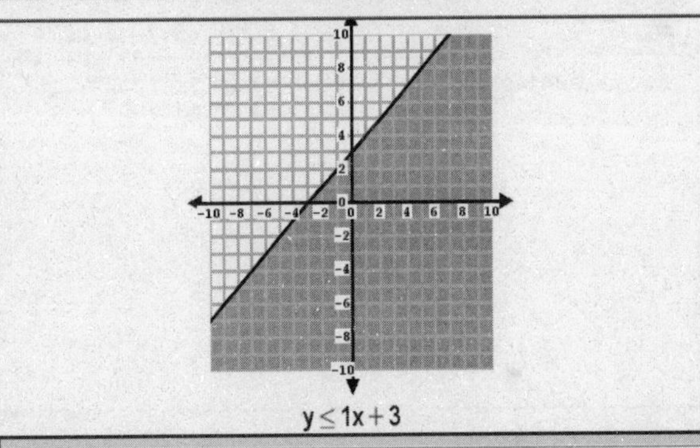

What is different from the graph above and the graph at right?

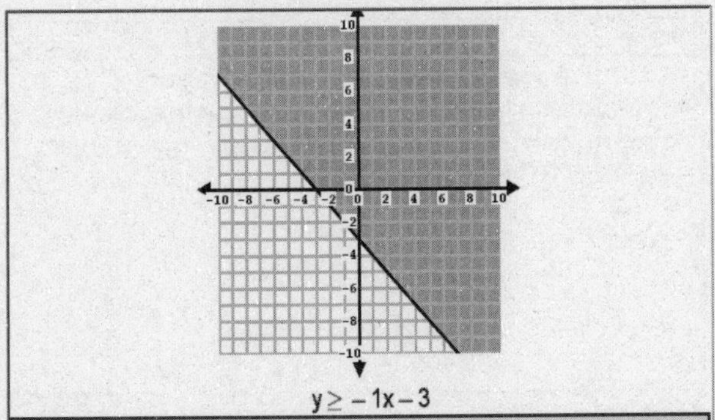

Greater than or equal to—note the line is solid, therefore included in the solution set.

Rate of change problems are applications of linear equations in which the rate is the slope of the line. An input value (x) determines an output value (y). One quantity changes (like distance or cost) at a specific rate depending on a different quantity (like time or money). The rate can be increasing or decreasing, but the quantities will most commonly be positive (since they are measured amounts) and therefore the graphs will be in the first quadrant.

Graphing Rate of Change Problems

1. Determine the units used to measure the change.
2. Determine which unit is dependant on the other, make that the y-variable.
3. Construct the axes with appropriate measures.
4. Graph the line.

Applications

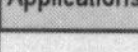

Many rates of change, like miles per hour, dollars per pound and micrograms per cubic centimeters can be graphed as linear equations.

Application

Joe plans to drive a constant 50 miles per hour (mph) on a road trip. This relationship can be written as a linear equation in miles (y) and hours (x), as $y = 50x$.

The y-value depends on how long Joe drives (x). The y-axis is labeled in 20 mi increments. The x-axis is in 1/2 hour increments.

Application

Joe plans to drive a constant 50 miles per hour (mph) on a road trip. This relationship can be written as a linear equation in miles (y) and hours (x), as $y = 50x$.

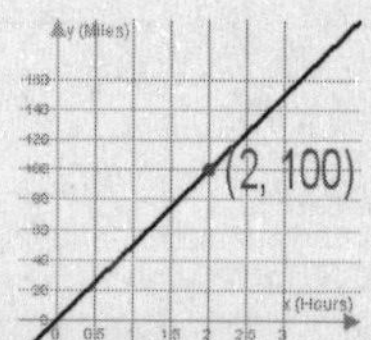

After 2 hours, Joe will have gone 100 miles.

Change x to get y. Ordered pairs represent how long (x is time) and how far (y is distance traveled). 50 miles/hour is the rate of change, because Joe will go 50 miles in one hour.

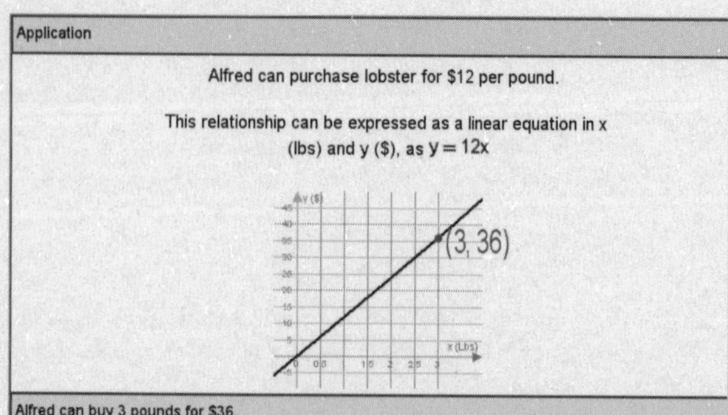

Application
Alfred can purchase lobster for $12 per pound.
This relationship can be expressed as a linear equation in x (lbs) and y ($), as y = 12x
y ($)
(3, 36)
x (Lbs)
Alfred can buy 3 pounds for $36.

The price depends on how much you buy. Ordered pair solutions are how many pounds and price. The cost per pound is the rate of change, and is represented by the slope of the line.

Application

A dopamine concentration is 26.6 micrograms per cubic centimeter (cc). This relationship can be written as a linear equation with cubic centimeters (x) and micrograms (y) as: $y = 26.6x$

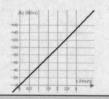

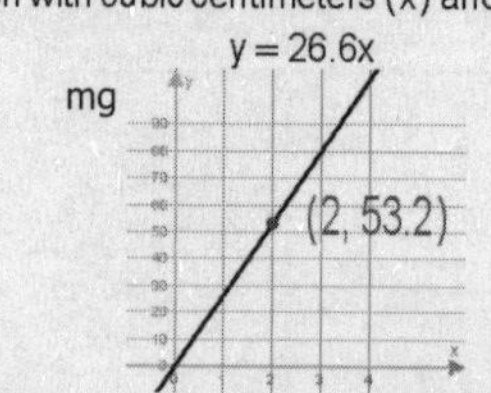

2 ccs delivers 53.2 micrograms.

From the graph you can determine how much dopamine is in each cc. The volume determines the amount of dopamine.

All linear equations can be represented by **y = mx + b**. When **x** and **y** measure physical quantities, slope becomes the **rate of change**. The input value, **x**, determines the output value, **y**, by the rate of change factor. In the visualizations presented here **x** is gallons and **y** is the number of miles that can be driven. The output value **y** is determined by the input value **x** times the rate of change (**m**) plus any initial conditions (**b**).

Can you determine how many miles you get on a gallon of gas without knowing the rate your car gets per gallon?

What does rate represent?

What happens to the line as the rate changes? What happens to the point on the line as x increases?

Does the faster you drive influence the number of miles? Can this be determined by the graph? What else do you need to know?

Can **x** ever be negative? What happens when **x** is zero?

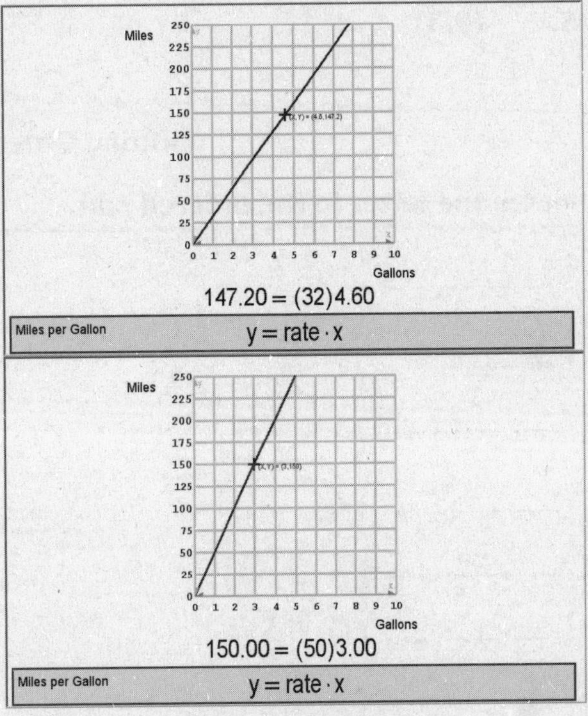

How many miles can you go on 2.5 gallons?

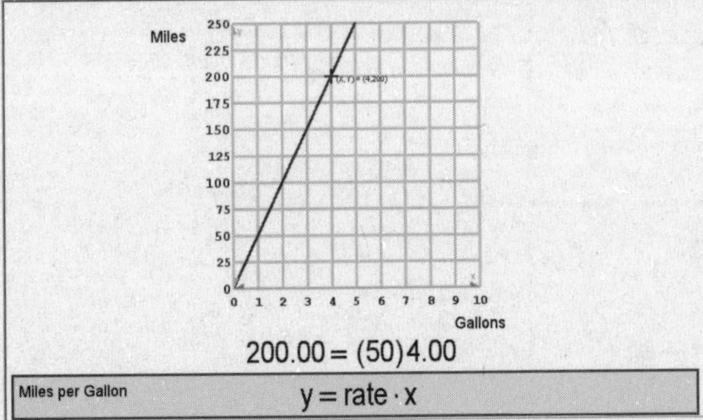

What kind of vehicle gets 50 mpg? How many gallons are required to travel 300 miles?

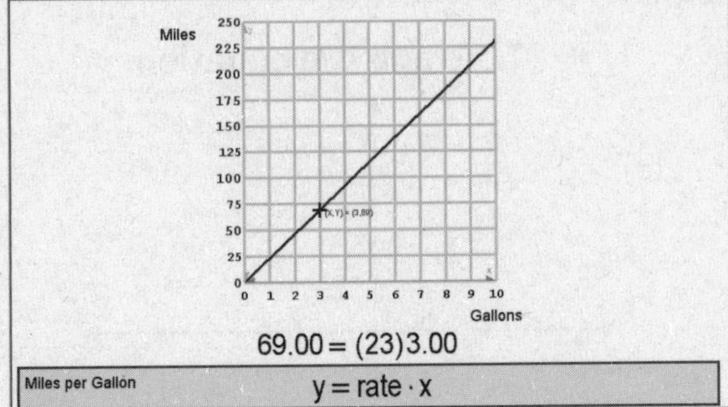

How do you use the graph to determine how many gallons of gas are needed for a 250 mile round trip?

Ordered Pairs as solutions

Which of the following ordered pairs are solutions to $2x - 5y = 12$?

1. **(-1,-2)**

2. **(1,2)**

3. **(6,0)**

4. **(-3,-3.6)**

Which of the following ordered pairs are solutions to $2x^2 + y^2 = 9$?

5. **(0,3)**

6. **(0,-3)**

Plotting Ordered Pairs

Match the letter to the ordered pair.

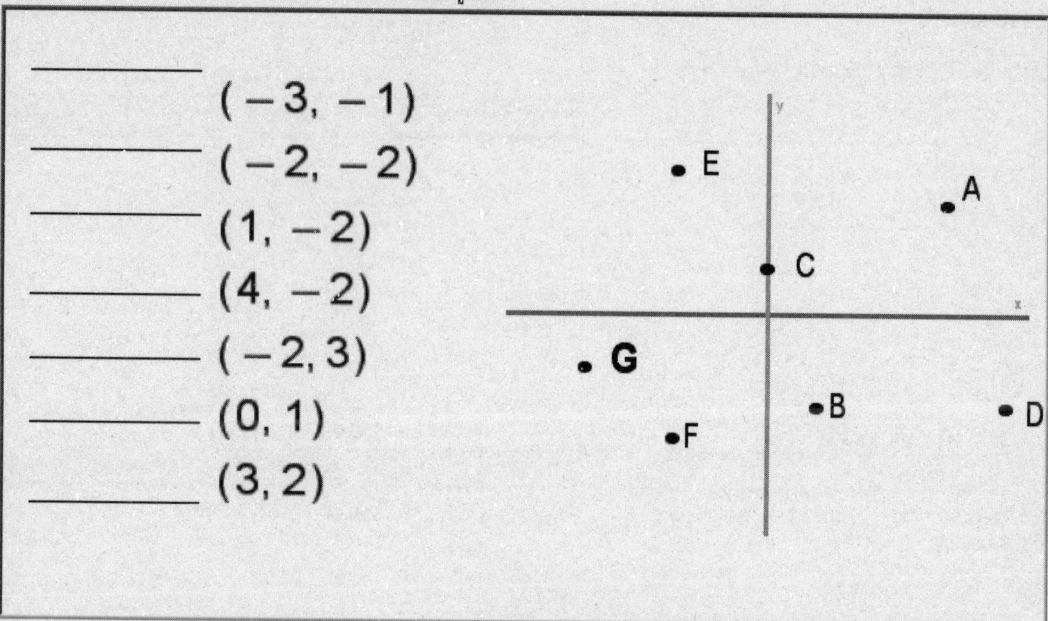

Table of Values

1. Fill in a table of values.

x	y=2x-5	Ordered Pair

2. Graph the equation.

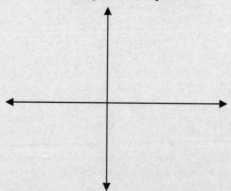

y = mx + b

Describe the slope as +, -, or 0.

1. m is ________ **2. m is ________** **3. m is ________**

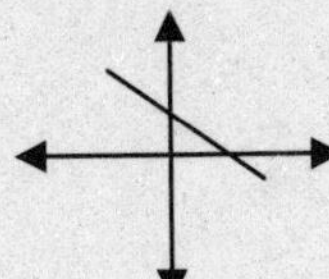

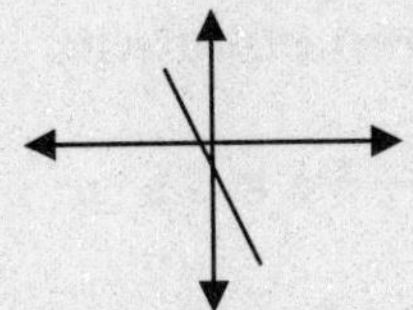

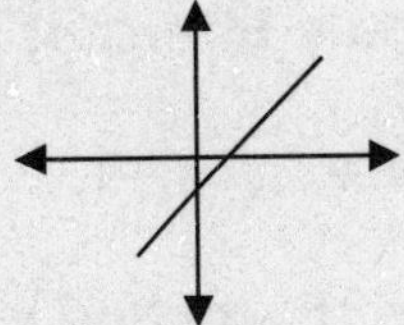

From the graphs above, estimate the y-intercept.

4. b = __________ **5. b = __________** **6. b = __________**

x– and y– Intercepts

From the graph :

1. The x-intercept is __________

2. The y-intercept is __________

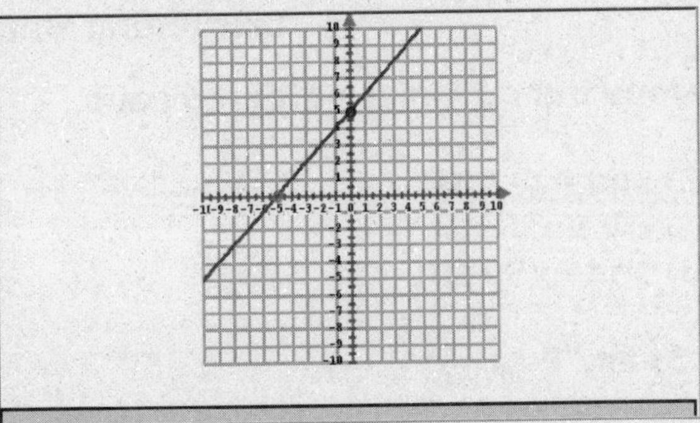

Find the x– and y– intercepts from the given equation.

3. y = 5x – 10

x-intercept = _____

y-intercept = _____

4. y = –2x + 6

x-intercept = _____

y-intercept = _____

5. y = x – 2

x-intercept = _____

y-intercept = _____

Ax + By = C Intercepts

Find the x-intercept from the given equation.

1. $2x - 5y = 8$
2. $-2x + y = -4$
3. $3x - 9y = -15$

Find the y-intercept from the given equation.

4. $-7x + 3y = -9$
5. $2x - 5y = 15$
6. $3x + 7y = -14$

6. **Find the x– and y-intercepts and draw the graph of the following equation:**
   $3x - 5y = -15$

   x-intercept ________
   y-intercept ________

Calculating Slope

Find the slope from the given ordered pairs.

1. $P_1(3,2)$ and $P_2(-2,5)$ m= ______________
2. $P_1(0,0)$ and $P_2(9,-15)$ m= ______________
3. $P_1(-2,3)$ and $P_2(4,-6)$ m= ______________
4. $P_1(-3,-2)$ and $P_2(7,-2)$ m= ______________

Parallel Lines

Which lines are parallel to: $y = \frac{1}{2}x - 3$

1. $y = \frac{1}{2}x - 5$ Yes ________ No ________
2. $y = \frac{2}{3}x - 3$ Yes ________ No ________
3. $y = -\frac{1}{2}x + 3$ Yes ________ No ________
4. $y = \frac{1}{2}x - 4$ Yes ________ No ________
5. $3x + 6y = 12$ Yes ________ No ________

Perpendicular lines

Which lines are perpendicular to: $y = \frac{1}{2}x - 3$

1. $y = \frac{-1}{2}x - 3$ Yes ________ No ________
2. $y = -2x - 5$ Yes ________ No ________
3. $y = 2x + 6$ Yes ________ No ________
4. $y = -2x - 3$ Yes ________ No ________
5. $3x - 6y = 12$ Yes ________ No ________

Slope-Intercept

1. Identify the slope, y-intercept, and graph y = 3x+2

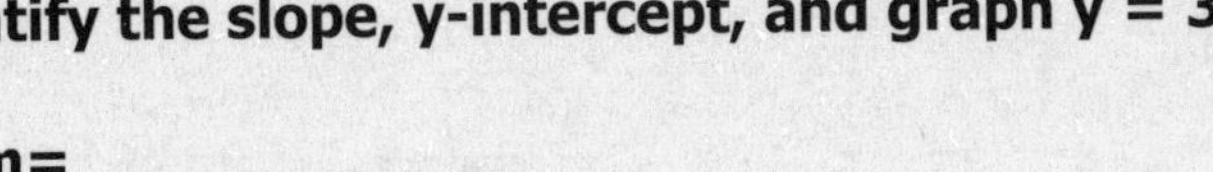

m=_______

b=_______

2. Which graph matches the equation: y=-2x+1?

a. 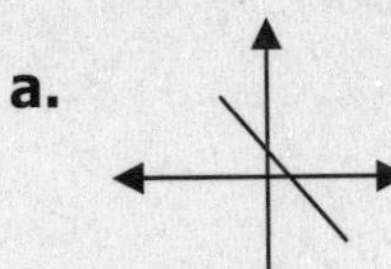

b. 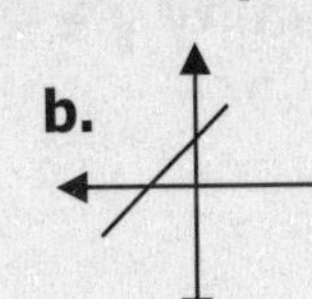

c. 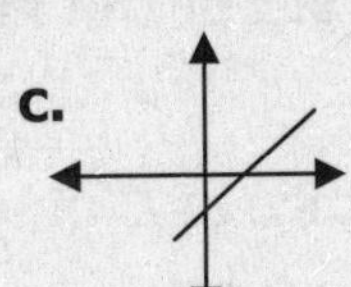

d. 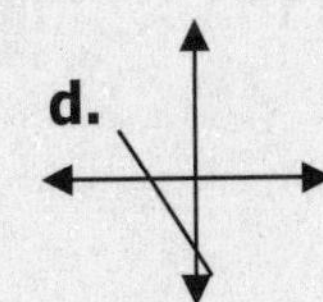

Point-Slope Equation

1. Identify x_1, y_1, m, and graph the equation: y – 2 = 3(x+1).

x_1 = _____

y_1 = _____

m = _____

2. Which graph matches the equation: y+3 = 2(x-1)

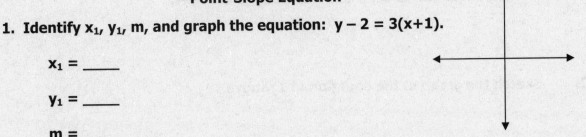

a. 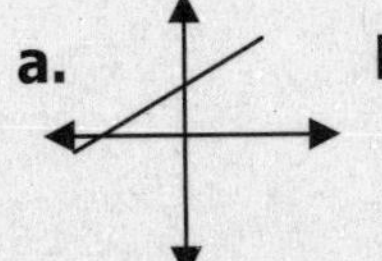

b. 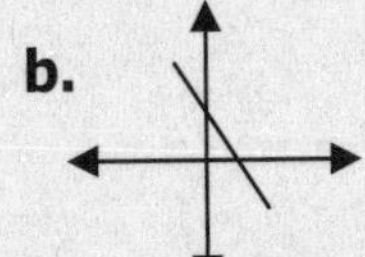

c. 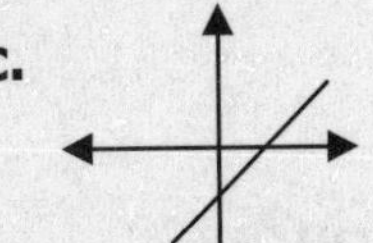

d. 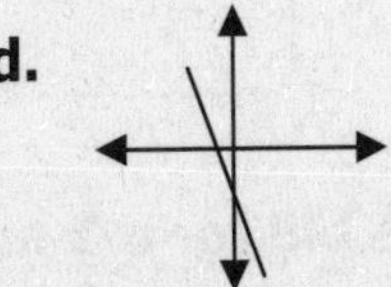

Graphing Inequalities

1. Graph the following inequality: $y > 2x - 3$

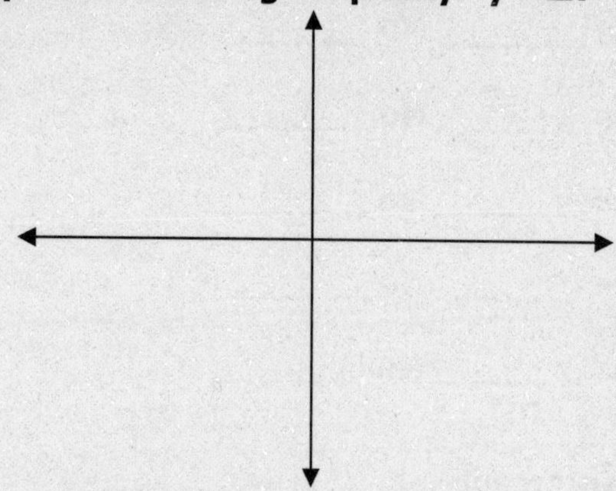

2. Which is the graph of $y > x + 2$?

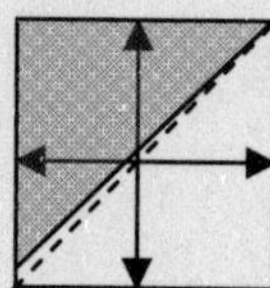 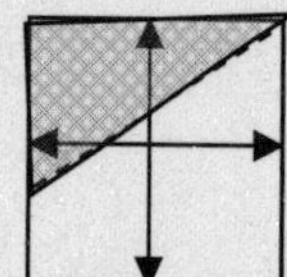 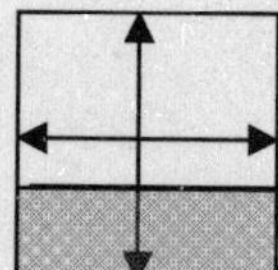 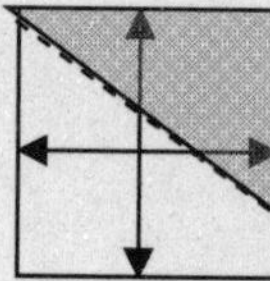

3. Is the point (2,3) in the solution set of the inequality $y \geq 2x - 5$?

Rate of Change

A taxi charges 45 cents per quarter of a mile.

1. Write an equation to calculate the metered charges.

2. Sketch the graph of the equation in 1. above.

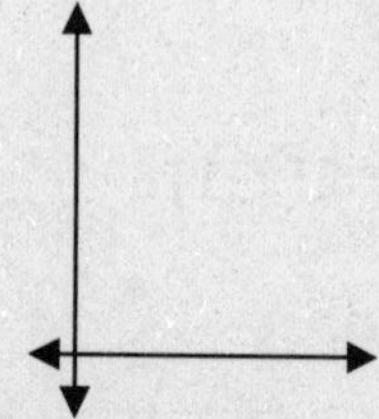

3. How much is the bill for a 3 mile trip?

9. Systems of Equations

In the real world, most situations require more than two variables to describe them. For example, we can describe the simple motion of a ball in two variables: distance and time. But to describe the weather, we need many more variables. We seek to describe such situations with a system of **linear equations**, one for each variable we have. This enables us to find a solution for each variable. So, if we have two equations in two variables, we can find a solution, or the exact values of the variables that solve both.

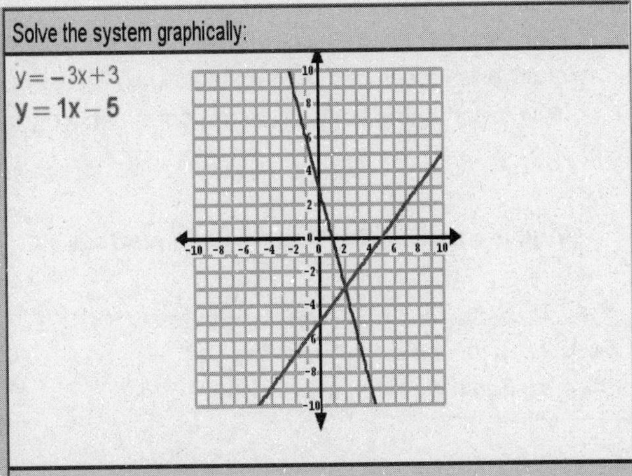
Solve the system graphically:
y = −3x + 3
y = 1x − 5
Graph the second equation.

Systems of linear equations are two or more linear equations taken together as a set. A graph of such a system has two or more lines intersecting. The point where the lines cross is **the only point the lines have in common**, therefore it **is the only point that satisfies both equations.**

Systems of equations have many real-world applications, from cost-revenue analysis to calorie-weight predictions. Finding a solution to a cost-revenue system means to find the break-even point — the point where cost equals revenue, where the cost line crosses the revenue line.

Graphing and Solving Systems of Equations

Step 1: Graph the first equation.
Step 2: Graph the second equation.
Step 3: Find the point of intersection.

Systems of Equations

$$y = m_1x + b_1$$
$$y = m_2x + b_2$$

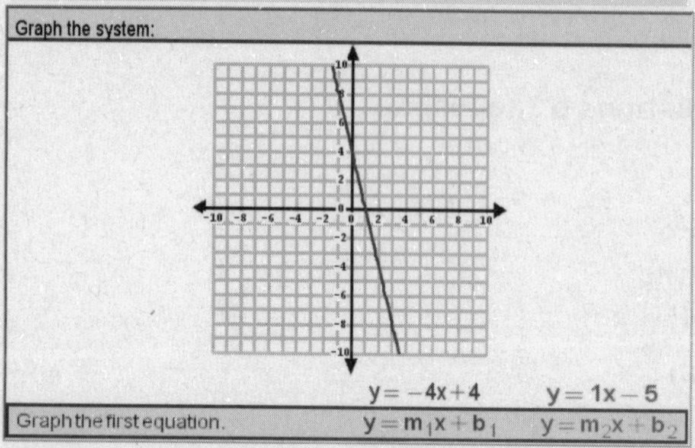
Graph the system:
y = −4x + 4
y = 1x − 5
Graph the first equation.
y = m1x + b1
y = m2x + b2

Step 1: Graph the first line: **y = -4x+4**. Graph by any method.

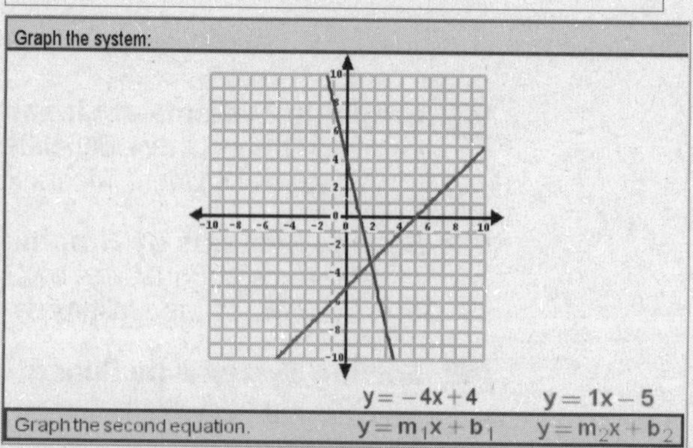
Graph the system:
y = −4x + 4
y = 1x − 5
Graph the second equation.
y = m1x + b1
y = m2x + b2

Step 2: Graph the second line: **y=x-5**. Graph by any method.

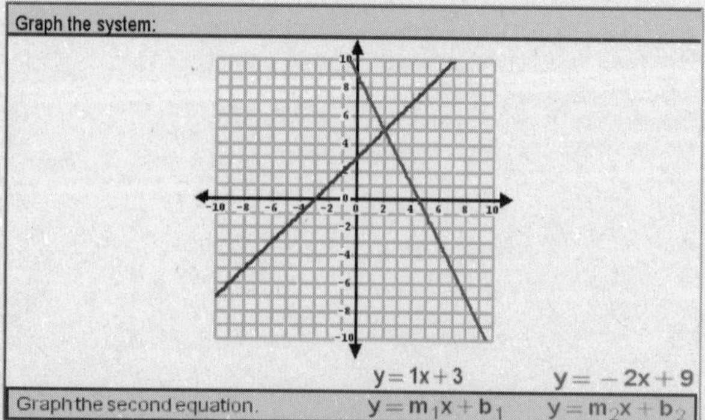
Graph the system:
y = 1x + 3
y = − 2x + 9
Graph the second equation.
y = m1x + b1
y = m2x + b2

Point 2 is dynamic. Change slopes and intercepts to examine any two-equation system. **Two equations crossing at a single point are called consistent.**

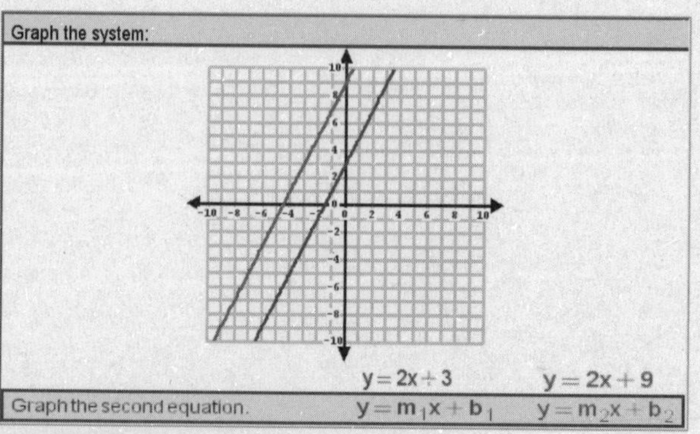
Graph the system:
y = 2x + 3
y = 2x + 9
Graph the second equation.
y = m1x + b1
y = m2x + b2

Special Case: Parallel lines have no points in common and do not intersection. **Parallel lines are called inconsistent.**

Systems of equations are two or more equations taken as a set. In real-world applications, systems of linear equations examine two (or more) linear relationships to determine what point they have in common. One of the processes for solving the system is to graph the lines and then to determine where they intersect.

For systems of equations, visualize two intersecting lines graphed on the same set of axes. Use the joystick to change the slopes and **y**-intersects to make new systems.

What determines the quadrant of the answer? Can the slopes be equal? What happens if the **y**-intercepts are the same? Can the slopes and **y**-intercepts of the two lines be equal? Can both lines have positive slopes? Can they both have negative slopes? Do perpendicular lines intersect?

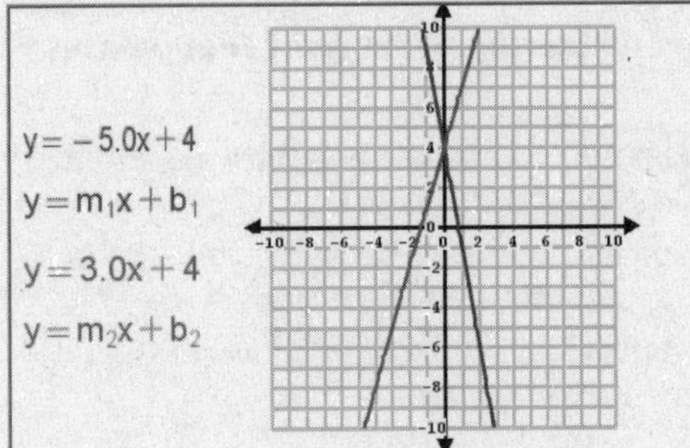

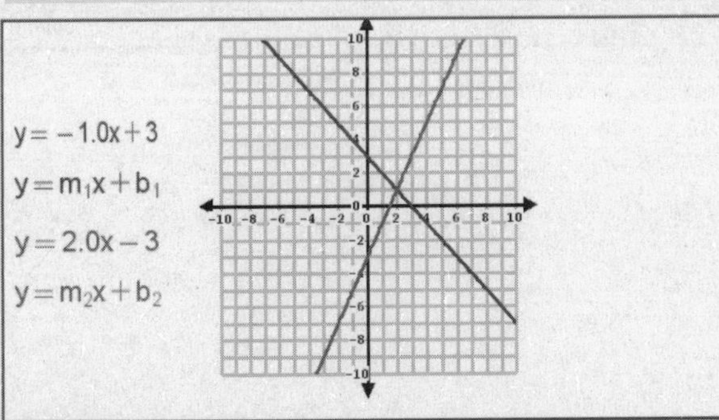

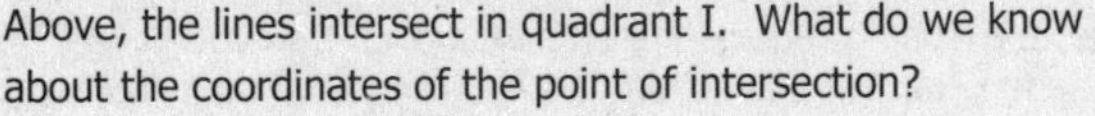

Above, the lines intersect in quadrant I. What do we know about the coordinates of the point of intersection?

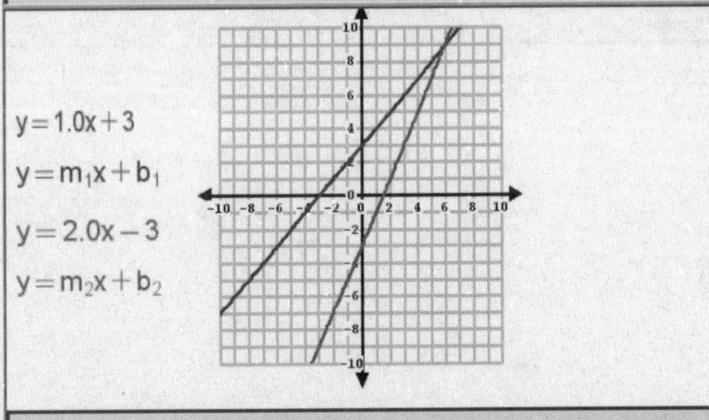

What happens when both slopes are positive? Can two increasing lines cross in any of the four quadrants?

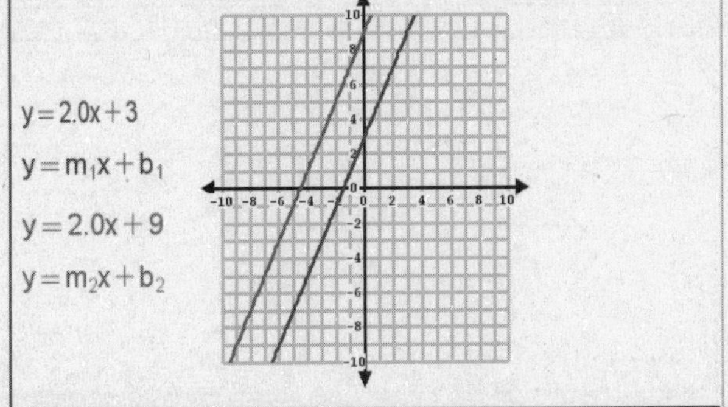

Special Case I: Parallel lines do not intersect. How do you determine if two lines are parallel?

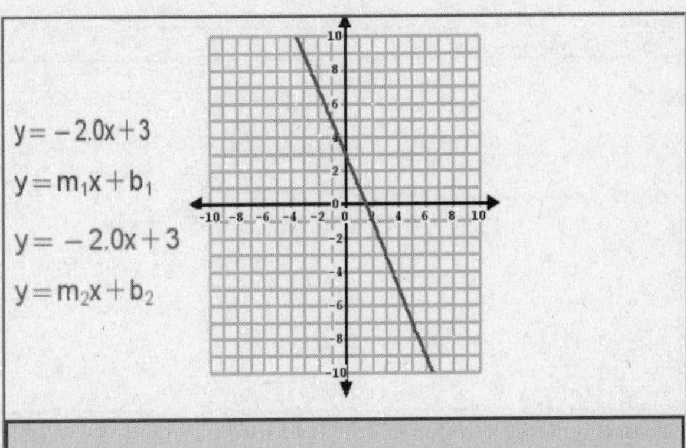

If the slopes and intercepts are the same, the lines are the same and these systems are called **dependent**.

Systems of Linear Inequalities

EnableMath

Systems of linear inequalities define a region and not just a single point. Graphing systems of inequalities begins with graphing each inequality separately and then determining the overlapping region as the answer.

Hint: Always graph inequalities in **y=mx+b** form. Self-check by correct shading. For > shade above the line and for < shades below the line.

Graphing and Solving Systems of Inequalities

Step 1: Graph the first inequality. Lightly shade the appropriate side of the line.

Step 2: Graph the second inequality. Lightly shade the appropriate side of the line.

Step 3: Find the region of intersection where the two shaded areas overlap.

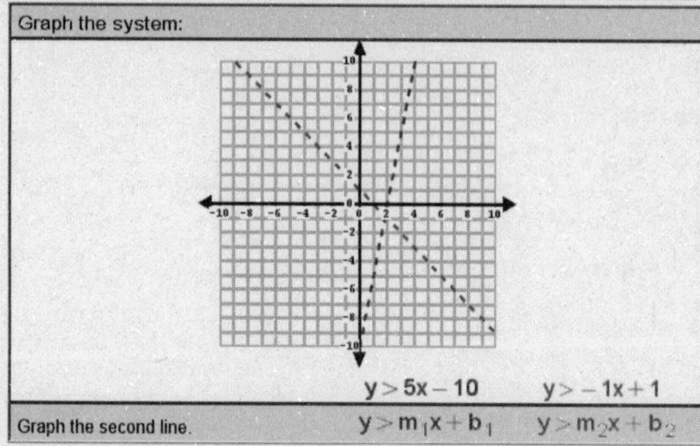

Notice that both lines are dotted to show that these lines are not included. Think about which regions are to be included. On paper, lightly shade the regions.

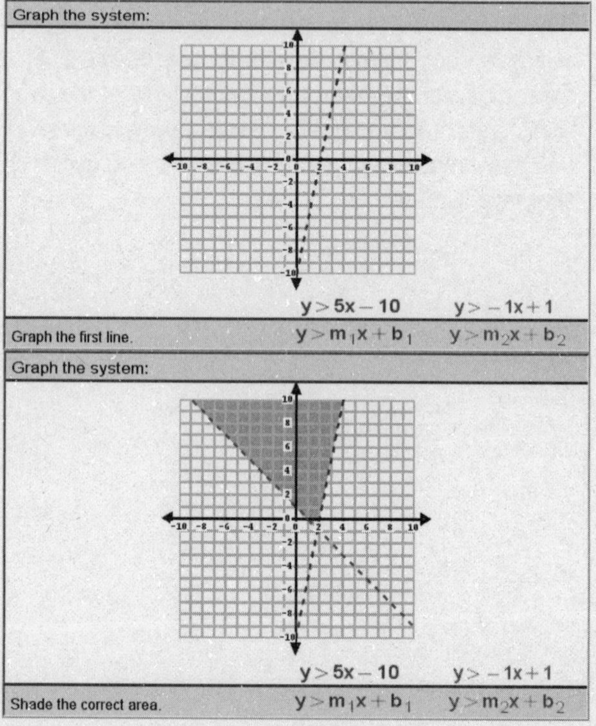

The overlapping regions are shown above. Can you determine the "top" of a line from the "bottom" of a line? Will > always shade the top of the line?

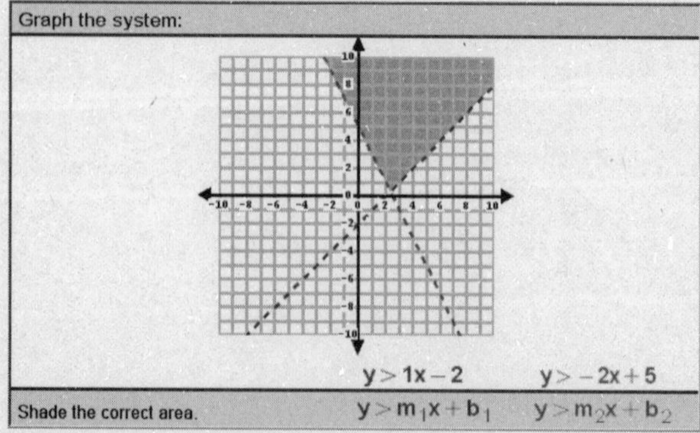

The slope of line 1 positive and its function values increase linearly with x. The slope of line 2 is negative and its functional values decreasing linearly.

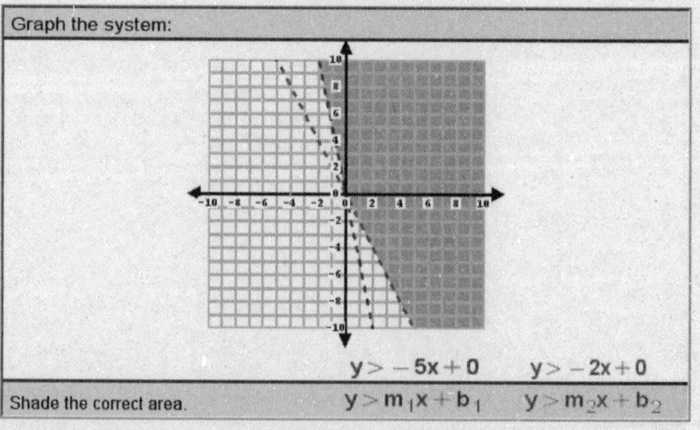

Both lines have a negative slope.

Systems of Linear Inequalities

Systems of linear inequalities define a region of points. What affect does the slope of the lines have on defining that solution region? As you play with these graphs, see if you can guess what regions will be solutions to these systems of linear inequalities.

Can both slopes be positive? Can both be negative and have intersecting regions? Can the lines be parallel? Can the lines be perpendicular? Can one line be horizontal and one vertical? What type of lines would only use the first quadrant as the overlapping region? Do the y-intercepts determine which quadrant is used?

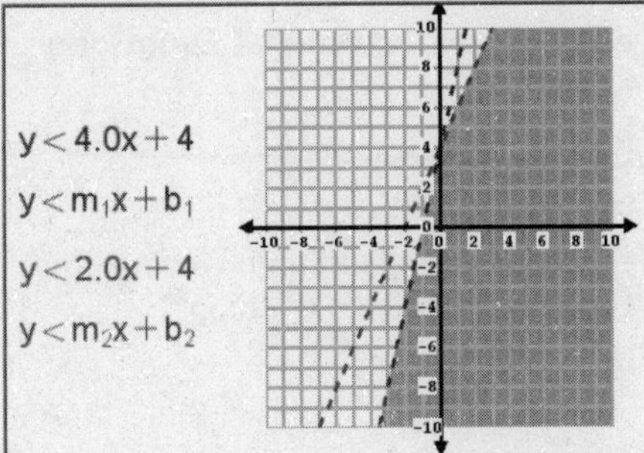

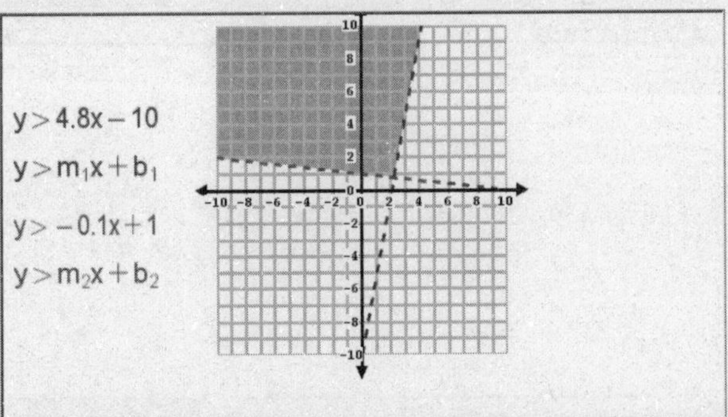

To self-check, mentally test (0,0). Is (0,0) part of the system answers above?

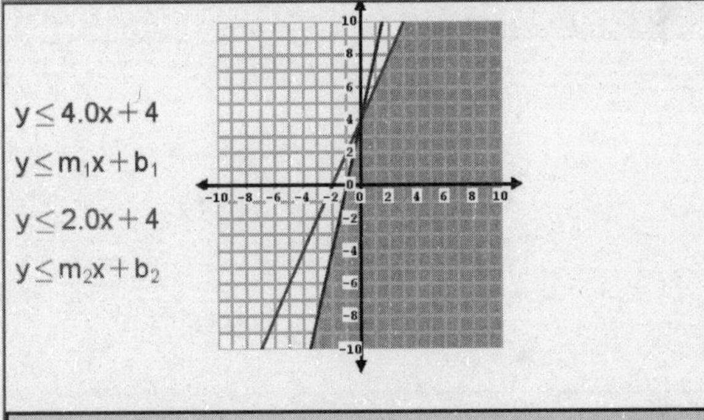

If greater than shades the region above the line, does less than define the region below the line?

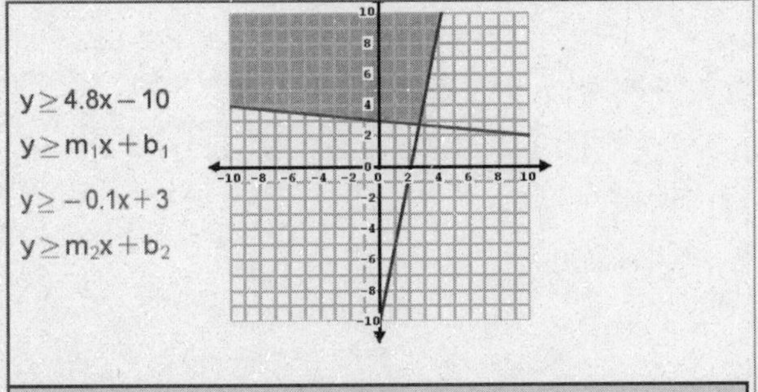

What region is shaded when both inequalities are >.

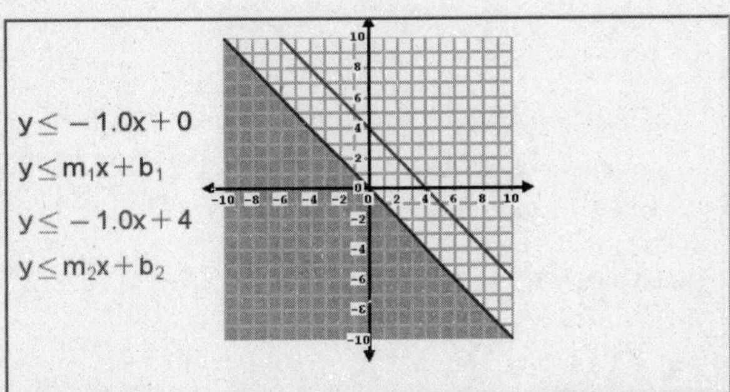

Can parallel lines associated with inequalities define a solution region?

Solving a system of linear equations by graphing means to find the point of intersection of the lines forming the system. **The point of intersection is the only point that satisfies both equations.**

After graphing two (or more) intersecting lines, determine the coordinates of the point of intersection by inspection. Read along the **x**-axis for the **x**-coordinate and along **the y**-axis for the **y**-coordinate. Report answers as ordered pairs.

Graphing and Solving Systems of Equations

Step 1: Graph the first equation.

Step 2: Graph the second equation.

Step 3: Find the point of intersection by reading the **x** and **y** coordinates from the graph.

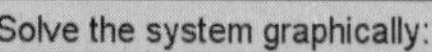

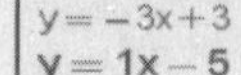

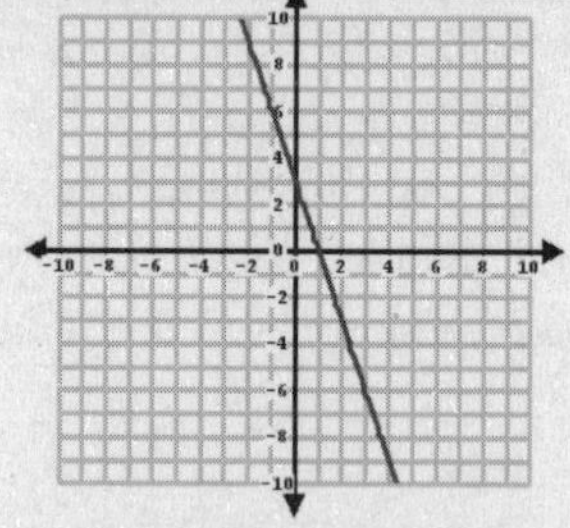

Graph the first equation.

Solve the system graphically:

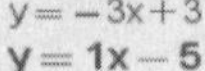

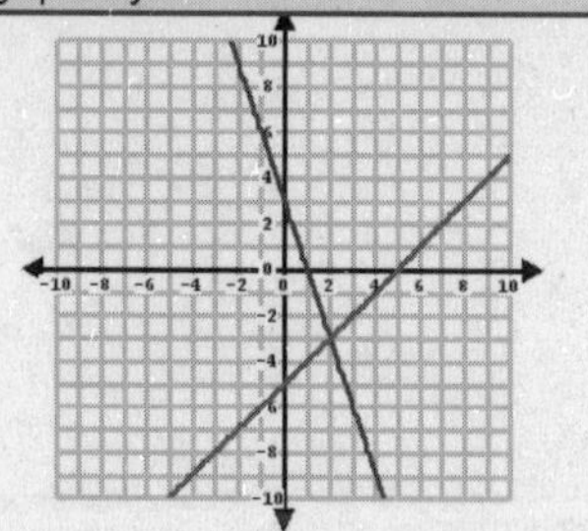

Graph the second equation.

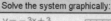

Locate the point of intersection.

Solve the system graphically:

y= −3x+3
y= 1x−5

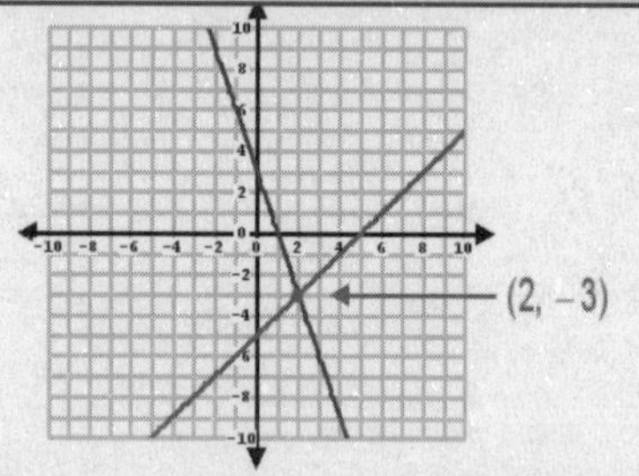

The solution is the point of intersection.

Read the coordinates of the point of intersection **(2.-3)**. The point **(2,-3)** satisfies both equations. Try it: Substitute **2** for **x** and **−3** for **y** in both equations.

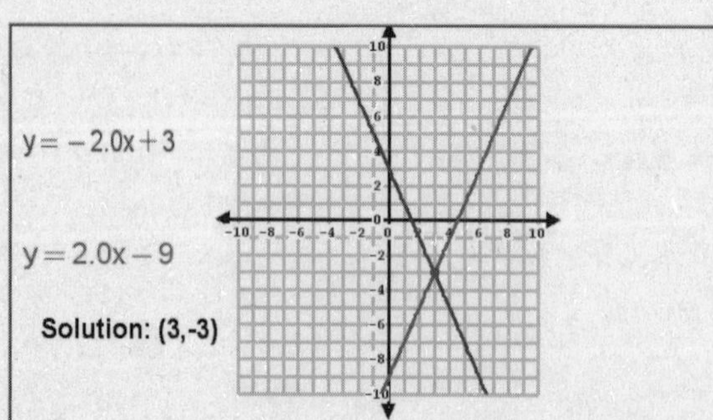

Follow along the **x**-axis for the **x**-coordinate, and along the **y**-axis for the **y**-coordinate.

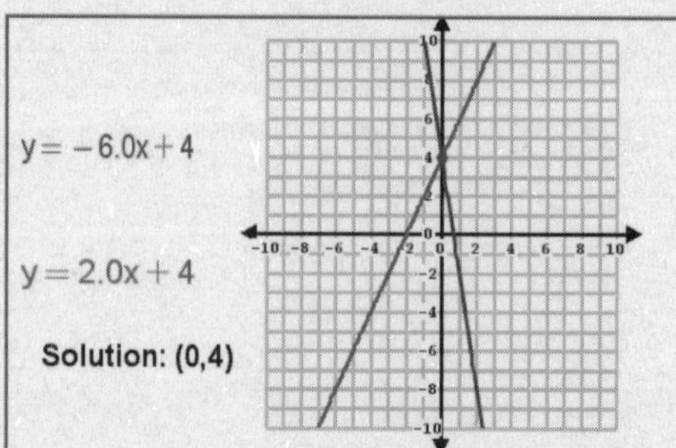

If the points are difficult to read, look for clues to finding the point of intersection in the system equations.

Systems of linear equations are solved when the coordinates of the point of intersection are found. This point of intersection satisfies both equations. **Visually, the solution is the point where the lines cross.** Read the coordinates of the solution point from its position on the grid.

Use the joystick to change slopes and y-intercepts and investigate the graph of any **two-equation linear system**.

How do you know if the point of intersection satisfies both equations? Can two lines have no intersection? Can two lines have more than one intersection point? Can both slopes be positive and still cross? Can both slopes be negative and still cross? What slopes and y-intercepts ensure that the point of intersection is in Quadrant I?

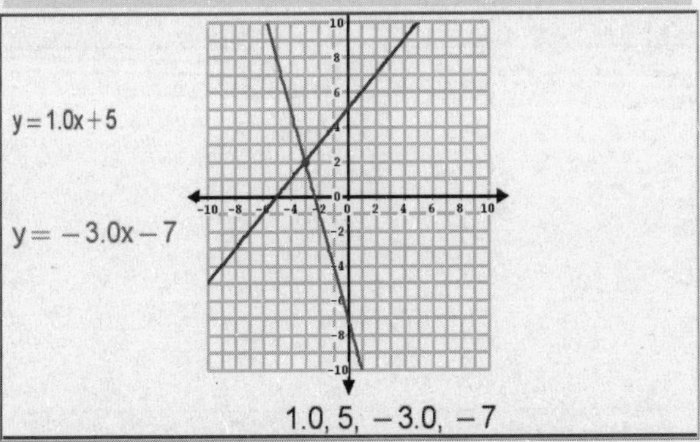

Read the coordinates of the intersection point from the grid. This point is located at (-3,2). Does the point (-3,2) satisfy both equations? (Check your solution algebraically.)

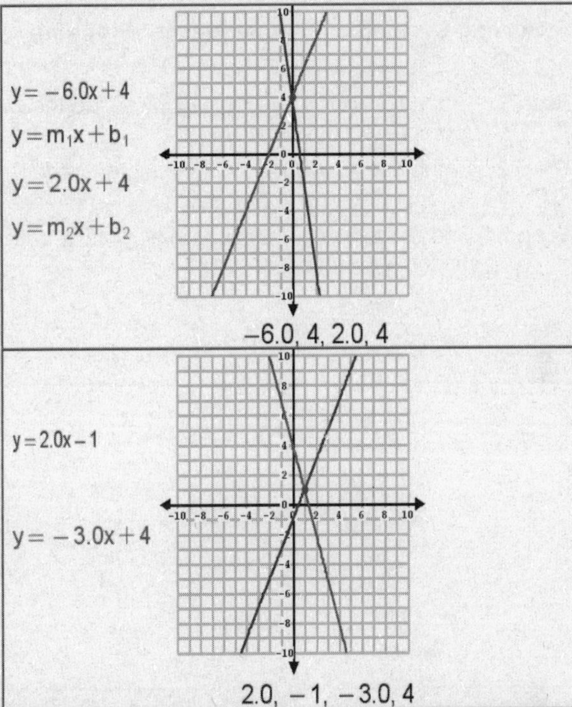

Read the intersection point as (1,1). Does (1,1) satisfy both equations? Lines that intersect are called **independent**.

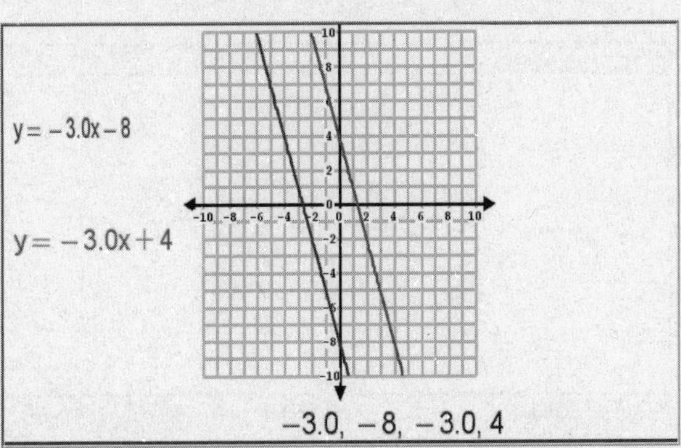

Parallel lines have no point of intersection. These lines are called **inconsistent**.

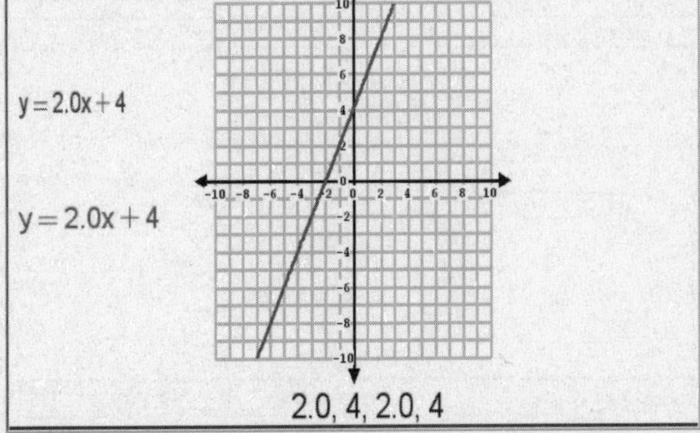

Lines with the same slopes and intercepts are called **dependant**. How many solutions are there to the system above?

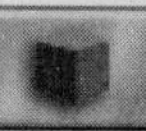

Solving Systems of Inequalities by Graphing

EnableMath

The solution to a system of linear inequalities is a region bounded by two (or more) lines. The region is the set of all points satisfying both (all) inequalities in the system.

Solving the system by graphing means to show a graph of the region bounded by the inequalities of the system.

Solving Systems of Inequalities by Graphing

Step 1: Graph the first inequality. Lightly shade the appropriate side of the line.

Step 2: Graph the second inequality. Lightly shade the appropriate side of the line.

Step 3: Find the region of intersection where the two shaded areas overlap.

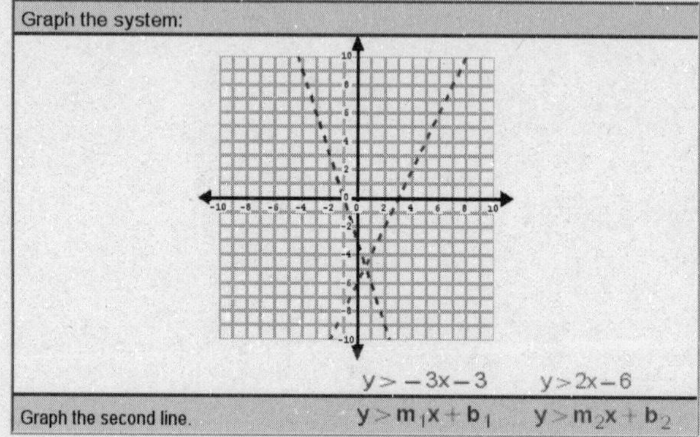

Remember that > and< use dotted lines. Note which side of the lines are to be included—use the test point (0,0) if you are not sure.

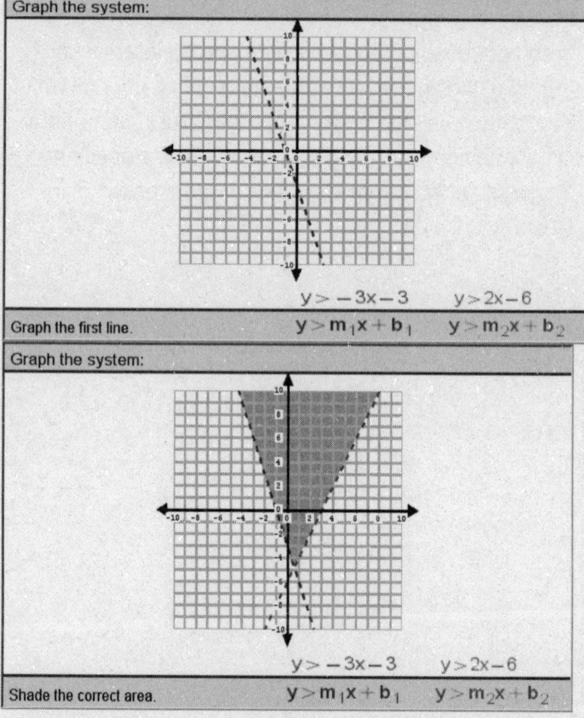

On paper, each inequality would be shaded and the overlapping part would be the solution region. You can double check by testing points inside or outside the region.

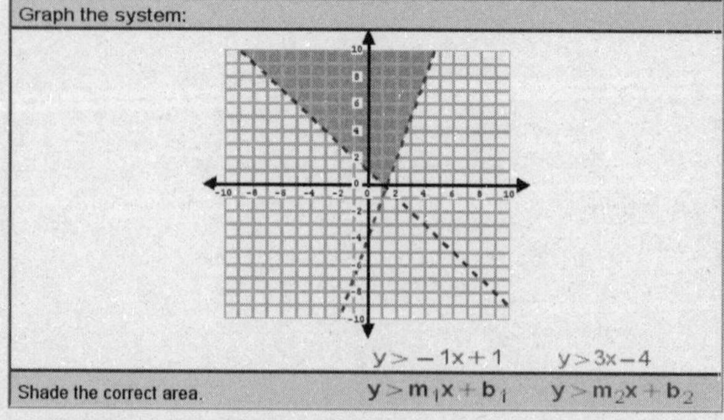

Greater than — will look like this.

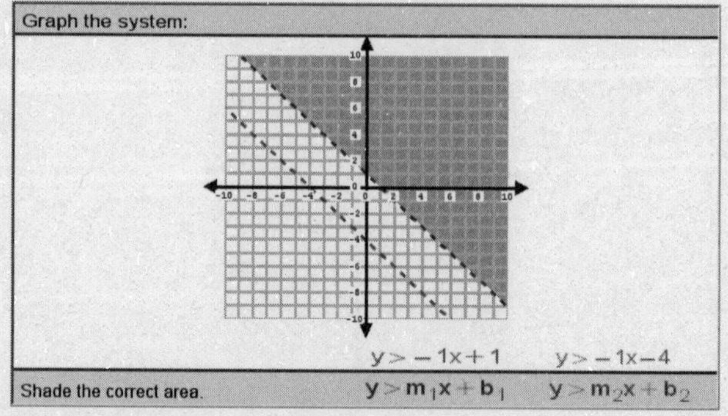

Parallel lines **CAN** have solution regions.

Solving systems of inequalities visually means graphing each inequality and determining the region that is common to both (or all, if more than two).

Use the joystick to change slopes and y-intercepts.

What happens if the inequalities are mixed?

Does it make a difference if a > inequality is in a system with a < inequality?

Can > and $\leq$ be in the same system?

Can two parallel lines be in the same system?

What inequalities would choose the inside part of two parallel-line inequalities?

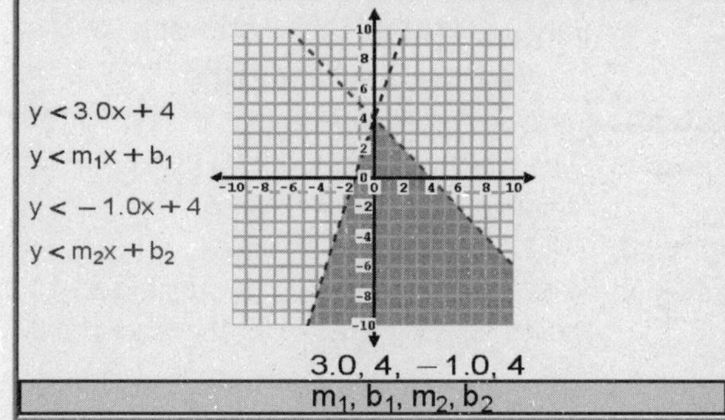

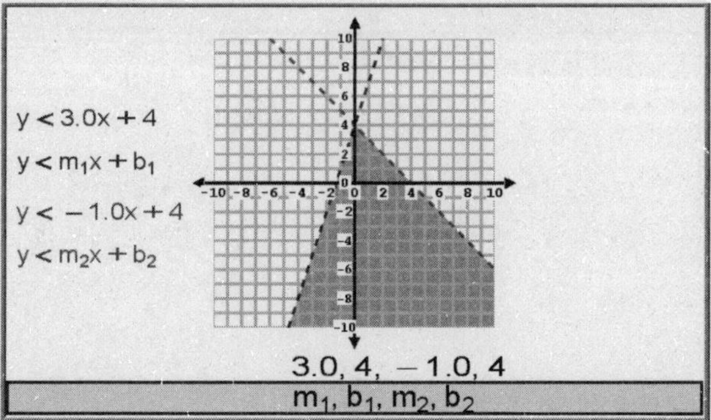

Point 1: Notice that the shaded region is "below" each line, as opposed to "above" the line as in > inequalities. Test point (0,0) to double check each shaded region.

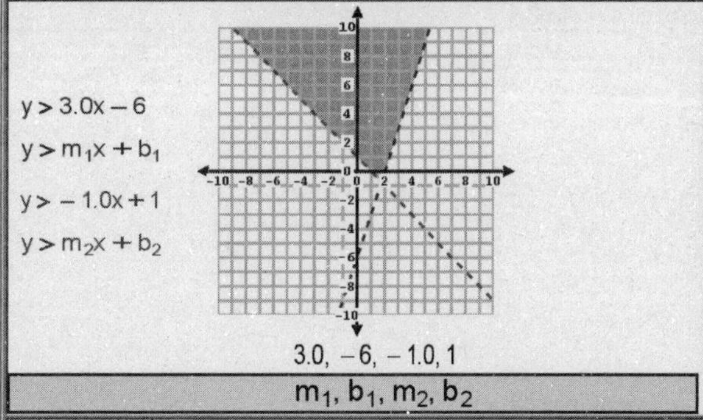

Point 2: *Greater than.* The lines are **NOT** included in the solution region.

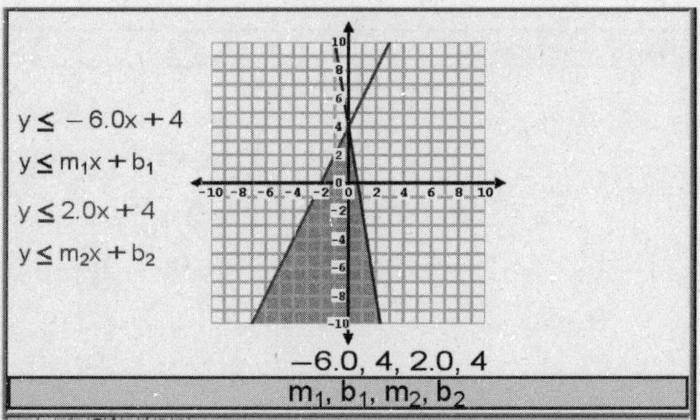

Point 3: *Less than or equal to.* The line **IS** included in the solution region.

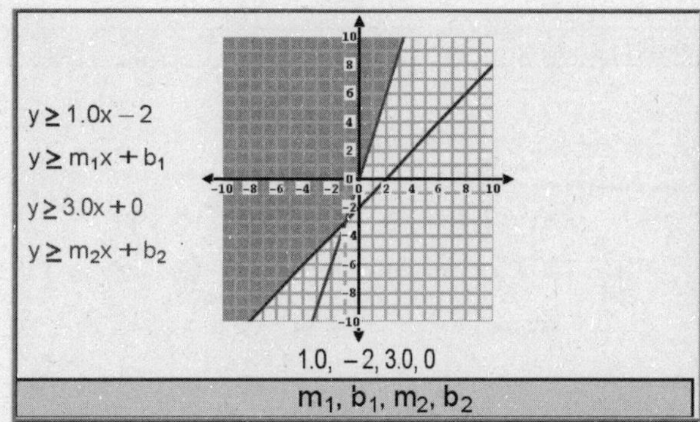

Point 4: *Greater than or equal to.* The line **IS** included in the solution region.

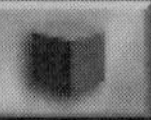

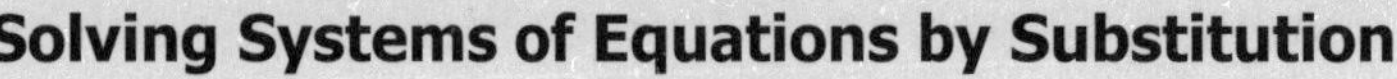

Solving Systems of Equations by Substitution

EnableMath

Solving systems of linear equations by substitution is the first of two algebraic ways to solve a system of equations. You solve for one variable in one equation and then substitute that solution for the other variable in the other equation.

Solve for **x** or **y** (your choice) and then substitute that expression for **x** (or **y**) into the other equation. This yields the value for the **y-coordinate**. Substitute that answer back into the first equation to find the value for the **x-coordinate**.

The following work shows how to solve for **x** first. The concept shows solving for **y** first. Choose either way.

Solving Systems by Substitution

Requires 2 substitutions

Step 1: Solve one equation for x *or* y.

Step 2: Substitute the above result for the chosen variable in the other equation.

Step 3: Solve for the coordinate value.

Step 4: Substitute the value from step 3 into either original equation to solve for the other coordinate.

Solve by substitution:

$$-3x+2y=1$$
$$2x-4y=-6$$

You may choose to solve for either variable in either equation. In the bottom equation, we solve for x.

Solve by substitution:

$$-3x+2y=1$$
$$2x-4y=-6$$
$$2x=-6+4y \Rightarrow x=-3+2y$$

Solve the second equation for x.

Step 1: Solve the bottom equation for **x**. **x** becomes an expression in terms of **y**. We say, "Solve for x in terms of y."

Solve by substitution:

$$-3x+2y=1$$
$$2x-4y=-6$$
$$2x=-6+4y \Rightarrow x=-3+2y$$
$$-3(-3+2y)+2y=1 \Rightarrow 9-6y+2y=1$$

Substitute this x into the first equation for x.

Step 2: Substitute **(-3 + 2y)** for **x** in the top equation.

Solve by substitution:

$$-3x+2y=1$$
$$2x-4y=-6$$
$$2x=-6+4y \Rightarrow x=-3+2y$$
$$-3(-3+2y)+2y=1 \Rightarrow 9-6y+2y=1$$
$$9-4y=1 \Rightarrow -4y=-8 \Rightarrow y=2$$

Solve for y.

Step 3: Find the coordinate value for **y** (solve for y). Think, "Substitute **x** to find **y**." The answer is taking shape: **(__,2)**.

Solve by substitution:

$$-3x+2y=1$$
$$2x-4y=-6$$
$$2x=-6+4y \Rightarrow x=-3+2y$$
$$-3(-3+2y)+2y=1 \Rightarrow 9-6y+2y=1$$
$$9-4y=1 \Rightarrow -4y=-8 \Rightarrow y=2$$
$$x=-3+2y \Rightarrow x=-3+2(2) \Rightarrow x=1$$

Use this y to get x.

Step 4: Substitute the **y**-coordinate in **either** equation to get the **x**-coordinate. Substitute **y** to find **x**. The coordinates of the point of intersection are **(1,2)**.

Graphing systems of equations is not always the most efficient way to arrive at the solution. It gives a visual representation, but coordinates can be hard to determine. An algebraic process for solving systems of equations is more exact, allowing for decimal and fractional answers, and is usually quicker. We've limited the work to integer answers so that the process is easy to visualize.

Why do we use **y=mx+b** form for substitution? Which is found first, **x** or **y**?

Use the joystick to explore these dynamic examples.

How do you know which equation to use to solve for **y**? How do you determine if you solve for **x** or **y**? Can the slopes help determine which variable to solve for? How do you find slope if the equation is in **Ax + By = C** form? What does the top equation look like in **Ax+By = C** form?

What if both equations were in **y = mx + b** form; what substitution would be handy?

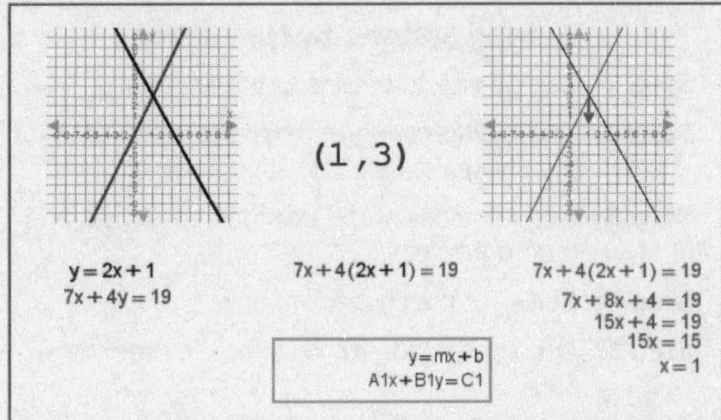

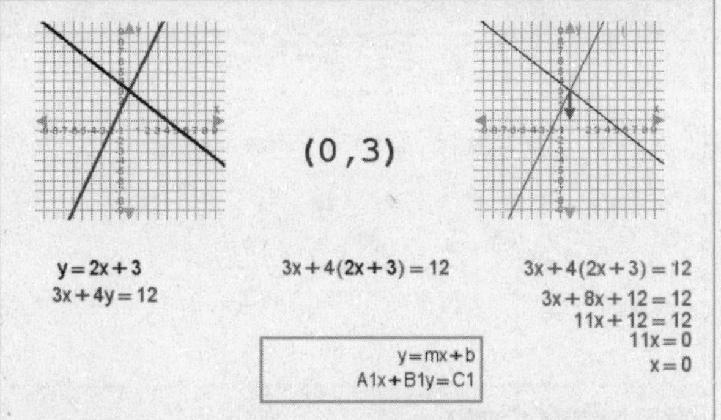

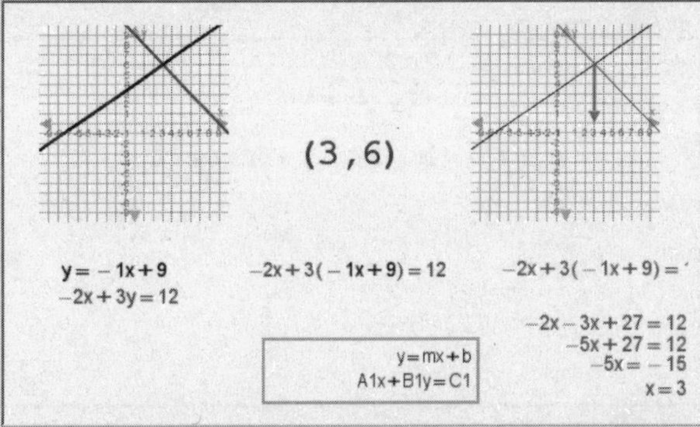

Quick check: Substitute the ordered pair into both equations. Does the point satisfy both equations?

Can you solve the second equation for **y** instead of the first one? What happens? Does it take fewer or more steps? Can you solve for **x** rather than **y**?

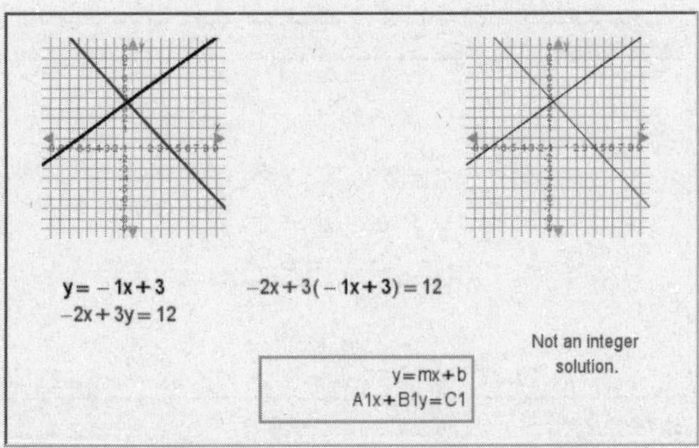

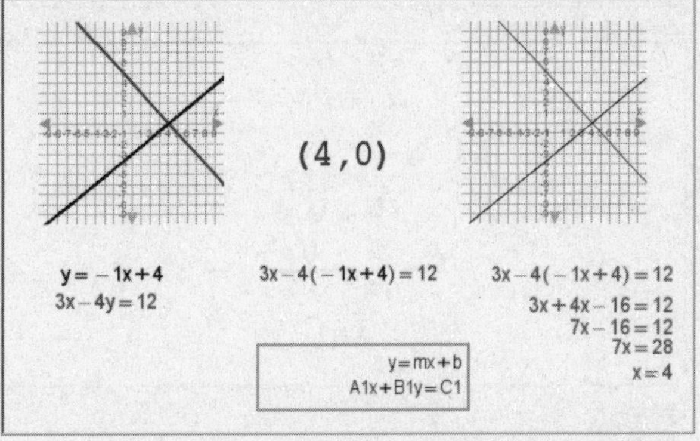

Does this system have a solution? What is an approximation of the solution?

How do you find the value of **y** when you know the value of **x**?

Solving Systems of Equations by Elimination

EnableMath

Solving a system of linear equations by elimination, sometimes called **addition**, is an algebraic process used to find the ordered pair solution.

Two basic principles of equations can be employed in this process: You can add (or subtract) any number to both sides of an equation and you can multiply both sides by any non-zero number.

Each side of an equation is an equivalent value or an expression. Therefore, corresponding sides of equations can be added or subtracted.

Solving Systems by Elimination

Step 1: Decide which variable to eliminate first.

Step 2: Use multiplication to make the coefficients of the chosen variable additive inverses.

Step 3: Add left sides of the changed equations and then right sides.

Step 4: Solve for the chosen variable.

Step 5: Use substitution to solve for the other variable.

$$\mathbf{x + y = 3}$$
$$\mathbf{2x - 5y = -1}$$

Step 1: to eliminate x.

Step 2: multiply top equation by –2

$$\mathbf{-2x - 2y = -6}$$
$$\underline{\mathbf{2x - 5y = -1}}$$

Step 3: add $\mathbf{0 \quad -7y = -7}$

Step 4: solve $\mathbf{y = 1}$

Step 5: substitute $\mathbf{x + (1) = 3}$

$\mathbf{x = 2}$ $\quad$ **(2,1)**

Solve by elimination:

$$-3x + 2y = 1$$
$$2x - 4y = -6$$
$$2(-3x + 2y = 1) \Rightarrow -6x + 4y = 2$$

Multiply the first equation by 2.

The above choice is to eliminate **y**. *Think: If I multiply the top equation by **2**, then the **y**-coefficients are additive inverses.*

Multiply both sides of the top equation by **2**.

Solve by elimination:

$$-3x + 2y = 1$$
$$2x - 4y = -6$$
$$2(-3x + 2y = 1) \Rightarrow -6x + 4y = 2$$
$$\begin{array}{r} -6x + 4y = 2 \\ +\quad 2x - 4y = -6 \\ \hline -4x \quad = -4 \end{array}$$

Add the equations to eliminate y.

Rewrite and align the equations. Add left sides and then right sides of the equations.

Solve by elimination:

$$-3x + 2y = 1$$
$$2x - 4y = -6$$
$$2(-3x + 2y = 1) \Rightarrow -6x + 4y = 2$$
$$\begin{array}{r} -6x + 4y = 2 \\ +\quad 2x - 4y = -6 \\ \hline -4x \quad = -4 \end{array}$$
$$x = 1$$

Solve for x.

Divide both sides of the resulting equation by –4 to solve for **x**.

Solve by elimination:

$$-3x + 2y = 1$$
$$2x - 4y = -6$$
$$2(-3x + 2y = 1) \Rightarrow -6x + 4y = 2$$
$$\begin{array}{r} -6x + 4y = 2 \\ +\quad 2x - 4y = -6 \\ \hline -4x \quad = -4 \end{array}$$
$$x = 1$$
$$-3(1) + 2y = 1 \Rightarrow -3 + 2y = 1 \Rightarrow 2y = 4 \Rightarrow y = 2$$

Use this x to get y.

Substitute 1 for **x** in either equation to solve for y. How do you know if your answer is correct?

Solving Systems of Equations by Elimination

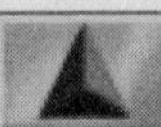

One of the properties of equations is that **an equation can be changed on one side if an equivalent change is made on the other side**.

Why can we multiply both sides of an equation by a non-zero number? Why can we add two equations together?

Use the joystick to change the equations; change **m** and **n** until **y** is eliminated. Change the value of **x** and watch the crosses move until the solution is reached.

How do you know what to multiply by when changing an equation?

How do you choose which variable to eliminate?

Can you eliminate both variables?

Why do the coefficients of the chosen variable need to be additive inverses?

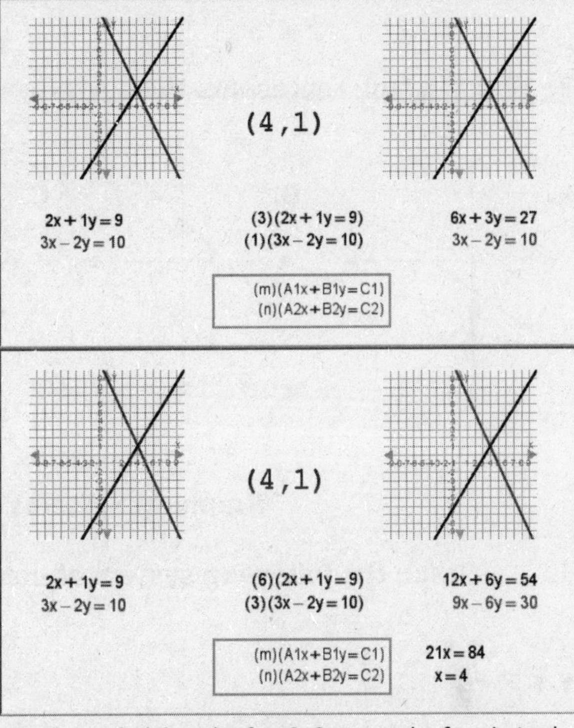

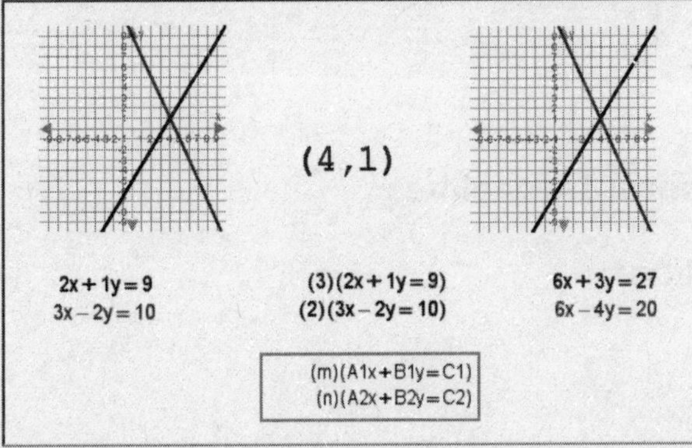

Why did this combination not yield a solution? Do the **x's** add out? Do the **y's** add out?

How do you find the value for **y**? Can you solve for **y** instead of **x**? Is it easier to use 4 to find **y** or to rework the system to solve for **y**?

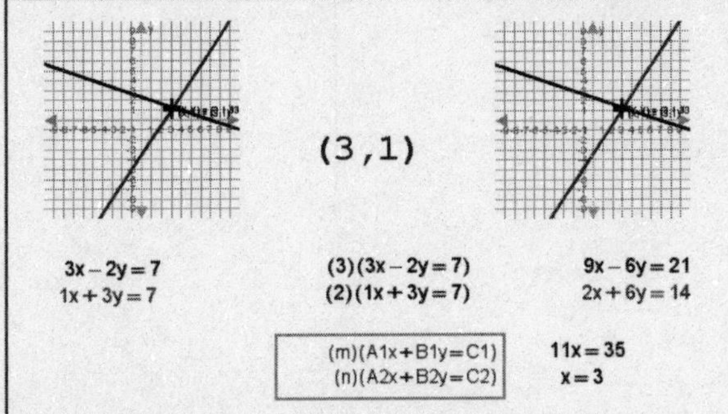

Does the cross match up with the solution?

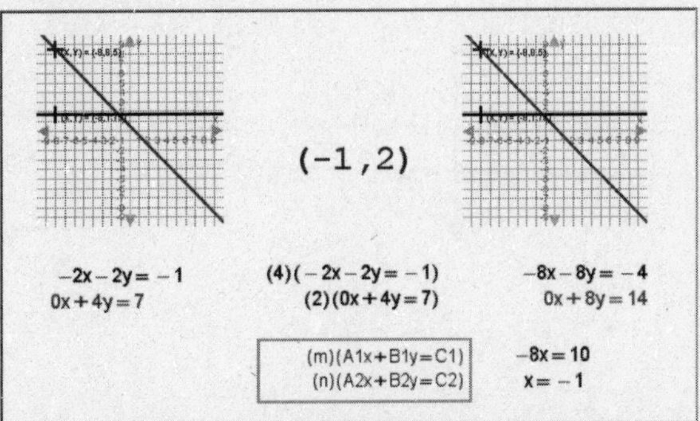

What happens when one of the lines is horizontal? Is there a short cut? If the lines are vertical, which variable is a solution?

Graphing Systems of Linear Equations

1. Graph the following system of equations:

$$y = 2x - 5$$
$$y = -3x + 2$$

2. Which graph represents the system: $y = x + 2$, $Y = -x + 5$

A.

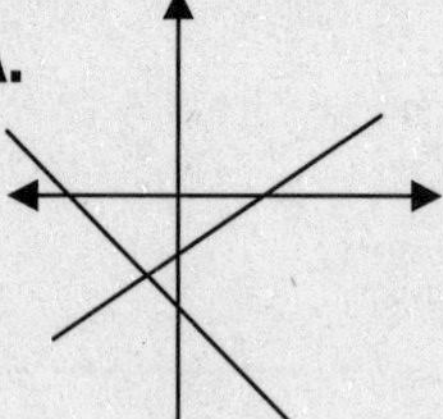

B.

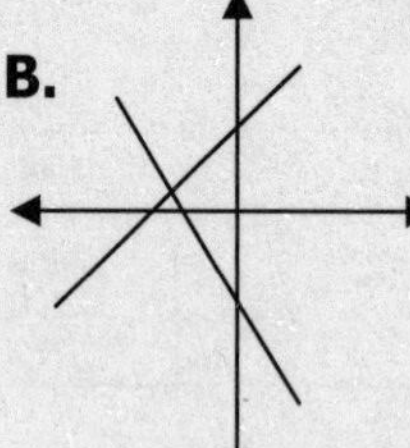

C.

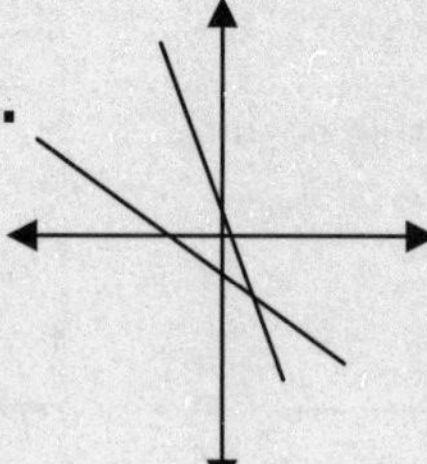

D.

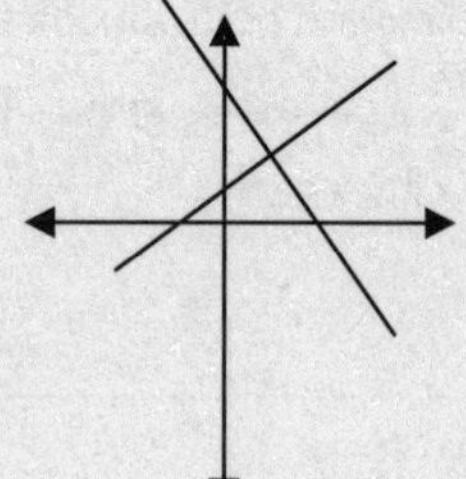

Graphing Systems of Linear Inequalities

1. Graph the following system of inequalities:

$$y > -2x + 1$$
$$y < x - 3$$

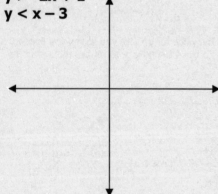

$$y = \frac{2}{3}x - 5$$
$$y = \frac{-1}{2}x + 2$$

Solving Systems of Equations by Graphing

1. Determine the ordered pair solution to the system:

$y = -2x + 5$
$y = 2x - 2$

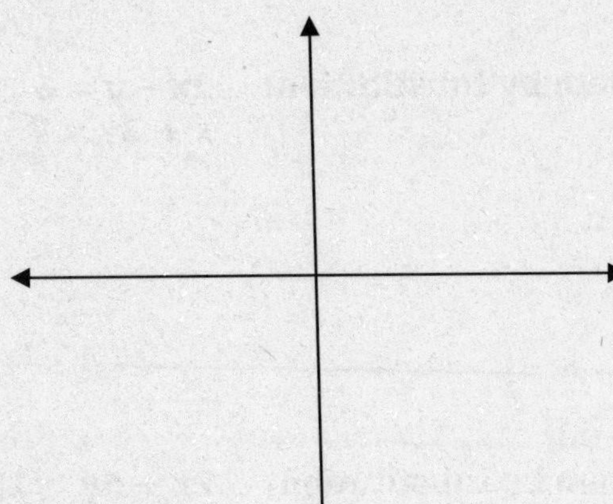

2. Determine the solution to each system.

A. $y = x - 1$
$y = -x + 3$

B. $y = \frac{2}{3}x - 2$
$y = \frac{-1}{3}x + 1$

C. $y = 2x + 2$
$y = -x - 1$

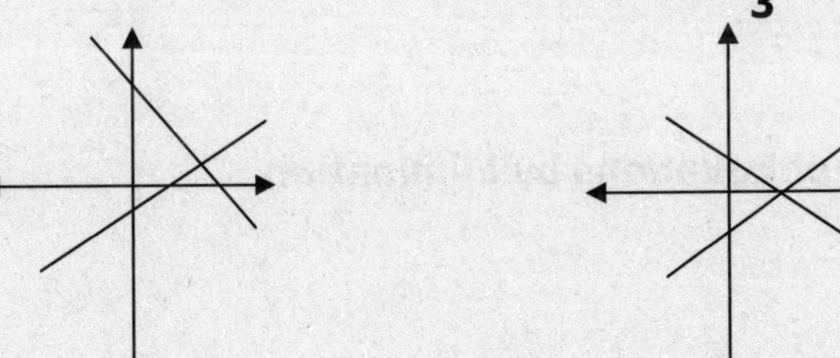

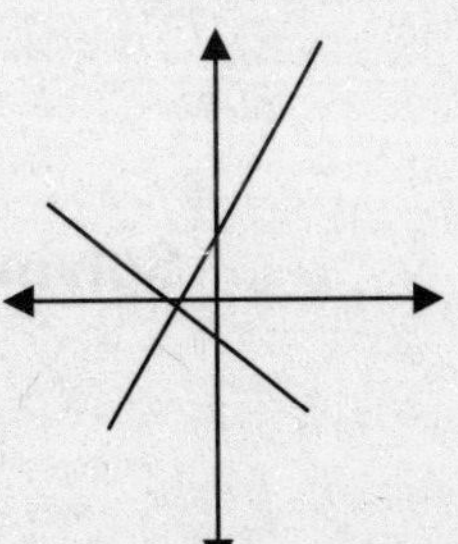

Solving Systems of Inequalities by Graphing

Graph the system: $y > -1x + 2$
$y \leq 2x - 3$

Solving Systems of Equations by Substitution

1. **Solve the system by substitution:** $2x - y = 6$
   $x + 3y = 7$

2. **Solve the system by substitution:** $2x + 5y = 12$
   $5x + 2y = 10$

Solving Systems of Equations by Elimination

1. **Solve the system by elimination:** $4x - y = 6$
   $2x + 5y = 7$

2. **Solve the system by elimination:** $2x + 6y = 5$
   $3x + 4y = 8$

10. Geometry

Geometry, from the Greek *Geo* for earth and *metry* for measure, is the study of shapes. Here we introduce you to some of its basic concepts. Every closed shape has a perimeter, an edge, and an area. Every shape made of straight lines has angles associated with it. The simplest of closed shapes that can be made of straight lines are triangles. At the end of this modules you will learn the Pythagorean Theorem and use it to calculate lengths and distances.

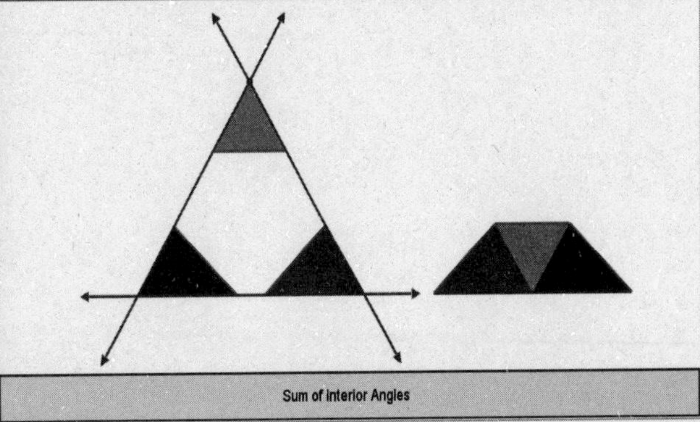

Perimeter is the measure of the distance around the edge of a geometric figure. Whether a square, rectangle, triangle or a polygon (many sided figure), you calculate the perimeter by measuring the length of each side and adding these distances together. Since perimeter is a measure of distance, distance units (like meters or inches) are usually included.

Perimeter

- Rectangle: 2L +2W
- Square: 4s
- Triangle: a + b + c

Perimeter

Perimeter is the total length around the outside of a shape.
For instance, the perimeter of

6cm

4cm 4cm

6cm

is 4cm + 6cm + 4cm + 6cm = 20cm.

Take a "walk" around the above rectangle. Can you see that the perimeter is 2(length + width)? Rectangles can be described by their dimensions. The above rectangle is a "4 by 6" rectangle.

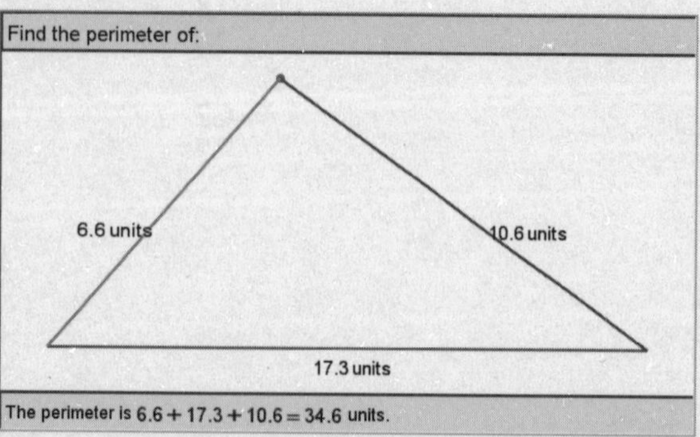

No matter what shape triangle is given, the perimeter is the sum of the lengths of the sides.

Perimeter

Perimeter is the total length around the outside of a shape.

Find the perimeter of:

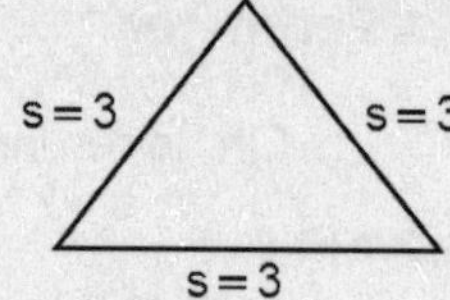

The perimeter is $3 + 3 + 3 = 9$.

The sides of the above triangle are equal. An algebraic way to represent the perimeter of equilateral triangles is **3s**. No units are given in the above example. Does it change the answer if yards or meters are chosen?

To visualize the perimeter of a geometric figure, take a "walk" around the figure, counting the paces (units) as you go.

The number line at the bottom is measuring the distance the red dot moves. Increase **t** with the joystick and watch as the red dot moves around the figure

What distance does the red dot travels from the beginning position to the opposite corner?

How can the distributive property be used to simplify finding the perimeter of a rectangle?

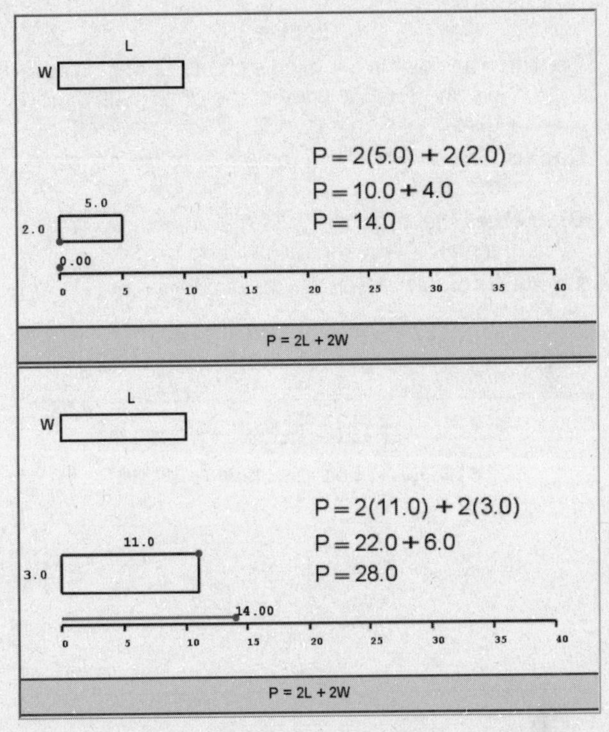

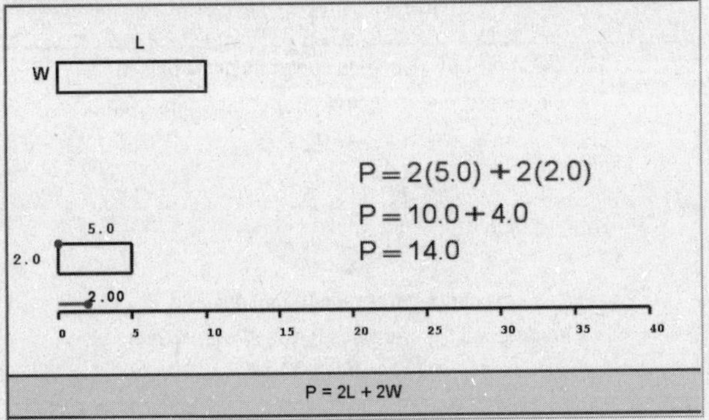

What does the first part or "leg" of the trip correspond to?

If you are half way "home" how much more do you have to go?

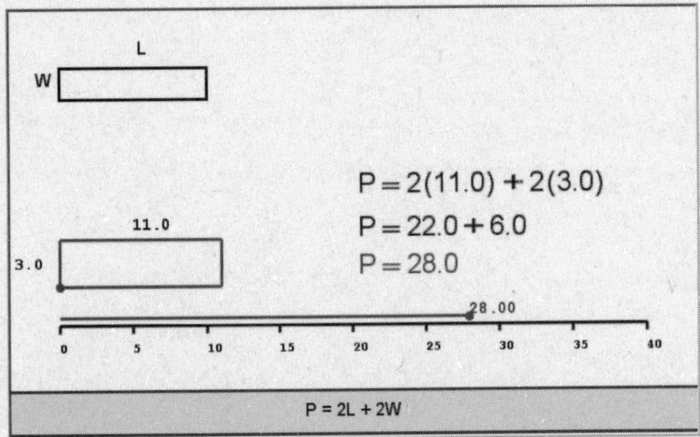

The walk is complete. How many "paces" does it take to walk around the figure?

Circumference

The perimeter of a circle is called the **circumference**. It is the measure of the distance around the outside of a circle. The ratio of the circumference to the diameter is a very special number which is called pi (π), the 16th letter of the Greek alphabet.

π is an irrational number, which is a non-terminating, non-repeating decimal. The decimal approximate for π is 3.14. With computers, mathematicians have calculated π to millions of decimals places.

Circles

Center: The point in the middle of a circle that is equidistant from the edge of the circle in all directions.

Radius: The distance from the center to the edge of the circle.

Diameter: The distance across the circle through the center. Twice the radius.

Circumference: The distance around a circle.

π is an irrational number.
That means it has a non-repeating decimal.
The first few digits of π are:
3.141592653589793238...
π is commonly approximated as 3.14.
When asked for an exact answer, please use π (read as pi).
When asked for an approximate answer, please use 3.14.

π has a special relationship with circles.
It is the ratio of the circumference to the diameter.

Circumference = C (d) $\pi = \frac{C}{d}$

Any circle, no matter how large or small has the same ratio of the circumference to the diameter. Try it!

The perimeter of a circle is called its circumference.
The circumference of a circle depends on its radius.

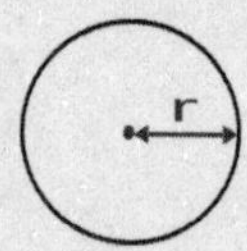

The circumference of a circle is $2\pi r$.
For instance, if the radius is 3, the circumference is:
$2\pi(3) = 6\pi \approx 18.84$

Once the radius is known you can calculate the circumference from the ratio for π. **$C=2\pi r$** is the usual formula for the circumference of a circle.

The diameter of a circle is equal to $2r$.

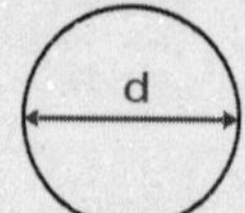

The circumference of a circle can also be written as πd.
For instance, if the diameter is 6, the circumference is:
$\pi(6) = 6\pi \approx 18.84$

The formula for the circumference can be written as either

$c= 2\pi r$ or **$C=\pi d$.**

The **circumference** is the distance around a circle—its perimeter. The visualization is to take a "walk" around the circle, counting the "paces" as you go.

Below, the distance traveled around the circumference is marked off on the number line. Change **t** (time) and follow the red dot as it move around the circumference. The length of the circumference is measured along the number line.

When do you use **radius** and when do you use **diameter** to find circumference? Which is used most often in describing circular objects?

Does it make any difference which you use, the diameter or radius?

What do you need to know to calculate the perimeter of a semi-circle?

What do you get if you divide the circumference by the diameter?

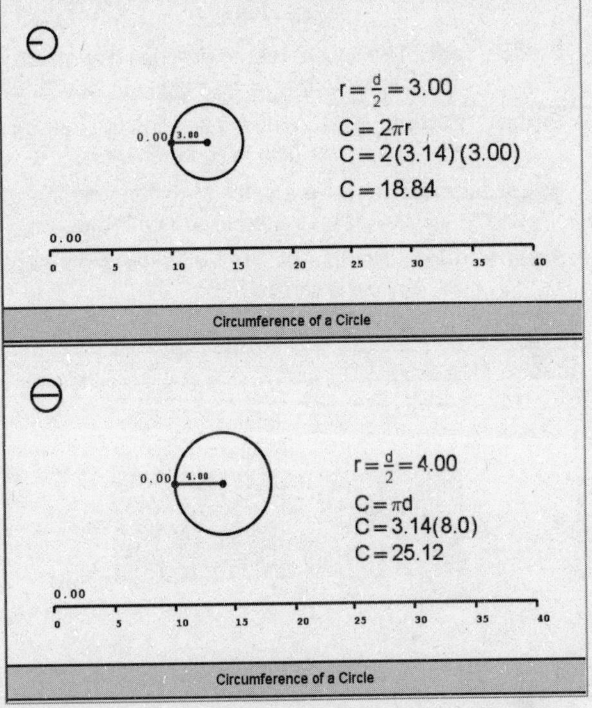

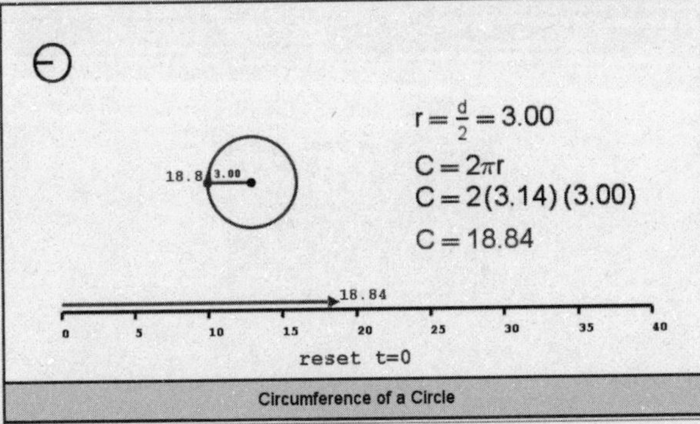

What determines the size of a circle?

In the formula for circumference, what factor stays the same whether you use diameter or radius?

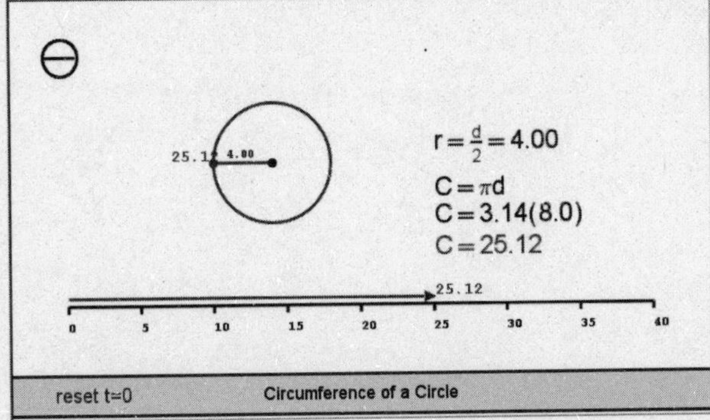

Does the diameter of the circle affect the value of π?

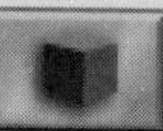

Area of a Rectangle

The **area** of a geometric figure is the amount of surface enclosed by its perimeter. Area is determined by counting up how many unit squares fit inside the figure. For that reason, the measurement units for area are called "square" units (feet, inches, meters, centimeters, etc.).

Find the area of a rectangle by multiplying its length times its width.

Area Units

Square feet: Use square feet to describe how much carpet to buy or how big your house is.

Square meters: Measure how much sod to plant for the soccer field in square meters.

Square inches: How big a patch to fix the hole in the quilt is measured in square inches.

Square miles: Measure the size of the flood damage by using square miles.

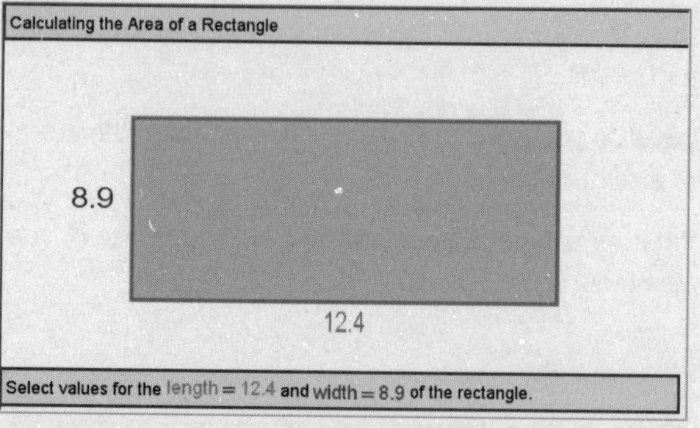

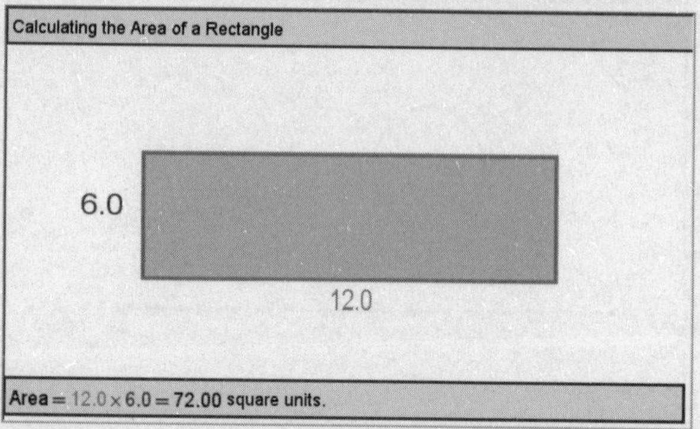

Attach the units as appropriate. The above rectangle will require 72 square units to cover the surface.

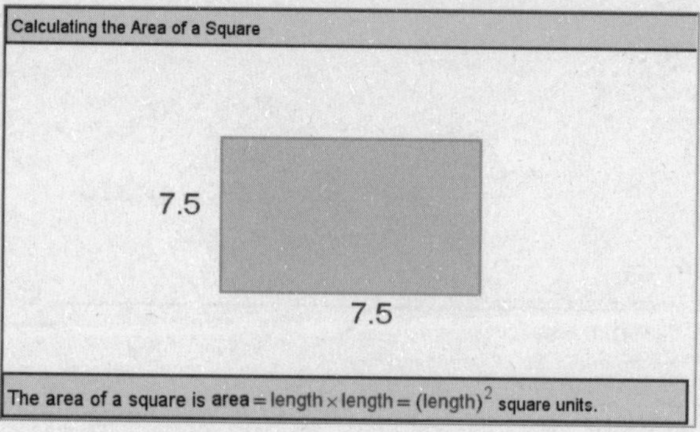

Calculating the Area of a Square
7.5
7.5
The area of a square is area = length × length = (length)² square units.

Sometimes you will see the area of a square formula written as either $\mathbf{A = s^2}$ or $\mathbf{A = l^2}$.

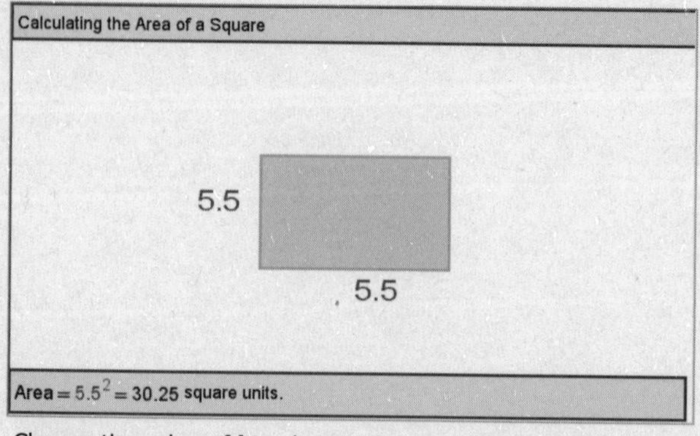

Change the value of **l** to change the size of the square.

You have seen this concept many times, as we have described multiplication as unit squares arranged in a rectangle. To find area using this visualization multiplying the length and width of each side. The total number of unit squares that fill the rectangular area represent the number of square units.

What affect do the units have on the area product?

How does the concept change for finding the area of a square?

If you double the length will you double the area?

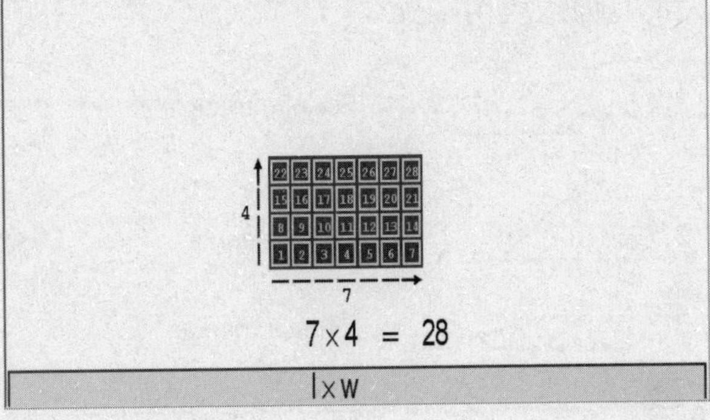

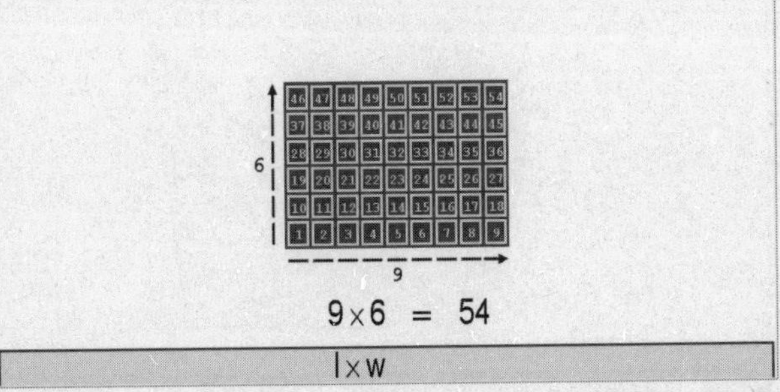

How does changing the size of the rectangle change the area?

Area of a Triangle

EnableMath

In order to calculate the area of a triangle, the length of the **base** and **height** of the triangle must be known. The height is found by measuring the distance from the top of the triangle to the base. Once the height is found, you can envision a rectangle with the **height** as length and the **base** as width. The area of the triangle is

$$A = \frac{1}{2}bh$$

The height of a Triangle

1. Scalene triangle
2. Right Triangle
3. Obtuse triangle

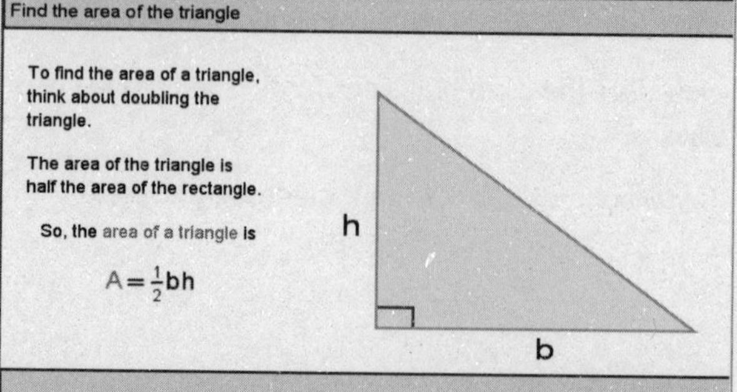

Find the area of the triangle
To find the area of a triangle, think about doubling the triangle.
The area of the triangle is half the area of the rectangle.
So, the area of a triangle is
$A=\frac{1}{2}bh$
h
b

Find the area of the triangle

To find the area of a triangle, think about doubling the triangle, so that a rectangle is formed.

The area of the triangle is half the area of the rectangle.

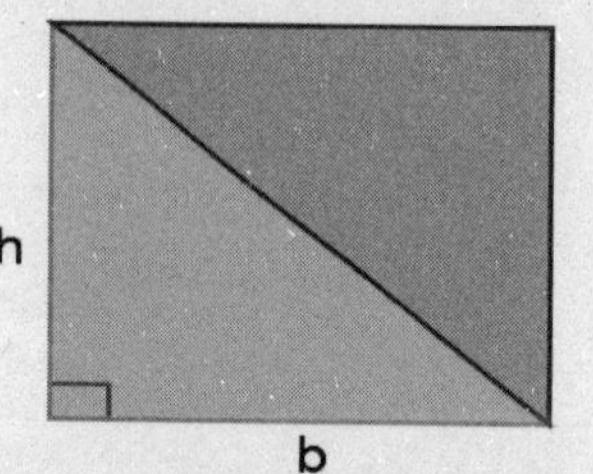

h
b

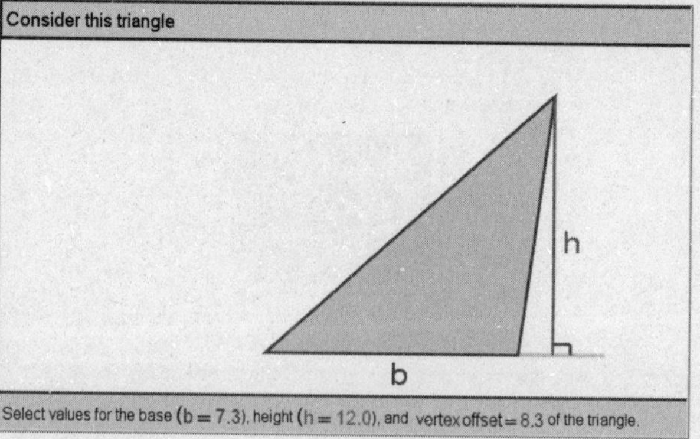

Consider this triangle
h
b
Select values for the base (b = 7.3), height (h = 12.0), and vertex offset = 8.3 of the triangle.

Once the triangle is doubled, the height becomes the length and the base becomes the width. The area of the triangle is 1/2 the area of the rectangle.

Draw additional lines until the triangle looks like a rectangle, with the height the same as the length, as below, left.

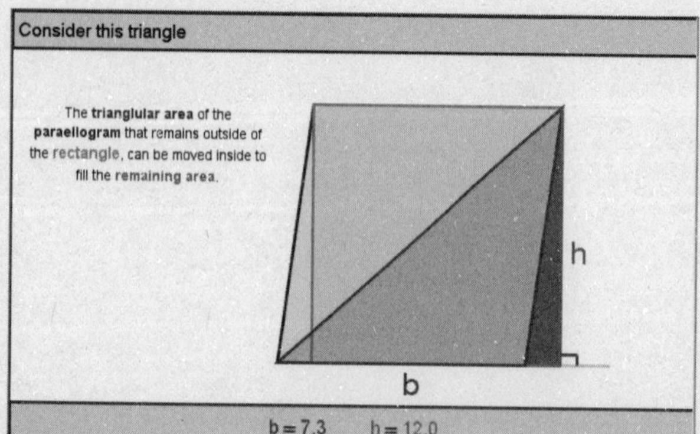

Consider this triangle
The triangular area of the paraellogram that remains outside of the rectangle, can be moved inside to fill the remaining area.
h
b
b = 7.3 h = 12.0

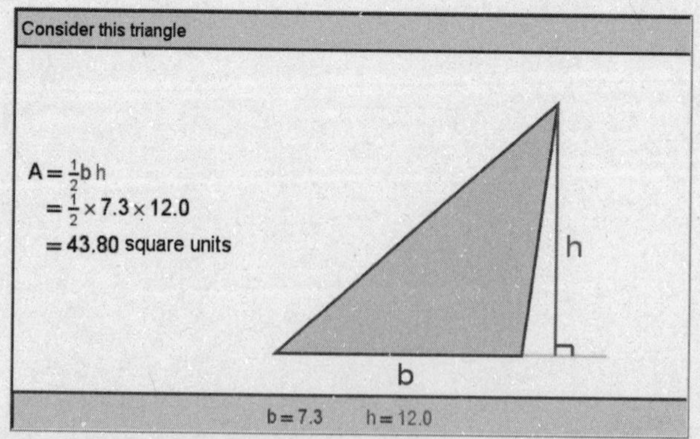

Consider this triangle
$A=\frac{1}{2}bh$
$=\frac{1}{2}\times 7.3\times 12.0$
$=43.80$ square units
h
b
b = 7.3 h = 12.0

The height is equal to the length and the base is the width. The area of the triangle is 1/2 the area of the rectangle.

The area A of the triangle is **A=½bh**.

To find the **area** of a triangle, visualize the triangle inside a rectangle. The area of the triangle is exactly 1/2 the area of the rectangle, no matter what shape the triangle takes.

This seems obvious for a right triangle (bottom), but it does not seem obvious for other types. You can change the form of this triangle by moving the vertex back and forth. Investigate and you can see that the formula **Area=1/2(base)(height)** holds true for all triangles.

How does changing the shape of a triangle by moving the triangle's vertex horizontally affect the area?

If the height and base are the same, will changing the position of the vertex change the area?

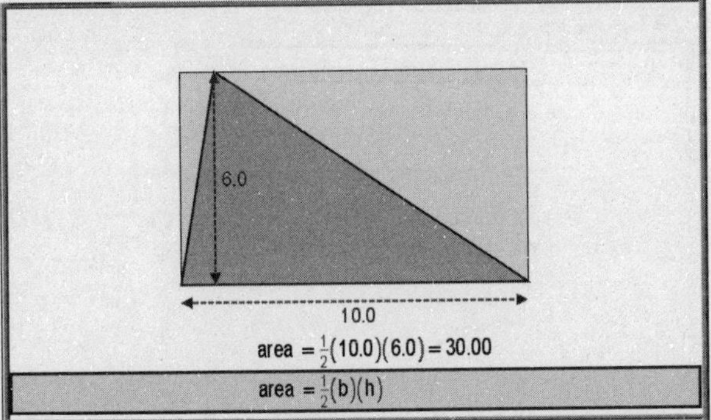

Can every triangle fit into a corresponding rectangle? What happens to the **height** as the shape changes?

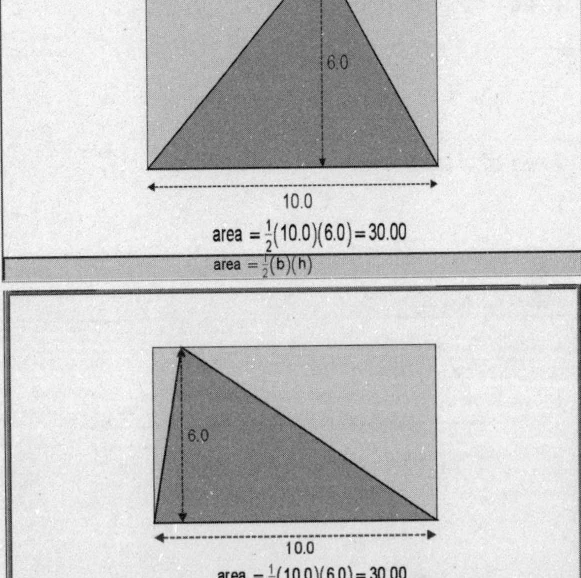

What is the area of the rectangle? Is the area of the triangle equal to half that amount?

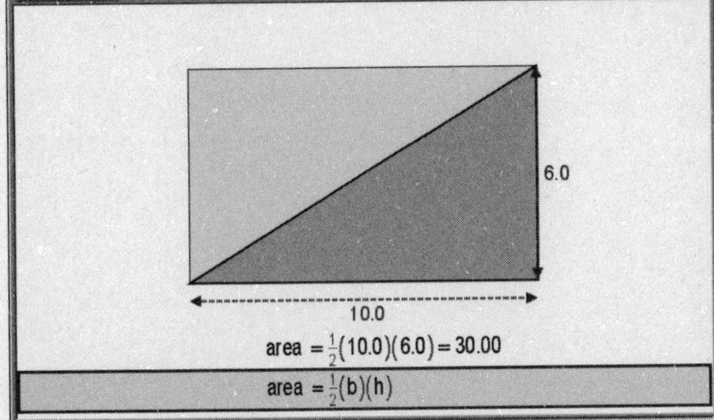

This is a right triangle — the area formula is easiest to see here. Change **b** and **h** to change the size of the triangle.

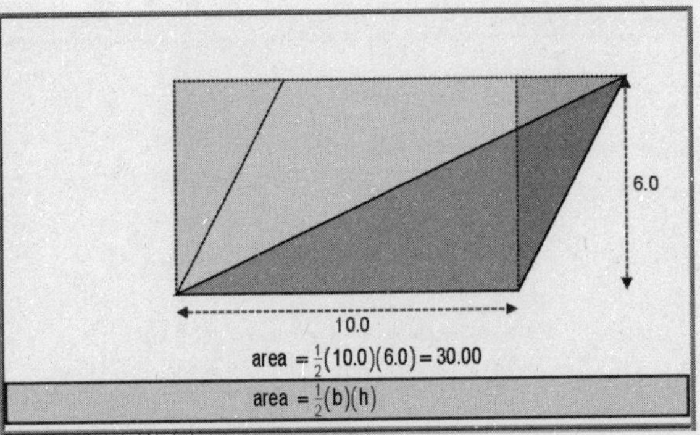

Is the formula true even for this triangle? Notice that the height is taken outside the perimeter.

Area of Parallelograms & Trapezoids

EnableMath

Parallelograms and Trapezoids are **quadrilaterals**, like rectangles they all have four sides.

Parallelograms are like rectangles except that their corners are not square (right angles). They are called parallelograms because their opposite sites are parallel to each other.

Trapezoids have two parallel sides, their other two sides can be any length.

Area of a parallelogram: $A = bh$

Area of a trapezoid: $A = \frac{1}{2}(b_1 + b_2)h$

Consider this parallelogram:

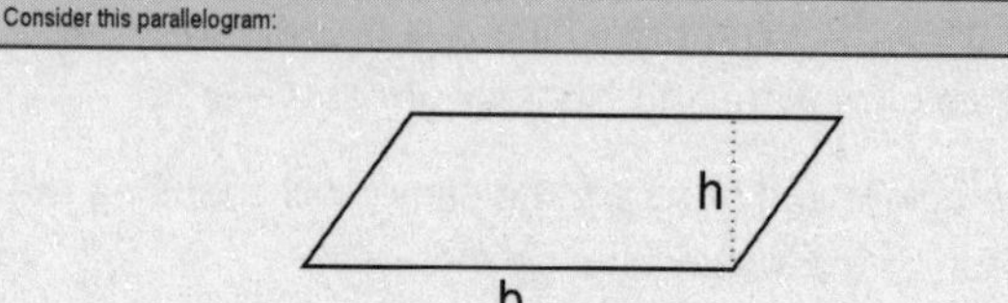

Because of the properties of parallelograms,

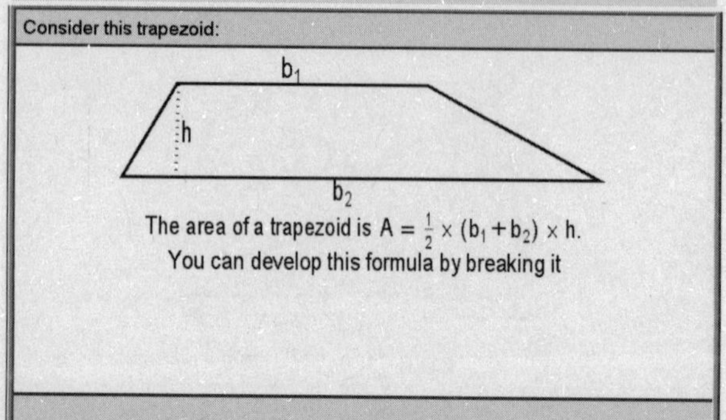

Consider this trapezoid:
b1
h
b2
The area of a trapezoid is A = 1/2 × (b1 + b2) × h.
You can develop this formula by breaking it

Once the figure is rearranged we can see that it forms a rectangle. Since the area of a rectangle is **lw**, the area of a parallelogram is **bh**, where **b** is the width and **h** is the length.

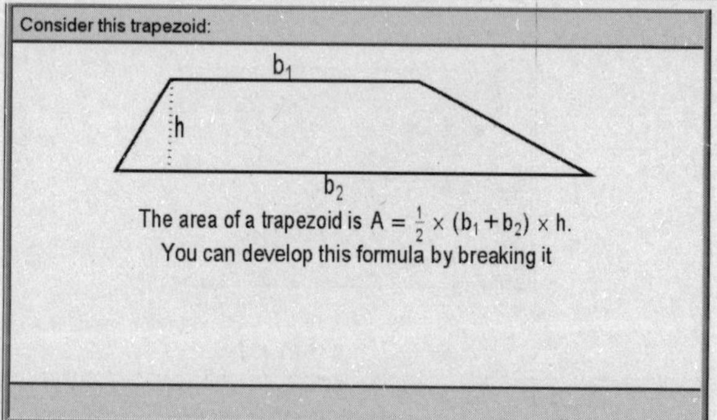

Consider this trapezoid:
b1
h
b2
The area of a trapezoid is A = 1/2 × (b1 + b2) × h.
You can develop this formula by breaking it

Increase the length of the top side b_1 by b_2. Similarly add the length of the top side b_1 to the bottom side b_2, so that the top and bottom sides are now equal in length (b_1+b_2). The lengths of these parallel sides will resemble a parallelogram. Since the parallel sides are now doubled, we divide that length by 2 and multiply by the height.

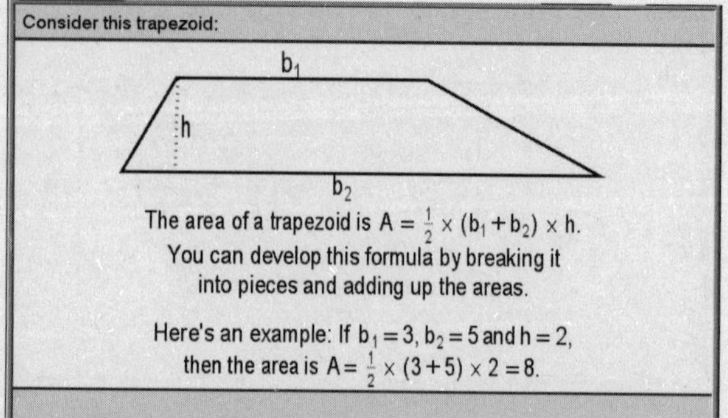

Consider this trapezoid:
b1
h
b2
The area of a trapezoid is A = 1/2 × (b1 + b2) × h.
You can develop this formula by breaking it
into pieces and adding up the areas.
Here's an example: If b1 = 3, b2 = 5 and h = 2,
then the area is A = 1/2 × (3 + 5) × 2 = 8.

Once both bases and the height are known, substitute their values into the formula and use order of operations to simplify.

Breaking shapes into simpler components is sometimes necessary so that area and perimeter can be measured. In the visualizations below, the parallelograms are rearranged so that the triangle section from one side (dark lines) is appended to the other side (light lines) so that a rectangle is formed. The trapezoids are outlined in a dark line while the attached upside down figure is in a light outline.

Both visualizations are dynamic, investigate through selecting values for $\mathbf{b_1}$, $\mathbf{b_2}$, and **h**.

Do you see one parallelogram or two? Which is the original?

Does it make a difference in finding the area?

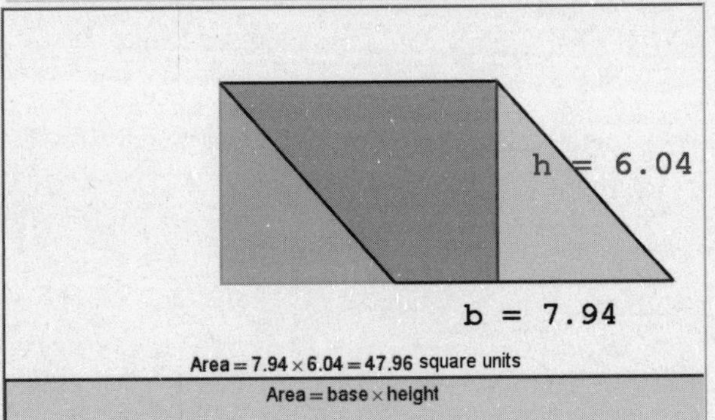

What determines the size of the triangle portion to be "rearranged"? How does the size of the base angles affect area?

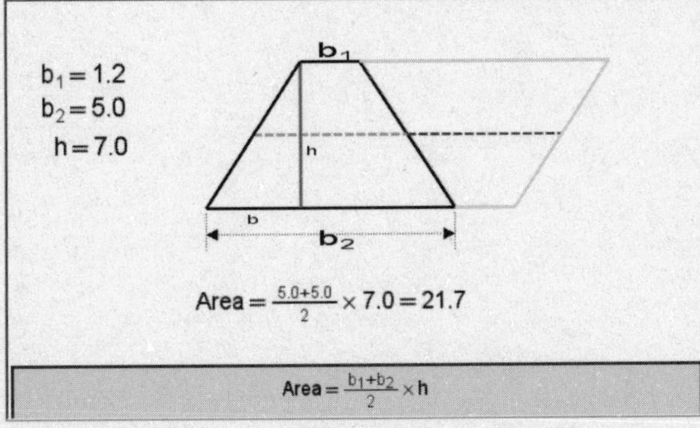

Once the bases and height are known, how can you put that information to use in finding the area?

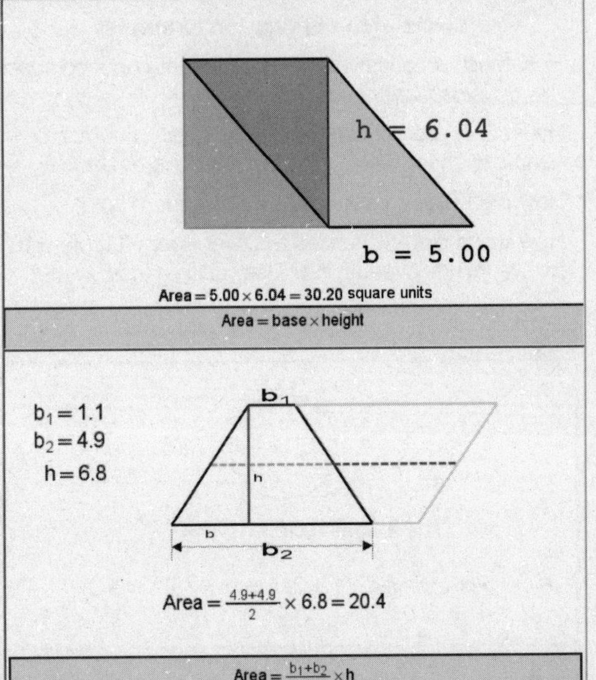

Notice the "shadow" trapezoid? Once the shadow is turned upside-down and attached, what's the base of the new parallelogram?

Area of a Circle

EnableMath

The area of a circle depends upon the irrational number pi (π).

The formula for area of a circle is: $A = \pi r^2$

Circle area application examples

How much area is available to store data on a compact disk? Use square centimeters.

How much ground can a sprinkler soak if the rotator head can shoot water 12 feet? Use square feet.

How many paint cans can fit into a square box?

How much cloth is needed to cover a round table with twelve inches overlapping? Use square yards.

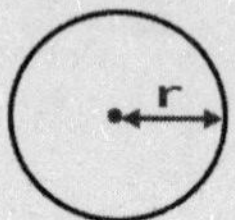

The area of a circle is $A = \pi r^2$.

For example, if $r = 3$, $A = \pi \times (3)^2 = 9\pi$.

Square the area and then multiply by 3.14. Remember to attach the appropriate square units as needed.

π is an irrational number.
That means it has a non-repeating decimal.
The first few digits of π are:
3.141592653589793238...
π is commonly approximated as 3.14.
When asked for an exact answer, please use π (coded as pi).
When asked for an approximate answer, please use 3.14.

The formula for the area of a circle is $\mathbf{A = \pi r^2}$, where **r** is the radius of the circle.

Use the joystick to change the length of the radius. Watch the area of the circle get larger as **r** increases, and decrease as the length of **r** decreases.

If you double the radius, do you double the area?

Can you find the area of a circle if you know its diameter?

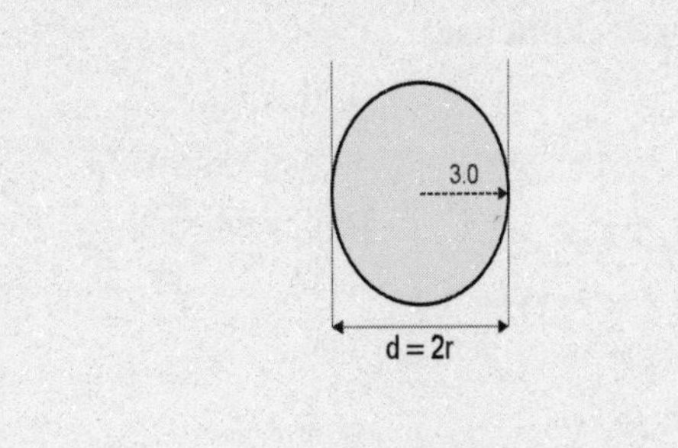

Area $= \pi(3.0)^2 = 28.27$

Area $= \pi(1.0)^2 = 3.14$

What part of the circle determines the size of the area? Is 1/3 the radius the same as 1/3 the area?

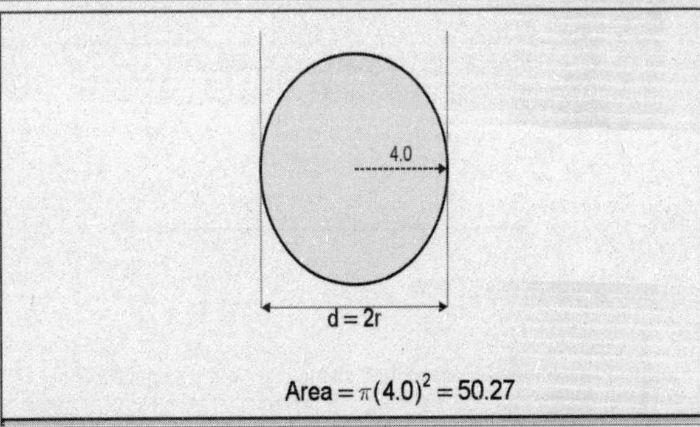

If the radius increases by 1 unit, how will that change the area?

Classifying Angles

Building vocabulary is an important step in understanding any concept in any field of study, job, or career situation. Understanding the meaning of words like "acute angle" or "supplementary angle" are key to being able to make use of geometric concepts.

Vocabulary check list

- ✓ Ray
- ✓ Vertex
- ✓ Angle
- ✓ Degree
- ✓ Acute angle
- ✓ Right angle
- ✓ Obtuse angle
- ✓ Straight angle
- ✓ Complementary
- ✓ Supplementary

A half-line like this is called a ray.

An angle is formed when two rays meet.

Angles can be measured in degrees.
There are 360° in an entire circle.

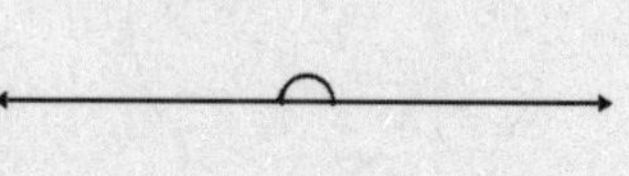

That means there are 180° in a half-circle or straight line.

Each degree is 1/360. Angles are measures in degrees depending on how much of the circle they take up.

Angles are classified according to how big they are.

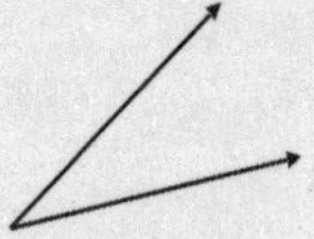

90° angles are called right.

Angles less than 90° are called acute.

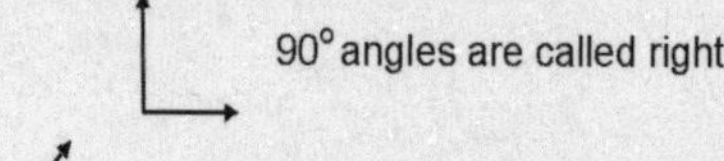

Angles greater than 90° are called obtuse.

These are the three types of angles and all angles fall into one of the three categories.

Complementary Angles

Two angles are called complementary if they can be put together to make a right (90°) angle.
For instance, the complement of a 20° angle is:

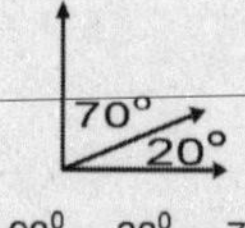

$90^0 - 20^0 = 70^0$.

If you know that two angles are complementary, and you know one of them, subtract from 90° to find the other one.

Supplementary Angles

Two angles are called supplementary if they can be put together to make a (180°) angle.
For instance, the supplement of a 20° angle is:

160° 20°

$180^0 - 20^0 = 160^0$.

If two angles are supplementary and you know one, subtract from 180° to get the other one.

Visualize angles like the hands on an analog clock. One hour is a complete circle of the minute hand, 360°. 15 minutes corresponds to 15 degrees, 1/4 of the circle; 1/2 hour is a straight angle or line and so on. What has to happen in order for the clock analogy to represent measurement of angles?

If the little hand is on three and the minute hand is on six, how many degrees is indicated?

What time is it at angle 0?

If you know two angles are complementary, and you know one of them, what do you do to find the other one?

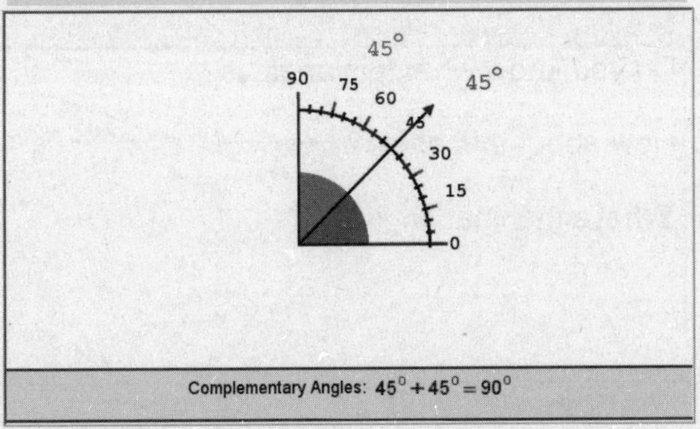

Complementary Angles: $45^\circ + 45^\circ = 90^\circ$

Notice that the end of an angle is called the vertex. Measure the angle beginning at 0 and turning counter-clockwise.

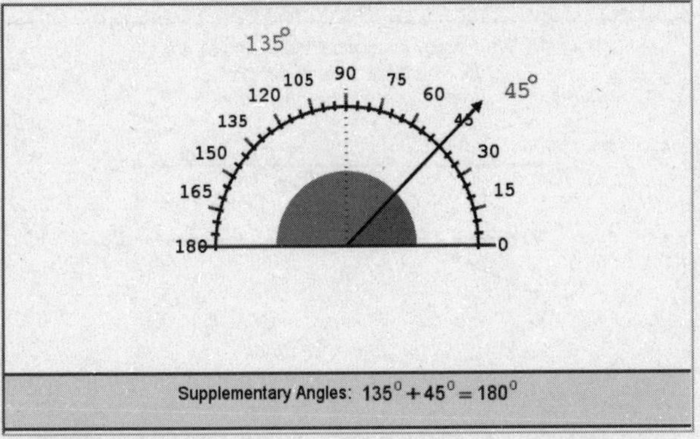

Supplementary Angles: $135^\circ + 45^\circ = 180^\circ$

Will supplementary angles always have one acute angle and one obtuse angle?

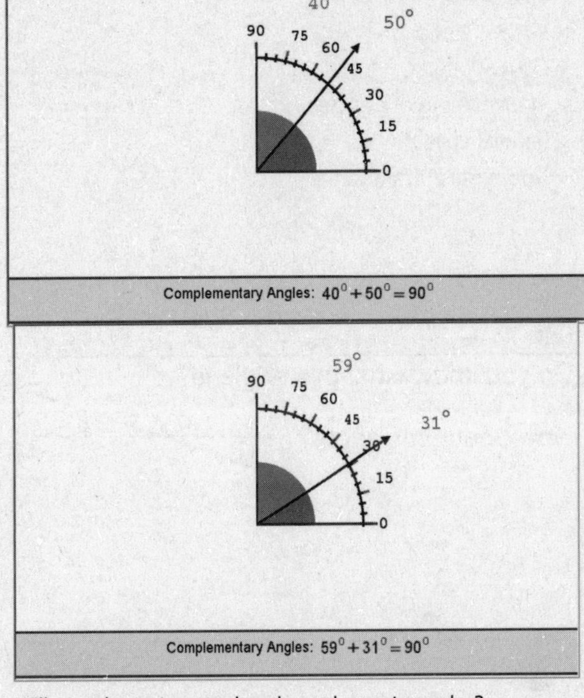

Complementary Angles: $40^\circ + 50^\circ = 90^\circ$

Complementary Angles: $59^\circ + 31^\circ = 90^\circ$

Will complementary angles always be acute angles?

Intersecting Lines and Angles

Now that we can classify angles and know the difference between complementary and supplementary angles, we can apply this knowledge to situations involving intersecting and parallel lines. Intersecting lines form a set of **vertical angles**. Two parallel lines crossed by a non-parallel line, or **transversal**, form two sets of corresponding vertical angles. If we know any one of the angle measures, we can use it to find all of the missing angle measures.

More vocabulary...

- ✔ Vertical angles
- ✔ Corresponding angles
- ✔ Alternate interior angles
- ✔ Parallel lines
- ✔ Non-parallel transversal

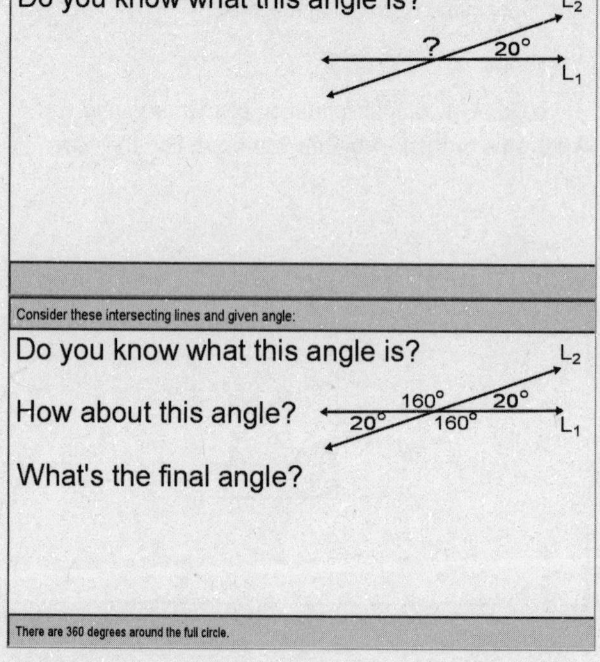

Consider these intersecting lines and given angle:
Do you know what this angle is?
L2
?
20°
L1
Consider these intersecting lines and given angle:
Do you know what this angle is?
How about this angle?
What's the final angle?
L2
160°
20°
20°
160°
L1
There are 360 degrees around the full circle.

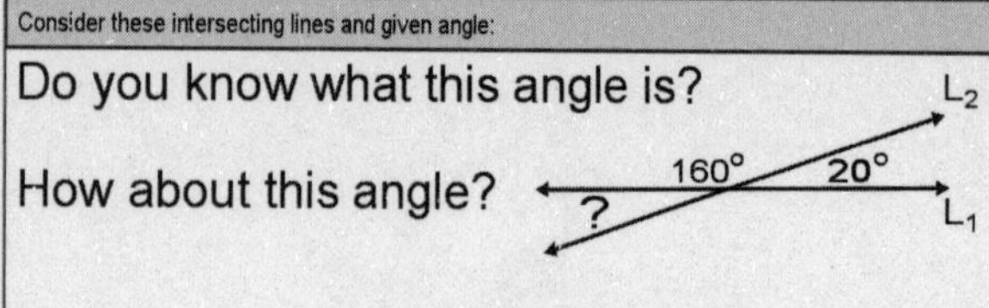

Consider these intersecting lines and given angle:
Do you know what this angle is?
How about this angle?
L2
160°
20°
?
L1

The first two angles are supplementary on L1. The new unknown angle is supplementary to angle 160° on L2.

Notice that the intersecting lines form two sets of equivalent angles called *vertical* angles.

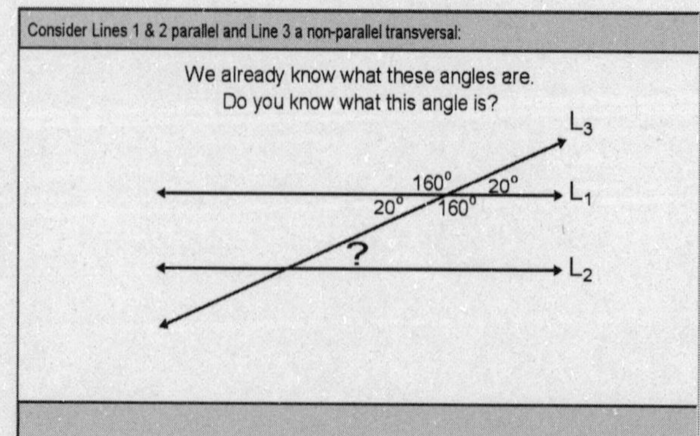

The unknown angle is equivalent to its corresponding angle—the angle in the same position. It is also equal to its alternate interior angle—the other 20° angle in the figure above.

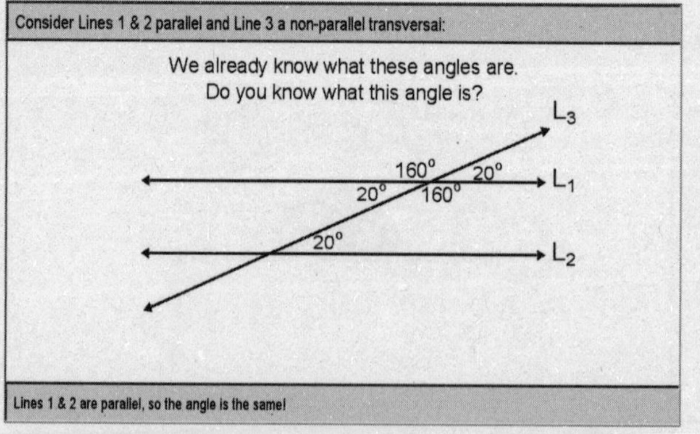

Consider Lines 1 & 2 parallel and Line 3 a non-parallel transversal:
We already know what these angles are.
Do you know what this angle is?
L3
160°
20°
L1
20°
160°
20°
L2
Lines 1 & 2 are parallel, so the angle is the same!

Once we know one of the angles, we can find all the others.

Two distinct lines can either intersect, forming two pairs of vertical angles, or they can be parallel. If two parallel lines are crossed by another line, two sets of corresponding vertical angles are formed. If the measure of any one of the angles is known, the other angles can be found.

We start out with the definition of an acute angle. You can change this angle to right or to obtuse.

Do intersecting lines always form two acute and two obtuse angles?

How do you know which two angles are equal when two lines intersect?

What's the difference between corresponding angles and vertical angles?

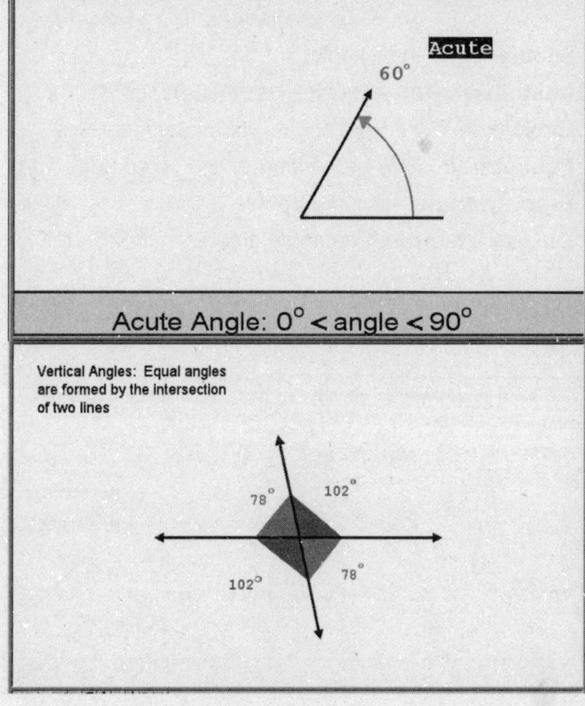

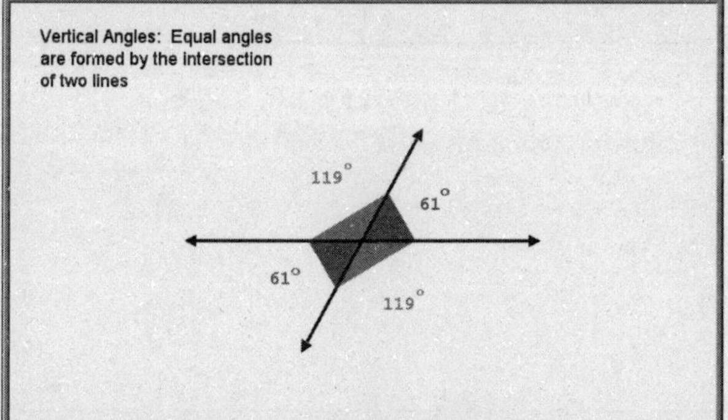

Can you pick out the corresponding angles?

The four angles between the parallel lines are called interior angles. Which pairs of interior angles are equal?

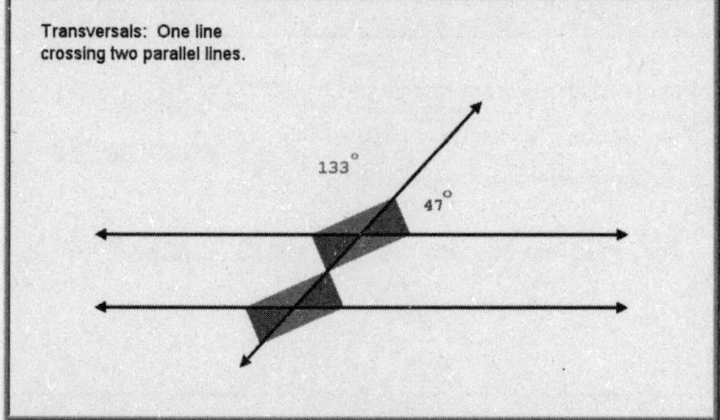

When you have a transversal across two parallel lines are the opposite angles still always equal.

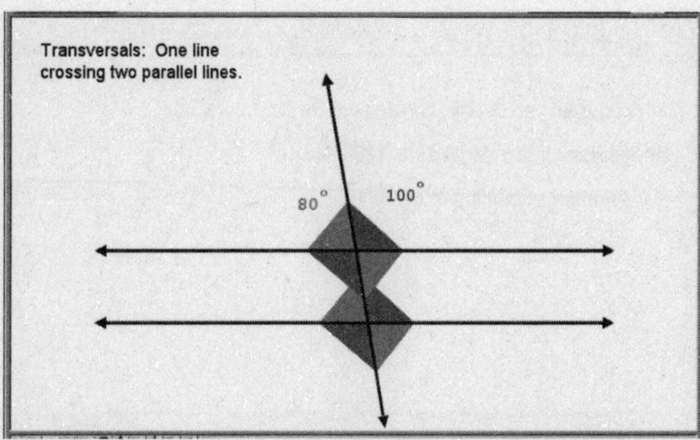

Can you find the value of every angle in this transversal?

Angles of a Triangle

EnableMath

Triangles have three sides and three angles. The sum of the angles of a triangle add to 180°. Triangles can be classified either by the size of their angles or by how many of their angles are the same. Once a triangle is classified, the shape and relative sizes of the angles can be pictured.

Triangle Basics

Scalene: No equal angles

Acute triangle: All angles less than 90°

Isosceles: Two equal angles and two equal sides

Equilateral: Three equal angles and equal sides

Right triangle: One right angle

Obtuse triangle: One angle greater than 90°

One way to classify a triangle is by the size of its interior angles.

If all three of the angles are less than 90°, it's an acute triangle.

If it has a 90° angle, it's a right triangle.

If it has an angle greater than 90°, it's an obtuse triangle.

Another way to classify a triangle is by how many angles are the same.

If all three of the angles are the same, it's called equilateral.

If two of the angles are the same, it's called isosceles.

If none of the angles are the same, it's called scalene.

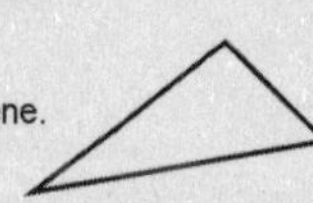

If the description of a triangle is an isosceles right triangle, then I know exactly what kind of triangle I have: A right triangle with two sides the same length and the angles are 45°, 45°, and 90°.

The interior angles of any triangle sum to 180°.

For instance, if two angles are 120° and 40°,

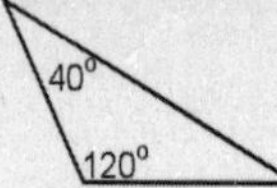

Add the two given angle measures and subtract for 180°.

The interior angles of any triangle sum to 180°.

For instance, if two angles are 120° and 40°,

then the remaining angle is 20°.

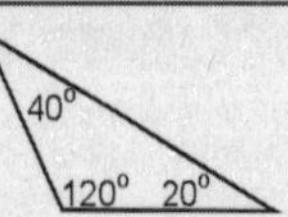

Notice that the largest angle is across from the longest side and the smallest angle is across from the shortest side.

The interior angles of any triangle sum to 180°.

For instance, if two angles are 120° and 40°,

then the remaining angle is 20°.

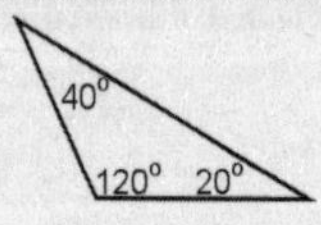

The angles in an equilateral triangle are all 60°, because $\frac{180^\circ}{3} = 60^\circ$.

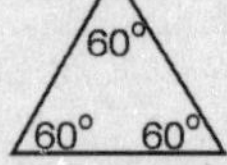

An equilateral triangle can also be called equiangular for obvious reasons.

The sum of the interior angles of a triangle is 180°.

Using that information and some basic vocabulary about triangles, can you describe what an equilateral (equiangular) triangle looks like?

Can you determine the size of one angle of a right triangle if you know that one is 30°?

Can a triangle have more than one obtuse angle?

Can a triangle have more than one right angle?

Can a triangle have three acute angles?

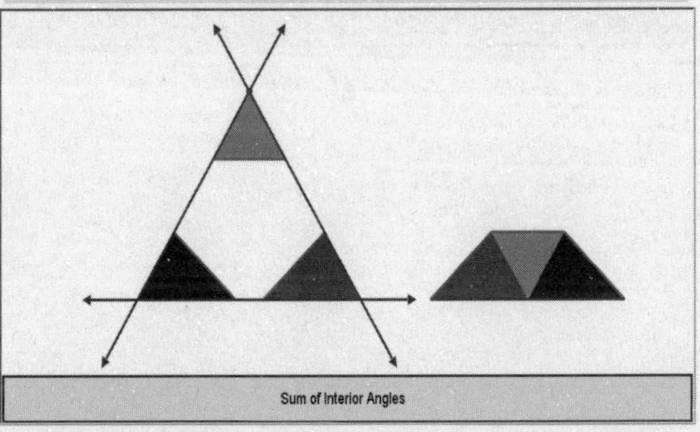

Sum of Interior Angles

If you put the angles together they form a line – 180°. Try it with a paper triangle. Tear off the corners and align the angles. Did you get a straight line?

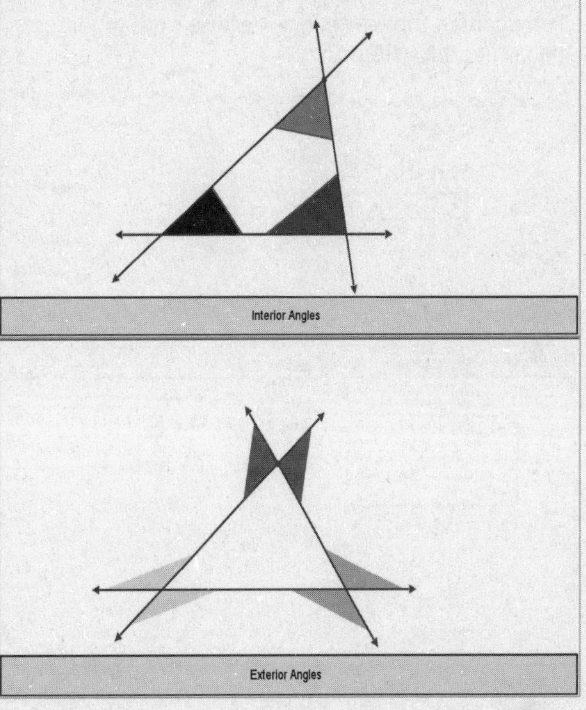

Interior Angles

Exterior Angles

What is the sum of an interior angle and one of its exterior angles?

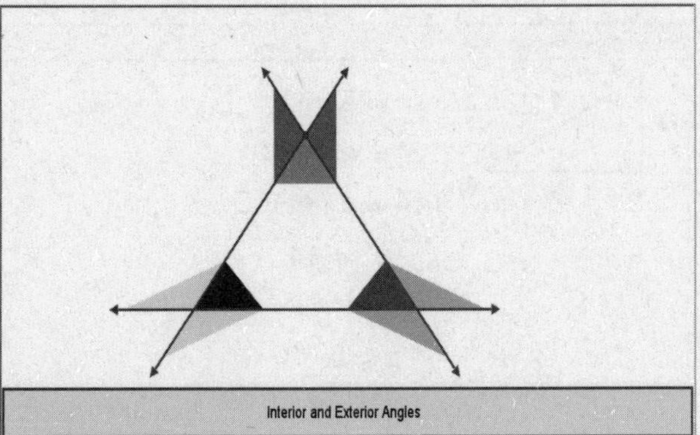

Interior and Exterior Angles

Do we know the missing angles on each corner (vertex)?
What kind of angle is it?

Pythagorean Theorem

EnableMath

The **Pythagorean Theorem** is used to find the measures of the sides of right triangles. It connects the measure of the hypotenuse—the side opposite the right angle—with the other two sides. The Pythagorean Theorem states that $\mathbf{a^2 + b^2 = c^2}$, where **a** and **b** are the length of the sides (or legs) of a triangle and **c** is the hypotenuse. If you know two of the sides of a right triangle, you can substitute and solve for the other side.

Pythagorean triples—triangles whose sides are in proportion to the pattern:

3, 4, 5

3, 8, 10

15, 20, 25

Pythagoras and his followers are credited with proving the following theorem about right triangles in about 500 BC:

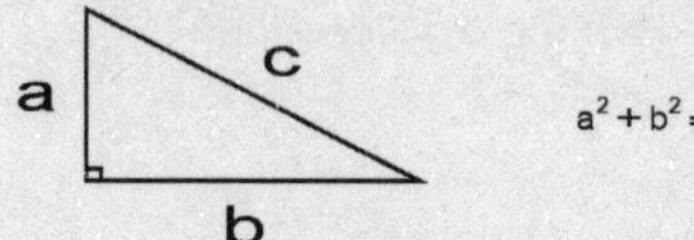

$a^2 + b^2 = c^2$

a and b are called legs or sides.
c, which is opposite the right angle, is called the hypotenuse.

$a^2 + b^2 = c^2$

Find the length of the hypotenuse of this right triangle:

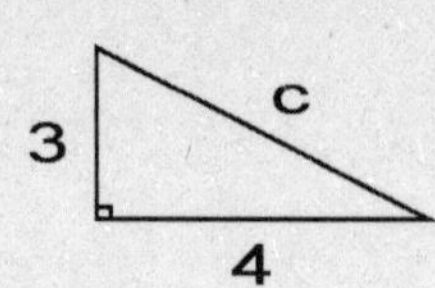

$c^2 = a^2 + b^2$

$c^2 = 3^2 + 4^2$

$c^2 = 9 + 16$

$c^2 = 25$

So, $c = 5$.

c is a length, so it's positive. $a^2 + b^2 = c^2$

Pythagorean triples are always integer values.

Approximate the length of the hypotenuse of this right triangle:

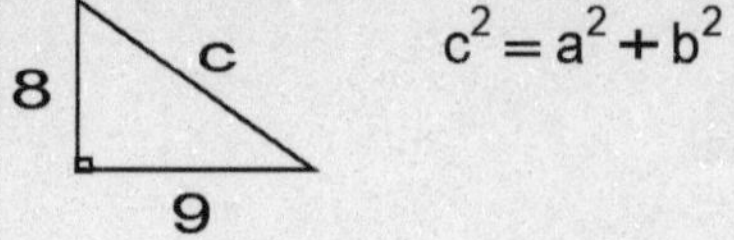

$c^2 = a^2 + b^2$

$a^2 + b^2 = c^2$

What value of **c** makes this a Pythagorean triple?

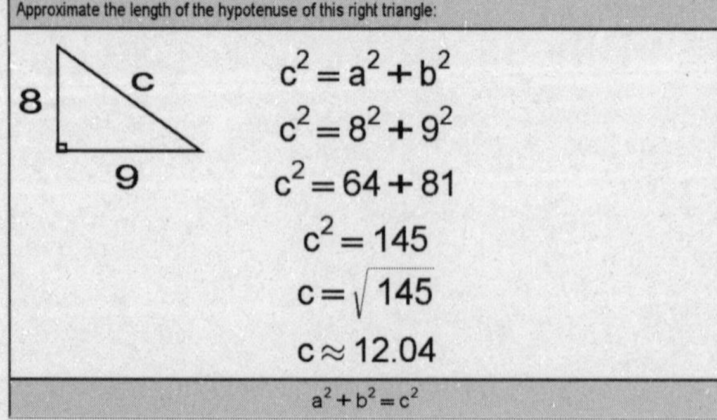

Think of this as a real world problem: You go west 9 miles and then north 8 miles, how far have you traveled from your start?

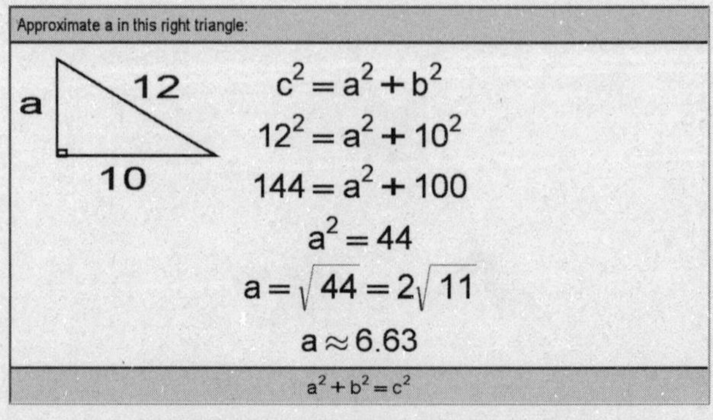

To find the length of **a**, factor the radical and then take the square root of the non-perfect factor.

There are many ways to prove the **Pythagorean Theorem**. Here we show one of them. This is a dynamic visualization of a proof, change the values of **a** and **b** and watch the rectangles and the triangles change.

The proof presented here is in sequence. Go through it point by point. You can change the size of the triangles by changing **a** and **b**. Can you find some Pythagorean triples using the visualizations depicted below?

When you use the Pythagorean Theorem, why do you only need to use the positive square root?

Can you find any other proofs of the Pythagorean Theorem?

What happens if you change the size of one side? Do you have to change the size of each side?

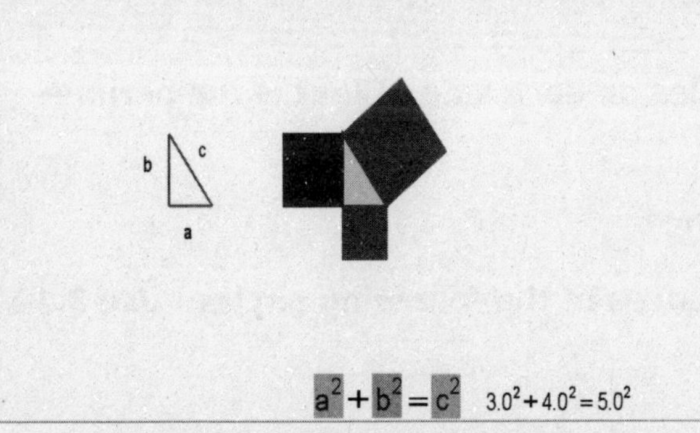

Form a square from each side of the right triangle. If the sides were marked off in units, how many square units would make up the blue (base) square if a=3? How many if side b=4? How many if the hypotenuse is c=5?

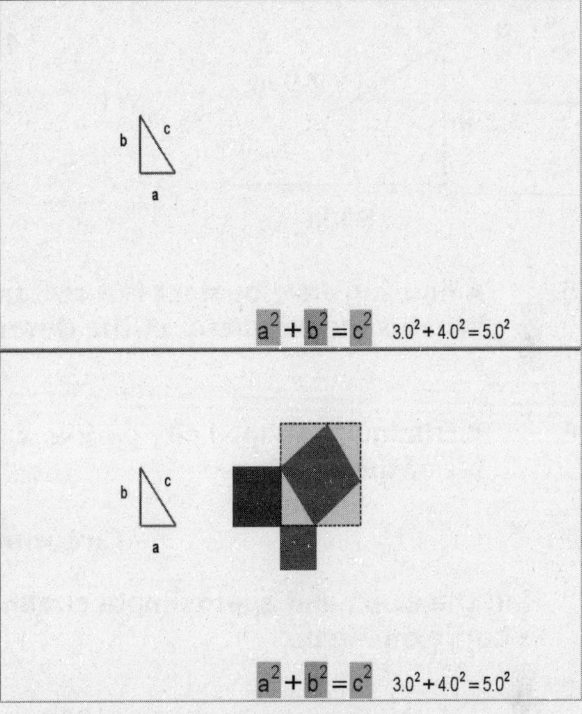

The next step is to augment the hypotenuse square with three more triangles equivalent to the original triangle. Do you see the four triangles that make up the square about the hypotenuse?

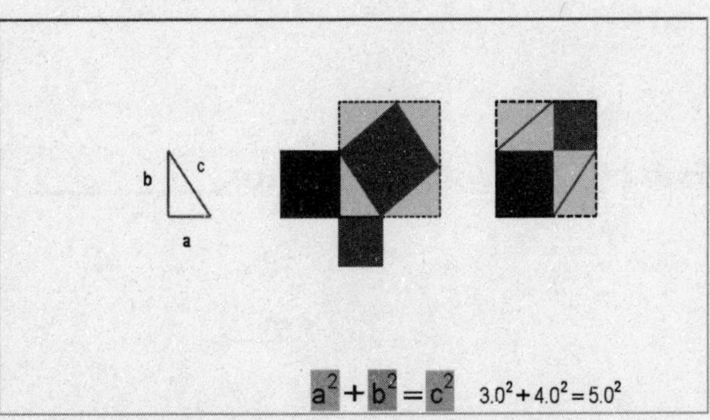

Finally, the side **a** and **b** squares are filled in with four replicas of the triangle forming an equivalent square to the hypotenuse square. What are the equivalent parts?

Perimeter

Find the perimeter of the following figures.

1. **2.**

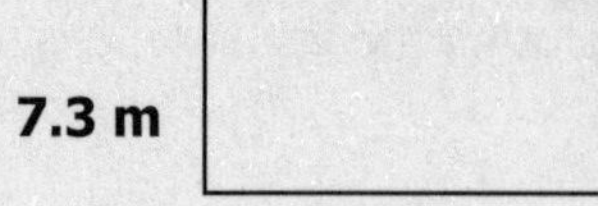

3.

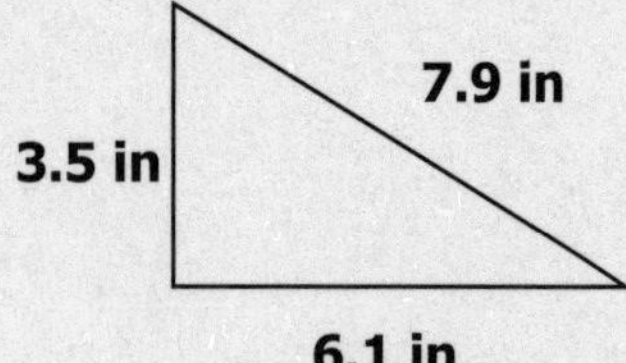

4.

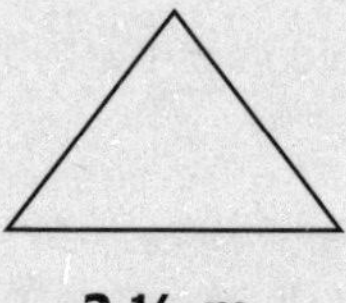

5. **A housing development is a rectangular 4 blocks long and 6 blocks wide. What is the perimeter of the development in blocks?**

6. **A triangular shaped city park is 2.6 miles on each side. What is the perimeter of the park?**

Circumference

Find the exact and approximate circumferences of the following circles. Use 3.14 to approximate pi.

1.

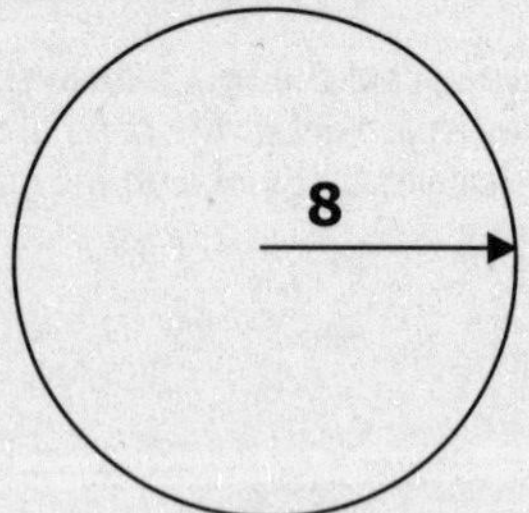

2.

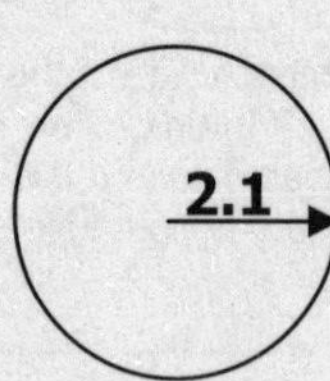

Exact _____ **Approximate** __________ **Exact** _______ **Approximate** __________

3.

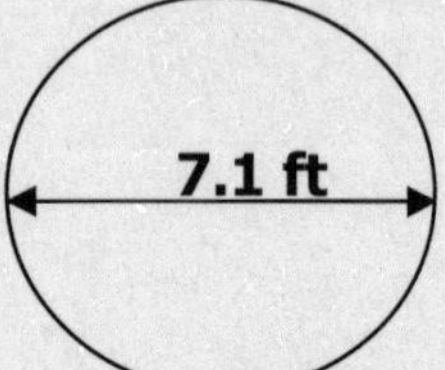

4.

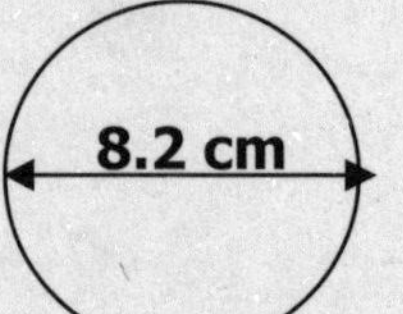

Exact _______ **Approximate** ________ **Exact** ___________ **Approximate** ________

Area of a Rectangle

Find the area of the following figures.

1.

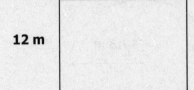

12 m

14 m

2.

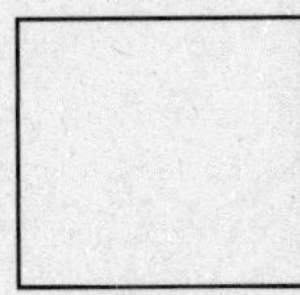

8.2 km

3.

11 in

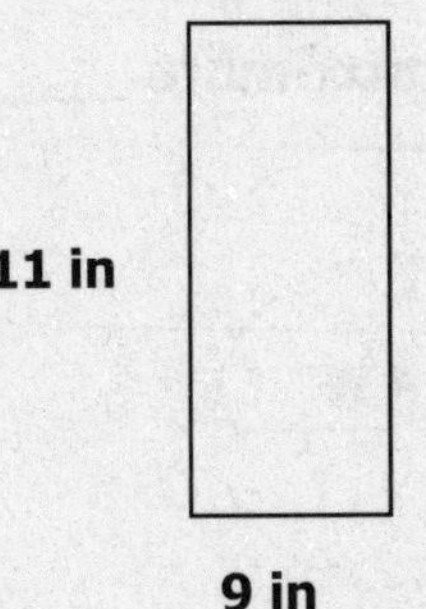

9 in

4.

1.2 ft

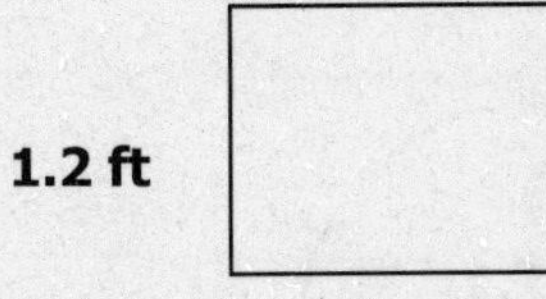

1.7 ft

5. A housing development is a rectangular 4 blocks long and 6 blocks wide. What is the area of the development in blocks?

6. A square shaped city park is 2.6 miles on each side. What is the area of the park?

Area of a Triangle

Find the area of the following triangles.

1.

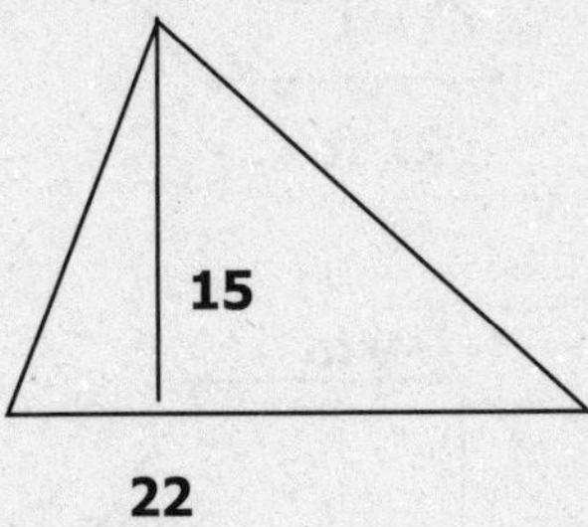

22

2.

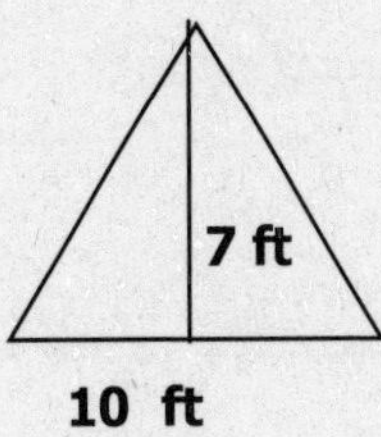

10 ft

3.

6 m

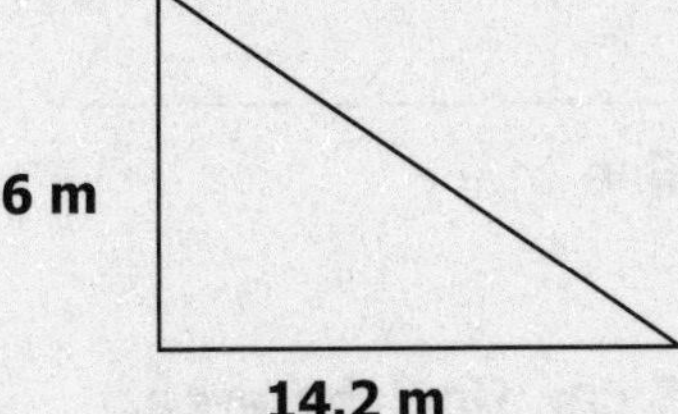

14.2 m

4.

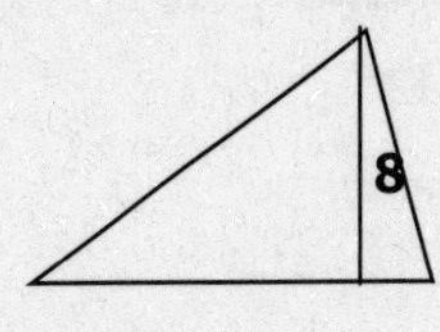

15

5. A triangle has a base of 7.2 cm and a height of 5.3 cm. What is the area of the triangle?

Area of a Circle

Find the exact and approximate areas of the following circles. Use 3.14 to approximate pi.

1.

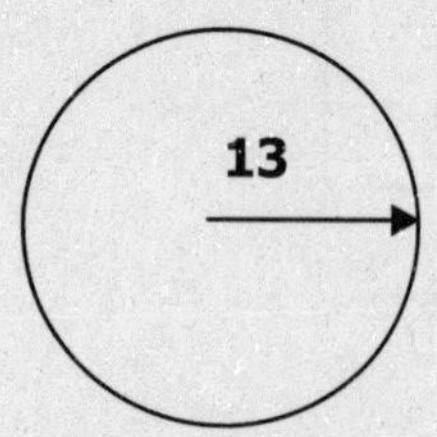

2.

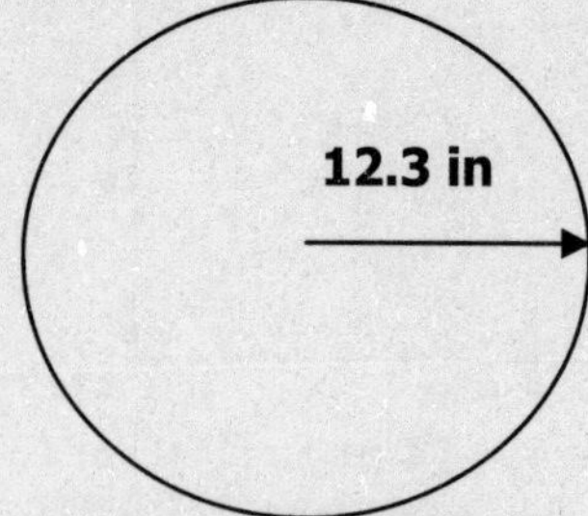

Exact __________Approximate _________ Exact___________ Approximate _________

3.

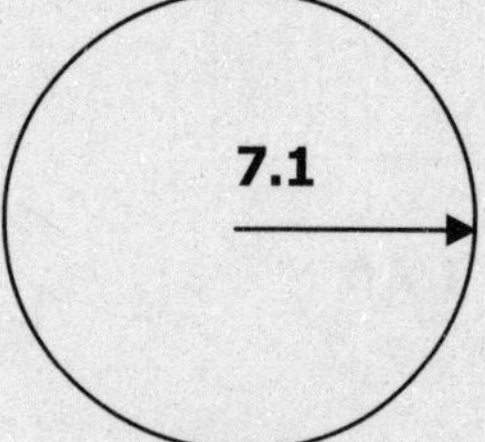

4.

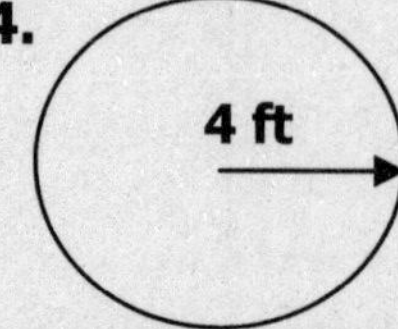

Exact __________Approximate _________ Exact___________ Approximate _________

Area of a Parallelogram & Trapezoid

Find the area of the following figures:

1.

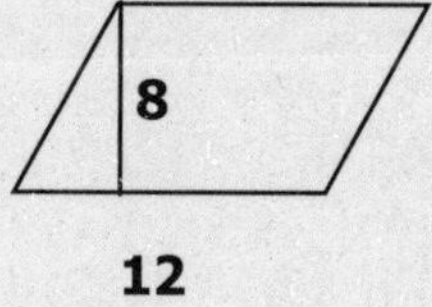

2.

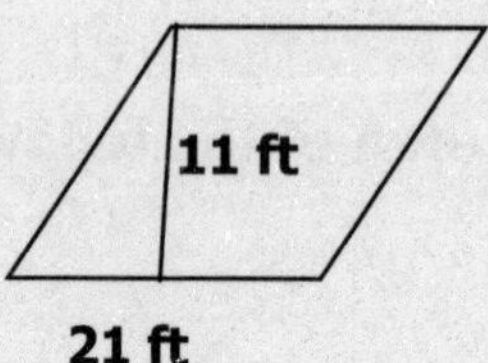

3.

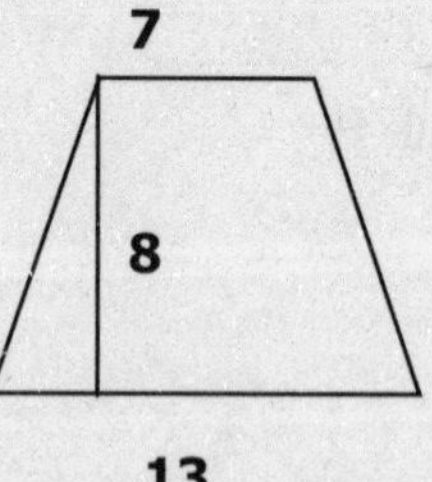

4.

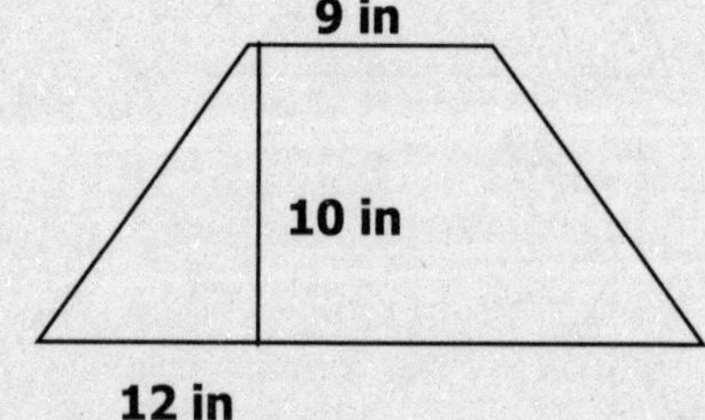

5. A parallelogram of base 11.2 cm and height of 23.5 cm, find the area.

6. A trapezoid has base 1 = 2.3 and base 2 = 5.7 and a height of 3.8. Find the

Classifying angles

Use the following words to fill in the blanks: acute, obtuse, right, straight.

1. **An angle measuring 23º is a _______________ angle.**

2. **An angle measuring 90º is a _______________ angle.**

3. **An angle measuring 91º is a _______________ angle.**

4. **An angle measuring 180º is a _______________ angle.**

5. **Find the complement of an angle that measures 47º. __________.**

6. **Find the supplement of an angle that measures 47º. __________.**

Intersecting Lines and Angles

Fill in the values for all the angle measures.

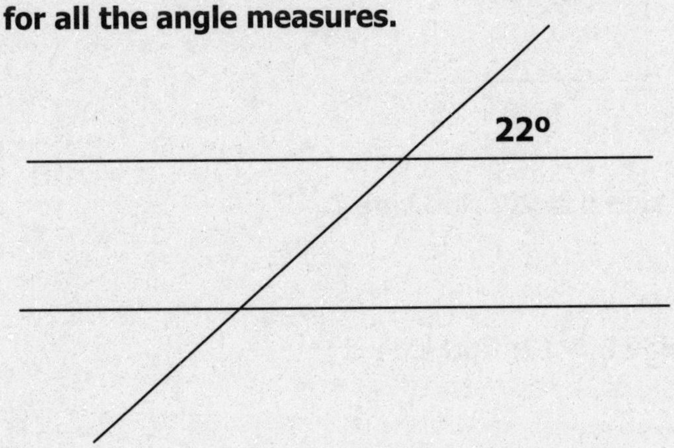

22º

Angles of Triangles

Use the following words to fill in the blanks: acute, obtuse, right.

1. Angles measuring 77º, 75º, 28º make a(n)______________ triangle.

2. Angles measuring 23º, 68º, 89º make a(n) ______________ triangle.

3. Angles measuring 90º, 45º, 45º make a(n) ______________ triangle.

4. Angles measuring 31º, 100º, 49º make a(n) ______________ triangle.

5. Find the third angle of a triangle if two angles are 47º and 52º. __________

6. Find the third angle of a triangle if two angles are 102º and 43º. _________

Pythagorean Theorem

Use the Pythagorean Theorem to find the length of the indicated side. Round to tenths.

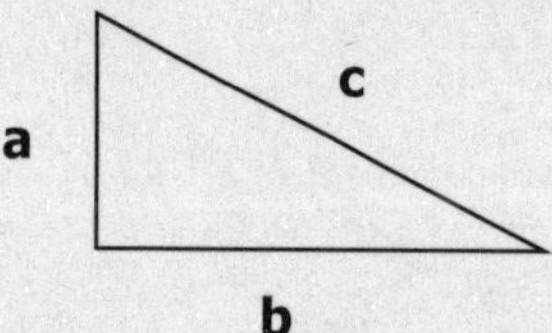

1. Side a = 12 and side b = 20; find side c.

2. Side a = 3 and side b = 12; find side c.

3. Side a = 10 and hypotenuse = 26, find side b.

4. Side b = 8 and hypotenuse = 12, find side b.

11. Polynomials

Thus far, we have been dealing with linear expressions and equations. These monomials have **variables to the first power**. *Nomial* is another word for *term*, and *poly* means *many*. A monomial is a single term and a *polynomial* can have *many terms.* The simplest polynomials are in one variable and each term has that variable raised to a different power or exponent. Remember, only like variables raised to the same power can be added.

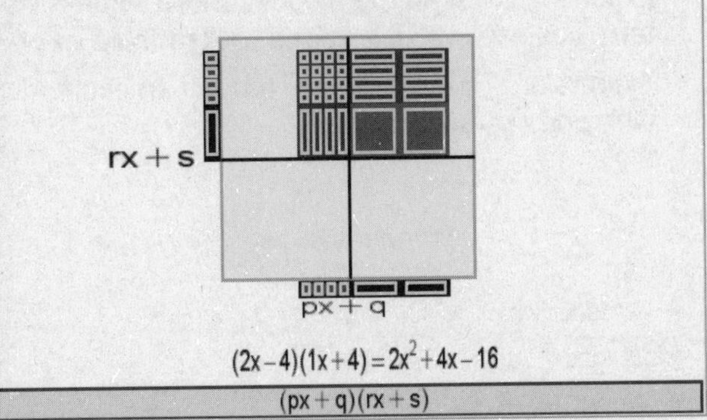

In the **order of operations**, one of the top-ranking processes is **evaluating exponents**. This ranking underscores the importance of correctly evaluating exponents and having an understanding of their affect on variables and expressions. When evaluating or simplifying exponential expressions, you must follow a set of rules called the **Rules (or Laws) of Exponents**. These rules allow variable expressions to be combined or simplified into a term containing just a variable raised to an exponent. Later in the module, these same rules will be used to simplify an expression so that each term has each variable raised to **a unique exponent**.

Expressions (and later, each term in an expression) are simplified when each variable is used once with one *positive* exponent.

Exponent Rules

- Product Rule: $\mathbf{x^a * x^b = x^{(a+b)}}$
- Quotient Rule: $\mathbf{x^a / x^b = x^{(a-b)}}$
- Power Rule: $\mathbf{(x^a)^b = x^{(a*b)}}$
- Zero Exponent Rule: $\mathbf{x^0 = 1}$
- Negative Exponent Rule: $\mathbf{x^{-a} = 1/x^a}$

Product Rule:

$$x^2 \cdot x^3$$

$x^a \cdot x^b = x^{a+b}$

Product Rule:

$$x^2 \cdot x^3$$
$$x^2 \cdot x^3 = x^{2+3}$$
$$x^2 \cdot x^3 = x^5$$

$x^a \cdot x^b = x^{a+b}$

Point 1: Any time two of the same base (number or variable) are multiplied, **add exponents**.

Remember: $x = x^1$ If a variable has no exponent it is understood that the exponent is 1.

Quotient Rule:

$$\frac{x^3}{x^2}$$
$$\frac{x^3}{x^2} = x^{3-2}$$
$$\frac{x^3}{x^2} = x^1$$

$\frac{(x^a)}{(x^b)} = x^{a-b}$

Point 2: If you forget, list all the factors and divide out the common factors. If the result is a variable raised to a negative exponent, rewrite it in the denominator.

Power Rule:

$$(x^3)^4$$
$$(x^3)^4 = x^{3 \cdot 4}$$
$$(x^3)^4 = x^{12}$$

$(x^a)^b = x^{a \cdot b}$

Point 3: Power rule: Use scratch paper to write out all the factors: (xxx)(xxx)(xxx)(xxx) = x^{12}.

Simplify:

$$x^3 \cdot x^{-7}$$
$$= x^{3+-7}$$
$$= x^{-4}$$
$$= \frac{1}{x^4}$$

Points 4-6: Use the rules as needed to simplify to one base to a positive exponent.

Exponents follow set patterns independent of the value of their base. If you understand how to read the patterns of exponents and to follow the rules for combining and simplifying exponents, you will be better prepared to use business and scientific information such as **debt analysis, interest and investment growth, cell reproduction, population growth**, and many more interesting topics in the news everyday.

Here we visualize exponents using stacks. The exponent **n** is across the horizontal axis. The vertical axis shows the value of the base taken to that exponent. You can see that it does not grow or shrink linearly.

Positive exponents: What happens to whole numbers as exponents get larger? What happens to fractions as exponents get larger?

Negative Exponents: What happens to whole numbers as exponents get smaller? What happens to fractions as exponents get smaller?

How does the pattern for 1/2 (right and below) compare to the pattern for 2? 3? 10? 1/4? 1/3?

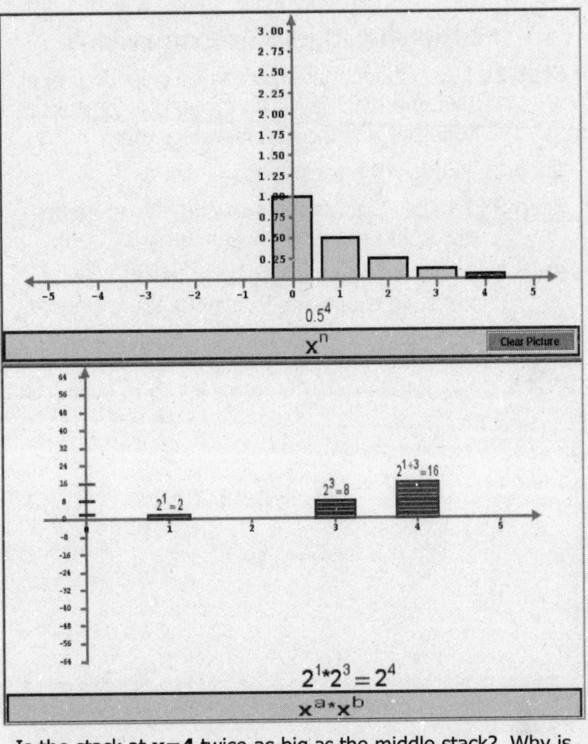

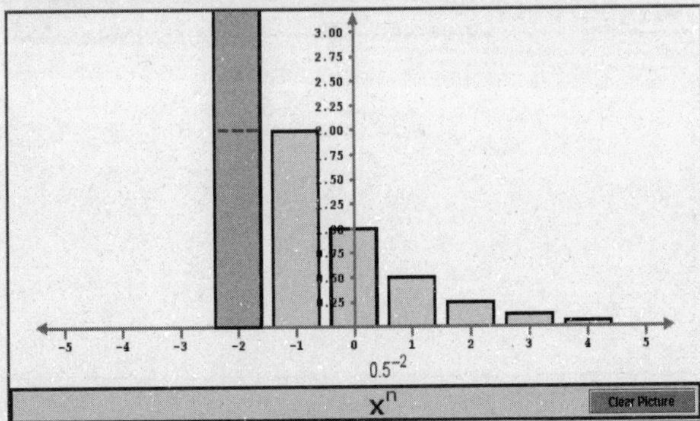

Why does the value of **n** increase as the exponents decrease?

Is the stack at **x=4** twice as big as the middle stack? Why is that the case? How much bigger is stack at **x=3** than the stack at **x=1**?

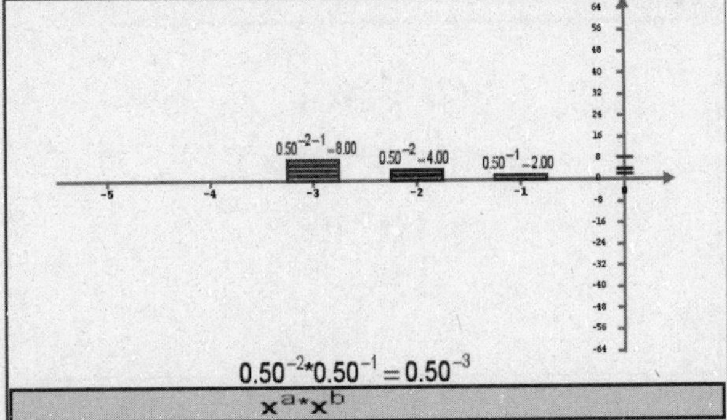

What does playing with this visualization suggest to you about fractions and negative exponents? Are any of the y-values negative?

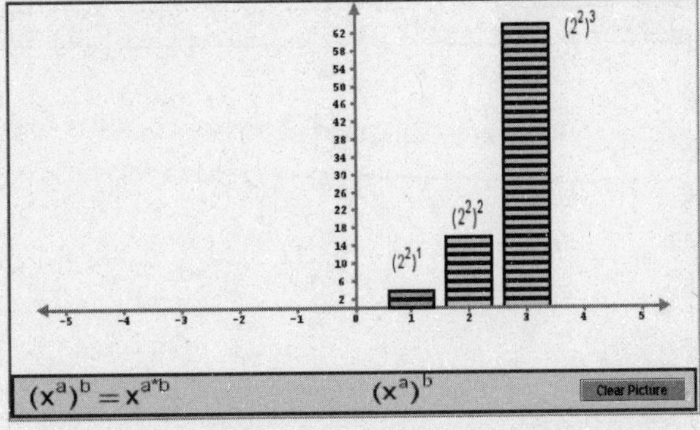

When **x=2** and **a=2,** what is the value within the parentheses? What is the value of the expression when **b**=1, 2, and 3? Does this follow the pattern for 4 to the same powers?

Multiplying algebraic expressions makes use of the **associative and commutative properties of multiplication** and the **rules of exponents**. The associative property allows constants and variables to be "moved" so they can be grouped together. Constants can then be multiplied; variable expressions can be simplified according to exponent rules: multiply like bases by adding exponents.

An algebraic expression is **simplified** when there is only one constant factor and one of each variable factor raised to a positive power. In order to keep positive exponents, use the definition of negative exponents to write the expression in simplified form.

Multiplying Algebraic Expressions

Step 1: Use the commutative and associative properties of multiplication to group the constants together and the variables together.

Step 2: Multiply the constants.

Step 3: Multiply the variables by adding exponents according to the exponent rules.

Step 4: If the exponent is negative, use the law of negative exponents to change the exponent to a positive integer.

Multiply:

$$-2x(6x^2)$$
$$= -12x^3$$

Add the powers of x. $ax(bx^2)$

Multiply:

$$-4x^3(4x^5)$$
$$= -16x^8$$

Add the powers of x. $ax^c(bx^d)$

Grouping constants together is usually done mentally. Double-check the signs, so that a sign error does not occur.

Add the exponents to get the exponent of the variable.

Multiply:

$$-3x^2(-2x^{-5})$$
$$= 6x^{-3}$$
$$= \frac{6}{x^3}$$

Rewrite as a positive exponent. $ax^c(bx^d)$

Adding exponents results in a negative exponent for **x**. Be sure to use the rules of exponents to leave only positive powers.

Simplify:

$$(-2x^4)^3$$
$$= (-2)^3(x^4)^3$$
$$= -8x^{12}$$

Multiply the powers of x. $(ax^b)^c$

Exponent rule: **Product to Power**: Each factor is raised to the third power.

Alternative thinking: $(-2x^4)(-2x^4)(-2x^4) = -8x^{12}$

Simplify:

$$(2x^3)^4(4x^3)^2$$
$$= (2)^4(x^3)^4(4)^2(x^3)^2$$
$$= 16x^{12}16x^6$$
$$= 256x^{18}$$

Add the powers. $(ax^b)^c \cdot (dx^e)^f$

Double use of the product-to-power rule: Once each power is determined, combine constants and then variables by adding exponents. Note: Think of 2 as 2^1 and 4 as 4^1.

Two single-term expressions multiply to form a single-term expression. What properties are used to allow us to find these products? What role do exponents play in finding the products? What "mental" math manipulations are performed in each multiplication?

The visualizations show manipulations of constants, variables, and exponents. Therefore, zero is sometimes shown as a constant or an exponent, and not simplified. Negative exponents are left as they are rather than being rewritten.

How do you determine the exponent of **x**? How do you determine the exponent of **y**? How do you determine the constant? What rule allows you to mentally pick out the constants to multiply? Do the sign rules apply for integers? Do the sign rules apply to exponents?

$$\left(2x^2y^2\right)\left(3x^3y^1\right)=6x^5y^3$$

$(ax^my^n)(bx^py^q)$

$$\left(2x^2y^2\right)\left(3x^3y^1\right)=6x^5y^3$$

$(ax^my^n)(bx^py^q)$

Why do you add exponents in a multiplication problem?

$$\left(2x^{-3}y^2\right)\left(3x^3y^1\right)=6x^0y^3$$

$(ax^my^n)(bx^py^q)$

If you are subtracting exponents are you always dividing?

$$\left(2x^{-3}y^2\right)\left(3x^{-1}y^1\right)=6x^{-4}y^3$$

$(ax^my^n)(bx^py^q)$

The multiplication is complete, but how would you simplify the above problem?

Dividing single-term algebraic expressions is a similar process to multiplying single term algebraic expressions. **Work with constants, then variables.** Simplify constants by either dividing or leaving them in fraction form, then simplify variables either by rewriting them as negative exponents or by using the **power rule of exponents**.

Dividing Algebraic Expressions

Step 1: Divide constants if possible. If not, leave them in place.

Step 2: Rewrite variables with negative exponents as necessary, so that all variables are in the numerator.

Step 3: Multiply like variables by adding their exponents.

Step 4: Rewrite so that all exponents are positive.

Simplify:

$$\frac{x^3}{x^8} = x^3x^{-8} = x^{3+-8} = x^{-5} = \frac{1}{x^5}$$

$\frac{x^a}{x^b}$

Alternatively, use the power rule for quotients: Subtract exponents, top minus bottom.

Simplify:

$$\frac{-3x^{-2}y^{-3}}{9x^{-3}y^{-4}} = \frac{-x^{-2}y^{-3}x^3y^4}{3} = \frac{-x^{-2+3}y^{-3+4}}{3} = \frac{-xy}{3}$$

Notice that the variables in the denominator have negative exponents — when they move to the numerator they are transformed to positive exponents.

Simplify:

$$\frac{x^5}{x^2} = x^5x^{-2} = x^{5+-2} = x^3$$

$\frac{x^a}{x^b}$

Simplify:

$$\frac{-8x^3y^{-2}}{-2x^5y^4} = 4x^3y^{-2}x^{-5}y^{-4} = 4x^{3+-5}y^{-2+-4} = 4x^{-2}y^{-6} = \frac{4}{x^2y^6}$$

Step 2 yields 4 as the constant factor, and all the variables from the denominator are written in the numerator with negative exponents. The final step is to rewrite so all exponents are positive.

Think about dividing algebraic expressions as **grouping all the constants together**. Begin by grouping all the **x**'s together and all the **y**'s together. You have then parsed (separated out) your problem into manageable "sub-problems". You can even bracket the portions so that you can see exactly where each factor belongs. In the visualization, we colored the factors blue for **powers of x** and red for **powers of y**.

What two ways can be used to simplify the expressions presented here?

Hint: The purpose here is to "see" the exponents. For this reason, zero exponents are included and not evaluated to 1.

$$\frac{x^2y^5}{x^4y^2} = x^{-2}y^3$$
$$= \frac{y^3}{x^2}$$

$$\frac{x^my^n}{x^py^q}$$

$$\frac{x^0y^5}{x^4y^2} = x^{-4}y^3$$
$$= \frac{y^3}{x^4}$$

$$\frac{x^my^n}{x^py^q}$$

What happens when the exponent in the numerator is larger than the exponent in the denominator?

$$\frac{x^0y^1}{x^{-3}y^2} = x^3y^{-1}$$
$$= \frac{x^3}{y^1}$$

$$\frac{x^my^n}{x^py^q}$$

What happens when the denominator has the larger exponent?

$$\frac{x^4y^5}{x^4y^2} = x^0y^3$$

$$\frac{x^my^n}{x^py^q}$$

What happens when the exponents are equal?

Defining Polynomials

Algebraic Expressions are made up of any meaningful combination of constants, variables, exponents, roots, and symbols of enclosure. Terms of an algebraic expression are separated by addition or subtraction signs. A special class of algebraic expressions are polynomials. **Polynomials** are sums made up of expressions that take the form ax^n, where **n** is a positive integer.

Classifying Polynomials

Mono—one term

Bi—two terms

Tri—three terms

Poly—many terms (four or more)

Degree of a term: The exponent of the variable or the sum of the exponents if more than one variable is present.

Degree of a polynomial: The degree of the highest term in the polynomial.

Monomials

Monomials have one term.
Some examples of monomials are:

$3x^2$

x^3

4

$2x$

Binomials

Binomials have two terms.
Some examples of binomials are:

$3x^2+7x$

x^3-27

$4+x$

$2x-3$

Count the number of terms.

Trinomials

Trinomials have three terms.
Some examples of trinomials are:

$3x^2+7x+5$

x^3-x+27

$4+x+6x^2$

x^4-2x-3

Count the number of terms.

Find the degree of these polynomials:

The degree of a polynomial is the highest power in the polynomial.

$8x^3-27$ has a degree of 3.

$4+x+6x^2$ has a degree of 2.

$2x-3$ has a degree of 1.

4 is $4x^0$, so the degree is 0.

Identify the degree of each term. Then the degree of the highest term is the degree of the polynomial.

Visualizing **trinomials of degree two** is an extension of what has been used in past modules: number bars, variable bars, and squares. These bars and squares vary as **x** varies.

How would you visualize a polynomial of degree 3? Can we draw a visualization of degree 4 or more?

What if **b** is a negative number?

How do you represent a binomial?

How many ways can you represent a binomial?

How do you represent a monomial?

What components are necessary to represent a trinomial?

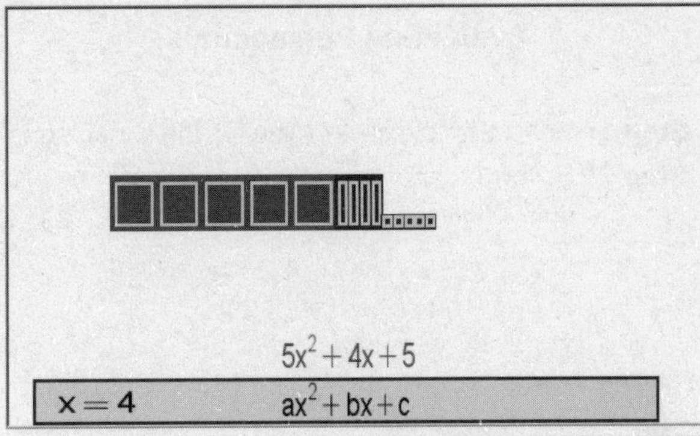

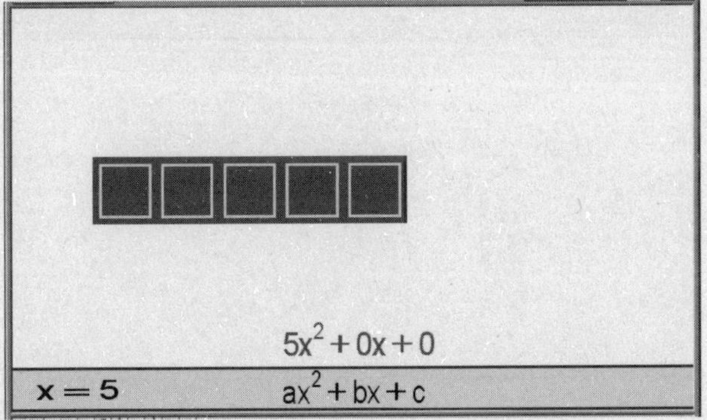

If **b** and **c** =0 then what does the polynomial look like?

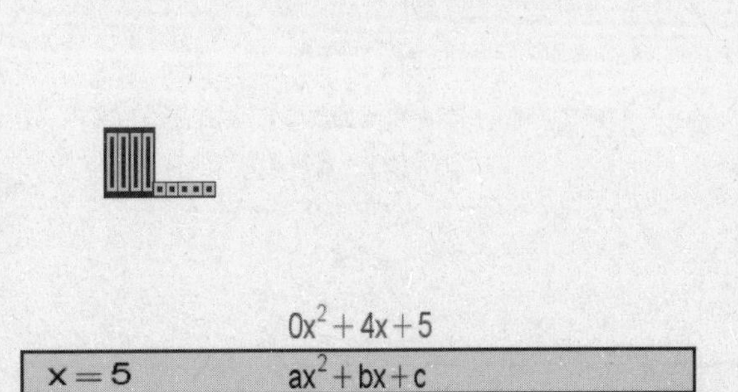

If **a=0,** what's missing from the visualization?

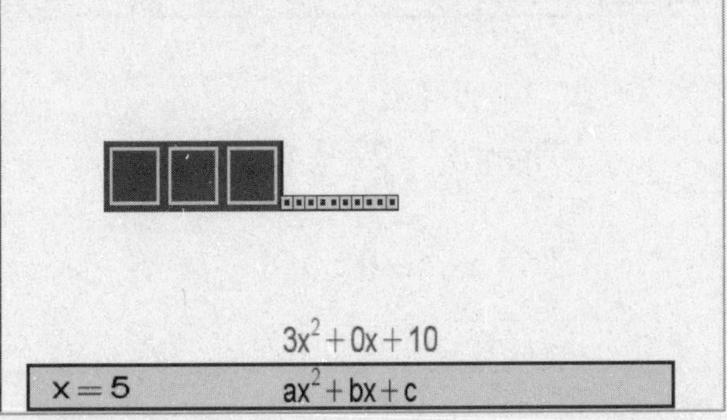

What's missing?

Do the big squares hold a number bar with 25 units in it in the above visualization?

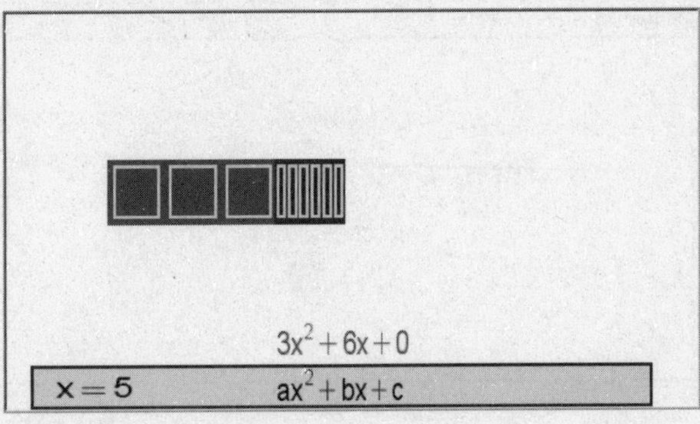

What if **c=12**? How would that be represented?

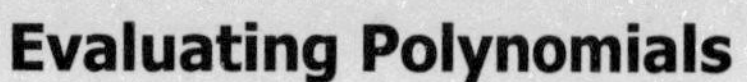

Evaluating Polynomials

EnableMath

Polynomials are algebraic expressions with constants and variables raised to various powers. If the polynomial has **only one variable**, we call it **a polynomial in x** (or whatever the variable is) and if it has more than one variable, we call it a **polynomial in x and y**, and so on. Each of the variables can take on different values, and then the polynomial can be **evaluated** for those value. Substitute the values in for the variables and use **order of operations** to evaluate.

Evaluating Polynomials

Step 1: Substitute the given value for the variable(s).

Step 2: Follow order of operations to evaluate the polynomial.

Substitute:

Let $x = -3$.

Then, $3x^2 - 2x - 4 = 3(-3)^2 - 2(-3) - 4$

$3x^2 - 2x - 4$

Substitute:

Let $x = -3$.

Then, $3x^2 - 2x - 4 = 3(-3)^2 - 2(-3) - 4$

$= 3(9) + 6 - 4$

$= 27 + 2$

$= 29$

$3x^2 - 2x - 4$

Point 1: Step 1 (above right) and step 2 (above) show how to evaluate a polynomial.

Substitute:

Let $x = 2$.

Then, $3x^2 - 2x - 4 = 3(2)^2 - 2(2) - 4$

$= 3(4) - 4 - 4$

$= 12 - 8$

$= 4$

$3x^2 - 2x - 4$

Point 2: Substitute 2 for **x**—always show the substitution so that sign mistakes are avoided. Follow order of operations to complete the process.

Substitute:

Let $x = 2$.

Then, $x^3 - 27 = (2)^3 - 27$

$= 8 - 27$

$= -19$

$x^3 - 27$

Point 3: Substitute, then evaluate.

Substitute:

Let $x = 3$.

Then, $x^3 - 27 = (3)^3 - 27$

$= 27 - 27$

$= 0$

$x^3 - 27$

Point 4: This is called the difference of cubes. Note that 27 is a perfect cube.

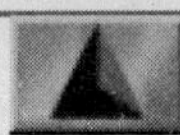

You can visualize the evaluation of a polynomial as filling its space with unit bars. We have shown this to you side by side, the expression on the left and the same space filled with a number bar on the right. How many units fill a a variable bar an **x**? How many will fill a square $\mathbf{x^2}$?

Can the representation for $2x^2 + 3x$ be evaluated for anything other than 5?

What happens when you change **x**?

What happens when you change **a** (the coefficient of the squared term)?

What happens when you change **b** (the coefficient of the linear term)?

$5x^2 + 4x = 5(3^2) + 4*3 = 57$

$x = 3$ $ax^2 + bx$

Is the number bar on the right made up of 57 units?

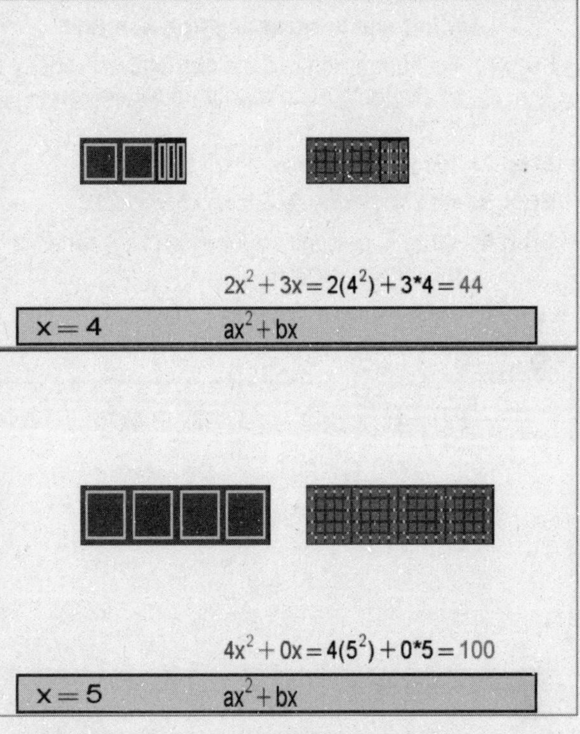

The coefficient of **x** is 0—what effect does that have on the $\mathbf{x^2}$ portion?

Adding polynomials makes use of the distributive properties of real numbers.

Adding polynomials is straight forward:

Identify like terms and add their coefficients. Like terms have exactly the same variable factors raised to the same exponent.

Subtracting polynomials:

Use the distributive property to find the opposite of each term in the second polynomial, then add them. Subtracting two numbers is the same as adding the opposite of the second number. For review, see section 6. The Real Numbers.

Adding and Subtracting Polynomials

Step 1: For subtraction use the distributive property to distribute –1 to each term within parentheses.

Step 2: Identify like terms.

Step 3: Add like terms by adding coefficients.

Step 4: Write in descending (or ascending) order of the chosen variable.

Add these polynomials:

$$(2-3x)+(-5+6x)$$
$$=2-3x-5+6x$$
$$=2-5-3x+6x$$
$$=-3+3x$$
$$=3x-3$$

$(a+bx)+(c+dx)$

Subtract these polynomials:

$$(2-4x-2x^2)-(3-2x+4x^2)$$
$$=2-4x-2x^2-3+2x-4x^2$$

Colors indicate like terms. $(a+bx+cx^2)-(d+ex+fx^2)$

Step 1 is to distribute the –1 to each term in the second polynomial. This is equivalent to finding the opposite of each term.

Subtract these polynomials:

$$(2-4x-2x^2)-(3-2x+4x^2)$$
$$=2-4x-2x^2-3+2x-4x^2$$
$$=2-3-4x+2x-2x^2-4x^2$$
$$=-1-2x-6x^2$$
$$=-6x^2-2x-1$$

$(a+bx+cx^2)-(d+ex+fx^2)$

Once the –1 is distributed, identify like terms and combine. Write in descending order of the variable, **x**.

Subtract these polynomials:

$$(2x^3-4x^2-4x)-(3x^2-2x+4)$$
$$=2x^3-4x^2-4x-3x^2+2x-4$$

$(ax^3+bx^2+cx)-(dx^2+ex+f)$

Point 3: Distribute the –1 to the second polynomial. Notice that $2x^3$ and -4 do not have a like terms.

Subtract these polynomials:

$$(2x^3-4x^2-4x)-(3x^2-2x+4)$$
$$=2x^3-4x^2-4x-3x^2+2x-4$$
$$=2x^3-4x^2-3x^2-4x+2x-4$$
$$=2x^3-7x^2-2x-4$$

$(ax^3+bx^2+cx)-(dx^2+ex+f)$

Write in descending order of the variable. We do this to standardize the polynomial and quickly see a host of things about it.

Adding and Subtracting Polynomials 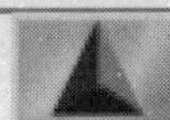

Like terms are visualized with squares, variable bars, and number bars.

Adding and subtracting polynomials is simply counting up the number of each different kind.

How many squares are required to represent a polynomial whose $\mathbf{x^2}$ coefficient is **a**?

Is addition of polynomials commutative?

Is subtraction of polynomials commutative?

How do you know if the coefficient of a term is positive or negative?

Can a term have 0 as its coefficient?

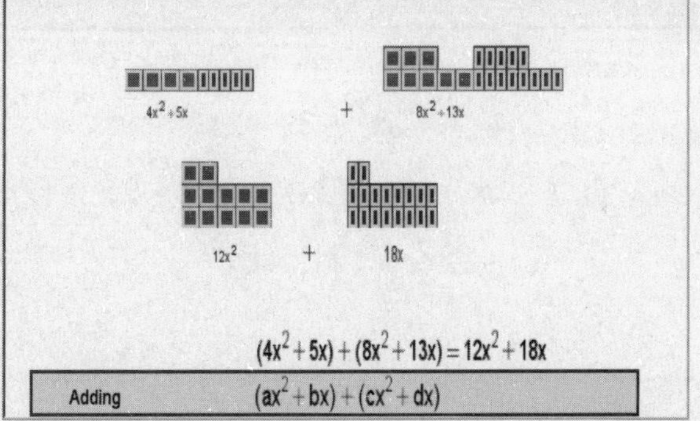

$4x^2+5x$ + $8x^2+13x$
$12x^2$ + $18x$
$(4x^2+5x)+(8x^2+13x)=12x^2+18x$
Adding $(ax^2+bx)+(cx^2+dx)$

Combine the squares and the bars and count how many. What's the short cut?

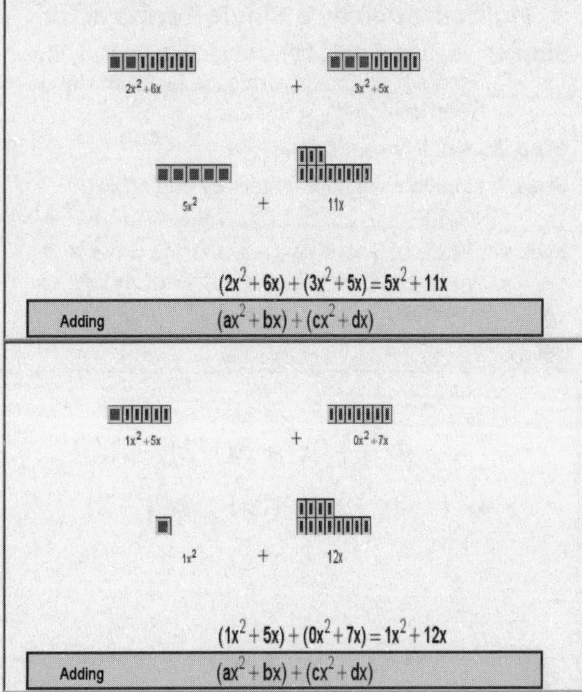

What's "missing" in the second polynomial?

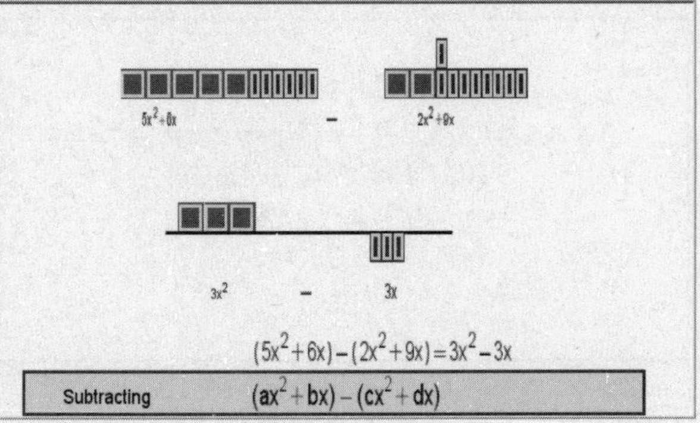

Why is the **3x** part under the line? What does it mean for a term to be negative?

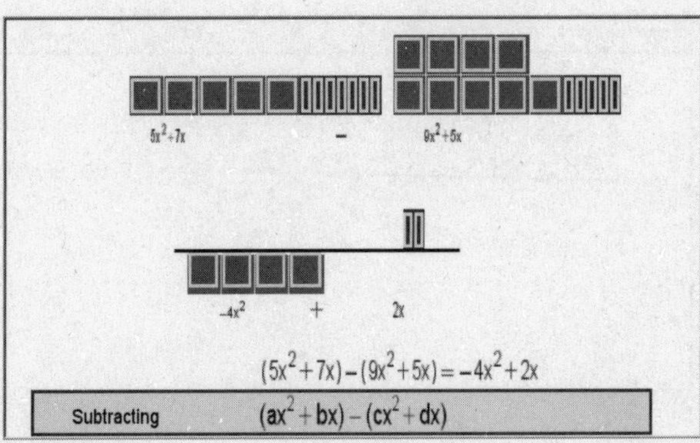

What does it mean to have $\mathbf{-4x^2}$?

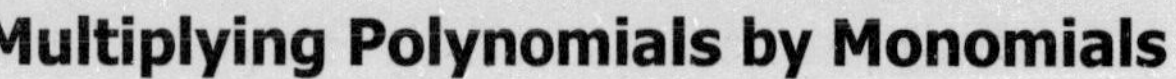

Multiplying Polynomials by Monomials

EnableMath

Use the **distributive property** to multiplying a **monomial** and a polynomial.

Each term inside the parentheses (polynomial) is multiplied by the monomial term outside the parentheses.

Multiplication by a Single-Term Factor

Step 1: Use the distributive property to multiply the single term factor with each factor in the parentheses.

Step 2: Multiply coefficients.

Step 3: Multiply variable factors by adding exponents.

Step 4: Write polynomials in decreasing order and write algebraic expressions with positive exponents.

Distribute:

$$-2x(3x+4)$$
$$-2x(3x)+-2x(4)$$
$$-6x^2-8x$$

Distribute:

$$4x^3(-3x^2+3x-2)$$
$$4x^3(-3x^2)+4x^3(3x)+4x^3(-2)$$

Point 2: Step 1 shows $\mathbf{4x^3}$ multiplied with each term within the parentheses.

Distribute:

$$4x^3(-3x^2+3x-2)$$
$$4x^3(-3x^2)+4x^3(3x)+4x^3(-2)$$
$$-12x^5+12x^4-8x^3$$

Step 2 shows how the coefficients and variables are multiplied.

Distribute:

$$2x^{-2}(-3x+2)-4x^{-3}(2x-3)$$
$$2x^{-2}(-3x)+2x^{-2}(2)+-4x^{-3}(2x)+-4x^{-3}(-3)$$

Distribute the factor to each term.

Distribute:

$$2x^{-2}(-3x+2)-4x^{-3}(2x-3)$$
$$2x^{-2}(-3x)+2x^{-2}(2)+-4x^{-3}(2x)+-4x^{-3}(-3)$$
$$-6x^{-1}+4x^{-2}-8x^{-2}+12x^{-3}$$
$$-6x^{-1}-4x^{-2}+12x^{-3}$$
$$\frac{-6}{x}+\frac{-4}{x^2}+\frac{12}{x^3}$$

Next, multiply coefficients. Then, multiply variables by adding exponents. Make sure expressions are written with positive exponents.

This is an important visualization. We will use again and again. Play with it!

The product is a rectangle. It can be in any 1, or in all of the 4, quadrants. It has two factors. In **Point 1**, the first factor is a constant, and in **Point 2,** it is a variable.

Hint: Use small numbers so that the visualizations are easier to see. Make sure to try negative coefficients and negative constants.

Is multiplication of a monomial and a binomial commutative?

Which quadrants hold positive coefficients?

What two factors determine the number of x^2-squares?

What two factors determine the number of x-bars?

When will there be no unit bars?

Can there ever be zero x-bars?

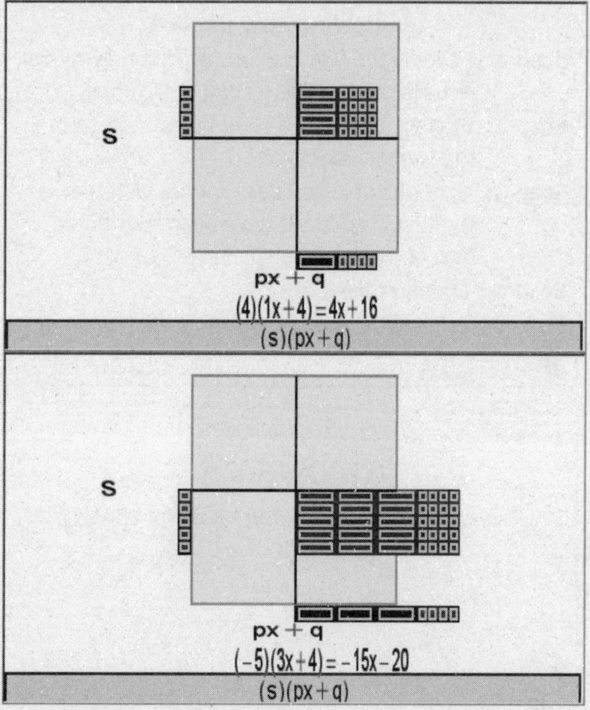

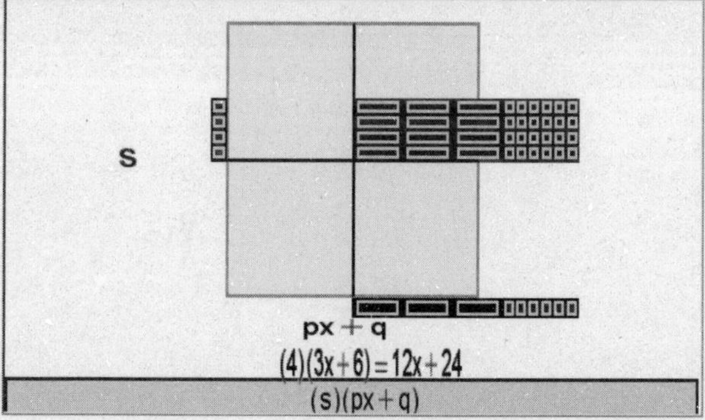

What determines how many x-bars in the product above? Why is this product in Quadrant I? Is it positive or negative?

Why is this product in Quadrant IV? Is it positive or negative?

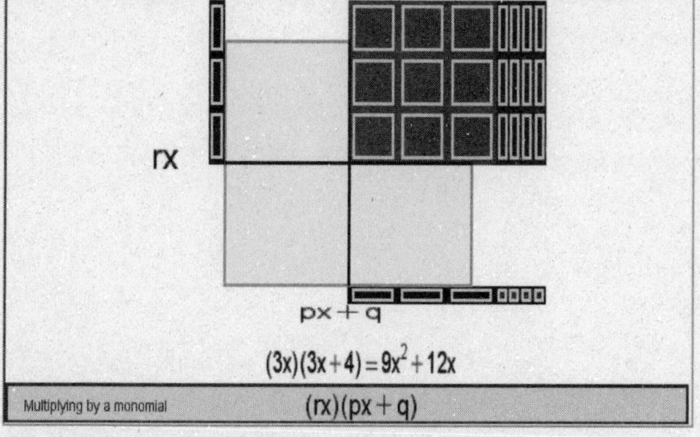

Point 2: What determines the number of x^2's? What happened to the unit bar?

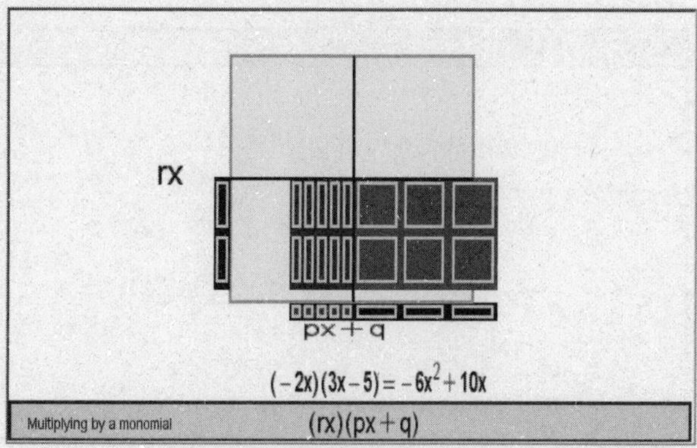

How can part of the product be in one Quadrant and part be in another Quadrant?

Multiplying Polynomials by Polynomials

EnableMath

Multiplying two polynomials requires each term to be multiplied **by every other term**. The product of each of these separate terms is called a **Partial Product** and the resulting product is the sum of all the partial products.

The Distributive Property allows multiplication to be distributed over addition. Therefore, it gives us a pattern for performing multiplication of polynomials. Whether the factors are binomials, trinomials, or higher order polynomials, using the distributive property pattern is a way of keeping your work logical and orderly.

Multiplying Polynomials

Step 1: Multiply the first term of the first polynomial to each term in the second polynomial.

Step 2: Multiply the second term times each term in the second polynomial.

Step 3: Continue in a like manner until all terms in the first polynomial have been distributed over the second polynomial.

Step 4: Combine like terms.

Step 5: Write in descending-power order.

Multiply (or distribute):

$$(-2x^3+3)(4x^2-5x)$$
$$= -2x^3(4x^2)+-2x^3(-5x)+3(4x^2)+3(-5x)$$
$$= -8x^5+10x^4+12x^2-15x$$

First, distribute $-2x^3$ from the first parentheses to each term of the second parentheses, $4x^2$ and $-5x$. Notice that the sign "goes with" the term to determine the sign of the product term. Next, distribute the 3 to each term.

Multiply (or distribute):

$$(3x^4-2x^2+4)(-7x^3+5x-6)$$
$$= -21x^7+15x^5-18x^4+14x^5-10x^3+12x^2-28x^3+20x-24$$
$$= -21x^7+29x^5-18x^4-38x^3+12x^2+20x-24$$

Combine like terms.

The process is the same, no matter how many terms are multiplied. Like terms are color-coded on the screen.

Multiply (or distribute):

$$(2x-3)(-4x+5)$$
$$= 2x(-4x)+2x(5)+-3(-4x)+-3(5)$$
$$= -8x^2+10x+12x-15$$
$$= -8x^2+22x-15$$

Multiply (or distribute):

$$(-2x^2-3x)(2x^2-4x+5)$$
$$= -2x^2(2x^2)+-2x^2(-4x)+-2x^2(5)+-3x(2x^2)+-3x(-4x)+-3x(5)$$
$$= -4x^4+8x^3-10x^2-6x^3+12x^2-15x$$
$$= -4x^4+2x^3+2x^2-15x$$

Multiply $-2x^2$ times each term in the second polynomial, then multiply $-3x$ times each term. Combine like terms and make sure the product is written in descending order of the variable.

Visualize this product of two binomials as a **rectangle** made up of 4 parts: The squares, vertical variable bars, horizontal variable bars, and number bars. The two binomials are the lengths of each side of the rectangle, they are also the factors of the polynomial.

The quadrant tells us whether that product is positive or negative, and the combination of all 4 of these rectangles or products is the full expression of the product of the binomials. Visually, we do not actually combine like terms, but algebraically, we definitely do.

Which terms multiply to make x bars? Which terms multiply to give x^2 squares? Which terms multiply to give unit bars?

How do you know if **partial products** are bars or squares?

Can any of the product terms be zero if the factor terms are not zero?

Why do you combine horizontal and vertical x-bars?

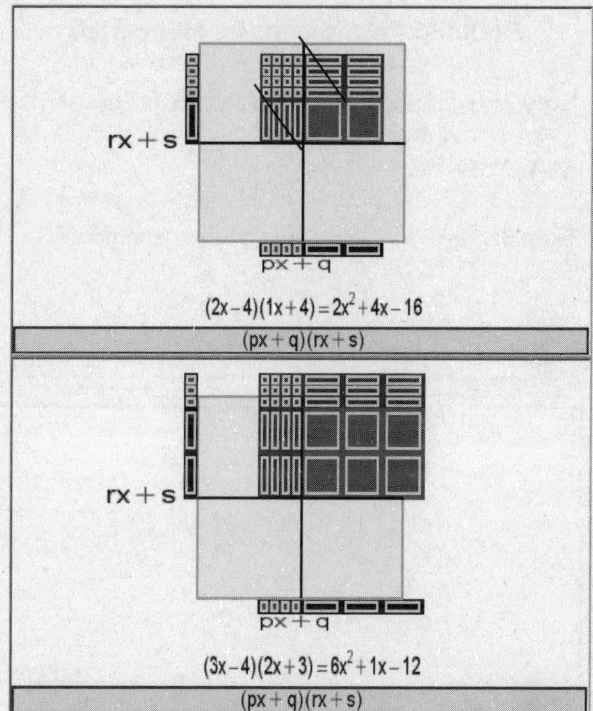

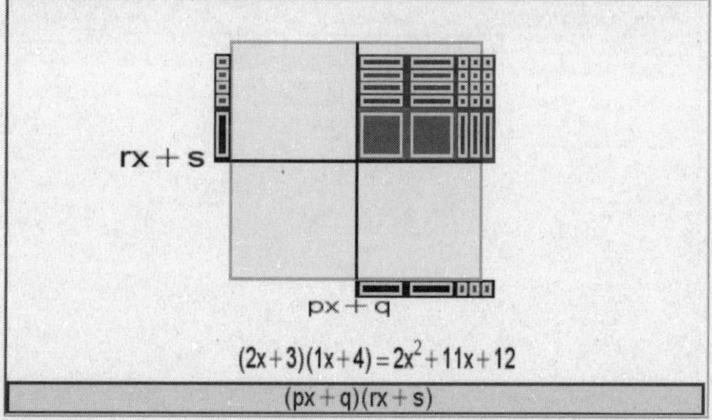

Which factors are shown by the 8 horizontal x-bars? Which factors are shown by the 3 vertical x-bars? Why are the x-bars added?

How do you get the **x** term in the product trinomial? Which factors multiply to form the $\mathbf{x^2}$ term? Why are the x-bars subtracted?

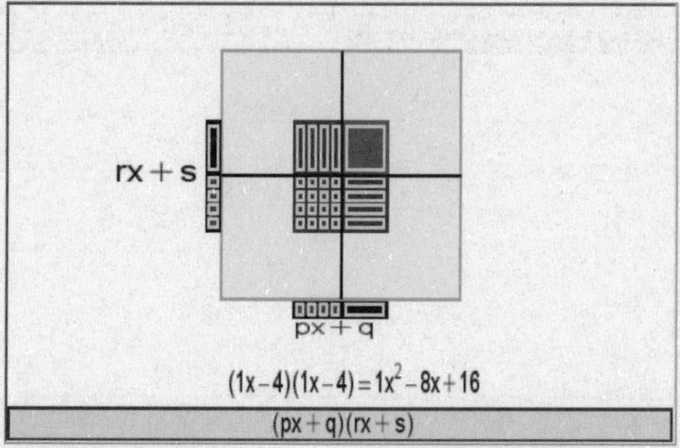

Special product: $(x - 4)^2 = x^2 - 8x + 16$. What do you notice about the first and last terms in the product? What do you notice about the middle term in the product?

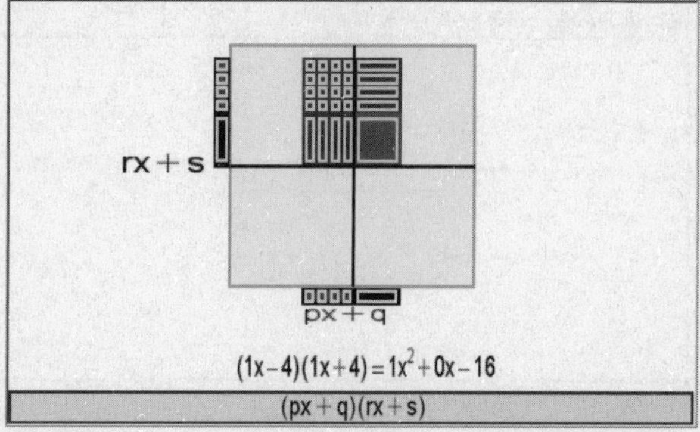

Special product: $(x - 4)(x + 4) = x^2-16$. What do you notice about the first and last terms in the product? What do you notice about the middle term in the product?

Dividing Polynomials by Monomials

EnableMath

The process of dividing a polynomial by a monomial is to **divide each term of the polynomial by the monomial**.

The number of terms in the polynomial is the number of terms in the quotient.

If there are no common factors between a term and the monomial divisor, then that term remains in the denominator, with the numerator unchanged. Check your work by multiplying the divisor times the quotient to get the original polynomial.

Dividing Polynomials by Monomials

Step 1: Break the polynomial apart so that each term is written over the denominator.

Step 2: Divide.

Step 3: Make sure there are no negative exponents

Divide this polynomial by this monomial:

$$\frac{3x^3+6x^2-9x}{3x}$$
$$=\frac{3x^3}{3x}+\frac{6x^2}{3x}-\frac{9x}{3x}$$

Break apart the fraction.

Divide this polynomial by this monomial:

$$\frac{3x^3+6x^2-9x}{3x}$$
$$=\frac{3x^3}{3x}+\frac{6x^2}{3x}-\frac{9x}{3x}$$
$$=x^2+2x-3$$

Simplify.

Each term is divided by the monomial. The quotient is in descending power of the variable.

Divide this polynomial by this monomial:

$$\frac{x^3-2x^2+3x}{2x^2}$$
$$=\frac{x^3}{2x^2}-\frac{2x^2}{2x^2}+\frac{3x}{2x^2}$$

Break apart the fraction.

Each term is divided by the monomial.

Divide this polynomial by this monomial:

$$\frac{x^3-2x^2+3x}{2x^2}$$
$$=\frac{x^3}{2x^2}-\frac{2x^2}{2x^2}+\frac{3x}{2x^2}$$
$$=\frac{x}{2}-1+\frac{3}{2x}$$

Simplify.

Divide. Notice the order: It is in decreasing order of the variable. The quotient is a not polynomial, but it is an algebraic expression.

Divide this polynomial by this monomial:

$$\frac{x^3-2x^2+3x-2}{2x^2}$$
$$=\frac{x^3}{2x^2}-\frac{2x^2}{2x^2}+\frac{3x}{2x^2}-\frac{2}{2x^2}$$
$$=\frac{x}{2}-1+\frac{3}{2x}-\frac{1}{x^2}$$

Simplify.

Four or more terms work in the same way: Each term is divided by the monomial.

The visualization of **division of polynomials** looks very much like multiplication, because division is the inverse of multiplication.

Think backwards: Given a monomial or constant, what do you multiply it by to get the polynomial represented by the rectangles? If you have the product and one factor (say the horizontal one), then the result of division is the other factor (the vertical one).

If the divisor is the vertical factor, then the result is the factor horizontal factor and vice versa.

Is the quotient always a binomial?

What determines the number of terms in the quotient?

What two multiplication statements can be made from a division statement?

If the divisor is a constant, is the degree of the quotient the same as the degree of the polynomial? What if the divisor is a variable?

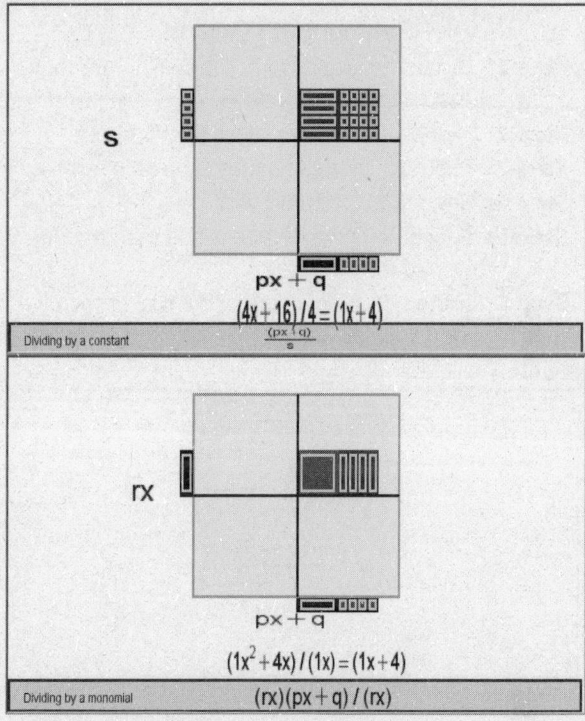

Is dividing by **x** equivalent to dividing by 1?

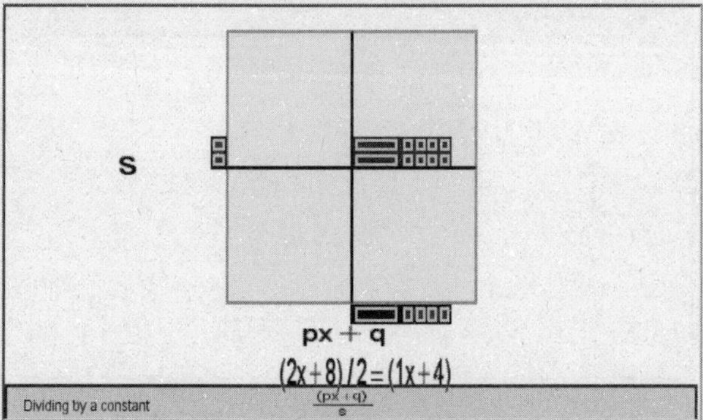

Does dividing by a positive constant always put the results on the right side of the **y**-axis?

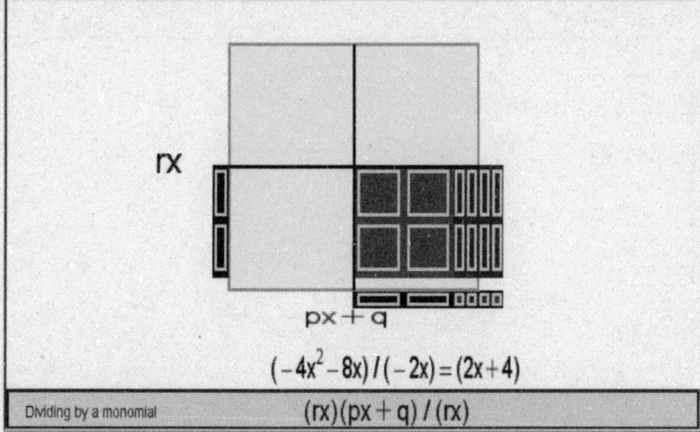

Does dividing by a variable with a negative coefficient always yield a positive quotient? How do you determine the sign of the terms in a quotient?

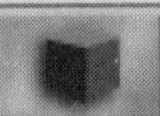
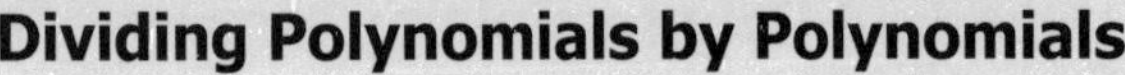

Dividing Polynomials by Polynomials

EnableMath

Long division, the tormentor of 10-year olds everywhere, is very useful for dividing polynomials.

The algorithm for dividing polynomials is exactly the same: **divide, multiply, subtract, bring down**. The difference is that instead of using numbers, we use the terms in the polynomial. The first thing to do is rewrite the division using the long division symbol:

$$polynomial\ 1 \overline{\smash{)}\, polynomial\ 2}$$

Polynomial Division

Step 1: Divide the lead term of the divisor into the lead term of the dividend.

Step 2: Multiply the answer times the divisor.

Step 3: Subtract. (Add the opposite of each term.)

Step 4: Bring down the next term.

Step 5: Repeat until the degree is less than the degree of the divisor.

Step 6: If there is a remainder, write it over the divisor as the last term.

Divide:

$$\frac{x^2+x-6}{x+3}$$

$$x+3\overline{\smash{)}\,x^2+x-6}$$

Divide:

$$\frac{x^2+x-6}{x+3}$$

$$\begin{array}{r} x \\ x+3\overline{\smash{)}\,x^2+x-6} \\ -(x^2+3x) \\ \hline -2x-6 \end{array}$$

Notice the first term in the quotient is written above the $\mathbf{x^2}$ term, the first term in the dividend. Distribute the negative through to subtract. Bring down the next term.

Divide:

$$\frac{x^2+x-6}{x+3}$$

$$\begin{array}{r} x-2 \\ x+3\overline{\smash{)}\,x^2+x-6} \\ -(x^2+3x) \\ \hline -2x-6 \\ -(-2x-6) \\ \hline 0 \end{array}$$

No remainder. Check your work by multiplying the quotient by the divisor. (x-2)(x+3).

Divide:

$$\frac{-2x^2-7x+6}{2x-1}$$

$$2x-1\overline{\smash{)}\,-2x^2-7x+6}$$

Set up the problem. Notice the sign of the lead coefficient. Divide $-2x^2$ by 2x.

Divide:

$$\frac{-2x^2-7x+6}{2x-1}$$

$$\begin{array}{r} -x-4+\frac{2}{2x-1} \\ 2x-1\overline{\smash{)}\,-2x^2-7x+6} \\ -(-2x^2+x) \\ \hline -8x+6 \\ -(-8x+4) \\ \hline 2 \end{array}$$

The remainder over the divisor is the final term in the quotient.

Division is the inverse process of multiplication. If you are given a product and one of the factors, what do you do to find the other factor?

The visualizations pictured here represent **trinomials divided by binomials.**

Will the quotient of a trinomial by a binomial always be a binomial? Do we always lose the highest power term when we divide a polynomial by a monomial?

What can you determine about the quotient from the location of the divisor and the quadrants of the dividend?

How do you determine if the terms in the quotient are positive or negative?

Can zero ever be the answer to a division problem?

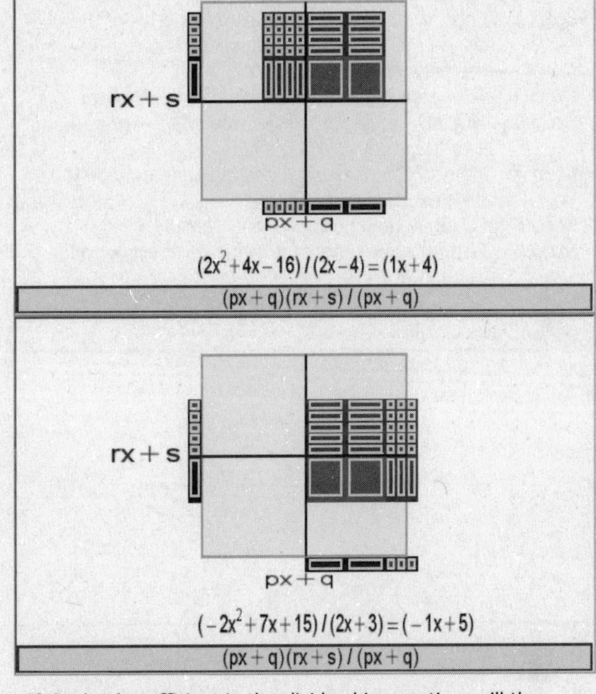

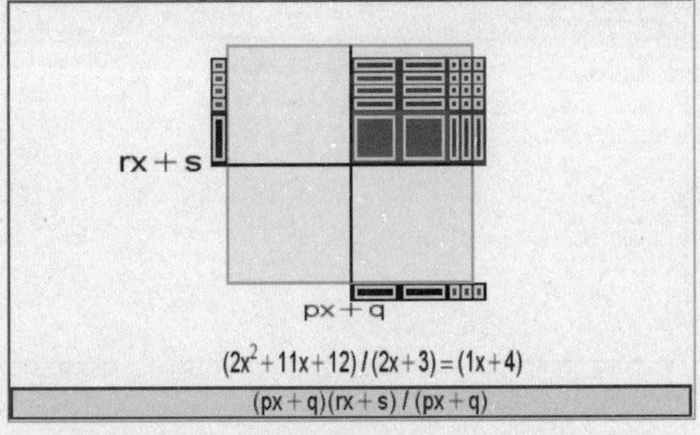

If the divisor has positive coefficients and a positive constant, what determines whether the quotient will have positive or negative terms?

If the lead coefficient in the dividend is negative, will the quotient always have a negative coefficient?

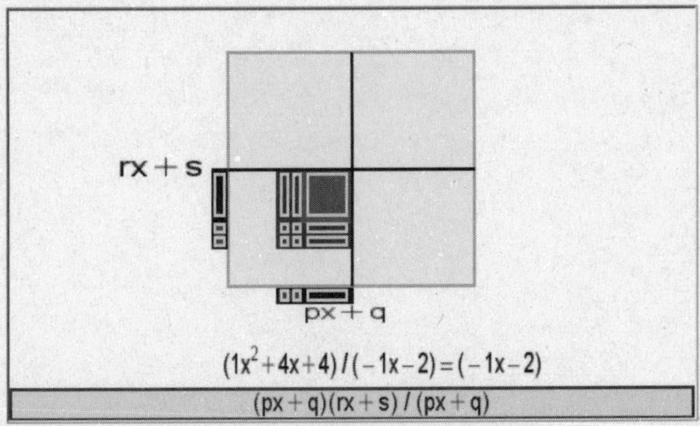

What do you notice about the shape of the dividend? What do you notice about the divisor and the quotient?

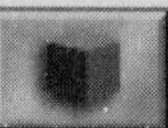

Synthetic Division

EnableMath

Long division can be a tedious process, so mathematicians developed an easier way to divide polynomials by binomials of the form **x+a** called **synthetic division.**

Division is performed with just the coefficients of the polynomial and the negative of the constant term in the binomial. All of the processes of long division are written in short hand to get the final answer. If there is a remainder, it can be written as a fraction, with the divisor as the denominator for the last term in the quotient.

Synthetic division has several applications in higher math courses, including finding roots for polynomial equations, which leads to the Fundamental Theorem of Algebra.

Synthetic Division Steps

Step 1: Enter the negative of the constant term of the divisor on the outside of a frame and the coefficients of the polynomial on the inside.
Step 2: Bring down the first coefficient to the answer.
Step 3: Multiply the constant times the coefficient and add it to the second coefficient.
Step 4: Multiply the constant times the sum and add it to the next coefficient.
Step 5: Continue until no coefficients remain.
Step 6: Write that in terms of **x** with the remainder as a fraction over the divisor.

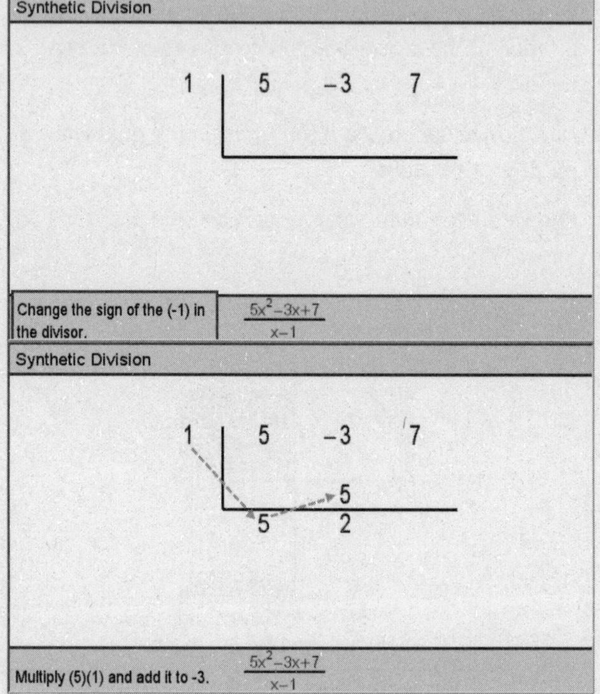

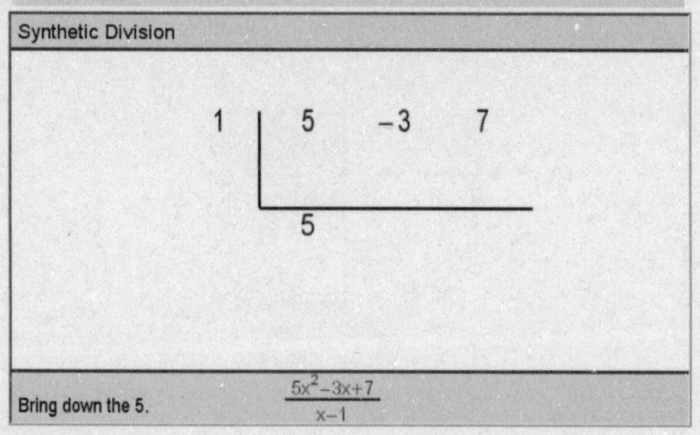

Step 2: Set up the frame and bring down the first coefficient.

Step 3: Multiply 1 times 5, and add to -3.

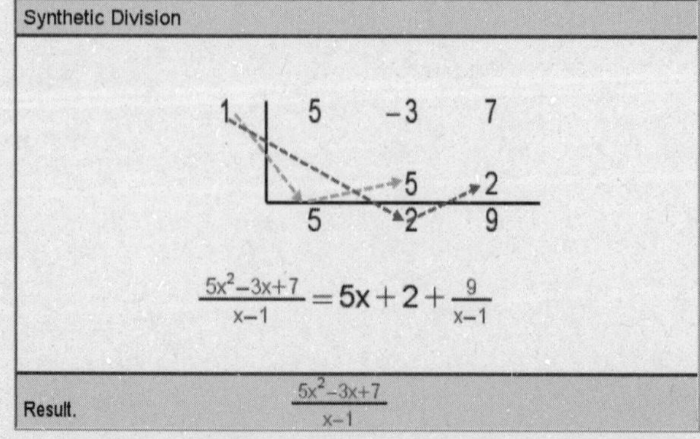

Steps 4–6: Multiply 1 times 2, and add it to 7. 9 is the remainder so the answer is written in terms of **x**, with the remainder as the last term of the algebraic expression.

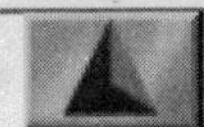

In math we take as many shortcuts as we can because computation can be tedious. Since we always write polynomials from left to right in descending order of their exponents, we can leave out the variables and the exponents and just focus on the coefficients. We put them into a "frame" and perform the division with numbers alone. This is the concept that synthetic division is based on.

These visualizations introduce two new symbols: **Q(x)** and **R(x)**, which we can think of as "**Quotient of x**" and "**Remainder of x.**" We call this functional notation. It is introduced in section 16. Functions.

What degree is the answer, compared to the original polynomial? How do you know if there is a remainder? If there is no remainder, what can you say about the divisor?

What does the graph look like if there is no remainder? What can you say about the quotient and divisor of there is no remainder? Can zero be used as a divisor? What about x+0? How does that fit into synthetic division?

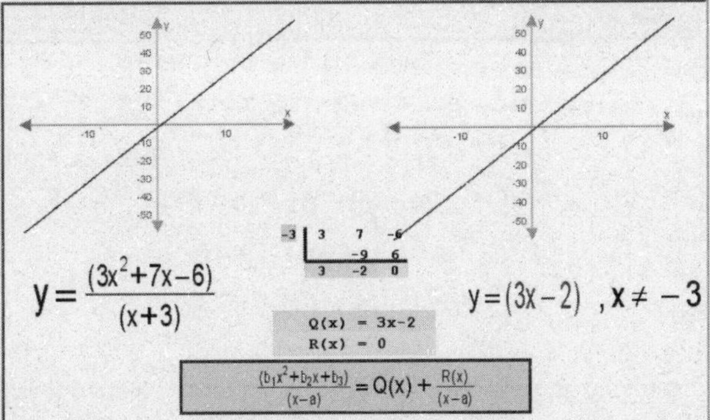

Is **x+3** a factor of **$3x^2+7x-6$**? How do you know?

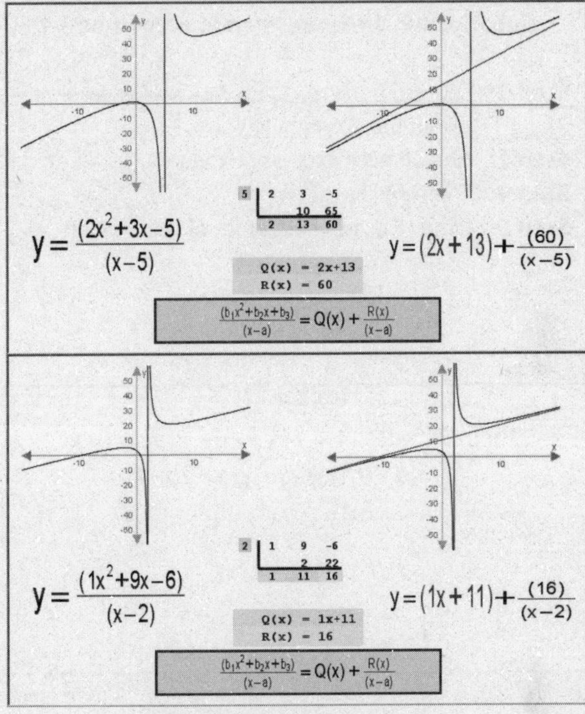

Will the remainder always be a constant?

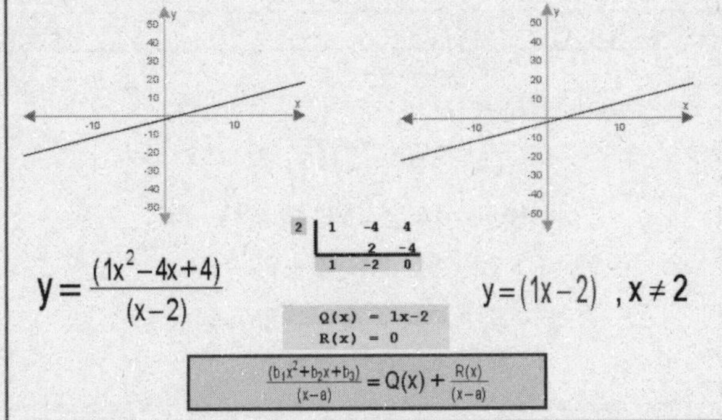

What do you notice about the divisor and the quotient in the above situation?

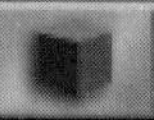
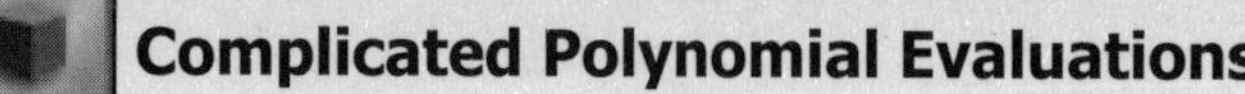

Complicated Polynomial Evaluations

EnableMath

We can substitute a value for the variable **(x)** in a polynomial. We can also substitute an expression with a new variable like **(a+2)** for **x** and simplify the polynomial in terms of the new variable. The new polynomial expression is sometimes called a **composite** of the two polynomials.

These processes are similar, but when substituting a number for **x**, the result is a value. When substituting an expression, the result is another polynomial. When we substitute a value for **x** in a polynomial, we use **order of operations** to evaluate the polynomial.

Substituting an Expression in a Polynomial

Step 1: Substitute the given expression for each variable in the polynomial.

Step 2: Expand each expression (square, cube, etc.).

Step 4: Combine like terms.

Step 5: Write in descending order of the variable.

Substitute:

Let $x = a + 2$.

Then, $3x^2 - 2x - 4 = 3(a+2)^2 - 2(a+2) - 4$

$3x^2 - 2x - 4$

Substitute:

Let $x = a + 2$.

Then, $3x^2 - 2x - 4 = 3(a+2)^2 - 2(a+2) - 4$

$= 3(a+2)(a+2) - 2(a+2) - 4$

$3x^2 - 2x - 4$

Point 1: Show the substitution and the expansion with the new expression. The expression **a+2** is to be expanded.

Substitute:

Let $x = a + 2$.

Then, $3x^2 - 2x - 4 = 3(a+2)^2 - 2(a+2) - 4$

$= 3(a+2)(a+2) - 2(a+2) - 4$

$= 3(a^2 + 2a + 2a + 4) - 2a - 4 - 4$

$= 3(a^2 + 4a + 4) - 2a - 8$

$= 3a^2 + 12a + 12 - 2a - 8$

$= 3a^2 + 10a + 4$

$3x^2 - 2x - 4$

Multiply **(a+2)(a+2)** to remove one set of parentheses. Follow through to simplify the expression. The new polynomial is in terms of **a**.

Substitute:

Let $x = a - 3$.

Then, $x^3 - 27 = (a-3)^3 - 27$

$= (a-3)(a-3)(a-3) - 27$

Distribute. $x^3 - 27$

Substitute and show the expansion.

Substitute:

Let $x = a - 3$.

Then, $x^3 - 27 = (a-3)^3 - 27$

$= (a-3)(a-3)(a-3) - 27$

$= (a-3)(a^2 - 3a - 3a + 9) - 27$

$= (a-3)(a^2 - 6a + 9) - 27$

$= a^3 - 6a^2 + 9a - 3a^2 + 18a - 27 - 27$

$= a^3 - 9a^2 + 27a - 54$

$x^3 - 27$

Multiply and simplify. The new polynomial is in terms of **a**.

Composite polynomials can be thought of as one polynomial being superimposed over another polynomial. Given a trinomial in **x**, what happens when **a** is substituted for **x**? What happens when **a+1** is substituted for **x**? Does that just add **1** to the polynomial? Are extra terms added? What effect does adding **−1** have on the polynomial?

Note: These visualizations work for positive coefficients. Negative coefficients can be hard to see, because we have to superimpose negative and positive representations.

How does substituting **a** for **x** change the polynomial?

Does changing the variable change the trinomial?

Does **a+3** triple the polynomial? Does it add three to the polynomial?

How does the constant term change from the original polynomial to the new one? What determines how much the constant increases? Will the constant ever decrease?

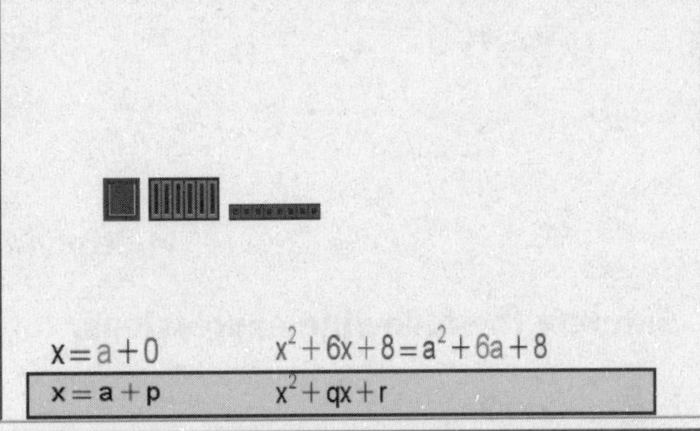

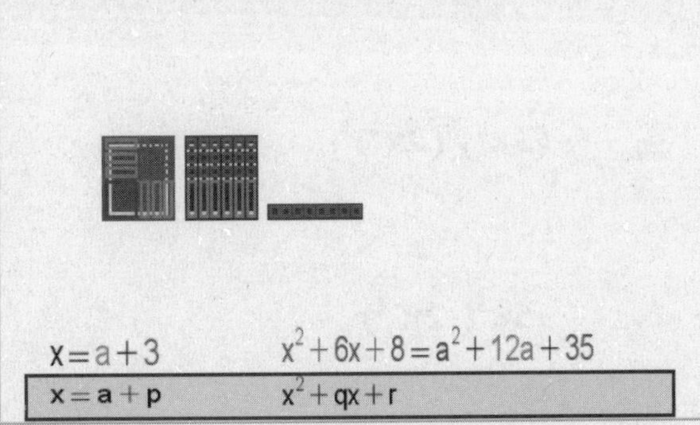

How do you get 12 **a**-bars? How do you get a number bar with 35 units?

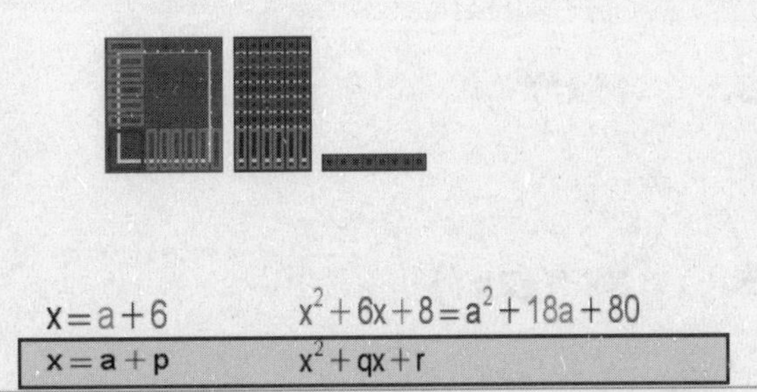

The original trinomial had 1 x^2-square and 6 x-bars. How many a-bars are in the **a+6** polynomial? What has been added to the x^2 square?

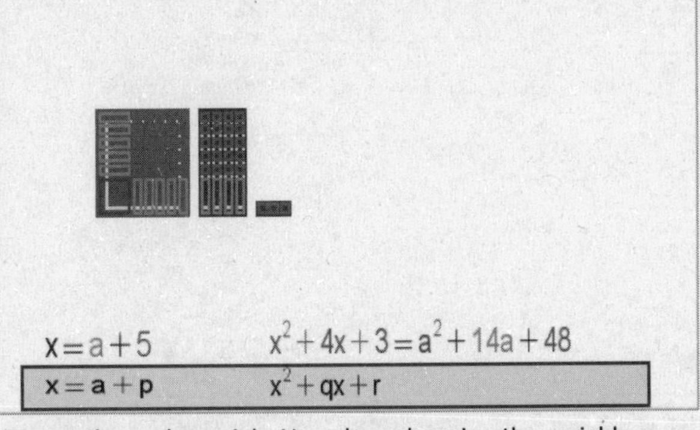

Try another polynomial. How does changing the variable **x** change the polynomial?

Rules of Exponents

1. **Mark the following as T(rue) or F(alse):**

______a. $x^0=0$ ______b. $x \cdot x^0=1$ ______c. $x \cdot x^{-1}=1$

2. **Evaluate the following:**

a. $2^2 \cdot 2^3$ b. $\frac{3^4}{3^2}$ C. $(2^2)^4$

Simplify the following.

3. $(x^2)(x^3)$ 4. $(x^{-7})^{-2}$ 5. $\frac{x^3}{x^{-2}}$ 6. $(2x^2)^4$

Multiplying Monomials

Simplify the following expressions:

1. $-2x(3x)$
2. $3x^2(2x^4)$
3. $(5x^2)^3$
4. $(3x^2)^3(2x^4)^3$
5. $3x^{-1}(-2x^{-3})$
6. $-5x^3(-2x^{-3})$

Dividing Monomials

Simplify each algebraic expression:

1. $\frac{x^5}{x^3}$ 2. $\frac{x^2}{x^{-5}}$ 3. $\frac{x^{-5}}{x^3}$

4. $\frac{x^{-4}}{x^{-3}}$ 5. $\frac{12x^{-3}y^{-1}}{-9x^3y^{-2}}$ 6. $\frac{3x^{-5}y^{-1}}{12x^{-1}y^2}$

Defining Polynomials

Identify the given algebraic expressions as M(onomial), B(inomial), T(rinomial), or P(olynomial):

1. $-5x^2 + 2$ ______

2. $2x^3 - 4x^2 + 2x - 3$ ______

3. $2 - 3x + 5x^2$ ______

4. 7 ______

What is the degree of each polynomial?

5. $-5x^2 + 2$ ______

6. $2x^3 - 4x^2 + 2x - 3$ ______

7. $2 - 3x + 5x^2$ ______

8. 7 ______

Evaluating Polynomials

Evaluate $2x^2 - 5x + 7$ for the following values of x:

1. Let $x = 3$ **2.** Let $x = -2$ **3.** Let $x = 0$

Evaluate $-3x^3 + 8$ for the following values of x:

4. Let $x = -1$ **5.** Let $x = 2$ **6.** Let $x = -2$

Evaluate each of the following for x = 2.

7. $x^2 - 7x + 4$ **8.** $x^3 - 5x + 3$

Adding and Subtracting Polynomials

Add or subtract as indicated:

1. $(5x^2 - 2x + 3) + (x^2 - 5)$ **2.** $(3x^2 + 2x - 1) + (X^2 + 4x + 7)$

3. $(3 - x + 2x^2) + (x - 6)$ **4.** $(5 + 2x^2) + (x + 3)$

5. $(2x^2 + 3x + 1) - (x^2 - 5x + 3)$ **6.** $(3 - x + 5x^2) - (4 - 7x)$

Multiplying Polynomials by Monomials

1. $-3x(2x - 7)$ **2.** $5x^3(2x^2 + 4x - 2)$

3. $2x^3(-4x^2 + 3x)$ **4.** $-x^3(-2x^2 + x - 3)$

5. $3x^{-4}(-5x^5)$ **6.** $x^{-2}(4x^3 + x^2) + 3x^{-2}(x^{-4} + 3x^{-2})$

Multiplying Polynomials by Polynomials

1. $(2x+3)(x+5)$

2. $(-5x+2)(3x+4)$

3. $(3x^2-5x)(2x^3+3)$

4. $(-x+x^3)(x^3+1)$

5. $(2x-5)(X^2+3x+7)$

6. $(x^2+2x+1)(3x^2+x+4)$

Dividing Polynomials by Monomials

1. $\dfrac{6x^3-4x^2+2x}{2x}$

2. $\dfrac{3x^3+7x^2-3}{3x^2}$

3. $\dfrac{5x^2+15x-60}{5x^2}$

4. $\dfrac{4x^2-12x+19}{2x^2}$

5. $\dfrac{-3x^2-7x-9}{-3x}$

6. $\dfrac{8x^4+2x^3-4x^2+6x-12}{4x^2}$

Dividing Polynomials by Polynomials

Use long division to divide each of the following:

1. $(3x^2+7x-3)\div(x-5)$

2. $(5x^2+3x-6)\div(2x+5)$

3. $(4x^2-12x+19)\div(4x+7)$

4. $(-3x^2-7x-9)\div(3x-1)$

12. Factoring

Polynomials can be combined through multiplication. Factoring is a method for reducing polynomials into a product of simpler polynomials. The factoring process undoes multiplication, enabling us to put a polynomial into its simplest form. Once a polynomial is in its reduced form we will solve for the roots of some of them. In this module you will investigate the critical steps involved with factoring polynomials, determining their roots, and solving equations. We approach the factoring of polynomials systematically. The key is to building up a repertoire of polynomials, so that you can quickly see both the form and the expected fac-

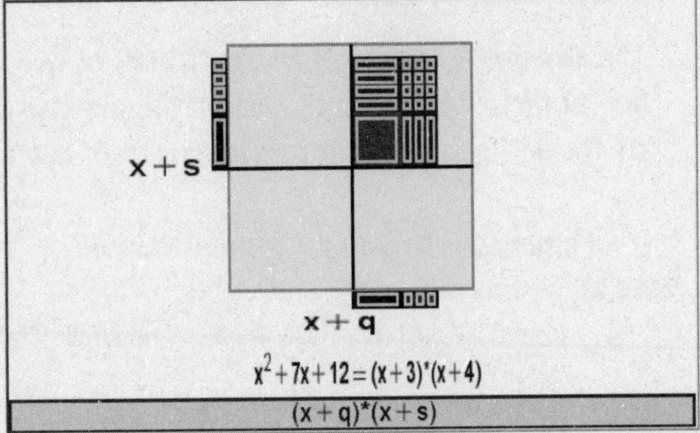

Greatest Common Factor

EnableMath

Factoring means to write numbers or expressions in terms of their multiplicative components. In pre-algebra and arithmetic we were interested in prime number factors. In this module we will extend that idea to include variable and binomial (having two terms) factors of algebraic expressions. Recall that the greatest common factor of two or more numbers is the largest number that divides every number in the set. The same is true for algebraic expressions.

The **Greatest Common Factor** (**GCF**) of two or more algebraic expressions is the largest combination of factors that divides each of the expressions. It is the product of largest common numerical coefficient factor and the largest power of each common variable.

Finding the Greatest Common Factor

Step 1: Find the GCF of the coefficients.

a. Factor each coefficient into its product of primes.

b. The GCF is the product of each factor raised to the largest power common to all.

Step 2: Find the GCF of the variables by taking the largest power of each variable common to all.

Find the greatest common factor of:

$$\{6, 12, 15\} = \{3 \cdot 2, 3 \cdot 4, 3 \cdot 5\}$$

GCF = 3

Find the greatest common factor of:

$$\{x^3, x^5, x^2\} = \{x^2(x), x^2(x^3), x^2(1)\}$$

$\text{GCF} = x^2$

Use scratch paper if needed to find the GCF of the coefficients. Above, the GCF of the variables is x^2—the largest power of the variable common to all.

Find the greatest common factor of:

$$\{15x^4, 20x^6, 10x^8\} = \{5x^4(3), 5x^4(4x^2), 5x^4(2x^4)\}$$

$\text{GCF} = 5x^4$

By inspection, 5 is the GCF of the coefficients and x^4 is the largest power of x common to all three.

Find the greatest common factor of:

$$\{12x^3y^2, 2xy, -6x^2y^3\} = \{2xy(6x^2y), 2xy(1), 2xy(-3xy^2)\}$$

$\text{GCF} = 2xy$

Notice that the variables are x and y and the largest common exponent for each is 1.

Find the greatest common factor of:

$$\{a^2b^2, 5ab, 15\} = \{ab \cdot ab, 5 \cdot ab, 5 \cdot 3\}$$

$\text{GCF} = 1$

Even though it looks like the above expressions have common factors, no factors but 1 are common to *all three* expressions.

Is there a way to determine if an algebraic expression can be factored?

Since multiplying factors yields a product, algebraic expressions that can be factored can be written as a product. Remember we visualize products as **rectangles**. If we can arrange the bars of an algebraic expression to be a rectangle, then that expression is factorable.

Is there more than one way? Which one is the GCF?

Change the **rx** factor (representing the GCF) to see the GCF.

In the figure to the right, what happens if the trial GCF is **2x** rather than **4x**?

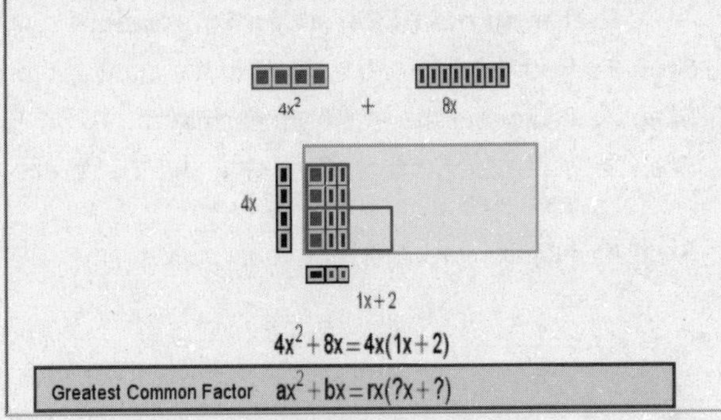

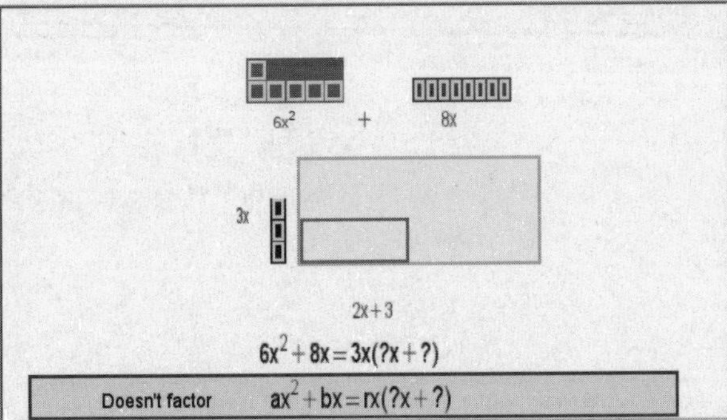

3x is the trial GCF. Is **3x** a factor of $\mathbf{6x^2+8x}$?

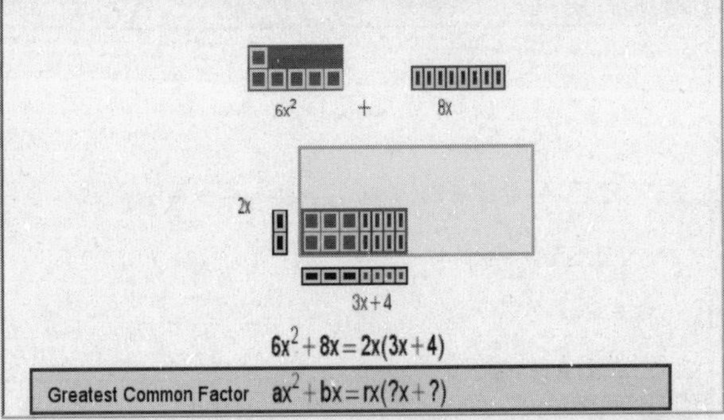

Change **rx**. Is **2x** a factor of $\mathbf{6x^2+8x}$? How do you know? Is it the GCF?

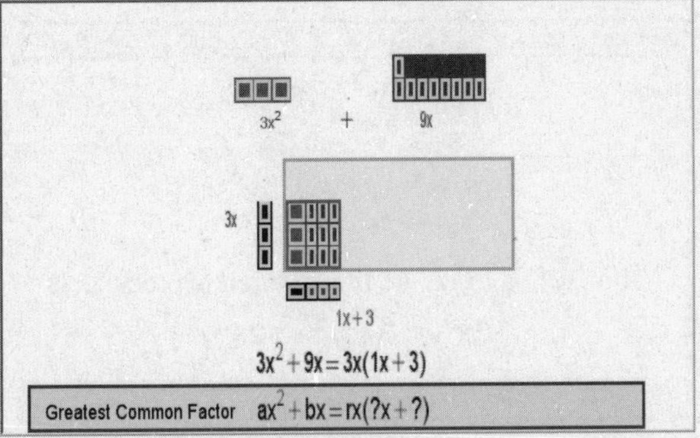

Can $\mathbf{3x^2}$ and **9x** be factored differently than represented above?

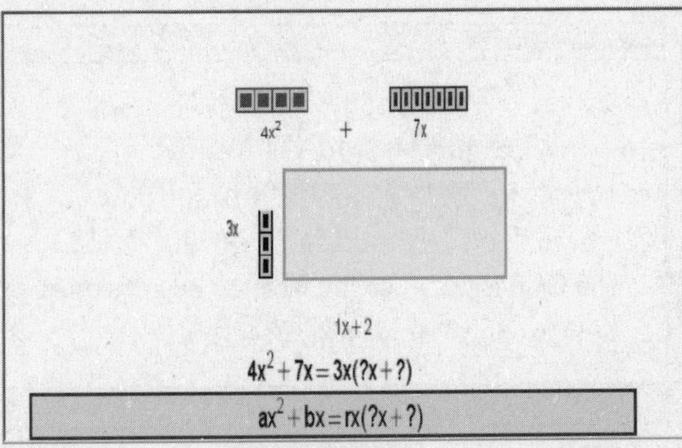

What is the GCF of $\mathbf{4x^2}$ and **7x**?

To factor an algebraic expression write it as the product of its GCF and its remaining factors.

Factoring the GCF from an Expression

Step 1: Find the GCF of the terms in the expression.

Step 2: Factor out the GCF from each term.

Step 3: Write the product of the GCF and the results from step 3.

Step 4: Multiply back to verify your answer.

Factoring Polynomials

$$10x^8 + 20x^6 - 15x^4 = 5x^4(2x^4 + 4x^2 - 3)$$

Write the polynomial as a product of its GCF and its remaining terms.

Factoring Polynomials

$$12x^3y^2 - 2xy + 6x^2y^3 = 2xy(6x^2y - 1 + 3xy^2)$$

Write the polynomial as a product of its GCF and its remaining terms.

Point 2: Use the Distributive Property to multiply back to check your work.

Factor out the GCF

$$\begin{aligned} 5u^6v^5 - 5u^4v^4 + 10u^5v &= 5\cdot 1u^6v^5 + 5\cdot(-1)u^4v^4 + 5\cdot 2u^5v \\ &= 5\cdot 1u^{4+2}v^5 + 5\cdot(-1)u^{4+0}v^4 + 5\cdot 2u^{4+1}v \\ &= 5\cdot 1u^{4+2}v^{1+4} + 5\cdot(-1)u^{4+0}v^{1+3} + 5\cdot 2u^{4+1}v^{1+0} \\ &= 5u^4v\left(u^2v^4 - v^3 + 2u\right) \end{aligned}$$

The factored polynomial is written as a product of its GCF and remaining terms.

Notice that $\mathbf{5u^4v}$ is a factor of each term. Above, each term is broken apart showing the factors. "Take out" $\mathbf{5u^4v}$ from each term.

Factor out the GCF

$$5u^2v^5 + 5u^7v^4 + 10u^5v^6$$

$$5\cdot 1u^2v^5 + 5\cdot 1u^7v^4 + 5\cdot 2u^5v^6$$

$$5\cdot 1u^{2+0}v^5 + 5\cdot 1u^{2+5}v^4 + 5\cdot 2u^{2+3}v^6$$

$$5\cdot 1u^{2+0}v^{4+1} + 5\cdot 1u^{2+5}v^{4+0} + 5\cdot 2u^{2+3}v^{4+2}$$

The GCF is $5u^2v^4$ so the factored expression is

$$5u^2v^4\left(1u^0v^1 + 1u^5v^0 + 2u^3v^2\right)$$

$$au^jv^k + bu^lv^m + cu^nv^o$$

Point 7: Step 2 shows the factors of the coefficients. Step 3 shows the **u's** and step 4 shows the **v's**. Take out the GCF and write it as a product with the remains.

Factor out the GCF

$$24x^9y^{15} - 16x^{12}y^3$$

$$8\cdot 3x^9y^{15} - 8\cdot 2x^{12}y^3$$

$$8\cdot 3x^{9+0}y^{15} - 8\cdot 2x^{9+3}y^3$$

$$8\cdot 3x^{9+0}y^{3+12} - 8\cdot 2x^{9+3}y^{3+0}$$

The GCF is $8x^9y^3$ so the factored expression is

$$8x^9y^3\left(3x^0y^{12} - 2x^3y^0\right)$$

$$au^jv^k - bu^lv^m$$

Point 8: What factor can be put in place for x^0 and y^0?

Factoring is un-multiplying—instead of the result being the rectangle formed by the factors, first form rectangle and then the factors are the dimensions of the sides. If an expression is factorable it is the result of a multiplication, a rectangle. Can you arrange the flats, bars and unit squares into a rectangular array?

Look back at the visualizations from the last assignment which show finding the GCF by factoring an expression with two terms. There we were interested in the GCF, **rx**; this time we are interested in both the GCF and the remaining factor. Which side of a rectangle represents the GCF? How do you read the answer?

What pattern is used to build the visual in **point 1?** Can you find another way to arrange the pieces into a rectangle?

Can you tell if an expression can be factored just by looking at the coefficients? Can you tell if an expression can be factored just by looking at the variables? How do you know if you have taken out the GCF and not just a lower common factor? Is every expression factorable?

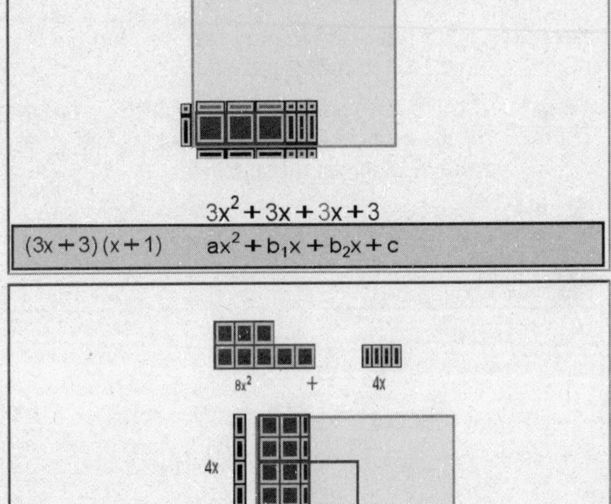

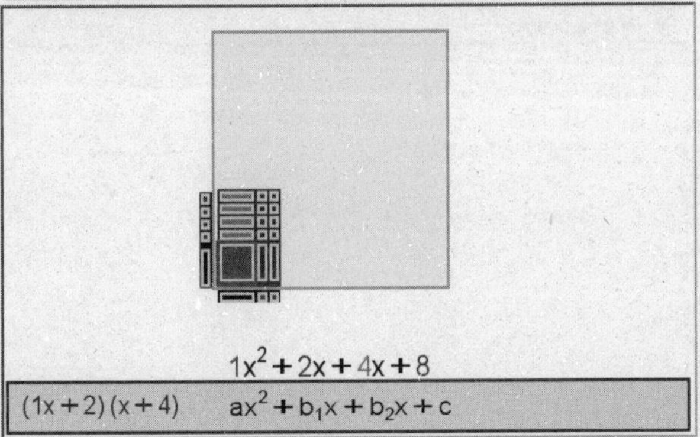

If the pieces can be arranged into a rectangle, then the simplified expression can be factored. Can you build an expression that is not factorable?

$8x^2$ + $4x$

$4x$

$2x+1$

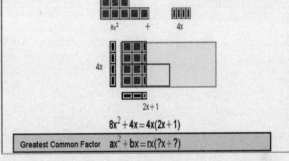

$8x^2 + 4x = 4x(2x + 1)$

Greatest Common Factor $ax^2 + bx = rx(?x + ?)$

Arrange the pieces into a rectangle. The common side is the factor. Is there another way to arrange the pieces to get a rectangle?

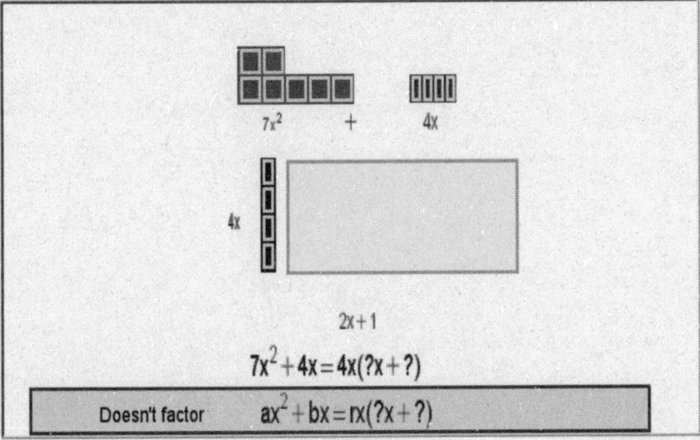

4x is not a factor. What is the GCF of the terms? Try other factors.

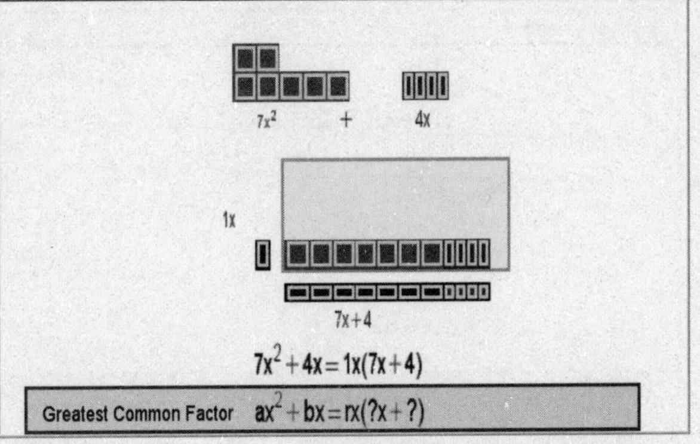

What is the GCF of the factors **7** and **4**? What is the GCF of factors $\mathbf{x^2}$ and **x**?

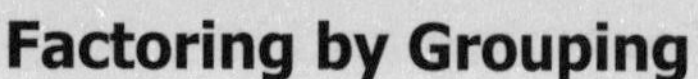

Factoring by Grouping

EnableMath

Factoring the **GCF** from an expression is useful in finding **binomial factors**. An expression with four terms is grouped so that the first two terms have a common factor and the last two terms have a common factor. If that result has two of the same binomial factors, then that common factor is taken out, leaving the remaining two terms as the other binomial factor.

Remember: 1 is a factor of everything.

Factor by grouping

Step 1: Group the first two terms together and the last two terms together.

Step 2: Factor the GCF from the first pair and another GCF from the second pair.

Step 3: If there is a common binomial factor from the results from step 2, factor it out, resulting in another binomial factor.

Step 4: Make sure there are no common factors remaining in the binomial pairs.

Factor by grouping:

$$6x^3+3x^2+10x+5$$
$$=6x^3+3x^2+10x+5$$
$$=3x^2(2x+1)+5(2x+1)$$
$$=(3x^2+5)(2x+1)$$

Factor by grouping:

$$x^3-2x^2+x-2$$
$$=x^3+x-2x^2-2$$
$$=x(x^2+1)-2(x^2+1)$$
$$=(x-2)(x^2+1)$$

Notice that the commutative property was used to rearrange the terms of the expression. This is an optional step. Try it without rearranging. Hint: 1 is a factor of everything.

When factoring the –2, watch the change of signs.

Factor by grouping:

$$2x^2+xy-4x-2y$$
$$=2x^2+xy-4x-2y$$
$$=x(2x+y)-2(2x+y)$$
$$=(x-2)(2x+y)$$

Notice the sign changes when –2 is factored. In order for the binomials to be common, the constants, variables and signs must be the same.

Factor by grouping:

$$zt-dt+zh-dh$$
$$=zt-dt+zh-dh$$
$$=t(z-d)+h(z-d)$$
$$=(t+h)(z-d)$$

Look for common terms. Two binomial factors are the result of factor by grouping.

The commutative, associative and distributive properties can be used to rearrange, group, and factor algebraic expressions. Given an expression with four terms, can two terms can be grouped together so that each pair has a GCF? Each pair of terms is a binomial. After factoring the GCF from the binomials, are the remaining binomials alike? Binomials that are alike can be factored. What factors are left when the binomial factors are taken out?

If an array of squares, variable bars, and unit bars can be made into a rectangle, what can you determine about the factors of the expression represented by the array? Can every factorable expression be arranged into a rectangular array? What happens when you increase the coefficient of a variable term in a binomial factor? Does the result increase, decrease, or remain the same?

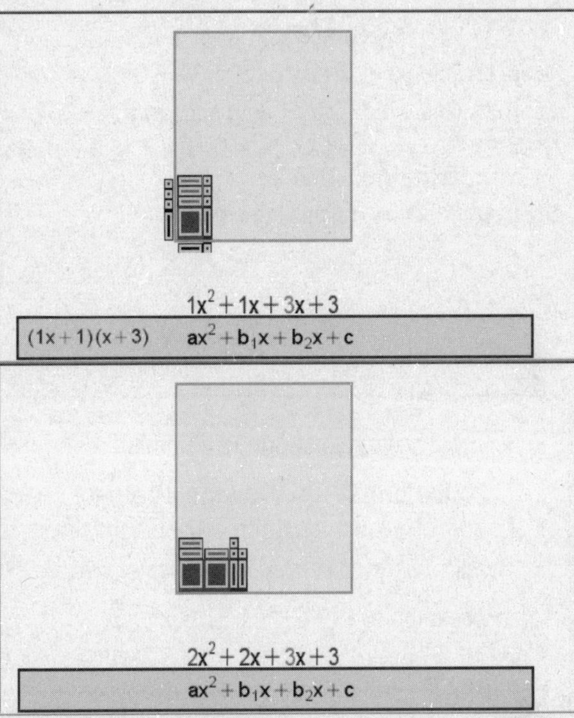

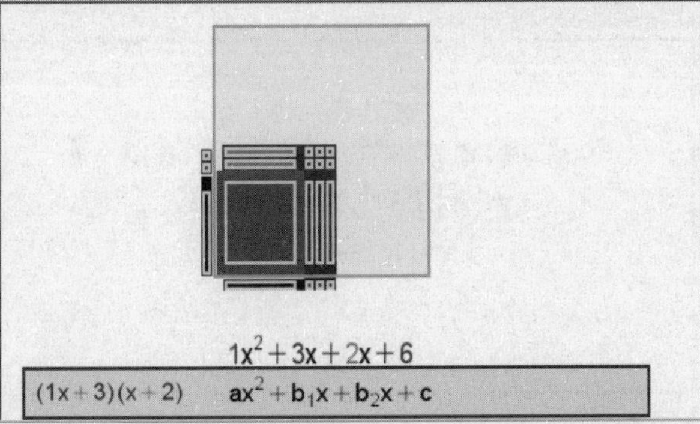

What is the factor from the first pair? What is the factor from the second pair?

This expression is factorable. Can you rearrange its objects units to make a rectangle?

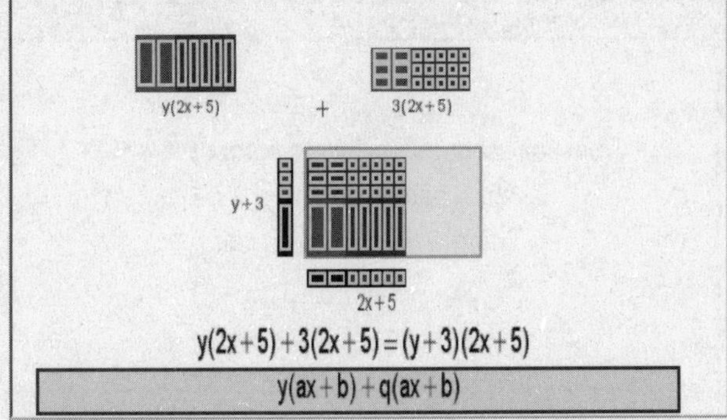

What binomial factor is common to both terms?

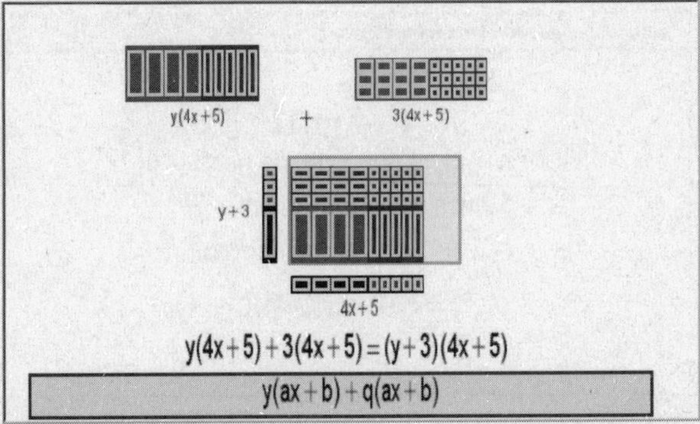

Here the pairs of factors are grouped into a rectangular array. How do you read off the factors?

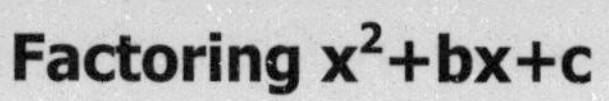

Factoring x^2+bx+c

EnableMath

Factoring is the process of breaking a product apart into its multiplicative components. Factoring undoes multiplication. A trinomial of the form $\mathbf{x^2 + bx + c}$ can be broken apart into two binomial factors if the sum of the factors of **c** add to **b**.

Note: Not all trinomials in the form $\mathbf{x^2 + bx + c}$ are factorable. If **c** does not have a pair of factors that add to **b,** then the trinomial is not factorable.

Factoring ax^2 + bx + c

Step 1: Find pairs of factors of **c**.

Step 2: Find which pair (if any) adds to **b**.

Step 3: Fill in the pattern **(x + __)(x + __)** with the factors from step 2.

Step 4: Check by multiplying back.

Multiply $(x+2)(x+3)$.

$(x+2)(x+3) = x^2+2x+3x+6 = x^2+5x+6$

How can we do the inverse operation?

How can we factor x^2+5x+6 to $(x+2)(x+3)$?

The key to factoring a trinomial of the form x^2+bx+c is to notice that b is the sum of the two constants in the binomial factors, while c is the product of the two constants.

For example, $(x+2)(x+3) = x^2+5x+6$.

Points 1 & 2: Here is the pattern for factoring a trinomial of the form x^2 + bx + c.

Factor this trinomial of the form x^2+bx+c:

x^2+6x-7

Possible pairs: -1 and 7 or 1 and -7

Which pair has a sum of 6?

-1 and 7 have a sum of 6.

$x^2+6x-7 = (x-1)(x+7)$

Point 3: Here are only two choices. Use trial and error or process of elimination to choose which pair adds to 6. Signs play a significant role in determining the correct factors.

Factor this trinomial of the form x^2+bx+c:

$x^2-7x+12$

What pairs of numbers have a product of 12?

Which pair has a sum of -7?

-3 and -4 are the right pair.

$x^2-7x+12 = (x-3)(x-4)$

Point 4: In time, factoring trinomials becomes a mental process. For now, use scratch paper to write out the factor pair and test it in the pattern.

Factor this trinomial of the form x^2+bx+c:

$x^2-3x-18$

What pairs of numbers have a product of -18?

Which pair has a sum of -3?

3 and -6 are the right pair.

$x^2-3x-18 = (x+3)(x-6)$

Point 5: Be careful to use the correct signs.

The representation of factoring begins with the product displayed in the middle of the axes. The factors are read from the left side and the bottom—the dimensions of the rectangle. Does it matter how the rectangle is arrayed? Can either side be listed first—is multiplication of binomials commutative?

Most trinomials are not factorable. However, all of the ones that we show here are because they are constructed from their factors. Use the joystick to change the values of **p** and **q**. How does changing the values of **p** and **q** affect the product of the binomial?

Notice how the unit bars (blue) pile up in each quadrant. How can that help you decide which sign to use?

How do you determine which quadrant goes with the bars? Will the squares always be located in the first quadrant? Can zero ever be used for **q** or **s**?

As a reminder: Quadrant I is positive, II is negative, III is positive, and IV is negative.

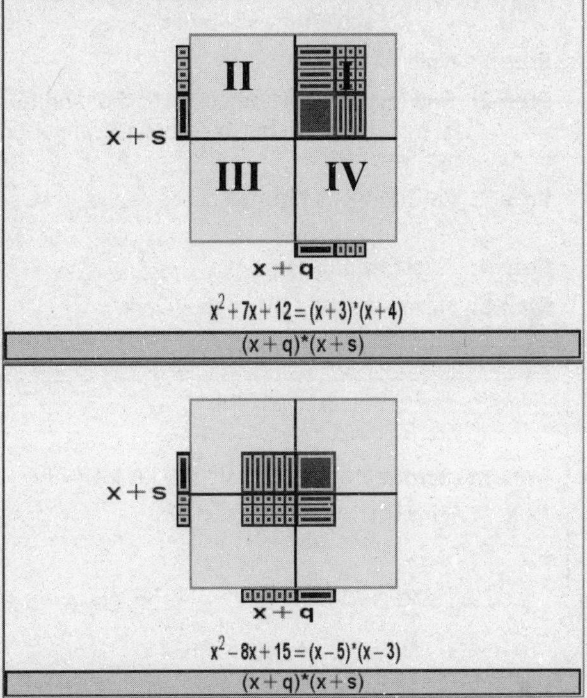

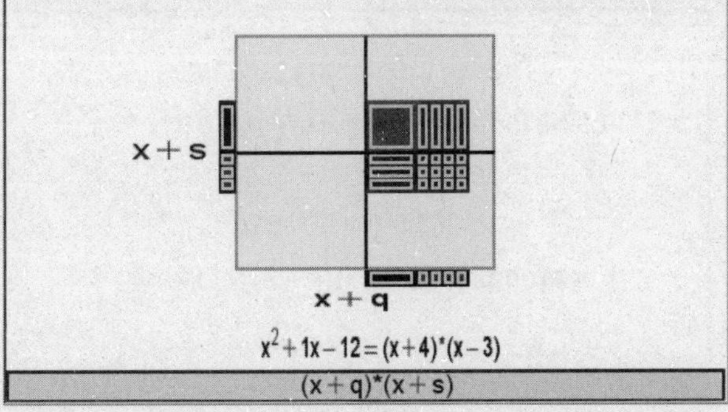

Notice that −3 is accounted for in quadrant III. Why are there bars in quadrant IV?

Here both **q** and **s** are negative. Are the unit bars positive or negative? Why?

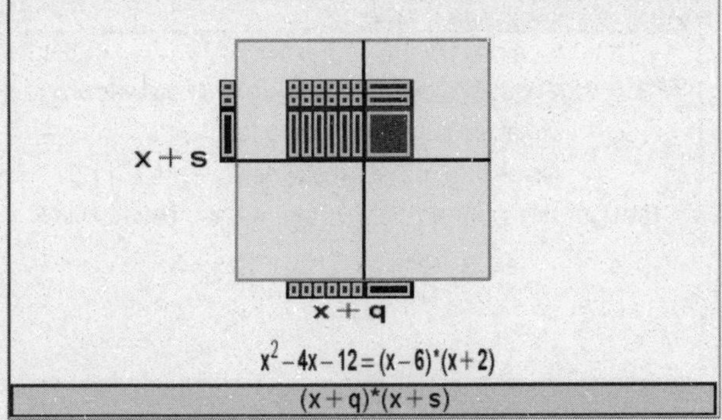

q is negative and **s** is positive. Are the unit bars positive or negative? Why? What if we reverse this and make **q** positive and **s** negative?

Factoring ax^2+bx+c

EnableMath

There are two effective and widely used methods for factoring trinomials of the form $\mathbf{ax^2 + bx + c}$. One method, **trial and error**, is usually done mentally or by using scratch paper. The second method, **factor by grouping**, is a step-by-step process. Both are presented here with a couple of examples.

Factoring ax^2+bx+c

Step 1: Multiply **a*c**.

Step 2: Find factors of the product **a*c** that add to **b**. If no factors exist, the trinomial cannot be factored.

Step 3: Rewrite **bx** as the sum of the results in step 2.

Step 4: Factor by grouping.

Step 5: Multiply back to check your work.

Factor this trinomial of the form ax^2+bx+c: **Use factor by grouping.**

$$8x^2+31x-4$$

What is the product of a*c? (8)(-4)=-32

What are the factors of -32 that add to 31? Only +32 and -1 work.

Rewrite bx (31x) with the factors of a*c:

$$8x^2+32x-x-4$$

Factor by grouping: 8x(x+4)-1(x+4)=(8x-1)(x+4)

$$8x^2+31x-4=(8x-1)(x+4)$$

$ax^2+bx+c=(px+q)(rx+s)$

Above and upper right show two examples using the factor by grouping method—sometimes called the a-c method. Once the factors of the **a*c** product that add to **b** are found (step 3), factor by grouping takes the guesswork away.

Factor this trinomial of the form ax^2+bx+c: **Use factor by grouping.**

$$12x^2-11x-5$$

What is the product of a*c? (12)(-5)=-60

What are the factors of -60 that add to -11? Only 4 and -15 work.

Rewrite bx (-11x) with the factors of a*c:

$$12x^2+4x-15x-5$$

Factor by grouping: 4x(3x+1)-5(3x+1)=(4x-5)(3x+1)

$$12x^2-11x-5=(4x-5)(3x+1)$$

$ax^2+bx+c=(px+q)(rx+s)$

The key to factoring a trinomial of the form ax^2+bx+c to $(px+q)(rx+s)$ is to notice that p*r is a, q*s is c, and p*s + q*r is b.

For example, $(2x+1)(x-3)=2x^2-5x-3$.

Here are clues to the mental process for factoring. It may take several tries to get the right combination, but the numbers used in most problems should be small enough to factor mentally.

Factor this trinomial of the form ax^2+bx+c:

$$2x^2+11x+5$$

Possible pairs for a = p*r: 1 and 2 or 2 and 1 (Positives only!)

Possible pairs for c = q*s: 1 and 5 or −1 and −5

Which p, q, r and s make b = p*s + q*r?

The right selections are: p = 2, q = 1, r = 1 and s = 5.

$$2x^2+11x+5=(2x+1)(x+5)$$

$ax^2+bx+c=(px+q)(rx+s)$

Trial and error is used along with the addition of some insight.

Factor this trinomial of the form ax^2+bx+c:

$$4x^2-14x+6=2(2x^2-7x+3)$$

What are the possible pairs for new a = p*r? (Positives only!)

What are the possible pairs for c = q*s?

Which p, q, r and s make new b = p*s + q*r?

The right selections are: p = 2, q = −1, r = 1 and s = −3.

$$4x^2-14x+6=2(2x-1)(x-3)$$

$ax^2+bx+c=(px+q)(rx+s)$

First remove common factors. That way the coefficients in the trinomial are as small as possible. Don't forget to write the constant term factor as a part of your answer.

Here we explore factoring trinomials of the form $\mathbf{ax^2 + bx + c}$ into two binomial factors. Here the leading coefficient is positive (**a>0**), and the coefficient of the linear term (**b**) and constant (**c**) re positive or negative. How do you determine the sign of the middle term? How do you determine the sign of the constant term? Is there any way for different pairs of binomial factors to yield the same product rectangle?

In these visualizations, the product rectangle is built from the binomial factors, so that the trinomials are factorable.

How does negative **s** affect the product rectangle? How does negative **q** affect the product rectangle? How can you tell if the middle term is going to be positive or negative? How do you know if the third term is going to be positive or negative? If the last term in the trinomial is positive, what do you know about the two constants in the binomial factors? If the constant term is negative what do you know about the factors?

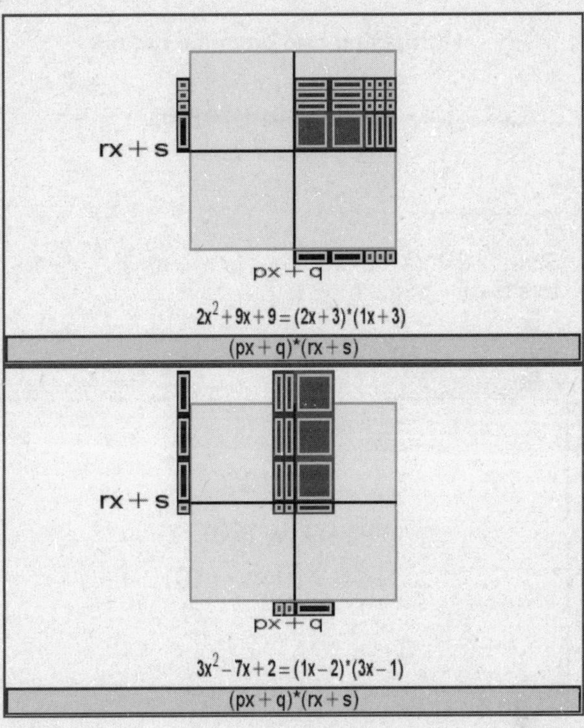

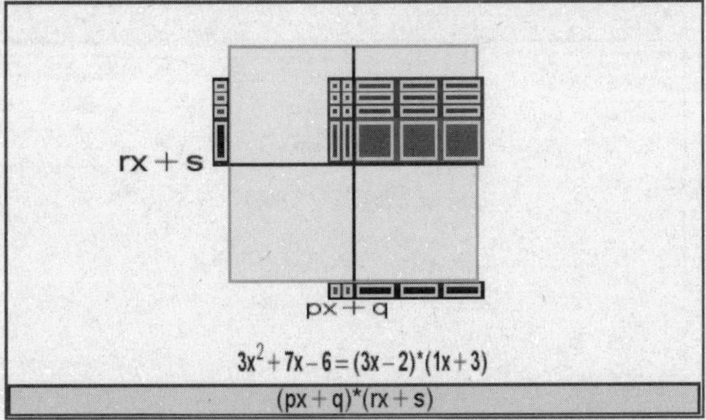

Is the variable **q** positive or negative? How does that impact the product rectangle? How does that impact the sign of the trinomial constant? How does that impact the middle term?

Both **p** and **q** are negative. What is the sign of the constant in the trinomial? How do you determine that the middle term is negative?

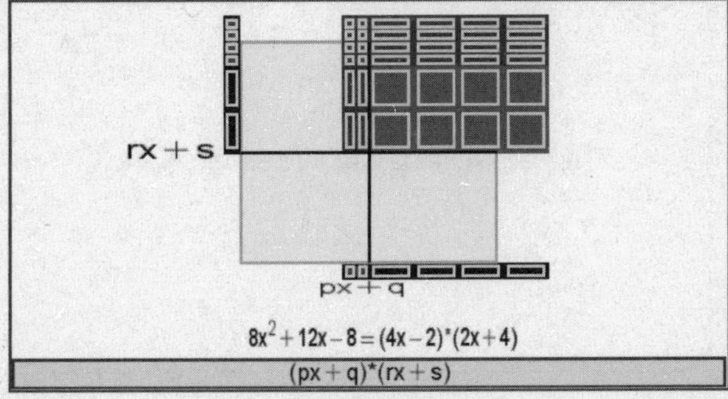

Is this factored completely?

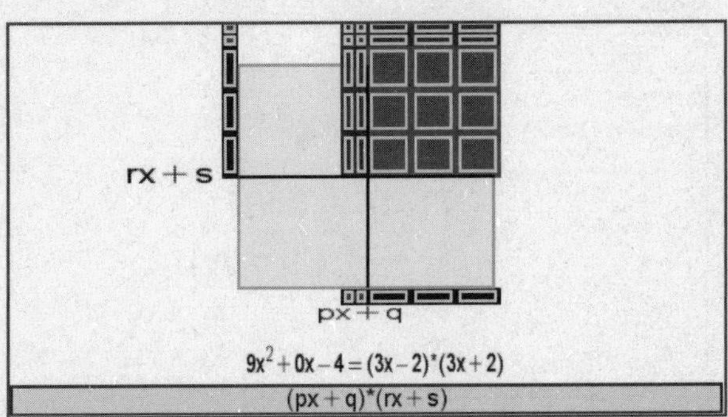

This one is a special case. What is the middle term of the trinomial? What do you notice about the first term? What do you notice about the constant term? The above pattern is called "**difference of squares.**"

Factoring the Difference of 2 Squares

There are some special cases which turn out to be both interesting and important. For example, most binomial factors form a trinomial product with three terms: a squared term, a middle term, and a constant term.

But binomial factors can also produce an expression where the middle term coefficient is zero. Some of these special cases have the form $\mathbf{a^2 - b^2}$ where a and b can stand for any combination of constants and variables that are perfect squares. This kind of expression is called, for obvious reasons, the *difference of squares* and it always factors as $\mathbf{(a + b)(a - b)}$. Notice the difference in signs between the two binomial factors.

Multiplying two binomial factors

$$(a + b)(a - b) = a^2 - ab + ba - b^2$$
$$= a^2 + 0ab - b^2$$
$$= a^2 - b^2$$

Since $(a + b)(a - b)$ multiplies to $a^2 - b^2$, $a^2 - b^2$ factors to $(a + b)(a - b)$.

The formula to factor a difference of squares is:

$$a^2 - b^2 = (a + b)(a - b)$$

Factor:

$$x^2 - 100$$
$$= (x)^2 - (10)^2$$
$$= (x + 10)(x - 10)$$

$a^2 - b^2 = (a + b)(a - b)$

The square root of $\mathbf{x^2}$ is **x** and square root of **100** is **10**.

Factor:

$$25 - 49x^2$$
$$= (5)^2 - (7x)^2$$
$$= (5 + 7x)(5 - 7x)$$

$a^2 - b^2 = (a + b)(a - b)$

Make sure the expression fits the difference of squares pattern. The square root of 25 is 5 and square root of $49x^2$ is 7x.

Factor:

$$9x^2 - 4y^2$$
$$= (3x)^2 - (2y)^2$$
$$= (3x + 2y)(3x - 2y)$$

$a^2 - b^2 = (a + b)(a - b)$

Any perfect square combinations work. *Think of the pattern as a perfect square minus another perfect square.*

There is NO formula to factor a sum of squares!

$\mathbf{a^2 + b^2}$ is not factorable!

Factoring the Difference of 2 Squares

Here is a visual demonstration that shows that the difference between two squares (a^2-b^2) is always **(a+b)(a-b)**, the product of the sum and the difference between their values.

*Hint: Don't be confused by our use of different letters, the general form remains the same! We are using **(x+a)(x-a)***

Visualize this as two squares (in this case we are using **x** for the length of the side of one of them and **a** for the length of the other. When we place one on top of the other, the area that remains is the difference between the two squares **(x^2-a^2).**

Animate (in the joystick) will show you how this difference factors into **(x+a)(x-a).**

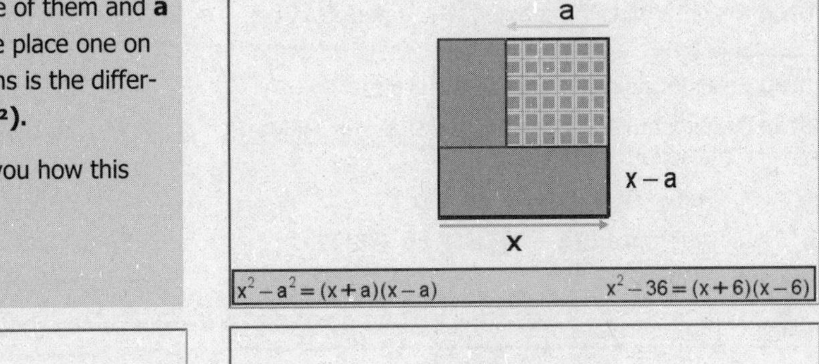

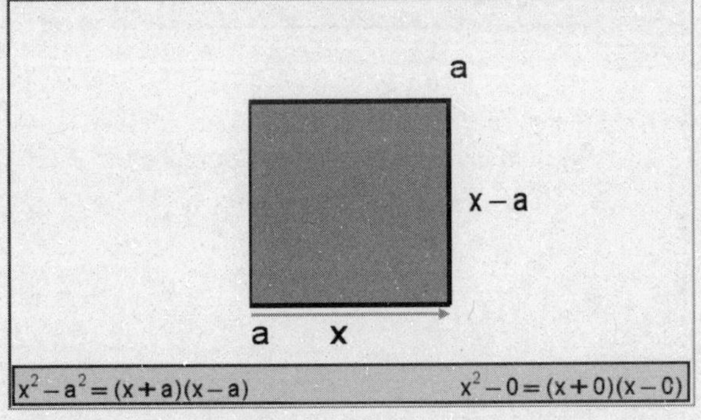

When a=0, the product is x^2. The length of each side is **x**. Now increase **a**. What happens?

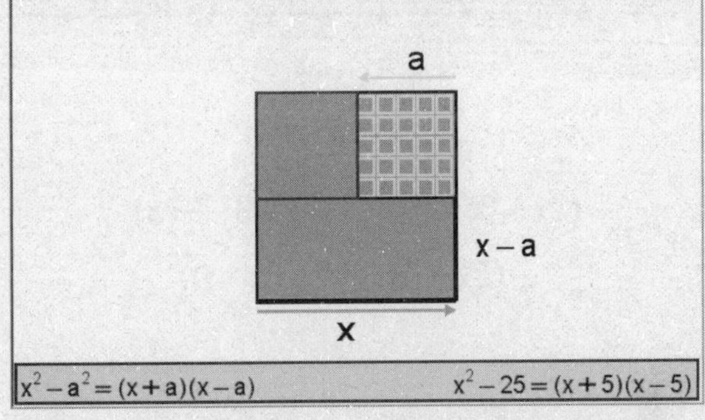

This is x^2 - a^2. What area is left when we subtract a^2 from x^2?

What are the dimensions of the block to the left of a^2?

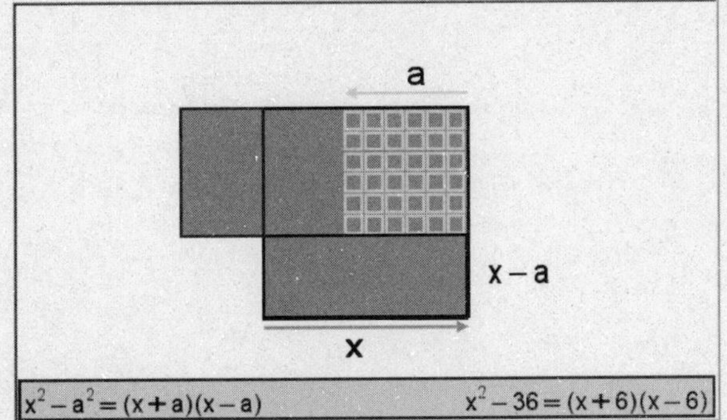

Select **animate** in the joystick and move that block. What are the dimensions of the block?

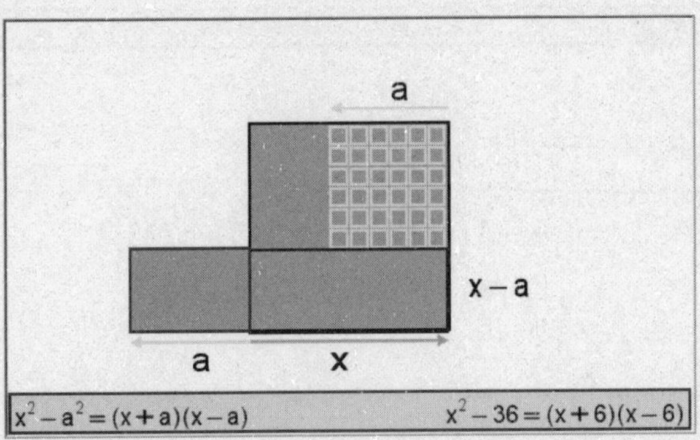

What are the dimensions of the two bottom rectangles taken together?

Like difference of squares, **sums and differences of cubes** are special cases and can be factored. There is a formula for factoring both sums and differences of cubes that can be memorized for use in more advanced topics in algebra. Once you know the pattern, you can fill in the formula with the appropriate values for **a** and **b**.

Factoring Sums and Differences of Cubes

Step 1: Determine if the binomial has perfect cube terms.

Step 2: Find the cubed root of both terms.

Step 3: Substitute the values from step 2 in the appropriate pattern.

Sums: $\mathbf{(a + b)(a^2 - ab + b^2)}$

Differences: $\mathbf{(a - b)(a^2 + ab + b^2)}$

Step 4: Simplify.

Factor:

$$8x^3 + 27$$
$$= (2x)^3 + (3)^3$$
$$= (2x+3)((2x)^2 - (2x)(3) + (3)^2)$$
$$= (2x+3)(4x^2 - 6x + 9)$$

$a^3 + b^3 = (a+b)(a^2 - ab + b^2)$

Perfect cubes $8x^3$ and 27; cubed roots are 2x and 3, respectively. Fill in the formula for sums and simplify.

Factor:

$$64x^3 - 1$$
$$= (4x)^3 - (1)^3$$
$$= (4x-1)((4x)^2 + (4x)(1) + (1)^2)$$
$$= (4x-1)(16x^2 + 4x + 1)$$

$a^3 - b^3 = (a-b)(a^2 + ab + b^2)$

Perfect cubes $64x^3$ and 1 and their cubed roots 4x and 1, respectively. Fill in the formula for difference and simplify.

The formula to factor a sum of cubes is:

$$a^3 + b^3 = (a+b)(a^2 - ab + b^2)$$

The formula to factor a difference of cubes is:

$$a^3 - b^3 = (a-b)(a^2 + ab + b^2)$$

Notice the sign patterns for both formulae.

The key to factoring sums and differences of cubes is recognizing prefect cubes in various forms.

$\mathbf{a^3+b^3}$ does not equal $(a+b)^3$ and $\mathbf{a^3-b^3}$ does not equal $(a-b)^3$.

Try multiplying **(a+b)(a+b)(a+b)** out by hand.

To factor a sum or difference of cubes, both terms must be perfect cubes.

How do you know if a number is a perfect cube?

How do you know if a variable is a perfect cube?

What is the sign pattern for factoring sums of cubes?

What is the sign pattern for difference of cubes?

$$8x^3 = 2^3x^3$$

Perfect Cubes p^3x^3

$$-64x^3 = -4^3x^3$$

Perfect Cubes p^3x^3

Why does the sign stay the same after taking cube roots of negative numbers?

$$a^3+b^3=(a+b)(a^2-ab+b^2)$$

$$a^3-b^3=(a-b)(a^2+ab+b^2)$$

$$8x^3+27=(2x+3)(4x^2-6x+9)$$

$p^3x^3+q^3$

What is the cubed root of $\mathbf{8x^3}$? What is the cube root of **27**?

$$a^3+b^3=(a+b)(a^2-ab+b^2)$$

$$a^3-b^3=(a-b)(a^2+ab+b^2)$$

$$64x^3-27=(4x-3)(16x^2+12x+9)$$

$p^3x^3+q^3$

What is the cube root of $\mathbf{64\ x^3}$?

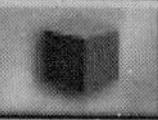

Factoring Perfect Squares

EnableMath

Perfect squares are quadratic expressions that can be factored into two copies of the same linear factor. Perfect squares are very important for some higher processes in mathematics.

When you factor the expression $\mathbf{x^2+6x+9}$, you get two copies of the same linear factor $\mathbf{(x+3)}$.

Factor this perfect square:

$$x^2+6x+9$$

Factor this perfect square:

$$x^2+6x+9$$
$$(x+3)(x+3)$$
$$(x+3)^2$$

Write as a square.

Once you have factored and there are two copies of the same factor, you can write the expression as a square.

Factor this perfect square:

$$2x^2-4x+2$$
$$2(x^2-2x+1)$$

Factor out the 2.

When there's a coefficient other than 1 on the $\mathbf{x^2}$ term, factor out that coefficient first to see if the resulting expression is a perfect square.

Factor this perfect square:

$$2x^2-4x+2$$
$$2(x^2-2x+1)$$
$$2(x-1)(x-1)$$
$$2(x-1)^2$$

Write as a square.

This quadratic expression is 2 times a perfect square.

You can visualize quadratic expressions that are perfect squares as a collection of x^2-squares, **x**-bars and unit bars that come together to form one big square.

What happens as you change the value of **x**?

If **a** and **c** are both perfect squares will the polynomial always be a perfect square?

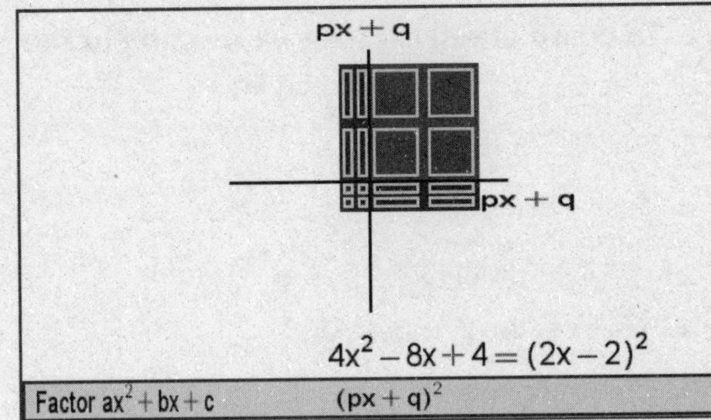

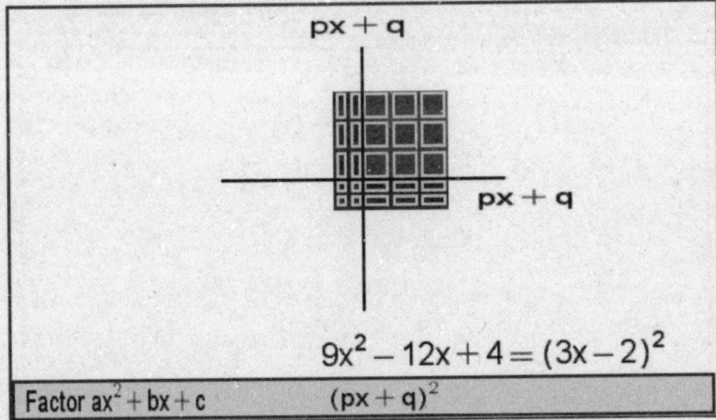

What happens as you change the values of **p** and **q**?

The process of completing the square is a method for factoring polynomials. If you can change the value of the **c** term in a quadratic to create a perfect square, then it can be factored.

To complete the square expression in the form x^2+bx+c

1. Find half of **b**.
2. Square that.
3. Add it and subtract it.
4. **$x^2+bx+(\frac{1}{2}b)^2 = (x+\frac{1}{2}b)^2$**
5. Combine constants.

Complete the square:

$$x^2+4x+5$$

Complete the square:

$$x^2+4x+5$$
$$x^2+4x+4+5-4$$

Add and subtract $(\frac{4}{2})^2$.

Here **b** is 4. So, half of b is 2. 2^2 is 4. So, here we add and subtract 4.

Complete the square:

$$x^2+4x+5$$
$$x^2+4x+4+5-4$$
$$x^2+4x+4+1$$
$$(x+2)^2+1$$

The first three terms are a square.

Now, the first three terms are equal to **$(x+2)^2$** - this is our **$(x+(\frac{1}{2})b)^2$** - and we have successfully completed the square.

Complete the square:

$$2x^2-12x+6$$
$$2(x^2-6x+3)$$

Factor out the 2.

Here, we have to factor out the coefficient of 2 first. Then, we can start to complete the square.

Complete the square:

$$2x^2-12x+6$$
$$2(x^2-6x+3)$$
$$2(x^2-6x+9+3-9)$$
$$2(x^2-6x+9-6)$$
$$2((x-3)^2-6)$$

The first three terms are a square.

Half of -6 is -3. $(-3)^2$ is 9. So, we add and subtract 9 to create the square $(x-3)^2$.

We saw in the last concept that you can visualize quadratic expressions that are perfect squares as a collection of $\mathbf{x^2}$-squares, **x**-bars and unit bars that come together to form one big square. In this concept, we'll experiment to see what we need to add in order to "complete the square."

What value of **c** completes this square?

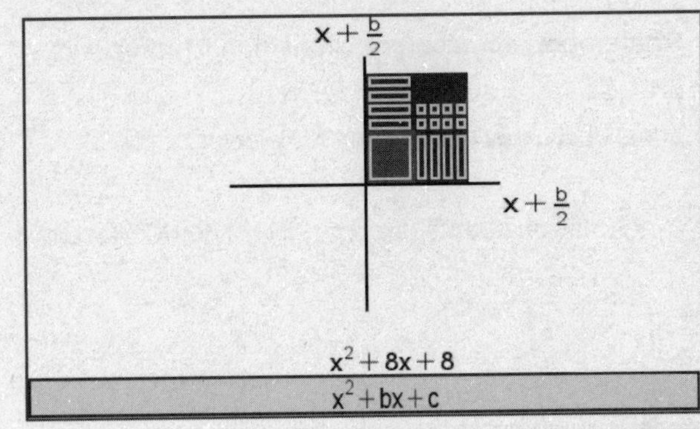

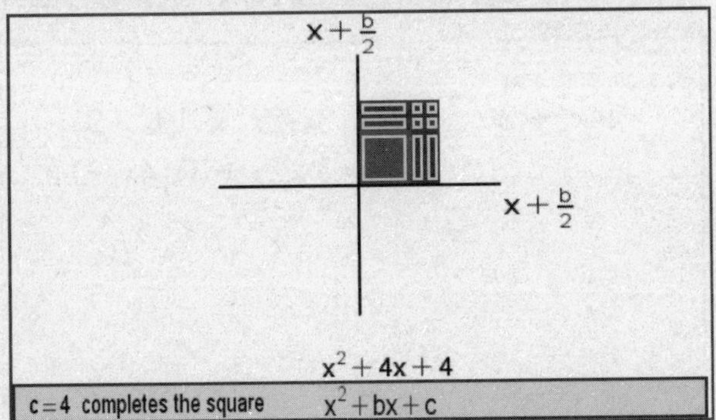

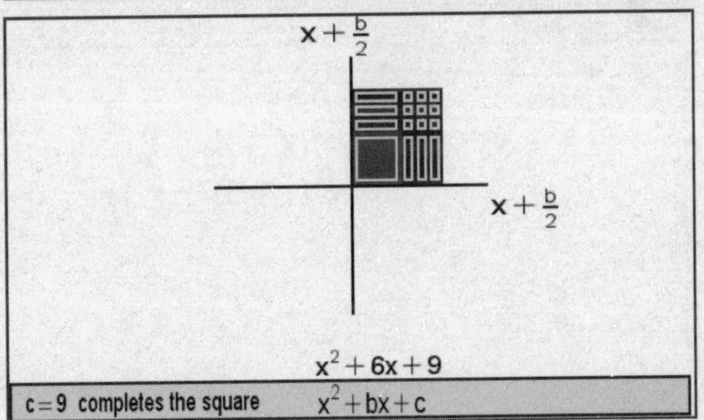

How is the value of **c** that completes the square related to **b**? Change the values of **b** and **c** and see if you can make a conjecture about the relationship between them.

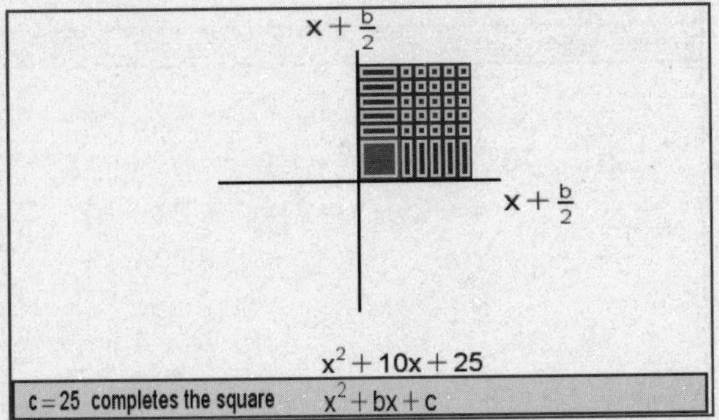

Sometimes variable expressions need to be factored in more than one step.

Always begin by looking for the greatest common factor (**GCF**) and factor that out first. Then, use the appropriate factoring methods on what is left. The factoring tools that you have learned so far are trinomial factoring, differences of squares, sums and differences of cubes ,and factoring by grouping.

Remember, some expressions don't factor.

Sums of squares ($a^2 + b^2$) do NOT factor.

Irreducible quadratics (like $x^2 + 3x + 9$) do NOT factor.

Factor completely:

$$x^4 - 4x^3 - 5x^2 =$$

Always factor out the GCF first!!

Factor completely:

$$\begin{aligned} x^4 - 4x^3 - 5x^2 &= x^2(x^2 - 4x - 5) \\ &= x^2(x-5)(x+1) \end{aligned}$$

Above, once the GCF was factored out, a trinomial was left to factor.

Factor completely:

$$\begin{aligned} 24x^3 + 30x^2 - 9x &= 3x(8x^2 + 10x - 3) \\ &= 3x(2x+3)(4x-1) \end{aligned}$$

Remember that the GCF is part of the factored form and must be part of the answer.

Factor completely:

$$\begin{aligned} x^4 - 16 &= (x^2+4)(x^2-4) \\ &= (x^2+4)(x+2)(x-2) \end{aligned}$$

Here, the GCF is 1. Next, we factored the difference of squares and then factored the resulting difference of squares again.

Factor completely:

$$\begin{aligned} 2x^7 - 16x^4 &= 2x^4(x^3 - 8) \\ &= 2x^4(x-2)(x^2+2x+4) \end{aligned}$$

The trinomial of the form $x^2 + bx + b^2$ doesn't factor.

After the GCF is factored out, a difference of cubes is left. Use the pattern for factoring difference of cubes.

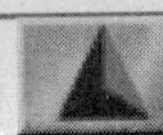

This concept is a little different from most concepts. It provides you with a flow chart for how to factor completely complicated variable expressions.

You can always refer back to this concept for a reference!

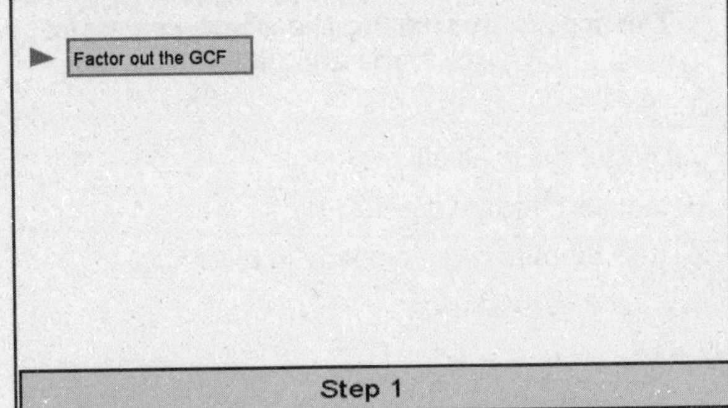

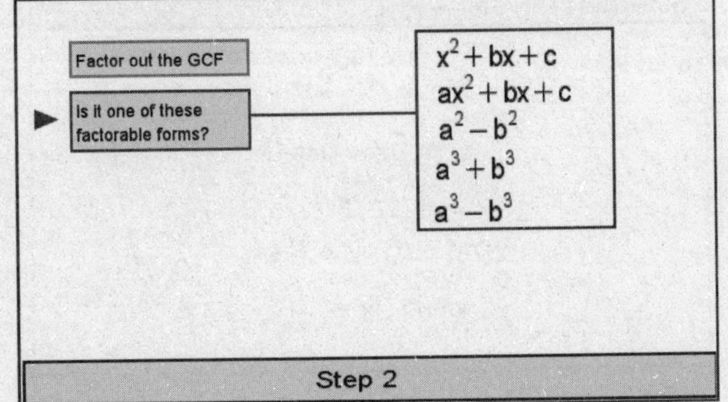

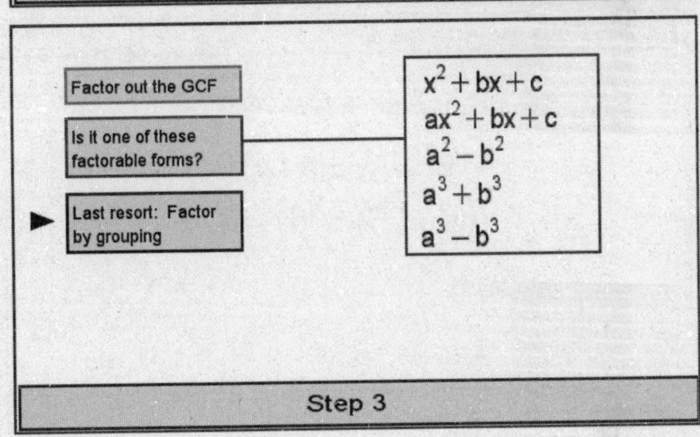

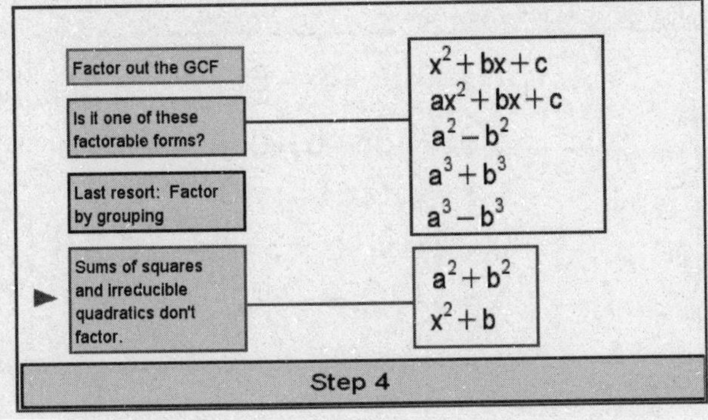

Finding the x-Intercepts of Parabolas

EnableMath

The graph of a quadratic equation is a parabola. The x-intercepts of a graph occur when **y=0**. So, to find the x-intercepts of a quadratic equation, set y=0, and solve for **x**:

$$0=ax^2+bx+c$$

Solving for **x** can be done by factoring the quadratic into two binomial factors and then setting each factor equal to zero. Use the zero factor property to solve. The zero factor property: if the product of two numbers is zero, at least one must be zero. If a*b=0, then a=0 and/or b=0.

The process for finding the x-intercepts of a quadratic equation

1. Set y=0.
2. Factor the quadratic.
3. Set each factor equal to zero.
4. Use the zero factor property to solve for x.
5. Check each solution.

Find the values of the x-intercepts of:

$$y=x^2+5x-6$$

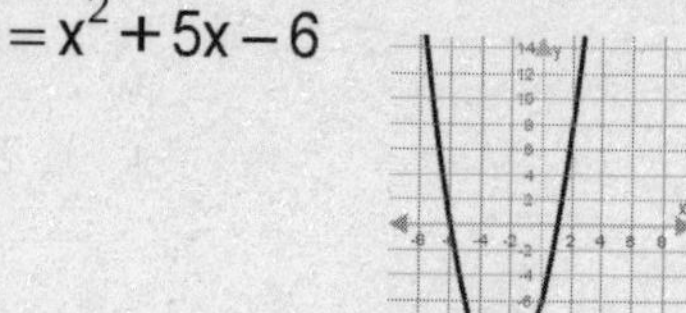

$y=ax^2+bx+c$

Find the values of the x-intercepts of:

$$y=x^2+5x-6$$
$$x^2+5x-6=0$$
$$(x-1)(x+6)=0$$

Factor the left side. $y=ax^2+bx+c$

First, set y=0. Next factor the quadratic.

Find the values of the x-intercepts of:

$$y=x^2+5x-6$$
$$x^2+5x-6=0$$
$$(x-1)(x+6)=0$$
$$x-1=0,\ x+6=0$$
$$x=1,\ x=-6$$

These are the x-intercepts. $y=ax^2+bx+c$

Set each factor equal to zero. The real solutions are the x-intercepts.

Find the values of the x-intercepts of:

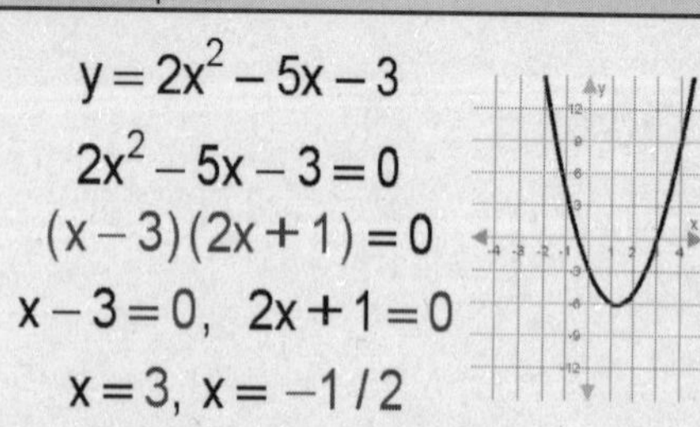

$$y=2x^2-5x-3$$
$$2x^2-5x-3=0$$
$$(x-3)(2x+1)=0$$
$$x-3=0,\ 2x+1=0$$
$$x=3,\ x=-1/2$$

These are the x-intercepts. $y=ax^2+bx+c$

Often one solution is positive and one is negative.

Find the values of the x-intercepts of:

$$y=6x^2+5x-6$$
$$6x^2+5x-6=0$$
$$(3x-2)(2x+3)=0$$
$$3x-2=0,\ 2x+3=0$$
$$x=2/3,\ x=-3/2$$

These are the x-intercepts. $y=ax^2+bx+c$

Use any means of factoring.

Finding the x-Intercepts of Parabolas

This is an introduction to graphing polynomials. The x-intercepts of a parabola are related to the factors of that quadratic equation. The visualization builds the parabola from the factors of a quadratic equation.

Change the values of **p, q, r** and **s** to see how the x-intercepts change. Does changing **p** and **q** affect **s** and **t**? Does changing **s** and **t** affect **p** or **q**?

What is the value of **y** at the x-intercept?

If **p** or **r** are negative, what happens to the graph?

Can **p** or **r = 0**? What happens?

As **p** increases, what happens to the parabola? What happens as **r** decreases? What happens as they increase?

What happens as **q** and **s** increase?

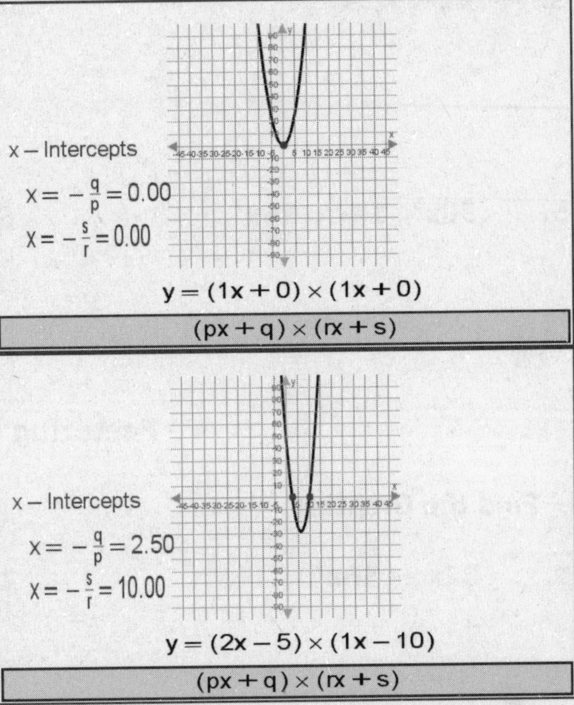

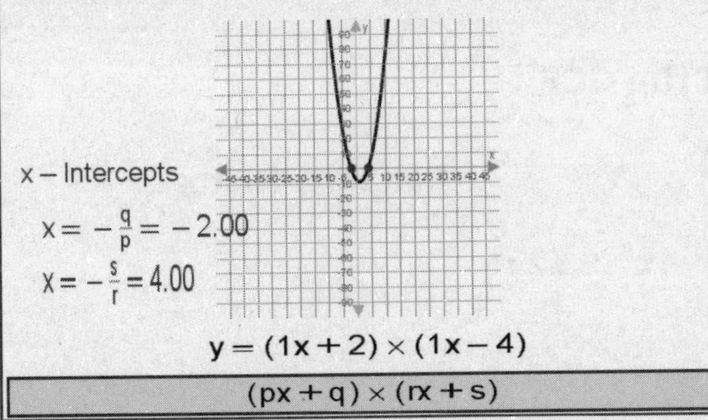

How are the values of **p, q, r** and **s** related to the **x-intercept** values? What quadratic is represented by the graph above?

What are the coordinates of the x-intercepts? Why does the graph intersect in two places?

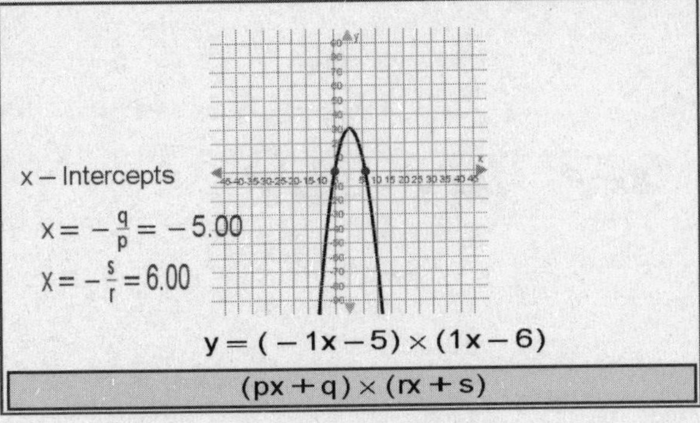

What is the quadratic equation for the above parabola? What is the coefficient of x^2?

Greatest Common Factor

Find the Greatest Com- mon Factor:

1. $27, 63, 99$

2. $48, 60, 72$

3. x^6, x^{11}, x^{15}

4. x^9, x^4, x^{12}

5. $30x^5, 12x^3, 36x^7$

6. $24x^5y^2, 18x^2y^8, 12x^3y^6$

Factoring and the GCF

— Find the Greatest Common Factor

1. $32x + 56x^2$

2. $4x^3 + 12x^4$

3. $12X^6 - 14x^{11} + 16x^{15}$

4. $7x^{12} + 14x^9 - 49x^4$

5. $30x^3 - 18x^5 - 36x^7$

6. $8x^3y^6 - 24x^5y^2 + 16x^2y^8$

Factor by Grouping

Factor the following:

1. $4x^2 + 16x + 3x + 12$

2. $3x^2 + 15x + 4x + 20$

3. $9x^3+12x^2+6x+8$

4. $15 - 9x - 5x^2 + 3x^3$

5. $10m + 4n - 6mn - 15m^2$

6. $rp - sp + rq - sq$

Factoring $x^2 + bx + c$

Factor the following trinomials

1. $x^2 + 13x + 40$

2. $x^2 + 12x + 35$

3. $x^2 + x - 56$

4. $x^2 - 5x - 14$

5. $x^2 - x - 56$

6. $x^2 + 4x - 12$

Factoring $ax^2 + bx + c$

Factor the following trinomials

1. $2x^2 + 13x + 15$
2. $2x^2 + 17x + 8$
3. $2x^2 + x - 36$
4. $12x^2 - 13x - 4$
5. $9x^2 - 18x - 16$
6. $6x^2 + 14x - 12$

The Difference of 2 Squares

Factor the following.

1. $x^2 - 36$
2. $x^2 - 9$
3. $9x^2 - 16$
4. $49x^2 - 64$
5. $12x^2 - 48$
6. $9x^2 - 16y^2$

Sums and Differences of Cubes

Factor the following.

1. $x^3 + 64$
2. $x^3 - 125$
3. $27x^3 - 64$
4. $8x^3 + 64$
5. $16x^3 + 2$
6. $125x^3 - 8y^3$

Factoring Perfect Squares

Factor the perfect square.

1. x^2-2x+1

2. $2x^2-4x+2$

3. $-x^2-6x-9$

Completing the Square

Complete the square.

1. x^2-2x+6

2. $x^2-6x+12$

3. $2x^2-4x+8$

4. $2x^2-4x+3$

Factoring Completely

Factor completely.

1. $5x^3+5x^2-60x$

2. $2x^4-32$

3. $2x^6-54x^3$

Finding the x-Intercepts of Parabolas

Find the x-intercepts of the given equation.

1. $y=x^2+3x-40$

2. $y=4x^2-7x-15$

13. Rational Expressions & Equations

The word 'rational' stems from ratio and is not about making sense. Rationals are ratios or fractions. Rational equations are expressions or equations that involve fractions. Rational equations can be simplified. To add or subtract rational numbers we must find their least common denominators. To divide them we invert the divisor and multiply. You might want to revisit *6.3 Operations on Rationals* before you start this section. Rational equations may look complicated and scary but you can solve them by taking one step at a time.

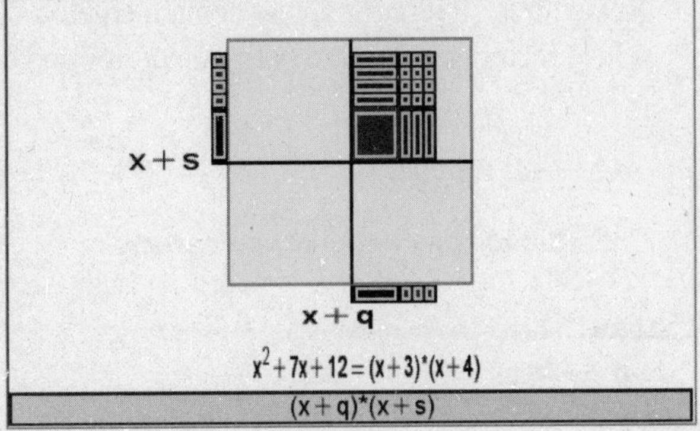

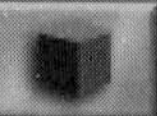

Simplifying Rational Expressions

Rational expressions are algebraic fractions. Like fractions in arithmetic, rational expressions should be written in simplest terms. In order to do this the numerator and denominator must be factored. Any common factors can be divided out. Once all common factors are removed, the rational expression is reduced.

Remember: Rational expressions are created by division. Single terms cannot be cancelled. Only whole factors common to both numerator and denominator can be cancelled.

Simplifying Rational Expressions

Step 1: Factor the numerator.

Step 2: Factor the denominator.

Step 3: Divide out pairs of factors common to both numerator and denominator.

Step 4: Rewrite in lowest terms.

Simplify:

$$\frac{x^2-16}{x^2-6x+8} = \frac{(x+4)(x-4)}{(x-2)(x-4)} = \frac{(x+4)\cancel{(x-4)}}{(x-2)\cancel{(x-4)}} = \frac{x+4}{x-2}$$

This is simplified.

This rational expression uses the difference of squares pattern to factor the numerator. The **(x-4)** factors divided out. Notice that the remaining constants CANNOT be reduced—they are NOT factors. Likewise, DO NOT reduce the **x** variables.

Simplify:

$$\frac{x^3-4x}{x^3+x^2-6x} = \frac{x(x^2-4)}{x(x^2+x-6)} = \frac{x(x+2)(x-2)}{x(x-2)(x+3)} = \frac{\cancel{x}(x+2)\cancel{(x-2)}}{\cancel{x}\cancel{(x-2)}(x+3)} = \frac{x+2}{x+3}$$

This is simplified.

Factor out the common **x** from each term. Divide out the common factors **x** and **(x-2).** Remember: DO NOT reduce the **x** variables from the final answer because they are NOT factors.

Simplify:

$$\frac{x^2-4x-5}{x^2+4x+3} = \frac{(x-5)(x+1)}{(x+1)(x+3)} = \frac{(x-5)\cancel{(x+1)}}{\cancel{(x+1)}(x+3)} = \frac{x-5}{x+3}$$

This is simplified.

Simplify:

$$\frac{2-3x}{3x-2} = \frac{-(-2+3x)}{(3x-2)} = \frac{-\cancel{(3x-2)}}{\cancel{(3x-2)}} = -1$$

This is simplified.

Look carefully at the above example. Notice that factoring out a −1 from the terms in the numerator reverses the signs of the terms. This is a common technique used to switch the signs of terms in either the numerator or denominator, so that common factors can be cancelled.

Two visualizations can guide your understanding of simplifying rational expressions. We show two algebraic expressions in rectangular arrays made up of number bars, variables bars, and squares. Rational expressions are **reducible** if the side of one rectangle is the same length as one side of the other rectangle. If you make one set of area factors equivalent—what happens to the corresponding factors?

We can also find common factors by graphing. Here we have graphed two quadratic equations. If they have a common **x-intercept**, then they have a common factor. Is this common x-intercept then one of the solutions?

Why does the expression on the right reduce when one set of dimensions is equivalent?

Does it matter which set of dimensions are equivalent?

What happens if one of the rectangles is a square?

When the graphs intersect other than at the x-intercept, can you tell if they have a common factor?

What if the graphs intersect at TWO x-intercepts?

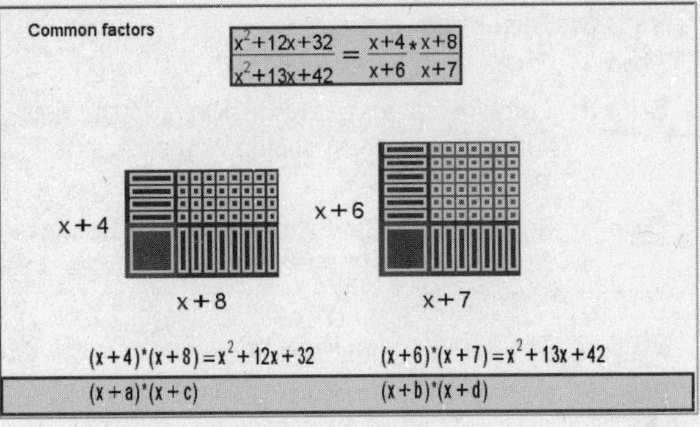

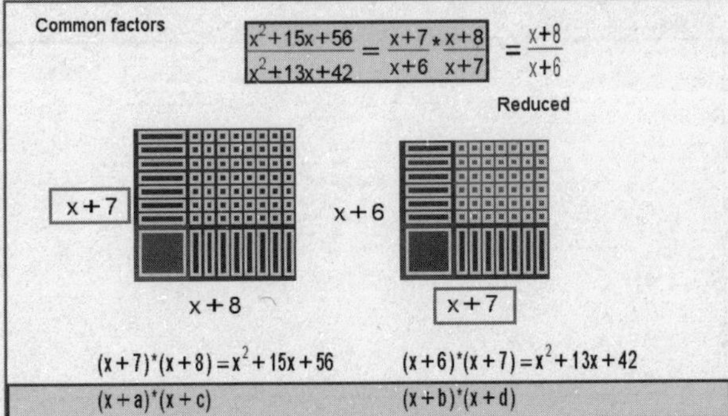

The above right frame shows two algebraic expressions that are not reducible. Changing **a** to 7 makes the factor x+7 the same as the right rectangle's bottom edge.

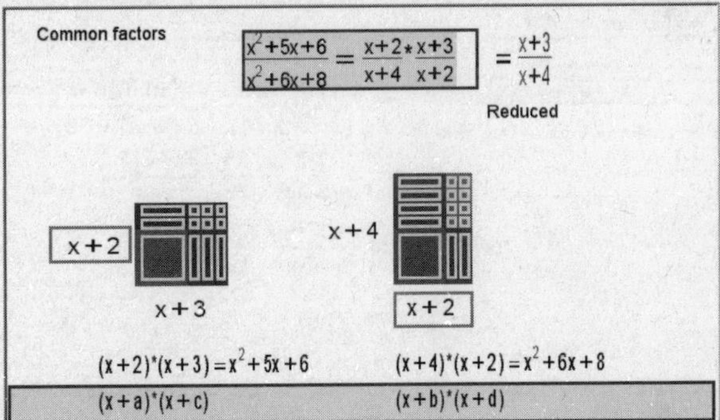

Here is a simpler rational equation. Both the numerator and the denominator are factorable and they have **(x+2)** as the common factor. If you change **b** to **3**, what will be the value of this rational equation?

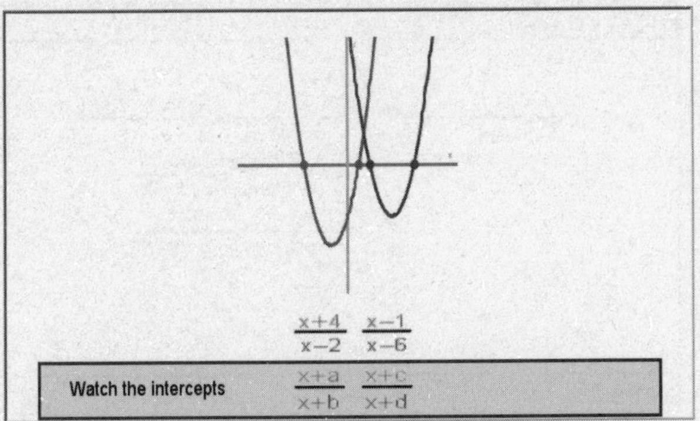

Advanced Visualization: We can graph the two quadratic equations. **These do not have a factor in common.**

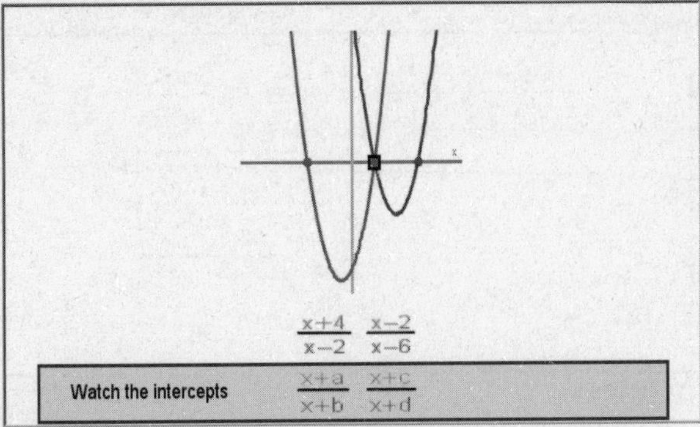

These do have a factor in common and can be reduced. Notice that this simplification means that there are now 3 distinct solutions to this rational equation not 4.

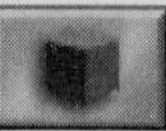

Multiplying Rational Expressions

Rational expressions can be multiplied just like regular fractions. The rule is: Multiply numerators for the new numerator and then multiply denominators for the new denominator. This process requires algebraic expressions to be reduced before multiplying. That way all factors common to both numerator and denominator can be removed allowing for simpler multiplications and no reducing at the end of the process.

Multiplying Rational Expressions

Step 1: Factor both numerators.

Step 2: Factor both denominators.

Step 3: Combine all numerator factors into the new numerator, thereby multiplying across numerators.

Step 4: Rewrite all denominator factors as the new denominator, thereby multiplying across denominators.

Step 5: Divide out common factors.

Step 6: Rewrite in final reduced form.

Multiply and simplify:

$$\frac{x^2-2x}{x^2-2x-3} \times \frac{x^2-9}{x^2+x-6} = \frac{x(x-2)}{(x-3)(x+1)} \times \frac{(x+3)(x-3)}{(x-2)(x+3)}$$
$$= \frac{x(x-2)(x+3)(x-3)}{(x-3)(x+1)(x-2)(x+3)}$$
$$= \frac{x(x-2)(x+3)(x-3)}{(x-3)(x+1)(x-2)(x+3)}$$
$$= \frac{x}{x+1}$$

Simplified form.

Determine and divide out all factors common in the numerator and denominator. Remember only whole FACTORS can be reduced. The **x**'s in the final answer are NOT factors.

Multiply and simplify:

$$\frac{x^3-x}{6x^2+6x-12} \times \frac{5x^2-20}{x^3-x^2-2x} = \frac{x(x^2-1)}{6(x^2+x-2)} \times \frac{5(x^2-4)}{x(x^2-x-2)}$$
$$= \frac{x(x+1)(x-1)}{6(x+2)(x-1)} \times \frac{5(x+2)(x-2)}{x(x-2)(x+1)}$$
$$= \frac{5x(x+1)(x-1)(x+2)(x-2)}{6x(x+2)(x-1)(x-2)(x+1)}$$
$$= \frac{5x(x+1)(x-1)(x+2)(x-2)}{6x(x+2)(x-1)(x-2)(x+1)}$$
$$= \frac{5}{6}$$

Simplified form.

Identify common factors and divide them out.

Simplify:

$$\frac{x^3-4x}{x^3+x^2-6x} = \frac{x(x^2-4)}{x(x^2+x-6)}$$
$$= \frac{x(x+2)(x-2)}{x(x-2)(x+3)}$$
$$= \frac{\cancel{x}(x+2)\cancel{(x-2)}}{\cancel{x}\cancel{(x-2)}(x+3)}$$
$$= \frac{x+2}{x+3}$$

This is simplified.

Multiply and simplify:

$$\frac{x^3-x}{6x^2+6x-12} \times \frac{5x^2-20}{x^3-x^2-2x} = \frac{x(x^2-1)}{6(x^2+x-2)} \times \frac{5(x^2-4)}{x(x^2-x-2)}$$
$$= \frac{x(x+1)(x-1)}{6(x+2)(x-1)} \times \frac{5(x+2)(x-2)}{x(x-2)(x+1)}$$
$$= \frac{5x(x+1)(x-1)(x+2)(x-2)}{6x(x+2)(x-1)(x-2)(x+1)}$$

Multiply.

Factor each term (numerator and denominator) completely using appropriate factoring methods—GCF, trinomial factoring, difference of squares, sums and differences of cubes, and/or factor by grouping.

Multiply and simplify:

$$\frac{x^2-2xy}{x^2-2xy-3y^2} \times \frac{x^2-9y^2}{x^2+xy-6y^2} = \frac{x(x-2y)}{(x-3y)(x+y)} \times \frac{(x+3y)(x-3y)}{(x-2y)(x+3y)}$$
$$= \frac{x(x-2y)(x+3y)(x-3y)}{(x-3y)(x+y)(x-2y)(x+3y)}$$
$$= \frac{x\cancel{(x-2y)}\cancel{(x+3y)}\cancel{(x-3y)}}{\cancel{(x-3y)}(x+y)\cancel{(x-2y)}\cancel{(x+3y)}}$$
$$= \frac{x}{x+y}$$

Simplified form.

Point 3: Factor, divide common factors, multiply remaining factors across numerators and denominators.

Multiplication of factors is visualized as a rectangle. When multiplying rational expressions the length of the sides of the rectangular are represented by the binomial factors. The two numerators multiply together to form one rectangle and the two denominators multiply to form the other rectangle. Watch what happens when one pair of factors divides out and reduces the rational expression.

Note: The bars that represent the sides are continuous—that is, x+2 is shown in blue; x+6 is 4 units larger. The small rectangle is within the larger rectangle represents the numerator product. The larger rectangle represents the denominator product.

Can any two pairs of factors divide out?

Can numerators divide each other out?

What happens when everything divides out?

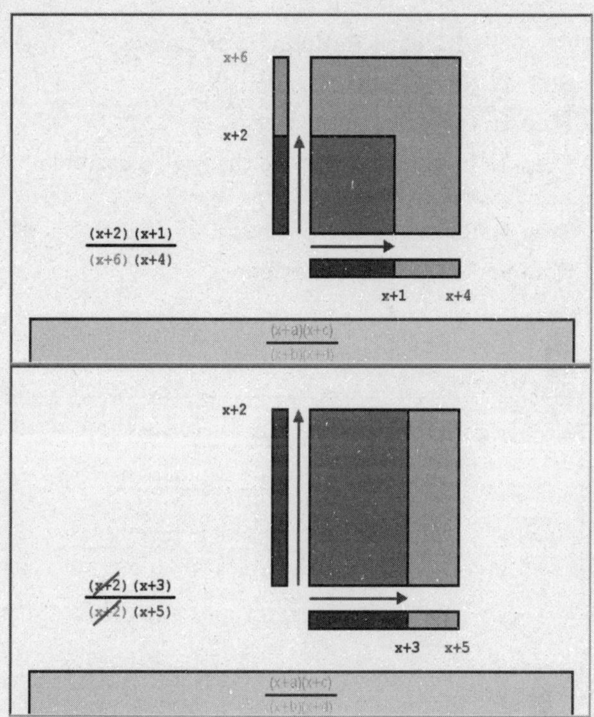

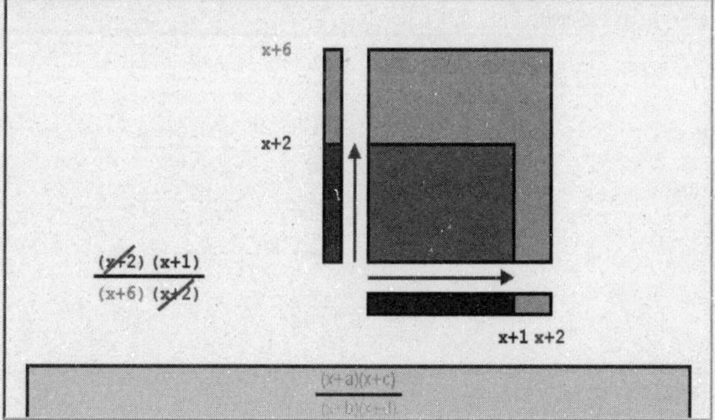

What part of the large rectangle represents the reduced answer?

The common x+2 factors represent "heights" of each rectangle.

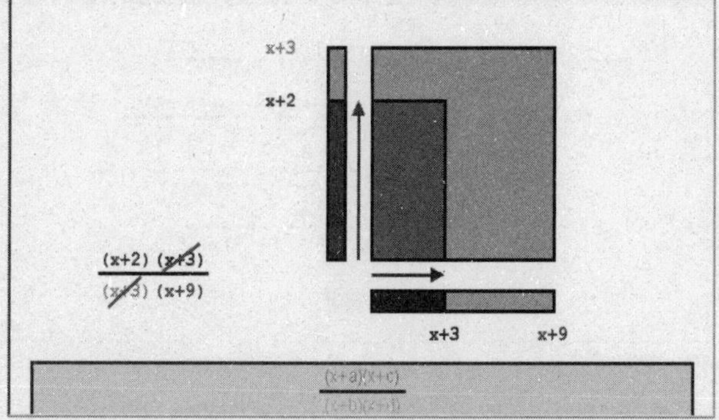

If **x=1**, what is the value of this rational expression?

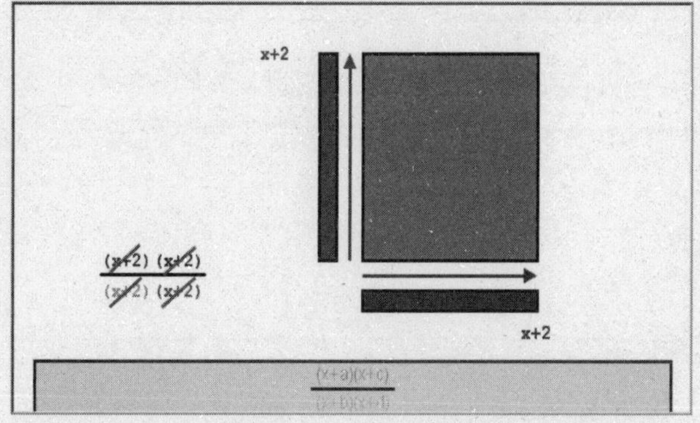

What do you get when the numerators and denominators are the same?

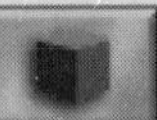

Dividing Rational Expressions

Division is the inverse operation of multiplication. Recall that to divide fractions, you invert the divisor and multiply. Do the exact same process for dividing rational expressions.

Let **a**, **b**, **c**, and **d** stand for any algebraic expression:

$$\frac{\frac{a}{b}}{\frac{c}{d}} = \frac{\frac{a}{b}\cdot\frac{c}{d}}{\frac{c}{d}\cdot\frac{d}{c}} = \frac{a}{b}\cdot\frac{d}{c}$$

Hint: Division can be expressed as two stacked expressions (fraction form) or with the division sign (÷) separating the two terms.

Dividing Rational Expressions

Step 1: Factor each numerator.

Step 2: Factor each denominator.

Step 3: Invert the divisor and change the operator sign to multiply.

Step 4: Reduce common factors.

Step 5: Rewrite in reduced form.

Divide and simplify:

$$\frac{x^2+4x+3}{x^2+2x-3} \div \frac{x^3+5x^2+6x}{x^2+3x} = \frac{x^2+4x+3}{x^2+2x-3} \div \frac{x(x^2+5x+6)}{x^2+3x}$$
$$= \frac{(x+1)(x+3)}{(x-1)(x+3)} \div \frac{x(x+2)(x+3)}{x(x+3)}$$

Factor the numerators and denominators.

Divide and simplify:

$$\frac{x^2+4x+3}{x^2+2x-3} \div \frac{x^3+5x^2+6x}{x^2+3x} = \frac{x^2+4x+3}{x^2+2x-3} \div \frac{x(x^2+5x+6)}{x^2+3x}$$
$$= \frac{(x+1)(x+3)}{(x-1)(x+3)} \div \frac{x(x+2)(x+3)}{x(x+3)}$$
$$= \frac{(x+1)(x+3)}{(x-1)(x+3)} \times \frac{x(x+3)}{x(x+2)(x+3)}$$

Invert and multiply.

After completely factoring both numerators and denominators, invert the second fraction and change the sign to multiply.

Divide and simplify:

$$\frac{x^2+4x+3}{x^2+2x-3} \div \frac{x^3+5x^2+6x}{x^2+3x} = \frac{x^2+4x+3}{x^2+2x-3} \div \frac{x(x^2+5x+6)}{x^2+3x}$$
$$= \frac{(x+1)(x+3)}{(x-1)(x+3)} \div \frac{x(x+2)(x+3)}{x(x+3)}$$
$$= \frac{(x+1)(x+3)}{(x-1)(x+3)} \times \frac{x(x+3)}{x(x+2)(x+3)}$$
$$= \frac{x(x+1)(x+3)(x+3)}{x(x-1)(x+3)(x+2)(x+3)}$$
$$= \frac{x+1}{(x-1)(x+2)}$$

Simplified form.

Only after inverting and changing the sign to multiply can you reduce common factors. Leave your answer in factored form.

Divide and simplify:

$$\frac{x^2-16}{x^3+6x^2+8x} \div \frac{x^2-2x-8}{x^3} = \frac{x^2-16}{x(x^2+6x+8)} \div \frac{x^2-2x-8}{x^3}$$
$$= \frac{(x+4)(x-4)}{x(x+2)(x+4)} \div \frac{(x-4)(x+2)}{x^3}$$

Factor the numerators and denominators.

Each expression is now in factored form.

Divide and simplify:

$$\frac{x^2-16}{x^3+6x^2+8x} \div \frac{x^2-2x-8}{x^3} = \frac{x^2-16}{x(x^2+6x+8)} \div \frac{x^2-2x-8}{x^3}$$
$$= \frac{(x+4)(x-4)}{x(x+2)(x+4)} \div \frac{(x-4)(x+2)}{x^3}$$
$$= \frac{(x+4)(x-4)}{x(x+2)(x+4)} \times \frac{x^3}{(x-4)(x+2)}$$
$$= \frac{x^3(x+4)(x-4)}{x(x+2)(x+4)(x-4)(x+2)}$$
$$= \frac{x^2}{(x+2)^2}$$

Simplified form.

Invert, change to multiplication, and then reduce common factors.

While we visualize division very differently then we do multiplication, remember that division is the inverse operations to multiplication. After we invert the divisor, the process for divide rational expressions is the same as when we multiply them.

By playing with this visualization you can develop a better feel for what happens when you are dividing rational expressions. It is not designed to show you how to divide them, but rather what the result looks like.

Which variables change the denominator?

Which variables change the numerator?

Which variables represent the length of the rectangle?

Which variables represent the width?

How does the visualization show division as the inverse of multiplication?

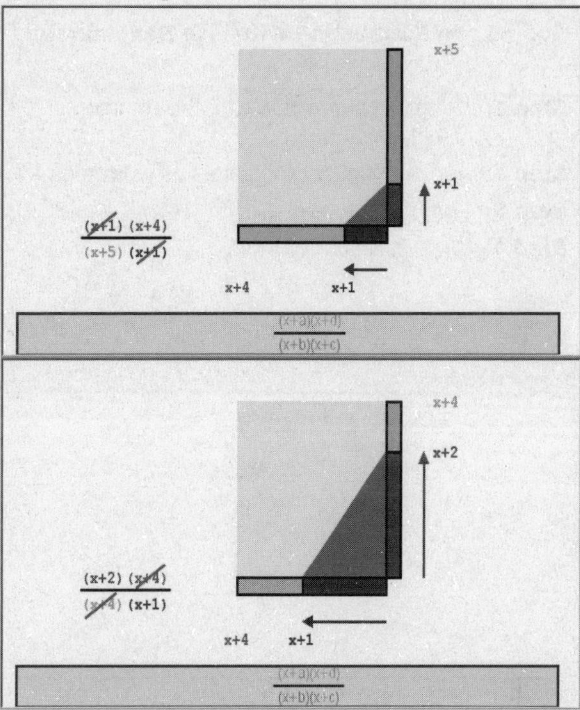

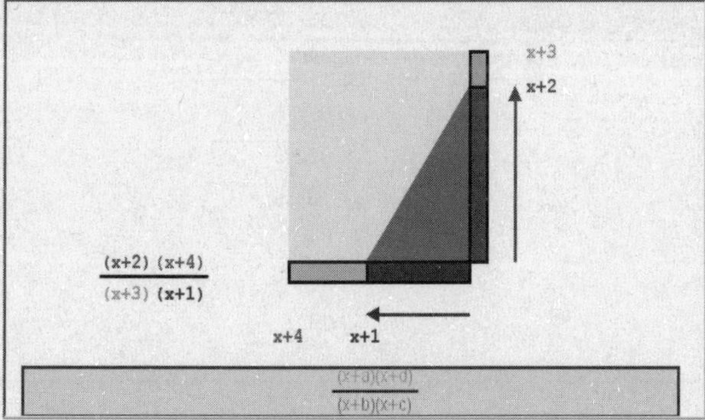

What is the area of the large triangle? As **c** increases, what happens to the area of the triangle?

What is the area of the rectangle? Once the common factors are divided out, what's the area of the remaining rectangle?

Add & Subtract with LIKE Denominators

Adding and subtracting rational expressions works just like adding and subtracting fractions. If the denominators are the same, combine the fractions by adding or subtracting their numerators. Remember that subtraction often requires multiplying an expression by −1 before combining like terms.

Note on use of −1: Multiply by −1 to subtract an expression; factor −1 from an expression to reverse the signs of the terms.

Adding and Subtracting with Like Denominators

Step 1: Write as one fraction with the common denominator.

Step 2: Add or subtract numerators as indicated.

Step 3: Combine like terms.

Step 4: Write in simplest form.

Add:

$$\frac{2}{x+3}+\frac{4}{x+3}=\frac{6}{x+3}$$

Write the sum of the numerators over the common denominator.

Subtract and simplify:

$$\frac{2x-7}{x^2-9}-\frac{x-4}{x^2-9}=\frac{2x-7-(x-4)}{x^2-9}=\frac{2x-7-x+4}{x^2-9}$$

Distribute the negative symbol.

Note that subtraction requires distributing **−1** to each term to be **subtracted** before combining like terms.

Subtract and simplify:

$$\frac{2x-7}{x^2-9}-\frac{x-4}{x^2-9}=\frac{2x-7-(x-4)}{x^2-9}=\frac{2x-7-x+4}{x^2-9}=\frac{x-3}{x^2-9}=\frac{x-3}{(x+3)(x-3)}=\frac{1}{x+3}$$

Simplify

Combine like terms and simplify to reduced form.

Add and simplify:

$$\frac{-4x+5}{2x^3-7x^2+6x}+\frac{2x-2}{2x^3-7x^2+6x}=\frac{-4x+5+2x-2}{2x^3-7x^2+6x}=\frac{-4x+5+2x-2}{2x^3-7x^2+6x}=\frac{-2x+3}{2x^3-7x^2+6x}=\frac{-(2x-3)}{x(2x-3)(x-2)}$$

Factor and cancel to simplify.

Point 3: Factor the numerator and denominator to check for common factors.

Note: Factor out −1 to change the sign of terms in the numerator.

Add and simplify:

$$\frac{-4x+5}{2x^3-7x^2+6x}+\frac{2x-2}{2x^3-7x^2+6x}=\frac{-4x+5+2x-2}{2x^3-7x^2+6x}=\frac{-4x+5+2x-2}{2x^3-7x^2+6x}=\frac{-2x+3}{2x^3-7x^2+6x}=\frac{-(2x-3)}{x(2x-3)(x-2)}=\frac{-1}{x(x-2)}$$

Simplify

Once all of the common factors have been reduced, the only remaining factor in the numerator is −1.

Add & Subtract with LIKE Denominators

Here we show a picture of two expressions with the same denominator and a picture of their sum.

Think about how the visualization could show the process of reducing a common factor. Would it be the same as simply taking away common bars and squares? Would it be like rearranging the numerator to show a common edge with the denominator?

Does changing the denominator change the process of adding numerators?

On scratch paper, put in a value for **x.** How does increasing the size of the denominator affect the sum? How does decreasing the denominator affect the sum? How do those changes affect the value of the rational expressions?

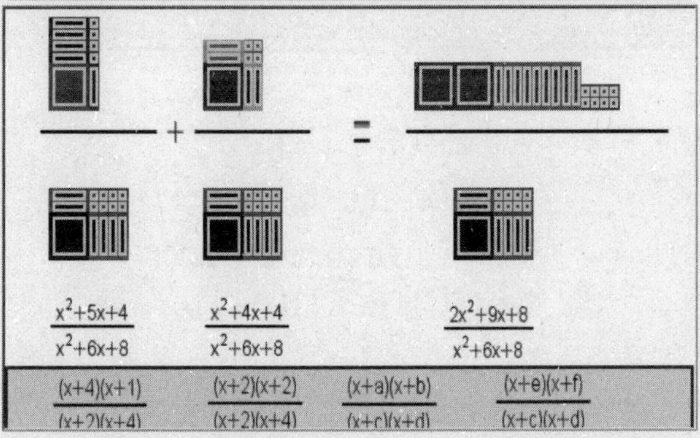

If the common denominator changes, but the numerators do not change, what happens to the sum?

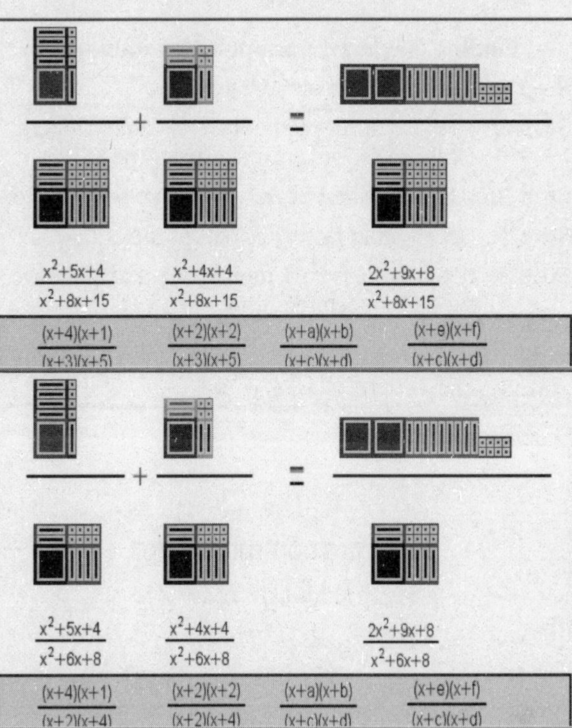

Is the answer in final form? Can $2x^2+9x+8$ be rearranged to form a rectangle (is it factorable)?

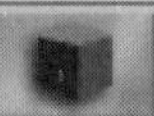

Finding the Least Common Denominator

To add or subtract rational expressions whose denominators are NOT the same requires finding a common denominator. The **Least Common Denominator (LCD)** is the least common multiple of the denominators. When algebraic expressions are in the denominators, write the expression with the fewest factors that all the denominators divide into evenly.

Finding the Least Common Denominator

Step 1: Factor each denominator.

Step 2: Look for factors common to all denominators; list those factors once as part of the LCD.

Step 3: Use the highest power of each common factor.

Step 4: List all other factors as part of the LCD.

Step 5: Combine all factors form step 2 and 3. Leave the LCD in factored form.

Find the Least Common Denominator (LCD) of:

$$x+2, x-5$$

The LCD is $(x+2)(x-5)$.

There are no factors in common.

Find the Least Common Denominator (LCD) of:

$$x, x(x-2)$$

The x is a common factor.

So, the LCD is $x(x-2)$.

Above right shows no common factors. Notice that each factor is a binomial. Above shows a monomial factor and a binomial factor.

Find the Least Common Denominator (LCD) of:

$$x^2-1, x^2-2x-3$$

$$(x+1)(x-1), (x-3)(x+1)$$

The $x+1$ is a common factor.

So, the LCD is $(x+1)(x-1)(x-3)$.

Point 3: The common factor is listed once, then the remaining factors. No multiplication is needed—leave the LCD in factored form.

Find the Least Common Denominator (LCD) of:

$$x^4-4x^3+4x^2, x^2-2x, x^3$$

$$x^2(x^2-4x+4), x(x-2), x^3$$

$$x^2(x-2)(x-2), x(x-2), x^3$$

Factor by appropriate methods. Above there are three expressions to factor. Note the common factors **x** and **(x-2).**

Find the Least Common Denominator (LCD) of:

$$x^4-4x^3+4x^2, x^2-2x, x^3$$

$$x^2(x^2-4x+4), x(x-2), x^3$$

$$x^2(x-2)(x-2), x(x-2), x^3$$

The x and $x-2$ are common factors.

So, the LCD is $x^3(x-2)^2$.

Point 4: The highest power on **x** is 3 and the highest power of **(x-2)** is 2; the LCD requires the highest powers of each common factor.

Finding the Least Common Denominator

When the sides of rectangles are the same, expressions represented by the rectangle have common factors. Look for ways to arrange the number bars, variable bars, and squares to form a rectangle. What dimensions make up the LCD when two rectangles have an equal dimension?

Parabolas are the graphs of quadratic equations. Two parabolas that are graphed on the same set of coordinate axes will have intersecting x-intercept(s) if they have a common factor(s). How many x-intercepts will two quadratics have if they intersect at one x-intercept? How many factors will the LCD have?

Compare the dimensions of the rectangles; what factors represent the LCD? How could you represent expressions with two common factors? What is the LCD if the rectangles do not have sides with the same dimensions?

If two parabolas do not intersect, what can you assume about common factors? Can two parabolas intersect at more than one x-intercept point? What should the graph look like if the LCD has fewer factors than the product of the two denominators?

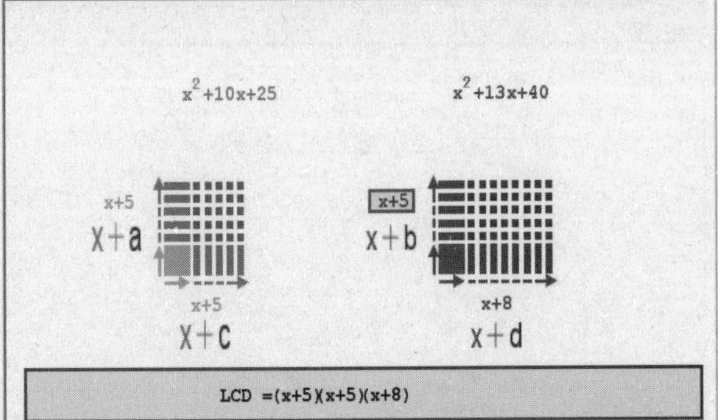

What are the common factors? The rectangle on the right side is a square—how is that useful in determining the LCD?

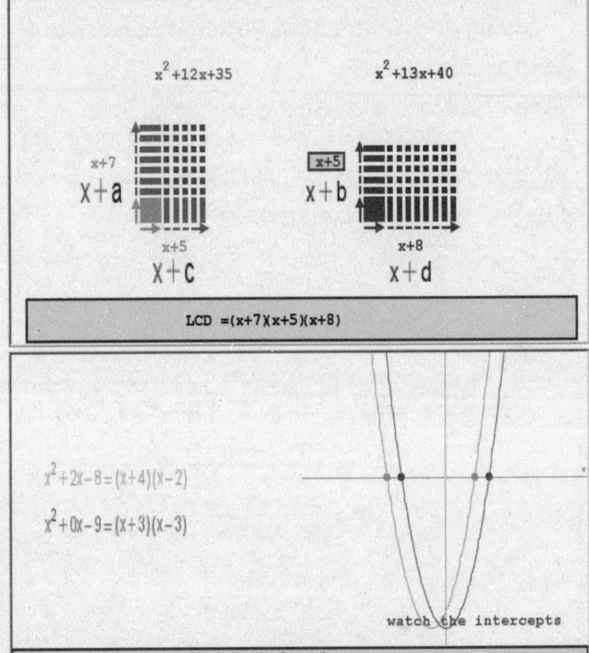

If two parabolas are graphed on the same axis, how many distinct factors are represented in this graph? What is the LCD?

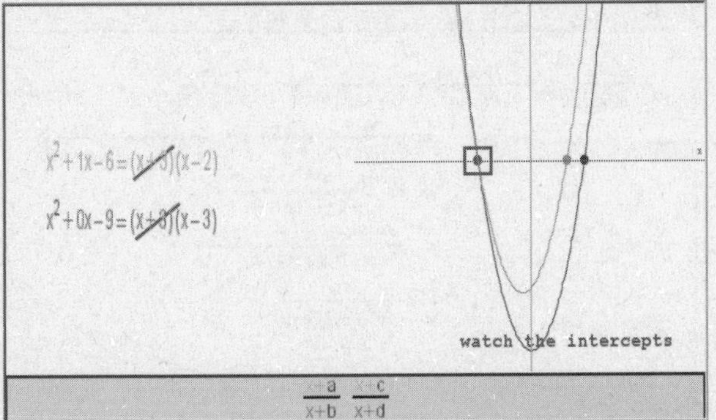

Above shows two parabolas intersecting on the x-axis. Which point do they have in common? How many factors are in the LCD?

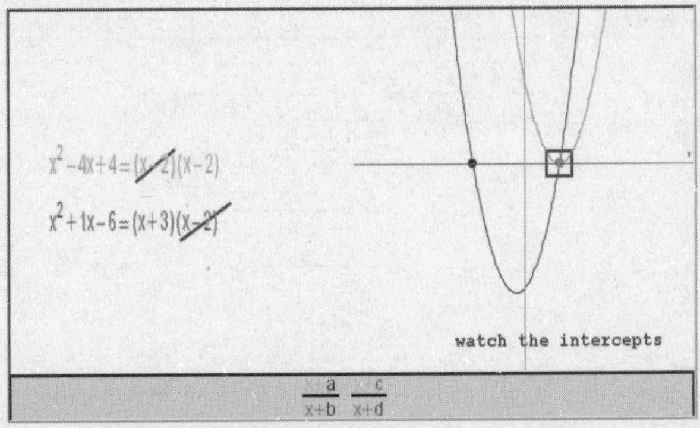

How many distinct factors are in the LCD? What power does the (x-2) factor require? Why?

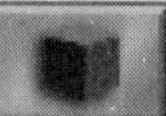

Adding & Subtracting with UNLIKE Denominators

To add or subtract rational expressions their denominators must be the same, which is the same requirements for adding or subtracting fractions in arithmetic. After finding the LCD, each rational expression must be changed to an equivalent expression using the new denominator. The process uses the same principle as reducing rational expressions — the **Fundamental Principle of Fractions.** If **A**, **B**, and **C** represent algebraic expressions, then $\frac{A}{B} \Leftrightarrow \frac{A \cdot C}{B \cdot C}$.

This principle allows us to build fractions by multiplying the same expression to both numerator and denominator, or reduce to lowest terms by dividing the same expression from both.

Adding and Subtracting Rational Expressions

Step 1: Find the LCD.

Step 2: Change each rational expression to an equivalent rational expression with the LCD.

Step 3: Add or subtract numerators.

Step 4: Write in simplest terms.

Add:

$$\frac{2}{x-3}+\frac{3}{x+2}=\frac{2}{x-3}\left(\frac{x+2}{x+2}\right)+\frac{3}{x+2}\left(\frac{x-3}{x-3}\right)$$
$$=\frac{2(x+2)+3(x-3)}{(x-3)(x+2)}$$

Combine over common denominator.

Add:

$$\frac{2}{x-3}+\frac{3}{x+2}=\frac{2}{x-3}\left(\frac{x+2}{x+2}\right)+\frac{3}{x+2}\left(\frac{x-3}{x-3}\right)$$
$$=\frac{2(x+2)+3(x-3)}{(x-3)(x+2)}$$
$$=\frac{2x+4+3x-9}{(x-3)(x+2)}$$
$$=\frac{5x-5}{(x-3)(x+2)}$$
$$=\frac{5(x-1)}{(x-3)(x+2)}$$

Simplify.

Once the LCD is found, multiply each fraction by any "missing" factors. (Notice that each step requires either multiplying or simplifying.)

Subtract:

$$\frac{x+3}{x^2}-\frac{x-2}{x(x+1)}=\frac{x+3}{x^2}\left(\frac{x+1}{x+1}\right)-\frac{x-2}{x(x+1)}\left(\frac{x}{x}\right)$$
$$=\frac{(x+3)(x+1)-(x-2)x}{x^2(x+1)}$$

Combine terms over common denominator.

Think of building each rational expression as the opposite of reducing—instead of reducing common factors, multiply them back to the numerator and the denominator. Watch the operator sign for subtraction—the –1 applies to the entire expression.

Subtract:

$$\frac{x+3}{x^2}-\frac{x-2}{x(x+1)}=\frac{x+3}{x^2}\left(\frac{x+1}{x+1}\right)-\frac{x-2}{x(x+1)}\left(\frac{x}{x}\right)$$
$$=\frac{(x+3)(x+1)-(x-2)x}{x^2(x+1)}$$
$$=\frac{x^2+x+3x+3-x^2+2x}{x^2(x+1)}$$
$$=\frac{6x+3}{x^2(x+1)}$$
$$=\frac{3(2x+1)}{x^2(x+1)}$$

Simplify

Once the rational expressions have been combined over the LCD, combine like terms and leave in factored form. Make sure the fraction is reduced to lowest terms.

Add:

$$\frac{x-4}{x^2+4x-5}+\frac{x+3}{x^2+7x+10}=\frac{x-4}{(x+5)(x-1)}+\frac{x+3}{(X+5)(x+2)}$$
$$=\frac{x-4}{(x+5)(x-1)}\left(\frac{x+2}{x+2}\right)+\frac{x+3}{(x+5)(x+2)}\left(\frac{x-1}{x-1}\right)$$
$$=\frac{(x-4)(x+2)+(x+3)(x-1)}{(x+5)(x-1)(x+2)}$$
$$=\frac{x^2+2x-4x-8+x^2-x+3x-3}{(x+5)(x-1)(x+2)}$$
$$=\frac{2x^2-11}{(x+5)(x-1)(x+2)}$$

Simplify.

Same process—just larger expressions. The most common mistake is a sign error. Double check for negative signs.

The visualizations below represents the process of adding rational expressions with unlike denominators. Build each fraction to the common denominator by multiplying by the appropriate factor. (We recommend that you draw out this step on scratch paper to help yourself visualize the process.) Next, add the numerators. How do you determine the factors of the LCD? Once the numerators are added, is the problem finished? How do you know when the rational expressions are in reduced form?

Why can't you add rational expressions without finding a common denominator?

What happens to the rational expressions as the value for **x** changes? Can **x = 0**? Can **x = 1**? Can **x < 0**? Can **x** be any number?

Remember: Division by 0 is undefined, because dividing by 0 is not physically possible.

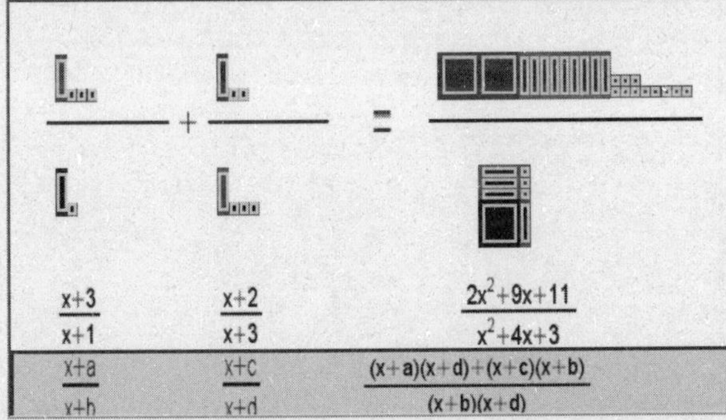

What values determines the number of rectangles in the numerator? Which rectangles make up the numerator?

$\frac{x+1}{x+2} + \frac{x+2}{x+4} = \frac{2x^2+9x+8}{x^2+6x+8}$

$\frac{x+a}{x+b} \quad \frac{x+c}{x+d} \quad \frac{(x+a)(x+d)+(x+c)(x+b)}{(x+b)(x+d)}$

What do you multiply **x+1** by to change to the common denominator? What do you multiply **x+2** by?

$\frac{x+5}{x+1} + \frac{x+4}{x+5} = \frac{2x^2+15x+29}{x^2+6x+5}$

$\frac{x+a}{x+b} \quad \frac{x+c}{x+d} \quad \frac{(x+a)(x+d)+(x+c)(x+b)}{(x+b)(x+d)}$

$\frac{x+3}{x+1} + \frac{x+2}{x+4} = \frac{2x^2+10x+14}{x^2+5x+4}$

$\frac{x+a}{x+b} \quad \frac{x+c}{x+d} \quad \frac{(x+a)(x+d)+(x+c)(x+b)}{(x+b)(x+d)}$

What happens when the value of **x** becomes very small? When **x=1**, does the process differ from adding regular fractions?

Rational Expressions in General

Rational expressions can take on many forms. A rational expression is a fraction whose numerator or denominator contains a fraction. Writing rational expressions in reduced form can require all four basic operations in the same problem.

There are two approaches to simplifying rational expressions. One way is to simplify numerator and denominator separately, and then reduce to lowest terms as a final step. The other way is to multiply both numerator and denominator of the main fraction by the LCD of the denominators. Both are effective.

	Method I	**Method II**
Step 1	Simplify numerator.	Find the LCD.
Step 2	Simplify denominator.	Multiply top and bottom of the main fraction by the LCD.
Step 3	Divide fractions.	Reduce.
Step 4	Reduce.	

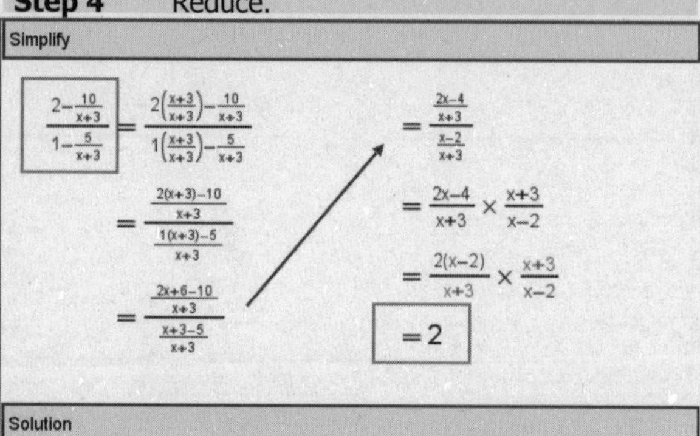

Key steps: simplify the numerator, then the denominator, then divide the resulting fractions. As you step through the solution process work the problem through with a pencil and paper.

Simplify

$$\frac{2-\frac{10}{x+3}}{1-\frac{5}{x+3}} = \frac{2\left(\frac{x+3}{x+3}\right)-\frac{10}{x+3}}{1\left(\frac{x+3}{x+3}\right)-\frac{5}{x+3}}$$

$$= \frac{\frac{2(x+3)-10}{x+3}}{\frac{1(x+3)-5}{x+3}}$$

Put terms over common denominator.

$$\frac{2-\frac{10}{x+3}}{1-\frac{5}{x+3}}$$

Multiply both numerator and denominator by the LCD

$$= \left[\frac{2-\frac{10}{x+3}}{1-\frac{5}{x+3}}\right]\left[\frac{x+3}{x+3}\right]$$

$$= \frac{2(x+3)-\frac{10}{1}}{1(x+3)-\frac{5}{1}}$$

$$= \frac{2x-4}{x-2}$$

$$= \frac{2(x-2)}{(x-2)} = 2$$

Method II

Get rid of the fractions in the denominators by multiplying them away. Sometimes Method II saves steps, sometimes Method I saves steps. In this case Method II seems to be more efficient.

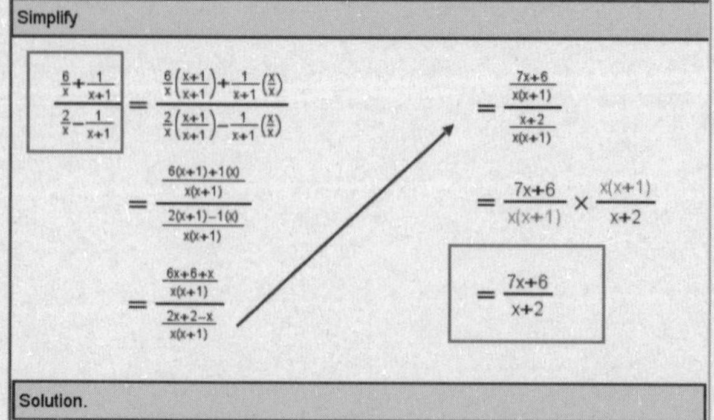

Hint: Put parentheses around the main numerator and another set around the main denominator. That way you can be sure each part is accounted for.

$$\frac{\frac{6}{x}+\frac{1}{x+1}}{\frac{2}{x}-\frac{1}{x+1}}$$

Multiply *each term* in the top and bottom by the LCD.

$$= \left[\frac{\frac{6}{x}+\frac{1}{x+1}}{\frac{2}{x}-\frac{1}{x+1}}\right]\left[\frac{x(x+1)}{x(x+1)}\right]$$

$$= \frac{6(x+1)+1x}{2(x+1)-x}$$

$$= \frac{7x+6}{x+2}$$

Method II

Hint: Keeping track of all the factors requires concentration and clear, readable work. Use as much space and scrap paper as needed, and make sure your work is easy to follow.

Eliminating one set of denominators turns complex rational expressions into regular rational expressions. After identifying the main fraction in a complex rational expression, multiply numerator and denominator by the LCD of the denominators.

How do you know which fractions make up the main fraction?

What determines the denominators to use as the LCD?

What happens when the "wrong" CD (common denominator) is used?

In the frame to the right what is x^0/x^0? What is x^n/x^n? Change **n** to 1—what happened? Change **n** to 3—what happened?

Change **n** to 5 as in the frame below—what happened?

What would change if the denominator of the numerator was a binomial?

$$\left(\frac{8+\frac{1}{x^7}}{9+\frac{1}{x^5}}\right)\frac{x^4}{x^4}=\frac{8x^4+\frac{1}{x^3}}{9x^4+\frac{1}{x}}$$

$$\left(\frac{a+\frac{1}{x^b}}{c+\frac{1}{x^d}}\right)\frac{x^n}{x^n}$$

$$\left(\frac{7+\frac{1}{x^7}}{5+\frac{1}{x^3}}\right)\frac{x^5}{x^5}=\frac{7x^5+\frac{1}{x^2}}{5x^5+x^2}$$

$$\left(\frac{a+\frac{1}{x^b}}{c+\frac{1}{x^d}}\right)\frac{x^n}{x^n}$$

The LCD is x^5. What would happen if x^6 or x^8 was used as the CD?

$$\left(\frac{2+\frac{1}{x^4}}{3+\frac{1}{x^3}}\right)\frac{x^4}{x^4}=\frac{2x^4+1}{3x^4+x}$$

$$\left(\frac{a+\frac{1}{x^b}}{c+\frac{1}{x^d}}\right)\frac{x^n}{x^n}$$

How does changing the values of **a**, **b**, **c**, **d**, and **n** affect the problem solving process?

Solving Proportions

A **proportion** is an equation made up of two (or more) equal ratios. A ratio is a rational expression. The terms of a proportion are the four parts: $\frac{A}{B} = \frac{C}{D}$.

The unknown can be in any of the four locations (in the numerator or denominator of each ratio). Proportions are solved by finding the **cross product** and then solving for the unknown variable.

Proportions are used to solve a wide array of practical application problems from statistics to geometry.

Note: For a review of ratios and proportions, see section 4. Ratio and Proportions.

Solving Proportions

Step 1: Find the cross product by multiplying the numerator of one ratio with the denominator of the other ratio.

Step 2: Solve for the unknown.

Step 3: Check by substituting back into the original proportion.

Solve for x:

$$\frac{3}{7} = \frac{12}{x}$$
$$3x = 7(12)$$
$$x = \frac{7(12)}{3}$$
$$x = 7(4)$$
$$x = 28$$

The variable can be located in any of the four possible positions.

Solve for x:

$$\frac{4}{x} = \frac{20}{15}$$
$$4(15) = 20x$$
$$\frac{4(15)}{20} = x$$
$$\frac{4(5)(3)}{4(5)} = x$$
$$3 = x$$

Sometimes you can solve a proportion mentally. What do you have to multiply by to change 4 to 20? Divide 15 by that number to find **x.**

Solve for x:

$$\frac{4}{5} = \frac{x}{35}$$
$$4(35) = 5x$$
$$\frac{4(35)}{5} = x$$
$$4(7) = x$$
$$28 = x$$

Solve for x:

$$\frac{x}{8} = \frac{49}{56}$$
$$56x = 8(49)$$
$$x = \frac{8(49)}{56}$$
$$x = \frac{8(7)(7)}{8(7)}$$
$$x = 7$$

Find the cross product and solve. To check your solution substitute 7 for x in the original proportion and solve. Does 7/8=49/56?

Since ratios are rational expressions, we represent them with right triangles. In a proportion where two ratios are equal, the two right triangles representing each of the ratios would have the same slope. They would be **similar triangles**. If two triangles are similar, they are proportional. The legs of the right triangles are the terms of the proportions pictured here. Use the joystick to make proportional triangles.

How do you know which triangle represents which proportion? How do you know when you have solved a particular proportion? How do you know when two triangles are similar?

Does changing the position of the unknown in a proportion make a difference to the process of finding the

What happens to the slopes when the triangles are proportional?

As **x** increases, what happens to the slope of the purple triangle?

What happens if **x < 0**?

Change **a, b,** and **d** so that the triangles are in different quadrants.

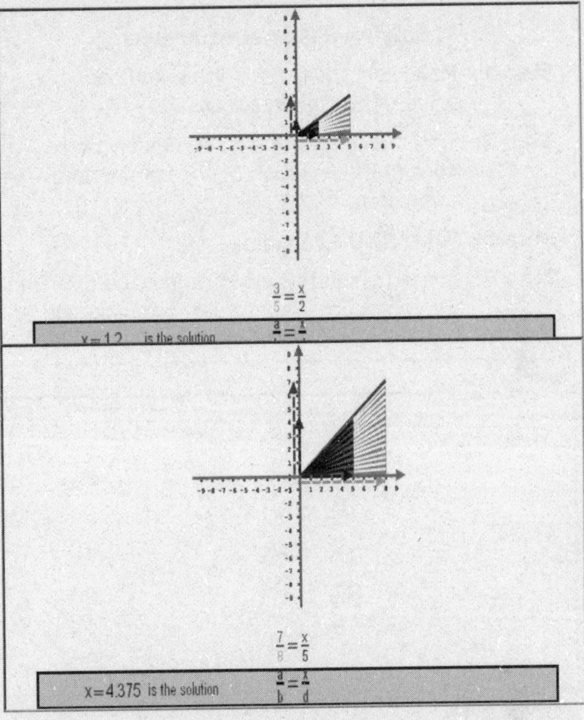

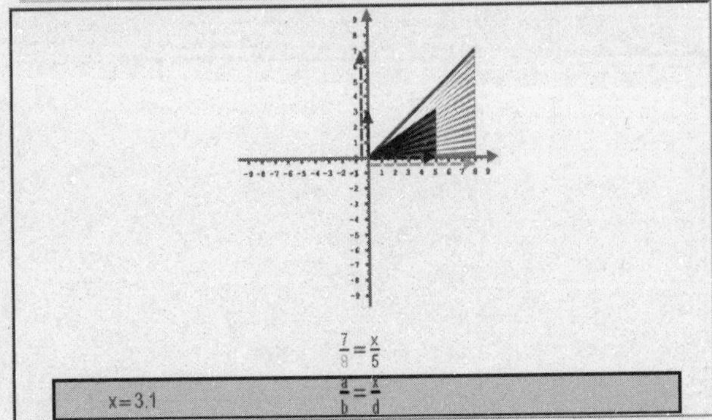

Test values for **x**. Does **x** need to increase or decrease to make these two triangles similar?

Can you think of a real life application for this situation?

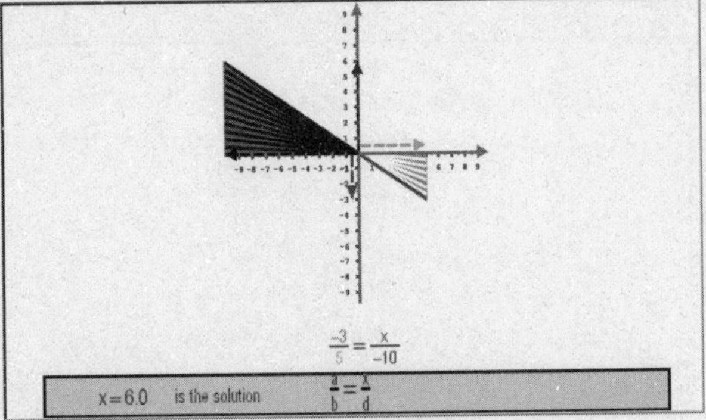

Here both sides of the proportion are negative. Why? How do you know the triangles are similar? Does **x=6** solve the proportion?

Solving Rational Equations

Solving rational equations makes use of the process of solving proportions. Rational equations are often proportions whose terms are expressions. If the terms of the equation can be put into the form of a proportion, cross multiply to solve. If not, multiply both sides of the equation by the common denominator and then solve.

Remember: Division by zero is undefined, because it is not consistent with division by other numbers. A solution that results in zero for either denominator is not included in the set of solutions.

Solving Rational Equations

Step 1: Make sure the form of the equation is two equal rational expressions.

Step 2: Find the cross product OR multiply both sides of the equation by the common denominator.

Step 3: Solve for the variable.

Step 4: Check by substituting back into the original equation. Eliminate values that make either

Solve for x:

$$\frac{2}{x-2} = \frac{6}{9}$$

$$2(9) = 6(x-2)$$

Cross multiply.

Solve for x:

$$\frac{2}{x-2} = \frac{6}{9}$$

$$2(9) = 6(x-2)$$

$$18 = 6x - 12$$

$$30 = 6x$$

$$5 = x$$

Divide both sides by 6.

Point 1: Find the cross product by multiplying one numerator with the other denominator; then solve. Check 5 to see if it is an acceptable answer. (Substitute 5 for x in the equation and solve.)

Solve for x

$$\frac{x+6}{10} = \frac{8}{x-5}$$

$$(x-5)(x+6) = 8(10)$$

$$x^2 + x - 30 = 80$$

$$x^2 + x - 110 = 0$$

$$(x+11)(x-10) = 0$$

$$x+11 = 0 \qquad x-10 = 0$$

$$x = -11 \qquad x = 10$$

These are the solutions.

Point 3: Cross multiplying resulted in a quadratic equation. Set the quadratic equal to zero and solve. Make sure both answers work.

Solve for x:

$$\frac{c}{x} + 1 = b$$

$$\frac{c}{x} = b - 1$$

$$c = x(b-1)$$

$$x = \frac{c}{b-1}$$

Divide by the coefficient of x. Answer.

Point 4: If **x** can be isolated, even if it is a denominator, you can use cross multiplication to solve.

Solve for x

$$\frac{2}{x} + \frac{3}{y} = 1$$

$$xy\left(\frac{2}{x} + \frac{3}{y}\right) = 1 \cdot xy$$

$$2y + 3x = xy$$

$$2y = xy - 3x$$

$$2y = (y-3)x$$

$$x = \frac{2y}{y-3}$$

Divide. Answer. $\frac{a}{x} + \frac{b}{y} = 1$

Point 5: Solve by multiplying both sides by the common denominator, **xy**. Isolate **x** on either side and solve in terms of **y**.

Just like proportions, picture rational equations as similar triangles. When the sides are proportional, the slopes of the triangles' hypotenuses are equal and the triangles are 'similar'.

Use the joystick to change the rational expressions. Create triangles that are located in each quadrant. What can you determine about the variable if the triangles are in opposite quadrants? The same quadrant?

Can the variable be 0? Can **x** be <0?

Can the triangles be in any quadrant?

What happens to the triangles when a value is entered so that the denominator is zero?

What happens when **x** is negative?

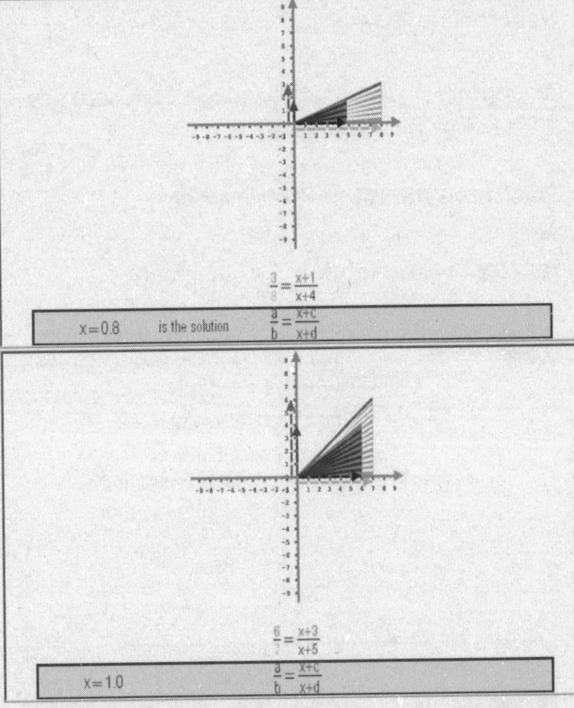

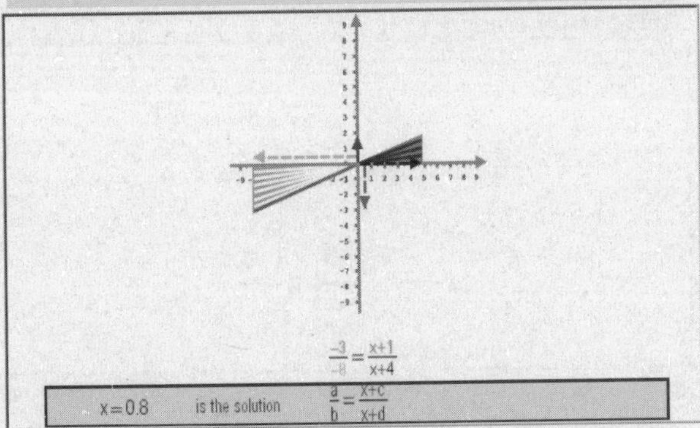

Are the triangles still similar? What's different about this visualization from the one above right?

Does the value of **x** have to increase or decrease to make the triangles proportional?

As **x** increases, what happens to the slope?

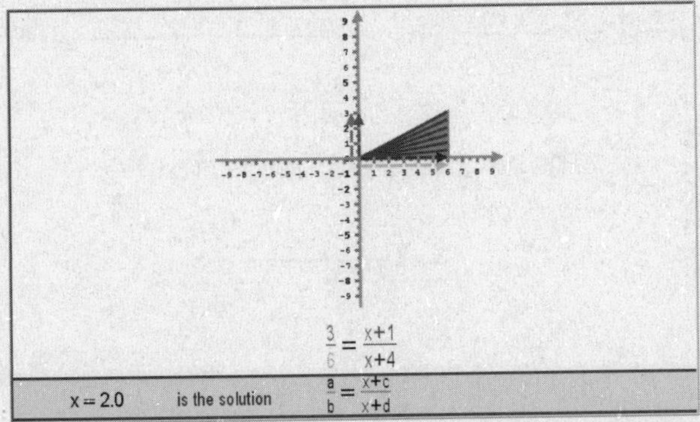

When the solution is found, what is the value of the numerator on the right side? What is the value of the denominator? Is the right side proportional to the left side?

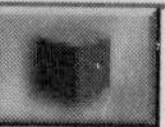

Introducing Asymptotes

A rational equation in the form $y = \dfrac{ax + b}{cx + d}$ graphs as a **hyperbola** that has tails that approach straight lines called **asymptotes**. The asymptotes, in this case, are parallel and perpendicular to the x-and y-axes (vertical and horizontal). Once the asymptotes are in place, the graph is sketched with the tails approaching, but not touching, the asymptotes.

Hyperbola: The shape of the graph of $y = \dfrac{ax + b}{cx + d}$

Asymptotes: Lines that the graph of a function approach, but do not touch.

Vertical Asymptote: The line x=-d/c.

Horizontal Asymptote: The line y=a/c.

Vertical Asymptotes

When graphing $y = \frac{ax+b}{cx+d}$,

$x = \frac{-d}{c}$ will be a vertical asymptote

$y = \frac{(ax+b)}{(cx+d)}$

Vertical Asymptotes

When graphing $y = \frac{ax+b}{cx+d}$,

$x = \frac{-d}{c}$ will be a vertical asymptote

because that value of x

makes the rational expression undefined.

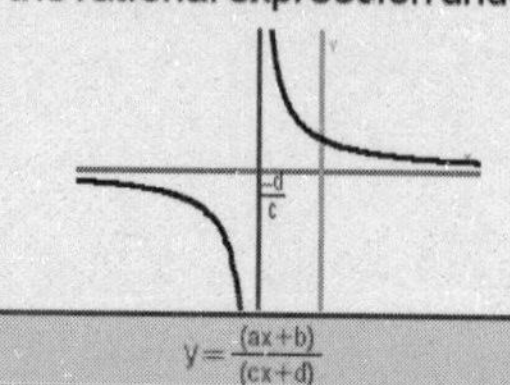

$y = \frac{(ax+b)}{(cx+d)}$

Find out what makes the denominator equal zero by solving **cx + d = 0** for **x.**

Find the vertical asymptote of:

$$y = \frac{1}{2x-7}$$

The vertical asymptote is $x = \frac{7}{2}$.

$y = \frac{(ax+b)}{(cx+d)}$

Solve for **x: 2x-7=0.**

Horizontal Asymptotes

When graphing $y = \frac{ax+b}{cx+d}$,

$y = \frac{a}{c}$ will be a horizontal asymptote.

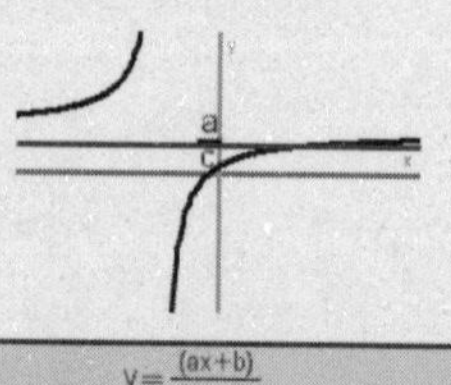

$y = \frac{(ax+b)}{(cx+d)}$

Make sure the rational expression part is in the correct forma. Then, **y=a/c** is the horizontal asymptote.

Find the horizontal asymptote of:

$$y = \frac{5x-3}{2x-7}$$

The horizontal asymptote is $y = \frac{5}{2}$.

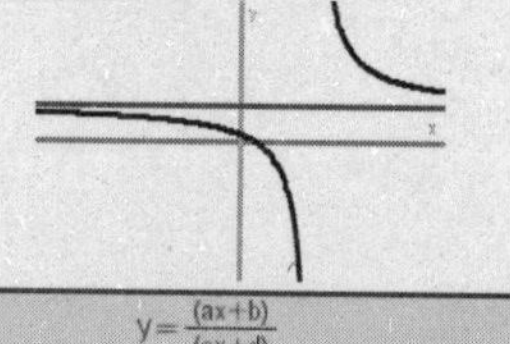

$y = \frac{(ax+b)}{(cx+d)}$

Find the horizontal asymptote by reading the coefficients of **x.**

The graphs of rational equations are **hyperbolas.** They may look like parabolas which are produced by quadratic equations, but they are very different. If we could graph a parabola on a huge screen we would see it continue to spread wider and wider. If we did the same with a hyperbola, we would find it squeezed between two lines. These lines are called the **asymptotes**, which means "not intersecting," in Greek.

Identifying the asymptotes of rational equations enables us to quickly visualize and sketch their graphs.

What is the equation of a horizontal asymptote?

What is the equation of a vertical asymptote?

How close does the hyperbola get to a asymptote?

How many asymptotes does one hyperbola have?

What can you determine about the intersection of the asymptotes?

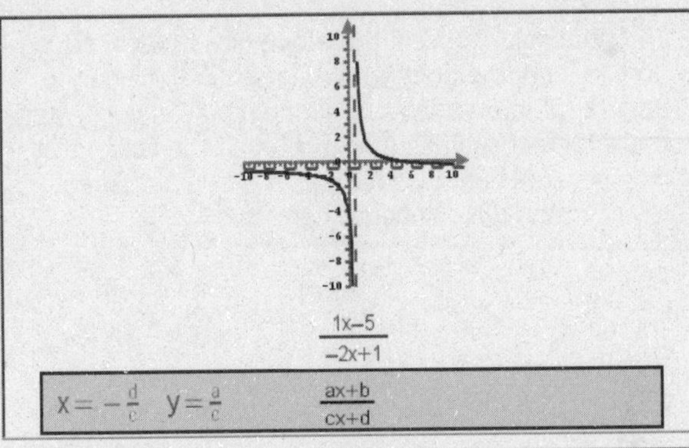

$\frac{1x-5}{-2x+1}$
$x=-\frac{d}{c}$ $y=\frac{a}{c}$ $\frac{ax+b}{cx+d}$

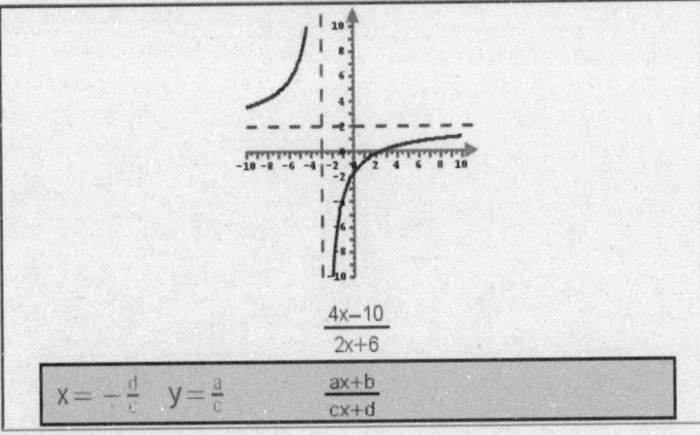

$\frac{4x-10}{2x+6}$
$x=-\frac{d}{c}$ $y=\frac{a}{c}$ $\frac{ax+b}{cx+d}$

What are the asymptotes?

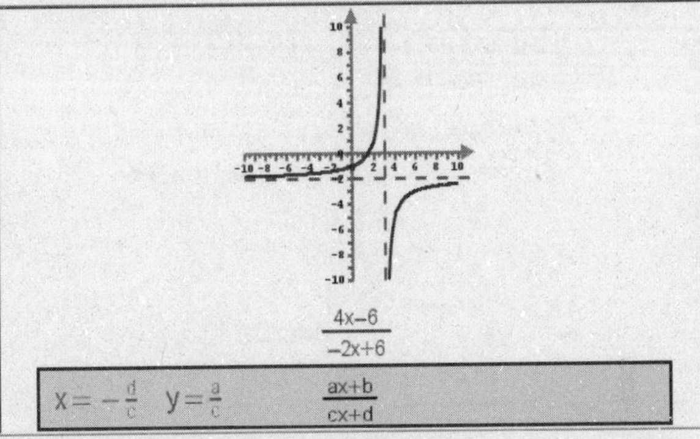

$\frac{4x-6}{-2x+6}$
$x=-\frac{d}{c}$ $y=\frac{a}{c}$ $\frac{ax+b}{cx+d}$

Is the vertical asymptote dependent on the numerator or on the denominator of the rational equation?

What parameters is the horizontal asymptote dependent on?

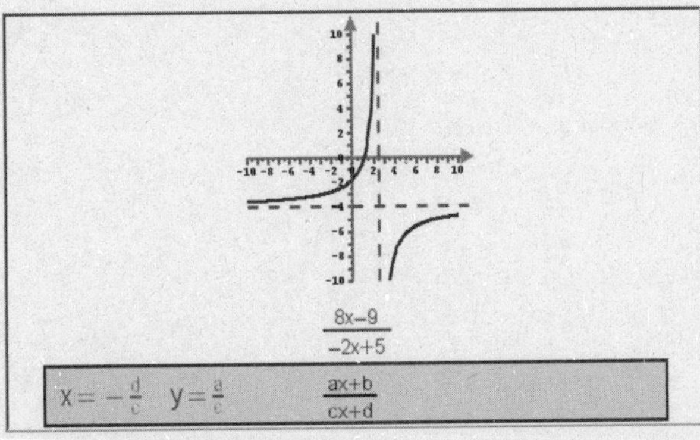

$\frac{8x-9}{-2x+5}$
$x=-\frac{d}{c}$ $y=\frac{a}{c}$ $\frac{ax+b}{cx+d}$

How would you change these asymptotes to reflect this graph like the graph on the right?

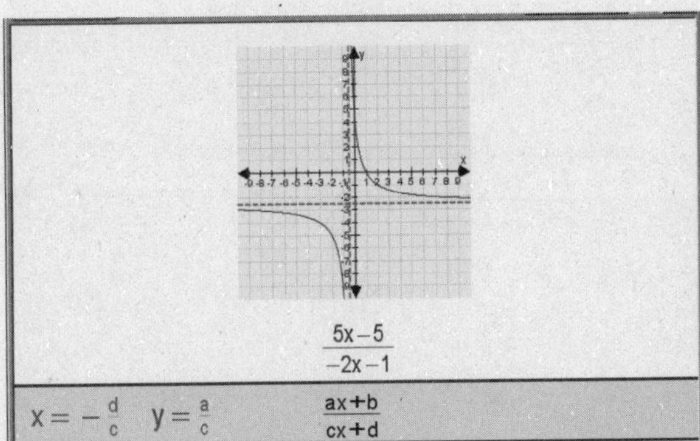

$\frac{5x-5}{-2x-1}$
$x=-\frac{d}{c}$ $y=\frac{a}{c}$ $\frac{ax+b}{cx+d}$

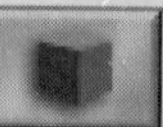

Solving Rational Expressions Graphically

Rational expressions can be set to equal **y** and then graphed. Rational equations in one variable can be solved by graphing. To solve a system of rational equations set each expression equal to y, graph them, and identify any points of intersection. If the graphs intersect, then the x-value at the point of intersection will be a solution.

To find a solution from the graph of a rational equation, identify the point(s) of intersection. Once the point(s) of intersection are found, you can verify that it is a correct solution by substituting the value of **x** into the equation and solving. If a true statement results, then the solution is correct.

The solution(s) of a rational equation are the points of intersection on the graph. For example, one of the solutions ($x = 2$), of $\frac{3x+2}{x+2} = \frac{x+4}{x+1}$ is shown on this graph:

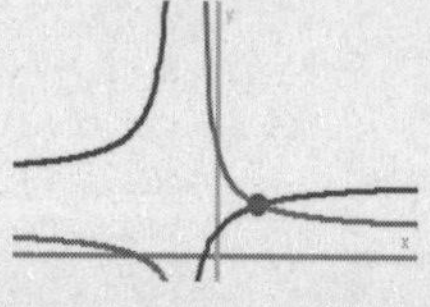

Notice that the left side (in blue on the computer) is graphed separately from the right side (pink). Since the graphs cross at **x=2**, 2 is a solution to the equation. To algebraically check, substitute 2 into both sides of the equation. If 8/4=6/3, then **x=2** does solve the equation.

The solution(s) of a rational equation are the points of intersection on the graph.

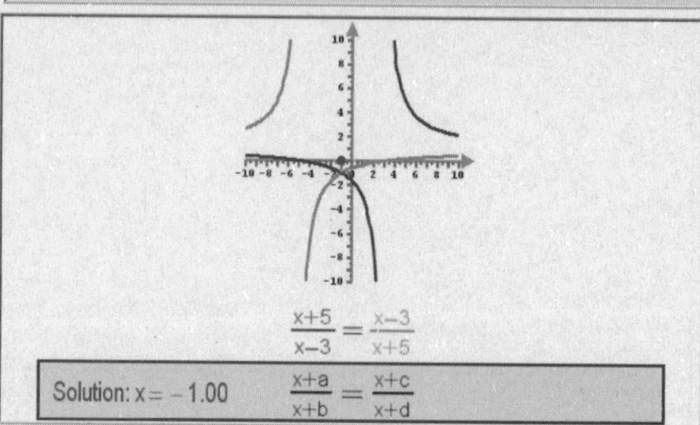

Here the graphs cross at **x** =-1. Is **x** =-1 a solution?

Systems of linear equations were solved graphically by finding their point of intersection in section 9. Systems of Equations. This method also applies to solving non-linear systems of equations. A point that two graphs share, is a solution to both equations. While linear equations have only one point of intersection, non-linear equations may have multiple points of intersection and, thus, multiple solutions. Rational equations can be solved if one or more points on the graph of the equation intersect.

How do you determine where the graphs intersect? How do you know if the value of **x** is positive, negative or zero? Can the graphs of a rational equation have more than one solution?

At right, the solution was computed by the computer.

How can you verify if the computer's solution is accurate or an estimated value?

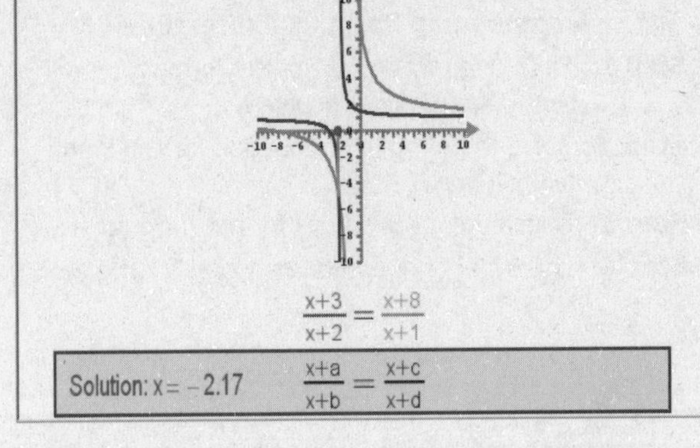

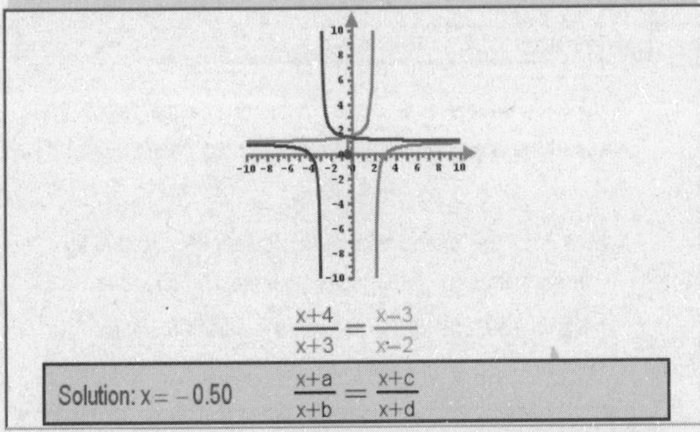

Reading the solution is tricky—what guides do you have in reading the correct answer?

How do you know if the answer you read from the graph is correct?

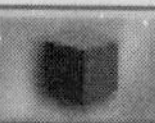

Manipulating Rational Equations

Scientists and engineers use formulas to model, simulate, and solve problems. Depending on the specific problem being addressed, standard formulas may need to be algebraically manipulated so that the unknown variable is put in terms of what is known. Isolating the unknown variable makes it easier to perform calculations and keep track of units. Manipulating equations often results in the unknown variable being set equal to a rational expression.

Manipulating Rational Expressions

Step 1: Determine which part of the formula represents the unknown quantity.

Step 2: Solve the formula or equation for the identified variable.

Step 3: Substitute given values for the formula.

Step 4: Use order of operations to solve for the unknown.

Gravitational Potential Energy

Gravitational potential energy is equal to the weight of an object times the height of the object.

$$GPE = wh$$

How does the GPE (in Joules) of a 500 Newton boulder change as the height (in meters) changes?

$$GPE = (500\ N)(60\ meters) = 30000\ Joules$$

Change h to explore! $GPE = wh$

Gravitational Potential Energy

What if we want to vary the GPE instead of the height? We can manipulate the equation GPE=wh to see how the weight changes as the GPE varies:

$$w = \frac{GPE}{h}$$

Consider a cliff that is 250 meters high. If the GPE (in Joules) of the object changes, how does the weight (in Newtons) change?

$$w = \frac{7500\ Joules}{250\ meters} = 30\ Newtons$$

Change GPE to explore! $GPE = wh$

Solve for **w** and then substitute values for **GPE** and **h**.

Kinetic Energy

The kinetic energy of an object in motion is equal to half the mass of the object times the velocity of the object squared.

$$KE = \frac{1}{2}mv^2$$

How does the kinetic energy (in Joules) of a 30,000 kg boat change as the velocity (in meters/s) changes?

$$KE = \frac{1}{2}(30,000\ kg)(2\ meters/s)^2 = 60000\ Joules$$

Change v to explore! $KE = \frac{1}{2}mv^2$

This one is already in the form we need. Just substitute the given values and simplify.

Kinetic Energy

The kinetic energy of an object in motion is equal to half the mass of the object times the velocity of the object squared.

$$KE = \frac{1}{2}mv^2$$

How does the kinetic energy (in Joules) of a 30,000 kg boat change as the velocity (in meters/s) changes?

$$KE = \frac{1}{2}(30,000\ kg)(4\ meters/s)^2 = 240000\ Joules$$

Change v to explore! $KE = \frac{1}{2}mv^2$

Observe what happens to **KE** as **v** doubles.

Kinetic Energy

What if we want to vary the KE instead? We can manipulate the equation $KE = \frac{1}{2}mv^2$ to find the mass as KE changes for a constant velocity:

$$m = \frac{2KE}{v^2}$$

Consider a rock falling at 40 m/s. As the KE (in Joules) changes, what is the mass (in kg)?

$$m = \frac{2*40000\ Joules}{(-40m/s)^2} = 50kg$$

Change KE to explore! $KE = \frac{1}{2}mv^2$

Solve for **m** before substituting the given values.

If you think of a linear equation in the form **y = mx + b**; then the value of **y** is dependant on whatever you substitute for x. We call x the **independent variable** and y the **dependent variable**. Notice the difference in the graphs below when the independent variable changes from **V** to **T**.

What is the shape of the graph when the independent variable is **T**?

What is the shape of the graph when the independent variable is **V**?

If a graph is linear, what do you know about the equation? If a graph is hyperbolic in form, what can you say about the equation?

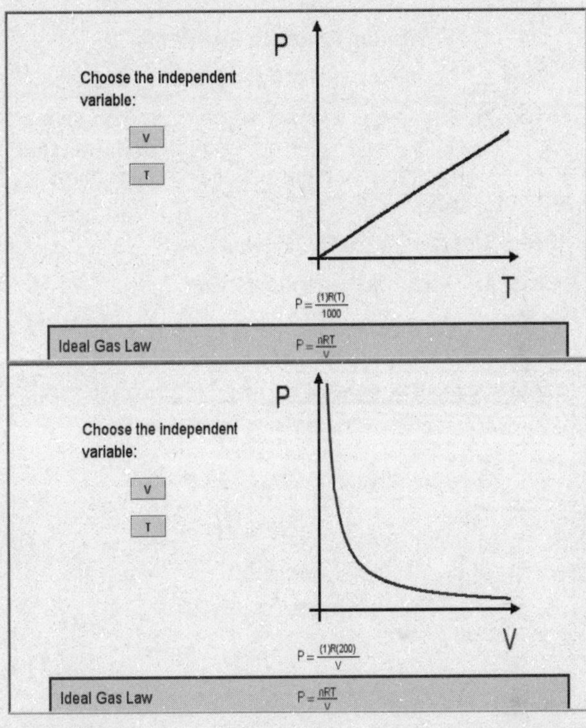

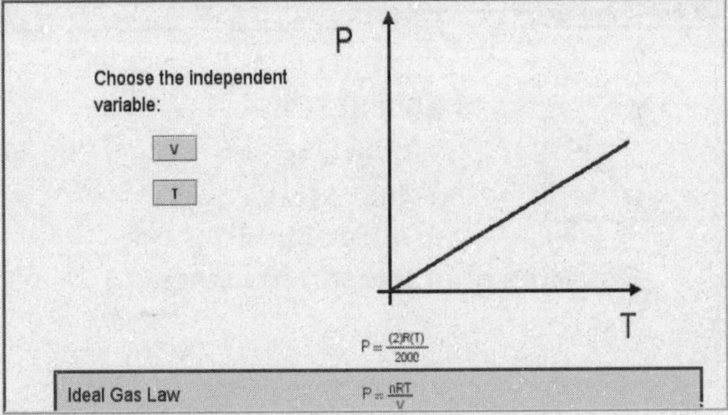

What happens to the slope of the line as **V** increases?

Why is the graph a hyperbolic shape when **V** is the independent variable?

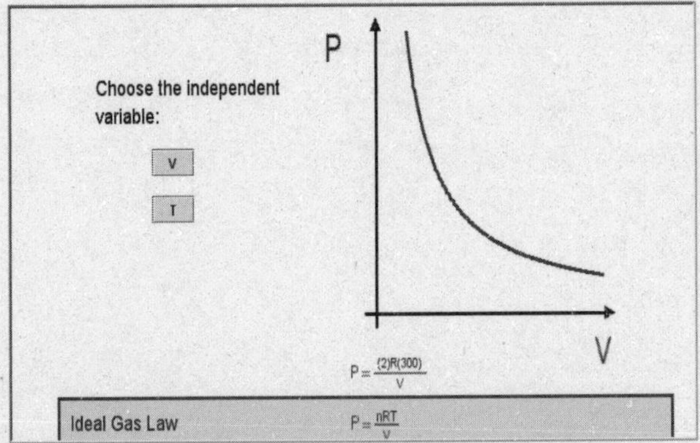

What happens to the shape of the curve as **T** decreases?

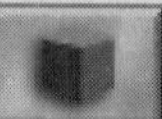

Similar Triangles

Triangles that are the same shape are called similar. Corresponding angles are equal. Corresponding sides of similar triangles are proportional.

Similar Triangle Problems

Step 1: Determine which sides are corresponding.

Step 2: Set up a proportion so that corresponding sides are across from each other in an equation (both numerators or both denominators).

Step 3: Solve for the unknown.

Step 4: Discard extraneous answers.

If these two triangles are similar, find x:

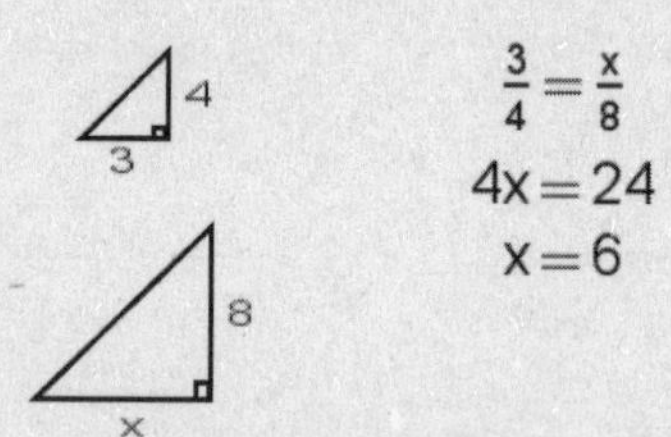

If these two triangles are similar, find x:

12

x

24

x + 5

$$\frac{x}{12} = \frac{x+5}{24}$$

$$24x = 12(x+5)$$

$$24x = 12x + 60$$

$$12x = 60$$

$$x = 5$$

Notice that corresponding sides are proportional. Substitute 5 back to check your answer.

Is 5/12 = 10/24?

If these two triangles are similar, find x:

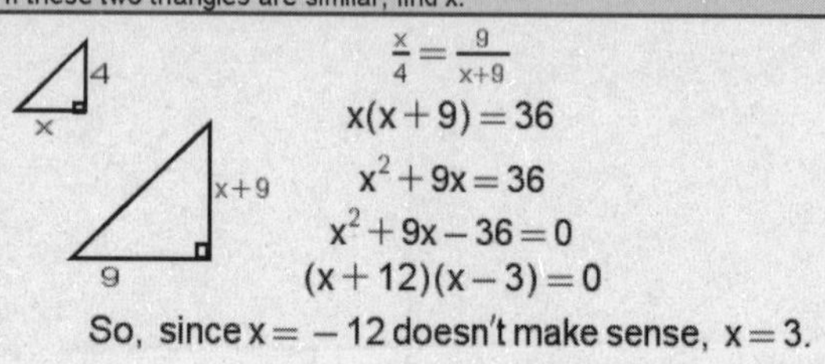

4
x
x+9
9
x/4 = 9/(x+9)
x(x+9) = 36
x² + 9x = 36
x² + 9x − 36 = 0
(x + 12)(x − 3) = 0
So, since x = −12 doesn't make sense, x = 3.

Solving the above problem results in a quadratic equation with two solutions. Why should the –12 be discarded? Does it work as a solution?

Two similar triangles are presented in the visualizations below. What happens when the triangles are shifted, rotated, or changed in size? Are the triangles still similar? How do you know?

Shift the triangles until they overlap. What can you determine about the angles?

What can you determine about the sides?

Are they still similar of their positions change?

You can align the triangles to make sure they are similar. What if you then rotated the triangles—would they still be similar?

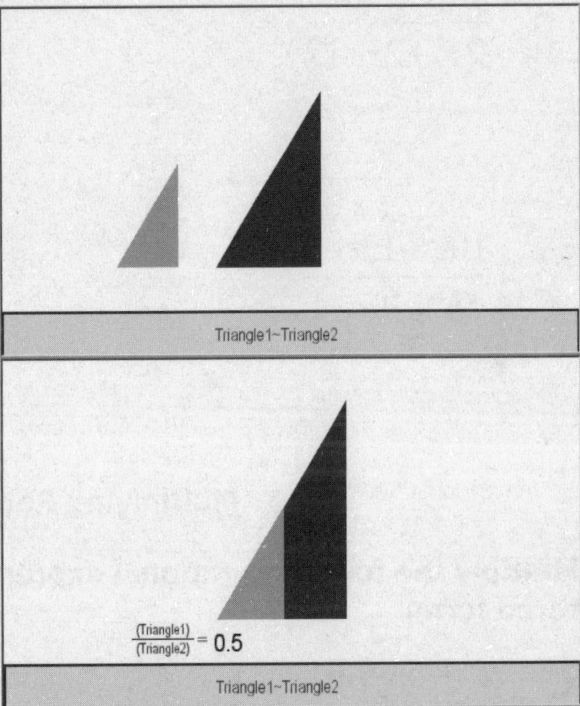

Change **a** to change the size of the triangles. What effect does that have on the similarity of the triangles?

Simplifying Rational Expressions

Write the following rational expressions is reduced form.

1. $\dfrac{x^2-7x+12}{x^2-6x+8}$

2. $\dfrac{x^2+x-12}{x^2+2x-8}$

3. $\dfrac{x^3+x^2+6x}{2x^2+2x+12}$

4. $\dfrac{x^2-16}{x^2+2x-8}$

5. $\dfrac{10x^2-13x-3}{5x^2-19x-4}$

6. $\dfrac{8-2x^2}{4x^2-16x+16}$

Multiplying Rational Expressions

Multiply the following rational expressions. Leave your answers in factored form.

1. $\dfrac{x^2-5x+6}{x^2-4x+4}\cdot\dfrac{x^2-4}{x^2-7x+12}$

2. $\dfrac{x^2+10x+25}{x^2+2x-15}\cdot\dfrac{3x-9}{2x^2+11x+5}$

3. $\dfrac{x^2-7x+12}{x^2+2x+4}\cdot\dfrac{x^3-8}{x^2-5x+6}$

4. $\dfrac{x^2-xy-x+y}{x^2-1}\cdot\dfrac{x^2+2x+1}{x-y}$

Dividing Rational Expressions

Divide the following rational expressions.

1. $\dfrac{x^2-7x+12}{x^2-6x+8} \div \dfrac{x^2+x-12}{x^2+2x-8}$

2. $\dfrac{x^3+x^2-6x}{2x^2+4x-16} \div \dfrac{x^2-x-12}{2x^2-32}$

3. $\dfrac{10x^2-13x-3}{2x^3-16} \div \dfrac{5x^2-19x-4}{4x^2+8x+16}$

4. $\dfrac{\dfrac{3x^3-27x}{x^2-x-6}}{\dfrac{2x^3+12x^2+18x}{x^2+5x+6}}$

Adding and Subtracting with LIKE Denominators

Add or subtract as indicated

1. $\dfrac{2x-3}{x^2-8x+15} - \dfrac{x+2}{x^2-8x+15}$

2. $\dfrac{x-3}{x^2-1} + \dfrac{x+5}{x^2-1}$

3. $\dfrac{2x+11}{(x+2)(x+7)} + \dfrac{5x+3}{(x+2)(x+7)}$

4. $\dfrac{5x^2}{x^2-2x-10} - \dfrac{2x+7}{x^2-2x-10}$

5. $\dfrac{5x^2}{x^2-4x-12} - \dfrac{3x^2+8}{x^2-4x-12}$

6. $\dfrac{1-x^2}{x^2-x-12} + \dfrac{x^2+1}{x^2-x-12}$

Finding the Least Common Denominator

Find the LCD for the following.

1. $(x+3), (x-2), (x+4)$

2. $4y(x+1), xy, 4(x+1)$

3. $x^2 + 12x + 35, 3x + 21$

4. $x^2 - x - 6, x^2 - 4$

5. $x^2 - 5x + 6, x^2 - 3x + 4$

6. $2x^2 - 50, 3x^2 + 14x - 5$

Adding & Subtracting with UnLIKE Denominators

1. $\frac{2x+5}{x-1}+\frac{x-3}{x+2}$

2. $\frac{x+3}{x-4}-\frac{x-3}{x+2}$

3. $\frac{x-7}{x^2-7x+12}+\frac{x-3}{x^2-6x+9}$

4. $\frac{x+5}{9-x^2}+\frac{x-4}{x^2-9}$

5. $\frac{x+5}{x^2-2x+1}-\frac{x^2+3x+2}{x^3-2x^2+x}$

6. $\frac{x+5}{x^3-x}+\frac{x-3}{x^2+2x+1}$

Rational Expressions in General

1. $$\frac{1-\frac{1}{x}}{2+\frac{3}{2x}}$$

2. $$\frac{\frac{x+2}{3}}{\frac{2}{x+3}}$$

3. $$\frac{\frac{x^2-5+6}{x^2-25}}{\frac{x^2-6x+9}{x^2-8x+15}}$$

4. $$\frac{\frac{1}{x^2}+\frac{2}{x}+1}{2-\frac{1}{x}-\frac{3}{x^2}}$$

5. $$\frac{\frac{1}{2x}-\frac{y}{2x^2}}{\frac{1}{4}-\frac{y}{4x}}$$

6. $$\frac{\frac{x^2+x+xy+y}{xy+y}}{\frac{x^2+x-xy-y}{x^2+x}}$$

Solving Proportions

Solve the following proportions.

1. $$\frac{5}{6}=\frac{x}{24}$$

2. $$\frac{5.3}{9.6}=\frac{x}{1.4}$$

3. $$\frac{5}{9}=\frac{12}{x}$$

4. $$\frac{6}{x}=\frac{72}{84}$$

5. $$\frac{x}{8}=\frac{36}{24}$$

6. $$\frac{x}{12}=\frac{2.9}{18}$$

Solving Rational Equations

Solve for x in each of the following.

1. $$\frac{5}{6}=\frac{x+3}{21}$$

2. $$\frac{x-5}{12}=\frac{1}{8}$$

3. $$\frac{8}{x+6}=\frac{x}{2}$$

4. $$\frac{6}{x-3}=\frac{x-4}{5}$$

5. $$\frac{5}{6}=\frac{x+1}{x+4}$$

6. $$\frac{2}{x+3}=\frac{x+5}{12}$$

7. $$\frac{4x+3}{3}=\frac{3x+11}{4}$$

8. $$\frac{x+5}{6}=\frac{3}{x-2}$$

Introduction to Asymptotes

Write the vertical and horizontal asymptotes for the following rational equations.

1. $y = \dfrac{7x+3}{2x-4}$

Horizontal Asymptote ______________

Vertical Asymptote ______________

2. $y = \dfrac{-2x+3}{x-6}$

Horizontal Asymptote ______________

Vertical Asymptote ______________

3. $y = \dfrac{x-1}{2x-5}$

Horizontal Asymptote ______________

Vertical Asymptote ______________

4. $y = \dfrac{3x+5}{-4x-1}$

Horizontal Asymptote ______________

Vertical Asymptote ______________

5. $y = \dfrac{9x+5}{-2x-7}$

Horizontal Asymptote ______________

Vertical Asymptote ______________

6. $y = \dfrac{2x+4}{3x-1}$

Horizontal Asymptote ______________

Vertical Asymptote ______________

Finding Solutions Graphically

Read a solution from the graph.

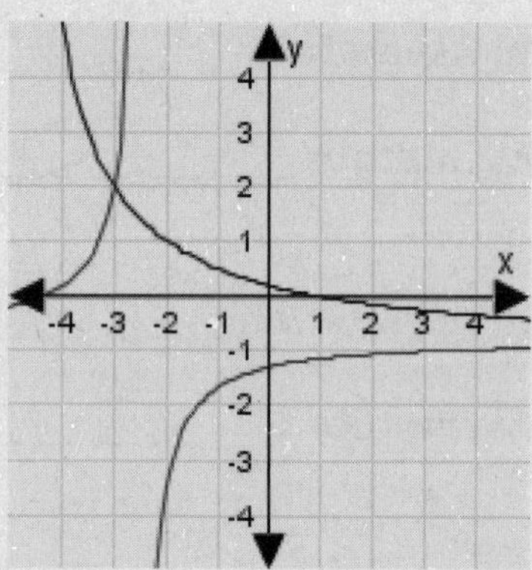

$$\frac{-3x-13}{4x+10}=\frac{x-1}{-x-5}$$

x = ______

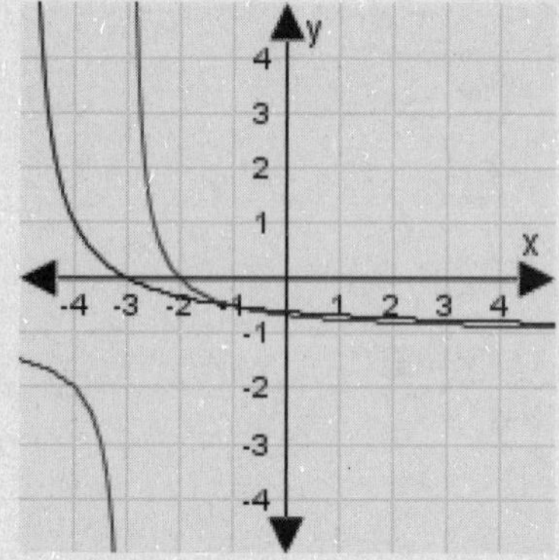

$$\frac{2x+4}{-2x-6}=\frac{x+3}{-x-5}$$

x = ______

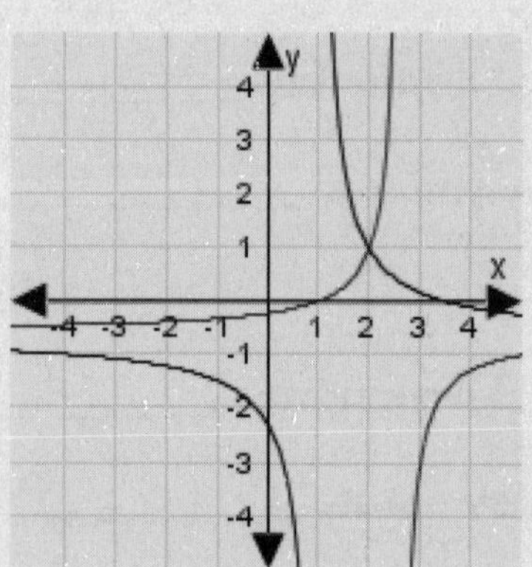

$$\frac{3x-3}{13-5x}=\frac{7-2x}{3x-3}$$

x = ______

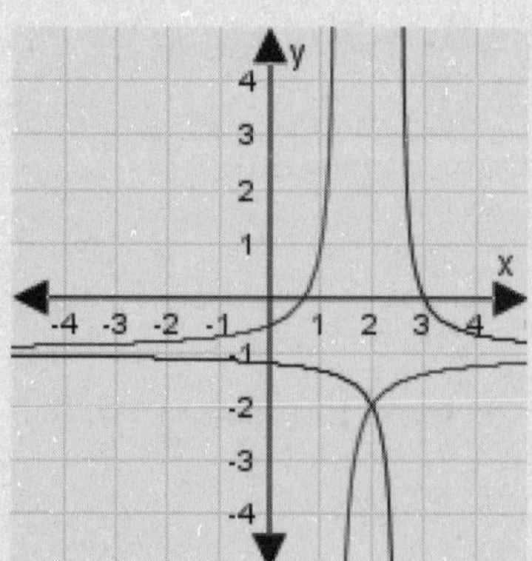

$$\frac{3x-2}{4-3x}=\frac{12-4x}{4x-10}$$

x = ______

Manipulating Rational Equations

Find the indicated value.

1. Your IQ is found by multiplying 100 to your mental age and dividing by your chronological age.

$$IQ = \frac{100 \cdot m}{c}$$

A. Solve for mental age:

B. Find your mental age if your IQ is 120 and you are 20.

2. The cost of running a hair dryer is found by multiplying the wattage times the rate per kilowatt-hour times the time, all divided by 1000.

$$c = \frac{wrt}{1000}$$

A. Solve for wattage, w.

B. Find the wattage if it costs 14.4¢ for 6 minutes at 2¢ per kilowatt-hour.

Similar Triangles

Set up a proportion and solve for x in each of the following.

1. 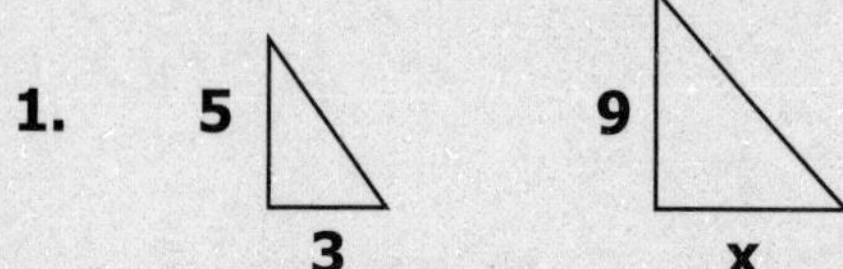

2. 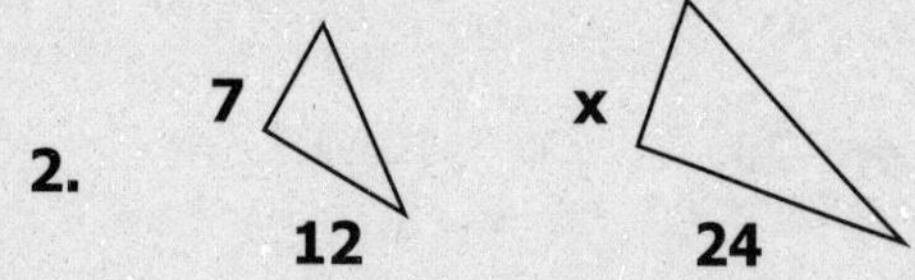

3. 8 X+2 x 15

4. x x+4 14 2x+5

14. Exponents & Radicals

Radical expressions are more than just finding square roots, cube roots, and so on. They can be manipulated in equations and used to solve application problems. Radical expressions can be written in several forms, as well as added, subtracted, multiplied and divided. When radicals are expressed in exponential form, all of the rules of exponents apply. We will begin studying exponents and radicals by learning to translate between forms and to express each in reduced form. You will draw on your skills of working with fractions and exponents from previous modules.

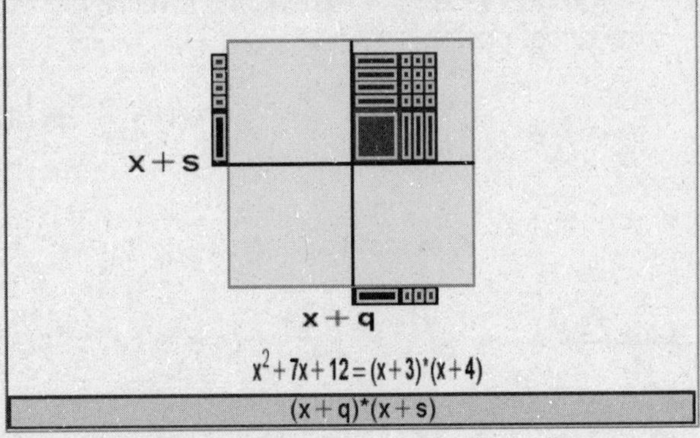

Roots and radicals can be written as powers, expressed as fractional or **rational exponents** defined by the following pattern:

$$\sqrt[n]{x} = x^{\frac{1}{n}}$$

Following the laws of exponents, if there are powers and roots involved, you can still write that as a fractional power:

$$\sqrt[n]{x^m} = \left(\sqrt[n]{x}\right)^m = x^{\frac{m}{n}}$$

Rational Exponents

$$\sqrt{x} = x^{\frac{1}{2}} \qquad \sqrt[3]{x} = x^{\frac{1}{3}} \qquad \sqrt[4]{x} = x^{\frac{1}{4}}$$

All *exponent rules* hold for rational exponents; use the product, quotient and power rules as needed.

Hint: powers can be switched from the numerator to the denominator (and vice versa) by making the power negative. $\frac{1}{x^n} = x^{-n}$

Write as a rational exponent:

$$\sqrt[3]{x} = x^{\frac{1}{3}}$$

Write as a rational exponent:

$$\frac{1}{\sqrt{(x)}} = \frac{1}{x^{\frac{1}{2}}}$$

$$= x^{\frac{-1}{2}}$$

Above, the square root is written as a 1/2 power and then made negative to bring it to the numerator.

Write as a rational exponent:

$$\sqrt{x^5}$$

$$= x^{5/2}$$

Write as a rational exponent.

Above, there is both a power and a root. Remember, the **power** becomes the **numerator** of the fractional exponent and the **root** becomes the **denominator**.

Write as a rational exponent:

$$\left(\sqrt[3]{x}\right)^7 = \left(x^{\frac{1}{3}}\right)^7$$

$$= x^{\frac{7}{3}}$$

Multiply the exponents.

It doesn't matter if the root or the power is on the inside. The power still goes on the top of the fractional power and the root still goes on the bottom of the fractional power.

Write as a rational exponent:

$$\left(\frac{1}{\sqrt[4]{x}}\right)^3 = \left(\frac{1}{x^{\frac{1}{4}}}\right)^3$$

$$= \left(x^{-\frac{1}{4}}\right)^3$$

$$= x^{-\frac{3}{4}}$$

First, we changed the fourth root to a 1/4 power. Then we made it negative to bring it to the numerator. Finally, we raised it to the third power.

We can display exponents on a number line. As the expression above the number line changes depending on the exponent, the decimal or fractional equivalent is graphed. Change the exponent in each of the visualizations to see how fractional exponents affect the base number.

What does the numerator of a rational exponent represent? What does the denominator represent? What happens if a rational exponent can be reduced to lowest terms?

What does a rational exponent represent?

What is the difference between a rational exponent and an integer exponent?

Can a rational exponent be negative?

What happens when the exponent is 1? 0? 0.5?

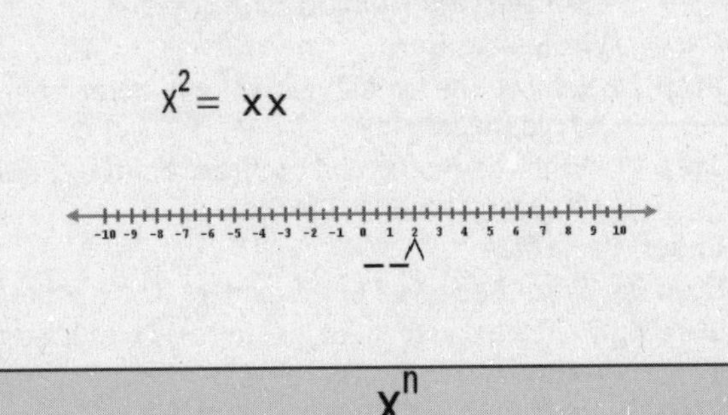

$x^5 = xxxxx$

-10 -9 -8 -7 -6 -5 -4 -3 -2 -1 0 1 2 3 4 5 6 7 8 9 10

x^n

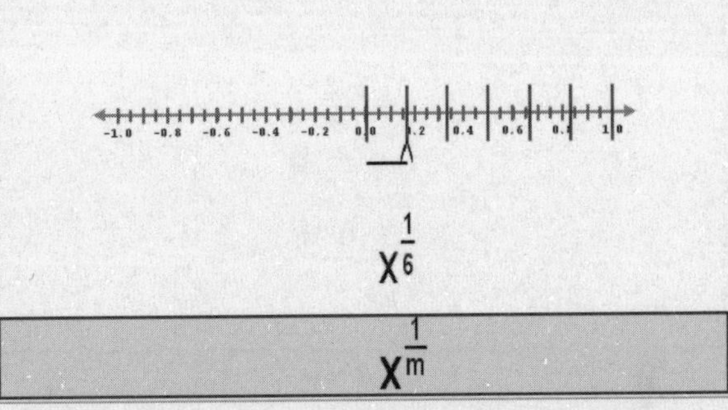

$x^{\frac{1}{6}}$

$x^{\frac{1}{m}}$

Point 1: What happens to the number of x's when the vale of the exponent **n** changes?

Point 2: What happens when you change the root (**m**)? What would the value of **x** have to be for the expression to be equal to a whole number?

$$\sqrt[6]{x^9} = \left(\sqrt[6]{x}\right)^9 = x^{9/6} = x^{3/2}$$

-10 -9 -8 -7 -6 -5 -4 -3 -2 -1 0 1 2 3 4 5 6 7 8 9 10

$\sqrt[6]{x^9}$

$\sqrt[m]{x^n}$

$$\frac{1}{\sqrt[4]{x^3}} = \frac{1}{\left(\sqrt[4]{x}\right)^3} = x^{-3/4} = x^{-3/4}$$

$\frac{1}{\sqrt[4]{x^3}}$

$\frac{1}{\sqrt[m]{x^n}}$

Point 3: What happened to the fractional exponent? How does reducing fractions work with exponents? What happens when the power and the root are the same?

Point 4: Both the root on the inside (with the power on the outside) and the root on the outside (with the power on the inside) are shown. Does the fractional exponent change in either situation?

Simplifying Radical Expressions

EnableMath

Radical expressions must be written in **simplest form**. That means that no perfect root factors can be under the radical and no common factors between any exponent and root.

To simplify radicals involving constants, you need to factor out the largest perfect square factor, then take the root as the coefficient of the radical of the other factor. For review, see Module 6.

To simplify radical expressions involving *variables*, you need to convert to rational (fractional) powers and reduce them to lowest terms.

Simplifying Radical Expressions

Case: Whole numbers

Step 1: Remove the largest perfect root factor from whole the number.

Step 2: Write the root as the coefficient of the radical containing the other factor.

Case: Variables

Step 3: Write the radical and exponent as a fraction.

Step 4: Remove common factors to reduce to lowest terms.

Step 5: Rewrite in radical form if necessary.

Simplify:

$$\sqrt{54}$$
$$=\sqrt{9}\sqrt{6}$$

Factor out perfect squares.

Simplify:

$$\sqrt{54}$$
$$=\sqrt{9}\sqrt{6}$$
$$=3\sqrt{6}$$

With constants, first factor out perfect squares. The square root is the coefficient of the radical factor

Simplify:

$$\sqrt{80}$$
$$=\sqrt{16}\sqrt{5}$$
$$=4\sqrt{5}$$

The largest perfect square factor of 80 is 16.

Simplify:

$$\sqrt{x^6}$$
$$=x^{6/2}$$
$$=x^3$$

With variables, first convert to a rational exponent, then reduce (if possible).

Simplify:

$$(\sqrt[3]{x})^{12}$$
$$=x^{12/3}$$
$$=x^4$$

It doesn't matter if the root is on the outside or inside of the power.

If perfect root factors can be found, then a radical expressions can be simplified. The perfect roots may be whole numbers or variables. This concept lets you change the values on radicals involving constants and variables to determine whether they simplify or not. You can control which factors, variables, exponents, and roots to use to explore exponent rules and to simplify radical expressions.

Does the product of perfect square factors always make a perfect square?

What happens as you change the values of **x**, **y** and **m** in **Point 1**? Why does this scenario always simplify?

Can you always find a power to "cancel out" with a root?

What happens if a rational exponent is an improper fraction? What happens to the whole number part when the exponent is written as a mixed number?

$\sqrt{(576)} = \sqrt{(64)} \times \sqrt{(9)} = 24$

$\sqrt{(64)} \times \sqrt{(9)}$

$\sqrt[m]{x^m} \times \sqrt[m]{y^m}$

$\sqrt[3]{1000} = \sqrt[3]{125} \times \sqrt[3]{8} = 10$

$\sqrt[3]{125} \times \sqrt[3]{8}$

$\sqrt[m]{x^m} \times \sqrt[m]{y^m}$

What perfect cube factors are in 1000? Are there perfect cube factors in 10,000?

$\left(\sqrt[9]{x}\right)^{10} = \sqrt[9]{x^{10}} = x\sqrt[9]{x^1}$

$\left(\sqrt[m]{x}\right)^n$

Point 2: What happens as you change the values of **m** and **n**? What happens when you "take out" a factor from under the radical?

$\left(\sqrt[6]{x}\right)^4 = \sqrt[6]{x^4}$

Doesn't simplify $\left(\sqrt[m]{x}\right)^n$

Can you change the radical to fraction form and reduce? The rational exponent reduces to 2/3? Is $x^{2/3}$ equivalent to $x^{4/6}$? How do you know?

Adding & Subtracting Radicals

To add and subtract radicals, we can think of radicals are the same as **like terms**. Radicals are **like** when they have the same **radicand** and the same **index**. If the two or more radical factors are exactly the same, then they can be combined by adding the coefficients of the radical factor—just like when we add like variable terms. Sometimes you can see from the beginning of a problem that two radicals are the same, but sometimes you'll need to simplify before you can see what radicals you're really dealing with.

Adding and Subtracting Radicals

Step 1: Write each radical term in simplest form.

Step 2: Compare radicands and indices—note like terms.

Step 3: Combine like radicals by adding coefficients.

Subtract:

$$7\sqrt{2}-4\sqrt{2}$$

The $\sqrt{2}$ is a like term, so we can combine.

Subtract:

$$7\sqrt{(2)}-4\sqrt{(2)}=3\sqrt{(2)}$$

The radicands and indices are the same; combine by adding coefficients .

Add:

$$\sqrt{(75)}+\sqrt{(27)}=\sqrt{(25)}\sqrt{(3)}+\sqrt{(9)}\sqrt{(3)}$$
$$=5\sqrt{(3)}+3\sqrt{(3)}$$
$$=8\sqrt{(3)}$$

The original radicals are not the same. Once we simplify each one through removing perfect square factors, we can combine by adding the 5 and 3 for the coefficient of radical 3.

Subtract:

$$\sqrt{(20x^5)}-x^2\sqrt{(45x)}=$$

Things get a little more tricky when radical terms involve both constants and variables. In a case like this, you have to break apart the square roots of the constants and variables and simplify as much as possible, before you can combine.

Subtract:

$$\sqrt{(20x^5)}-x^2\sqrt{(45x)}=\sqrt{(20)}\sqrt{(x^5)}-\sqrt{(45)}x^2\sqrt{(x)}$$
$$=\sqrt{(20)}x^{\frac{5}{2}}-\sqrt{(45)}x^2\,x^{\frac{1}{2}}$$
$$=\sqrt{(20)}x^{\frac{5}{2}}-\sqrt{(45)}x^{\frac{5}{2}}$$
$$=\sqrt{(4)}\sqrt{(5)}x^{\frac{5}{2}}-\sqrt{(9)}\sqrt{(5)}x^{\frac{5}{2}}$$
$$=2\sqrt{(5)}x^{\frac{5}{2}}-3\sqrt{(5)}x^{\frac{5}{2}}$$
$$=-\sqrt{(5)}x^{\frac{5}{2}}$$

Combine the $\sqrt{5}x^{\frac{5}{2}}$ like terms.

Notice that line 3 uses rational exponent form for the variable exponent—the variable part is NOT under the radical. After simplifying, we can see that both terms have the same radical and the same variable factor—they are like terms.

This concept allows you to experiment with various radical term combinations to see how they can be simplified and combined. Notice how the expressions are built by looking at the variables you control with the joystick—this can give you insight into what it takes to reduce radical expressions and to combine like radical terms.

What variable will be left as the radical factor? What determines which factors become the coefficients? How do you know you will always have a perfect radical factor to reduce?

What changes when you change the values of **a** and **b** with the joystick?

What changes when you change the values of **m** and **r** with the joystick?

Can each of these examples be written in rational exponent form before they are simplified?

$$\sqrt[6]{40960}+\sqrt[6]{466560}=4\sqrt[6]{10}+6\sqrt[6]{10}$$
$$=(4+6)\sqrt[6]{10}$$
$$=10\sqrt[6]{10}$$

$\sqrt[m]{a^m \times r}+\sqrt[m]{b^m \times r}$

$$\sqrt[6]{1458}+\sqrt[6]{128}=3\sqrt[6]{2}+2\sqrt[6]{2}$$
$$=(3+2)\sqrt[6]{2}$$
$$=5\sqrt[6]{2}$$

$\sqrt[m]{a^m \times r}+\sqrt[m]{b^m \times r}$

How do you know that 1458 has a perfect 6th root factor?

$$\sqrt[6]{1458}+\sqrt[6]{8192}=3\sqrt[6]{2}+4\sqrt[6]{2}$$
$$=(3+4)\sqrt[6]{2}$$
$$=7\sqrt[6]{2}$$

$\sqrt[m]{a^m \times r}+\sqrt[m]{b^m \times r}$

What if the radical index changed to 4? How would that change the expression? Would the result be the same?

$$\sqrt[4]{2}+\sqrt[4]{32}=1\sqrt[4]{2}+2\sqrt[4]{2}$$
$$=(1+2)\sqrt[4]{2}$$
$$=3\sqrt[4]{2}$$

$\sqrt[m]{a^m * r}+\sqrt[m]{b^m * r}$

Can this be written in rational exponent form? What would the answer look like?

$$\sqrt[4]{5}+\sqrt[4]{80}=1\sqrt[4]{5}+2\sqrt[4]{5}$$
$$=(1+2)\sqrt[4]{5}$$
$$=3\sqrt[4]{5}$$

$\sqrt[m]{a^m * r}+\sqrt[m]{b^m * r}$

Change **r** to 5. How did that change the expression?

Multiplying Radicals

EnableMath

Multiplying radicals is a two step process. If the indices are the same, multiply the radicands (also called **arguments**) together and then simplify. Alternatively, simplify first, multiply coefficients, and then multiply radicands. Simplify again, if necessary.

For multiplying radicals use the following rule: $\sqrt[n]{a} \cdot \sqrt[n]{b} = \sqrt[n]{ab}$

If there is a variable in the radicand, simplify by changing to rational exponent form. Then, add exponents.

Multiplying Radicals

For whole numbers: Multiply coefficients and then multiply radicand arguments. The radical index stays the same. Simplify by removing the highest perfect root factor.

For variables: Change to rational exponent form and add exponents.

Multiply:

$$\sqrt{(50)}\sqrt{(2)} =$$

Multiply:

$$\sqrt{(50)}\sqrt{(2)} = \sqrt{(100)}$$
$$= 10$$

Simplify the radical expression.

Above, we multiplied the 50 and 2 to get 100. The square root of 100 is 10.

Multiply:

$$\sqrt{(3)}\sqrt{(21)} = \sqrt{(63)}$$
$$= \sqrt{(9)}\sqrt{(7)}$$

Factor out perfect squares.

After multiplying, look for perfect root factors. 9 is a perfect square root factor of 63. The above expression is not simplified until the perfect root factor is removed from the radical.

Simplify:

$$\sqrt{(3)}\left(\sqrt{(6)} + 2\sqrt{(7)}\right) = \sqrt{(3)}\sqrt{(6)} + 2\sqrt{(3)}\sqrt{(7)}$$
$$= \sqrt{(3 \cdot 6)} + 2\sqrt{(3 \cdot 7)}$$

Use the Multiplication Property of Radicals.

Distributive Property holds for radicals. Multiply and then simplify radicals. Combine terms when possible.

Multiply:

$$x\sqrt[4]{x} = x \cdot x^{\frac{1}{4}}$$
$$= x^{1+\frac{1}{4}}$$
$$= x^{\frac{5}{4}}$$

The exponent for **x** is 1. Add 1 and 1/4 to get 5/4—leave it in improper fraction form.

Multiplying radicals almost always requires some simplifying. Same radicands multiply together under the radical and their coefficients multiply together outside the radical. Will it be easier to simplify before or after multiplying? Do variables require the same index? Can variables raised to 1 be multiplied by variables under a radical? This concept lets you explore what happens when you multiply radicals.

What happens as you change **a, b** and **m** in **Point 1** and **Point 2**?

How does changing the index change the factors of **a** and **b**?

What happens if you simplify before you multiply?

Can a variable always be expressed with a rational exponent? What happens when a variable has an exponent of a whole number? Can $\mathbf{x^3}$ be expressed as a rational exponent? Can it be expressed as a perfect fourth root?

$$\sqrt[3]{5}\times\sqrt[3]{1600}=\sqrt[3]{8000}$$
$$=20$$

$\sqrt[m]{a}\cdot\sqrt[m]{a^{m-1}b^m}$

$$\sqrt[4]{6}\sqrt[4]{1728}=\sqrt[4]{6}\sqrt[4]{6^3\cdot 8}$$
$$=6\sqrt[4]{8}$$

$\sqrt[m]{a}\sqrt[m]{a^{m-1}\cdot b}$

Multiply radicands.

$$\sqrt[5]{2}\sqrt[5]{32}=\sqrt[5]{2}\sqrt[5]{2^4\cdot 2}$$
$$=2\sqrt[5]{2}$$

$\sqrt[m]{a}\sqrt[m]{a^{m-1}\cdot b}$

If **a=b,** does the extra factor make the second radical a perfect root?

$$x\sqrt[3]{x^4}=\sqrt[3]{x^3\cdot x^4}$$
$$=\sqrt[3]{x^7}$$
$$=x^{\frac{7}{3}}$$

$x\sqrt[m]{x^a}$

Point 3: What's the exponent on **x** outside the radical? If the radical part is written in fraction exponent form, what do the exponents add to? What is another way to write the answer?

$$x\sqrt[5]{x^4}=\sqrt[5]{x^5\cdot x^4}$$
$$=\sqrt[5]{x^9}$$
$$=x^{\frac{9}{5}}$$

$x\sqrt[m]{x^a}$

Point 3: What happens as you change the value of **m**? Is there a short cut for getting to the improper fractional exponent?

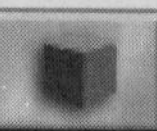

Rationalizing Denominators

EnableMath

Sometimes, we encounter fractions where the denominator has a radical factor. Remember that numbers that are not perfect roots are irrational numbers. To be in simplest form denominators should be rational numbers. We can make an irrational denominator rational through a process called **rationalizing the denominator**. To rationalize a denominator, we multiply the fraction numerator and denominator by the irrational factor (radical factor) we want to get rid of and simplify if possible. Sometimes the irrational is part of an expression. In that case we multiply by the ***conjugate*** of the expression: $(a + \sqrt{b})$ use $(a - \sqrt{b})$.

Hint: Don't forget that for any number, $\sqrt{a} * \sqrt{a} = a$

Rationalizing the Denominator

Step 1: Identify the radical factor in the denominator.

Step 2: Multiply both numerator and denominator by the radical factor or conjugate of the expression containing a radical.

Step 3: Simplify the numerator.

Step 4: Simplify the denominator clearing it of the radical factor.

Step 5: Simplify the fraction by removing common factors.

Rationalize the denominator of:

$$\frac{1}{\sqrt{(2)}} = \frac{1}{\sqrt{(2)}} \times \frac{\sqrt{(2)}}{\sqrt{(2)}}$$

Multiply by $\frac{\sqrt{2}}{\sqrt{2}}$.

Rationalize the denominator of:

$$\frac{1}{\sqrt{(2)}} = \frac{1}{\sqrt{(2)}} \times \frac{\sqrt{(2)}}{\sqrt{(2)}}$$

$$= \frac{\sqrt{(2)}}{2}$$

Now, the denominator is rational.

Multiply to clear the radical in the denominator. After multiplying, be sure to reduce the resulting fraction to lowest terms.

Rationalize the denominator of:

$$\frac{2}{3\sqrt{(3)}} = \frac{2}{3\sqrt{(3)}} \times \frac{\sqrt{(3)}}{\sqrt{(3)}}$$

$$= \frac{2\sqrt{(3)}}{3(3)}$$

$$= \frac{2\sqrt{(3)}}{9}$$

Now, the denominator is rational.

Above, we multiplied and divided by the square root of 3 to rationalize the denominator. After changing the denominator to a rational number, check to make sure the fraction is in lowest terms.

Rationalize the denominator of:

$$\frac{3}{\sqrt{(5)}+2} = \frac{3}{\sqrt{(5)}+2} \times \frac{\sqrt{(5)}-2}{\sqrt{(5)}-2}$$

Multiply by the "conjugate."

Rationalize by multiplying by the conjugate. Multiplying by the conjugate "clears" the radical from the denominator.

Rationalize the denominator of:

$$\frac{3}{\sqrt{(5)}+2} = \frac{3}{\sqrt{(5)}+2} \times \frac{\sqrt{(5)}-2}{\sqrt{(5)}-2}$$

$$= \frac{3(\sqrt{(5)}-2)}{5+2\sqrt{(5)}-2\sqrt{(5)}-4}$$

$$= 3\sqrt{(5)} - 6$$

Now, the denominator is rational.

Notice that the denominator radicals add out. In this case, the denominator simplifies to 1. Notice also, that the radical appears in the numerator.

In order for fractions with radicals to be in lowest terms, there should not be a radical in the denominator. How can you use the rules for changing fractions to eliminate the radical in the denominator? What do you need to multiply by in order to change the denominator to a rational number?

In this concept, you will explore equivalent fractions. One fraction will have a radical in the denominator and the other fraction will have a rational denominator. Explore what happens when you change the values of **a**, **b** and **c**.

What happens when a changes? What happens when **b** changes? What happens when **c** changes?

What determines what radical factor to multiply to the numerator and denominator?

When can you reduce a fraction to lowest terms?

$$\frac{7}{5\sqrt{(3)}} = \frac{7\sqrt{(3)}}{15}$$

$\frac{b}{c\sqrt{(a)}}$

$$\frac{7}{5\sqrt{(6)}} = \frac{7\sqrt{(6)}}{30}$$

$\frac{b}{c\sqrt{(a)}}$

What factor has been used to rationalize the denominator? Are the fractions still equivalent? How do you know?

$$\frac{2}{5\sqrt{(6)}} = \frac{1\sqrt{(6)}}{15}$$

$\frac{b}{c\sqrt{(a)}}$

What happened to the 2 in the numerator? Where did the 15 come from?

$$\frac{2}{7\sqrt{(6)}} = \frac{1\sqrt{(6)}}{21}$$

$\frac{b}{c\sqrt{(a)}}$

When can you reduce a fraction? Is the 1 necessary in the above expression? How did the radical 6 get moved from the denominator to the numerator?

Dividing Radicals

Dividing radical expressions is like reducing fractions: Divide common factors from numerators and denominators. With radical constants, an extra caution is that the radicals need to have the same index in order to divide factors. The following patterns show that you can divide before or after factoring out the root.

$$\sqrt[n]{\frac{b}{c}}=\frac{\sqrt[n]{b}}{\sqrt[n]{c}} \; and \; \frac{\sqrt[n]{ab}}{\sqrt[n]{ac}}=\sqrt[n]{\frac{ab}{ac}}=\frac{\sqrt[n]{b}}{\sqrt[n]{c}} \qquad \text{also} \qquad \frac{\sqrt[n]{ab}}{\sqrt[n]{ac}}=\frac{\sqrt[n]{a}\cdot\sqrt[n]{b}}{\sqrt[n]{a}\cdot\sqrt[n]{c}}=\frac{\sqrt[n]{b}}{\sqrt[n]{c}}$$

Dividing Radicals

Constants: Divide common factors within like radical indices. Rationalize the denominator.

Variables: Write the numerator and denominator using rational exponents. Divide by subtracting exponents.

Divide:

$$\frac{\sqrt{(6)}}{\sqrt{(2)}}=$$

Divide:

$$\frac{\sqrt{(6)}}{\sqrt{(2)}}=\frac{\sqrt{(2)}\sqrt{(3)}}{\sqrt{(2)}}$$
$$=\sqrt{(3)}$$

Above, both the numerator and denominator have a factor in common. Once we cancel out the common factor, we're left with a simplified solution.

Divide:

$$\frac{\sqrt{(5)}}{\sqrt{(35)}}=\frac{\sqrt{(5)}}{\sqrt{(5)}\sqrt{(7)}}$$
$$=\frac{1}{\sqrt{(7)}}$$
$$=\frac{1}{\sqrt{(7)}}\times\frac{\sqrt{(7)}}{\sqrt{(7)}}$$
$$=\frac{\sqrt{(7)}}{7}$$

The numerator and denominator have a factor in common, so we can divide (cancel) that factor out. Next, we'll need to simplify by rationalizing the denominator.

Divide:

$$\frac{x^2}{\sqrt[3]{x}}=\frac{x^2}{x^{\frac{1}{3}}}$$
$$=x^{2-\frac{1}{3}}$$
$$=x^{\frac{5}{3}}$$

When working with variables, convert to rational powers and subtract.

Simplify:

$$\frac{\sqrt[3]{t}}{\sqrt[5]{t}}=\frac{t^{\frac{1}{3}}}{t^{\frac{1}{5}}}$$
$$=t^{\frac{1}{3}-\frac{1}{5}}$$
$$=t^{\frac{5}{15}-\frac{3}{15}}$$
$$=t^{\frac{2}{15}}$$

$$\frac{\sqrt[a]{t}}{\sqrt[b]{t}}$$

Convert to rational exponents; subtract exponents to divide.

When you think about division, think about reducing common factors. If you can find common factors to eliminate, you can simplify by dividing. This concept lets you explore what happens when you divide radicals. There are two points, one with constants using square roots—the patterns are similar for higher roots. The other point uses variables. Notice how each expression is built from the variables you control with the joystick.

How do you know if a radical expression can be divided? How do you determine what factors divide out? What would happen if there were no common factors?

What happens as you change the values of **a** and **b** in **Points 1** and **2**?

Do constants follow exponent rules like variables do? Can you subtract exponents to divide constants? What has to be the same? (Try it on the problem to the right.)

$$\frac{\sqrt{(8)}}{\sqrt{(4)}} = \sqrt{(2)}$$

$$\frac{\sqrt{(a \times b)}}{\sqrt{(b)}}$$

$$\frac{\sqrt{(14)}}{\sqrt{(7)}} = \sqrt{(2)}$$

$$\frac{\sqrt{(a \times b)}}{\sqrt{(b)}}$$

What would happen if you rationalized the denominator before dividing out the common factor? Would the result be the same?

$$\frac{\sqrt{(7)}}{\sqrt{(35)}} = \frac{\sqrt{(5)}}{5}$$

$$\frac{\sqrt{(a)}}{\sqrt{(a \times b)}}$$

What was the common factor above? How did the denominator change to 5?

$$\frac{\sqrt{(7)}}{\sqrt{(35)}} = \frac{\sqrt{(5)}}{5}$$

$$\frac{\sqrt{(a)}}{\sqrt{(a \times b)}}$$

How do you change x^5 to a square root? Is $x^{10/2}$ the same as x^5?

$$\frac{x^2}{\sqrt[2]{x}} = x^{\frac{(4-1)}{2}}$$
$$= x^{\frac{3}{2}}$$

$$\frac{x^n}{\sqrt[m]{x}}$$

Does $x^2 = x^{4/2}$? What would happen if n=0?

Solving Radical Equations

EnableMath

Radical equations are equations with the variable under a radical. The first step in solving radical equations is to isolate the radical part. Next, remove the radical part by squaring, cubing, or raising both sides of the equation to the nth power.

One caution: Sometimes squaring (cubing and so on) may add something called **extraneous roots**. Always check to make sure answers are **real numbers** and that all solutions make sense. One particular caution—the radicand of a square root (or other even root) must be positive in order to get a real number.

Solving Radical Equations

Step 1: Isolate the radical on one side of the equation.

Step 2: Square (or cube or fourth...) both sides.

Step 3: Solve for **x**.

Step 4: Check all solutions.

Solve for x:

$$\sqrt{x} = 7$$
$$(\sqrt{x})^2 = 7^2$$
$$x = 49$$

Solve for x:

$$\sqrt{x} + 2 = 0$$
$$\sqrt{x} = -2$$

Subtract 2 from both sides.

Above, we have to subtract 2 from both sides to isolate the square root.

Solve for x:

$$\sqrt{x} + 2 = 0$$
$$\sqrt{x} = -2$$

So, there are NO real solutions.

The square root function does not yield negative numbers.

Even though it looks like squaring both sides will yield a good answer, checking the solution shows that it doesn't work. *When the square root of a number is equal to a negative number, there are NO REAL SOLUTIONS.*

Solve for x:

$$\sqrt{x-3} = 5$$
$$(\sqrt{x-3})^2 = 5^2$$
$$x - 3 = 25$$
$$x = 28$$

Remember: Isolate the radical; square both sides; then, solve for **x**. Does the solution work?

Solve for x:

$$\sqrt[3]{2x-3} = \sqrt[3]{x}$$
$$(\sqrt[3]{2x-3})^3 = (\sqrt[3]{x})^3$$
$$2x - 3 = x$$
$$x - 3 = 0$$
$$x = 3$$

The process works the same with cube (and higher order) roots. Always check the answer in the original equation.

Square roots have graphs that curve in a predictable way (see examples below). Cubed roots have a distinctive pattern, as do fourth, fifths, and so on. We can use these patterns to show a picture of solutions to particular equation. This concept lets you explore equations involving a square root.

We graph sides of equations separately. The constant right side of the equation is graphed as the horizontal blue line (y=c) and the square root on the left side is graphed as the red curve. What do you call the point where the graphs intersect?

How does **x** change as you change **b**? What change do you see in the red curve?

What happens if the radical part is a negative number?

Can **x** be negative?

Can **c** be negative?

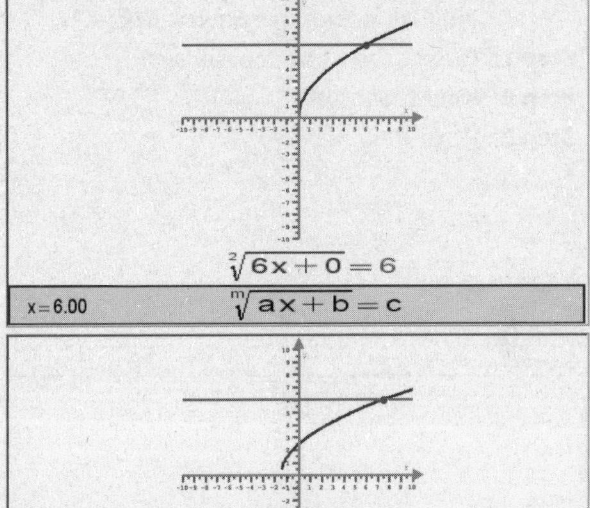

How does **x** change as you change **a**? What change do you see in the red curve?

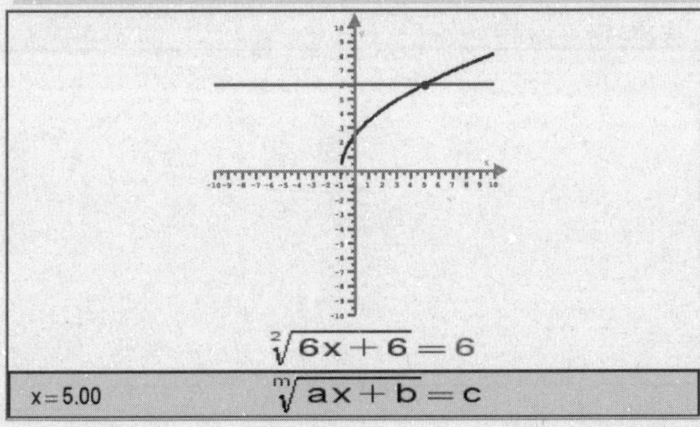

At what point does y=6 intersect with the red curve? What do you know about that point?

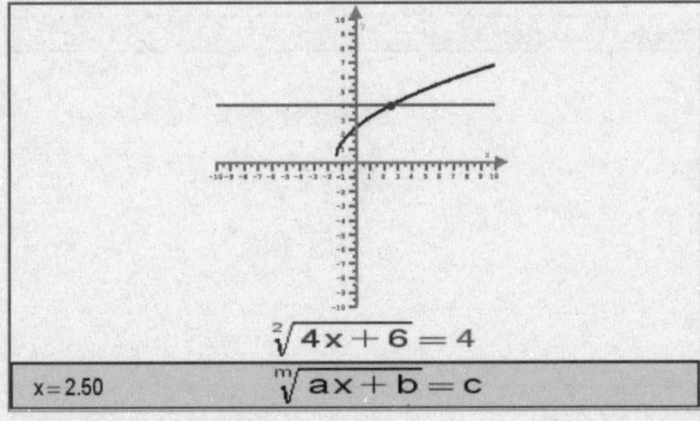

What happens as you change **c**?

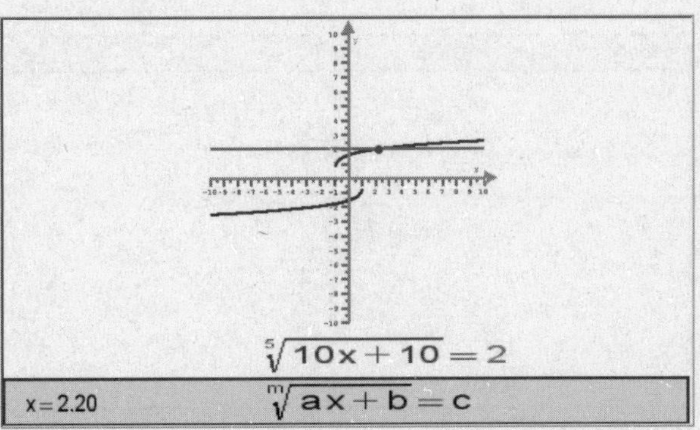

Explore what happens as you change the value of **m**. Do you notice the difference when **m** is even versus when **m** is odd? Why do you think that happens?

Imaginary Numbers

In the previous assignment, we found that the process for solving some equations yielded square root with negative valued radicands. When this occurred we said that this result was not **real**. We now define this type of solution as **imaginary**. **Imaginary numbers** denoted with the letter **i**, where

$$i = \sqrt{-1}$$

Imaginary numbers are not part of the Real Number System. Together with the Reals, imaginary numbers form the **Complex Number System**. Complex numbers are in the form **w = a +bi,** where **a** represents the real part and **b** is the imaginary part of the number. Complex number system has its own rules for combining and simplifying imaginary, or complex numbers. Imaginary numbers have real world uses in engineering and other science applications.

Simplifying Negative Square Roots

Step 1: Factor $\sqrt{-1}$ from the radicand.

Step 2: Simplify as usual.

Step 3: Replace $\sqrt{-1}$ by **i**.

What is i?

Throughout the history of mathematics, mathematicians kept coming across an important quantity:

$$\sqrt{-1}$$

This was thought to be only an imaginary quantity, so, mathematicians named it i for imaginary.

$$\sqrt{-1} = i$$

Powers of i:

$$i^2 = (\sqrt{-1})^2 = -1$$
$$i^3 = i^2 i = -1i = -i$$
$$i^4 = i^2 i^2 = (-1)(-1) = 1$$
$$i^5 = i^4 \cdot i = 1i = i$$

So, the powers of i cycle endlessly though i, -1, $-i$ and 1.

So, for instance, $i^{83} = -i$.

The powers of **i** cycle through i, -1, -i and 1 endlessly. You can always recreate the list by the equality i = $\sqrt{-1}$

Simplify this imaginary number:

$$\sqrt{-9}$$
$$= \sqrt{9}\sqrt{-1}$$
$$= 3i$$

Rewrite $\sqrt{-1}$ as i.

To simplify imaginary numbers, we can pull out any perfect squares and rewrite $\sqrt{-1}$ as **i**.

Simplify this imaginary number:

$$\sqrt{-12}$$
$$= \sqrt{4}\sqrt{3}\sqrt{-1}$$
$$= 2\sqrt{3}i$$

Rewrite $\sqrt{-1}$ as i.

Sometimes, we'll still have a square root left after we simplify. The entire constant and radical factors are coefficients of **i.**

Simplify this imaginary number:

$$-3\sqrt{-50}$$
$$= -3\sqrt{25}\sqrt{2}\sqrt{-1}$$
$$= -3*5\sqrt{2}i$$

Rewrite $\sqrt{-1}$ as i.

Remember: When there is a negative number under a square root, the quantity is imaginary.

In this concept, we explore the patterns of the imaginary number (**i**), which equals $\sqrt{-1}$.

Can you determine the value for **i** raised to *any power*?

Is there a pattern you can use to determine the value of **i**?

In **Point 1**, we'll figure out what happens as we raise **i** to different powers.

What happens as you change the value of **a** in **Point 1**? Do you notice any patterns? What do you think would happen when a = 200?

How is simplifying radical expressions with **i** different than expressions without **i**?

Does **i** always represent a negative number?

Can all negative numbers be replaced by **i**?

$$i^2 = -1$$

i^a

$$i^5 = i$$

i^a

Once you find the pattern, can you guess what **i** raised to any number will be?

$$\sqrt{-24} = 2\sqrt{6}\,i$$

$\sqrt{a^2 b}$

How are these simplifications like those we do on real numbers involving square roots?

$$-2\sqrt{-8} = -4\sqrt{2}\,i$$

$c\sqrt{a^{2}*b} =$

If the number under the radical was positive, how would the answer be different? Can you think of a way to describe the procedure you'd use to simplify imaginary numbers?

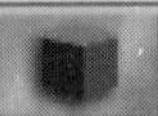

Adding & Subtracting Complex Numbers

EnableMath

Complex numbers have a real number part and an imaginary number part. Complex numbers use the pattern **a + bi** , where **a** is the real part and **b** is the imaginary part of the number. You can think of **b** as the coefficient of **i**. A complex numbers and its conjugate form a **complex conjugate pair**, **a + bi** and **a – bi** .

Notice: The only difference between a complex number and its conjugate is the sign difference between the real and imaginary parts.

Complex numbers can be added, subtracted, multiplied and divided.

Adding and Subtracting Complex Numbers

Addition: Add real parts (terms) by adding coefficients or constants and then add imaginary parts (terms) by adding coefficients of i.

Subtraction: Distribute the negative subtract sign to both parts of the subtracted term. Proceed as for addition by combining real parts together and then imaginary parts.

What are complex numbers?

Complex numbers are a combination of real and imaginary numbers. For instance, $3+2i$ is a complex number with a real part of 3 and an imaginary part of 2.

$a+bi$

What are complex conjugates?

Complex conjugates are a very useful tool in mathematics. The complex conjugate is found by negating the imaginary part of a complex number. For instance, the complex conjugate of $3+2i$ is $3-2i$.

$a+bi,\ a-bi$

Find any complex conjugate pair by using the opposite sign of the imaginary coefficient.

Add these complex numbers:

$$3+2i+5-4i$$

$a+bi+c+di$

You add or subtract complex numbers by "combining like terms." In other words, you combine the real parts together and separately combine the imaginary parts together.

Add these complex numbers:

$$3+2i+5-4i$$
$$=3+2i+5-4i$$
$$=8-2i$$

$a+bi+c+di$

Above, the 3 and the 5 combine to make 8 and the 2i and –4i combine to make –2i.

Subtract these complex numbers:

$$3+2i-(5-4i)$$
$$=3+2i-5+4i$$
$$=-2+6i$$

Combine like terms. $a+bi-(c+di)$

Don't forget to distribute your negative sign to both terms when you subtract!

When we graph a complex number (**a + bi**), we graph **a** (the real part) as the x-coordinate and **b** (the imaginary part) as the imaginary-coordinate. We now have a picture of all complex numbers in the complex coordinate plane. In this concept, you can explore how we graph complex numbers. You can also explore how to add and subtract complex numbers with **point 2**. Two complex numbers are graphed along with their sum. How can subtraction be represented?

What happens when the coefficient of **i** is 0? What happens when the real number part is 0?

Can all real numbers be represented as a complex number?

Is adding complex numbers commutative? Is adding complex numbers associative?

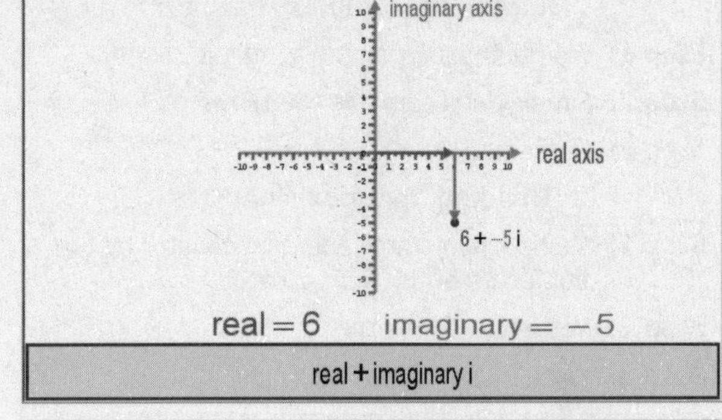

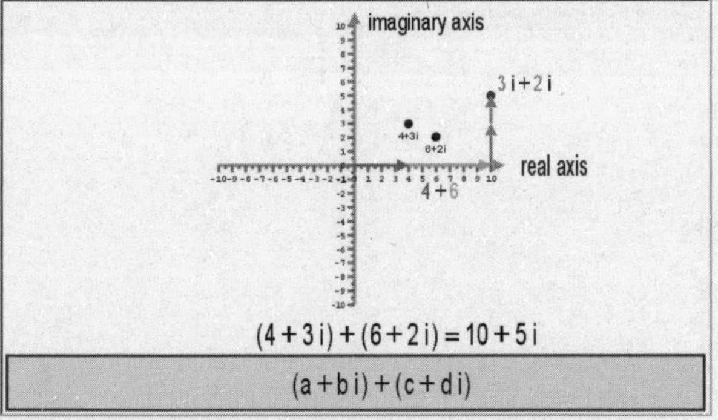

Point 2 lets you explore graphically what happens when we add two complex numbers together. How does changing the values of **a, b, c** and **d** change the sum?

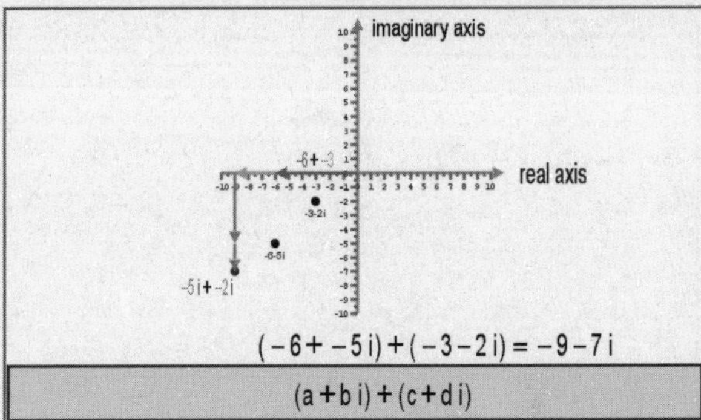

Negative numbers are as you would expect. Does adding two negative imaginary parts give a smaller number.

Multiplying & Dividing Complex Numbers

EnableMath

Multiplying complex numbers is just like multiplying binomials. You distribute, making sure each term is multiplied by every other term. Simplifying also includes eliminating $\mathbf{i^2}$ whenever possible.

Dividing complex numbers is like simplifying radical expressions; you have to change the denominator into a real number. Dividing complex numbers requires you to multiply by the complex conjugate of the denominator (this will give you a real denominator) and then simplify.

Hint: Don't forget that $i^2 = -1$.

Multiplying Complex Numbers

Step 1: Distribute as for binomial multiplication.

Step 2: Simplify and combine like terms.

Step 3: Swap out –1 for each i^2.

Dividing Complex Numbers

Step 1: Multiply numerator and denominator by the conjugate of the denominator.

Step 2: Multiply and simplify.

Step 3: Write in a + bi format.

Multiply these complex numbers:

$$(2-3i)(-1+4i)$$
$$=(2)(-1)+(2)(4i)+(-3i)(-1)+(-3i)(4i)$$

Distribute.

Multiply these complex numbers:

$$(2-3i)(-1+4i)$$
$$=(2)(-1)+(2)(4i)+(-3i)(-1)+(-3i)(4i)$$
$$=-2+8i+3i-12i^2$$
$$=-2+8i+3i+12$$
$$=10+11i$$

Combine like terms.

For this multiplication, we distribute, then convert i^2 to –1 and simplify.

Divide these complex numbers:

$$\frac{-2+3i}{-2-1i}$$
$$=\left(\frac{-2+3i}{-2-1i}\right)\left(\frac{-2+1i}{-2+1i}\right)$$

Multiply and divide by the conjugate (eliminating the imaginary part of the denominator).

For a division problem, the first step is to multiply and divide by the complex conjugate of the denominator. Here the denominator is –2-1i, so the complex conjugate is –2+1i.

Divide these complex numbers:

$$\frac{-2+3i}{-2-1i}$$
$$=\left(\frac{-2+3i}{-2-1i}\right)\left(\frac{-2+1i}{-2+1i}\right)$$
$$=\frac{4-2i-6i-3}{4-2i+2i+1}$$
$$=\frac{1-8i}{5}$$

Simplify.

When we multiply a complex number by its conjugate to clear a denominator, the imaginary parts of the denominator divide out.

Divide these complex numbers:

$$\frac{-2+3i}{-2-1i}$$
$$=\left(\frac{-2+3i}{-2-1i}\right)\left(\frac{-2+1i}{-2+1i}\right)$$
$$=\frac{4-2i-6i-3}{4-2i+2i+1}$$
$$=\frac{1-8i}{5}$$
$$=\frac{1}{5}+\frac{-8}{5}i$$

Divide through by the real denominator.

Don't forget that we usually like to see our final answers in **a + bi** format.

As always, we visualize multiplication as a rectangle. In **Point 1**, we see what happens graphically when we multiply two complex numbers. The brown sections are the real numbers and the red and blue sections are the imaginary numbers. Can you see what happens as you change the values of **a, b, c** and **d**?

In **Point 2**, we see what happens when you divide complex numbers by simplifying the denominator to a real number. What happens as you change the values of **a, b, c** and **d**?

Is multiplication commutative?

What happens when you multiply a complex pair?

What happens when you square a complex number?

When dividing two complex numbers, how do you check your answer?

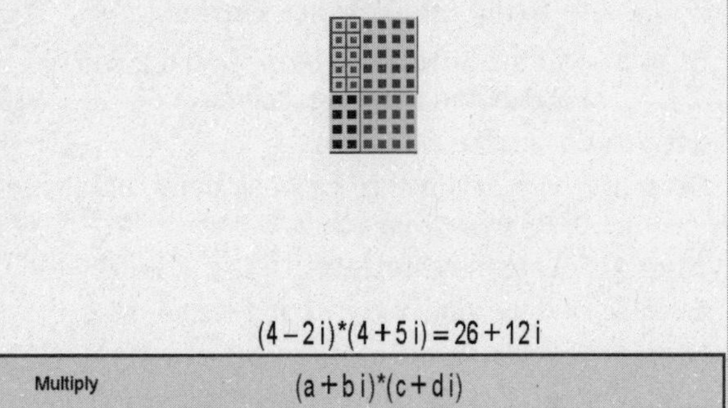

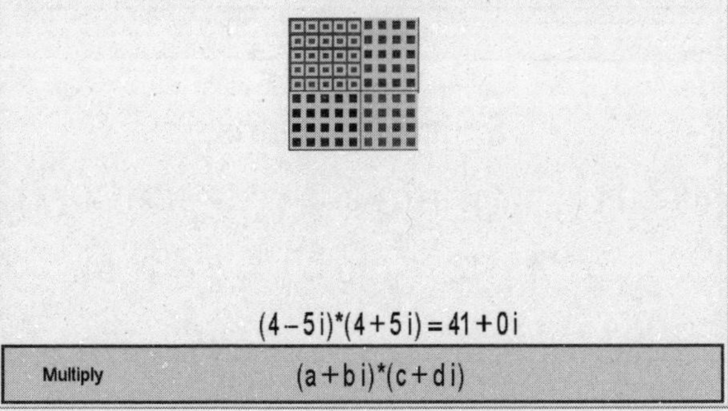

Point 1: What happens to the red and blue areas when a=c and b=-d? What happened to the middle terms?

Where did the imaginary parts go?

$$\frac{2+2i}{-2+0i} = \frac{2+2i}{-2+0i} * \frac{(-2-0i)}{(-2-0i)}$$

$$= \frac{-4-4i}{4} = \frac{-1}{1} + \frac{-1}{1}i$$

Divide $\frac{a+bi}{c+di}$

Point 2: Explore what happens as you change the values of **a, b, c** and **d**. Can you rewrite the above answer so that it looks easier to read?

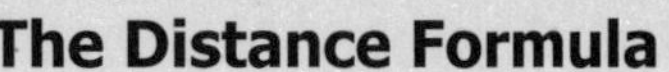

The Distance Formula

It is often necessary to find the distance between two points in a coordinate plane.

The distance between two points $P_1(x_1,y_1)$ and $P_2(x_2,y_2)$ is:

$$d=\sqrt{(x_2-x_1)^2+(y_2-y_1)^2}$$

Using the Distance Formula

Step 1: Find the **difference** between the **x** coordinates of the two given points.

Step 2: Square the difference.

Step 3: Find the difference between the **y** coordinates of the two given points.

Step 4: Square the difference.

Step 5: Find the sum of step 2 and step 4.

Step 6: Find the square root.

Find the distance between the points:

$$P_1(-1,\ -1) \text{ and } P_2(1,\ 3)$$

$d=\sqrt{(x_2-x_1)^2+(y_2-y_1)^2}$

Find the distance between the points:

$$P_1(-1,\ -1) \text{ and } P_2(1,\ 3)$$

So, the distance is:

$$d=\sqrt{(1-\ -1)^2+(3-\ -1)^2}=\sqrt{(2)^2+(4)^2}$$

$d=\sqrt{(x_2-x_1)^2+(y_2-y_1)^2}$

If we place those quantities into their correct places in the distance formula, this is what we get. Take care when there are double negatives!

Find the distance between the points:

$$P_1(-1,\ -1) \text{ and } P_2(1,\ 3)$$

So, the distance is:

$$d=\sqrt{(1-\ -1)^2+(3-\ -1)^2}=\sqrt{(2)^2+(4)^2}$$

$$=\sqrt{4+16}=\sqrt{20}=\sqrt{4}\sqrt{5}=2\sqrt{5}$$

$d=\sqrt{(x_2-x_1)^2+(y_2-y_1)^2}$

Simplify using order of operations to get our final answer.

The **distance formula** is based on the **Pythagorean Theorem, $a^2+b^2=c^2$**. To solve this equations for **c**, we first take the square root of both sides. If we think of constructing a right triangle around the two points (with hypotenuse between the two points), we can see that the length of one side is $\mathbf{x_2 - x_1}$ and the length of the other side is $\mathbf{y_2 - y_1}$. The Pythagorean Theorem states that the length (**d**) between the points $\mathbf{(x_1, y_1)}$ and $\mathbf{(x_2, y_2)}$ is given by,

$$d = \sqrt{(x_2 - x_1)^2 + (y_2 - y_1)^2}$$

If the value of **c** in the Pythagorean Theorem is the same as **d** in the distance formula, what corresponds to **a** and **b**?

Do any two points work?

Does this work in the complex plane?

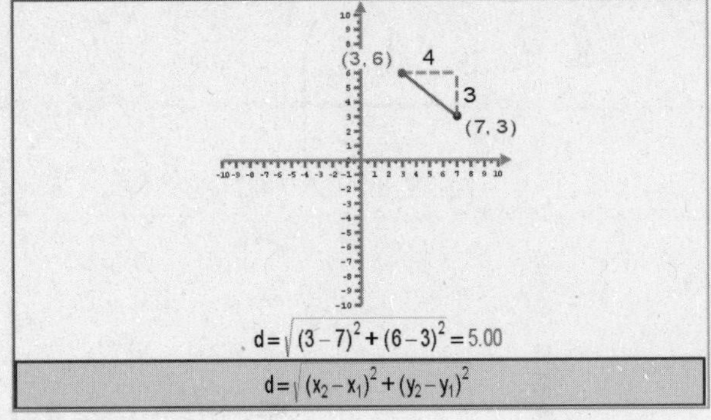

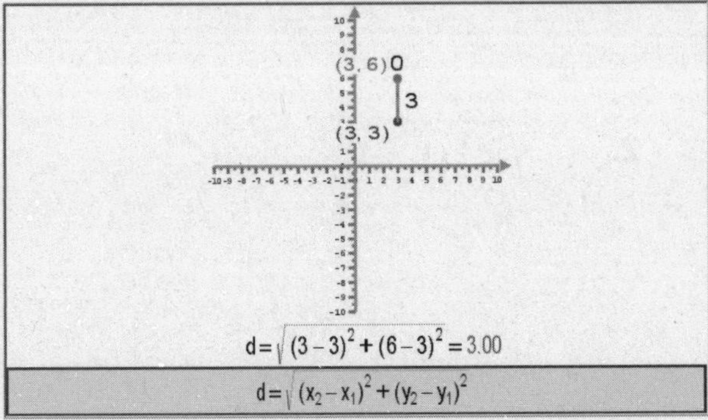

Explore what happens as you change the values of the points.
What happens when the two points have equal **x**-values?

Radicals and Rational Exponents

Write as a rational exponent:

1. $\sqrt[4]{x}$

2. $\sqrt[8]{x^7}$

3. $\left(\dfrac{1}{\sqrt{x}}\right)^{13}$

4. $\left(\dfrac{1}{\left(\sqrt{x}\right)^5}\right)$

Simplifying Radical Expressions

Simplify:

1. $\sqrt{63}$

2. $\sqrt{810}$

3. $\sqrt{x^{30}}$

4. $\sqrt[7]{x^{70}}$

Adding & Subtracting Radicals

Add or subtract as indicated.

1. $8\sqrt{5}+2\sqrt{5}$

2. $\sqrt{96}-\sqrt{24}$

3. $\sqrt{125}+\sqrt{20}$

4. $\sqrt{20x^7}-x^3\sqrt{80x}$

5. $\sqrt{32x^5}+x^2\sqrt{8x}$

Multiplying Radicals

Multiply.

1. $\sqrt{2}*\sqrt{40}$

2. $\sqrt{2}*\sqrt{24}$

3. $x^5 * x^{\frac{3}{5}}$

4. $x^{10} * x^{\frac{5}{4}}$

Rationalizing Denominators

Rationalize.

1. $\dfrac{1}{2\sqrt{7}}$

2. $\dfrac{5}{7\sqrt{6}}$

Dividing Radicals

Divide.

1. $\dfrac{\sqrt{77}}{\sqrt{7}}$

2. $\dfrac{\sqrt{5}}{\sqrt{30}}$

3. $\dfrac{x^2}{\sqrt[6]{x}}$

4. $\dfrac{x^3}{\sqrt[3]{x}}$

Solving Radical Equations

Solve for x:

1. $\sqrt{x} = 10$

2. $\sqrt{x} - 15 = -4$

3. $\sqrt{x+3} = 1$

4. $\sqrt[3]{4x+8} = \sqrt[3]{3x+12}$

Imaginary Numbers

Evaluate

1. i^9

2. $\sqrt{-160}$

Adding & Subtracting Complex Numbers

1. 2-2i + (-4-i)

2. 6+3i-(-4-2i)

Multiplying & Dividing Complex Numbers

1. (5+2i)(-1+3i)

2. $\dfrac{-2+3i}{-1-2i}$

3. $\dfrac{-4-2i}{3+i}$

The Distance Formula

Find the distance between the two given points.

1. (-2, -1) and (-1, 1)

2. (1.5, -0.5) and (4.5 and, 9.5)

3. (-3, -5) and (-4, -1)

3. (0,2) and (3, 12)

15. Quadratic Equations

Quad means *square* in Latin. A quadratic equation is polynomial where the highest order term is a square; it is thus said to be a second order polynomial. Quadratic equations are very important for two reasons:

1) They can represent a wide variety of things like *motion* in the real world, and **2)** We can find solutions for them. While there is a general formula for solving quadratic equations, it requires a good deal of calculation and taking square roots. Therefore, we look for tricks, special cases that are easier to solve.

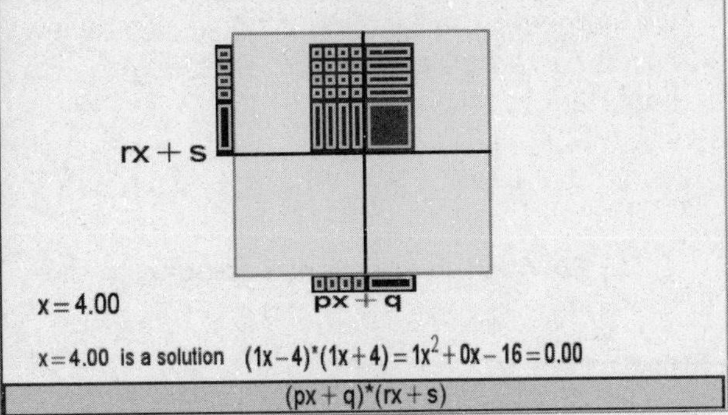

Solving quadratic equations is very useful in many real world applications. The solutions (or roots) of quadratic equations can be found using many different methods. The first technique we'll learn to use is called **solving by factoring**.

This method is useful when you can easily factor the given equation using the factoring processes we learned in the Factoring Module. To review factoring techniques, the Factoring Module sections called *Factoring and the GCF*, *Factoring* ax^2+bx+c and *Factoring the Difference of 2 Squares* are important to take a look at.

Solving Quadratics By Factoring

Step 1: Make sure one side is equal to 0.

Step 2: Factor the other side using the appropriate factoring technique(s).

Step 3: Use the zero factor property to solve.

Step 4: Check both answers by substituting back into the original equation.

Solve for x:

$$x^2+5x-6=0$$
$$(x-1)(x+6)=0$$
$$x-1=0,\quad x+6=0$$
$$x=1,\quad x=-6$$

These are the solutions. $ax^2+bx+c=0$

Solve for x:

$$2x^2-5x-3=0$$
$$(x-3)(2x+1)=0$$

Factor the left side. $ax^2+bx+c=0$

Here, one side is equal to zero, so we factor the other side.

Solve for x:

$$2x^2-5x-3=0$$
$$(x-3)(2x+1)=0$$
$$x-3=0,\quad 2x+1=0$$
$$x=3,\quad x=-1/2$$

These are the solutions. $ax^2+bx+c=0$

We set each factor equal to zero to determine the solutions. The next step is to check to make sure your answers are correct.

Solve for x:

$$6x^2=-5x+6$$

$ax^2+bx+c=0$

The example above must be rearranged so that one side is equal to zero. Add 5x and –6 to both sides to move them over to the left side. For ease of factoring, it is customary to keep the x^2 term positive, otherwise, it makes no difference which side of the equal side you choose.

Solve for x:

$$6x^2=-5x+6$$
$$6x^2+5x-6=0$$
$$(3x-2)(2x+3)=0$$
$$3x-2=0,\quad 2x+3=0$$
$$x=2/3,\quad x=-3/2$$

These are the solutions. $ax^2+bx+c=0$

Then we factor and set each factor equal to zero. Check your work by substituting 2/3 and –3/2 back into the original equation.

You can visualize factored quadratics as number bars, variable bars and x^2 squares. A quadratic equation that is factorable must be a product: It forms a rectangle. When it does, the factors are the lengths of two adjacent sides. Build factorable quadratics by changing **p, q, r,** and **s**. Find solutions by changing **x**.

What happens horizontally when the value of **x** is **−q/p**? What happens vertically when the value of **x** is **−s/r**? How many solutions can a quadratic equation have?

What value of **x** makes the equation true? Change the value of **x** until you reach a solution.

What happens to the squares and bars when you reach a solution?

Will there always be a positive and a negative solution?

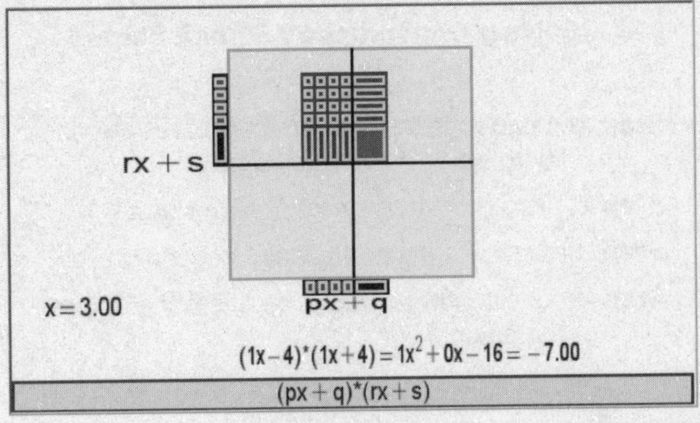

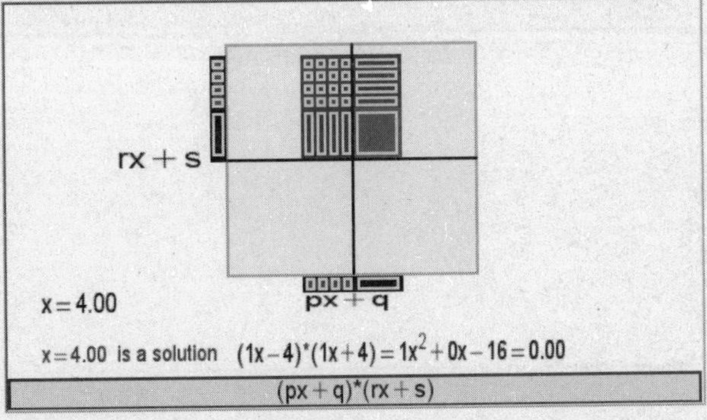

Here, **x=4** makes the equation true. Can you find another value of **x** that is a solution?

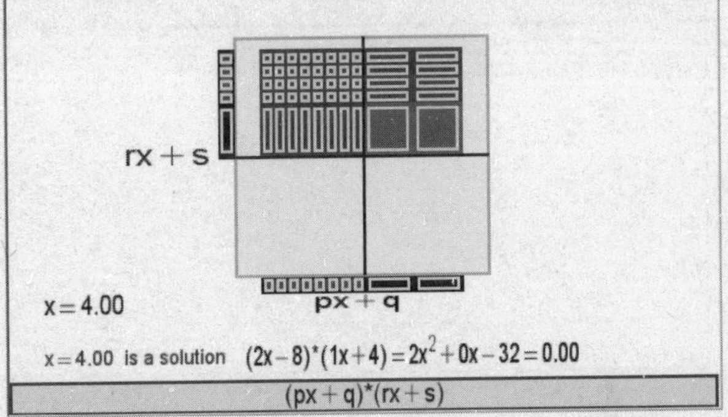

What happens as you change the values of **p** and **q**? **r** and **s**?

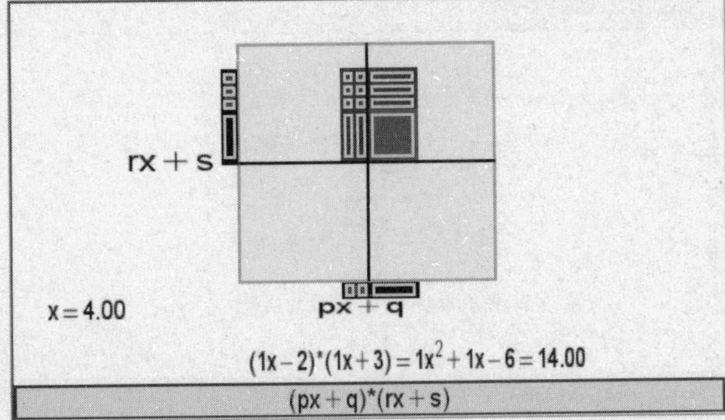

See if you can find the two solutions for the above equation. What happens to the boxes and bars when you reach a solution?

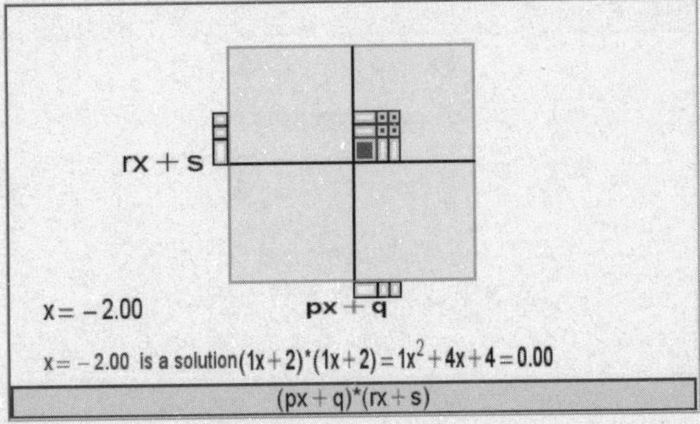

How many different factors (solutions) does this quadratic have?

Solving with Square Roots

EnableMath

If one or both sides of a quadratic equation can be written as a perfect square it can be solved by taking the *square root* of both sides. Consider the simple case of $x^2 = 25$. Take the square root of both sides: $\sqrt{x^2} = \sqrt{25}$. The solution, of course, is 5 or −5, because those are the only two numbers that yield 25 when squared.

Note: There are two solutions when taking the square root of both sides — the positive solution and the negative solution.

Solving Quadratics By Square Roots

Step 1: Rearrange so that perfect squares are on both sides of the equal sign.

Step 2: Take the square root of both sides.

Step 3: Solve for the positive and negative cases.

Step 4: Check both solutions back into the original equation.

Solve for x:

$$(x-2)^2=9$$
$$\sqrt{(x-2)^2}=\sqrt{9}$$

Take the square root of both sides.

Solve for x:

$$(x-2)^2=9$$
$$\sqrt{(x-2)^2}=\sqrt{9}$$
$$x-2=\pm 3$$
$$x-2=3,\ x-2=-3$$
$$x=5,\ x=-1$$

These are the solutions.

Since there is an isolated perfect square on both sides, we can take the square root of both sides. Using both the positive and negative square roots, we find the two solutions.

Solve for x:

$$(x+3)^2-4=0$$

Rearrange the above equation by adding 4 to both sides.

Solve for x:

$$(x+3)^2-4=0$$
$$(x+3)^2=4$$
$$\sqrt{(x+3)^2}=\sqrt{4}$$
$$x+3=\pm 2$$
$$x+3=2,\ x+3=-2$$
$$x=-1,\ x=-5$$

These are the solutions.

Take the square root of both sides, and then use both the positive and negative roots to find the two solutions to the quadratic equation.

Solve for x:

$$(x+2)^2+1=0$$
$$(x+2)^2=-1$$
$$\sqrt{(x+2)^2}=\sqrt{-1}$$

The $\sqrt{-1}$ isn't real.

There are NO real solutions.

The above equations looks as if it fits the pattern perfectly. Proceeding to the solution step we hit a snag: There are no real solutions when you take the square root of a negative number!

You can visualize quadratic equations with perfect squares as squares. Then, you can easily see what the positive solution is: the length of one side. Change the value of **x** until it fits the square formed by the constant p^2.

What values can you enter for **p**? What values can you enter for **x**?

What value of **x** makes this equation true?

Why is just the positive square root shown in the visualizations? Can you "visualize" a negative square root?

Why don't you need to take the positive and negative square roots of BOTH sides?

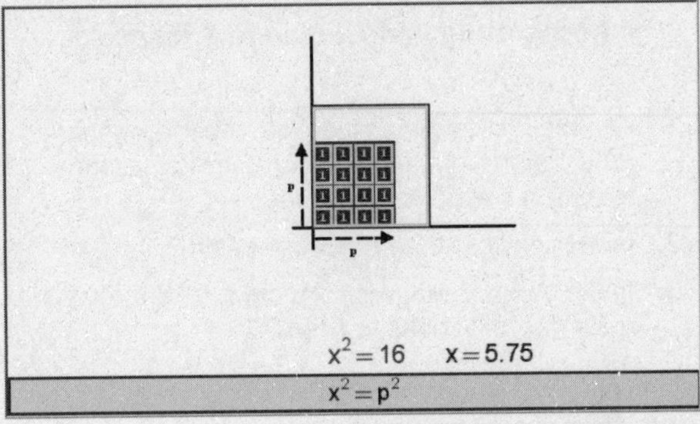

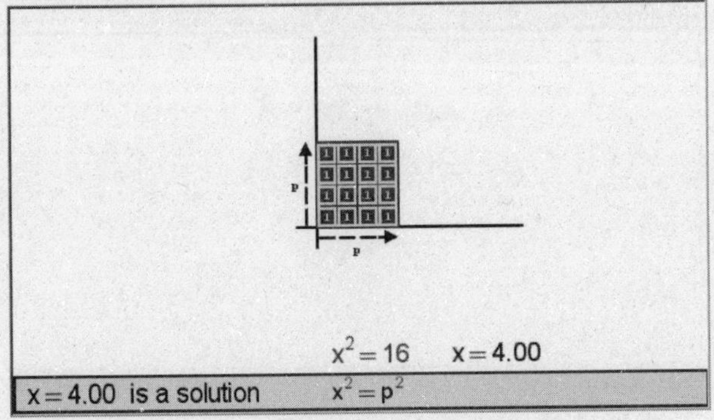

Here, **x=4** makes the equation true. What other value of **x** would make this equation true?

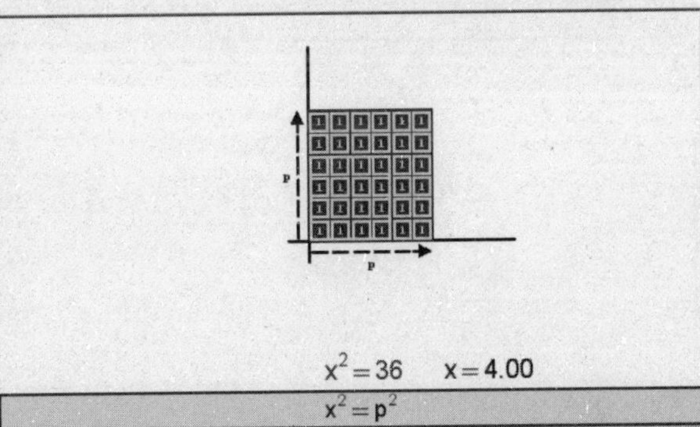

What happens as you change the value of **p**?

Factoring Perfect Squares

EnableMath

Quadratic expressions are called **perfect squares** if they can be factored into two copies of the same linear factor. Recognizing and making perfect squares makes it quick and easy to solve some quadratic equations. The pattern of a perfect square trinomial looks like $x^2 + 2ax + a^2$ which factors into two linear factors $(x+a)$ and $(x+a)$, copies of the same linear factor. Multiply to see that $(x+a)^2$ equals the product $x^2 + 2ax+a^2$.

Recognizing Perfect Square Trinomials

1. Can the first term be made into a perfect square? (You may have to factor a constant before the term is in perfect square form.)
2. Is the constant term a perfect square?
3. Is the middle term twice the product of the square roots of the first and last terms?

Factor this perfect square:

$$x^2+6x+9$$

Factor this perfect square:

$$x^2+6x+9$$
$$(x+3)(x+3)$$
$$(x+3)^2$$

Write as a square.

Notice that 6x is $2*\sqrt{x^2}\sqrt{9}$. Once you have factored the quadratic and there are two copies of the same factor, you can write the expression as a square.

Factor this perfect square:

$$2x^2-4x+2$$
$$2(x^2-2x+1)$$

Factor out the 2.

When there's a coefficient other than 1 on the $\mathbf{x^2}$ term, you'll factor out that coefficient first to see if the expression is a perfect square.

Factor this perfect square:

$$2x^2-4x+2$$
$$2(x^2-2x+1)$$
$$2(x-1)(x-1)$$
$$2(x-1)^2$$

Write as a square.

This quadratic expression is 2 times a perfect square.

You can visualize quadratic expressions that are perfect squares as a collection of x^2 squares, **x** bars and unit bars that come together to form one big square. The sides of the square form the factors. The visualizations were built from the expression $(px+q)^2$ so that all expressions generated will be perfect squares. You can change **p, q,** and **x.**

Can a perfect square quadratic expression be factored into a pair of *different* factors from the ones shown? Can the units, bars, and x^2s be arranged into a different square? Can they be arranged into a different rectangle?

What happens as you change the value of **x**?

What are the factors of the middle term for *every* perfect square quadratic?

Can the factors be a perfect square?

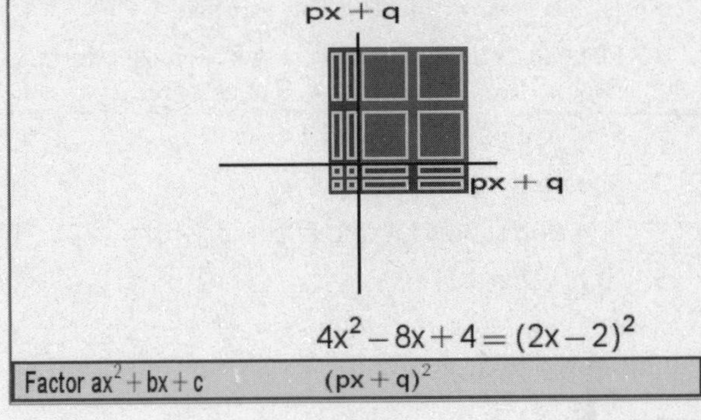

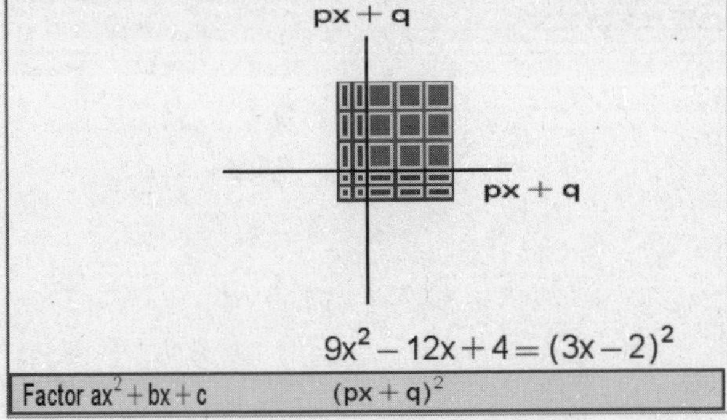

What happens as you change the values of **p** and **q**?

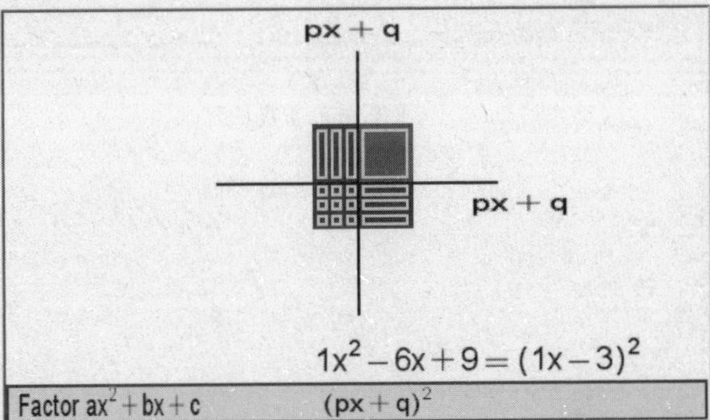

What relationship do you see between the **c** term and the **b** term in the quadratic equation of these perfect square equations.

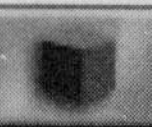

Completing the Square

We can change a quadratic equation into a perfect square quadratic. We call this process **completing the square**. We consider quadratics of the form $\mathbf{x^2+bx+c}$. For a quadratic to be a perfect square, the constant or **c** term must be a square number, to find out what that number is, we take half of **b**, the coefficient of the middle term, and then square that number.

Completing the Square

1. Make sure the expression is in $x^2 + bx + c$ form. Factor the coefficient of x^2 if necessary.
2. Find half of **b**
3. Square that.
4. Add ***and*** subtract it to the expression.
5. It now looks like:

$$x^2 + bx + \left(\frac{b}{2}\right)^2 = \left(x + \frac{b}{2}\right)^2$$

Complete the square:

$$x^2+6x+?$$
$$x^2+6x+9$$
$$x^2+6x+9$$
$$(x+3)^2$$

Add $(\frac{b}{2})^2$

This is in perfect square form.

The quadratic expression is a perfect square.

Complete the square:

$$x^2+4x+5$$
$$x^2+4x+4+5-4$$

Add and subtract $(\frac{4}{2})^2$.

Our **b** here is 4. So, half of that is 2. 2^2 is 4. So, here we add 4 to our perfect square and subtract 4 from the rest of the expression.

Complete the square:

$$x^2+4x+5$$
$$x^2+4x+4+5-4$$
$$x^2+4x+4+1$$
$$(x+2)^2+1$$

The first three terms are a square.

Now, the first three terms are equal to $\mathbf{(x+2)^2}$ - this is our $\mathbf{(x+(1/2)b)^2)}$ - and we have successfully completed the square. Notice that 5 – 4 was combined to 1.

Complete the square:

$$2x^2-12x+6$$
$$2(x^2-6x+3)$$

Factor out the 2.

Here, we have to factor out the coefficient of 2 first so that the coefficient of the $\mathbf{x^2}$ term is 1. Then, we can start to complete the square.

Complete the square:

$$2x^2-12x+6$$
$$2(x^2-6x+3)$$
$$2(x^2-6x+9+3-9)$$
$$2(x^2-6x+9-6)$$
$$2((x-3)^2-6)$$

The first three terms are a square.

Half of -6 is -3. $(-3)^2$ is 9. So, we add and subtract 9 to create the square $(x-3)^2$.

We saw in the last concept that you can visualize quadratic expressions that are perfect squares as a collection of x^2 boxes, **x** bars and unit squares that come together to form one big square. In this concept, we'll experiment to see what we need to add in order to "complete the square." Use the joystick to change **c** until the square is complete.

What gives you information on what value **c** should be? How does the pattern of squaring a binomial help determine the pattern for completing the square?

What value of **c** completes this square?

Why do you take half of **b** and square it to find **c**?

Can any quadratic expression be manipulated to complete the square?

Why are unit squares connected with **c**? Why are bars connected with **b**?

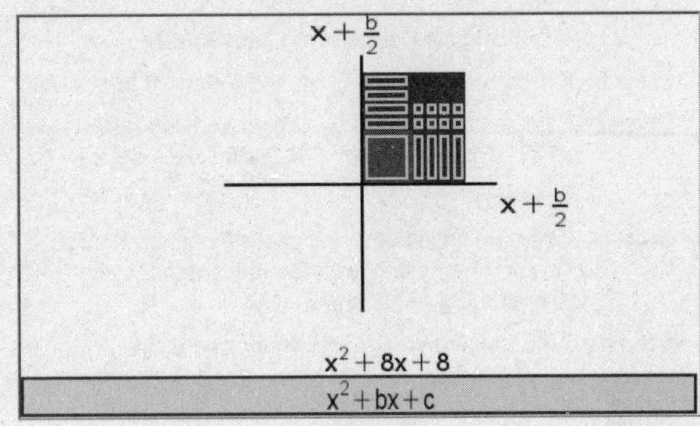

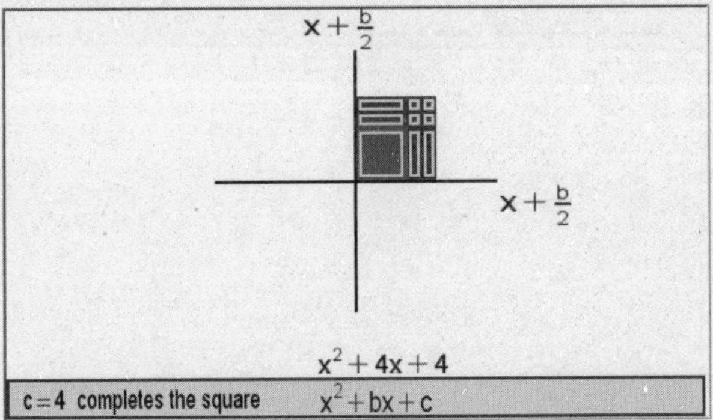

How is the value of **c** that completes the square related to **b**? Change the values of **b** and **c** and see if you can make a conjecture about the relationship between them.

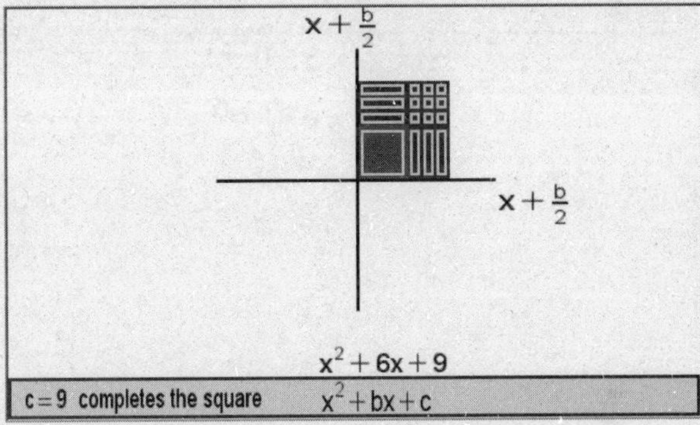

How many bars are there on each side of the square?

Does $(\frac{1}{2}b)^2$ always give you the value of **c**?

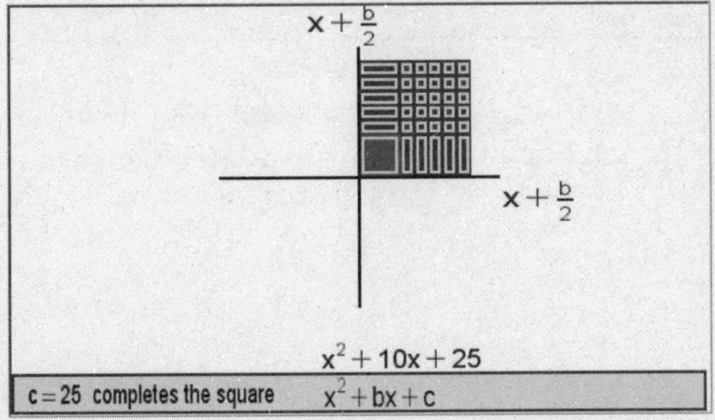

How many unit squares are needed to complete the square?

Solving by Completing the Square

EnableMath

In the previous assignment we completed the square with expressions. Here we complete the square with equations and we can then use this method to solve some quadratic equations. After completing the square, the process is to isolate the squared binomial on one side of the equal sign and then take the square root of both sides.

Don't forget to find both the positive and negative roots!

Solving By Completing the Square

Step 1: Put the expression into $\mathbf{x^2 + bx + c = 0}$ form.

Step 2: Complete the square by adding and subtracting $\mathbf{(b/2)^2}$ to the left side (**OR *both*** sides—see concepts).

Step 3: Write the complete square as a binomial squared and add or subtract the left over constant to the other side of the equal sign.

Step 4: Take the **+** and **–** square root of both sides.

Step 5: Solve and check.

Solve for x:

$$x^2+2x-3=0$$

Solve for x:

$$x^2+2x-3=0$$
$$x^2+2x+1-3-1=0$$
$$(x+1)^2-4=0$$

The square is completed.

It is in the correct form; complete the square by adding and subtracting 1.

Solve for x:

$$x^2+2x-3=0$$
$$x^2+2x+1-3-1=0$$
$$(x+1)^2-4=0$$
$$(x+1)^2=4$$
$$x+1=\pm 2$$
$$x+1=2x+1=-2$$
$$x=1, x=-3$$

These are the solutions.

Add 4 to both sides, then take the square root of both sides. Don't forget both the positive and negative roots. Solve for **x** in both cases. Both answers check.

Solve for x:

$$-2x^2+4x+6=0 \Rightarrow -2(x^2-2x-3)=0$$
$$-2(x^2-2x+1-3-1)=0 \Rightarrow -2((x-1)^2-4)=0$$

Complete the square.

In order to complete the square, you must factor out any coefficients other than 1 on the $\mathbf{x^2}$ term first, then complete the square.

Solve for x:

$$-2x^2+4x+6=0 \Rightarrow -2(x^2-2x-3)=0$$
$$-2(x^2-2x+1-3-1)=0 \Rightarrow -2((x-1)^2-4)=0$$
$$(x-1)^2+-4=0$$

Divide by -2.

Once you factor out the coefficient of the $\mathbf{x^2}$ term, you can divide both sides by the coefficient in order to be ready to solve with square roots.

When you graph a quadratic equation, you can find the solutions to it, if they are real, by looking for the **x-intercepts**.

Change **s** until the value of **s** completes the square. Notice that **s** is added to BOTH sides of the equation. Is that the same as adding and subtracting the same value to one side of the equation? Here we are looking for "the rest" of the constant to complete the square—what value of **s** needs to be added in order for the constant to become the perfect square that is $(b/2)^2$?

What value for **s** is added to both sides to complete the square?

What does the parabola look like if the value of **b** is 0?

Can a parabola have only one real solution? What would that parabola look like?

Can it have no real solutions? What would that parabola look like?

Can **a** be negative?

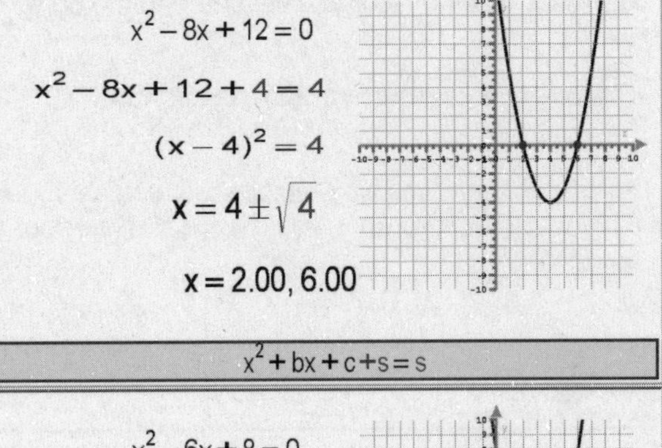

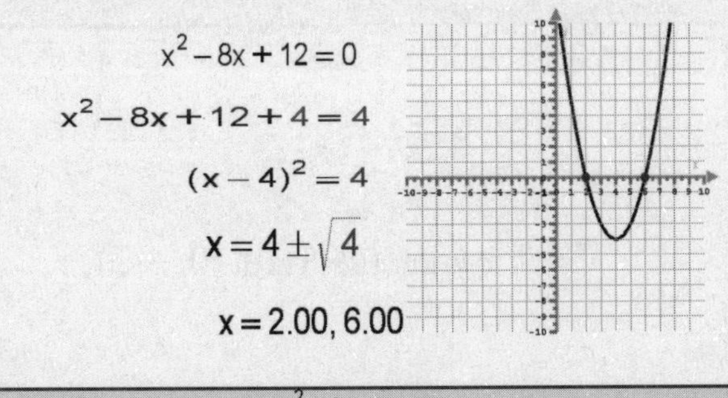

How is **s** related to **b** and **c**? How do we know to add 4 to both sides?

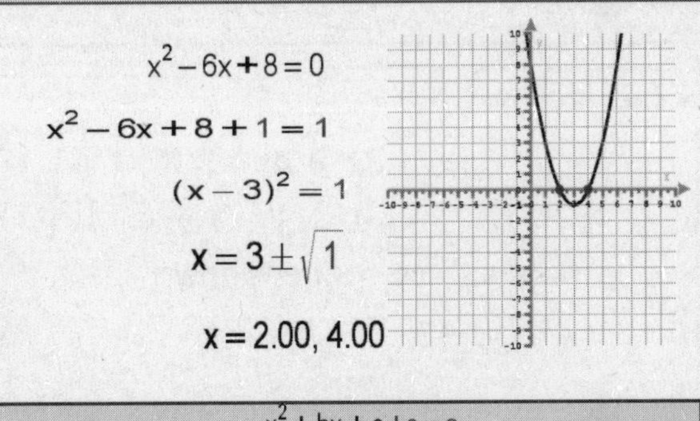

Change the values of **b to –6** and **c to 8**; Why does **s** have to be **1**? Can you find values for **b** and **c** that make **s=0**?

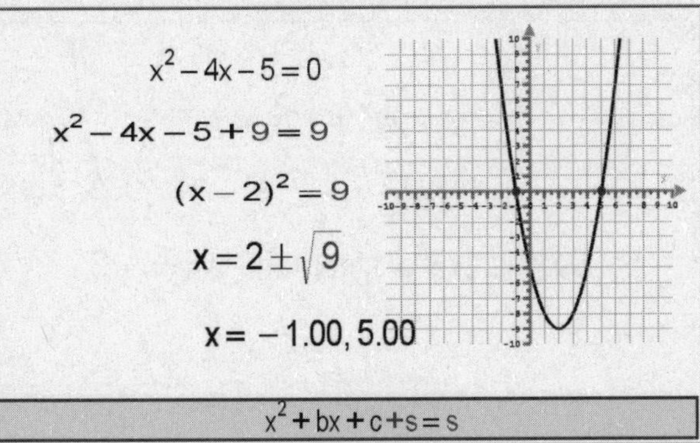

How do we know to add 9? Do the roots check?

Coefficients of Quadratic Equations

EnableMath

The graph of a quadratic equation is called a **parabola**. Quadratic equations have the form $y=ax^2+bx+c$, where **a**, **b** and **c** are constant coefficients. Each of these constants affects the graph of the equation in different ways.

- **a** controls how fast the parabola grows vertically and whether the parabola will open up or down. (**a**>0 opens up, **a**<0 opens down.)
- **c** controls the y-intercept. (The y-intercept is at (0,**c**).)
- **b** helps to control the **vertex** (the x coordinate of which is -**b**/(2**a**)) and the **axis of symmetry** (which is x=-**b**/(2**a**)) of the parabola.

Parabolas generally look like the figure to the right.

This parabola opens up because **a** is positive.

Points 1-3 are dynamic examples, so feel free to explore what happens when you change the values of **a**, **b** and **c**.

Does $y=2x^2+5x-7$ open up or down?

$$y=2x^2+5x-7$$
$$a=2$$
$$a>0\text{, so, the parabola opens up.}$$

$y=ax^2+bx+c$

Does $y=-3x^2+4x+5$ open up or down?

$$y=-3x^2+4x+5$$
$$a=-3$$
$$a<0\text{, so, it opens down.}$$

$y=ax^2+bx+c$

This parabola opens down because **a** is negative.

Find the value of the y-intercept of:

$$y=2x^2-6x-3$$
$$c=-3$$
$$\text{So, the y-intercept is at }(0,-3).$$

$y=ax^2+bx+c$

The **y-intercept** is at (0,**c**). Here it is at (0,-3).

Find the x-value of the vertex of:

$$y=3x^2-12x+2$$
$$x=\frac{-b}{2a}=\frac{+12}{2(3)}$$
$$\text{So, the x value of the vertex is 2.}$$

$y=ax^2+bx+c$

The **x** value at the **vertex** is –**b**/(2**a**). Here it is 2. We could easily find out the y value at the vertex by substituting **x=2** into the quadratic equation.

Find the equation for the axis of symmetry of:

$$y=2x^2+12x+2$$
$$x=\frac{-b}{2a}=\frac{-12}{2(2)}=-3$$
$$\text{So, the axis of symmetry is }x=-3.$$

$y=ax^2+bx+c$

The equation for the axis of symmetry is **x=-b/(2a).**

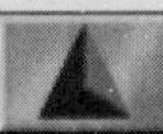

The general form of a quadratic equation is $y=ax^2+bx+c$. Which one of these coefficients, **a**, **b**, or **c**, would you change to make a parabola that opens up flip over and open down? Which one of the coefficients would you change to move the parabola up and down? Which coefficient makes the parabola "wider" or "skinnier"?

Change the values of **a**, **b** and **c** one at a time to see how they change the graph. It's a good idea to start by setting **b** and **c** equal to **0.**

What does the vertex have in common with the axis of symmetry?

How do you know if the vertex represents a maximum or minimum point on the parabola?

If you know **a** and **c**, can you determine if the parabola will have a maximum or minimum value?

How can you tell if a parabola has real solutions?

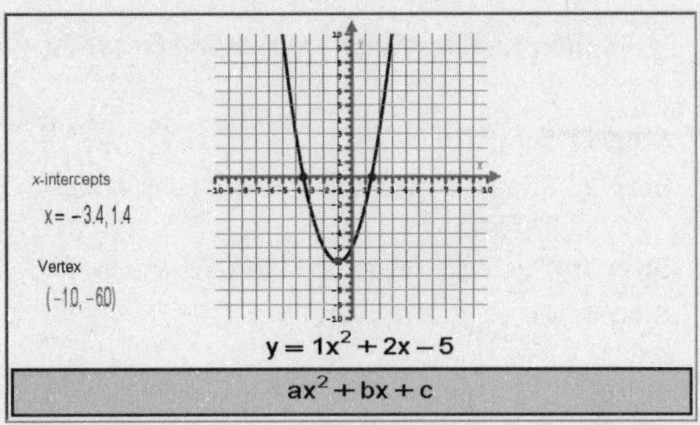

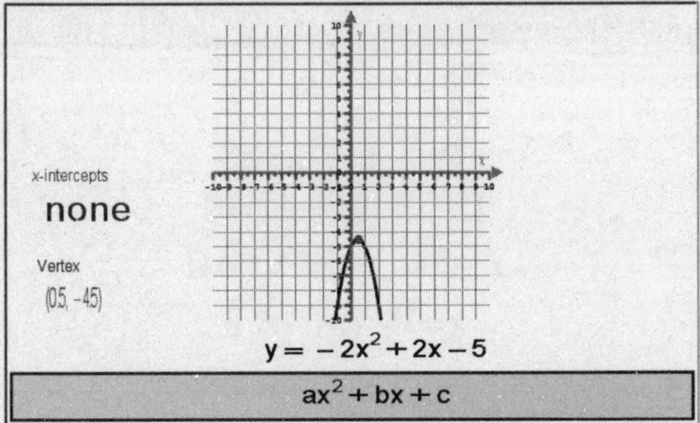

Which coefficient would you change to flip the graph over? What is the sign of that coefficient when the parabola opens down, as in the above graph?

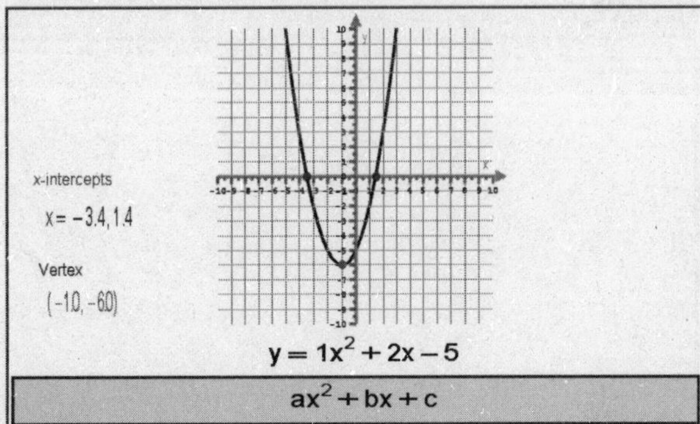

What happens as **a** goes from -1 to +1?

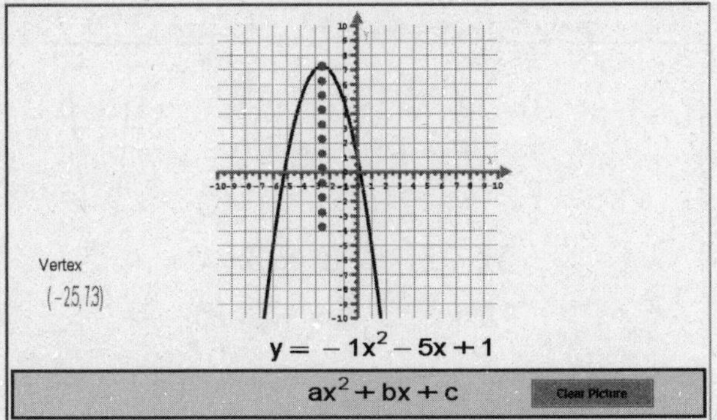

Point 2: Which coefficient do you change to move the parabola up and down? If **a>0, b>0** and **c>0**, does the graph have real solutions? In other words, does it cross the **x-axis**?

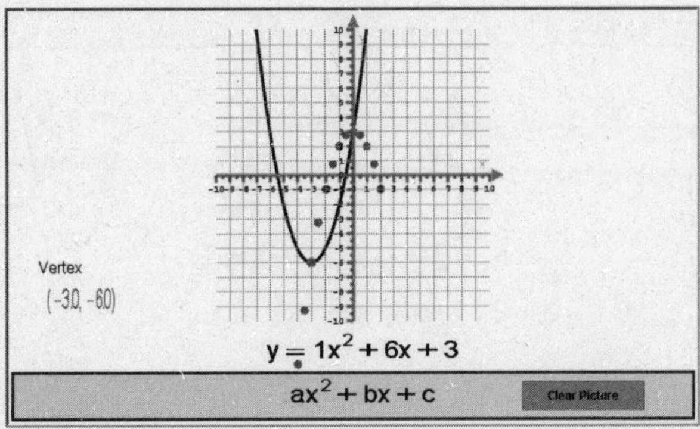

What does changing **b** do? How does it move the parabola? What shape does the motion of **b** produce?

The **x-intercepts** of a quadratic equation occur when **y=0**. So, if you set y=0, you have the equation:

$$0=ax^2+bx+c$$

Solve the equation for **x** to find the **roots**. Quadratic equations can have two roots, one root, or *no real roots.*

Finding Real Roots of a Quadratic Equation

Step 1: Set y=0.

Step 2: Solve the equation (by factoring or other methods).

Step 3: The real solutions are the x-intercepts.

Step 4: Check your answer.

Find the values of the x-intercepts of:

$$y=x^2+5x-6$$
$$x^2+5x-6=0$$
$$(x-1)(x+6)=0$$
$$x-1=0,\ x+6=0$$
$$x=1,\ x=-6$$

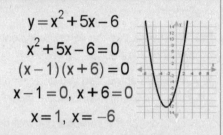

These are the x-intercepts. $y=ax^2+bx+c$

Find the values of the x-intercepts of:

$$y=2x^2-5x-3$$
$$2x^2-5x-3=0$$

Set y=0. $y=ax^2+bx+c$

First, set **y=0**.

Find the values of the x-intercepts of:

$$y=2x^2-5x-3$$
$$2x^2-5x-3=0$$
$$(x-3)(2x+1)=0$$
$$x-3=0,\ \ 2x+1=0$$
$$x=3,\ x=-1/2$$

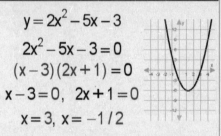

These are the x-intercepts. $y=ax^2+bx+c$

Then solve. The real solutions are the **x-intercepts**. Check both solutions to make sure no errors occurred.

Find the values of the x-intercepts of:

$$y=2x^2-5x-3$$
$$2x^2-5x-3=0$$
$$(x-3)(2x+1)=0$$
$$x-3=0,\ \ 2x+1=0$$
$$x=3,\ x=-1/2$$

These are the x-intercepts. $y=ax^2+bx+c$

Check: $2\cdot3^2-5\cdot3-3$ and $2\left(\frac{-1}{2}\right)^2-\frac{-5}{2}-3$

$18-15-3=0$ $\quad \frac{1}{2}+\frac{5}{2}-\frac{6}{2}=0$

Find the values of the x-intercepts of:

$$y=6x^2+5x-6$$
$$6x^2+5x-6=0$$
$$(3x-2)(2x+3)=0$$
$$3x-2=0,\ 2x+3=0$$
$$x=2/3,\ x=-3/2$$

These are the x-intercepts. $y=ax^2+bx+c$

Solve by factoring.

How are the **x-intercepts** of a parabola are related to the factors of that quadratic equation? If a quadratic equation is factorable (over the integers), then the factors can be written as **(px+q)** and **(rx+s)** where **p, q, r, s** are integers. To find the roots of the factorable quadratic, we set the factors equal to zero and solve for **x**: The roots are **x=-q/p** and **x=-s/r.**

Change the values of **p, q, r** and **s** to see how the x-intercepts change. What happens to the graph?

Will there always be one negative and one positive x-intercept?

What are the factors of a quadratic that has only one x-intercept?

How are the values of **p, q, r** and **s** related to the **x-intercept** values?

What must happen to make the parabola open down?

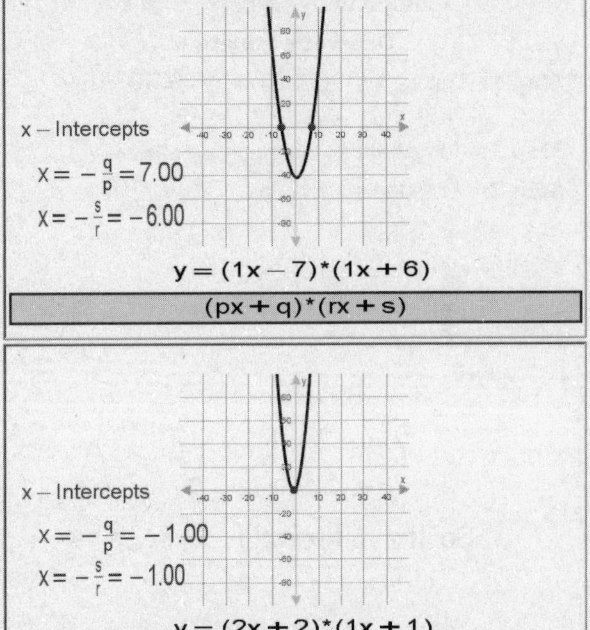

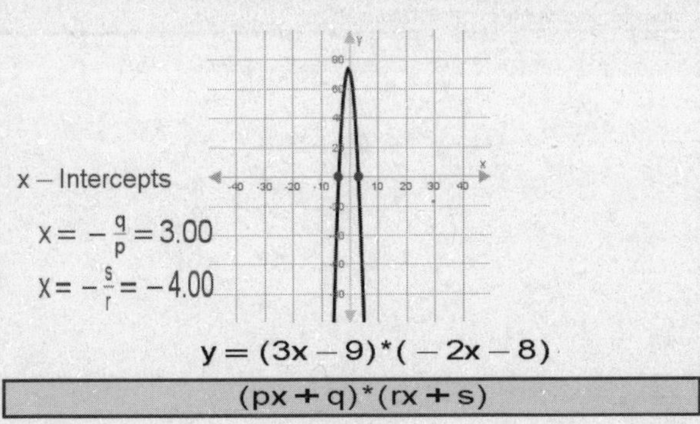

Can you change the direction that the parabola opens and not change the values of the intercepts?

What values of **q** and **s** give both intercepts the same value.

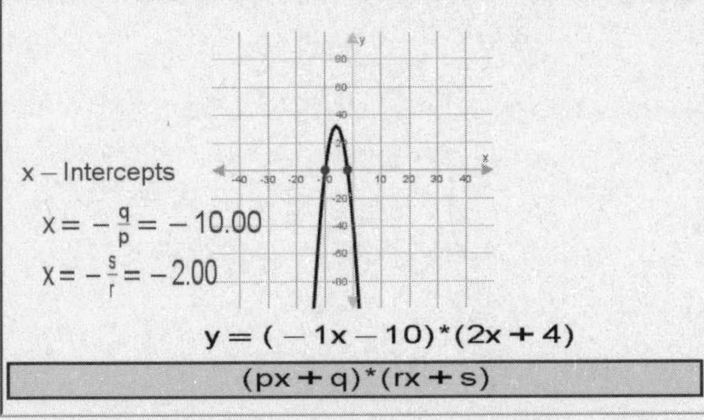

What values of **p, q, r,** and **s** make both intercepts negative?

Vertex Form $y=a(x-h)^2+k$

A quadratic equation has two parts, the quadratic or ax^2 term and the linear term **(bx+c).** As we have seen the ax^2 term is a parabola with its vertex at **(0,0)** and the **(bx+c)** term moves that vertex to a different point in the coordinate system. The *vertex form* of a quadratic equation is $y=a(x-h)^2+k$. This form of a quadratic equation represents moving that ax^2 parabola along the x-axis a distance **h** and moving it along the y-axis a distance **k**. When a quadratic equation is in this form, you can read the vertex of the parabola as **(h, k).** The form comes from completing the square on the general form of a quadratic $ax^2 + bx + c$, then renaming the more complex constant expressions **h** and **k.**

Notice that the equation has an (x-h) in it.

Finding the Vertex Form of a Quadratic Equation

Step 1: Ensure the quadratic is in $y = ax^2 + bx + c$ form.

Step 2: Complete the square on ax^2+bx+c.

Step 3: Write the equation as $y=a(x-h)^2 + k$.

The **vertex** of the parabola is (h, k).

Find the coordinates of the vertex of:

$$y=-2(x+1)^2-2$$
$$h=-1,\ k=-2$$
So, the vertex is at $(-1, -2)$.

$y=a(x-h)^2+k$

Notice that the **x** coordinate of the vertex, **h**, is negative.

Find the coordinates of the vertex of:

$$y=(x-2)^2+3$$

$y=a(x-h)^2+k$

Find the coordinates of the vertex of:

$$y=x^2+4x+5$$
$$y=x^2+4x+4+5-4$$
$$y=(x+2)^2+1$$

This is in vertex form. $y=a(x-h)^2+k$

Once the square is completed, it is in vertex form. In the above equation **h=-2** and **k=1**, so the vertex is at **(-2,1).**

Find the coordinates of the vertex of:

$$y=3x^2-6x+6$$
$$y=3(x^2-2x+2) \Rightarrow y=3(x^2-2x+1+2-1)$$
$$y=3((x-1)^2+1)$$
$$y=3(x-1)^2+3$$
$$h=1,\ k=3$$
So, the vertex is at (1, 3).

$y=a(x-h)^2+k$

Don't forget to factor out **a** first. Notice **a** was factored out, then the square was completed for **x-1**, and then to get it into final form, 3 (the **a** value) was distributed, removing the extra set of parentheses.

Vertex Form $y=a(x-h)^2+k$

A quadratic equation can be written in **vertex form : $y=a(x-h)^2+k$.** Vertex form makes it easy to read the coordinates of the vertex from the equation: **(h, k)**.

What direction does the x-coordinate of the vertex move the basic ax^2 parabola? How many units? What direction does the y-coordinate moves the parabola? How many units?

Use the joystick to change **h** and **k**.

As **h** increases, what happens to the parabola?

As **k** increases, what happens to the parabola?

Can you determine if a parabola has real roots by looking at the vertex?

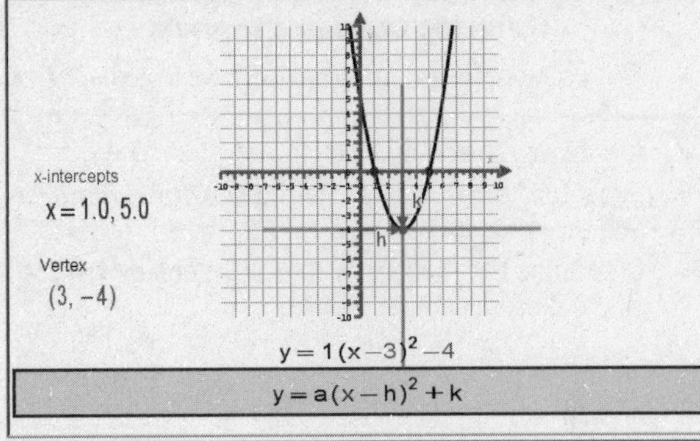

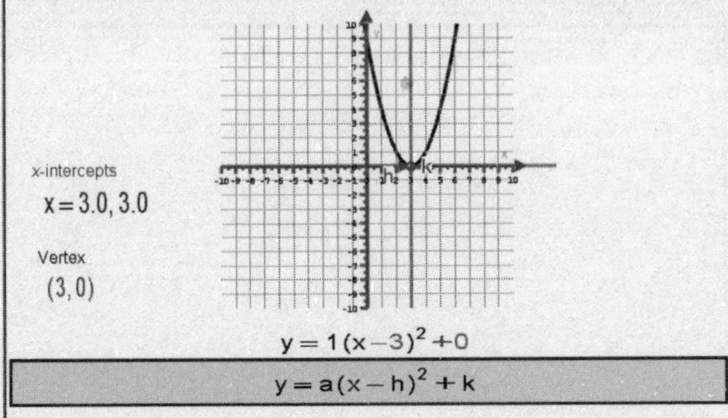

Where is the vertex of the parabola when **k=0**? What does the equation look like?

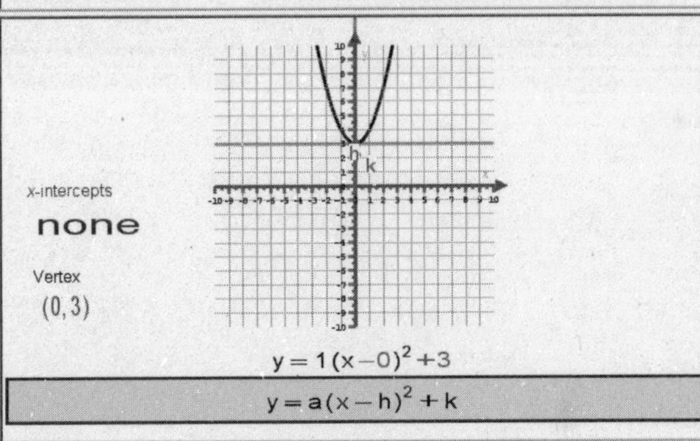

Where is the vertex of the parabola when **h=0**? Does the above quadratic have real solutions?

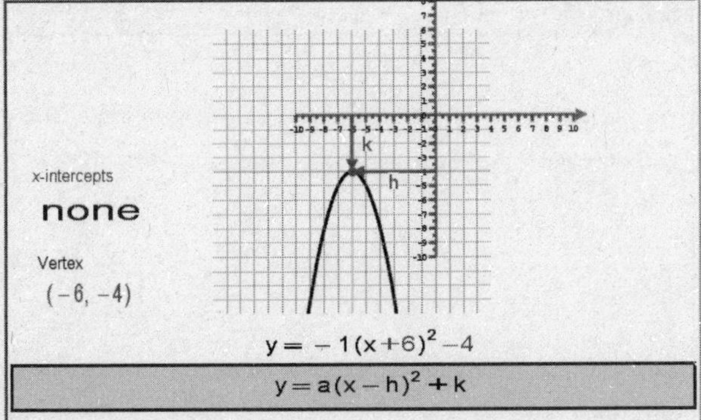

What values of **h** and **k** produce real solutions to a quadratic equation?

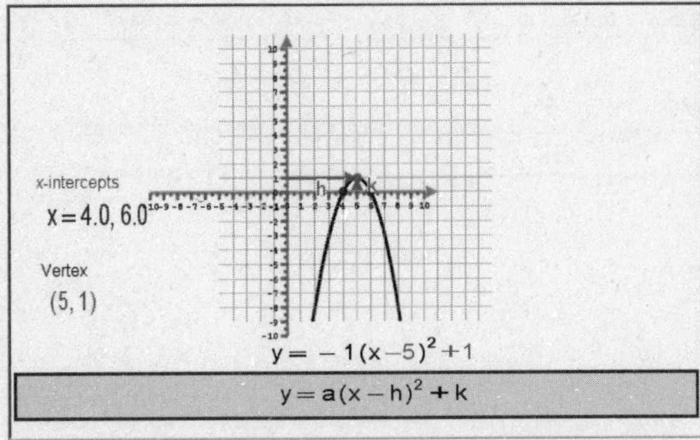

How does the vertex form help you picture quadratic equations and their parabolas? Can you determine what the equation looks like in standard form from vertex form?

Solving with the Quadratic Formula

EnableMath

If solving by factoring, solving with square roots or solving by completing the square aren't convenient, there exists a way to find the solutions to any quadratic equation in the form $\mathbf{ax^2+bx+c=0}$. Completing the square results in a way to solve any quadratic: the **quadratic formula.**

$$x=\frac{-b\pm\sqrt{b^2-4ac}}{2a}$$

The term inside the radical, $\mathbf{b^2-4ac}$, is called the **discriminant**. If the **discriminant is >0** there are two real solutions; if it is **=0**, there is one distinct solution; if it is **<0** there are NO REAL solutions.

Using the Quadratic Formula

- The equation or expression MUST be in $\mathbf{ax^2+bx+c}$ form.
- Identify **a**, **b**, and **c**.
- Substitute those values into the Quadratic Formula and solve for **x**.
- Determine the number of Real solutions by looking at the discriminate: $\mathbf{b^2-4ac}$.

A derivation for the quadratic formula:

$$ax^2+bx+c=0 \Rightarrow ax^2+bx=-c \Rightarrow x^2+\frac{b}{a}x=-\frac{c}{a}$$

$$x^2+\frac{b}{a}x+\frac{b^2}{4a^2}=\frac{b^2}{4a^2}-\frac{c}{a}$$

$$\left(x+\frac{b}{2a}\right)^2=\frac{b^2-4ac}{4a^2}$$

$$\sqrt{\left(x+\frac{b}{2a}\right)^2}=\pm\sqrt{\frac{b^2-4ac}{4a^2}}$$

$$x+\frac{b}{2a}=\frac{\pm\sqrt{b^2-4ac}}{2a} \Rightarrow x=\frac{-b\pm\sqrt{b^2-4ac}}{2a}$$

Simplify.

Solve for x:

$$2x^2+12x+14=0$$

$$ax^2+bx+c=0$$

The above example is in $ax^2+bx+c=0$ form, so **a=2, b=12** and **c=14**. We can use the quadratic formula to determine the solutions.

Solve for x:

$$2x^2+12x+14=0$$

$$x=\frac{(-b\pm\sqrt{(b^2-4ac)})}{(2a)}$$

$$x=\frac{(-12\pm\sqrt{((12)^2-4(2)(14))})}{(2(2))}$$

$$x=\frac{(-12\pm\sqrt{(32)})}{4}$$

$$x=-3+\sqrt{(2)},\ x=-3-\sqrt{(2)}$$

$$ax^2+bx+c=0$$

Use the quadratic formula and simplify. Notice that the discriminant is **>0**, so two real solutions are possible. Here we find the two solutions. Since square root of two is an irrational number, leave it in radical form.

Solve for x:

$$4x^2=16x+36$$

$$4x^2-16x-36=0$$

$$ax^2+bx+c=0$$

Remember, the equation HAS to be in $\mathbf{ax^2+bx+c=0}$ form, so above we had to manipulate the equation to get it to that form.

Solve for x:

$$4x^2=16x+36$$

$$4x^2-16x-36=0$$

$$x=\frac{(-b\pm\sqrt{(b^2-4ac)})}{(2a)}$$

$$x=\frac{(+16\pm\sqrt{((-16)^2-4(4)(-36))})}{(2(4))}$$

$$x=\frac{(16\pm\sqrt{(832)})}{8}$$

$$x=2+\sqrt{(13)},\ x=2-\sqrt{(13)}$$

$$ax^2+bx+c=0$$

Here we rearrange to get the equation into the proper form. Be careful of negative signs. We chose to move all terms to the left side to keep the $\mathbf{x^2}$ term positive.

The quadratic formula enables us to solve any quadratic equation. The term inside the radical b^2**-4ac** is called the **discriminant**. It can tell us a great deal about the solutions before we find the solutions. Think about the discriminant: What happens if it equals 0? What happens if it's negative? What happens if it's positive? What happens if it's not a perfect square?

$$x=\frac{-b\pm\sqrt{b^2-4ac}}{2a}$$

If the discriminant is greater than zero, what do you know about where the graph is located?

If the discriminant is less than zero what do you know about where the graph is located?

Can you determine if the graph opens up or down just by looking at the discriminant?

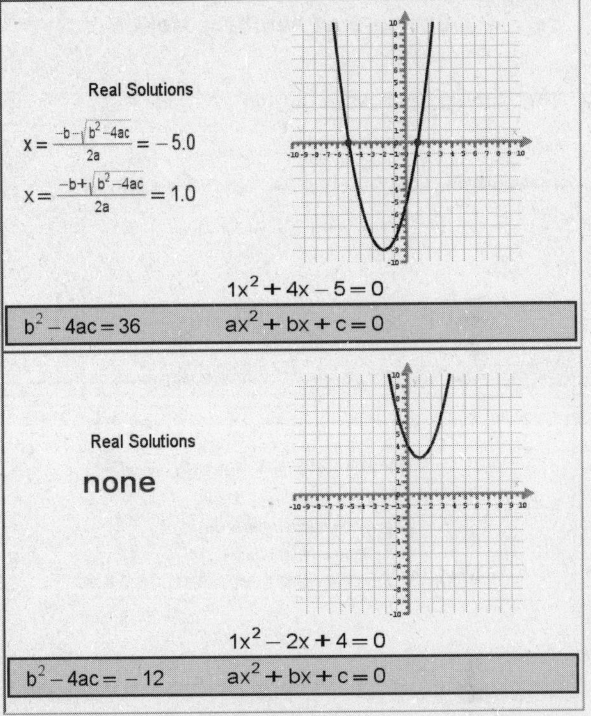

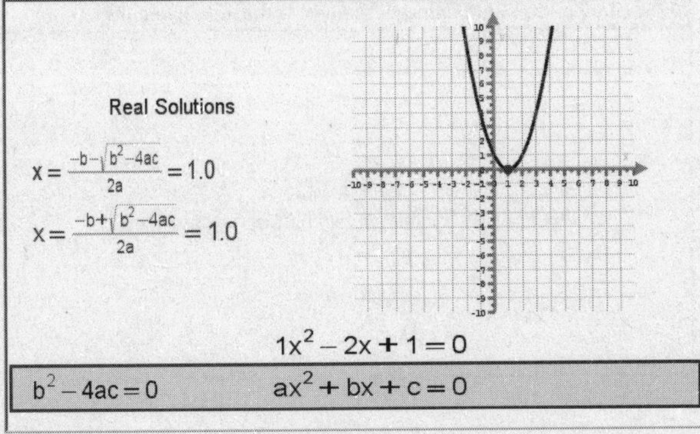

If the discriminant b^2**-4ac=0,** how many solutions will there be?

If the discriminant b^2**-4ac<0,** how many real solutions will there be?

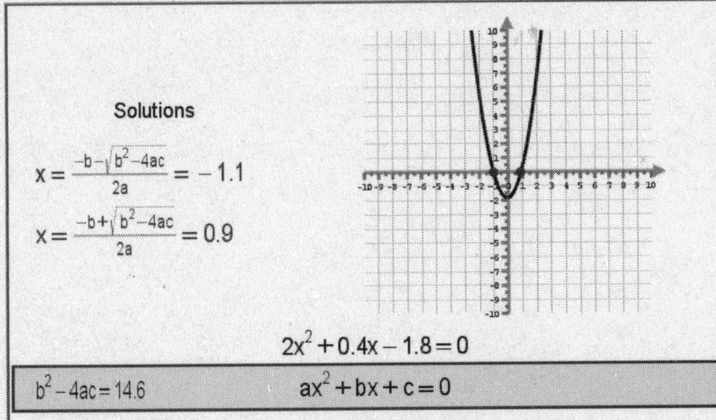

If the discriminant is b^2**-4ac>0,** how many real solutions will there be?

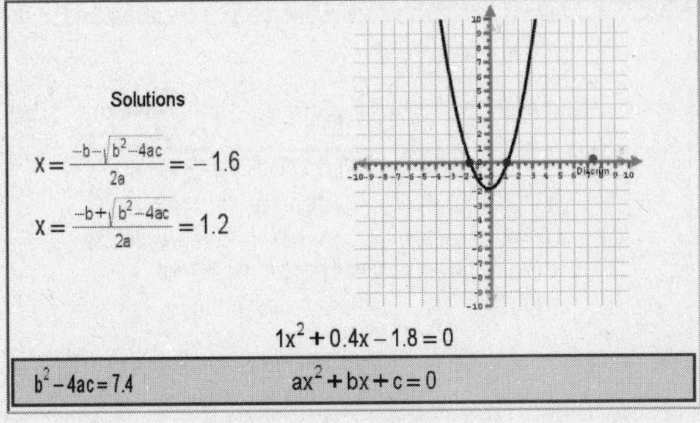

Point 2: Here we plotted the discriminant on the **x**-axis. Change **b** and **c**. What happens to the pink point? Where is there only one solution to the quadratic, where are there none?

Baseballs and other projectiles travel on **parabolic paths**. We can determine various things about the path of a projectile if we use the vertex form and general form of the parabola on which it travels. The vertex of the parabola represents the maximum height of the object. The coordinates (**h, k**) further describe how far it traveled (**h**) to reach the height (**k**). To find the length a ball travels from hit to catch, set the equation equal to 0 and solve for **x**.

Examples of Parabolic Motion

The path of a ball hit or thrown

The path of a cannon ball shot out of a cannon

What is the maximum height the baseball reaches?

The path of a baseball is given by:

$$y = \frac{-1}{300}(x-180)^2 + 108$$

where: x = length traveled (in feet)
and y = height (in feet).

Here, k = 108. So, the maximum height reached is 108 feet.

The equation is in vertex form. $y = a(x-h)^2 + k$

Here, **k=108**, so that is the maximum height the ball reaches.

At what point does the same ball hit the ground?

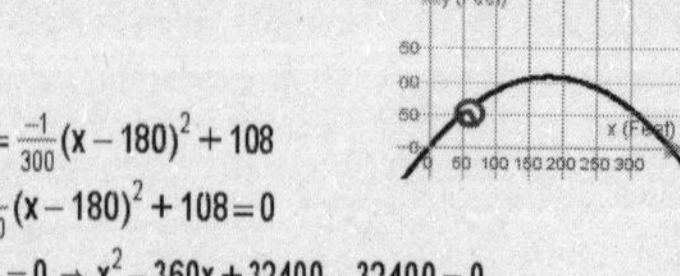

$$y = \frac{-1}{300}(x-180)^2 + 108$$

$$\frac{-1}{300}(x-180)^2 + 108 = 0$$

$$(x-180)^2 - 32400 = 0 \Rightarrow x^2 - 360x + 32400 - 32400 = 0$$

$x^2 - 360x = 0 \;\Rightarrow\; x(x-360) = 0 \;\Rightarrow$ So, the x-intercepts are 0 and 360.

So, the ball hits the ground after traveling 360 feet.

$y = a(x-h)^2 + k$

If we convert to general form and solve by factoring for the **x-intercept**, we can find out how far the ball travels before it hits the ground.

What is the maximum height the baseball reaches?

The path of a baseball is given by:

$$y = \frac{-1}{300}(x-180)^2 + 108$$

$y = a(x-h)^2 + k$

At what point does the same ball reach its maximum height?

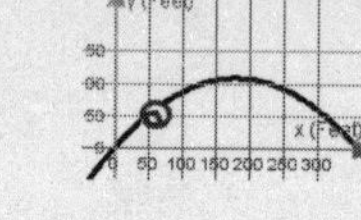

$$y = \frac{-1}{300}(x-180)^2 + 108$$

Here, h = 180.

So, the maximum height is reached 180 feet away from the batter.

$y = a(x-h)^2 + k$

h reveals when the ball reaches its maximum height. Here, **h=180**, so when the ball is 180 feet from the batter it achieves maximum height.

Baseballs, arrows, bullets, indeed most everything we throw or fire into the air is a projectile that follows a parabolic path. Galileo (1564-1642) was the first to discover this, just before the turn of the 17th century, when he rolled a ball down an inclined plane and measured distance vs. time. He found that he could describe its motion with a quadratic equation. Every falling body and every projectile that does not have too much air resistance follow a parabolic path. We can solve the quadratic equation that describe the motion of the object to find out how high it will go and how far it will go.

For some problems in which you want to find the highest point on the projectile's path, it is useful to use the vertex form of the quadratic equation as we have done here.

In physics classes, the standard form of the quadratic equation is used more often.

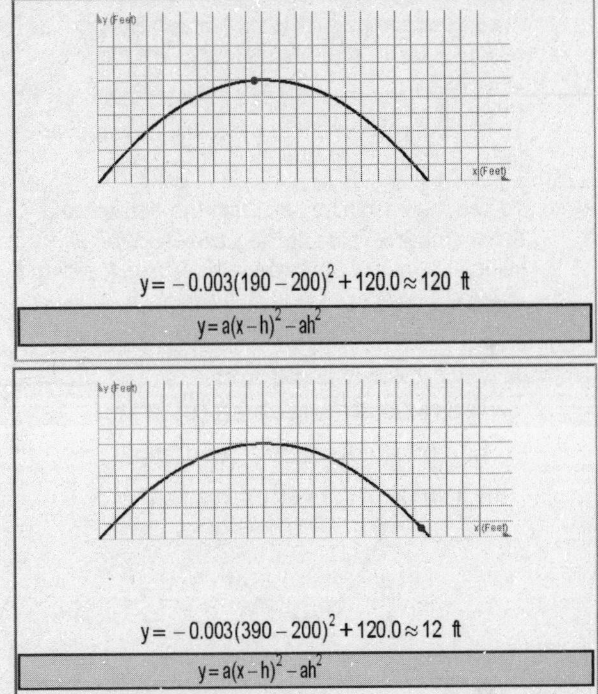

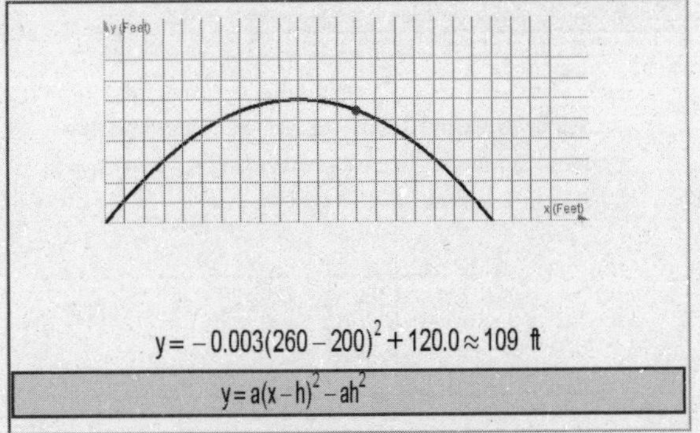

What happens to the baseball as you change **x**?

Where is the ball now?

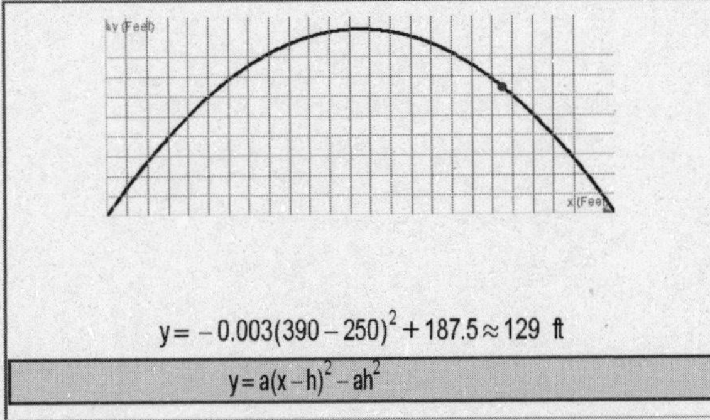

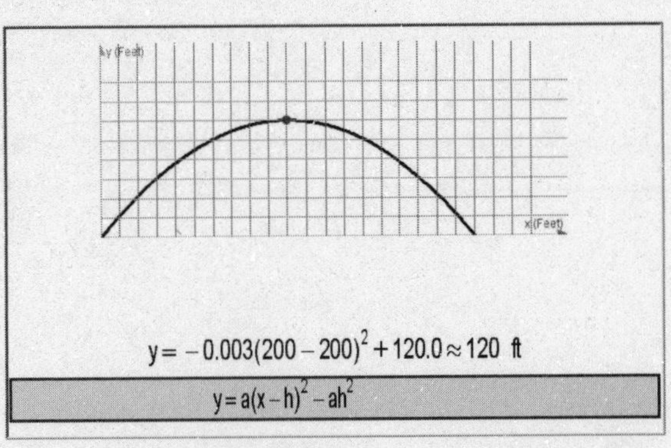

What happens to the flight path of the ball as you change **h**?

When does the ball reach maximum height? What relationship do **h** and **x** have then?

Seeing Complex Roots of Quadratics

EnableMath

The x-intercepts of a quadratic equation correspond to its real solutions. But even when the graph of a quadratic equation doesn't cross the x-axis, it still has roots (they're just not real). When there are no real roots for a quadratic equation, there are two complex roots. Complex roots come in **conjugate pairs (p + qi and p – qi).** The complex root has two parts, the real part, **p**, and the imaginary part, **qi**, where the imaginary part **i = √-1.**

You can see complex roots on a graph (just not as easily as you can see that real roots are the x-intercepts).

- To see the real part, find the **x** value at the vertex.
- To see the imaginary part, find the difference between the **x** value at the vertex and the **x** value at either of the two places *where the graph is twice as high* as it is at the vertex.

Even when a quadratic doesn't cross the x – axis, there are still two roots. In that case, the roots are a complex conjugate pair, $(p \pm qi)$. Most people don't know that you can see those complex roots on a graph, but, as you will see, you can!

$p \pm qi$

Seeing the Real Part (p) of the Complex Roots

The value of the real part (p) of the complex root pair of a quadratic is the x value at the vertex. Here, $p = 3$.

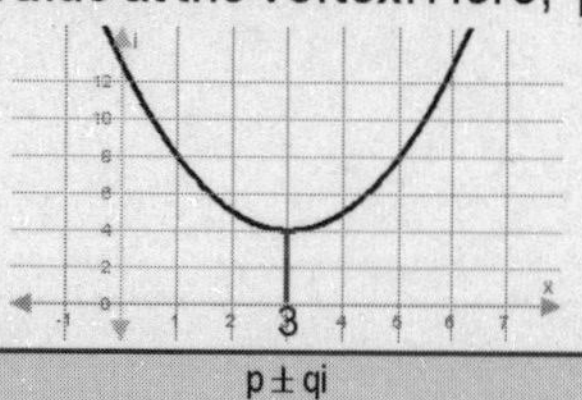

$p \pm qi$

Here, the **x** value at the vertex is **3**, so **3** is the **p**, or real part of the complex solutions.

Seeing the Imaginary Part (q) of the Complex Roots

The value of the imaginary part (q) of the complex root pair of a quadratic is the difference between the x value at the vertex and the x value at the points where the quadratic reaches twice its vertex height. Here, $q = 2$.

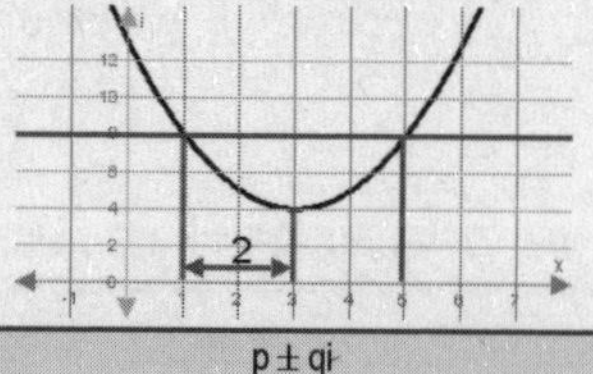

$p \pm qi$

Here, the graph is twice as high as the vertex at **x=1** and **x=5**. These places are 2 units away from **x=3** (at the vertex). So, 2 is the imaginary part of the solutions. The solutions are **3±2i.**

We have thus far been focused only on the real roots, the solutions of a quadratic equation. But there are roots to a quadratic equation even when the graph does not cross the x-axis. These roots are complex numbers (they have a real part and an imaginary part). How do you know when a quadratic has complex solutions? How do you know when a quadratic has real solutions?

Change the values of **a, b** and **c** to determine what looks different about the graph when the type of solutions change.

When are there complex solutions?

When are there real solutions?

Does the coefficient of **a** have to be positive to have complex solutions?

Can a quadratic have one real and one complex solution?

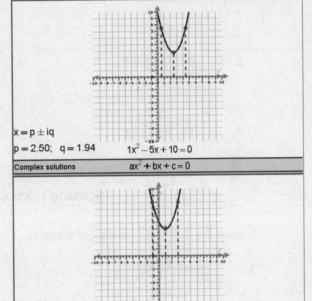

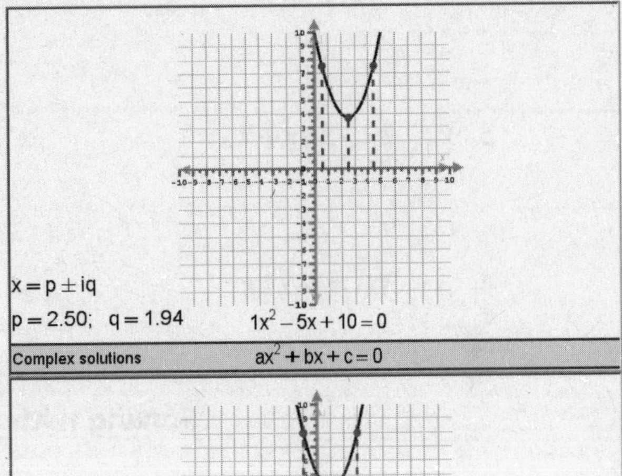

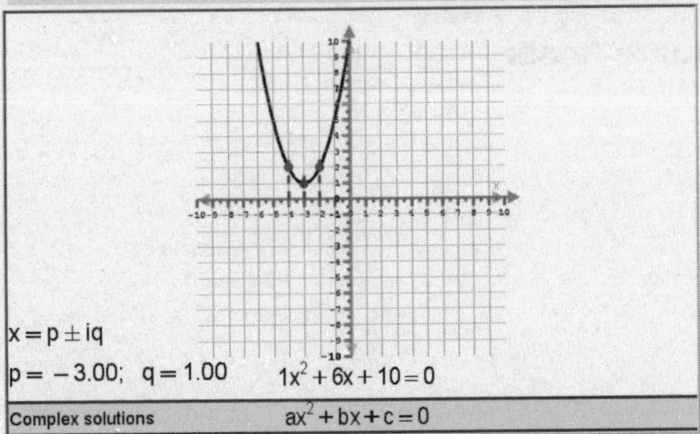

When there are two complex solutions, what on the graph corresponds to **p**?

$x = p \pm iq$

$p = 1.00$; $q = 2.00$ $1x^2 - 2x + 5 = 0$

Complex solutions $ax^2 + bx + c = 0$

When there are two complex solutions, what on the graph corresponds to **q**?

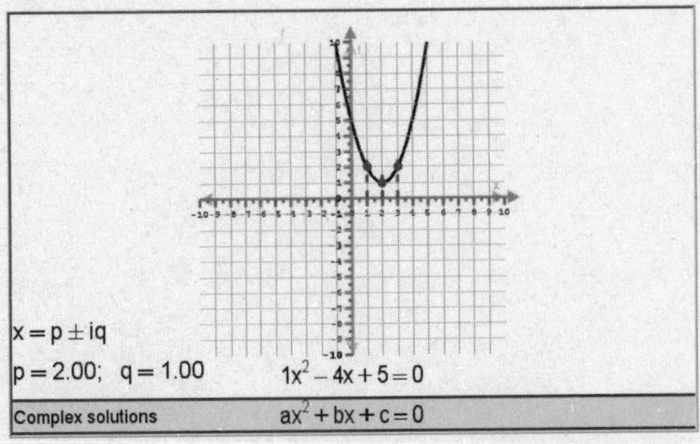

Can you figure out what these three lines on the graph mean?

Solving by Factoring

Solve by factoring:

1. $x^2-2x-15$

2. $x^2=9x-14$

3. $2x^2-15x+25=0$

4. $3x^2=4-11x$

Solving with Square Roots

Solve by taking the square root:

1. $(x-8)^2=49$

2. $(x+3)^2-64=0$

3. $(x-7)^2+25=0$

4. $(x+1)^2-7=2$

Factoring Perfect Squares

Factor the perfect square.

1. x^2-2x+1

2. $2x^2-4x+2$

3. $-x^2-6x-9$

Completing the Square

Complete the square.

1. x^2-2x+6

2. $x^2-6x+12$

3. $2x^2-4x+8$

4. $2x^2-4x+3$

Solving by Completing the Square

Solve by completing the square.

1. $x^2+12x+27=0$

2. $2x^2+16x-40=0$

3. $3x^2+30x-225=0$

Coefficients of Quadratic Equations

1. Does $y=5x^2+8x+4$ open up or down?

2. What is the y-intercept of $y=4x^2+5$?

3. What is the x value of the vertex of $y=-2x^2+12x-5$?

x-Intercepts

Find the x-intercepts of the given equation.

1. $y=x^2+3x-40$

2. $y=4x^2-7x-15$

Vertex Form $y=a(x-h)^2+k$

Find the vertex of the given parabola.

1. $y=(x+1)^2+3$

2. $y=(x-4)^2+4$

3. $y=x^2-2x+5$

Solving with the Quadratic Formula

Solve using the quadratic formula:

1. $x^2-12x+35=0$

2. $-3x^2=18-18x$

3. $2x^2=20x-56$

Applications

Consider this parabolic motion path for a baseball:

1. **What's the maximum height the ball reaches?**

$$y=\frac{-4}{395}(x-182)^2+116$$

2. **How far is the ball from the batter when it reaches its maximum height?**

3. **How far is the ball from the batter when it hits the ground?**

Seeing Complex Roots of Quadratics

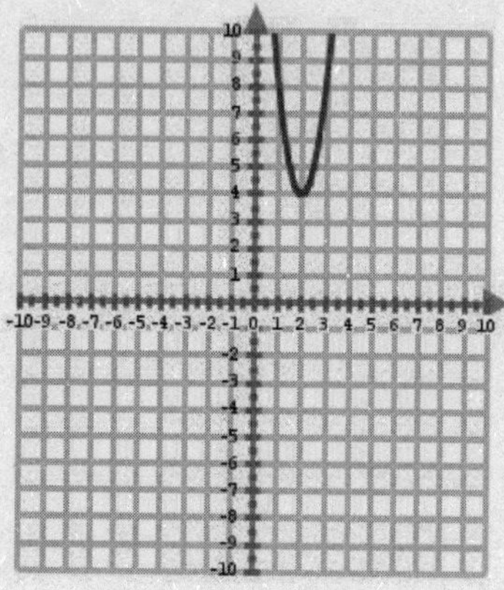

1. a. What is the real part of the complex solutions?

   b. What is the imaginary part of the complex solutions?

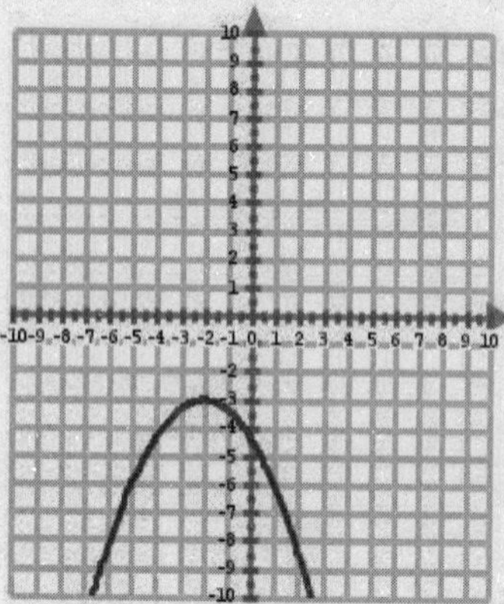

2. a. What is the real part of the complex solutions?

   b. What is the imaginary part of the complex solutions?

16. Introduction to Functions

The concept of a **function** is considered one of the most important concepts in mathematics. A function is a unique relation that transforms an input to an output. The input can be a numerical value, an algebraic expression, a quantity, or some other mathematical object. A functional transformation is a unique, one-to-one correspondence, meaning that each function input maps to one, and only one output. In math we visualize functions as graphs, tables, charts, or symbols. In this module you will develop your understanding of functions and how to manipulate their representations.

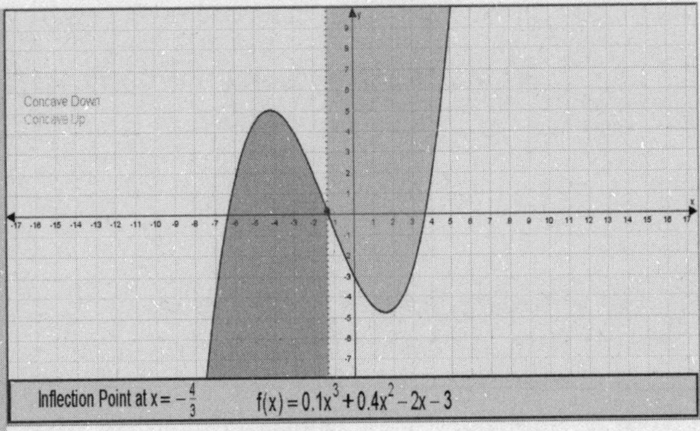

Equations in two variables have solutions that are **ordered pairs**. As you recall from **Modules 8** and **9**, ordered pairs are presented in the form of **(a, b)**, where **a** is an **x** value and **b** is a **y** value, and can be plotted on an x-y coordinate axis. Order is critical, meaning that the points (3, 4) and (4, 3) represent different locations on a graph.

An ordered pair is a solution to an equation if it satisfies the equation.

Testing Ordered Pair Solutions

Step 1: Make sure all variables are on one side of the equal sign.

Step 2: Substitute the first number in an ordered pair for the x value.

Step 3: Substitute the second number in the ordered pair for the y value.

Step 4: Use order of operations to simplify each side separately.

Step 5: Compare sides for equality.

Is (1,2) a solution to the equation?

$2x - 3y = -2$

Let $x = 1$ and $y = 2$.

Then, $2x - 3y = 2(1) - 3(2) = 2 - 6 = -4$.

So, $(1, 2)$ is not a solution of $2x - 3y = -2$.

$2x - 3y = -2$

Substitute 1 for **x** and 2 for **y**. Since $-4 \neq 2$, the solution does not work.

Is (-3,4) a solution to the equation?

$x^2 + y^2 = 25$

Let $x = -3$ and $y = 4$.

Then, $x^2 + y^2 = (-3)^2 + (4)^2 = 9 + 16 = 25$.

So, $(-3, 4)$ is a solution of $x^2 + y^2 = 25$.

$x^2 + y^2 = 25$

There are other ordered pair solutions to this equation. You can make a table of values to display ordered pair solutions.

Is (-4,-2) a solution to the equation?

$2x - 3y = -2$

Let $x = -4$ and $y = -2$.

Then, $2x - 3y = 2(-4) - 3(-2) = -8 + 6 = -2$.

So, $(-4, -2)$ is a solution of $2x - 3y = -2$.

$2x - 3y = -2$

Is (-2,2) a solution to the equation?

$x^2 + y^2 = 25$

Let $x = -2$ and $y = 2$.

Then, $x^2 + y^2 = (-2)^2 + (2)^2 = 4 + 4 = 8$.

So, $(-2, 2)$ is not a solution of $x^2 + y^2 = 25$.

$x^2 + y^2 = 25$

Make sure the substitutions replace just the variable by enclosing them in parentheses so that sign errors will be avoided.

Equations in two variables have an unlimited number of solutions. Finding solutions or checking to see if an ordered pair is a solution of a particular equation requires substituting values for the variables. You can change the equation on the screens on the Web by changing **A, B,** or **C** and you can find different ordered pairs that solve the equation by changing **x** for the first number in the ordered pair and **y** for the second number in the ordered pair. Can you predict if an ordered pair will be a solution before doing the math? Can you find more than one value for **x** that works for one value for **y**? Can you find more than one value for **y** for one value for **x**?

If (2, 3) is a solution (at right) is (3, 2) a solution?

Can the same ordered pair be a solution to different equations?

Find an *x* and a *y* that solve the equation.

$$ax + by = c$$
$$2x + 5y = 17$$

$$2(1) + 5(2) = 12$$

(1, 2) is not a solution to $2x + 5y = 12$.

Find an *x* and a *y* that solve the equation.

$$ax + by = c$$
$$2x + 5y = 17$$

$$2(1) + 5(3) = 17$$

(1, 3) is a solution to $2x + 5y = 17$.

Which should you change, **x** or **y**? Does it matter? Which causes the biggest change in the solution? Why?

Find an *x* and a *y* that solve the equation.

$$ax + by = c$$
$$3x + 2y = 10$$

$$3(2) + 2(2) = 10$$

(2, 2) is a solution to $3x + 2y = 10$.

If **x=0**, what does **y** have to be in the above equation? If **y** is negative will **x** be negative as well?

Find an *x* and a *y* that solve the equation.

$$ax + by = c$$
$$3x + 2y = 10$$

$$3(8) + 2(-7) = 10$$

(8, −7) is a solution to $3x + 2y = 10$.

If **x** is negative will **y** always be positive? Are there other solutions to the above equation? How do you organize the solutions?

Table of Values

EnableMath

Organize ordered pair solutions to equations in two unknowns by using a *table of values.* The table columns can be arranged showing **x**, the *independent variable* or *input value*, in the first column, followed by the equation (here represented in function notation, **f(x),** instead of **y**) with substitutions, and then the ordered pair solution. The graph can be plotted from the ordered pair solutions listed in the last column. The process for graphing an equation using a table of values is reviewed below.

Graphing Using a Table of Values

Step 1: Pick any number for the input value, x.

Step 2: Substitute that value for x and solve to find y, the output value.

Step 3: List the chosen x and corresponding y value as an ordered pair.

Step 4: Plot the ordered pair solution on a coordinate axis.

Step 5: Connect the points.

Plot the graph of f(x)=2x+1 using a table of values:

x	2x+1	(x, 2x+1)
−2	2(−2)+1=−3	(−2, −3)

Plot the graph of f(x)=2x+1 using a table of values:

x	2x+1	(x, 2x+1)
−2	2(−2)+1=−3	(−2, −3)
−1	2(−1)+1=−1	(−1, −1)
0	2(0)+1=1	(0, 1)

Try "easy" numbers that will "come out even" because they are easier to plot than fractions or decimals. In these examples **x** is the independent variable because we use that value to determine **y**. The **y** value is *dependant* on what we choose for **x**.

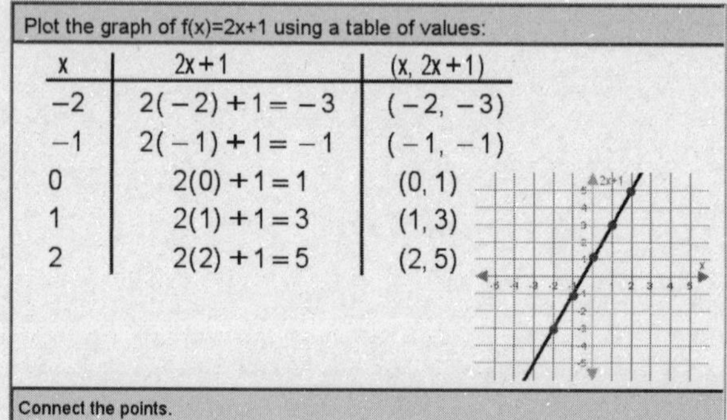

Plot the graph of f(x)=2x+1 using a table of values:

x	2x+1	(x, 2x+1)
−2	2(−2)+1=−3	(−2, −3)
−1	2(−1)+1=−1	(−1, −1)
0	2(0)+1=1	(0, 1)
1	2(1)+1=3	(1, 3)
2	2(2)+1=5	(2, 5)

Connect the points.

Once a clear pattern has been established, connect the points. The above is a linear equation and the graph is a straight line.

Organizing information in a *table of values* is common practice. Use appropriate headings to identify steps in the process or information relevant to the task. In the visualizations below, the task is to graph the line from a table of values. Column headings are chosen as **x**, the **independent variable** or **input**, and **y**, the **dependant variable** or **output**.

You can change the equation by changing **a**, **b**, or **c**. Change the table by changing the value of the independent variable, **x**, and/or the **xStep**—which generates the table based on how many "steps" from the original **x** you want. Does it matter what **xStep** is to get the pattern to plot the graph? Does the graph change if **xStep** changes?

Does it matter which values you pick for **x**?

Will changing **x** change the graph of the line?

Why can't you control the value of **y** with the joystick?

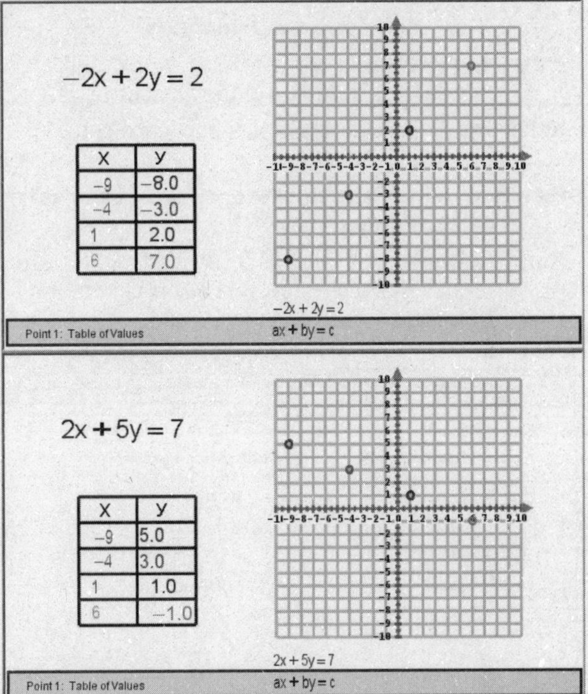

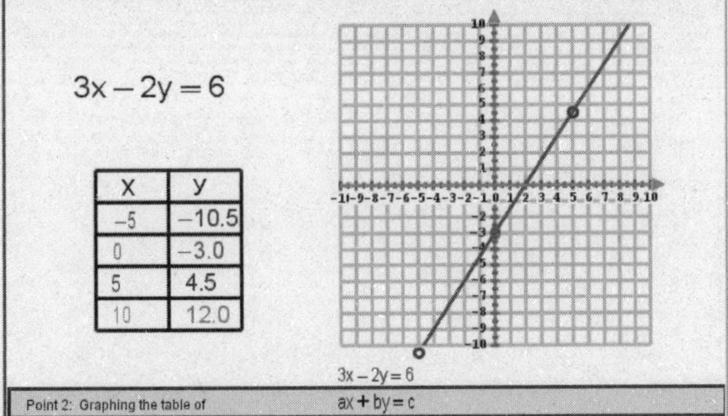

$3x - 2y = 6$
x | y
−5 | −10.5
0 | −3.0
5 | 4.5
10 | 12.0
$3x - 2y = 6$
Point 2: Graphing the table of
$ax + by = c$

Are there any values between −5 and 0 that could be included? How do we get to see those points?

Can other values be included? Can you find two different **x** values with the same y value? Can you find one **x** value with two different **y** values?

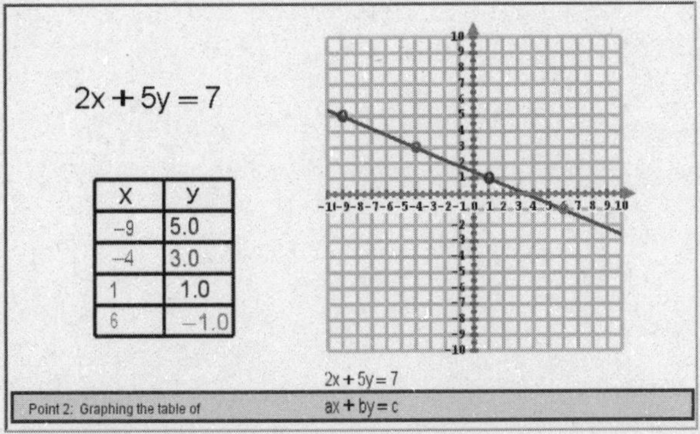

$2x + 5y = 7$
x | y
−9 | 5.0
−4 | 3.0
1 | 1.0
6 | −1.0
$2x + 5y = 7$
Point 2: Graphing the table of
$ax + by = c$

After finding the ordered pairs and plotting them on the grid, connect the points to draw the line. What if one of the points was not in line with the others?

Introduction to Functions

EnableMath

A *relation* is a correspondence or mapping between two sets of numbers, an ***input*** set, called the ***domain***, and an ***output*** set, called the ***range***. Relations are ordered pairs of numbers written in the form of (a, b).

Functions are special relations, where each input value (x) corresponds to *only one* output value (y). The function ***rule*** defines what to do with the input value to get to the output value. A function can be represented in symbols (an equation), as a table, or as a graph. Functions are named using letters, either upper or lower case, with the variable enclosed in parentheses, like f(x), g(x), A(x), and so on.

Relations and Functions

Function Notation: f(x) is read as "f of x" and means "find the value of the function at x".

Relation: Any meaningful correspondence between two sets of numbers.

Function: Any relation that assigns every input value only one output value.

Rule: How the input value gets changed to the corresponding output value. Usually given in symbolic form.

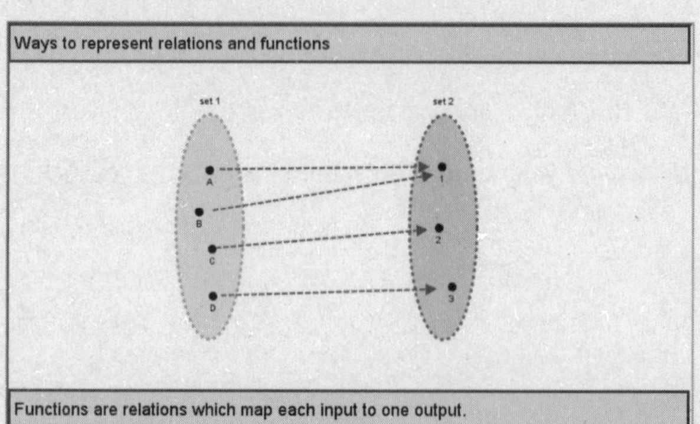

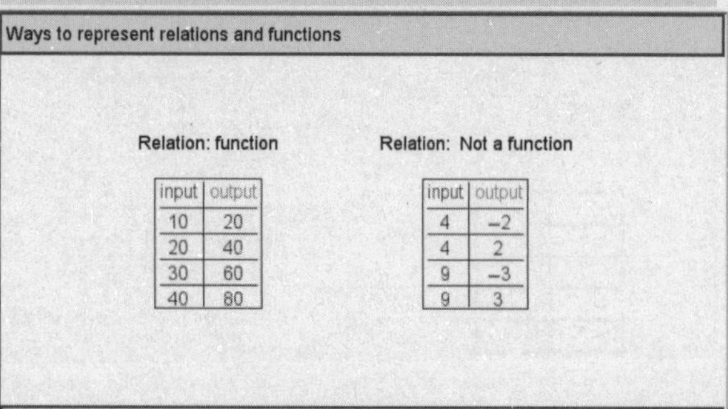

Ways to represent relations and functions

Relation: function

input	output
10	20
20	40
30	60
40	80

Relation: Not a function

input	output
4	−2
4	2
9	−3
9	3

Tables

Notice that the input values in the second table each have two output values. Think of what function rule could be used in table 1 and what relation could be described in table 2 above.

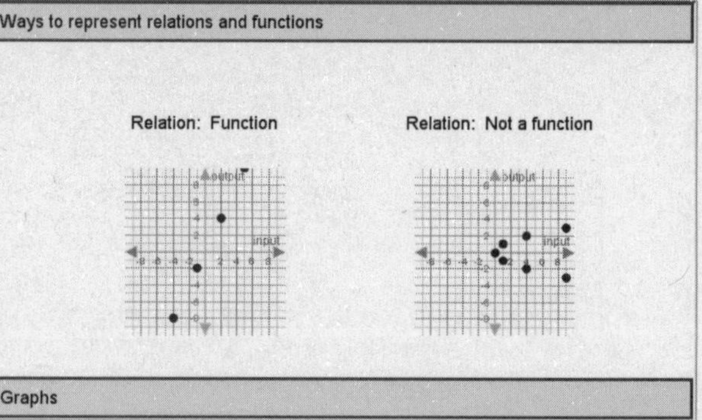

Notice that for each **x** value there is only one **y** value in the first graph. In the second graph, every **x** value has two **y** values, except for the point (0, 0).

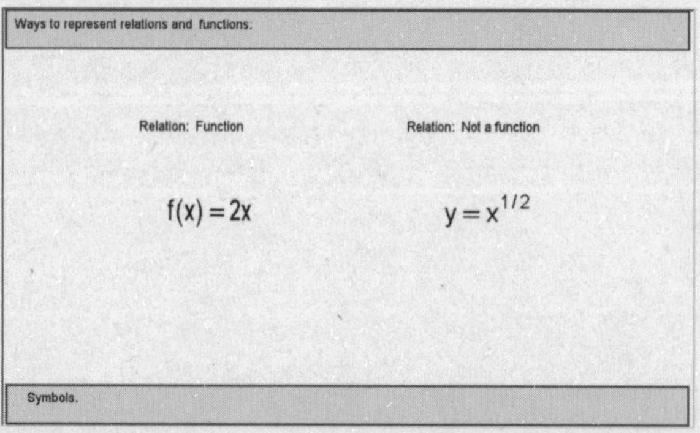

Notice the difference in notation between the two equations above. In the function, no matter what value you choose for x, there is only one value for f(x). The second equation is not a function—the fraction exponent means square root.

A **function** defines a process for taking one or more input numbers and producing a single number output. In other words, a function defines the relationship between its input and output values. A functional rule, or equation, tells us what needs to be done to an input number to determine its corresponding output number.

Tables, **graphs**, and **equations** are algebraic tools for expressing functional relationships. Each of these function representations communicate the same information about the function, but represent the information in different ways. Which representation you choose to use to represent a function with depends on which most effectively communicates the information that you are interested in. The key is to learn how to see how each representation communicates the same information and to become comfortable switching between them.

Variable: A letter standing in for an unknown quantity or changeable number.

Independent Variable: The input into a function, most often represented by x or t.

Dependent Variable: The output from a function, often represented by y or f(x), this number *depends* on the functional rule.

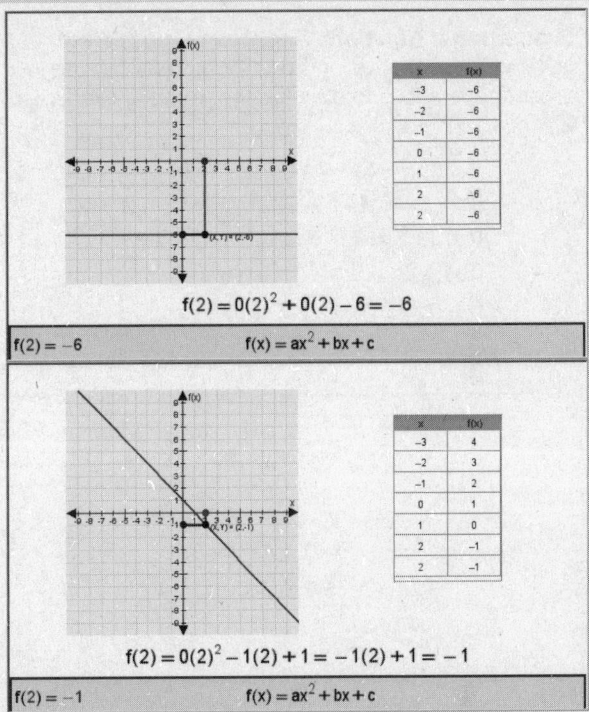

x	f(x)
-3	-6
-2	-6
-1	-6
0	-6
1	-6
2	-6
2	-6

x	f(x)
-3	4
-2	3
-1	2
0	1
1	0
2	-1
2	-1

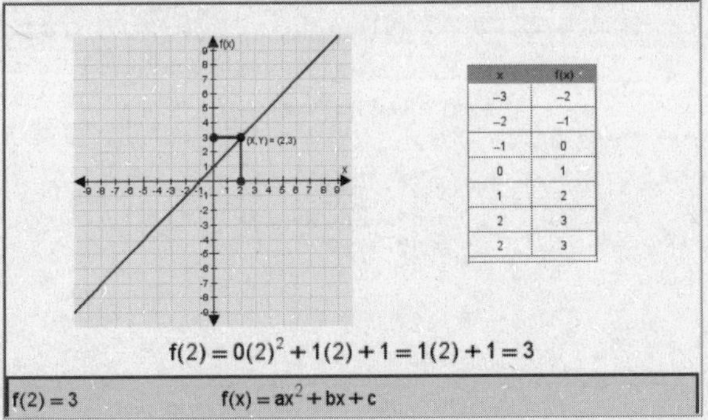

x	f(x)
-3	-2
-2	-1
-1	0
0	1
1	2
2	3
2	3

Changing the values of the variables **a**, **b**, and **c** changes the functional rule. What happens when a=0 and b=0? What does the graph look like when just a=0? Can you locate the ordered pairs in the table on the graph?

Keep a=0 and change the value of **b**. What does the line look like when b<0, b==0, and b>0? How could you make a graph of the function from the order pairs of the function displayed in the table?

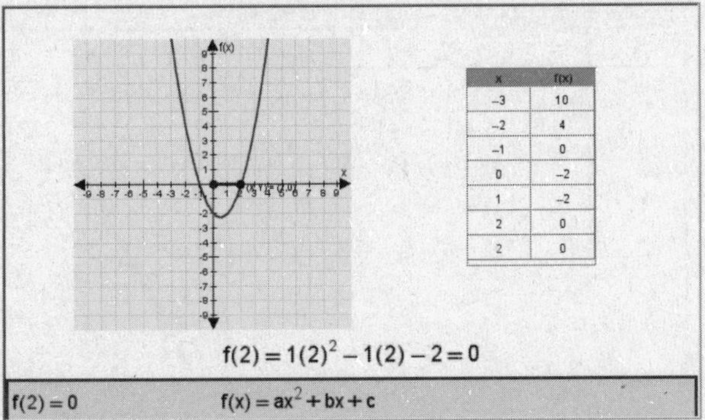

x	f(x)
-3	10
-2	4
-1	0
0	-2
1	-2
2	0
2	0

How does the function change when you make a>0? How has the shape of the graph changed? Find the ordered pairs of the function on the graph.

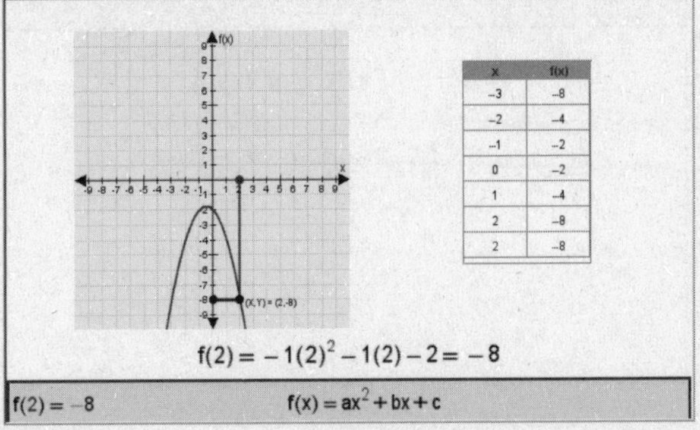

x	f(x)
-3	-8
-2	-4
-1	-2
0	-2
1	-4
2	-8
2	-8

Now make a<0. How has the graph changed? What happens to the graph as you change the values of **b** and **c**?

One of the important features of functions is that the way they are written helps keep track of exactly what is happening when evaluating for a particular value. It is a shorthand way to give a lot of information with very little writing. In later lessons, function notation will be used to indicate how to combine more than one function and to write one function in terms of another function.

To evaluate f(x) means to substitute the number, variable, or expression inside the parentheses in place of the variable in the function and then simplify the right side of the equal sign.

Evaluating a function: Replace the variable with a given value or expression from the domain and use order of operations to evaluate the resulting expression.

Given: $f(x) = 3x + 2$

$f(3) = 3(3) + 2 = 8$

$f(-2) = 3(-2) + 2 = -4$

$f(0) = 3(0) + 2 = 2$

$f(a) = 3a + 2$

$f(a+1) = 3(a+1) + 2 = 3a + 5$

Functional Notation

Functional notation is convenient and powerful.

f(x) is read "f of x."

f(−1) is read "f of -1." It means "replace each x in f(x) with the value -1.

If $f(x) = 2x^2 - 3x + 4$

then $f(-1) = 2(-1)^2 - 3(-1) + 4 = 9$.

Find $f(-2)$ if $f(x) = 3x^2 - 2x - 4$.

$$\begin{aligned} f(-2) &= 3(-2)^2 - 2(-2) - 4 \\ &= 3(4) + 4 - 4 \\ &= 12 + 0 \\ &= 12 \end{aligned}$$

Substitute the value −2 into the function for **x** and evaluate. The final statement can be written as f(-2) = 12 showing both the domain value and the range value. The statement means the value of the function at −2 is 12.

Find $f(4)$ if $f(x) = x^3 - 27$.

$$\begin{aligned} f(4) &= (4)^3 - 27 \\ &= 64 - 27 \\ &= 37 \end{aligned}$$

Whatever domain value is given, substitute it into the function and then evaluate. Above we get the statement f(4) = 37 showing both the domain value and the range value.

Find $f(a+2)$ if $f(x) = 2x - 4$.

$$f(a+2) = 2(a+2) - 4$$

Expressions can be used as well as values. Above, shows the first step in substituting a + 2 for x. The answer expressed in terms of **a** is f(a+2)=2a.

Plot the graph of f(x)=2x+1 using a table of values:

x	$f(x) = 2x + 1$	(x,f(x))
−2	$2(-2) + 1 = -3$	(−2, −3)
−1	$2(-1) + 1 = -1$	(−1, −1)
0	$2(0) + 1 = 1$	(0, 1)
1	$2(1) + 1 = 3$	(1, 3)
2	$2(2) + 1 = 5$	(2, 5)

The process is to go from input—through rule—to ordered pair—to graph.

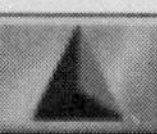

Functions are defined by a function rule; an input value gets "processed" by the rule to give an output value. The first visual shows the concept as a "function machine" with input "processing" to "output". The second visual shows the graph of a quadratic equation with a table of values.

Use the joystick to change the function (change **a**, **b**, and, **c**) and input value, x. For each value of x we can see a different value for f(x). Does every input value have an output value? Input values and output values form ordered pairs. What do the collection of ordered pairs look like for a particular function—what does the graph of the function look like?

Is there any value for x where the given function does not have a value? What values can be used as input values?

Can you describe the output values for the given functions? What output values are not used for each function?

What does f(0) mean? Why is it an important function value?

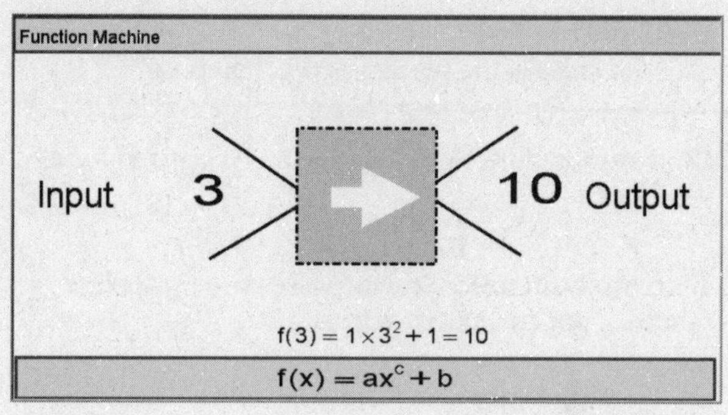

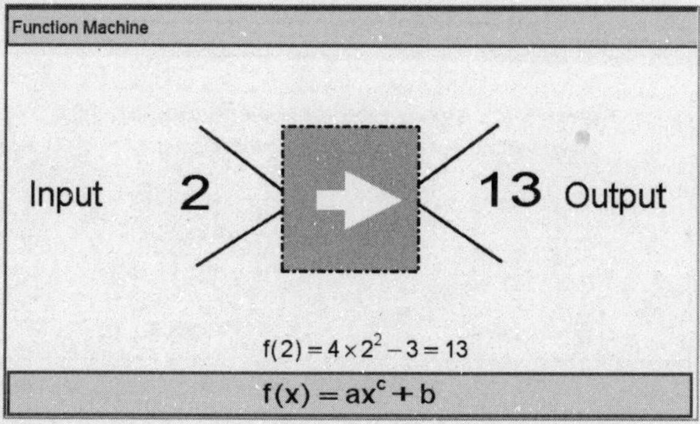

What ordered pair is represented by the function machine above? What graph is represented by the function rule? What is f(0)?

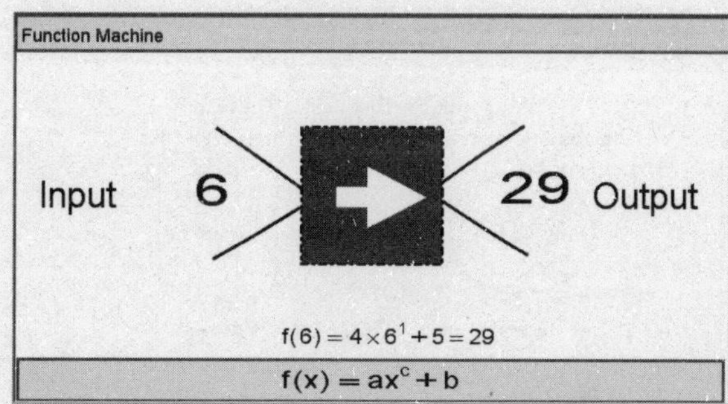

What ordered pair is represented above? What is f(0)? What is f(1)? What does the graph of the ordered pairs look like?

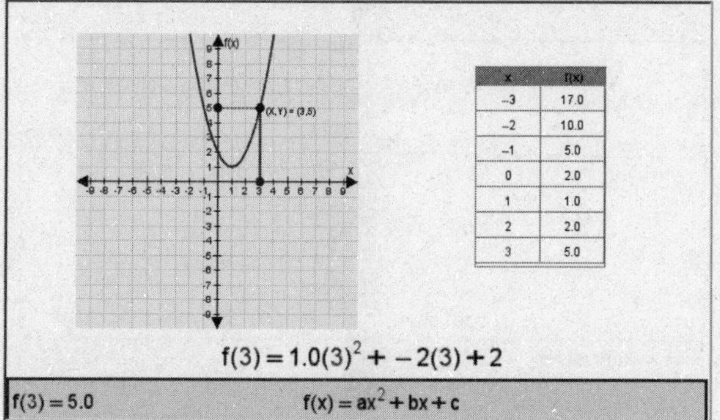

x	f(x)
–3	17.0
–2	10.0
–1	5.0
0	2.0
1	1.0
2	2.0
3	5.0

How are the f(x) values found? Can you pick an f(x) value and then find an x value? Do the f(x) values *depend* on what value is picked for x?

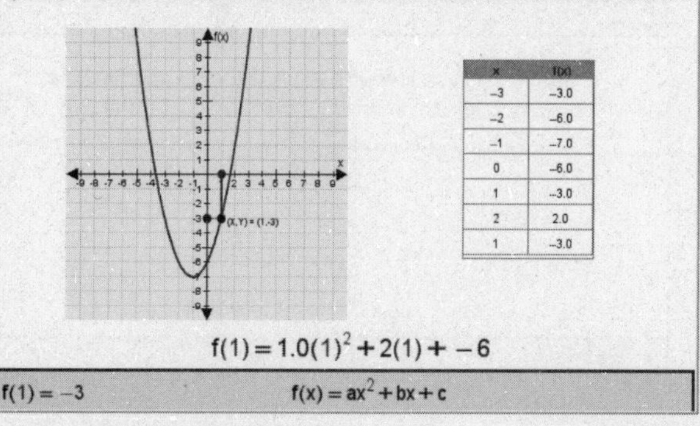

x	f(x)
–3	–3.0
–2	–6.0
–1	–7.0
0	–6.0
1	–3.0
2	2.0
1	–3.0

What happens to the y-coordinate when the x values change? What does x=0 yield? What values for y are not possible from the given graph?

Is it a function of x?

EnableMath

A function must have one and only one output value for every input number.

A function can be presented graphically, on a coordinate axis. The horizontal axis (x-axis) represents the input values. In order for the relation to be a function, any given x value can form an ordered pair with only one y value. We can visualize this by thinking of a straight line parallel to the y axis passing through each successive x on the graph. The line can only hit (cross) the graph once for each x value.

Vertical Line Test: Are there any points where a vertical line crosses the function more than once?

Continuous Function: The function is defined for all values of x.

Discrete Function: Specific values are mapped or graphed; not continuous values.

Is it a function?

In order for a relationship to be a function of x, it must pass the vertical line test. In other words, for every value of x, there must not be more than one y.

The Vertical Line Test: Continuous

A graph passes the vertical line test if no vertical line crosses the graph more than once.

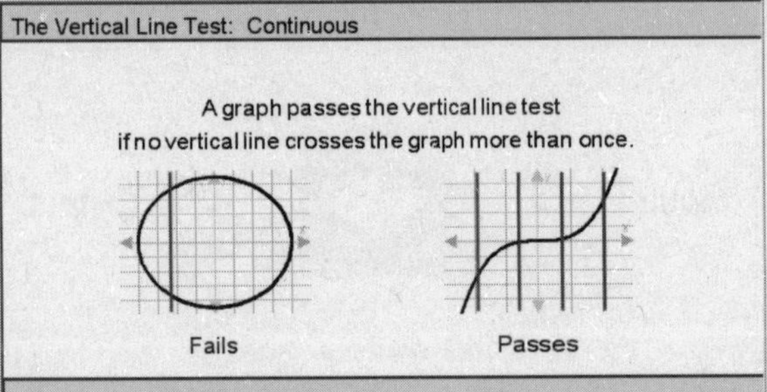

In the first figure above, the vertical line cuts the circle in two points for a single value of **x**.

The Vertical Line Test: Discrete functions

The graph of a discrete function passes the vertical line test if no vertical line crosses more than one point.

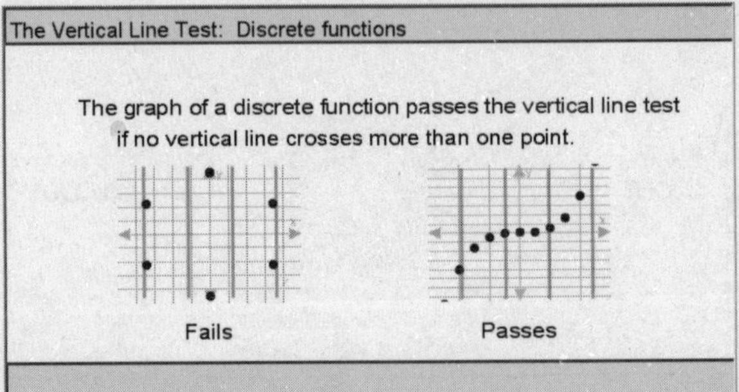

Are there points where a vertical line crosses the function in more than one place?

Tables

A function is a rule in which each input has exactly one output.

x	f(x)
2	3
4	4
6	5
8	6

This is a function.

Notice that each input has only one output. This is a function.

Tables

A function is a rule in which each input has exactly one output.

x	f(x)
2	3
2	–3
6	5
6	6

This is not a function.

This table of values does not represent a function because f(x=2)= 2 and –3. Once you have found one exception, you do not have to look any further.

Functions are special relations that map each input to one, and only one, output value.

The **Vertical Line Test** is used to determine if the graph of a relation is a function. A vertical line must not cross the graph of a function more than once (there can be one and only one Function Bar for each value of x).

Using the joystick, increase or decrease the value of **x** to move the red, dashed vertical line. Can you find a value for **x** where the red line crosses the graph more than once? If so, then the relation is not a function.

Can all the input values of a function map to the same output value? Do they have to?

How do you know what values of **x** to use?

How do you know if all values of **x** are included?

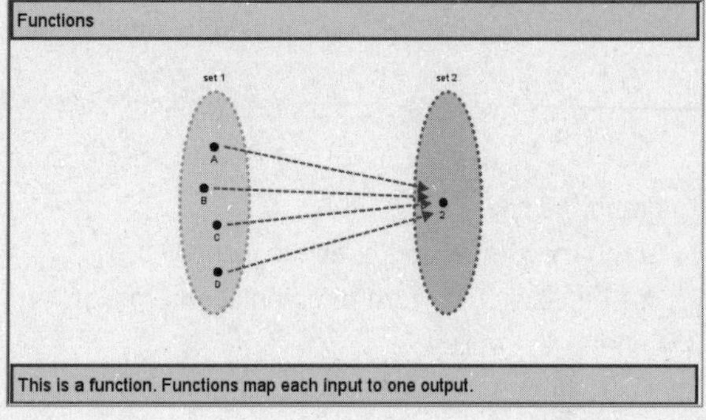

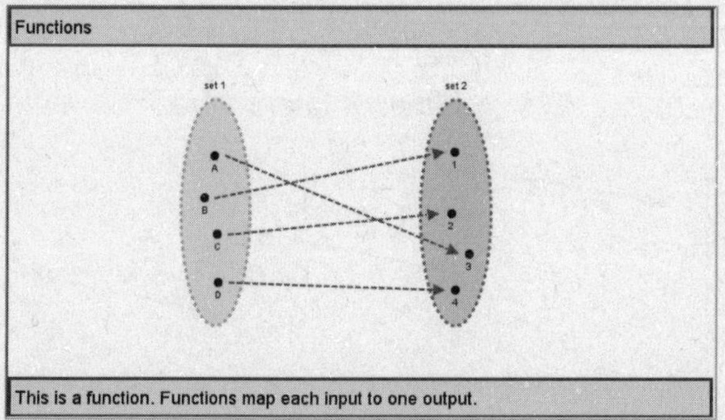

Above, A maps to 3, B maps to 1, C maps to 2, and D maps to 4. Since each input maps to only one output a functional relationship exists between the elements in set 1 and set 2.

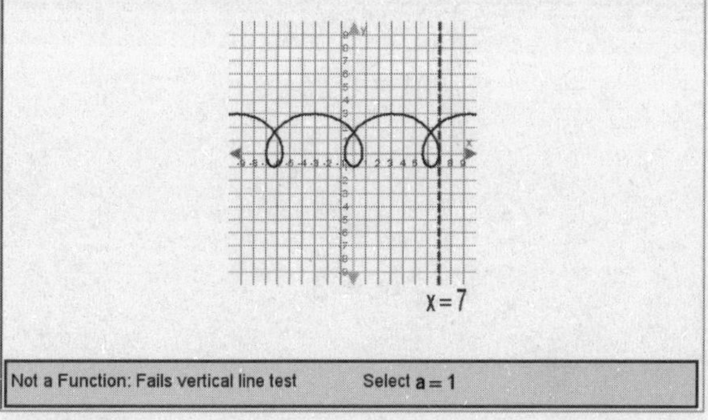

Change the value of **x** to see what happens to the red line. Can you find a value for **x** that crosses the function more than once?

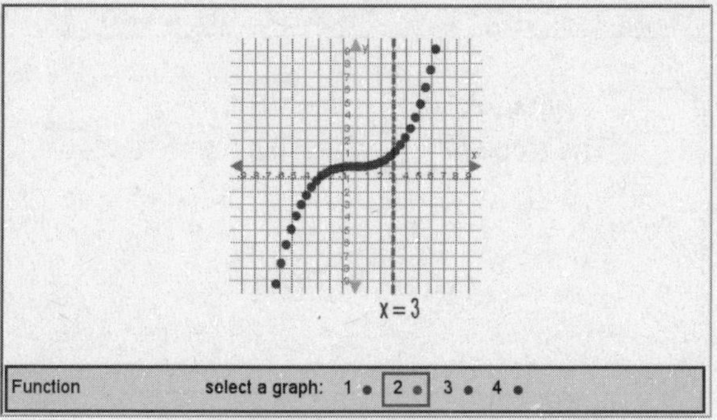

How do you know this is a function? Do you have to check every point? Can you determine the pattern in the above function?

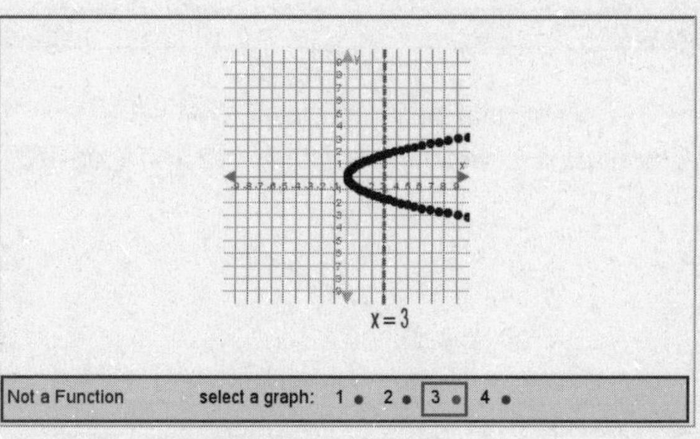

Why is this not a function?

Linear Functions

EnableMath

Linear functions graph as straight lines. A quick review of some of the important information about lines is presented below. This time, function notation is used. Instead of y=mx+b, use f(x)=mx+b. You can assume f(x)=y for all graphs.

To review more about graphing straight lines go to **Module 8**.

Given two points on a line you can find its slope using:

$$m = \frac{y_2 - y_1}{x_2 - x_1}$$

To graph the line:

1. Graph the y-intercept, b, as the point (0,b).
2. Use the slope (rise/run) to graph another point.
3. Connect the points.

A linear function of the form f(x)=b where b is a real number is called a constant function and graphs as a horizontal line.

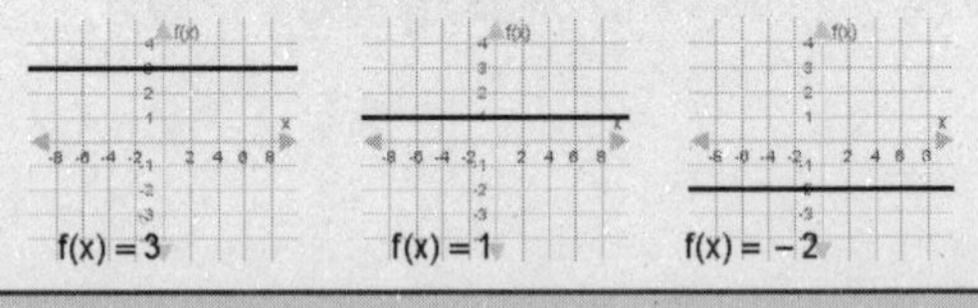

Calculate the slope between the two points:

$(-1, -2)$ and $(1, 4)$

$$m = \frac{y_2 - y_1}{x_2 - x_1}$$

$$m = \frac{4 - -2}{1 - -1}$$

$$m = \frac{6}{2}$$

$$m = 3$$

Given any two points, find the change in y to the change in x. Make sure the x and y values are corresponding.

In a linear function f(x)=mx+b, b is the y – intercept.

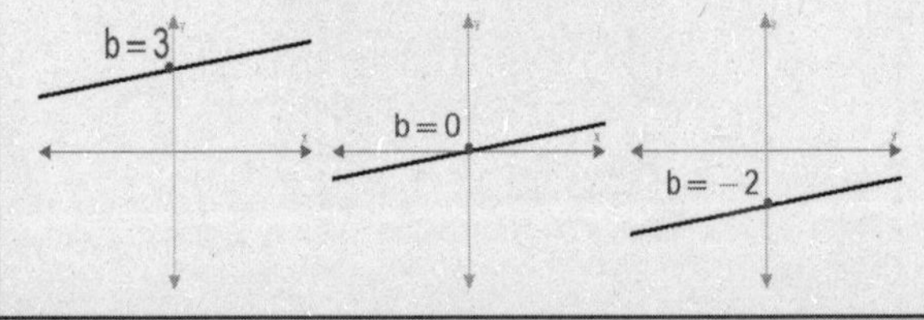

For any line f(x)=mx+b, the y-intercept is f(0). If the equation is in f(x)=y=mx+b form, the y-intercept is at the point (0,b).

Graph:

$f(x) = \frac{2}{3}x - 3$

First, plot the y – intercept, $b = -3$.

The slope is $\frac{2}{3}$, which means a rise of 2 and a run of 3.

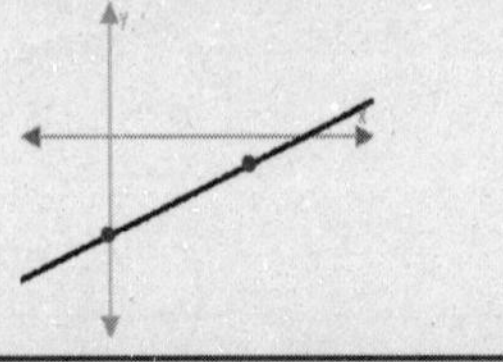

Connect the points.

The slope is positive so the line is rising.

Graph:

$f(x) = -\frac{2}{3}x + 1$

First, plot the y – intercept, $b = 1$.

The slope is $-\frac{2}{3}$, which we rewrite as $\frac{-2}{3}$

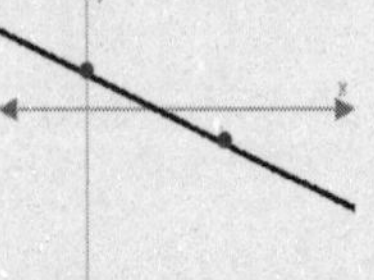

Connect the points.

The slope is negative so the line is falling.

Linear function, or lines, can be described using function notation. All lines can be identified by their s**lope** and their **y-intercept** or **x-intercept**. Do all lines have an x-intercept? Do all lines have a y-intercept?

Can you describe the domain of any given line? Can you describe the range?

What kind of information does the slope relay? How do you know if the line is rising (increasing) or falling (decreasing)?

What point corresponds to f(0) for any line?

How can you determine if a line represents a constant function? What is the slope of a constant function?

What is the slope of a vertical line?

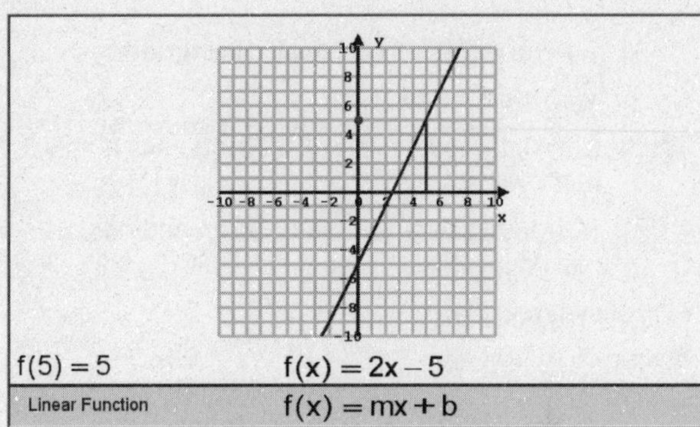

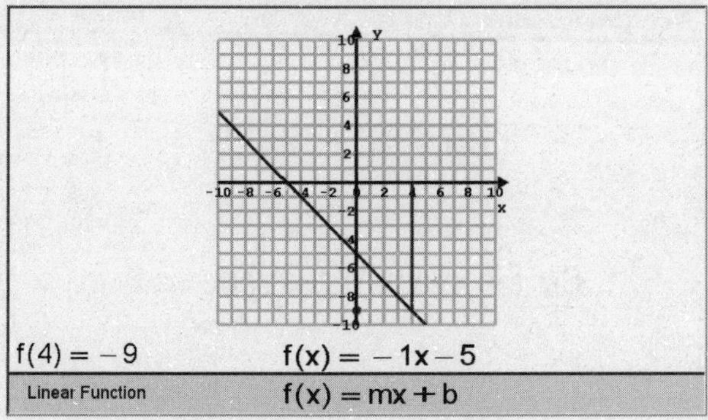

As **x** increases, does **f(x)** increase or decrease?

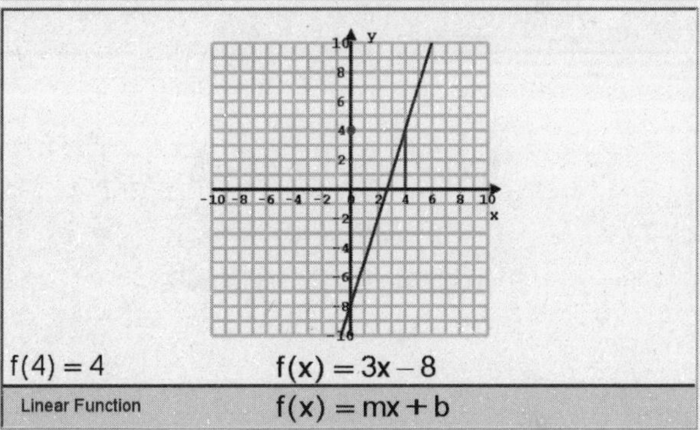

As **x** increases, does **f(x)** increase or decrease?

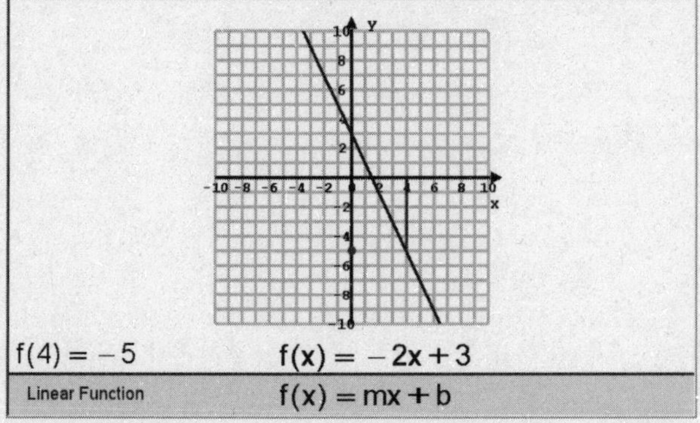

What is f(0)? What is the slope? Is the line rising or falling?

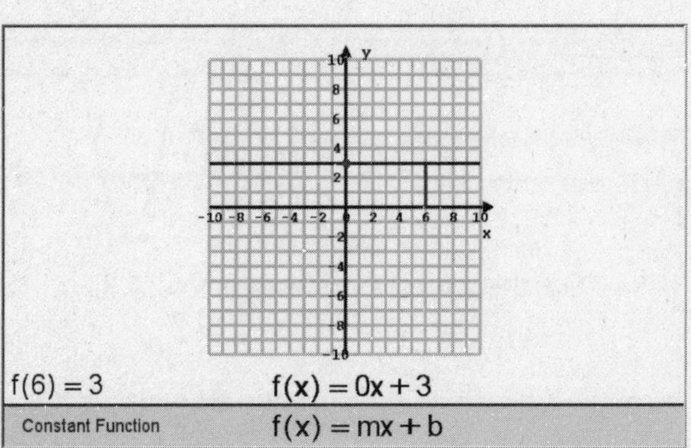

What do you notice about the slope? What is the slope of any constant function?

Quadratic Functions: Characteristics

EnableMath

Quadratics can be written in general polynomial form as a function $\mathbf{f(x) = ax^2 + bx + c}$. The variable is always raised to the second degree. Quadratic functions always graph in the shape of a parabola. The parabola is symmetric about a line called the **axis of symmetry**. That means that if you fold a parabola along the axis of symmetry all of the points would "match up" from one side to the other. The tip of the parabola is called the **vertex** and it is an ordered pair (x, f(x)), where f(x) represents either the **maximum** or **minimum** function value.

Properties of Quadratic Functions

Given: $\mathbf{f(x) = ax^2 + bx + c}$

Then: If a>0, the parabola opens up and has a minimum value.

If a<0, the parabola opens down and has a maximum value.

Axis of symmetry: x = –b/2a

Vertex: (x, y), where $x = \frac{-b}{2a},\ y = \frac{4ac - b^2}{4a}$

Does $f(x) = 2x^2 + 5x - 7$ open up or down?

$$f(x) = 2x^2 + 5x - 7$$
$$a = 2$$
$$a > 0,\ \text{so, it opens up.}$$

$f(x) = ax^2 + bx + c$

Does $f(x) = -3x^2 + 4x + 5$ open up or down?

$$f(x) = -3x^2 + 4x + 5$$
$$a = -3$$
$$a < 0,\ \text{so, it opens down.}$$

$f(x) = ax^2 + bx + c$

First, make sure the equation is in the correct form, and then, identify the value of **a** to determine if the parabola opens up or down.

Find the x value of the vertex of:

$$f(x) = 3x^2 - 12x + 2$$
$$x = \frac{-b}{2a} = \frac{+12}{2(3)}$$

So, the x value of the vertex is 2.

$f(x) = ax^2 + bx + c$

When the equation is in the correct format, find the **x** value of the vertex by simplifying –b/2a. You can find the y value of the vertex either by finding f(-b/2a) or by simplifying the above formula for y.

Find the equation for the axis of symmetry of:

$$f(x) = 2x^2 + 12x + 2$$
$$x = \frac{-b}{2a} = \frac{-12}{2(2)}$$

So, the axis of symmetry is $x = -3$.

$f(x) = ax^2 + bx + c$

The axis of symmetry goes through the vertex, therefore the axis of symmetry is the line x= -b/2a.

A quadratic function graphs as a parabola. From the standard form of a quadratic equation, $\mathbf{f(x) = ax^2 + bx + c}$, we can determine whether the parabola opens up or down, what the axis of symmetry is, and determine its vertex.

If you know the parabola opens up, can you find the minimum value of the function? If it opens down, can you find the maximum value?

You can control **a, b, c** and **x** in the visualizations below.

How do you determine if the parabola opens up or down?

What does the axis of symmetry do to help graph the parabola?

How much do you need to know in order to get a reasonable picture of what the graph should look like?

What happens if **a** is a fraction?

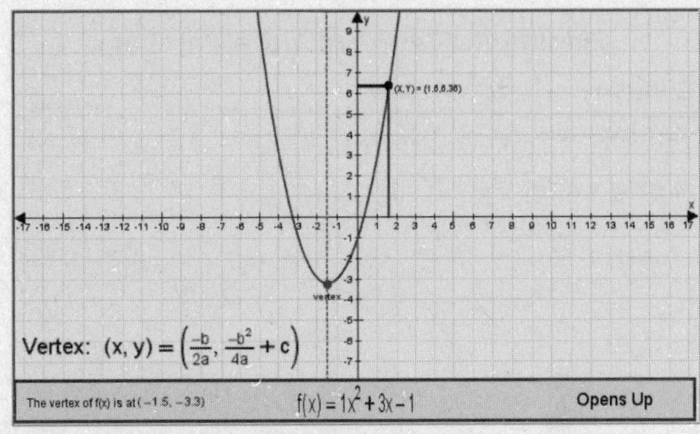

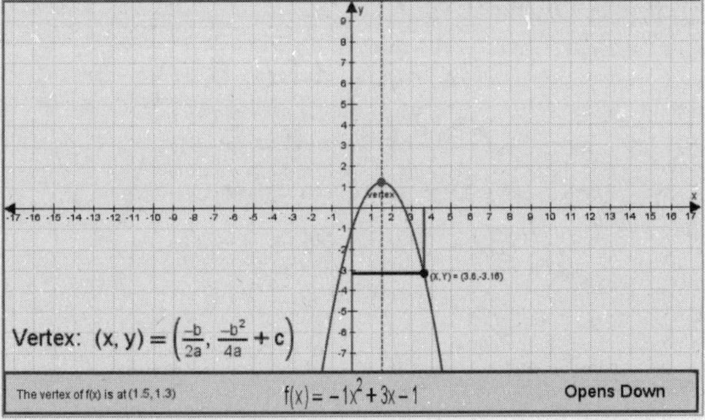

Does the above parabola have a maximum or minimum value? Change **x** to determine the **y** value of the vertex.

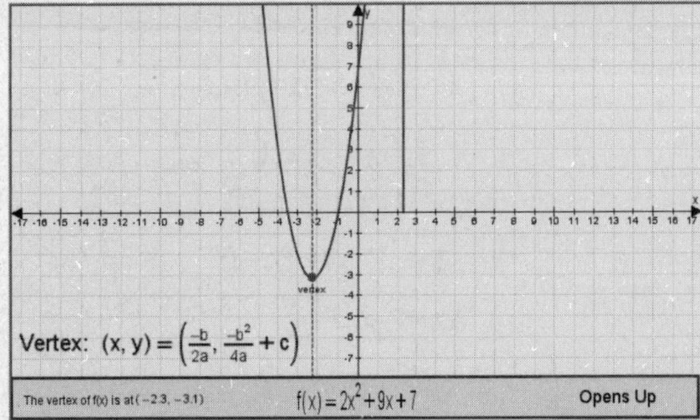

The **x** value above is 3 but the **y** value is off the graph. Does that mean there is no **y** value? If there is one, how do you find it?

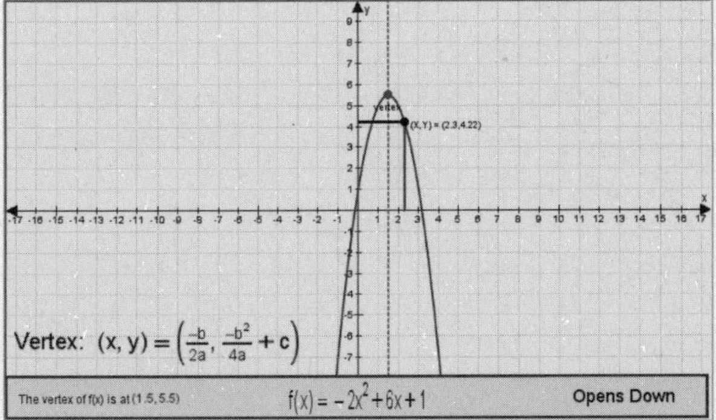

If you trace the **x** value to the vertex, is the **y** value a maximum or minimum functional value? How do you know? What can you determine about the range of the function?

Quadratic Functions: Intercepts

EnableMath

As you remember with graphing lines, critical points to consider are where the line crosses the **x** and **y** axes. The same is true for quadratic functions. A quadratic function will cross the **y** axis once and can cross the **x** axis either zero, once or twice. Finding the x-intercepts means to find the roots of the equation by setting it equal to zero and solving for the **x** variable. Remember, since a quadratic equation is to the second power it can have zero, one, or two roots.

Finding the Intercepts of a Parabola

Given: $f(x) = ax^2 + bx + c$

Y-intercept: Find f(0) or (0, c)

X-intercepts: Solve for x in $ax^2 + bx + c = 0$

Find the value of the y-intercept of:

$$f(x) = -2x^2 + 2x + 4$$

$$c = 4$$

So, the y-intercept is at (0, 4).

$f(x) = ax^2 + bx + c$

Find the values of the x-intercepts of:

$$f(x) = x^2 + 5x - 6$$

$$x^2 + 5x - 6 = 0$$

$$(x-1)(x+6) = 0$$

$$x - 1 = 0,\ x + 6 = 0$$

$$x = 1,\ x = -6$$

$f(x) = ax^2 + bx + c$

The equation is set equal to zero and the resultant quadratic is factored. Once the intercepts and vertex are found, the graph can be sketched accurately.

Find the values of the x-intercepts of:

$$f(x) = 6x^2 + 5x - 6$$

$$6x^2 + 5x - 6 = 0$$

$$(3x-2)(2x+3) = 0$$

$$3x - 2 = 0,\ 2x + 3 = 0$$

$$x = 2/3,\ x = -3/2$$

$f(x) = ax^2 + bx + c$

From inspecting the equation, the y-intercept is –6; the x intercepts can be found by setting the equation equal to zero and solving for **x**.

The **y-intercept** is where a graph crosses the **y** axis. An **x-intercept** is where the graph crosses the **x** axis. Since the value for **y** is zero at an x-intercept, the x-intercept is a *root* of the equation, that is we can *solve* $ax^2 + bx + c = 0$ for x.

Use the joystick to control the shape of the parabolas by changing **a**, **b**, and **c**. The green dots show the x-intercepts and the red dot shows the y-intercept.

When will a parabola have only one x-intercept?

When will a parabola have no x-intercepts?

Will a parabola always have a y-intercept?

When will the y-intercept be at the vertex?

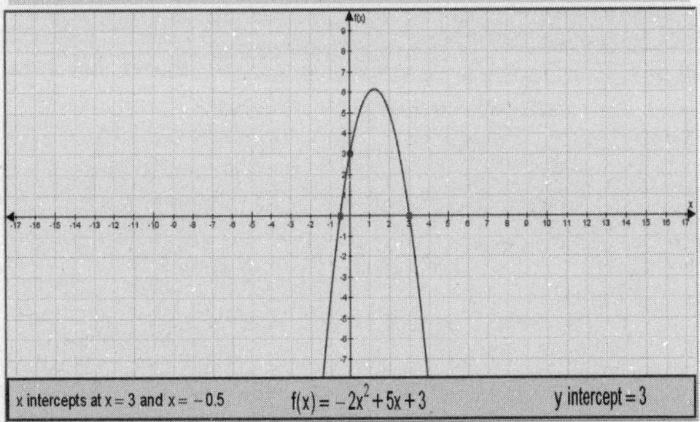

Where does the graph cross the y-axis? Where does it cross the x-axis? What do you know about the x-intercepts and the axis of symmetry?

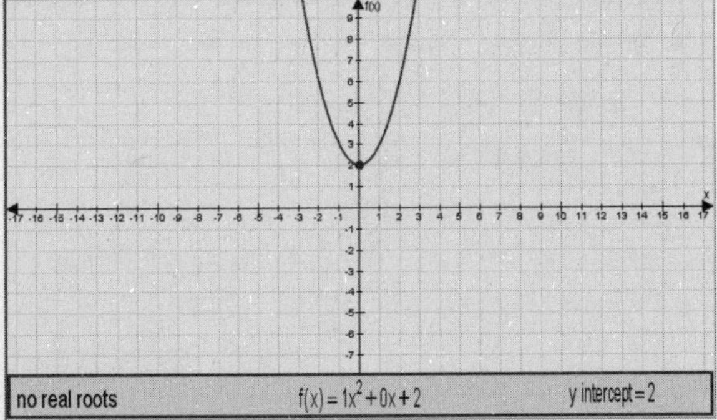

What happens if to the parabola when you let a = -1? Are there still no real roots?

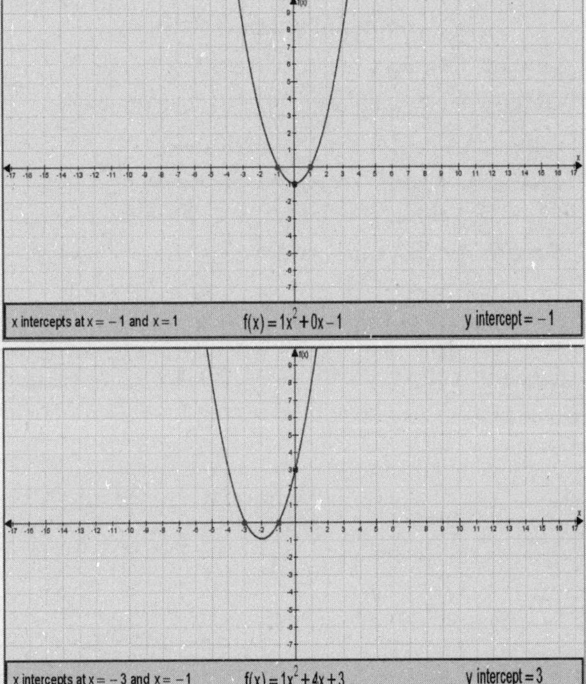

If you know the y-intercept and the equation for the axis of symmetry, can you find another point on the graph?

Identifying Common Functions

EnableMath

Functions can be classified and identified by the shapes of their graphs. A linear function graphs to a straight line; a quadratic function graphs as a parabola. The graph gives information about the equation and the equation gives information about the graph.

Step through the examples online. Try to determine which type of function is presented by looking just at the graph.

Common Function Shapes

Linear: A straight line; x is to the first power

Quadratic: A parabola; x is to the second power

Cubic: A lazy s; x is to the third power

Absolute Value: A **v** shape; x will always be within the absolute value symbols

Square root: A slow upward curve; x will always be under a radical

Rational: A hyperbola; an algebraic fraction

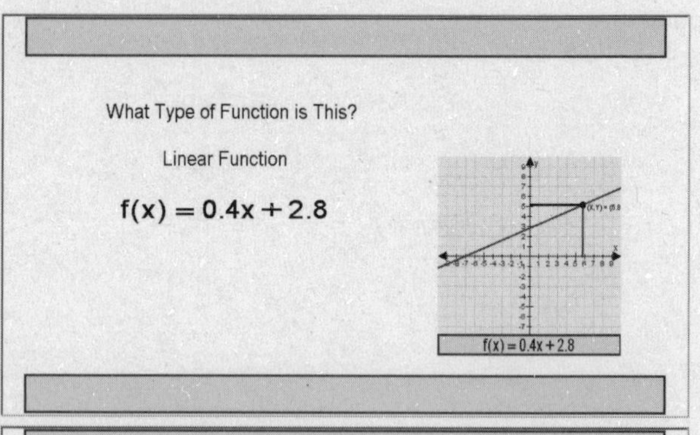

What Type of Function is This?
Linear Function
f(x) = 0.4x + 2.8
f(x) = 0.4x + 2.8

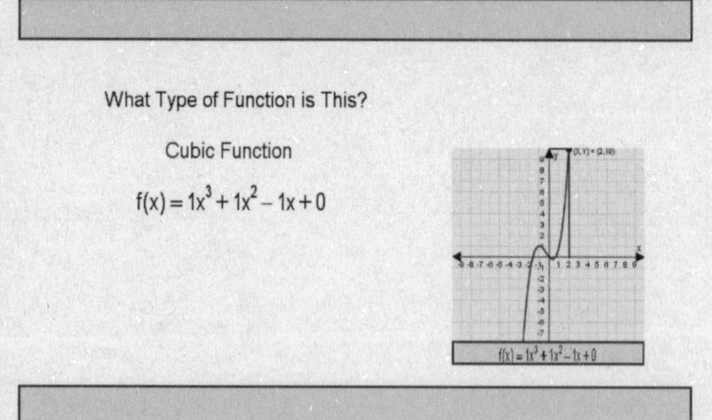

What Type of Function is This?
Cubic Function
f(x) = 1x³ + 1x² – 1x + 0

All cubic functions have x^3 and all have the same shape graph. The graph might be pulled or stretched, but you can expect it to follow the basic shape of the above graph.

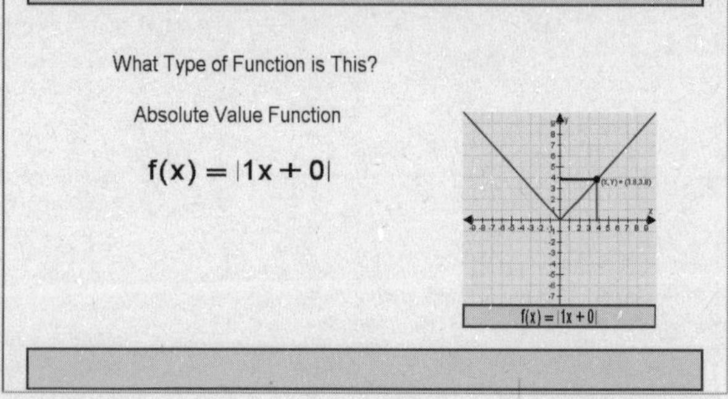

What Type of Function is This?
Absolute Value Function
f(x) = |1x + 0|
f(x) = |1x + 0|

The absolute value function looks like a **v** because both positive and negative values give a positive result; absolute value functions usually have positive y values. Think about pairs of absolute values like 2 and –2; 10 and –10; 1000 and –1000...

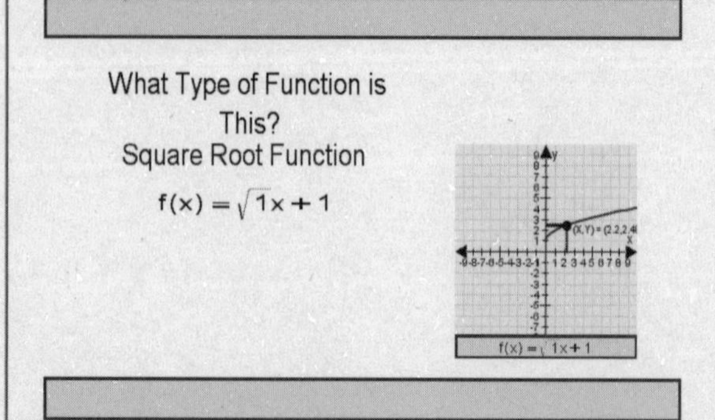

What Type of Function is This?
Square Root Function
f(x) = √1x + 1

Notice where the y-intercept is. Begin the curve there.

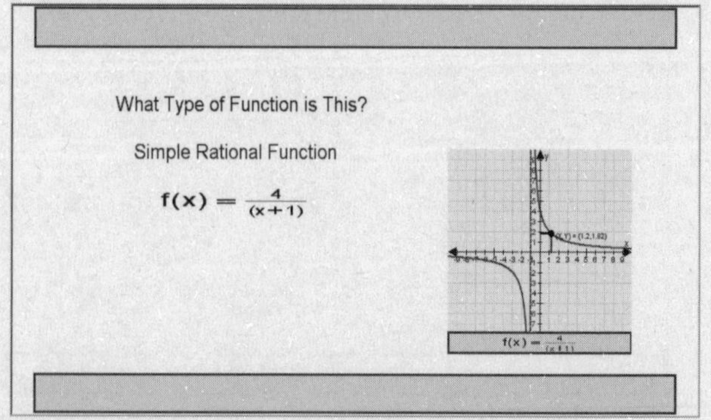

What Type of Function is This?
Simple Rational Function
f(x) = 4/(x + 1)

Notice that the function seems to have two parts divided by the asymptotes. Anytime a function looks like the one above, think about a rational expression.

The purpose of identifying common functions is to link the visualization of the graph of the function with the type of equation. The graphs below and on-line are examples of patterns of functions. Change the coefficients to see how the equation parameters change the graph. Does changing **a** always change direction? Does increasing the constant term always shift the graph vertically up or down? What do you have to change to shift the graph left or right?

What point on the graph is determined by the constant term?

How does changing the size of **a** affect the shape of a quadratic function?

What would you have to change to get the absolute value function to graph in quadrants III and IV?

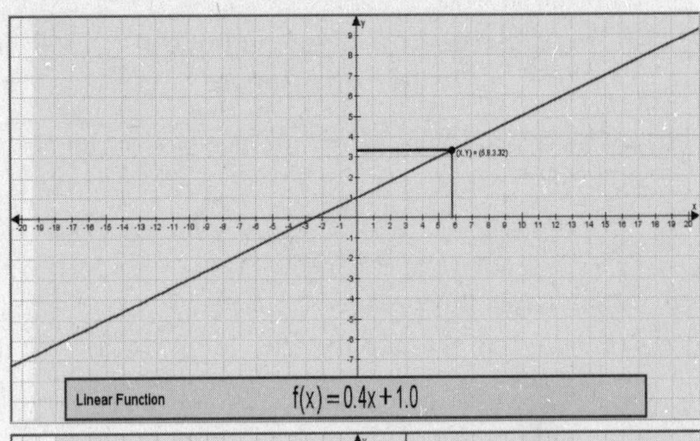

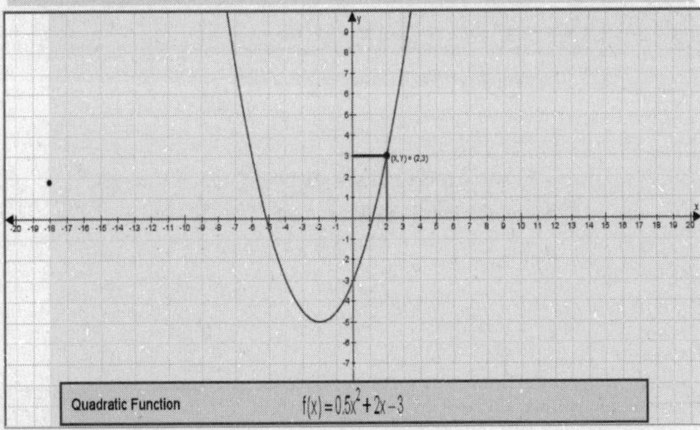

How does changing **a** change the graph? How does changing **b** change the graph?

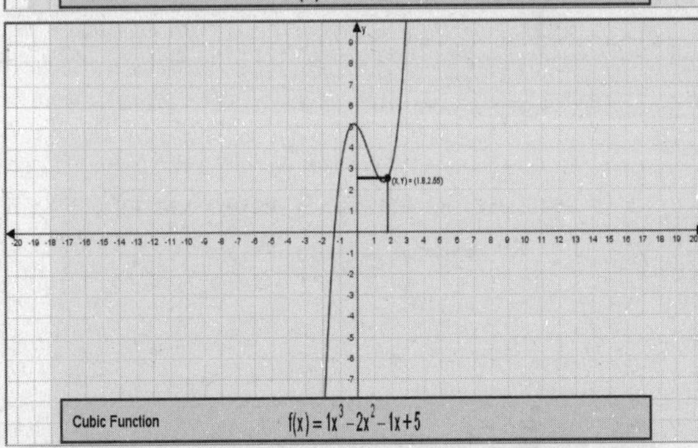

Can you change the graph so that it looks as if it's a linear function? What could you do to ensure that that doesn't happen?

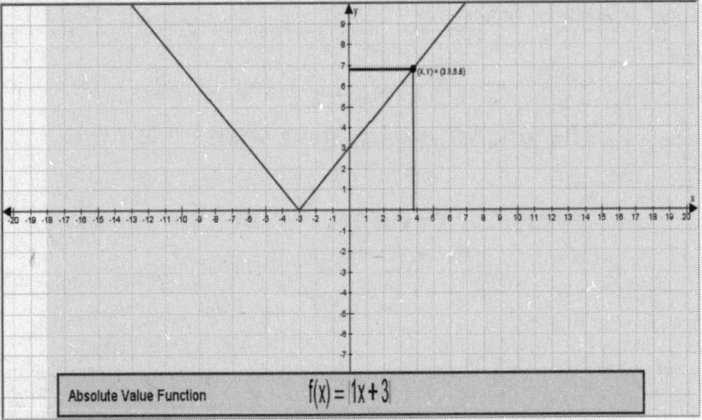

Is this graph symmetric? What is the axis of symmetry?

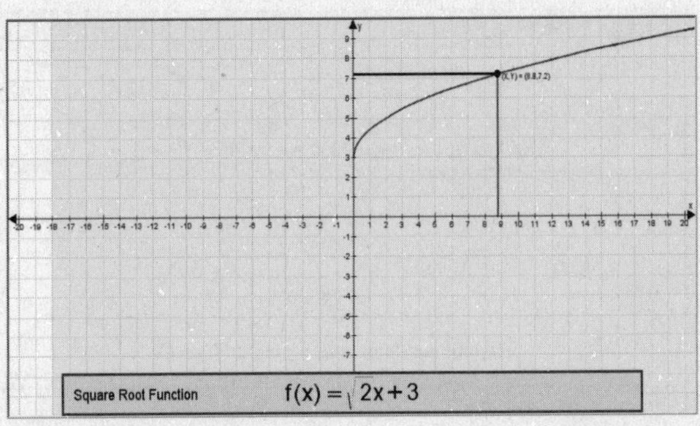

How does changing **a** affect the graph of the function?

Domain and Range

Looking at the graph of a function or its equation helps us determine the **domain** and **range**. The description can be verbal or symbolic. There is no set process for determining the domain and range of functions, instead we must analyze each equation or graph using all the rules and principles available to us. For our purposes, the domain values are all real numbers for which the function is defined. To find the domain, find any values that make the function undefined and eliminate those values from the set of all real numbers.

Questions for Determining the Domain and Range

1. Are there any values for **x** for which the function is undefined?
2. Are there gaps or spaces in the graph, or regions where the graph does not exist?
3. What do the range values look like?
4. Are there critical values to test?

Graphically find the domain and range of:

$$f(x) = x^2 + 1$$

(0, 1)

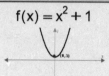

D: all real numbers

R: $y \geq 1$

The range is all of the resulting y values.

Algebraically find the domain and range of:

$$f(x) = x^2 + 1$$

x can take any value. So, D: all real numbers.

x^2 is always ≥ 0. So, R: $y \geq 1$.

The range is all of the resulting y values.

We know x^2 is defined for any value and is always positive or zero. If x^2 is zero, y=1; therefore, **y** can be anything greater than or equal to 1.

Algebraically find the domain and range of:

$$f(x) = \frac{1}{x-1} + 3$$

If $x = 1$, the function is undefined. So, D: $x \neq 1$.

The numerator is never $= 0$. So, R: $y \neq 3$.

The range is all of the resulting y values.

Any **x** values that make the denominator undefined are eliminated form the domain. Analyze the range values: Since the fraction can be very large or very small, depending on what x is, the best we can say is that it can never be zero (the numerator is never zero), so **y** can't equal 3.

Algebraically find the domain and range of:

$$f(x) = \frac{3}{4x+10}$$

The function is undefined where $4x + 10 = 0$.

$$4x = -10$$

$$x = \frac{-10}{4} = -\frac{5}{2}$$

So, D: $x \neq -\frac{5}{2}$

The numerator is never=0. So, R: $y \neq 0$.

The range is all of the resulting y values.

Set the denominator equal to zero and solve for x to eliminate those values from the domain.

Algebraically find the domain and range of:

$$f(x) = \sqrt{x+2} + 3$$

The function is undefined when $x + 2 < 0$.

So, D: $x \geq -2$.

Square roots yield results that are ≥ 0.

So, R: $y \geq 3$.

For square roots, the radicand must be positive for the answer to be a real number. Set the radicand ≥0 to find the domain. Analyze to find the range.

We show the domain and the range on a graph by coloring the part of the x-axis that represents the domain and the part of the y-axis that represents the range of the function.

When the graph is a parabola the domain is shown along the whole x-axis. Why is this? Imagine that you can zoom out and see more and more of this graph. How would it look?

Some functions have a domain that starts at one point and is then continuous to the right or the left on the x-axis. Take a look at **Point 2**. And some functions may have a discontinuous range, that is they are not defined for some points in the domain. Take a good look at **Point 3**.

The domain is shown on the screen in teal and the range in light green.

Are there critical values that make the function undefined?

Can you determine if the range values are all positive? Or all negative? Or all greater than (or less than) a constant?

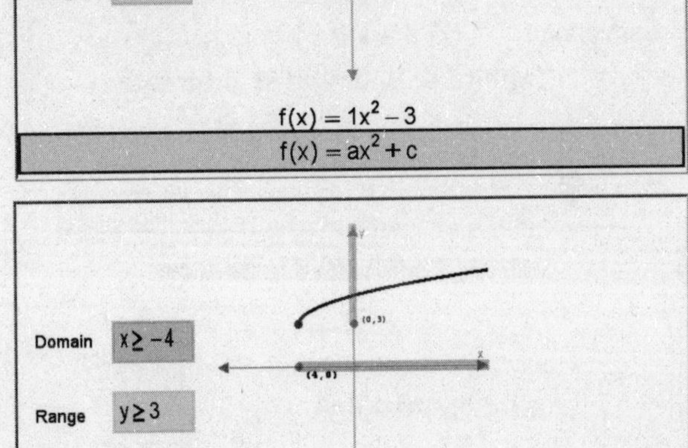

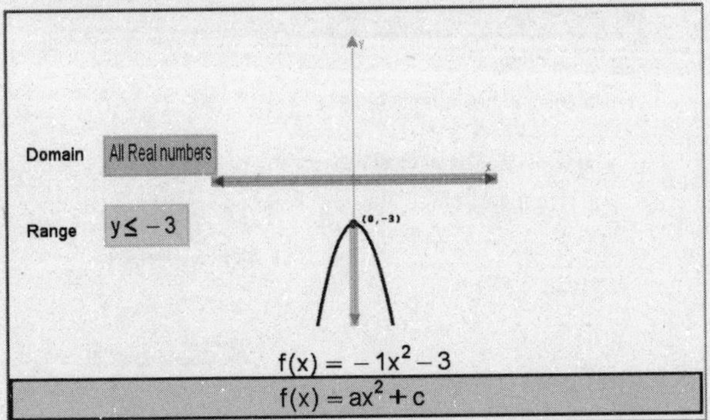

When a<0 and the parabola opens down. What is the range of the parabola above?

Domain $x \geq -4$, Range $y \geq 3$, $f(x) = \sqrt{x+4} + 3$; $x \geq -a$, $y \geq b$, $f(x) = \sqrt{x+a} + b$

Why can't x= −5? Find the range: What happens when x= −4? What do you know about the range values? Will there ever be a negative f(x) value? How do you know?

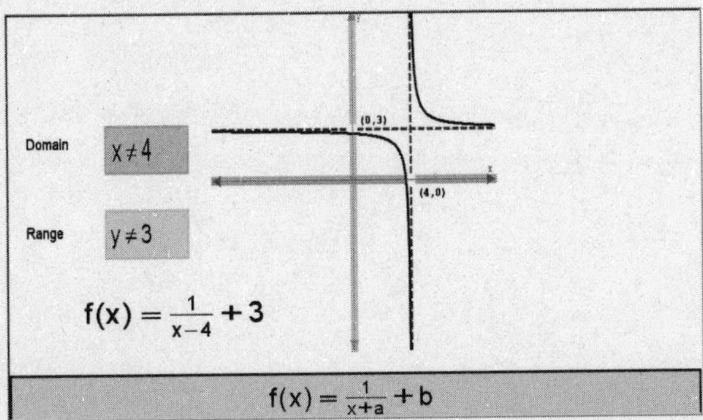

Why is one point taken out of the domain for this function?

Intervals

EnableMath

Intervals are continuous sections or parts of the Real numbers shown on graphs or symbolically. All real numbers within the defined boundaries are included. Intervals are described in set notation using inequality statements, interval notation using brackets and/or parentheses with the endpoint values, and, on graphs by a closed or open circle at the endpoints. Using intervals allows us to describe parts of a graph without describing the entire graph.

Interval notation is commonly used in mathematics to show the **bounds** of the interval described by the *endpoints*. Use parentheses to show the endpoint is not included and brackets to show the endpoint is included.

Finite or Bounded Intervals

	Set Notation	Interval Notation
Closed:	$\{x \mid a \le x \le b\}$	$[a,b]$
Open:	$\{x \mid a < x < b\}$	(a,b)
Semiopen:	$\{x \mid a < x \le b\}$	$(a,b]$
Semiopen:	$\{x \mid a \le x < b\}$	$[a,b)$

Infinite or Unbounded Intervals

Use ∞ or $-\infty$ to indicate positive or negative infinity.

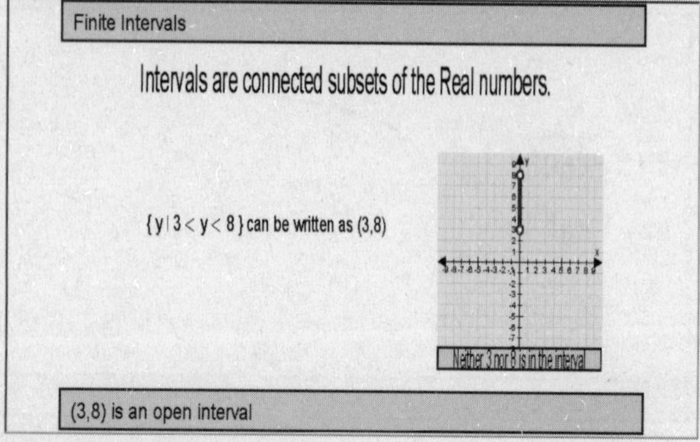

The open interval above does not include values 3 and 8, but is open for values up to 3 and up to 8 as close as we want to get.

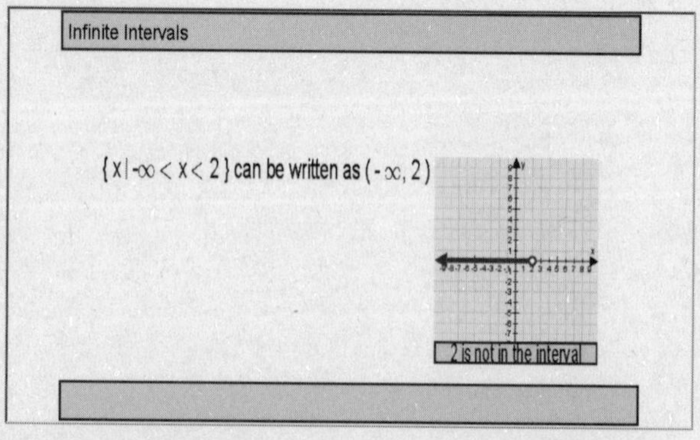

The above example shows a negative infinite open interval with an upper bound of 2.

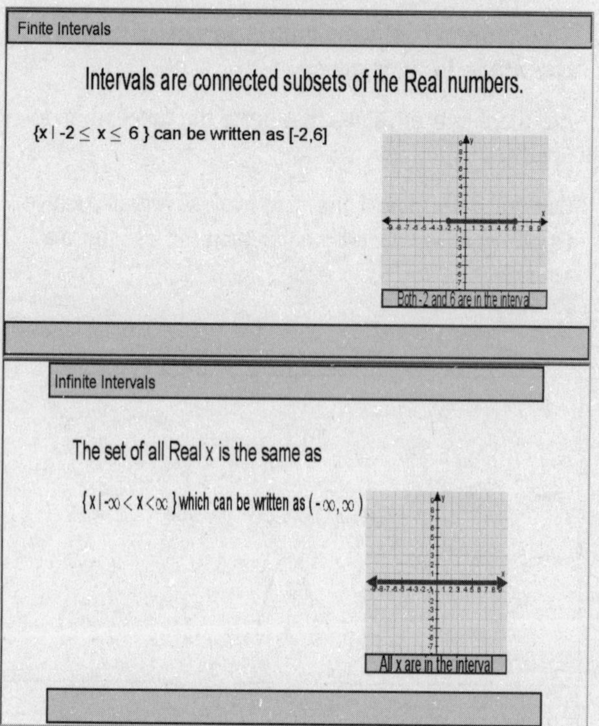

All real numbers are included. Notice that the interval notation used is open; infinity is a concept, not a value or number.

Sometimes we need to limit what domain or range values to use. We can define the intervals we want included by naming the endpoints. The mathematical meaning of interval is exactly like the everyday meaning. It is a segment or range of values in times, space, or events. In business a profit margin is an interval.

You can set the upper and lower bounds by clicking and dragging on the appropriate red dashed line.

How do you know if a value is included in an interval?

Can you always find a maximum value over an interval?

Can you always find a minimum value over an interval?

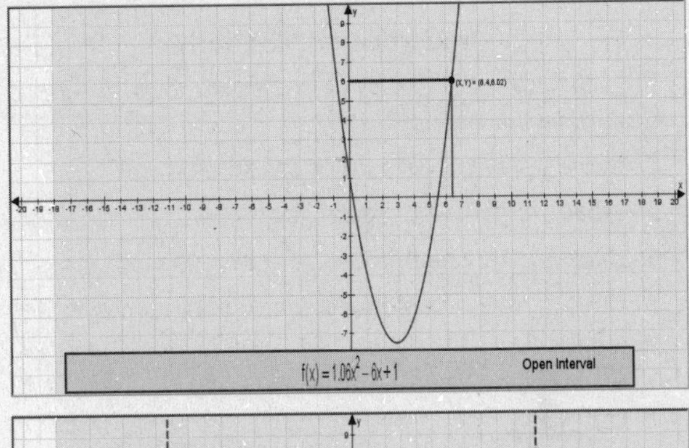

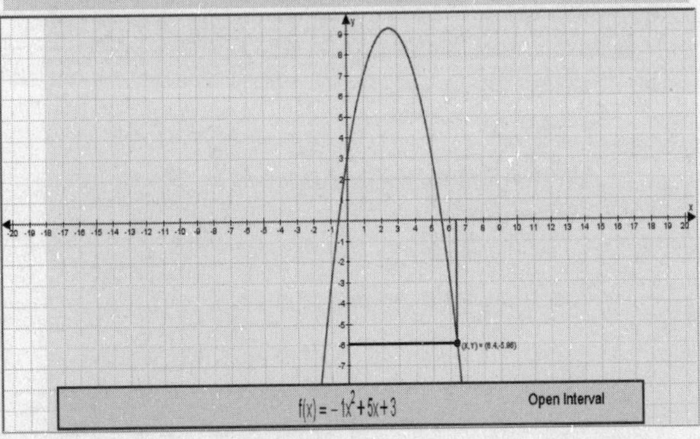

Are any interval bounds apparent? Can the range can be describes as an open infinite interval? How can the domain be described in interval notation?

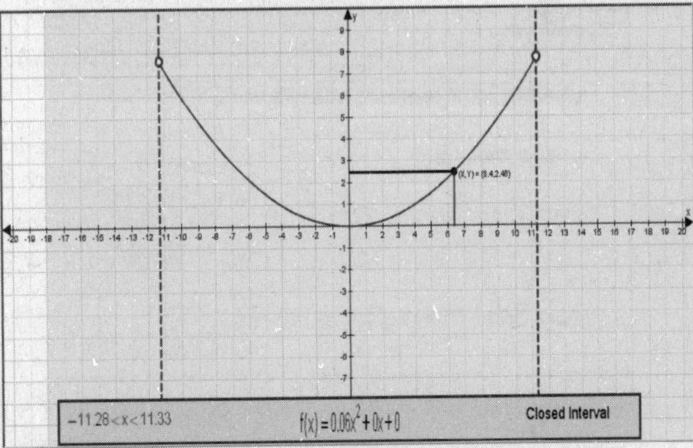

Are the endpoints of the interval included? What are the range values over the domain interval? How would you write the domain using interval notation? What's the minimum function value over the given interval?

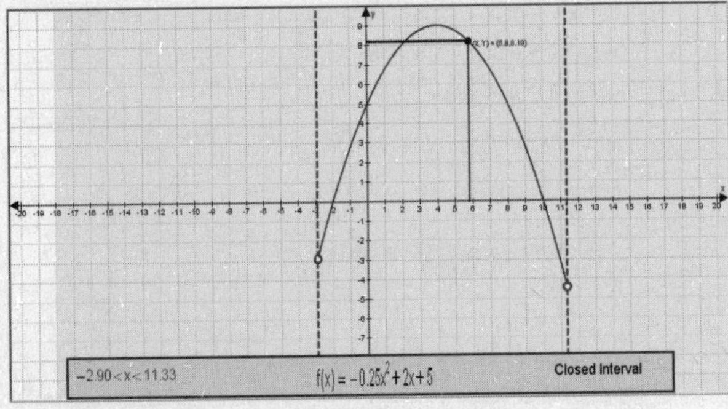

Are the endpoints of the interval included? What are the range values over the domain interval?

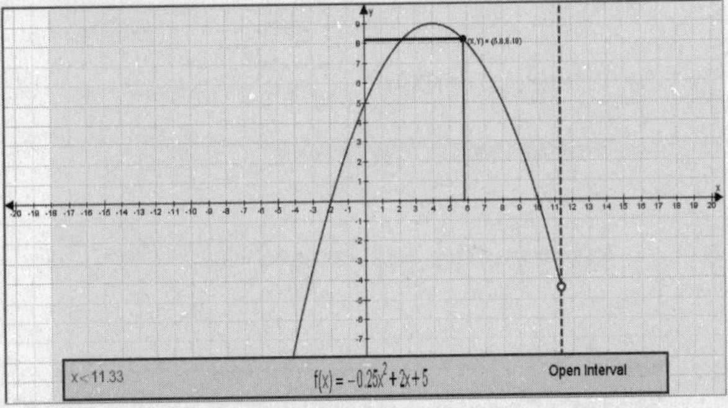

How would you write the domain using interval notation? What's the maximum function value over the interval? Is there a minimum function value?

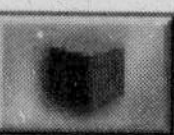

Graphs of functions or curves can be described in several ways. We have already seen that lines can be rising (if the slope is positive) or falling (if the slope is negative). Curves described over intervals can be describes by their concavity. Curves can be concave up (think—can it hold water?) or concave down. Functions change *concavity* at an *inflection point*. An inflection point is located at a *critical value*. If a graph is concave up over an interval it has a local *minimum value*; if it is concave down over an interval it has a *local maximum* value.

Properties of Functions

1. Is the curve increasing or decreasing over a defined interval?
2. Is the curve concave up or concave down?
3. What are the x-intercepts (roots)?
4. Does it have one or more inflection points?
5. Does it have a local maximum or minimum over an interval?

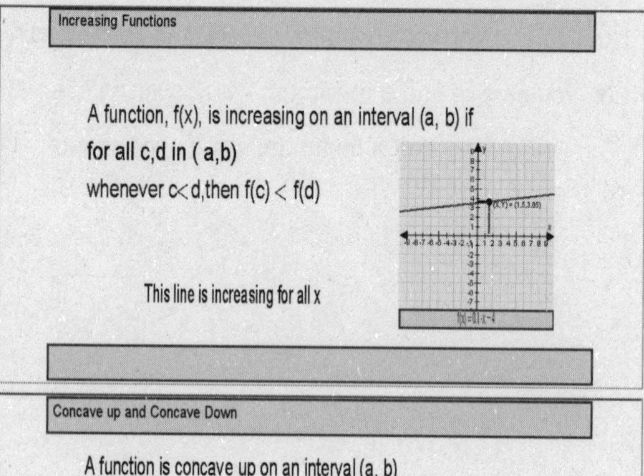

Increasing Functions
A function, f(x), is increasing on an interval (a, b) if
for all c,d in (a,b)
whenever c<d,then f(c) < f(d)
This line is increasing for all x

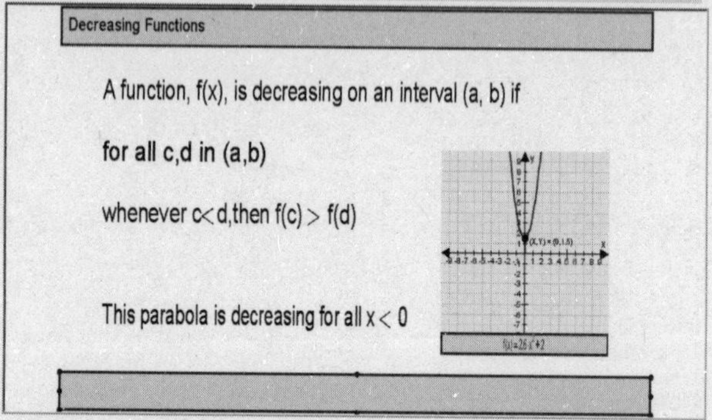

Decreasing Functions
A function, f(x), is decreasing on an interval (a, b) if
for all c,d in (a,b)
whenever c<d,then f(c) > f(d)
This parabola is decreasing for all x < 0

Test both sides of the vertex. Since 2<3 and f(2)<f(3) the graph is rising for all x>0.

Hint: Travel along the interval left to right, from the smallest x value to the largest x value.

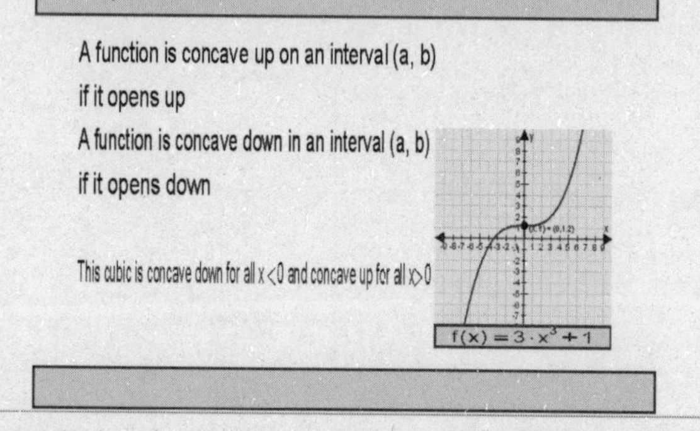

Concave up and Concave Down
A function is concave up on an interval (a, b)
if it opens up
A function is concave down in an interval (a, b)
if it opens down
This cubic is concave down for all x<0 and concave up for all x>0
f(x) = 3·x³ + 1

Concavity is a description of the shape. Note where concavity changes. The point indicated on the graph is very close to the inflection point of (1, 0). That is where the function values change from positive to negative; the graph changes from rising to falling, the concavity changes from up to down.

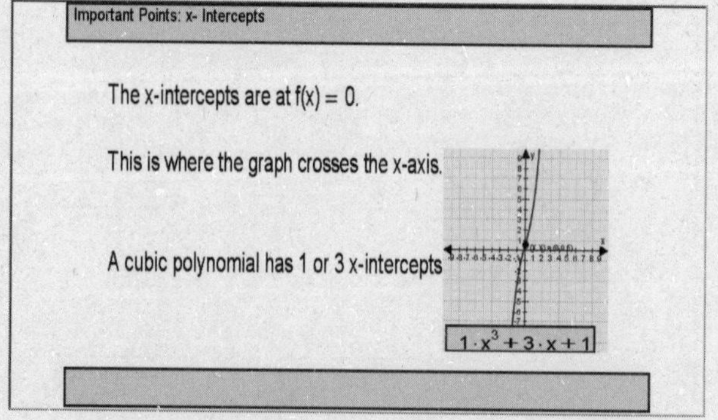

Important Points: x- Intercepts
The x-intercepts are at f(x) = 0.
This is where the graph crosses the x-axis.
A cubic polynomial has 1 or 3 x-intercepts
1·x³ + 3·x + 1

Find x-intercepts by setting the equation equal to zero and solving for **x**, if possible.

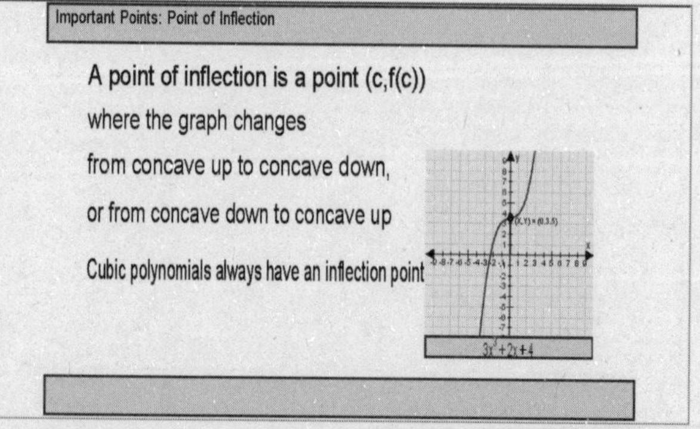

Important Points: Point of Inflection
A point of inflection is a point (c,f(c))
where the graph changes
from concave up to concave down,
or from concave down to concave up
Cubic polynomials always have an inflection point

A critical point is an inflection point where a graph changes concavity. In the above graph the critical point is (0,4). Note the change in function values as well as concavity.

Curves can be described by the way they look. Parts of curves can be described or examined over defined intervals.

If a function is concave up or down are the functional values increasing or decreasing over an interval? Are the functional values increasing or decreasing? Does it have an inflection point? Can you find a local maximum or minimum value over an interval?

Are the function values positive or negative over an interval?

Is the graph rising or falling?

Is there an inflection point?

Does knowing the classic shape of a graph help decide if critical points are in an interval?

How can you identify if a graph has a local maximum or minimum over an interval?

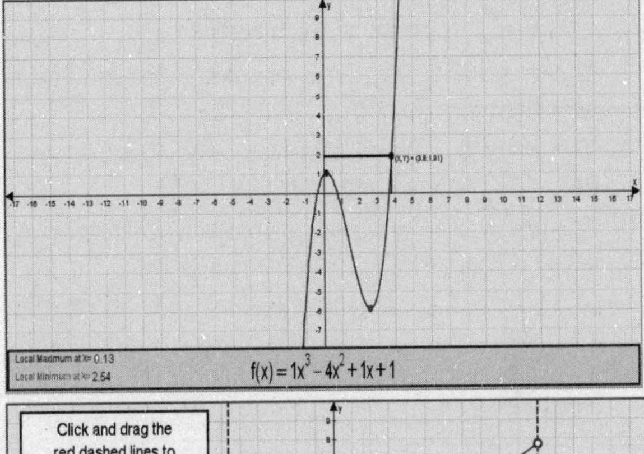

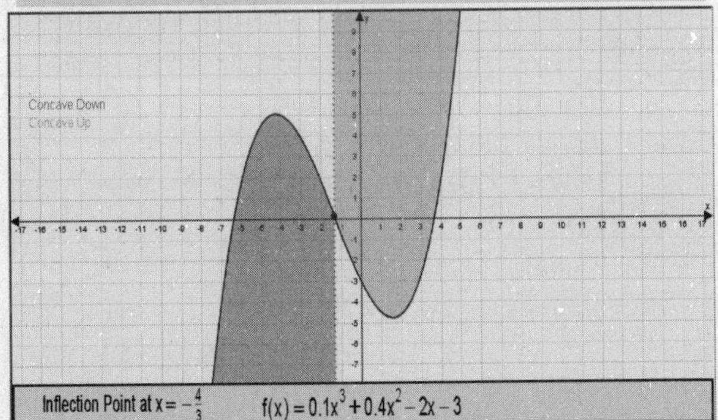

Is the inflection point a root of the function? Is it always a root of an equation? Change **a**, **b**, and **c** to see.

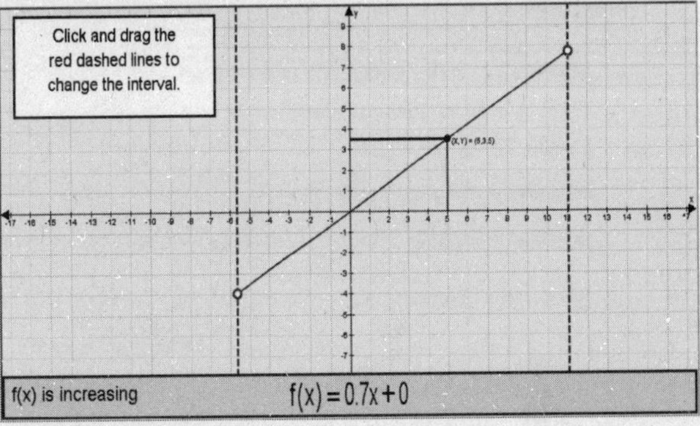

Does the line described above have a local maximum over the given interval?

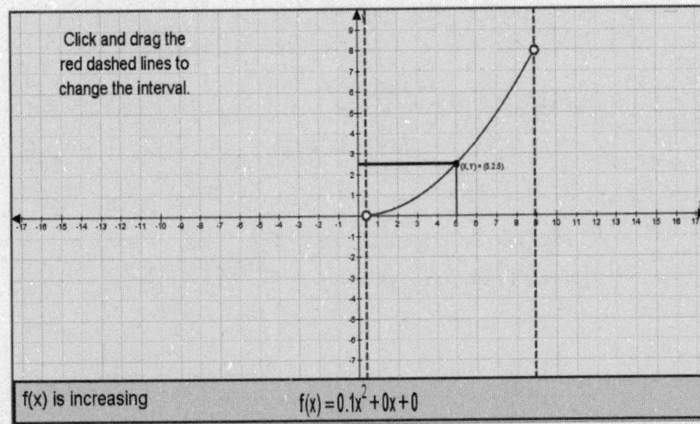

Are all increasing functions concave up?

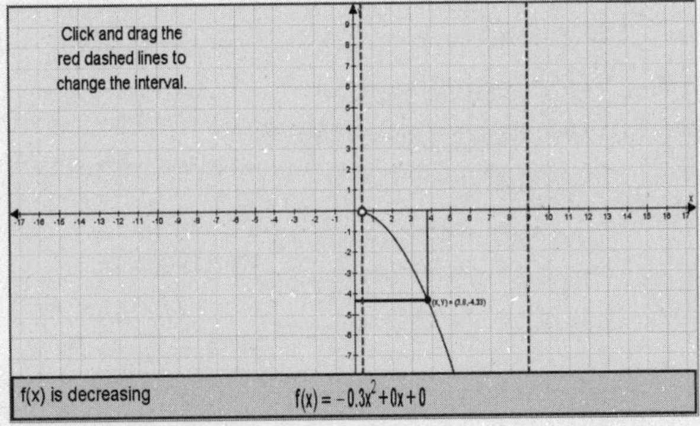

Is there a local minimum value for the function over the given interval? What does the local minimum value approach?

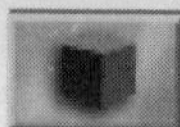

Symmetry

EnableMath

An intuitive definition for symmetry was given at the beginning of 16.2. We can now give an algebraic definition. We will consider functions that are symmetric about either a line x = a, y=x, the y-axis, and the origin. Below is a chart with tests of symmetry for the three cases. You can think of symmetry as folding along an axis or spinning at a point. The points matching up along the graph are called *reflections* of each other.

Tests of Symmetry

1. The graph of a function is symmetric about a line x=a if f(a-x) = f(a+x).
2. The graph of a function is symmetric about the y-axis if f(x) = f(−x). (an even function)
3. The graph of a function is symmetric about the origin if f(−x) = −f(x). (an odd function)

Note: The graph of a *relation* is symmetric about the x-axis if each point (x, y) and (x, -y) are on the graph.

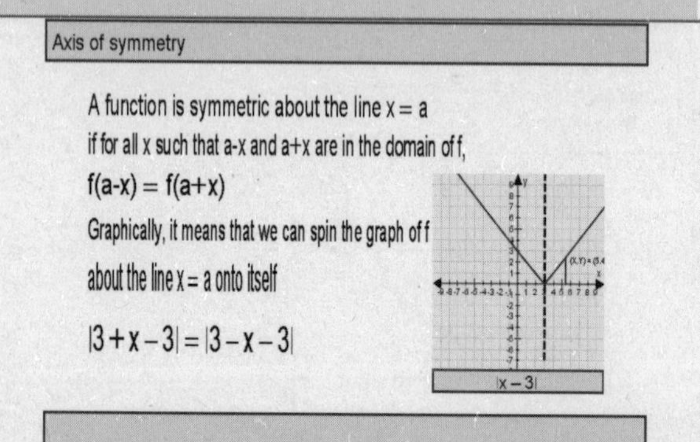

Axis of symmetry
A function is symmetric about the line x = a
if for all x such that a-x and a+x are in the domain of f,
f(a-x) = f(a+x)
Graphically, it means that we can spin the graph of f
about the line x = a onto itself
|3 + x − 3| = |3 − x − 3|
|x − 3|

Each point to the right of the line **x=3** are reflections of points to the left of the line (and vice versa). Notice that a point and its reflection point form a line perpendicular to the axis of symmetry.

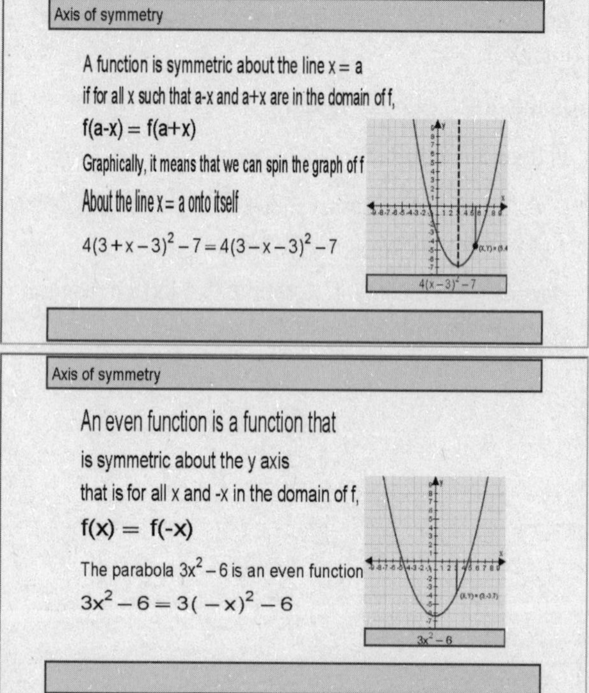

Axis of symmetry
A function is symmetric about the line x = a
if for all x such that a-x and a+x are in the domain of f,
f(a-x) = f(a+x)
Graphically, it means that we can spin the graph of f
About the line x = a onto itself
4(3 + x − 3)² − 7 = 4(3 − x − 3)² − 7
4(x − 3)² − 7
Axis of symmetry
An even function is a function that
is symmetric about the y axis
that is for all x and -x in the domain of f,
f(x) = f(-x)
The parabola 3x² − 6 is an even function
3x² − 6 = 3(− x)² − 6
3x² − 6

Substitute −x for **x** and compare. Notice that $3(-x)^2 - 6$ simplifies to $3x^2 - 6$.

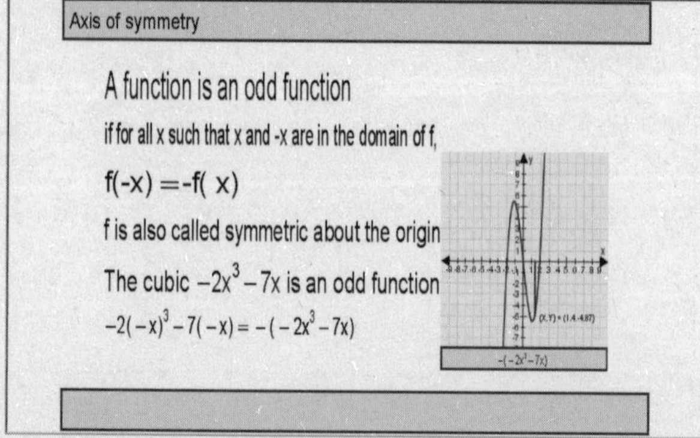

Axis of symmetry
A function is an odd function
if for all x such that x and -x are in the domain of f,
f(-x) = -f(x)
f is also called symmetric about the origin
The cubic −2x³ − 7x is an odd function
−2(− x)³ − 7(− x) = − (− 2x³ − 7x)
−(− 2x³ − 7x)

Substitute −x for x and compare to −f(x). Each side of the equation simplifies to $2x^3+7x$.

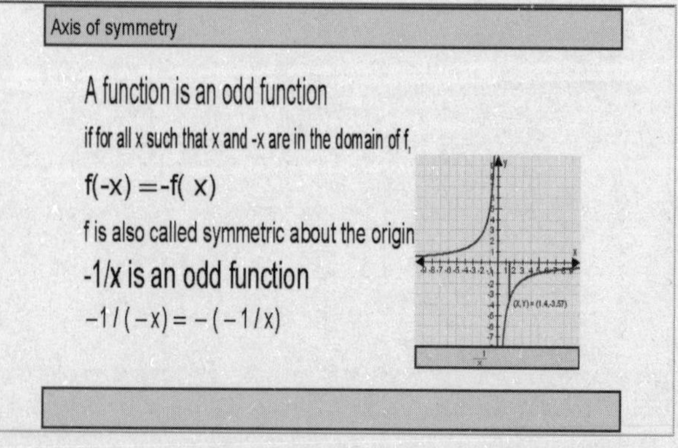

Axis of symmetry
A function is an odd function
if for all x such that x and -x are in the domain of f,
f(-x) = -f(x)
f is also called symmetric about the origin
-1/x is an odd function
−1 / (− x) = − (− 1 / x)

Of course we eliminate values for **x** that make the function undefined. The domain of the above function is {x|x!=0}. For all other values of **x**, the test holds.

If you know a graph is symmetric along an axis or at a point, you can either fold it or rotate it to match up points with their reflections along the graph.

Use the visualizations to look for patterns. What is the degree of each odd function? What is the degree of each even function?

What determines whether a function is even or odd?

Can any function be called even or odd?

What are the identifying traits of an even function?

What are the identifying traits of an odd function?

If you know one point on a symmetric function graph, how do you find its reflection point?

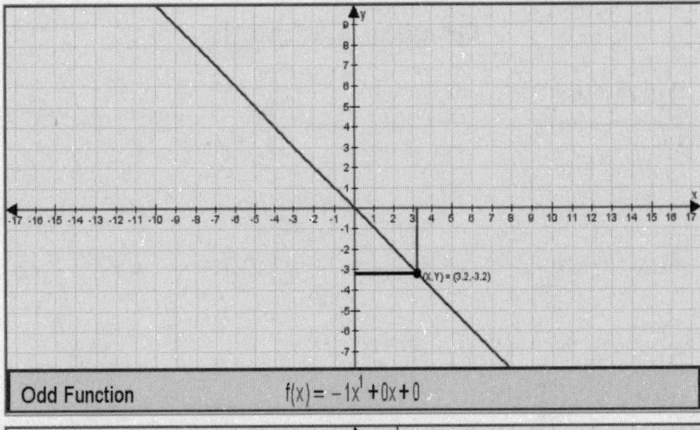

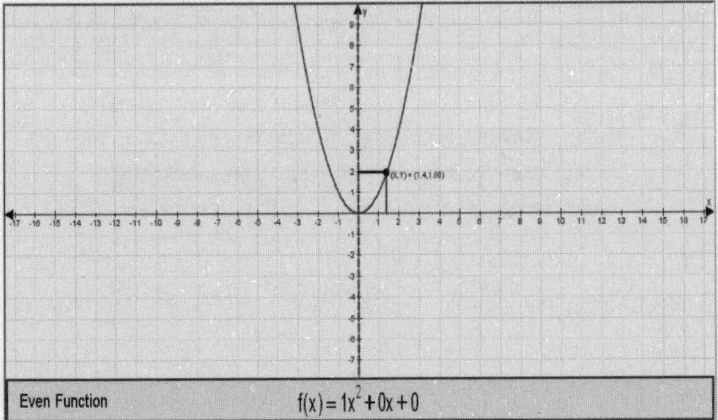

What point is the reflection of the given point? What is the minimum value of the function?

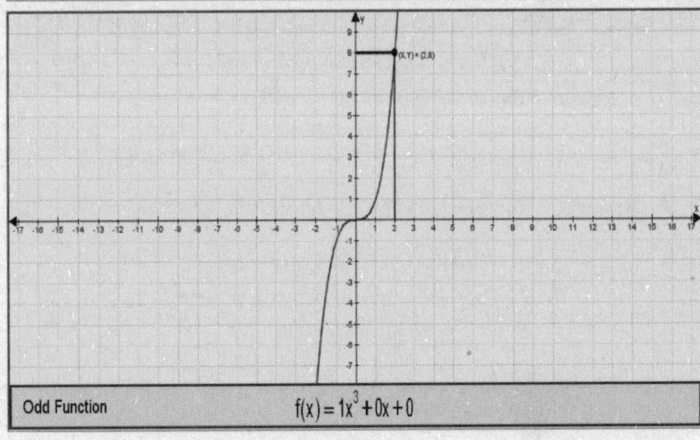

If you "spin" the graph what point reflects the given point of (2, 8)? How many real roots does the function have?

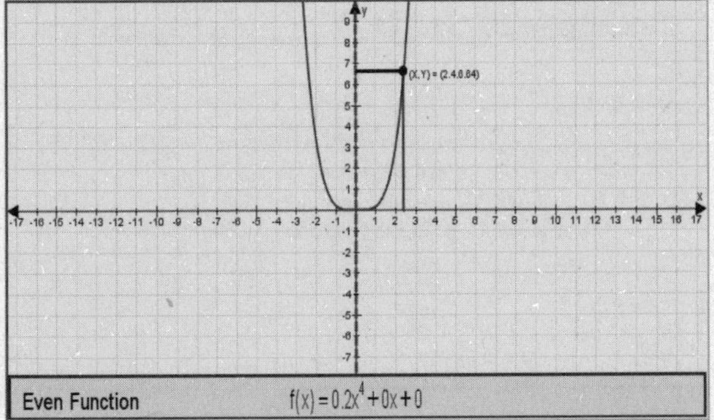

Can you determine if a function is even or odd by the degree of the function?

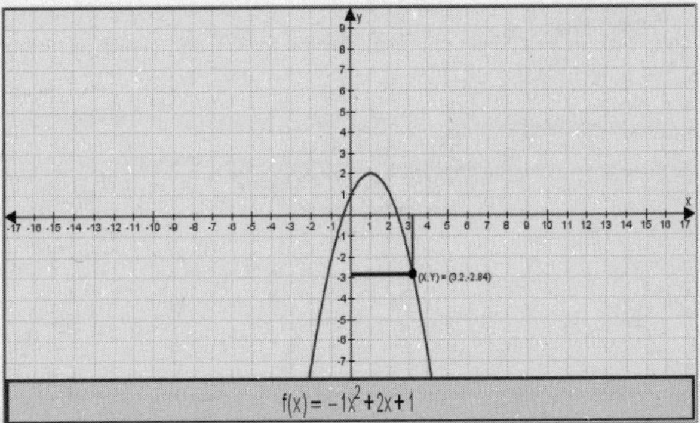

Is a parabola an even function? How do you know?

To add, subtract, and multiply (and, as addressed in the next section, divide) functions we use functional notation as a concise way to write complicated combinations of algebraic equations. If two functions, f and g, are defined by their function rules and the domain is given, then function arithmetic expressed as f(x) + g(x) can be shortened to (f+g)(x), or simply to f + g.

The domain of the function defined by each operation, f + g, f – g, and f*g, is the **intersection** of the domains of f and g.

Note: **Points 3** and **4** of the online examples provide a review of the intersection of sets.

Function Arithmetic

Operation			
Addition	f + g	(f+g)(x)	f(x) + g(x)
Subtraction	f – g	(f–g)(x)	f(x) – g(x)
Multiplication	f · g	(f·g)(x)	f(x) · g(x)

D = {x|x∈f and x∈g}

If $f(x)=x^2-2x+5$ and $g(x)=x^2+3x-7$,
you can easily find (f+g)(x), (f-g)(x) and (f*g)(x) by manipulation:

$$(f+g)(x)=(x^2-2x+5)+(x^2+3x-7)=2x^2+x-2$$

If $f(x)=x^2-2x+5$ and $g(x)=x^2+3x-7$,
you can easily find (f+g)(x), (f-g)(x) and (f*g)(x) by manipulation:

$$(f+g)(x)=(x^2-2x+5)+(x^2+3x-7)=2x^2+x-2$$

$$(f-g)(x)=(x^2-2x+5)-(x^2+3x-7)=x^2-2x+5-x^2-3x+7=-5x+12$$

$$(f\cdot g)(x)=(x^2-2x+5)(x^2+3x-7)$$
$$=x^4+3x^3-7x^2-2x^3-6x^2+14x+5x^2+15x-35$$
$$=x^4+x^3-8x^2+19x-35$$

Try it out: Does f(2) + g(2) = (f+g)(2)? Yes, because, by substitution:

f(2) = 5 and g(2)=3 and (f+g)(2) = 8.

The domains of f+g, f-g and f*g consist of all of the real numbers formed by the intersection of the domains of f and g.

Since the domains of f and g are all Real Numbers, the domains of f+g, f–g and f*g are the Reals as well.

Find the domains of f+g, f-g and f*g:

$f(x)=\sqrt{x-2}$ and $g(x)=\frac{1}{x+1}$
The domain of f(x) is $x\geq 2$.
The domain of g(x) is $x\neq -1$.

In order for f to be defined over the Real Numbers the radical expression must be greater than zero. To find the lower bound, set x-2 = 0. For g, **x** can be anything except –1. Why?

Find the domains of f+g, f-g and f*g:

$f(x)=\sqrt{x-2}$ and $g(x)=\frac{1}{x+1}$
The domain of f(x) is $x\geq 2$.
The domain of g(x) is $x\neq -1$.
The domains of f+g, f-g and f*g are all $x\geq 2$ (the intersection).

The restriction for **g** is outside the bounds of **f**. In symbols the domain of f+g is $[2,\infty)$.

Addition, subtraction, and multiplication of functions can be illustrated by looking at the graphs of each independent function and their corresponding sum, difference, or product. They often do things that we do not expect.

In order to be able to see how the graphs change, it is necessary to look at simple case, a parabola is combined with a straight line by either +, –, or *. You can change the coefficients, but cannot alter the number of terms in the functions. Can you describe what happens when a quadratic function is added to a linear function? How does changing the coefficients and constants move the graph?

As **b** increases, how does the parabola move? How does changing **b** change the results?

How does changing **a** effect the results? Which operation changes the graph the most?

What happens when **m** is negative? What happens when **a** is negative?

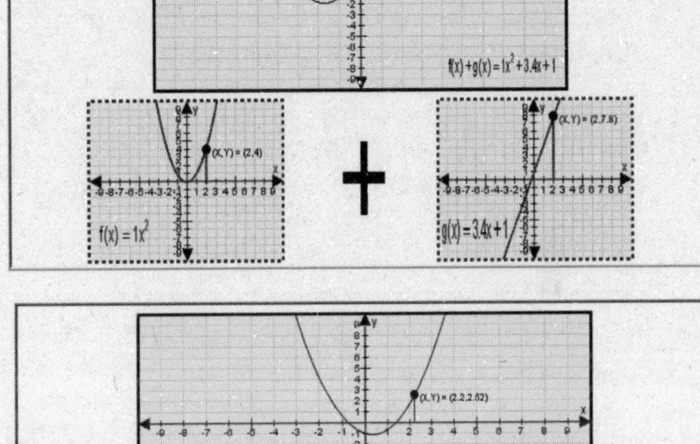

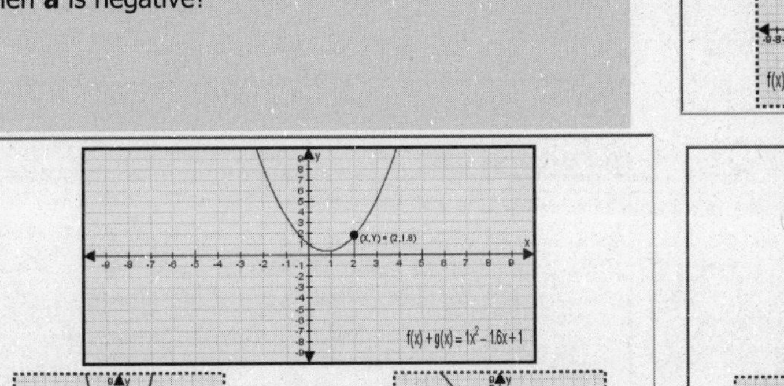

What happens when a linear function is added to a quadratic function? What does changing **m** do? What does changing **b** do? What does changing **a** do?

How is subtraction of two functions different from addition. What do you expect to happen when you subtract a linear function from a quadratic function?

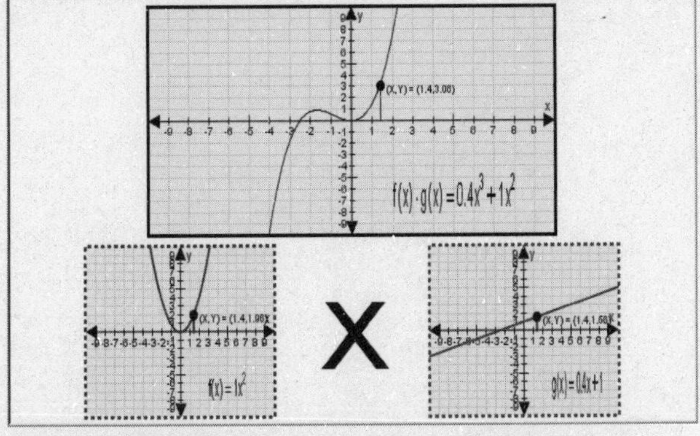

Does it make sense that multiplying a linear function times a quadratic function yields a cubic function? What affect does changing **m**, **b**, and **a** have on a cubic function?

Division of functions results in algebraic fractions—thus rational functions. Rational functions graph as hyperbola. Of particular interest in division of functions is determining the domain. For f+g, f-g, and f*g the domain was the intersection of the domains of f and g. There is an additional restriction in division: the denominator cannot equal zero. In order to find the domain of f/g, find the intersection of the domains of f and g and then find any values that make the denominator equal to zero. Eliminate those values from the domain.

Division of Functions

Define the Domain: find the domains of f and g and any values for x that make the denominator equal zero. Eliminate the excluded values from the intersection of domains of f and g.

f/g: Find f(x)/g(x) and write in simplest form by factoring numerator and denominator to reduce.

If $f(x)=x^2+2x-3$ and $g(x)=x^2-3x+2$,
you can easily find (f/g)(x) by manipulation:

$$(f/g)(x)=\frac{x^2+2x-3}{x^2-3x+2}$$
$$=\frac{(x+3)(x-1)}{(x-2)(x-1)}=\frac{x+3}{x-2}$$

The domain of f/g consists of all of the real numbers formed by the intersection of the domains of f and g except for those real numbers x such that $g(x)=0$.

Find the domain of each function. Find the intersection; then restricted values that make the denominator (g(x)) undefined.

Find the domain of f/g:

$f(x)=x^2+2x-3$ and $g(x)=x^2-3x+2$,
The domains of f and g are all real numbers.
$g(x)=0$ at $x=1$ and $x=2$. (Look at the factors!)

Factor x^2-3x+2 to $(x-1)(x-2)$. Clearly, $x \neq 1$ and $x \neq 2$. Eliminate those values from the intersection of the domains of f and g.

Find the domain of f/g:

$f(x)=x^2+2x-3$ and $g(x)=x^2-3x+2$,
The domains of f and g are all real numbers.
$g(x)=0$ at $x=1$ and $x=2$. (Look at the factors!)
So, the domain of f/g is $x<1 \cup 1<x<2 \cup x>2$.

Using set notation: $\{x|x\neq 1 \text{ and } x\neq 2;\ x\in \text{Reals}\}$

Division brings additional restrictions to the domain of **f** and **g**. We must make sure not to use any values that make the denominator equal to zero. The domain of f/g is the set of all numbers in the intersection of the domains of **f** and **g** AND excludes any value that makes g(x)=0.

In each of the visualizations, the denominator, g, is a linear function. The numerator is a quadratic. Pay careful attention to how **a**, **m**, and **b** affect the graph. Remember restrictions on the domain include the point where the linear function equals zero.

What effect do **b** and **m** have on the graph of f/g? What happens when **b=0**?

Can **m=0**? Can **m=0** AND **b=0**?

What happens when **a** is negative? Where does the graph of f/g reside when a is negative?

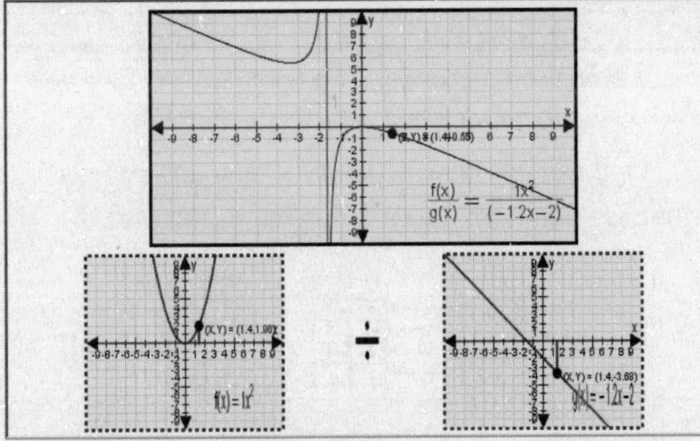

What value for **x** is restricted from the domain? What is the equation for the asymptote?

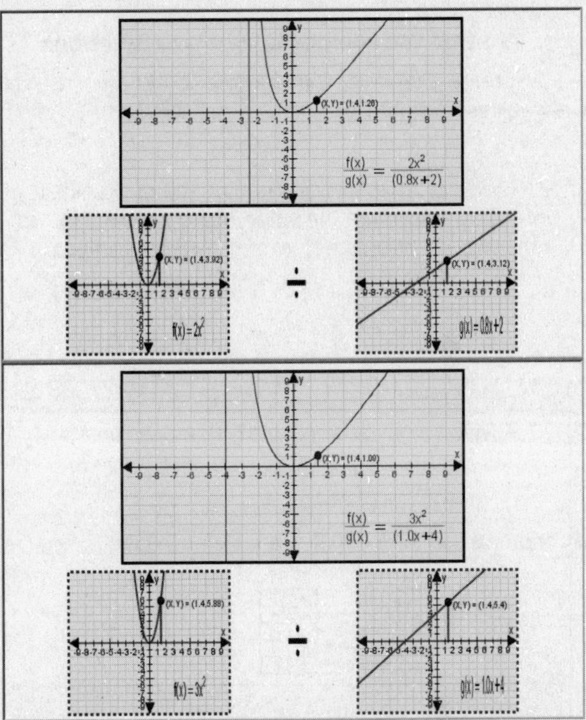

Are there any restrictions to the domain in the above function? Do you expect that there is a portion of the graph that is beyond **x=-10**? What change can bring the portion back into view?

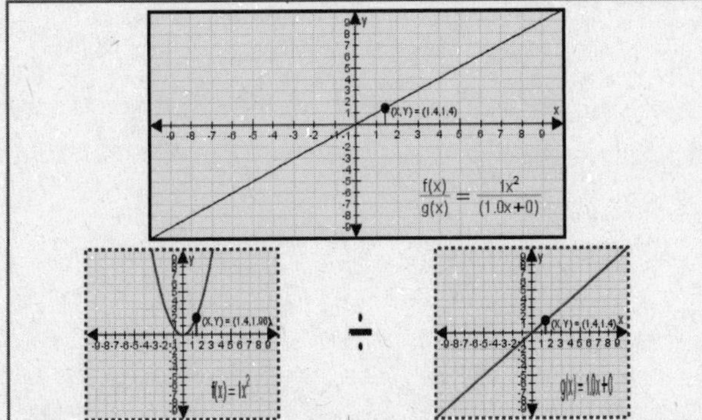

Begin with the simplest case and build from there. What happens as **b** increases? What happens as **m** increases? What happens as **a** increases.

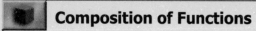

Functions can be combined, as you have seen, by the operations of addition, subtraction, multiplication and division. Another way to combine two functions is called **composition**. We define composition of functions, f°g, to be f(g(x)) - that is find g(x) and then use that value as an input value for f (x). Composition of functions, f°g, is read "f composite with g" or "f of g". The domain for f°g consists of the domain of g whose g(x) values are in the domain of f.

To find the composition of two functions

1. Create a table for transforming **x** into g(x). Select x values, evaluate g(x), and record values.

2. Create a table for transforming the g(x) values into f(x). Substitute the values for g(x) into f(x). In other words, calculate f(x=g(x)). Record values.

Given two functions f(x) and g(x), we can take a composition of g by f, which is written f(g(x)) or $f \circ g$. For example, if $f(x)=3x-1$ and $g(x)=x^2-2x$, then we can form f(g(x)) in a table as follows:

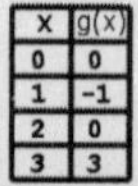

x	g(x)
0	0
1	-1
2	0
3	3

Given two functions f(x) and g(x), we can take a composition of g by f, which is written f(g(x)) or $f \circ g$. For example, if $f(x)=3x-1$ and $g(x)=x^2-2x$, then we can form f(g(x)) in a table as follows:

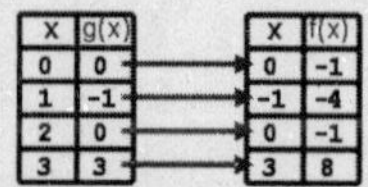

x	g(x)
0	0
1	-1
2	0
3	3

x	f(x)
0	-1
-1	-4
0	-1
3	8

The values for **g(x)** become the **x** values when finding **f(x)**.

Given two functions f(x) and g(x), we can take a composition of g by f, which is written f(g(x)) or $f \circ g$. For example, if $f(x)=3x-1$ and $g(x)=x^2-2x$, then we can form f(g(x)) in a table as follows:

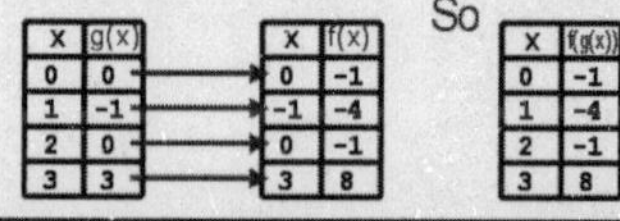

x	g(x)
0	0
1	-1
2	0
3	3

x	f(x)
0	-1
-1	-4
0	-1
3	8

So

x	f(g(x))
0	-1
1	-4
2	-1
3	8

Make a table relating **x** and **f(g(x))**, the composite function.

Algebraically, for the example $f(x)=3x-1$ and $g(x)=x^2-2x$,

then $f(g(x)) = f(x^2-2x) = 3(x^2-2x)-1 = 3x^2-6x-1$.

Also, $g(f(x)) = g(3x-1) = (3x-1)^2 - 2(3x-1)$

$= 9x^2-6x+1-6x+2 = 9x^2-12x+3$.

$f(g(x)) \neq g(f(x))$ usually!!!

Point 2: We can also solve this algebraically by using substitution.

A composite function is a function of a function. This is the first time that we do something with functions that we did not even imagine doing with equations. Composition of functions is one of the reasons that make the idea of functions and functional notation so powerful. Here we investigate this new process. It is a new operation that we have not had before!

Does a function of a function necessarily produce a more complicated function?

View 1 shows the composition of functions graphically.

View 2 shows it with tables

Switch between these two views with your joystick to gain a greater understanding of this new process.

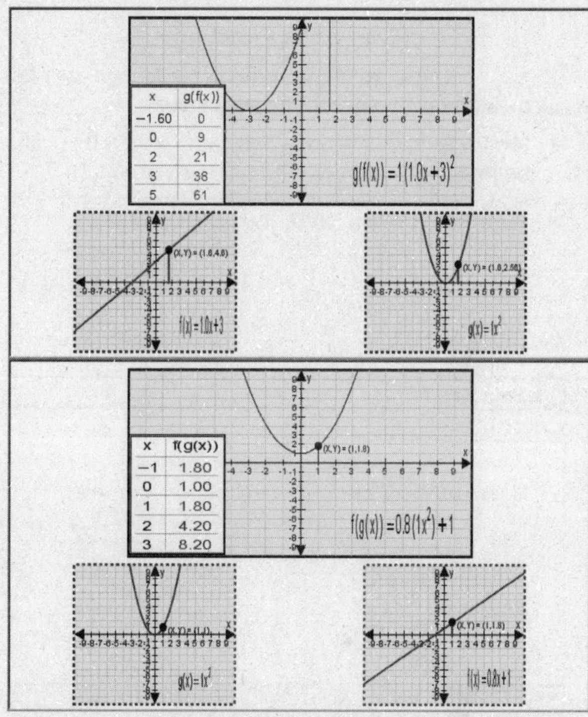

x	g(f(x))
−1.60	0
0	9
2	21
3	38
5	61

x	f(g(x))
−1	1.80
0	1.00
1	1.80
2	4.20
3	8.20

Change each of the coefficients **b** and **m**. How does each of these change the composite function?

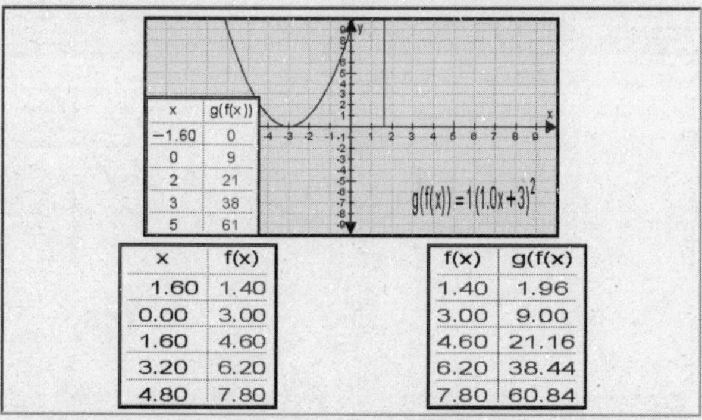

x	g(f(x))
−1.60	0
0	9
2	21
3	38
5	61

x	f(x)
1.60	1.40
0.00	3.00
1.60	4.60
3.20	6.20
4.80	7.80

f(x)	g(f(x))
1.40	1.96
3.00	9.00
4.60	21.16
6.20	38.44
7.80	60.84

To graph the composition of two functions you can create tables of values and transform individual points.

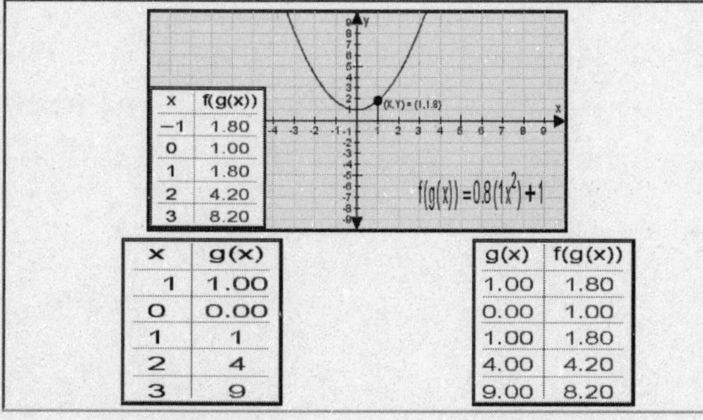

x	f(g(x))
−1	1.80
0	1.00
1	1.80
2	4.20
3	8.20

x	g(x)
1	1.00
0	0.00
1	1
2	4
3	9

g(x)	f(g(x))
1.00	1.80
0.00	1.00
1.00	1.80
4.00	4.20
9.00	8.20

Change **x** to watch the values in each of these tables change.

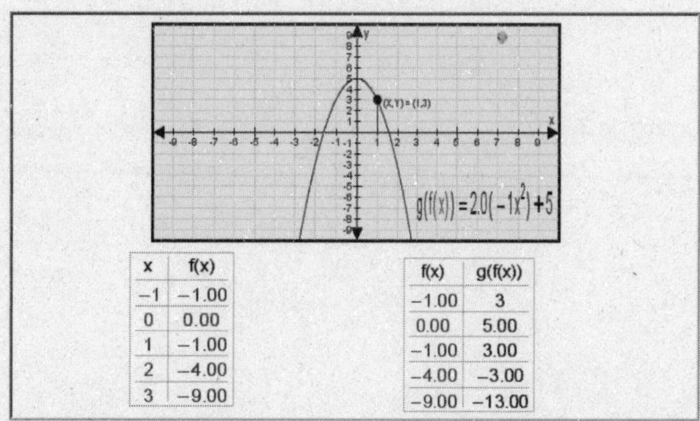

x	f(x)
−1	−1.00
0	0.00
1	−1.00
2	−4.00
3	−9.00

f(x)	g(f(x))
−1.00	3
0.00	5.00
−1.00	3.00
−4.00	−3.00
−9.00	−13.00

Change the coefficients **a**. How does each of these change the composite function?

Is it one-to-one?

Some functions have an **inverse**. The graph of the inverse is a *reflection* of the graph of the function along the line y=x . The equation of the inverse function can be found algebraically—we will do that in the next section. In order for a function to have an inverse it must be in the category of functions called **one-to-one**. A function is one-to-one if every input value matches up to a different output value. That means no two input values can match up to the same output value. Every output value matches up to exactly one input value. Graphically it means that the function must pass the **horizontal line test** as well as the vertical line test.

One-to-one Functions

1. Must pass the vertical line test: No **x** value can be matched with more than one **y** value.
2. Must pass the horizontal line test: No **y** value can be matched with more than one **x** value.
3. Have an inverse.

In order for a function to have an inverse, it must be one – to – one. A one – to – one function passes both the vertical line test and the horizontal line test.

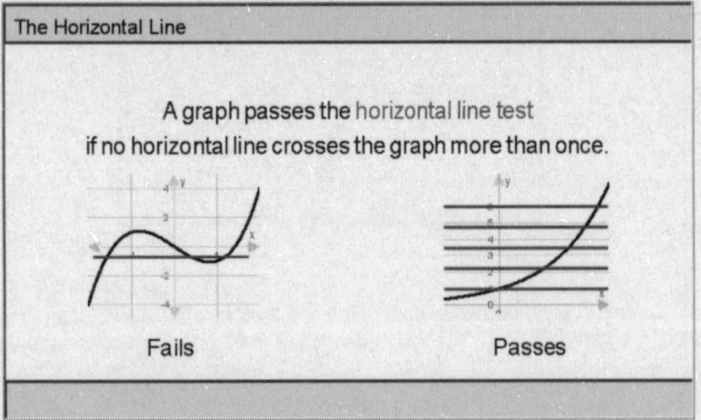

The Horizontal Line
A graph passes the horizontal line test
if no horizontal line crosses the graph more than once.
Fails
Passes

The first graph has three different **x** values for the same **y** value. Is it still a function?

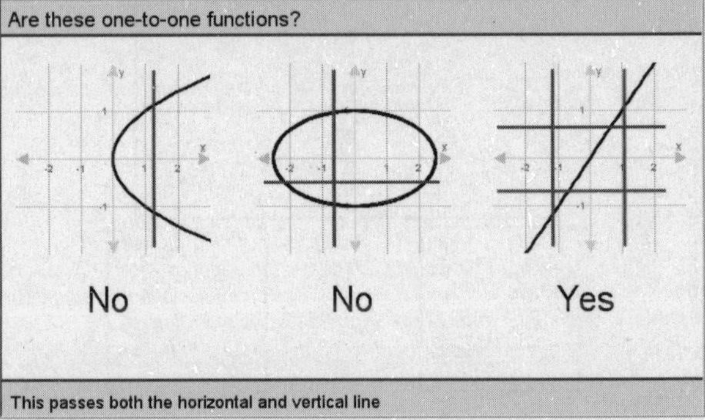

Think about the horizontal line as moving up and down along the y axis. It "cuts" the graph in at most one place on the third graph.

In order for a relation to be a function, no **x** value can map to more than one **y** value. A function is **one-to-one** if no **y** value has more than one **x** value mapped to it. Think about a reflection: every **x** and **y** value can be interchanged and you still have a function. Visually it means that the function can pass the horizontal line test: As a horizontal line passes through all **y** values it must cut the graph in at most one place for each **y** value.

Control the horizontal line (red) with **y** and the vertical (gold) line with **x**.

Can an even function ever be one-to-one?

What makes some cubic functions one-to-one and some not?

If you define the domain and range over an interval can an even function be one-to-one?

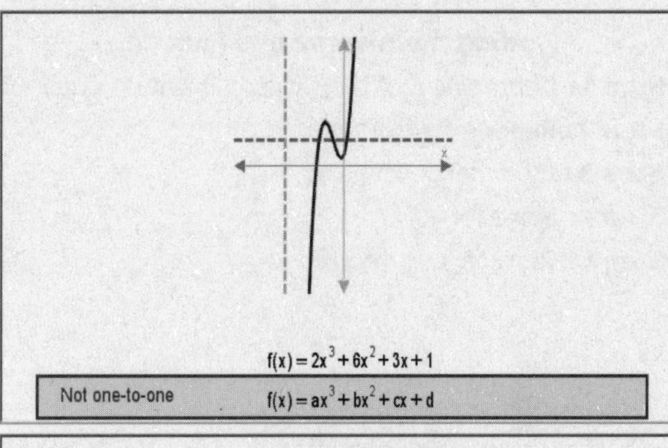

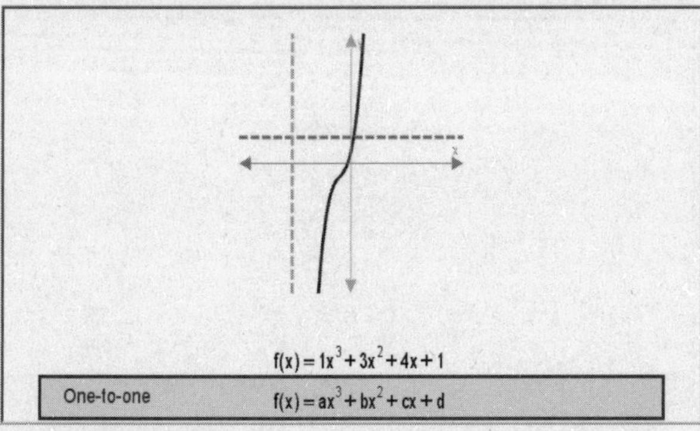

Is the above function still a cubic function? How many Real roots does it have?

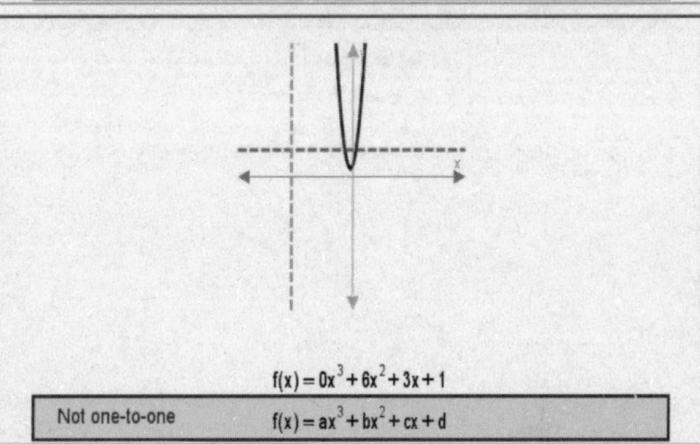

Is the above function an even function?

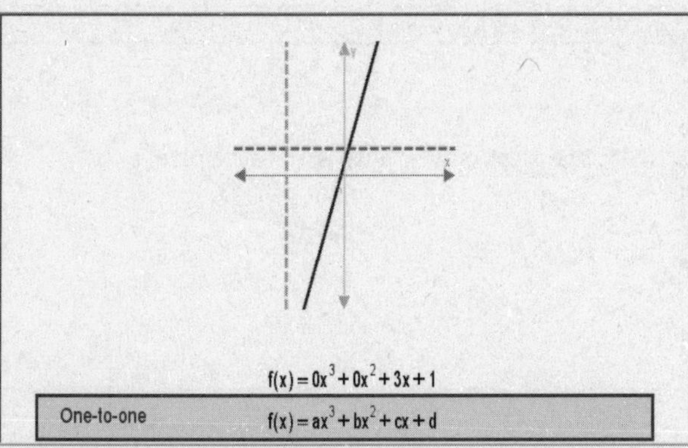

Are all lines one-to-one?

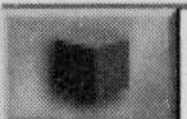

Finding the Inverse of a Function

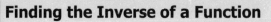

If a function is one-to-one it has an **inverse** where the x and y values are interchanged. The domain values become the range values and vice-versa. A function and its inverse are mirror images of each other; the graph of the inverse is reflected about the line y=x. The equation of the inverse can be found from the equation of the function by following the process described below. The inverse of f(x) is called "f inverse" and is written as $f^{-1}(x)$.

Finding the Inverse of a Function

Step 1: Determine that the function is one-to-one.

Step 2: Replace f(x) with y.

Step 3: Interchange x and y.

Step 4: Solve for y.

Step 5: Replace y with $f^{-1}(x)$.

Find the inverse function of:

$$f(x) = 2x + 1$$
$$y = 2x + 1$$
$$x = 2y + 1$$
$$x - 1 = 2y$$
$$\tfrac{1}{2}(x - 1) = y$$
$$\tfrac{x}{2} - \tfrac{1}{2} = y$$
$$\text{So, } f^{-1}(x) = \tfrac{x}{2} - \tfrac{1}{2}.$$

Graph the function and its inverse:

$$f(x) = 2x + 1$$
$$f^{-1}(x) = \tfrac{x}{2} - \tfrac{1}{2}$$

The graph of the inverse is a reflection over $y = x$.

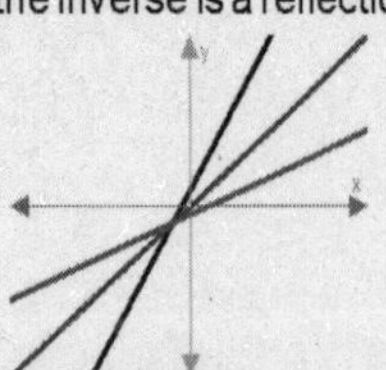

Here the axis of symmetry is the line y=x, which appears on screen in red (middle line here).

Find the inverse function of:

$$f(x) = \sqrt{x+2} + 3$$
$$y = \sqrt{x+2} + 3$$
$$x = \sqrt{y+2} + 3$$
$$x - 3 = \sqrt{y+2}$$
$$(x-3)^2 = y + 2$$
$$(x-3)^2 - 2 = y$$
$$\text{So, } f^{-1}(x) = (x-3)^2 - 2.$$

Note: The domain of the function is D: $x \geq -2$ and the range is R: $y \geq 3$. For the inverse, $f^{-1}(x)$, the domain becomes the range and the range becomes the domain.

Graph the function and its inverse:

$$f(x) = \sqrt{x+2} + 3$$
$$f^{-1}(x) = (x-3)^2 - 2$$

The graph of the inverse is a reflection over $y = x$.

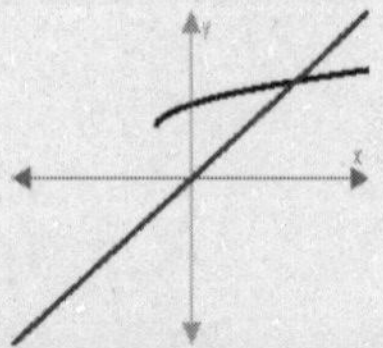

Graph the function (black on screen) and the axis of symmetry y=x (red on screen).

Graph the function and its inverse:

$$f(x) = \sqrt{x+2} + 3$$
$$f^{-1}(x) = (x-3)^2 - 2$$

The graph of the inverse is a reflection over $y = x$.

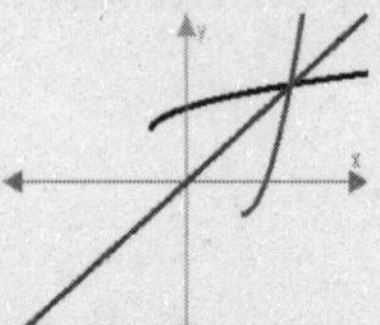

Next graph the inverse (purple on screen).

Finding the Inverse of a Function

A function and its inverse are reflections about the line y=x. Each x value is interchanged with its reflected y value. You can graph a function and its inverse from a table of values or from the equations.

Here are some simple functions and their inverses. One screen the function appears in blue and the inverse in red. The axis of symmetry is gray (point 1) or green (point 2).

What happens to the domain values when converting a function to its inverse? What happens to the range values?

As **x** changes, what happens to $f^{-1}(x)$?

If you draw a line from a point and its reflection, what relationship does that line have with the axis of symmetry?

How can you find the equation of a function if you know the equation of the inverse?

Will the inverse function always be one-to-one?

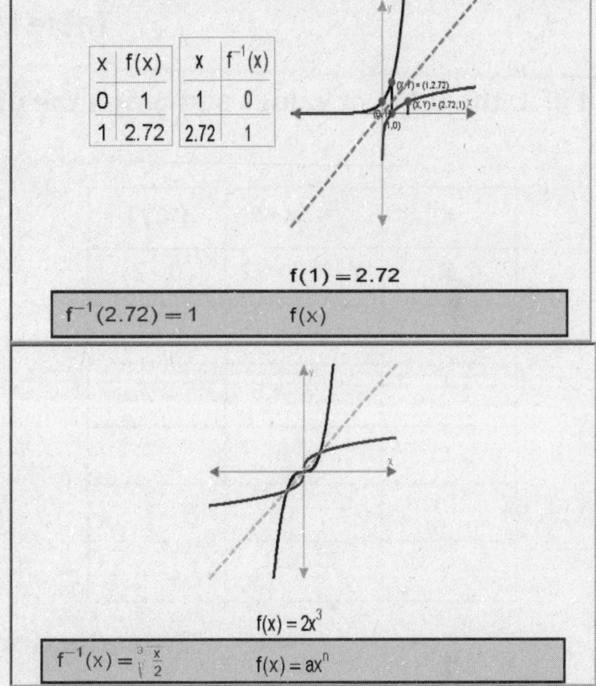

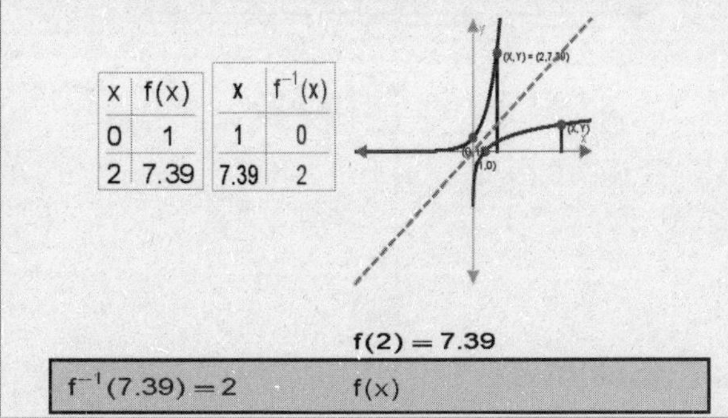

As **x** increases what happens to f(x)? What happens to the inverse, $f^{-1}(x)$? As **x** decreases what happens to f(x)? What happens to $f^{-1}(x)$?

Change **a** and **n** to see other functions and their inverses. What does **a** determine for the graphs? What does **n** determine? Which ranges are more restricted, those with even **n** or odd **n**?

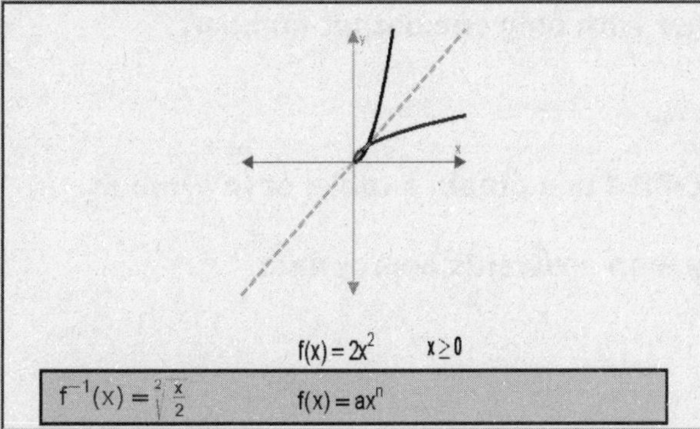

Why is the domain of f(x) restricted to x≥0? (Hint: is the graph of a parabola one-to-one?)

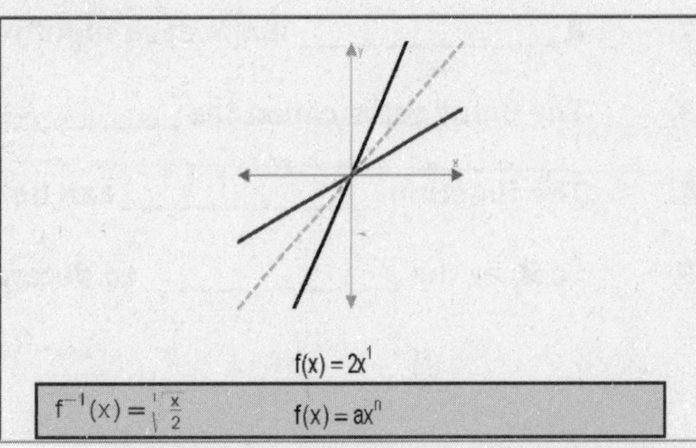

Are there restrictions on the domain or range for f(x) or $f^{-1}(x)$ in the above functions?

Ordered Pairs

Equation A is $x^2 + y^2 = 9$ and Equation B is $2x - y = 6$. Determine if the given ordered pair is a solution to A, B, both A and B, or neither A nor B.

1. (0, 3) ______________
2. (-3, 0) ______________
3. (0, 0) ______________
4. (3, 3) ______________
5. (3, 0) ______________
6. (5, 4) ______________

Table of Values

Fill in the table of values and graph the given equation.

x	y=3x-2	(x,y)
0	Y*0-2=-2	(0,-2)

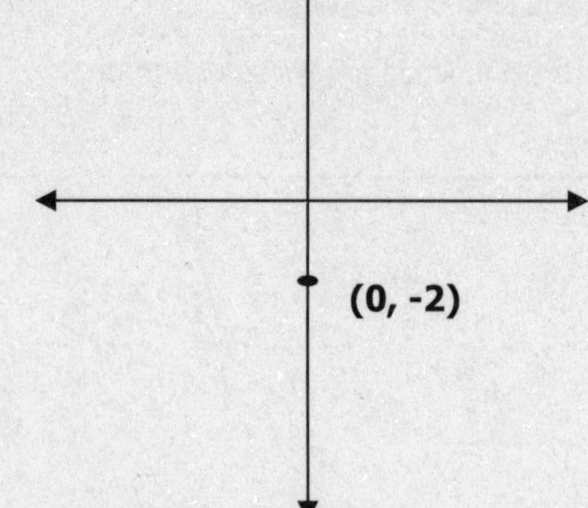

Introduction to Functions

Fill in the blank with the appropriate word to make a true statement. Use the words: domain, range, function, relation, input, output, rule, graph, table, symbols.

1. A ______________ is any correspondence between two sets of numbers.
2. A ______________ maps each input number with only one output number.
3. The input set is called the ______________.
4. The function ______________ can be described in a graph, a table, or in symbols.
5. Look at the ______________ to determine if an answer is appropriate.

Function Notation and Evaluation

Given the function: $f(x)=x^2 - 3x + 2$; find the following function values.

1. $f(2) =$ ________ **2.** $f(-1) =$ ________

3. $f(0) =$ ________ **4.** $f(t) =$ ________

5. $f(a + 1) =$ ________ **6.** $f(a + h) =$ ________

Is it a function of x?

Is it a function?

1.

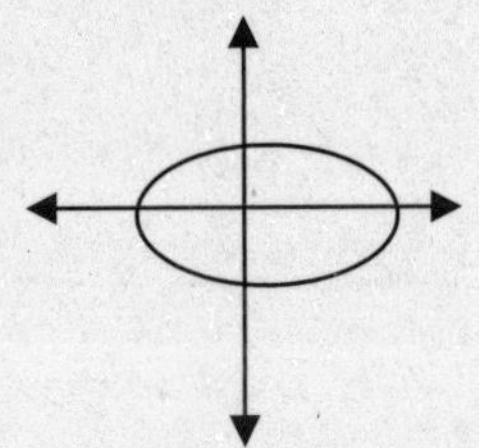

2.

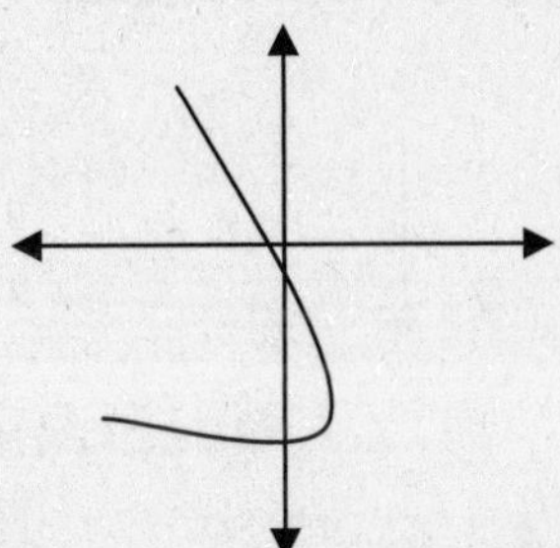

3.

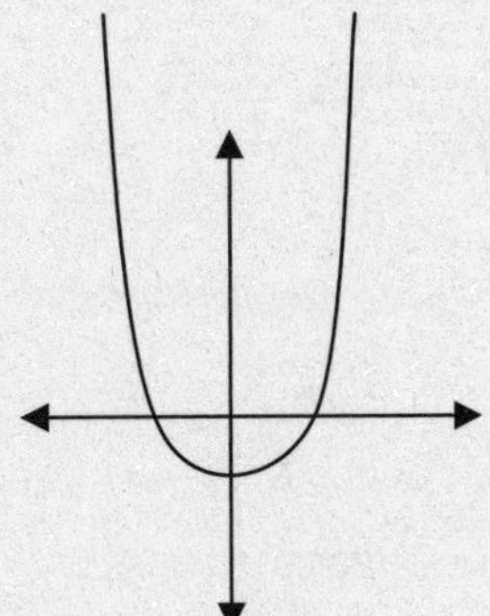

4.

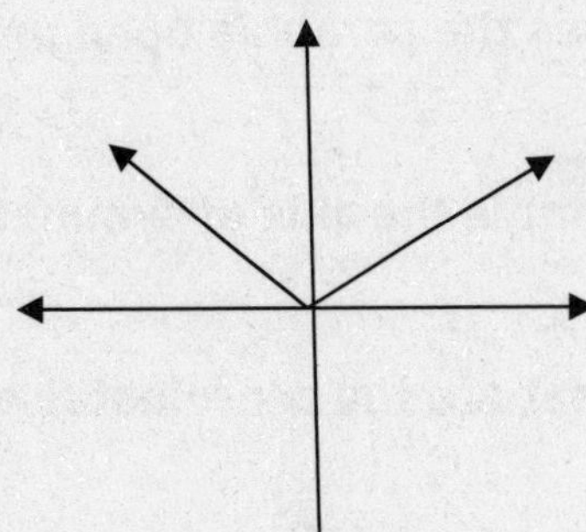

5.

x	f(x)
3	7
1	3
-1	-1
-3	-5

6.

x	f(x)
2	4
2	-4
0	0
1	1
1	-1

Linear Functions

1. Identify the slope and y-intercept of the line y = 2x –3.

m=__________ b=__________

2. Find the slope of the line connecting the two points (2,-3) and (-3, 4).

3. Graph: $f(x) = \frac{2}{3}x - 2$

4. Graph: $f(x) = \frac{-1}{2}x + 2$

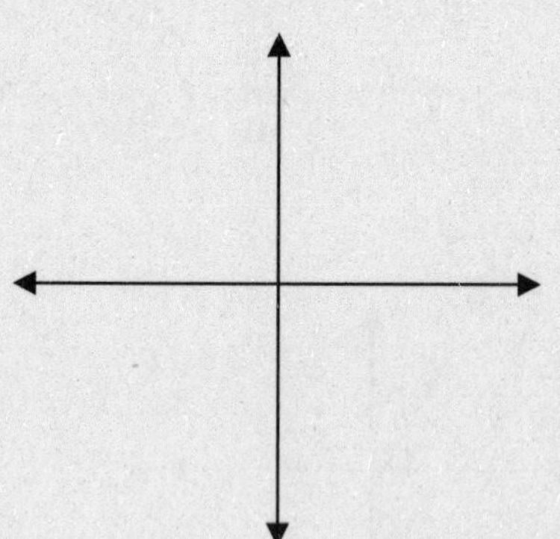

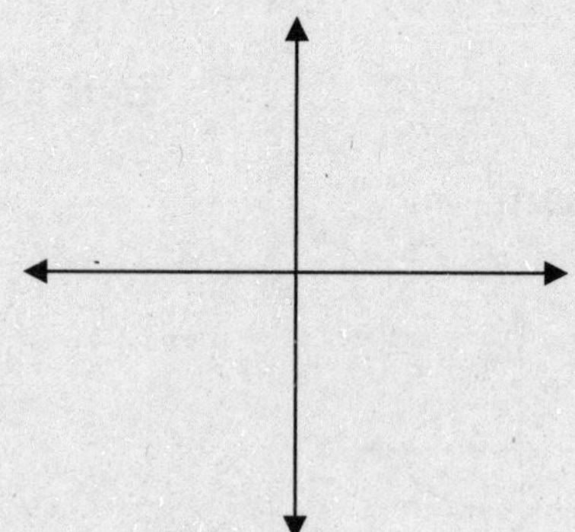

Quadratic Functions: Characteristics

Let $f(x) = 2x^2 - 4x + 1$.

1. Does the parabola open up or down?

2. What is the axis of symmetry?

3. What are the coordinates of the vertex?

x=__________ and y=__________

Quadratic Functions: Intercepts

Let $f(x) = 2x^2 - 3x + 1$.

1. The y intercept is __________ 2. The x intercepts are __________

Let $f(x) = -x^2 + 3x + 4$

3. The y intercept is __________ 4. The x intercepts are __________

Identifying Common Functions

Match the graph with the equation.

1. $f(x) = 2x + 3$ with ________.

2. $f(x) = x^2 + 3x + 4$ with________.

3. $f(x) = |x-2|$ with ________.

4. $f(x) = x^3 - 2x^2 + x + 1$ with ________.

5. $f(x) = \sqrt{2x} + 1$ with ________.

A.

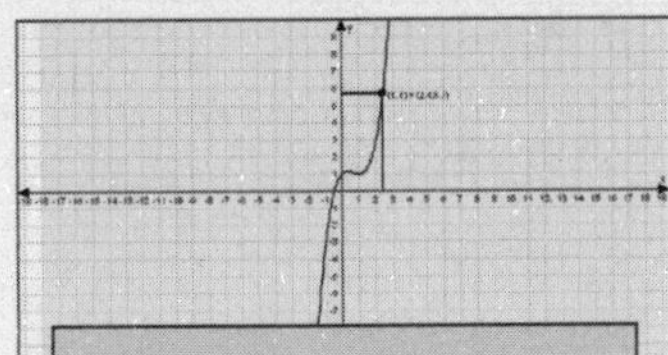

B.

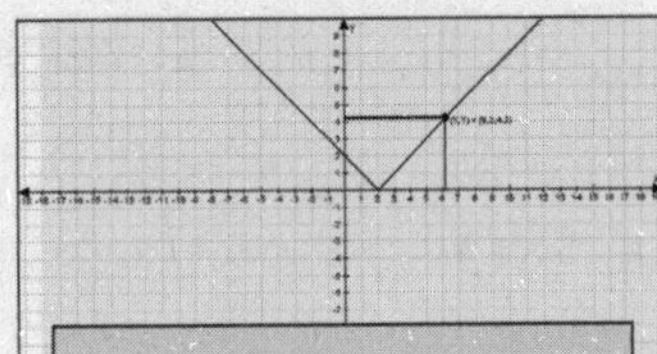

C.

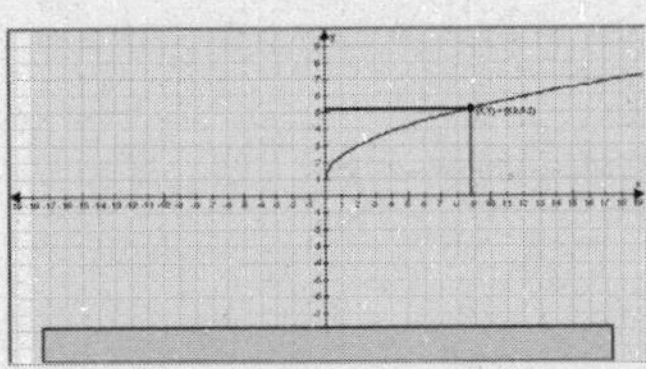

D.

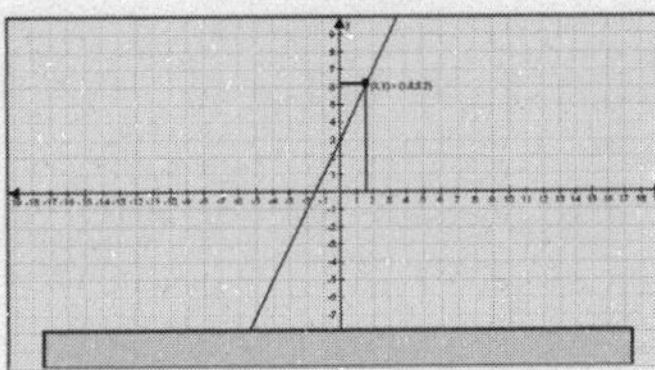

E.

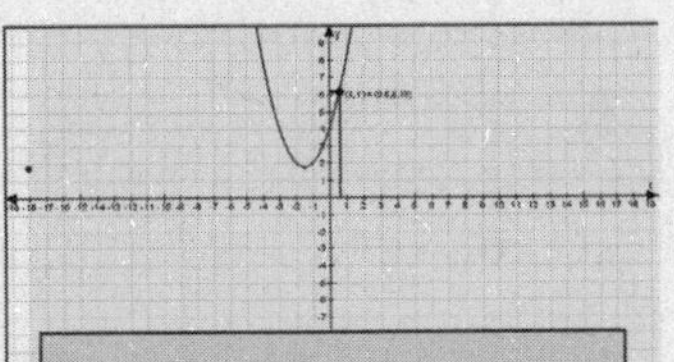

F.

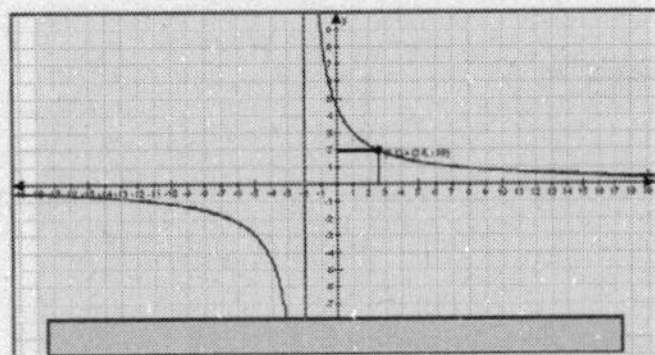

Domain and Range

Find the domain and range of the following functions.

1. f(x) = x – 2   D: R:
2. f(x) = x^2 +x – 2   D: R:
3. f(x) $\sqrt{3x} + 4$ =   D: R:
4. f(x) = $2 - \frac{1}{3x+2}$ D: R:

Intervals

Write in Interval Notation and then graph the set.

	Set	Interval Notation	Graph
1.	{x| -2 ≤ x ≤ 5}	________	
2.	{y| y < 3}	________	
3.	{x| x ≤ 7}	________	
4.	{x| 0 ≤ x < 7}	________	
5.	{x|x∈Reals}	________	
6.	{y|y>–3}	________	

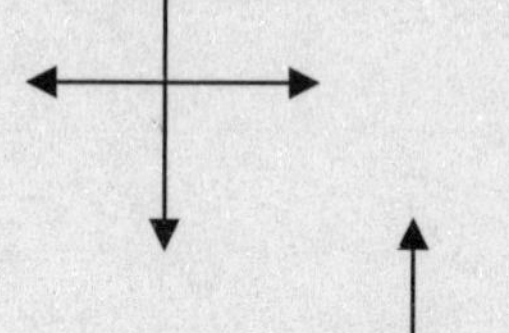

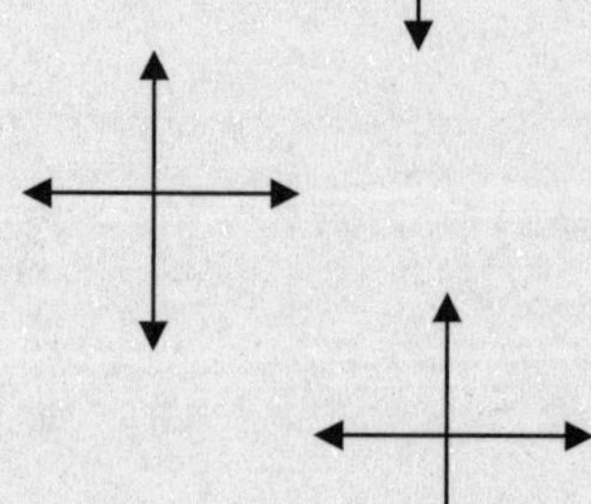

Properties of Curves

Use the following graph to answer the questions.

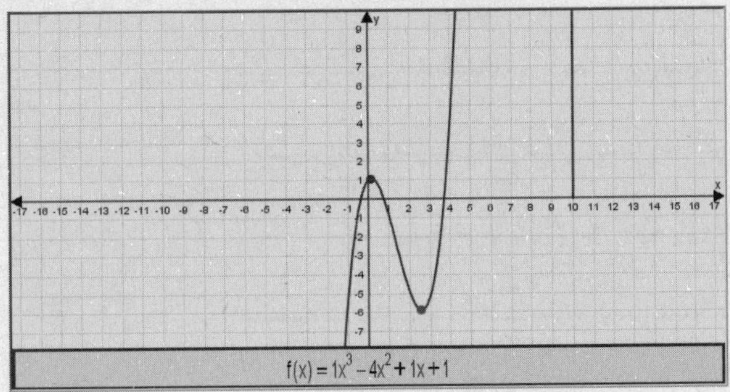

1. **The graph is _____________ over the interval [0, 2].**

2. **In the interval [-1, 2], the graph has a local ________________.**

3. **The graph is _____________ over the interval (-∞, 0].**

4. **The point (2.5, -6) is ____________________.**

5. **The graph is concave up over interval _______________.**

6. **The graph is concave down over the interval _______________.**

Symmetry

Are the functions EVEN, ODD, or NEITHER?

1. $f(x) = 3x^8 - 3$

2. $f(x) = 5x^3 - 2x$

3. $f(x) = 2x^3 - x^2$

4. $f(x) = \dfrac{5}{x - 2}$

5. $f(x) = |2x| - 3$

6. $f(x) = 2x^3 - \sqrt{x}$

f+g, f-g, f*g

Let $f(x) = 2x^2 - 3x + 7$ and $g(x) = 3x - 5$

1. Find f + g ______________________________

2. Find f – g ______________________________

3. Find f*g ______________________________

4. Find g – f ______________________________

f/g

1. If $f(x) = 2x - 6$ and $g(x) = x - 3$ find $f(x)/g(x)$ ________________

2. Find $g(x)/f(x)$ ________________

3. If $f(x) = x^2 - 5x + 6$ and $g(x) = 6x-12$ find f/g ________________

4. Find g/f ________________

5. If $f(x) = x^2 + 7x + 12$ and $g(x) = x^2 + 2x - 8$, find f/g ________________

6. Find g/f ________________

Composition of Functions

1. If $f(x) = x^2 - 6$ and $g(x) = x - 3$ find the following:

   A. $(f^\circ g)(2) =$

   B. $(f^\circ g)(-2) =$

   C. $(f^\circ g)(-1) =$

   D. $(f^\circ g)(x)$

2. If $f(x) = x^2 + 7x + 12$ and $g(x) = 2x - 8$, find $(f^\circ g)(3)$.

3. Find $(g^\circ f)(x)$

Is it one-to-one?

Determine if the graph is one-to-one.

1.

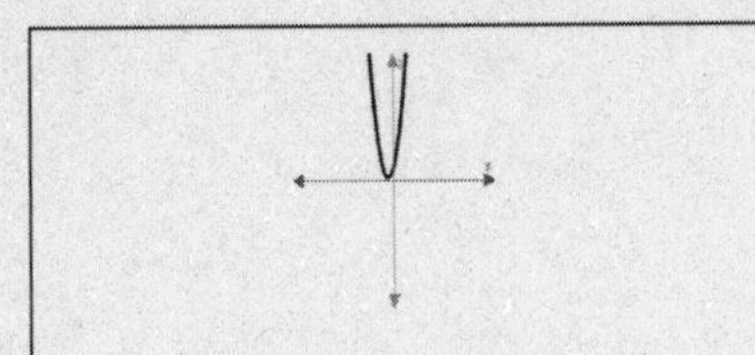

____

2.

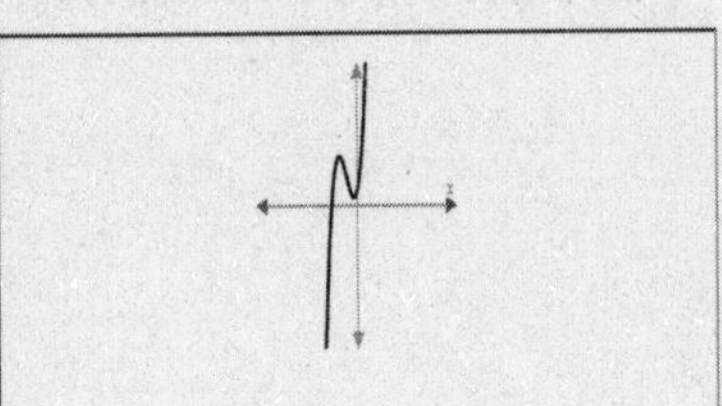

____

3.

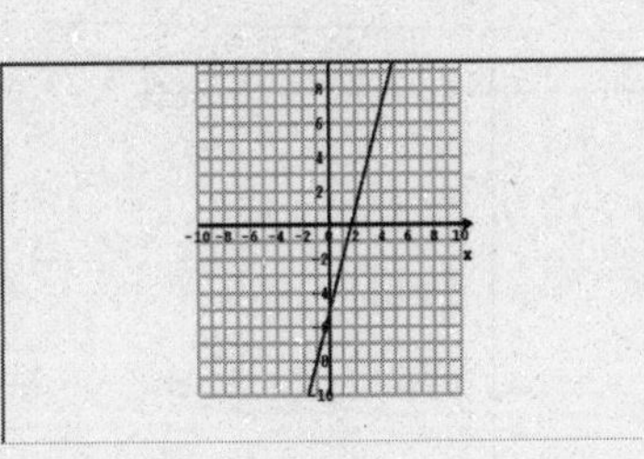

____

4.

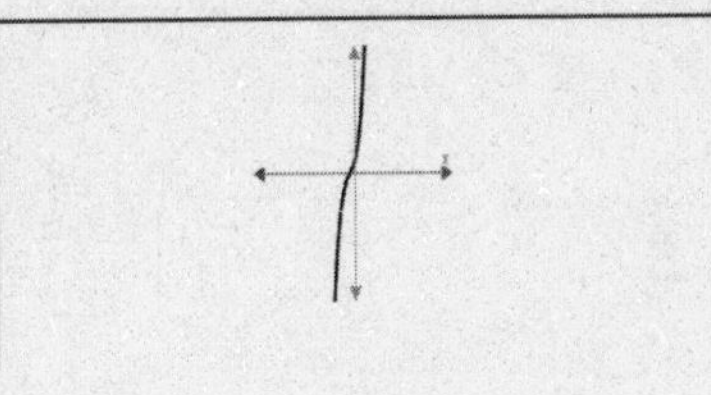

____

5.

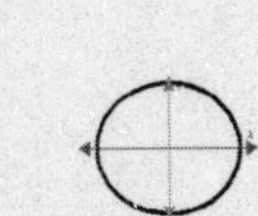

____

Finding the Inverse of a Function

1. **Find the inverse function of:** $f(x) = 2x + 3$

2. **Sketch f and f^{-1} on the same axes:**

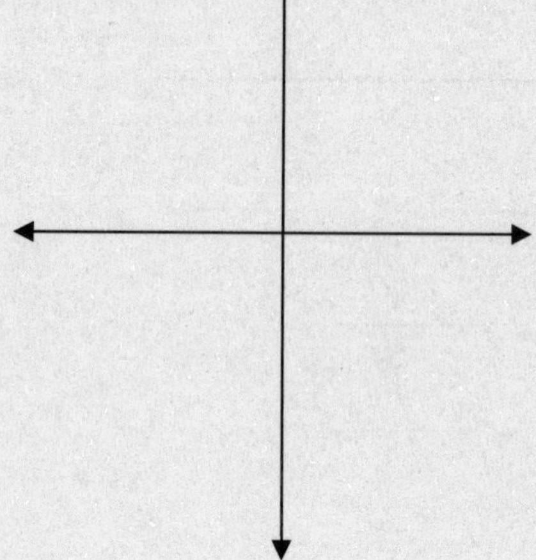

3. **Find the inverse of** $f(x) = \sqrt{x-1}+2$

4. **Sketch the graph of f and f^{-1}.**

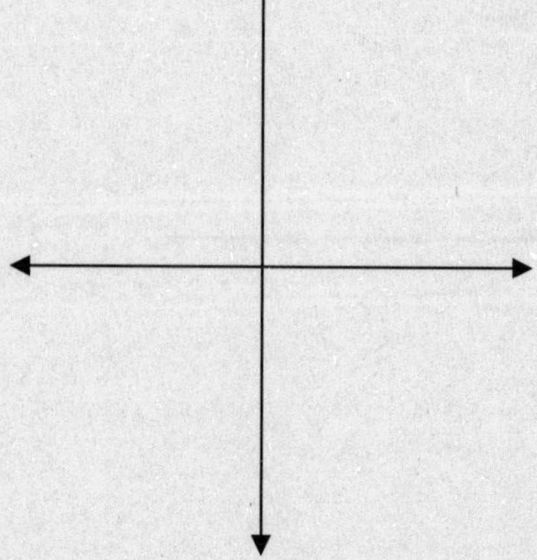